42nd European Photovoltaic Solar Energy Conference and Exhibition (EU PVSEC 2025)

Bilbao, Spain
22-26 September 2025

Volume 3 of 6

ISBN: 979-8-3313-2987-7

Printed from e-media with permission by:

Curran Associates, Inc.
57 Morehouse Lane
Red Hook, NY 12571

Some format issues inherent in the e-media version may also appear in this print version.

Copyright© (2025) by WIP – Renewable Energies
All rights reserved.

Printed with permission by Curran Associates, Inc. (2025)

For permission requests, please contact WIP – Renewable Energies
at the address below.

WIP – Renewable Energies
Sylvensteinstr. 2
81369 Munchen
Germany

Phone: +49 89 72012735
Fax: +49 89 72012791

wip@wip-munich.de

Additional copies of this publication are available from:

Curran Associates, Inc.
57 Morehouse Lane
Red Hook, NY 12571 USA
Phone: 845-758-0400
Fax: 845-758-2633
Email: curran@proceedings.com
Web: www.proceedings.com

42nd European Photovoltaic Solar Energy Conference and Exhibition (EU PVSEC 2025)

Bilbao, Spain
22-26 September 2025

Volume 3 of 6

42nd European Photovoltaic Solar Energy Conference and Exhibition

Proceedings of the International Conference

22 September – 26 September 2025

Edited by:

C. DEL CAÑIZO
Solar Energy Institute
UPM
Spain

R. KENNY
European Commission
Joint Research Centre
Italy

J. BERGMILLER
WIP Renewable Energies
Germany

J. DE GREGORIO
WIP Renewable Energies
Germany

Edition Team:

B. Yildiz
L. Großhans
A. Michaelsen
U.E. Birgi
WIP Renewable Energies
Germany

Photos at:

Coordination of the Technical Programme:
European Commission Joint Research Centre
Via E. Fermi 1
21020 Ispra (VA)
Italy

Institutional Support:
European Commission

Institutional PV Industry Cooperation:
SolarPower Europe
ESMC – European Solar Manufacturing Council

Supporting Organisations:
AUSTRALIAN PV INSTITUTE
ASOM – Alliance for Solar Mobility
BASQUE ENERGY CLUSTER
BILBAO CONVENTION BUREAU
EASE – European Association for Storage of Energy
ETIP PV – European Technology & Innovation Platform PV
GÜNDER – Turkish Solar Energy Society
IEA PVPS - IEA Photovoltaic Power Systems Programme
INSTITUTO SOLAR DE ENERGÍA SOLAR
LDES – Long Duration Energy Storage Council
NSEFI – National Solar Energy federation of India
NUS /SERIS – National University of Singapore / Solar Energy Research Institute of Singapore
UPM - Polytechnic University of Madrid

Supporting Associations:
EERA – European Energy Research Aliance
EREF – European Renewable Energies Federation
EUREC – The Association of European Renewable Energy Research Centres
VDMA Photovoltaic Equipment

Local Support:
ENTE VASCO DE LA ENERGÍA
EUH – University of the Basque Country

EU PVSEC 2025 realised by:

WIP Renewable Energies
Sylvensteinstr. 2, 81369 Munich, Germany
Tel: +49 89 720 12 735, Fax: +49 89 720 12 791
Email: pv.conference@wip-munich.de
www.eupvsec.org
www.wip-munich.de

Proceedings produced and published by:

WIP Renewable Energies
Sylvensteinstr. 2, 81369 Munich, Germany
Tel: +49 89 720 12 735, Fax: +49 89 720 12 791
Email: pv.conference@wip-munich.de
www.eupvsec.org
www.wip-munich.de

Legal notice
Neither the European Commission, the Organiser or the Publisher nor any person acting on their behalf is responsible for the use which might be made of the following information.

© 2025 WIP Renewable Energies
All rights reserved. No part of this publication may be reproduced in any form or by any electronic or mechanical means, including photocopying, recording or by any information storage and retrieval system without permission in writing from the copyright holder and the publisher.

Despite due diligence no liability for accuracy and completeness of the information and material offered in this document can be assumed by WIP Renewable Energies.

42nd EUROPEAN PHOTOVOLTAIC SOLAR ENERGY CONFERENCE AND EXHIBITION
22 SEPTEMBER – 26 SEPTEMBER 2025

EU PVSEC 2025 COMMITTEES

INTERNATIONAL SCIENTIFIC ADVISORY COMMITTEE (ISAC)

Chair

P. Szymanski, European Commission Joint Research Centre, Director of Energy, Transport and Climate, Petten, The Netherlands

Committee Members

V. Bermúdez Benito, Founder & Principal Consultant, Berbetin, Antibes, France

G.C. Eder, OFI, Vienna, Austria

P. Frankl, Head of the Renewable Energy Division, International Energy Agency, France

M. Getsiou, European Commission, DG RTD, Brussels, Belgium

S.W. Glunz, Head of Division Photovoltaics - Research, Fraunhofer ISE, Freiburg, Germany

N.M. Haegel, Director of the National Center for Photovoltaics, NREL, Golden, USA

R. Kenny, European Commission Joint Research Centre, Directorate for Energy and Transport and Climate, Ispra, Italy

S. Nowak, Managing Director of NET Nowak Energy & Technology, St. Ursen, Switzerland

R. Schlatmann, Chairman of ETIP PV, Head of the Solar Energy Division at Helmholtz-Zentrum Berlin, Germany

W.C. Sinke, TNO Energy Transition, The Netherlands

M. Topič, Head of Laboratory of Photovoltaics and Optoelectronics of the University of Ljubljana, Slovenia

P. Verlinden, Director at Amrock, Visiting Professor at Sun Yat-Sen University, Guangzhou, China

E. Voroshazi, Head of PV module process laboratory, CEA, Le Bourget-du-Lac, France

J. Bergmiller, Managing Director Events & Knowledge Transfer, WIP Renewable Energies, Munich, Germany

J. de Gregorio, Head of Unit, Scientific Services and Cooperation, WIP Renewable Energies, Munich, Germany

CONFERENCE EXECUTIVE COMMITTEE

Conference General Chair

C. del Cañizo, UPM, Madrid, Spain

Technical Programme Chair

R. Kenny, European Commission Joint Research Centre, Directorate for Energy and Transport and Climate, Ispra, Italy

Committee Members

W.C. Sinke, Program Development Manager, TNO Energy Transition, The Netherlands

S. Nowak, Managing Director of NET Nowak Energy & Technology, St. Ursen, Switzerland

M. Topič, Head of Laboratory of Photovoltaics and Optoelectronics of the University of Ljubljana, Slovenia

V. Bermúdez Benito, BERBETIN, France

E. Voroshazi, Head of PV Module Process Laboratory, CEA, Le Bourget-Du-Lac France

H. Ossenbrink, Former European Commission Joint Research Centre, Germany

J. Bergmiller, Managing Director Events & Knowledge Transfer, WIP Renewable Energies, Munich, Germany

J. de Gregorio, Head of Unit, Scientific Services and Cooperation, WIP Renewable Energies, Munich, Germany

2025 SCIENTIFIC COMMITTEE

Programme Technical Chair

R. Kenny, European Commission, Joint Research Centre, Italy

Topic Chairs

Topic 1: Silicon Materials and Cells

F. Schindler, Fraunhofer ISE, Germany

Topic 2: Thin Films and New Concepts

I. Gordon, imec, Belgium

Topic 3: Photovoltaic Modules and BoS Components

T. Barnes, NREL, USA

Topic 4: PV Systems Engineering, Integrated/Applied PV

A.M. Gracia Amillo, FUNDACION CENER, Spain

Topic 5: PV in the Energy Transition

C. Agraffeil, CEA / INES, France

Topic Organisers and Paper Review Experts

Topic 1: Silicon Materials and Cells

F. Schindler, Fraunhofer ISE, Germany

C. Fischer, Wacker Chemie, Germany

G. Hahn, University of Konstanz, Germany

K. Ding, Forschungszentrum Jülich, Germany

P. Roca i Cabarrocas, CNRS-LPICM, France

A. W. Weeber, TNO Energy Transition, The Netherlands

D. Muñoz, CEA / INES, France

S. W. Glunz, Fraunhofer ISE, Germany

K. Bothe, ISFH, Germany

M. Topic, University of Ljubljana, Slovenia

P. Fath, RCT-Solutions, Germany

S. Peters, Hanwha Q CELLS, Germany

M.P. Bellmann, SINTEF, Norway

A. Ciesla, UNSW, Australia

C. Hagendorf, Freiberg Instruments, Germany

X. Yu, Zhejiang University, China

J.S. Lee, KIER, South Korea

R. Brendel, ISFH, Germany

T. Dullweber, ISFH, Germany

J. Horzel, Fraunhofer ISE, Germany

W. Nemeth, NREL, United States of America

R. Turan, METU, Türkiye

F. Menchini, ENEA, Italy

W. Favre, CEA, France

J. Meier, Meier Technologies, Switzerland
J. Schmidt, ISFH, Germany
M. Wright, University of Oxford, United Kingdom
J. Zhao, CSEM, Switzerland
A. Morisset, CSEM, Switzerland
A. Richter, Fraunhofer ISE, Germany
J. Linke, ISC Konstanz, Germany
B. Geerligs, TNO Energy Transition, The Netherlands
S. Dubois, CEA, France
M. Hermle, Fraunhofer ISE, Germany
B. Terheiden, University of Konstanz, Germany
P. Delli Veneri, ENEA, Italy
T. Matsui, AIST, Japan
Y. Ohshita, Toyota Technological Institute, Japan
E. Bruhat, HOLOSOLIS, France
A. Augusto, Dalarna University, Sweden
F. Ferrazza, ENI S.p.A., Italy
A. Otaegi, UPV/EHU, Spain
M.C. Schubert, Fraunhofer ISE, Germany
H. Duman, KalyonPV, Türkiye
N. Usami, Nagoya University, Japan
Y. Zhu, UNSW, Australia
D. Brunner, RENA Technologies, Germany
A. Danel, CEA, France
C. Gerardi, 3Sun, Italy
H.J. Nonnenmacher, Meyer Burger, Germany
P. Verlinden, AMROCK, Australia
Q. Wang, Wang, Qi, China
W. Zhang, Zhang, Weiming, China
Y. Chen, Trina Solar Energy, China
E. Krassowski, CE Cell Engineering, Germany
M. Foti, 3Sun, Italy
D.L. Bätzner, Meyer Burger Research, Switzerland

Topic 2: Thin Films and New Concepts
I. Gordon, imec, Belgium
J.C. Goldschmidt, Marburg University, Germany
F. Schoofs, Oxford PV, United Kingdom
N. Kyranaki, Hasselt University, Belgium
S. Veenstra, TNO Energy Transition, The Netherlands
T. Aernouts, imec, Belgium
A.N. Tiwari, SOLTIWA, Switzerland
G. Siefer, Fraunhofer ISE, Germany
M. Edoff, Uppsala University, Sweden
A. Marti Vega, UPM, Spain
J. Poortmans, imec, Belgium
I. Ramiro, UPM, Spain
T. Magorian Friedlmeier, ZSW, Germany

S. Albrecht, HZB, Germany
S. Berson, CEA, France
P. Carroy, CEA, France
C. Case, Oxford PV, United Kingdom
G. Coletti, FuturaSun, Italy
S. De Wolf, KAUST, Saudi Arabia
U.W. Paetzold, KIT, Germany
H. Sivaramakrishnan Radhakrisnan, imec, Belgium
P. Schulze, Fraunhofer ISE, Germany
L. Wang, Technology Innovation Institute, United Arab
   Emirates
Y. Smirnov, Applied Materials, United States of America
B. Stannowski, HZB, Germany
F. Fertig, Hanwha Q CELLS, Germany
L. Lancellotti, ENEA, Italy
S. Cros, CEA, France
S. Hayase, The University of Electro-Communications, Japan
S. Huang, Macquarie University, Australia
M. Khenkin, HZB, Germany
C. Lin, National Taiwan University, Taiwan

M.S.H. Norton, University of Cyprus, Cyprus
P. Pistor, Pablo de Olavide University, Spain
W. Tress, Zurich University of Applied Sciences,
   Switzerland
A. Aguirre, imec, Belgium
D. Lan, UNSW Sydney, China
M. Saliba, University of Stuttgart, Germany
P. Manshanden, TNO Energy Transition, The Netherlands
L. Vesce, University of Rome II, Italy
I. Dogan, TNO Solliance, The Netherlands
Y. Kuang, imec, Belgium
M. Al Katrib, IPVF, France
M.I. Hossain, QEERI, Qatar
W.H. Chiu, Chang Gung University, Taiwan
C. Chen, Ming Chi University of Technology, Taiwan
C. Fell, CSIRO Energy Technology, Australia
G. Brammertz, imec, Belgium
T. Dalibor, Avancis, Germany
S. Ishizuka, AIST, Japan
A. Redinger, University of Luxembourg, Luxembourg
A. Romeo, University of Verona, Italy
V. Sittinger, Fraunhofer IST, Germany
M. Theelen, TNO/Solliance, The Netherlands
G. Timò, RSE, Italy
A. Kanevce, ZSW, Germany
A. Pérez-Rodríguez, IREC, Spain
R. Gutzler, ZSW, Germany
W. Witte, ZSW, Germany
T. Nishimura, Tokyo Institute of Technology, Japan
C. Qian, University of New South Wales, Australia
J.P. Connolly, CentraleSupelec, France
J.P. Kleider, CNRS/GeePs, France
I. Konovalov, University of Applied Sciences Jena, Germany
Y. Okada, University of Tokyo, Japan
M. Rusu, HZB, Germany
H. Meddeb, DLR, Germany
E. Saucedo, Universitat Politècnica de Catalunya (UPC),
   Spain
P. Vidal-Fuentes, FUNDACIÓ INSTITUT DE RECERCA
   EN ENERGIA DE CATALUNYA, Spain
C. Malerba, ENEA, Italy
C. Becker, HZB, Germany
D. Kuciauskas, NREL, United States of America
M. Ochoa, University of Cantabria, Spain
T. Tayagaki, AIST, Japan
S. Wasmer, WAVELABS Solar Metrology Systems,
   Germany
S. Zandi, UNSW, Australia
C. Messmer, University of Freiburg, Germany
J.B. Puel, Institut Photovoltaïque d'Ile de France (IPVF),
   France
S. Ternes, University of Rome II, Italy

Topic 3: Photovoltaic Modules and BoS Components
V. Bermúdez Benito, BERBETIN, France
R. Preu, Fraunhofer ISE, Germany
R. Gottschalg, Fraunhofer CSP, Germany
T. Barnes, NREL, United States of America
G. Friesen, SUPSI, Switzerland
G. Bardizza, TÜV Rheinland Solar, Italy

V. Barth, CEA, France
A. Faes, CSEM, Switzerland
A. Lennon, Sundrive Solar, Australia
M. Mittag, Fraunhofer ISE, Germany
M.A. Muñoz-García, UPM, Spain
H. Nagel, Fraunhofer ISE, Germany
S. Pietralunga, CNR, Italy
T. Timofte, ISC Konstanz, Germany

S. Feldbacher, PCCL, Austria
A. Halm, ISC Konstanz, Germany
H. Hanifi, AESOLAR, Germany
E. Warren, NREL, United States of America
S. Zhang, Trina Solar Energy, China
X. Zhen, Canadian Solar, China
G. Beaucarne, Dow Silicones Belgium, Belgium
T. Bejat, CEA, France
C. Camus, LayTec, Germany
U. Jahn, Fraunhofer CSP, Germany
G. Oreski, PCCL, Austria
M. Pander, Fraunhofer CSP, Germany
T. Sample, European Commission JRC, Italy
A. Morlier, imo-imomec, Belgium
C. Barretta, PCCL, Austria
P. Gebhardt, Fraunhofer ISE, Germany
C. Sen, UNSW, Australia
O. Arriaga Arruti, CSEM, Switzerland
X. Gu, NIST, United States of America
C. Xiao, Chinese Academy of Sciences, United States of America
R. Aninat, TNO/Solliance, The Netherlands
S. Mitterhofer, NIST, United States of America
B. Hoex, UNSW, Australia
E. Özkalay, SUPSI, Switzerland
M. Bokalič, University of Ljubljana, Slovenia
S. Bordihn, ISFH, Germany
M. Despeisse, CSEM, Switzerland
J. Govaerts, imec, Belgium
J. Lopez-García, STS-Certified, Spain
M. Pravettoni, Technology Innovation Institute, United Arab Emirates
T. Stoyanova Lyubenova, Joint Research Centre, Italy
C. Ulbrich, HZB, Germany
J. Moereke, Avancis, Germany
Y.S. Long, ITRI, Taiwan
D. Pavanello, European Commission JRC, Italy
A.K. Vidal de Oliveira, UFSC, Brazil
J. Bengoechea, CENER, Spain
M. Ernst, ANU, Australia
H. Ellis, European Commission JRC, Italy
B. Mihaylov, European Commission JRC, Italy
G. Chowdhury, 3E, Belgium
B. Aissa, QEERI - Qatar Environment and Energy Research Institute, Qatar

Topic 4: PV Systems Engineering, Integrated/Applied PV
A. Gracia Amillo, CENER, Spain
W.G.J.H.M. van Sark, Utrecht University, The Netherlands
K. Lappalainen, Tampere University, Finland
J.M. Almeida Serra, University of Lisbon, Portugal
I. Tsanakas, CEA, France
C. Buerhop-Lutz, HI ERN, Germany
D. Moser, Becquerel Institute Italia, Italy
F. Frontini, SUPSI, Switzerland
G.C. Eder, OFI, Austria
A. Scognamiglio, ENEA, Italy
A. Chatzipanagi, European Commission JRC, Italy
I. Antón Hernández, UPM, Spain
R.M.E. Valckenborg, TNO, The Netherlands
T. Reindl, SERIS, Singapore
J.R. Gonzalez, European Space Agency, The Netherlands
G. Mütter, Gerhard Mütter e.U., Austria
T. Merdzhanova, Forschungszentrum Jülich, Germany

V. Lara-Fanego, Solargis, Spain
A. Louwen, Eurac Research, Italy
A. Martinez Fernandez, European Commission JRC, Italy
T. Oozeki, AIST, Japan

J. Remund, Meteotest, Switzerland
M. Sengupta, NREL, United States of America
M. Zehner, Rosenheim Technical University of Applied Sciences, Germany
B. Nouri, German Aerospace Center, Spain
S. Poddar, UNSW, Australia
D. Bachour, HBKU/ Qatar Foundation, Qatar
J. Yang, NREL, United States of America
S. Bouguerra, imo-imomec, Belgium
C. Alonso-Tristán, UBU, Spain
M. Carbone, ENEL Green Power, Italy
M. Dennenmoser, BayWa r.e. Solar Projects GmbH, Germany
C.W. Hansen, Sandia National Laboratories, United States of America
A. Neubert, DNV Maritime Software GmbH, Germany
D. Berrian, Belectric, Germany
M. Oliosi, PVsyst, Switzerland
J. Moschner, KU Leuven / EnergyVille, Belgium
C. Bucher, BUAS, Switzerland
B. Wittmer, PVsyst SA, Switzerland
M. Bolen, SB Energy, United States of America
D. Daßler, Fraunhofer CSP, Germany
R. Einhaus, ZSW, Germany
P. Hacke, NREL, United States of America
A. Heimsath, Fraunhofer ISE, Germany
J. Lin, PV Guider, Taiwan
A. Migan-Dubois, GeePs, France
M. Rinio, University of Karlstad, Sweden
J.S. Stein, Sandia National Laboratories, United States of America
D. Stellbogen, ZSW, Germany
M. Theristis, Sandia National Laboratories, United States of America
A. Virtuani, CSEM, Switzerland
A. Driesse, PV Performance Labs, Germany
M. Øgaard, IFE, Norway
A. Nobre, SERIS, Singapore
T. Trupke, UNSW, Australia
C. Cornaro, University of Rome II, Italy
G. A. dos Reis Benatto, DTU, Denmark
S. Malik, Fraunhofer CSP, Germany
S. Lindig, Univers SAS, France
M.M. Nygård, Institute for Energy Technology, Norway
P. Alonso Gomez, BayWa r.e., Germany
Y. Assoa, CEA, France
P. Bonomo, SUPSI, Switzerland
V. D'Ambrosio, University of Naples Federico II, Italy
E. Román Medina, Tecnalia, Spain
L.H. Slooff, TNO Energy Transition, The Netherlands
S. Villa, TNO, The Netherlands
M. La Rosa, Glass to Power, Italy
T. Del Caño, Onyx Solar Energy, Spain
X. Zhihao, AIST, Japan
P. Sharif, ODTU-GUNAM, Türkiye
K. Umeda, TAISEI CORPORATION, Japan
S. Boddaert, CSTB, France
N. Lysgaard Andersen, DTU, Denmark
K. Meyer, ISFH, Germany
T. Biel, NET Nowak Energy & Technology, Switzerland
F. Colucci, ENEA, Italy
A. Pascaris, NREL, United States of America
C. Dupraz, INRAE, France
C. Alonso-García, CIEMAT, Spain
A. Lefort, BayWa, Germany
H.N. Riise, IFE, Norway
M.A. Schüler, Next2Sun Technology GmbH, Germany
P.J. Pérez-Higueras, University of Jaén, Spain
K. Oda, Agritree,

M. Berwind, Fraunhofer ISE, Germany
M. Dörenkämper, TNO, The Netherlands
M. Heinrich, Fraunhofer ISE, Germany
B. Newman, Lightyear, The Netherlands
A. Reinders, Eindhoven University of Technology, The Netherlands
T. Tanahashi, AIST, Japan
J. Leloux, LuciSun, Belgium
E. Shirazi, University of Twente, The Netherlands
K. Araki, University of Miyazaki, Japan
K. Nishioka, University of Miyazaki, Japan
R. Campesato, CESI, Italy
V. Khorenko, Azur Space, Germany
G. Kakoulaki, European Commission Joint Research Centre, Italy
H. Toyota, JAXA, Japan
P. Garcia-Linares, UPM, Spain
I. Weiss, Weiss, Ingrid, Germany
A. Hensel, Fraunhofer ISE, Germany
J.S. da Fernandes, Hochschule Offenburg, Germany
Y. Ueda, Tokyo University of Science, Japan
J. Braid, Sandia National Laboratories, United States of America

Topic 5: PV in the Energy Transition
J. Stierstorfer, WIP Renewable Energies, Germany
R. Pestana, R&D Nester, Portugal
P.J. Alet, CSEM, Switzerland
C. Agraffeil, CEA, France
K. WAMBACH, Wambach-Consulting, Germany
C. del Cañizo, UPM, Spain
L. Großhans, WIP Renewable Energies, Germany
M. Getsiou, European Commission DG RTD, Belgium
S. Nowak, NET Nowak Energy & Technology, Switzerland
C. Breyer, LUT University, Finland
I. Kaizuka, RTS Corporation, Japan
G. Masson, Becquerel Institute, Belgium
P. Baliozian, VDMA, Germany
L. Großhans, WIP Renewable Energies, Germany
C. Candelise, Bocconi University, Italy
S. Caneva, WIP Renewable Energies, Germany

G. Barchi, Eurac Research, Italy
R. Bründlinger, AIT, Austria
V. Efthymiou, University of Cyprus, Cyprus
M. Centeno Brito, University of Lisbon, Portugal
F. Carigiet, ZHAW, Switzerland
B. Gaiddon, HESPUL, France
F.Z. Ouchani, Green Energy Park, Morocco
M. Rennhofer, AIT, Austria
G. Adinolfi, ENEA, Italy
W. Schaffer, Salzburg Netz, Austria
A. Haber, e-control, Austria
G. Heilscher, Technische Hochschule Ulm, Germany
A. Anctil, Michigan State University, United States of America
S. Arancón, Plug and Play, Spain
S. Capaccioli, ETA - Florence Renewable Energies, Italy
V. Fthenakis, Columbia University, United States of America
G. Heath, NREL, United States of America
K. Komoto, Mizuho Research & Technologies, Ltd., Japan
W. Palitzsch, LuxChemtech, Germany
S. Ovaitt, NREL, United States of America
M. de Wild-Scholten, SmartGreenScans, The Netherlands
S. Herceg, Fraunhofer ISE, Germany
C. Polacchi, Eurac Research, Italy
N. Espinosa, Universidad de Murcia, Spain
E. Drahi, TotalEnergies OneTech, France
S. Guastella, RSE, Italy

H. Ossenbrink, Band Gap, Germany
D. Polverini, European Commission DG GROW, Belgium
N. Taylor, European Commission JRC, Italy
K.A. Weiß, Fraunhofer ISE, Germany
I. Kafedjiska, Helmholtz Zentrum Berlin, Germany
P. Malbranche, Solar Action, France
S. De Iuliis, ENEA, Italy
T. Haarberg, BNW-Energy, Norway
A. Nayfeh, Khalifa University, United Arab Emirates
E. Vartiainen, Fortum Renewables Oy, Finland
E. Veronese, Eurac Research, Italy
P. Sanchez-Friera, Solkeys, Spain
N. Cherradi, Desert Technologies, Saudi Arabia
S. Nold, Fraunhofer ISE, Germany
H.J.J. Yu, CEA, France
M. Beck, U.S. Department of Energy, United States of America
M. Woodhouse, NREL, United States of America
A.B. Cristóbal, UPM, Spain
G. Ruggieri, Insubria University, Italy
S. Tay, NUS, Singapore

Awards Coordinators

Student Awards Coordinator
A.H.M. Smets, Delft University of Technology, The Netherlands

Student Awards Committee
R. Kenny, EU PVSEC Technical Programme Chair, Italy
C. del Canizo, Conference Chair, UPM, Spain
E. Voroshazi, CEA, France
J. Poortmans, imec, Belgium
P.J. Alet, CSEM, Switzerland
S. Caneva, WIP Renewable Energies, Germany
A. Romeo, University of Verona, Italy
G. Friesen, SUPSI, Switzerland
F. Schindler, Fraunhofer ISE, Germany
J.C. Goldchmidt, Marburg University, Germany
D. Moser, Becquerel Institute, Italy
K. Ding, FZJ, Germany
W.C. Sinke, TNO Energy Transition, The Netherlands
M. Topic, University of Ljubljana, Slovenia
R. Schlatman, HZB, Germany
S. Glunz, Fraunhofer ISE, Germany
A.M. Vega, UPM, Spain
I. Kaizuka, RTS, Japan
P.D. Veneri, ENEA, Italy
J. Bengoechea, CENER, Spain

Poster Awards Coordinator
P. Malbranche, Solar Action, France

Poster Awards Committee
R. Kenny, European Commission JRC, Italy
C. del Canizo, UPM, Spain
W. van Sark, Utrecht University, The Netherlands
I. Tsanakas, CEA INES, France
L. Miranda, Oxford PV, United Kingdom
D. Munoz, CEA INES, France
I. Gordon, imec, Belgium
E. Roman, Tecnalia, Spain
G. Eder, OFI, Austria
I. Antón, UPM, Spain
S. Veenstra, TNO, The Netherlands
J.M. Almeida Serra, University of Lisbon, Portugal
T. Magorian Friedlmeier, ZSW, Germany
J. Stierstorfer, WIP Renewable Energies, Germany

G. Kakoulaki, European Commission JRC, Italy
T. Barnes, NREL, USA
T. Merdzhanova, Forschungszentrum Jülich, Germany

Highlights Committee
C. del Cañizo, UPM, Madrid, Spain
R. Kenny, European Commission Joint Research Centre, Directorate for Energy and Transport and Climate, Ispra, Italy
W.C. Sinke, TNO Energy Transition, The Netherlands
S. Nowak, Managing Director of NET Nowak Energy & Technology, St. Ursen, Switzerland
M. Topič, Head of Laboratory of Photovoltaics and Optoelectronics of the University of Ljubljana, Slovenia
V. Bermúdez Benito, BERBETIN, France

E. Voroshazi, Head of PV Module Process Laboratory, CEA, Le Bourget-Du-Lac France
H. Ossenbrink, Band Gap, Germany
J. Bergmiller, Managing Director Events & Knowledge Transfer, WIP Renewable Energies, Munich, Germany
J. de Gregorio, Head of Unit, Scientific Services and Cooperation, WIP Renewable Energies, Munich, Germany
S. Leanza, Marketing and PR Manager, WIP Renewable Energies, Munich, Germany
B. Yildiz, Project Manager Events & Knowledge Transfer, WIP Renewable Energies, Munich, Germany
F. Schindler, Fraunhofer ISE, Freiburg, Germany
I. Gordon, imec, Leuven, Belgium
T. Barnes, NREL, Evergreen, USA
A.M. Gracia Amillo, FUNDACION CENER, Sarriguren, Spain
C. Agraffeil, CEA / INES, Le Bourget-du-Lac, France

SUBJECT INDEX

Silicon Materials and Cells

Sessions 1CP.1, 1EP.3, 1AO.4, 1AO.5, 1AO.6, 1BO.1, 1BO.2, 1BO.3, 1BO.4, 1DO.9, 1BV.5, 1CV.2

Thin Films and New Concepts

Sessions 2CP.2, 2BO.1, 2CO.1, 2CO.2, 2DO.9, 2DO.6, 2DO.7, 2DO.8, 2AO.2, 2AO.3, 2AO.1, 2BO.8, 2BO.9, 2BO.10, 2BV.1, 2BV.2, 2CV.3

Photovoltaic Modules and BoS Components

Sessions 3CP.1, 3CP.3, 3CO.10, 3CO.11, 3DO.12, 3DO.16, 3DO.19, 3DO.20, 3BO.11, 3BO.12, 3BO.14, 3BO.15, 3AV.1, 3AV.2, 3AV.3

PV Systems Engineering, Integrated/Applied PV

Sessions 4AP.1, 4AO.7, 4AO.8, 4AO.9, 4DO.1, 4DO.3, 4BO.6, 4BO.7, 4CO.8, 4CO.9, 4DO.10, 4DO.17, 4BO.5, 4BO.16, 4BO.17, 4DO.2, 4DO.4, 4DO.5, 4CO.3, 4EO.2, 4BV.3, 4BV.4, 4CV.1, 4DV.1, 4DV.4,

PV in the Energy Transition

Sessions 5CP.1, 5CP.2, 5DO.14, 5DO.15, 5CO.4, 5CO.5, 5CO.6, 5DO.18, 5CO.4, 5CO.5, 5CO.6, 5DO.18, 5EO.3, 5EO.1, 5DV.2, 5DV.3,

Topic Code	Session Type	Day Codes
1 Silicon Materials and Cells	P = Plenary Session	A = Monday, 22 September 2025
2 Thin-Films and New Concepts	O = Oral Session	B = Tuesday, 23 September 2025
3 Photovoltaic Modules	V = Visual Session	C = Wednesday, 24 September 2025
4 Photovoltaic Systems		D = Thursday, 25 September 2025
5 Photovoltaics in the Energy Transition		E = Friday, 26 September 2025

e.g. 1AO.4 ⇒ 1= Silicon Materials and Cells, A=Monday, O=Oral session, 4=Session 4

FOREWORD

The European Photovoltaic Solar Energy Conference and Exhibition (EU PVSEC) stands as the World's leading and most renowned forum for PV research and development and the biggest conference on PV solar energy. In 2025, celebrating its 42nd edition, the EU PVSEC was the essential meeting and exchanging point for global PV experts from research, development, and industry.

Held from 22–26 September 2025 in Bilbao, Spain, the EU PVSEC 2025 was a resounding success, showcasing a wide range of cutting-edge research results. Bringing together both the Conference and the Exhibition, this edition attracted more than 1600 participants from 61 countries who contributed over 1000 presentations across various fields of science and technology. The event provided an essential platform for the exchange of knowledge and ideas on photovoltaic research, innovations, and applications. In the exhibition area 51 companies from all parts of the world welcomed visitors and presented their products and services.

Conference Highlights

The EU PVSEC covered a broad range of topics with an extensive programme that offers an opportunity for workers from across the entire field of photovoltaics to share their findings, as well as an opportunity for multidisciplinary learning. Rapid advances in materials, designs, and manufacturing processes reflect the accelerating expansion of the global PV market. The programme was arranged into 5 topics as follows:

- Silicon Materials and Cells;
- Thin Films and New Concepts;
- Photovoltaic Modules and Balance of System Components;
- PV Systems Engineering, Integrated/Applied PV;
- PV in the Energy Transition.

Communicating the key messages from the conference, not only to participants, but also to other researchers, key stakeholders, policy makers and the general public was an important added value. We thank the Highlights Committee, composed of selected members of the Scientific Committee, as well as the Session Chairs, for providing a comprehensive summary of the findings and state of the art research that were delivered during this year's event. Some key highlights are listed below, while further details may be found in the dedicated highlights presentation in the annex of these proceedings.

Cross-cutting themes:

- Demonstrated the versatility of solar technologies, spanning traditional and emerging application areas.
- Sustainability and circularity remain central, with research focused on reducing material use, such as replacing silver with copper, and advancing end-of-life management of modules.
- Ensuring long-term stability and predictable energy yield is equally essential, with many examples of studies on degradation mechanisms and efforts to elucidate their root-causes, such as in the case of UVID.

- The role of artificial intelligence across the PV value chain is rapidly expanding, from design to operations and maintenance, including among many others drone applications.

Latest Solar Innovations in Materials, Cells, Modules and PV Systems:

While silicon solar cells remain the cornerstone of PV technology, perovskite solar cells continue to stand out as the leading complementary technology to silicon, both as standalone devices and in tandem configurations. Research efforts are increasingly focused on enhancing stability, understanding degradation mechanisms, improving durability and scalability, and ensuring full industrial compatibility.

Many companies presented impressive results on industrial-size single-junction perovskite modules as well as perovskite-based tandem modules, and several new efficiency records were announced during the event. The rapid pace of innovation in cell and module architecture underscores the need for accelerated and more robust testing and qualification methodologies. Both the industry and the research community are moving swiftly to assess and improve reliability in this fast-evolving PV landscape.

A major focus in module research remains the optimisation of materials and packaging to ensure long lifetimes and predictable energy yields from high-efficiency cells. In parallel, many innovative advances in the operation and maintenance (O&M) of PV systems were presented and discussed.

Applications, Grid Integration and Storage

"PV can be deployed everywhere": from space applications to agrivoltaics, PV noise barriers, building-integrated photovoltaics (BIPV), floating PV systems, and even vehicles. Among these, agrivoltaics is gaining momentum as a promising dual land use approach, offering economic benefits for farmers while increasing resilience to climate change.

Flexibility solutions, particularly through battery storage, were recognised in many technical presentations as essential to accommodate higher PV penetration levels and to reduce energy curtailment. At the same time, strengthening grid infrastructure and enhancing grid management capabilities remain critical to enable the next phase of large-scale PV integration.

Photovoltaics in the Energy Transition

Options for re-establishing competitive module manufacturing in Europe were extensively analysed, including detailed policy recommendations for industrial support and market growth. Currently, a mismatch persists between global PV module installation rates and production rates, resulting in growing inventories and sharply reduced prices.

Finally, inclusiveness, diversity, citizen participation, awareness, education, and social engagement were underlined as vital dimensions of the sector's long-term sustainability and innovation capacity.

EU PVSEC 2025 Proceedings

Selection for inclusion in the conference was made by the Scientific Committee's paper review experts and topic organisers (see the listing on pages 010002-001-005), to whom we express our sincere gratitude for their comprehensive review work and overall contribution to the success of the conference.

The EU PVSEC 2025 Proceedings contain the full papers covering most of the highlights described above and more. The Proceedings provide a comprehensive overview of the PV solar sector, its current status and future prospects in science, research, innovation, development and deployment extending to 3,750 pages. In addition to the 299 submitted papers, the proceedings include 101 presentations (slides) shown during the plenary and oral presentations as well as 176 poster files of the visual presentations. In total this amounts to 576 publications.

The Conference Proceedings are published as downloadable files and are also fully accessible online. A DOI code (Digital Object Identifier) has been assigned to each paper. This ensures unequivocal and permanent identification and full citability. The EU PVSEC 2025 papers can be viewed and downloaded in a full free open access from the EU PVSEC's Proceedings website https://userarea.eupvsec.org/proceedings.

The proceedings of the EU PVSEC 2025 strengthen the commitment to providing quick and open access to high quality scientific results. This is a powerful source for targeted and quick information search and retrieval, enabling you to search by topic, keywords, paper title, DOI, author, or organization.

We are confident that these Proceedings will play an important role in providing a comprehensive overview of the current actors and activities in the global PV sector and that they will disseminate information on the state-of-the-art of technologies and applications. This can generate further research, add momentum to innovation and promote interest in PV worldwide.

We would like to cordially thank all authors and participants of the EU PVSEC 2025 for their contributions and look forward to welcoming you in Rotterdam, The Netherlands from 14 – 18 September 2026 at the EU PVSEC 2026, the 43rd European Photovoltaic Solar Energy Conference and Exhibition

The Editors

TABLE OF CONTENTS OF EU PVSEC 2025 PROCEEDINGS PAPERS

Oral SESSION 1AO.5 Si TOPCon Solar Cells and Related Processing Steps

Oral SESSION 1BO.2 Characterisation and Modelling of Si Solar Cells

Oral SESSION 1BO.3 Si Solar Cell Manufacturing Processes

[1] Anhalt University of Applied Sciences, Köthen, Germany; [2] Fraunhofer CSP, Halle, Germany

Oral SESSION 2AO.2 Advances in Chalcogenide Devices

Oral SESSION 2AO.3 III-V Based Devices | Tandem and Perovskite Solar Cells

Oral SESSION 2BO.10 Advanced Modelling and Characterisation of Perovskite Solar Cells

Sivaramakrishnan Radhakrishnan[1], Jef Poortmans[1], Johan Lauwaert[3], Bart Vermang[1]
[1] Hasselt Unversity, Genk, Belgium; [2] University of Cyprus, Nicosia, Cyprus; [3] Ghent University, Ghent, Belgium

Oral SESSION 2BO.8 Advanced Conversion Devices

Visual SESSION 2BV.1 New Materials, Devices and Conversion Concepts | New Modelling and Characterisation Techniques

Visual SESSION 3AV.2 PV Module Durability and Reliability

*Nathan Roosloot[1], Harsha Walpita[2], Christoph Seiffert[1], Jean Thomas[3],
Maarten Dörenkämper[4], Minne M. de Jong[4], Josefine H. Selj[1], Gaute Otnes[1]*
*[1] Institute for Energy Technology, Kjeller, Norway; [2] University of Oslo, Kjeller, Norway; [3]
Ciel et Terre, Lille, France; [4] TNO, Eindhoven, The Netherlands*

**Visual SESSION 3AV.3 PV Modules Characterisation and Performances
Assessment**

Cristian Terrados[1], Eva de la Viuda[1], Kabir Paul Sulca[1], Julian Anaya[1], Miguel Ángel González[1], Oscar Martínez[1]
[1] University of Valladolid, Valladolid, Spain

3BO.11.6 Luminescence Measurements of PV Modules with a Cost-Effective and Small-Sized Hood-Based Tool under Daylight Conditions   020206

Marc Köntges[1], Michael Siebert[1], Dieter Lorenz[2], Bernd Kuhrmann[2], Michael Fuß[2]
[1] ISFH, Emmerthal, Germany; [2] MBJ Solutions, Ahrensburg, Germany

Oral SESSION 3BO.12 Characterisation and Energy Rating of PV Modules

3BO.12.1 Developing a New I-V Translation Methodology in Accordance with IEC 60891:2021 Correction Procedure 1 and 2   020208

Wenhao Xu[1], Yating Zhang[1], Mengdi Liu[1], Christos Monokroussos[1], Werner Herrmann[2], Giorgio Bardizza[2], Harald Müllejans[3]
[1] TÜV Rheinland, Shanghai, China; [2] TÜV Rheinland Solar, Cologne, Germany; [3] European Commission JRC, Ispra, Italy

3BO.12.2 Characterization of Vehicle Integrated Photovoltaic Modules   020209

Ricardo Moruno[1], Francisco José Martín[1], Juan Manuel Redondo[1], Javier Malo[1], Luis Javier San José[1], Guido Vallerotto[1], Steve Askins[1], Rubén Núñez[1], César Domínguez[1], Ignacio Antón[1], Rebeca Herrero[1]
[1] UPM, Madrid, Spain

3BO.12.4 Estimating the Energy Yield of Bifacial Photovoltaics with the JRC's Photovoltaic Geographic Information System   020210

Nigel Taylor[1], Teodora Lyubenova[1], Lavanya Malarkannan[2], Nikos Alexandris[1], Alexandros Falangas[3], Robert Kenny[1], Ewan D. Dunlop[1], Blago Mihaylov[1]
[1] European Commission JRC, Ispra, Italy; [2] National Physical Laboratory, Teddington, United Kingdom; [3] TRASIS International, Brussels, Belgium

3BO.12.5 An Update on Energy Rating Amendments – Integration of Bifacial Modules   020211

Stefan Riechelmann[1], Hendrik Sträter[1], Ana María Gracia Amillo[2], Sophie Pelland[3], Anton Driesse[4]
[1] PTB, Braunschweig, Germany; [2] CENER, Pamplona, Spain; [3] Natural Resources Canada, Varennes, Canada; [4] PV Performance Labs, Freiburg, Germany

Oral SESSION 3BO.14 Characterisation and Outdoor Monitoring of Perovskite-based PV Modules

3BO.14.1 Outdoor Measurements of Perovskite Modules   020213

Hanna Ellis[1], Harald Müllejans[1], Ewan D. Dunlop[1], Tony Sample[1]
[1] European Commission JRC, Ispra, Italy

Oral SESSION 3BO.15 Outdoor Performances and Degradation Analysis of PV Modules

3CO.11.5 Indoor Characterization and Analysis of Reverse Breakdown Behavior of   020223
Solar Cells with Different Cell Architectures

Bengt Jaeckel[1], Jens Froebel[1], Matthias Pander[1], Andreas Maixner[2], Hamed Hanifi[2]
[1] *Fraunhofer CSP, Halle, Germany;* [2] *AESOLAR, Koenigsbrunn, Germany*

Plenary SESSION 3CP.1 Si PV Manufacturing: Pushing the Limits of Performance

3CP.1.2   IBC4EU: European Back Contact Technology   020225

Florian Buchholz[1], Daniel Tune[1], Tobias Meßmer[1], Jonathan Linke[1], Manjunath Prasad[1], Valentin D. Mihailetchi[1], Juras Ulbikas[2], Arne Dahle[3], Martijn Meereboer[4], Francesca Fabris[5], Erik Eikelboom[5], Tom Borgers[6], Rik Van Dyck[6], Filip Duerinckx[7], Hariharsudan Sivaramakrishnan Radhakrishnan[7], Timea Bejat[8], Samuel Harrison[8], Ashish Binani[9], Nicolas Guillevin[9], Jan Kroon[9], Yevgeniya Larionova[10], Thorsten Dullweber[10], Ofer Shochet[11], Isaac Rosen [11], Ingo Röver [12], Wolfram Palitzsch[12], Yasmin Zaror[13], Johannes Stierstorfer[14], Aurimas Radzevicius[15], Julius Denafas[16], Tuomas Vanhanen [17], Tuukka Savisalo[17], Maximilian Pospischil [18], Marian Breitenbücher [18], Özlem Coşkun[19], Melodie de l`Epine [20], Philippe Macé[20], Ian Kenchington[20]
[1] *ISC Konstanz, Konstanz, Germany;* [2] *Protechnology, Vilnius, Lithuania;* [3] *Norsun, Oslo, Norway;* [4] *Energyra, Westknollendam, The Netherlands;* [5] *Futurasun, Citadella, Italy;* [6] *IMEC, Genk, Belgium;* [7] *Hasselt Unversity, Genk, Belgium;* [8] *CEA, Le Bourget-du-Lac, France;* [9] *TNO, Petten, The Netherlands;* [10] *ISFH, Emmerthal, Germany;* [11] *Copprint, Jerusalem, Israel;* [12] *LuxChemTech, Freiberg, Germany;* [13] *WIP Renewable Energies, Munich, Germany;* [14] *WIP - Renewable Energies, Munich, Germany;* [15] *Valoe Cells, Vilnius, Lithuania;* [16] *Solitek, Vilnius, Lithuania;* [17] *Valoe, Mikkeli, Finland;* [18] *Highline Technologies, Freiburg, Germany;* [19] *Kalyon PV, Ankara, Türkiye;* [20] *Becquerel Institute, Brussels, Belgium*

Plenary SESSION 3CP.3 Perovskite – Silicon Tandems: Towards Commercialisation | PV Stability in the Field

3CP.3.4   Outdoor Performance and Reliability of Perovskite (Pk)-Silicon (Si)   020226
Tandems: >1 year of Monitoring in the NEXUS Project

Atse Louwen[1], Jordi Veirman[1], Alexander Astigarraga[1], Juan José Stivanello[1], David Moser[2], Perrine Carroy[3], Vincent Barth[3], Delfina Muñoz[3], Markus Lenz[4], Anika Sidler[4], Jorge Ferrando[5], Maximiliano Alejandro Senno[5], Henk J. Bolink[5], Talat Özden[6], Hisham Nasser[6], Shuaifeng Hu[7], Xinyi Shen[7], Henry Snaith[7]
[1] *Eurac Research, Bolzano, Italy;* [2] *Becquerel Institute Italy, Trento, Italy;* [3] *CEA / INES, Le Bourget-du-Lac, France;* [4] *School of Life Sciences FHNW, Muttenz, Switzerland;* [5] *University of Valencia, Paterna, Spain;* [6] *ODTÜ-GÜNAM, Ankara, Türkiye;* [7] *University of Oxford, Oxford, United Kingdom*

Oral SESSION 3DO.12 Innovative Encapsulation Materials

Oral SESSION 4DO.1 PV Tracking and Simulation

*Marcus Rennhofer[1], Philipp Mayer-Ullmann[1], Diana Maria Krainer[1],
Gusztav Ujvari[1], Janine Lichtenberger[1], Konrad Kainz[1], Vassilissa Neussl[1],
Bernhard Kubicek[1]*
[1] AIT, Vienna, Austria

Visual SESSION 4DV.4 PV System Engineering

Oral SESSION 5EO.1 Citizens Participation and Awareness

This presentation was selected by the Sc. Committee of the EU PVSEC 2025 for submission of a full paper to one of the EU PVSEC's collaborating peer-reviewed journals.

EFFECT OF GLASS BEADS ON THE SOLAR OPTICAL PROPERTIES OF THERMOPLASTIC ENCAPSULANTS FOR COLORED PV MODULES

Martin Huemer[1,3], Gernot M. Wallner[1,2], Andreas Brandstätter[3]
[1]Institute of Polymeric Materials and Testing, University of Linz, Austria
martin.huemer@jku.at
[2]Christian Doppler Laboratory for Superimposed Mechanical-Environmental Ageing of Polymeric Hybrid Laminates,
Institute of Polymeric Materials and Testing, University of Linz, Austria
gernot.wallner@jku.at
[3]Lenzing Plastics GmbH, Werkstrasse 2, 4860 Lenzing, Austria
a.brandstaetter@lenzing-plastics.com

ABSTRACT: A promising approach for producing colored photovoltaic (PV) modules is the incorporation of interference pigments into the front encapsulant. Besides several advantages such as spectrally selective reflection, higher efficiency or better durability, the main disadvantage of interference pigments are variations in specular reflectance depending on the angle [1]. The main objective of this work was to evaluate the potential of glass beads as diffusor pigments in colored PV encapsulants. Films varying in type (refractive index and particle size) and concentration of the glass beads were manufactured. Furthermore, films with a combination of glass fillers and interference pigments were analysed. Fourteen film grades were assessed by UV/Vis/NIR spectroscopy. The reflectance of the glass bead modified encapsulants was dependent on the refractive index and the particle size. The smallest beads with the highest reflectance index were not suitable. The transmittance of the film was below 80 %. However, the other glass grades were classified as an interesting option for homogenization fillers for colored PV encapsulants.
Keywords: Encapsulation, glass beads, spectroscopy

1 INTRODUCTION

Significant efforts have been devoted to the research of Building Integrated Photovoltaic (BIPV) systems and more aesthetically pleasing PV modules. Thereby, colored modules have to fulfil high optical requirements. To mitigate the often negatively perceived angular dependency of structural colors like interference pigments, light must be scattered. This can either be done by a rough surface of the front sheet or by directly incorporating scattering agents in the front encapsulant. While so far mainly $BaSO_4$ was used, in this study for the first time the potential of glass beads varying in particle size, index of refraction and content is assessed systematically.

2 EXPERIMENTAL

Forteen films made from a non-crosslinked thermoplastic polyolefin (TPO) were manufactured by Lenzing Plastics GmbH (Austria). The encapsulants differed in the concentration (low or high) and type of the glass beads (refractive index and particle size). Four films were equipped with both, glass beads and interference pigments. As references, a non-pigmented transparent and a blue-pigmented encapsulant film without glass beads were examined. The films were characterized by UV/Vis/NIR-spectroscopy in the range from 250 to 2500 nm in 5 nm steps on a Lambda 950 UV/Vis/NIR spectrometer (PerkinElmer, USA) equipped with a 150 mm integrating sphere. Hemispheric (T_h) and diffuse transmittance (T_d) as well as hemispheric reflectance (R_h) spectra were recorded. The spectral data were weighted with a reference air mass spectrum (AM1.5) source function and integrated over the solar range from 300 to 1250 nm according to equations (1)-(3), where "λ" is the wavelength. Hemispheric ($T_{h,sol}$) and diffuse solar transmittance ($T_{d,sol}$) and hemispheric solar reflectance ($R_{h,sol}$) values were deduced [2, 3]. Moreover, hemispheric solar absorbance ($A_{h,sol}$) and the solar haze were calculated with equations (4) and (5). To evaluate the expected relative efficiency (η_{rel}) of the PV modules, the hemispheric transmittance data was weighted with an AM1.5 source function and a spectral response function for a typical monocrystalline silicon cell (SR) (see equation (6)). The obtained values ($T_{h,sol}^{mSi}(i)$) were then normalized with equation (7) to those of the non-pigmented, transparent film ($T_{h,sol}^{mSi}(Tr)$).

$$T_{h,sol} = \frac{\int_{300}^{1250} (T_h)_\lambda (AM_{1.5})_\lambda d\lambda}{\int_{300}^{1250} (AM_{1.5})_\lambda d\lambda} \qquad (1)$$

$$T_{d,sol} = \frac{\int_{300}^{1250} (T_d)_\lambda (AM_{1.5})_\lambda d\lambda}{\int_{300}^{1250} (AM_{1.5})_\lambda d\lambda} \qquad (2)$$

$$R_{h,sol} = \frac{\int_{300}^{1250} (R_h)_\lambda (AM_{1.5})_\lambda d\lambda}{\int_{300}^{1250} (AM_{1.5})_\lambda d\lambda} \qquad (3)$$

$$A_{h,sol} = 100 - T_{h,sol} - R_{h,sol} \qquad (4)$$

$$Haze = \frac{T_{d,sol}}{T_{h,sol}} \times 100 \qquad (5)$$

$$T_{h,sol}^{mSi} = \frac{\int_{300}^{1250} (T_h)_\lambda (AM_{1.5})_\lambda \, SR_\lambda \, d\lambda}{\int_{300}^{1250} (AM_{1.5})_\lambda \, SR_\lambda \, d\lambda} \qquad (6)$$

$$\eta_{rel}(i) = \frac{T_{h,sol}^{mSi}(i)}{T_{h,sol}^{mSi}(Tr)} \times 100 \qquad (7)$$

3 RESULTS

The solar transmittance and reflectance spectra of the encapsulants filled with different glass beads are illustrated in Fig. 1 to Fig. 4. Furthermore, the calculated solar weighted properties as well as the expected relative efficiency of the films are listed in Table I and Table II. The first number of the diffusor pigment type refers to the refractive index (n) and the second to the average bead size. Encapsulants equipped with glass beads of high refractive index (n=2.15) revealed a significant higher hemispheric reflectance and lower hemispheric transmittance. Smaller particles with an average size of 2.2 µm increased the hemispherical reflection by a factor of 2 compared to a particle size of 7.6 µm. This is in good agreement with the Mie theory [4]. Due to the high reflectance and consequently lower transmittance, the glass beads G 2.25 – 2.2 are not reasonable for efficient PV modules. The relative efficiency dropped to 60 %. The films with the lower refractive index glass beads (n=1.5) did not differ in their optical properties. For both particle sizes the hemispheric reflectance and the diffuse transmittance were higher maintaining also a high hemispheric transmittance. Consequently, the haze of these films was noticeably increasing, probably leading to a reduction of the angular dependency of color perception of interference pigmented encapsulants. The hemispheric absorbance was not affected. Deviations by 1 to 2 % were primarily related to scattering losses at the edge of the film samples.

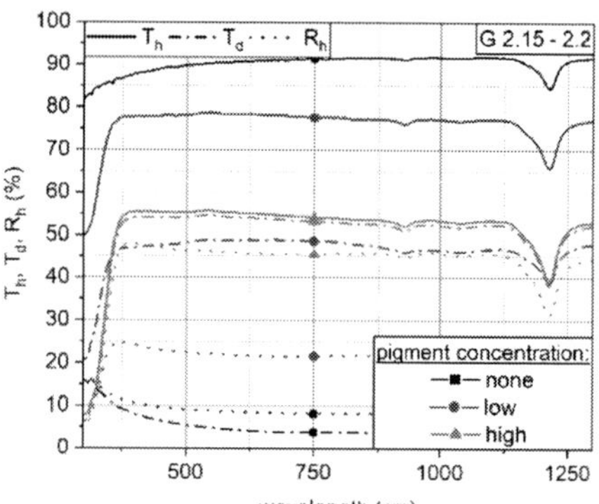

Figure 1: Hemispheric transmittance (T_h) and reflectance (R_h) and diffuse transmittance (T_d) spectra of the encapsulants filled with glass beads with a refractive index of 2.15 and a bead size of 2.2 µm.

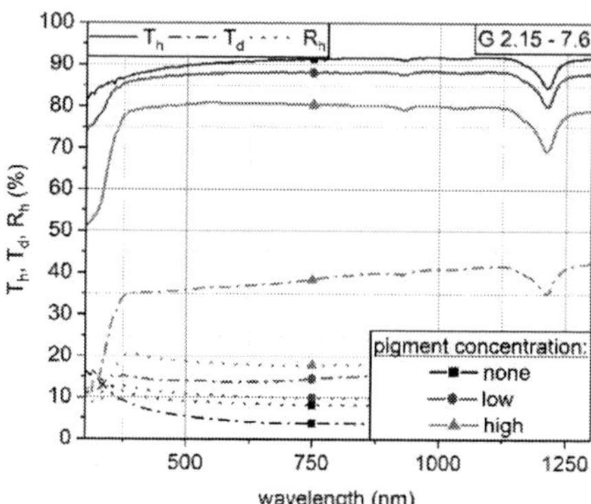

Figure 2: Hemispheric transmittance (T_h) and reflectance (R_h) and diffuse transmittance (T_d) spectra of the encapsulants filled with glass beads with a refractive index of 2.15 and a bead size of 7.6 µm.

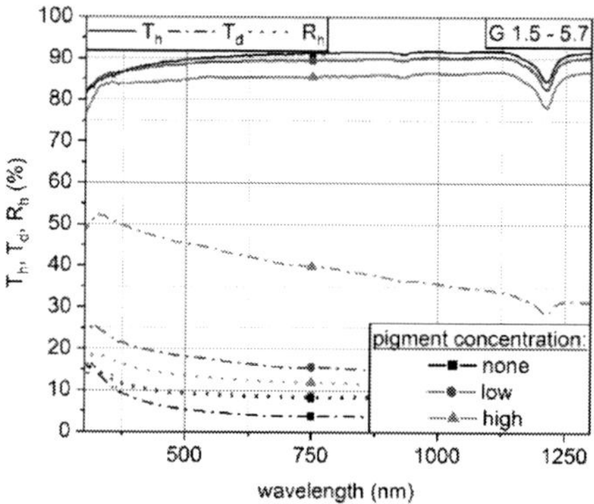

Figure 3: Hemispheric transmittance (T_h) and reflectance (R_h) and diffuse transmittance (T_d) spectra of the encapsulants filled with glass beads with a refractive index of 1.5 and a bead size of 5.7 µm.

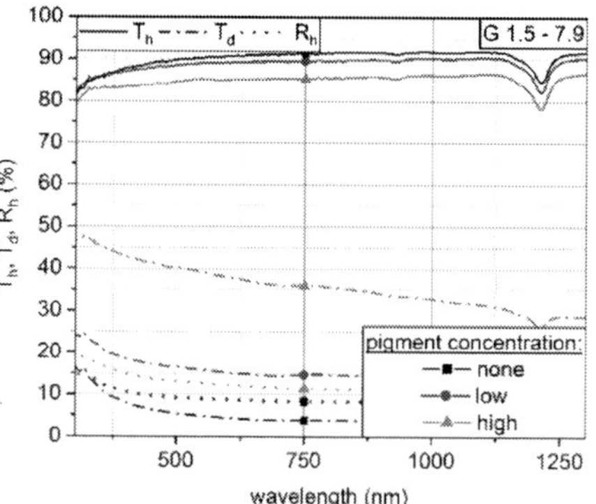

Figure 4: Hemispheric transmittance (T_h) and reflectance (R_h) and diffuse transmittance (T_d) spectra of the encapsulants filled with glass beads with a refractive index of 1.5 and a bead size of 7.9 µm.

In Fig. 5 the solar transmittance and reflectance spectra of the encapsulants containing various glass beads and the blue interference pigments are depicted. The same order of drop in transmittance and rise in reflectance as described above was found. Hence, it is not only possible to adjust the haze of the encapsulants but also the intensity of color perception. The reflectance spectra reveal a more pronounced shift to higher values especially at the lower, blueish wavelengths. For example, the embedding of G 1.5 – 5.7 led to a 4 % rise in reflectance at a wavelength of 600 nm, but a 13 % boost at 425 nm. Interestingly, the combination of the glass fillers with the interference pigments resulted in a minor increase of the absorbance. This slight delta may be a measuring artefact, as light is presumably scattered past the opening of the integrating sphere [5, 6]. The actual efficiency should be slightly higher than listed in Table II.

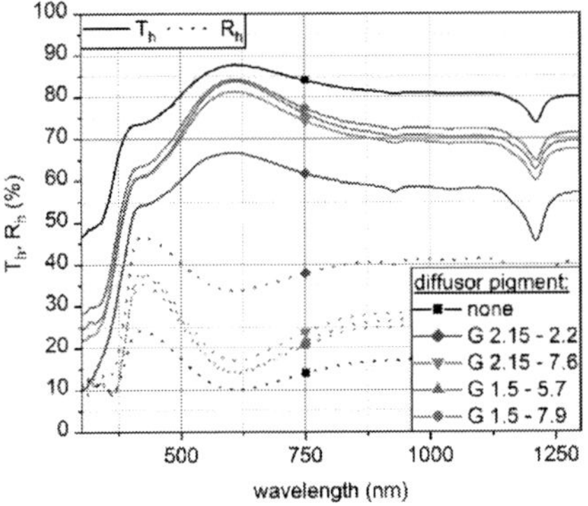

Figure 5: Hemispheric transmittance (T_h) and reflectance (R_h) spectra of the encapsulants filled with a blue interference pigment and different glass beads.

Table I: Solar weighted hemispheric transmittance and reflactance and diffuse transmittance of the investigated encapsulants.

diffuser pigment		blue pigment	$T_{h,sol}$	$T_{d,sol}$	$R_{h,sol}$
type	concentration		%	%	%
-	none	no	90	5	9
G 2.15 - 2.2	low	no	77	48	22
G 2.15 - 2.2	high	no	54	53	45
G 2.15 - 7.6	low	no	87	15	10
G 2.15 - 7.6	high	no	80	37	18
G 1.5 - 5.7	low	no	89	16	9
G 1.5 - 5.7	high	no	85	41	13
G 1.5 - 7.9	low	no	89	15	9
G 1.5 - 7.9	high	no	85	37	12
-	none	yes	81	21	15
G 2.15 - 2.2	medium	yes	59	53	38
G 2.15 - 7.6	medium	yes	71	40	25
G 1.5 - 5.7	medium	yes	74	40	22
G 1.5 - 7.9	medium	yes	72	40	23

Table II: Solar weighted hemispheric absorbance, solar haze and expected relative efficiency of the investigated encapsulants.

diffuser pigment		blue pigment	$A_{h,sol}$	Haze	η_{rel}
type	concentration		%	%	%
-	none	no	1	5	100
G 2.15 - 2.2	low	no	1	61	86
G 2.15 - 2.2	high	no	1	98	60
G 2.15 - 7.6	low	no	2	17	97
G 2.15 - 7.6	high	no	2	47	88
G 1.5 - 5.7	low	no	2	19	98
G 1.5 - 5.7	high	no	2	48	94
G 1.5 - 7.9	low	no	2	17	98
G 1.5 - 7.9	high	no	3	44	94
-	none	yes	3	26	91
G 2.15 - 2.2	medium	yes	3	90	67
G 2.15 - 7.6	medium	yes	4	56	80
G 1.5 - 5.7	medium	yes	4	54	83
G 1.5 - 7.9	medium	yes	5	55	82

4 CONCLUSIONS

The study revealed the possibility to manipulate the solar optical properties of encapsulants by incorporating glass fillers. While small glass beads with a high refractive index are not suitable for highly efficient PV modules, larger beads with a lower refractive index similar to the encapsulant material seem to be a reasonable approach. To assess the angular dependency of the encapsulants, color perception will be evaluated on double-glass module level. Furthermore, angle-dependent measurements will be conducted.

5 REFERENCES

[1] Perales E., Chorro E., Cramer W. R., Martinez-Verdú F. M., "Analysis of the colorimetric properties of goniochromatic colors using the MacAdam limits under different light sources," Appl. Opt., no. 50, pp. 5271–5278.
[2] Wallner, G. M., Platzer, W., and Lang, R. W., "Structure–property correlations of polymeric films for transparent insulation wall applications. Part 1: Solar

optical properties," Solar Energy, vol. 79, no. 6, pp. 583–592, 2005.

[3] R. E. Bird, R. L. Hulstrom, "Terrestrial solar spectral data sets," Sol. Energy 30, vol. 1983, pp. 563–573.

[4] Mie, G., "Beiträge zur Optik trüber Medien, speziell kolloidaler Metallösungen," Annalen der Physik, vol. 330, no. 3, pp. 377–445, 1908.

[5] D.I. Milburn and K.G.T. Hollands, "An analysis of thick-sample effects in the measurement of directional-hemispherical transmittance," Optics Communications, no. 118, pp. 1–8, 1995.

[6] Neugebauer, J., Wallner-Novak, M., Lehner, T., Wrulich, C., and Baumgartner, M., "Movable Thin Glass Elements in Façades," 195-202 Pages / Challenging Glass Conference Proceedings, Vol. 6 (2018): Challenging Glass 6, 2018.

Effect of Glass Beads on the Solar Optical Properties of Thermoplastic Encapsulants for Colored PV Modules

Martin Huemer[1,3], Gernot M. Wallner[1,2], Andreas Brandstätter[3]

[1] Institute of Polymeric Materials and Testing, University of Linz, Austria

[2] Christian Doppler Laboratory for Superimposed Mechanical-Environmental Ageing of Polymeric Hybrid Laminates, Institute of Polymeric Materials and Testing, University of Linz, Austria

[3] Lenzing Plastics GmbH, Werkstrasse 2, 4860 Lenzing, Austria

EU PVSEC 2025
Bilbao, 25th of September 2025

INTRODUCTION: CONCEPT FOR COLORED PHOTOVOLTAICS

Lenzing Plastics — Solpol

- Interference-pigmented thermoplastic polyolefin (TPO)

  - Terpolymer:

    - ~ 89.5 mol% ethylene

    - ~ 10 mol% acrylate

    - ~ 0.5% silane

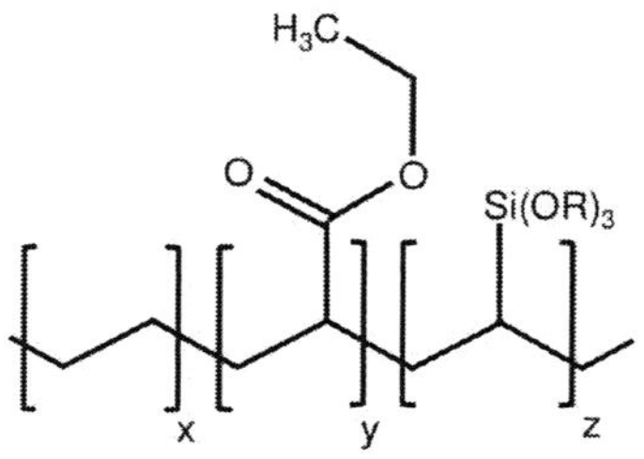

  - Additives:

    - Interference pigments

    - Diffusor pigment

    - Carbon Black

    - UV stabilizer

020228-002

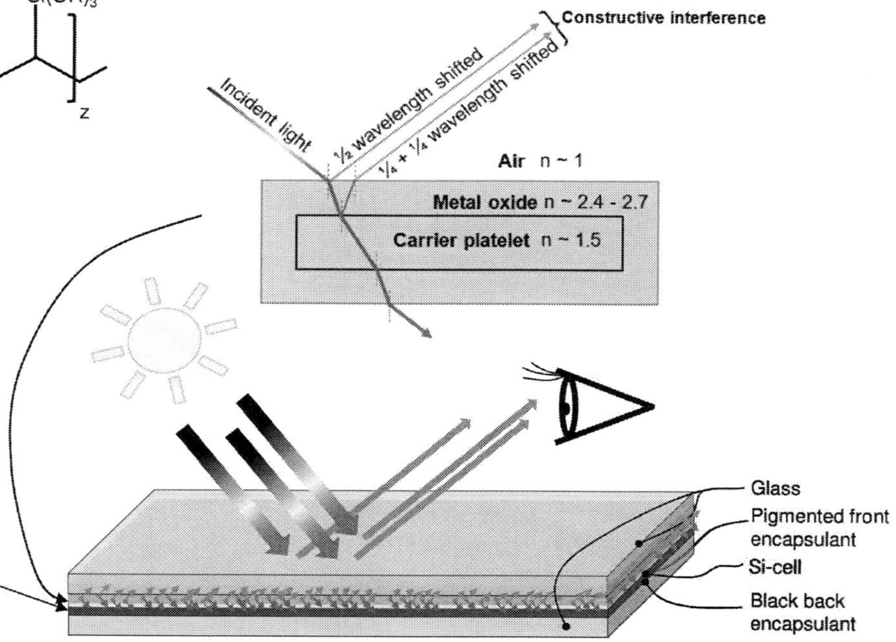

EXPERIMENTAL | INVESTIGATED ENCAPSULANTS

Lenzing Plastics — solpol

- 14 TPO encapsulants (450 µm) manufactured at Lenzing Plastics

diffuser pigment			blue interference
refractive index	average size in µm	concentration	pigment
-	-	-	no
2.15	2.2	low	no
2.15	2.2	high	no
2.15	7.6	low	no
2.15	7.6	high	no
1.5	5.7	low	no
1.5	5.7	high	no
1.5	7.9	low	no
1.5	7.9	high	no
-	-	-	yes
2.15	2.2	medium	yes
2.15	7.6	medium	yes
1.5	5.7	medium	yes
1.5	7.9	medium	yes

Photographic images of 450 µm x 25 mm x 25 mm films in front of a chessboard.

020228-003

EXPERIMENTAL | METHODS AND CALCULATIONS

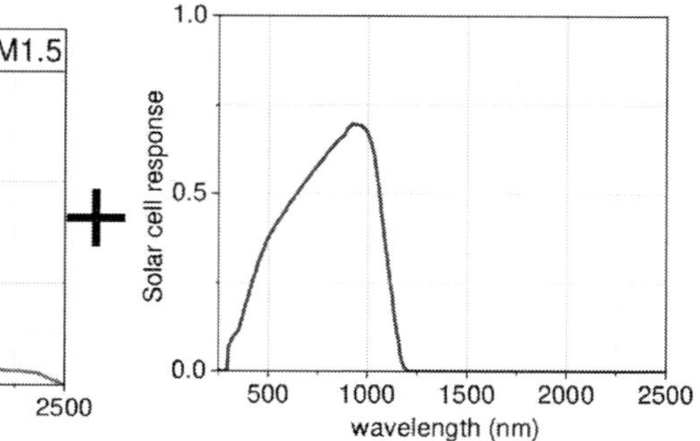

$$T_{h,sol} = \frac{\int_{300}^{1250} (T_h)_\lambda (AM_{1.5})_\lambda \, d\lambda}{\int_{300}^{1250} (AM_{1.5})_\lambda \, d\lambda}$$

$$T_{d,sol} = \frac{\int_{300}^{1250} (T_d)_\lambda (AM_{1.5})_\lambda \, d\lambda}{\int_{300}^{1250} (AM_{1.5})_\lambda \, d\lambda}$$

$$R_{h,sol} = \frac{\int_{300}^{1250} (R_h)_\lambda (AM_{1.5})_\lambda \, d\lambda}{\int_{300}^{1250} (AM_{1.5})_\lambda \, d\lambda}$$

$$A_{h,sol} = 100 - T_{h,sol} - R_{h,sol}$$

$$Haze = \frac{T_{d,sol}}{T_{h,sol}} \times 100$$

$$T_{h,sol}^{mSi} = \frac{\int_{300}^{1250} (T_h)_\lambda (AM_{1.5})_\lambda \, SR\lambda \, d\lambda}{\int_{300}^{1250} (AM_{1.5})_\lambda \, SR\lambda \, d\lambda}$$

$$\eta_{rel}(i) = \frac{T_{h,sol}^{mSi}(i)}{T_{h,sol}^{mSi}(Tr)} \times 100$$

020228-004

RESULTS | MICROSCOPIC IMAGES

Lenzing | Plastics | solpol

Microscopic images of the TPO encapsulants; upper row: high concentration of glass beads and no interference pigments; lower row: medium concentration of glass beads and blue interference pigments.

020228-005

RESULTS | SOLAR OPTICAL PROPERTIES
REFRACTIVE INDEX 2.15

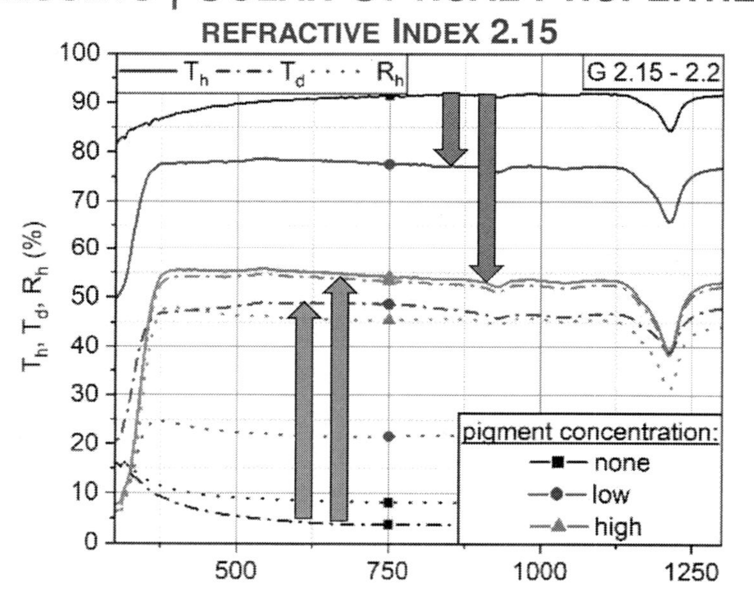

— Increased reflectance and diffuse transmittance

— Huge loss in hemispheric transmittance and estimated efficiency

$\Delta T_{h,sol}$	$\Delta T_{d,sol}$	$\Delta R_{h,sol}$	$\Delta A_{h,sol}$	ΔHaze	η_{rel}
-13	+43	+13	0	+56	86
-36	+48	+36	0	+93	60

— Less Increased reflectance and diffuse transmittance

— Lower loss in hemispheric transmittance

$\Delta T_{h,sol}$	$\Delta T_{d,sol}$	$\Delta R_{h,sol}$	$\Delta A_{h,sol}$	ΔHaze	η_{rel}
-3	+10	+1	+1	+12	97
-10	+32	+9	+1	+42	88

020228-006

RESULTS | SOLAR OPTICAL PROPERTIES

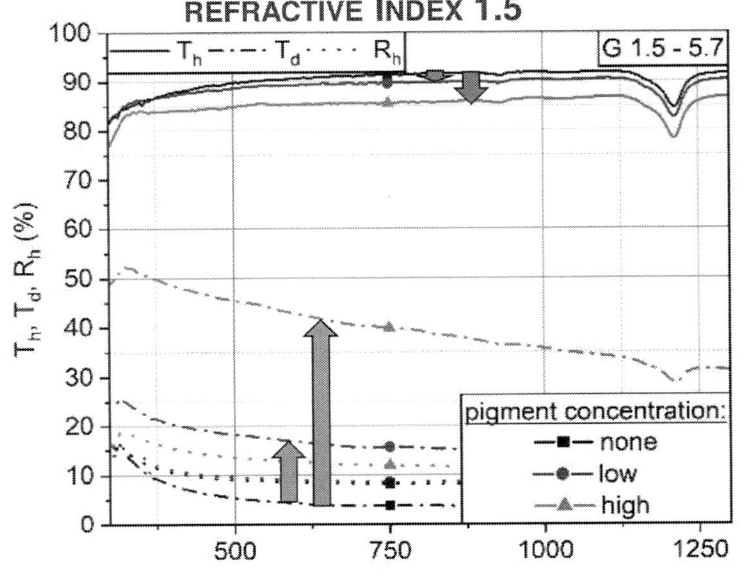

— Increased diffuse transmittance

— Almost no loss in hemispheric transmittance and estimated efficiency

$\Delta T_{h,sol}$	$\Delta T_{d,sol}$	$\Delta R_{h,sol}$	$\Delta A_{h,sol}$	ΔHaze	η_{rel}
-1	+11	0	+1	+14	98
-4	+36	+4	+1	+44	94

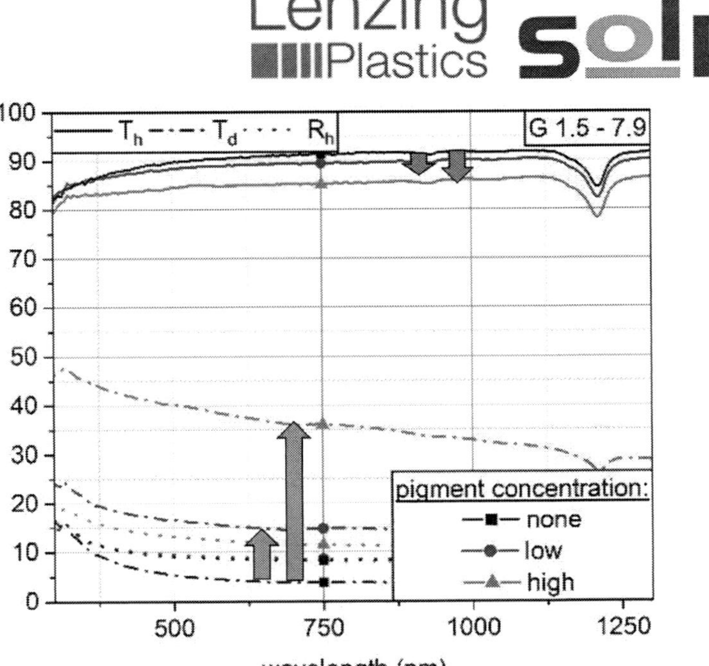

— Increased diffuse transmittance

— Almost no loss in hemispheric transmittance and estimated efficiency

$\Delta T_{h,sol}$	$\Delta T_{d,sol}$	$\Delta R_{h,sol}$	$\Delta A_{h,sol}$	ΔHaze	η_{rel}
-1	+10	0	+1	+12	98
-4	+32	+3	+2	+39	94

RESULTS | SOLAR OPTICAL PROPERTIES
INTERACTION OF DIFFUSER AND INTERFERENCE PIGMENT

	$\Delta T_{h,sol}$	$\Delta T_{d,sol}$	$\Delta R_{h,sol}$	$\Delta A_{h,sol}$	ΔHaze	η_{rel}
G 2.15 – 2.2	-22	+32	+23	0	+64	67
G 2.15 – 7.6	-10	+19	+10	+1	+30	80
G 1.5 – 5.7	-7	+19	+7	+1	+28	83
G 1.5 – 7.9	-9	+19	+8	+2	+32	82

— More pronounced shift of the reflectance at lower blueish wavelengths

Photographic images of 100 mm x 100 mm double glass laminates with a black back encapsulant and a blue front encapsulant with and without different glass beads.

020228-008

CONCLUSION AND OUTLOOK

Conclusion

- All investigated glass beads are increasing diffuse transmittance and haze

- Smaller particles result in pronounced increase in diffuse transmittance

- Higher refractive index leads to increased hemispheric reflectance

Outlook

- Angle-dependent color measurements

- Evaluating further diffusor pigments (chemistry, shape, size, refractive index, …)

- Producing multi-layered encapsulants

- Ageing stability

- Adherence testing:

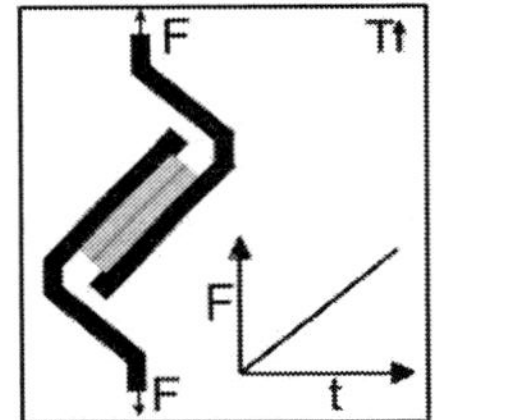
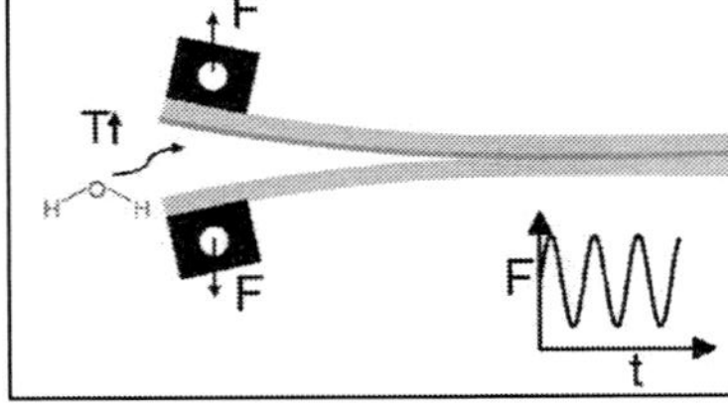

- Further applications (Agri-PV?)

Questions

- martin.huemer@jku.at

- https://colorquant.lenzing-plastics.com/

TOPCON PV Modules UV exposure: Uncovering Hidden Instabilities

Baloji Adothu[1,*], Shahzada Pamir Aly[1], Bengt Jaeckel[2], Matthias Pandar[2], Ralph Gottschalg[2], and Vivian Alberts[1]

[1]Research and Development Center, Dubai Electricity and Water Authority, Dubai, UAE.
[2]Fraunhofer Center for Silicon Photovoltaics CSP, Otto-Eissfeldt-Str. 12, 06120 Halle (Saale), Germany.

* Corresponding author: Phone +971 522 578980 | baloji.adothu@dewa.gov.ae

Abstract— The rapid expansion of GW-scale photovoltaic installations in desert environments is shifting the spotlight to the stability of new-generation PV module technologies under harsh conditions. High UV irradiance, a characteristic challenge of desert regions, has raised concerns about the long-term performance of emerging technologies, particularly the TOPCon PV modules, which technology is currently gaining rapidly increasing market share in the PV industry. In a collaborative study with leading solar institutes, TOPCON modules from different manufacturers were subjected to accelerated UV exposure at elevated temperatures to detect potentially hidden degradation pathways.

The results from our preliminary studies demonstrated a notable power degradation in 3 out of 5 TOPCon modules tested compared to PERC modules. In terms of the specific batches of PV modules considered, the three TOPCon modules that showed abnormal degradation exhibited power losses of around 8% after a UV dose exposure of 90 kWh/m². PERC modules exhibited lower values around 2% degradation (based on the UV aging study conducted at DEWA R&D). When UV exposure was combined with dark storage, the power degradation in the affected TOPCon modules increased significantly, reaching 13% to 16.5% (as observed in the UV aging study at F-CSP). Significant changes in the electrical parameters of the modules were observed after the UV exposure. However, light soaking was found to stabilize the performance of TOPCon modules after periods of dark storage. The combined impact of UV aging, dark storage, and light soaking revealed significant changes in the stability of TOPCon PV modules.

Electroluminescence (EL) imaging detected the formation of a distinct checkered pattern in some of the TOPCon modules, accompanied by intense UV fluorescence (UVF) at cell edges and along multi-busbar soldering points. Interestingly, these specific structural changes were not observed in the PERC modules, underscoring their stability after high-dose UV exposure. These findings highlight critical challenges and uncover the hidden instability of TOPCon, emphasizing the need for further interlaboratory testing and reliability studies to mitigate possible unknown degradation risks in high-UV environments.

Keywords— TOPCON PV Modules, PERC PV Modules, UV Exposure, UV instability, Performance

I. INTRODUCTION

The deployment of photovoltaic (PV) modules in desert regions has gained significant traction due to favorable environmental factors such as high solar irradiance, extended daylight hours, and generally clear skies. However, these regions also present extreme challenges to PV module performance and reliability due to harsh environmental conditions, including intense ultraviolet (UV) radiation, extreme temperatures, large temperature fluctuations, and the persistent accumulation of dust and soiling [1]. Despite technological advancements, the long-term impact of these conditions on module degradation and performance remains a concern and uncertain.

As the global PV market expands, new-generation PV technologies such as TOPCon (Tunnel Oxide Passivated Contact) modules have emerged as key players in PV industry. TOPCon technology uses an ultrathin tunnel oxide layer (1.2–1.5 nm) with poly-Si passivation to minimize recombination losses at the semiconductor/metal interfaces, while enhancing the electric field distribution in the depletion region. The combination of these effects leads to higher power conversion efficiency (PCE). Since 2022, this technologyhas emerged as a potential mainstream successor to PERC, offering efficiencies of 22–24% (with lab records above 26%), compared to PERC's 20–22% (lab record ~24%) [1–5]

The rapid expansion of gigawatt-scale solar farms has emphasized the importance of new advanced technologies with improved PCE and long-term stability.TOPCon currently shows real potential due to its promising efficiency gains over the previous mainstream technologies, like PERC (Passivated Emitter and Rear Cell) modules [1–5]While TOPCon provides better thermal and LeTID stability than PERC, UV stability may pose a significant challenge due to the sensitive nature of the tunnel oxide. Proposed degradation mechanisms include tunnel oxide and poly-Si passivation loss as well as hydrogen-related instabilities, making this an active area of research.

Desert environments are known to accelerate PV module degradation processes, with UV-induced degradation (UVID) being a dominant factor. This degradation primarily affects critical components such as encapsulants, backsheets, and interface and cell surface layers, leading to efficiency losses and shorter module deployment lifetimes [6–8]. Failure Mode and Effects Analysis (FMEA) conducted on desert-installed PV systems confirms that UVID poses a major reliability risk, particularly for evolving technologies like TOPCon, where stability under extreme UV exposure is not fully understood [9–11].

Compared to PERC modules, which are well understood, the unique design and materials of TOPCon cells and modules present the possibility of new degradation pathways that could compromise their long-term reliability in deserts. Laboratory observations reveal that while the degradation mechanisms in PERC modules are understood and predictable, the performance and reliability of TOPCon remain uncertain in the absence of long-term outdoor field studies. This is especially concerning, considering that TopCon modules have already been deployed at GW-scale in residential, commercial, and especially utility-scale projects.

This research investigates the degradation behavior and stability of TOPCON PV modules under accelerated UV exposure, incorporating the effects of dark storage and light soaking on their performance, considering a limited number of modules from various Tier 1 manufacturers. This study emphasizes the need for further interlaboratory and outdoor reliability studies to mitigate possible unknown or hidden degradation risks. A comprehensive understanding of the potential formation of unidentified early-stage and/or new classes of degradation mechanisms that may compromise the stability of TOPCON modules is essential for both the manufacturer and end users. By comparing the performance of TOPCON and PERC modules, the study aims to identify possible unknown degradation mechanisms that accelerate the degradation of TopCon modules in harsh desert climates.

II. METHODOLOGY

PV module selection: Batches of commercially available PERC and five TOPCON PV modules from a Tier 1 company were selected for this study. TOPCon and PERC are both types of modules that have undergone accelerated UV testing to compare their performance characteristics and degradation rates. TOPCon-PV1 and TOPCon-PV2 were utilised for continuous UV exposure test, while TOPCon-PV3, TOPCon-PV4, and TOPCon-PV5 were utilized for the UV test, followed by dark storage and light soaking process for studying their instabilities.

The study involves the collaborative studies of solar PV experts and leading research institutes to improve our understanding of potentially new or unknown degradation mechanisms in new generation solar PV technologies under UV exposure levels that represents typical desert conditions.

UV test conditions: The testing was conducted under short-circuit conditions and continued progressively up to 150 kWh/m² at a chamber temperature of 60 °C, using a UVTC-2 chamber (PSC Instrument GmbH). After each dosage interval of 30 kWh/m², comprehensive electrical characterization was performed to assess performance changes.

The cetisPV-Moduletest3 system from h.a.l.m. electronik GmbH is used to characterize the electrical parameters at AM1.5 Class A+A+A+ standards for solar simulation. Standard testing conditions (STC) are followed during the testing, which is conducted with an insolation of 1000 W/m² and a module temperature of 25°C. The duration of each test flash was 65 ms. EL images of PV modules captured using the CetisPV's EL-package. UV-FL imaging, which creates fluorescence images by illuminating the modules with UV light. The imaging was captured in dark room conditions.

III. RESULTS AND DISCUSSIONS

Fig.1 depicts the continuous UV exposure effect on the power degradation trend as a function of UV dose. The modules were exposed to UV irradiance on the front side during the UV test. The power degradation of PERC and two variants of TOPCon PV modules (TOPCon-PV1 and TOPCon-PV2) shows different behavior under continuous UV exposure test.

The TOPCon PV module exhibits the highest degradation in front side ((Fig.1a)), peaking at around 8%, followed by a slight recovery or stabilization. PERC module shows lower power degradation rates compared to TOPCon. Similar trends are observed in the rear side(Fig.1b) with TOPCon-PV2 again showing the highest degradation (~8%) under UV exposure, while TOPCon-PV1 and PERC exhibit more gradual and stable degradation patterns. Both TOPCon-PV2 and TOPCon-PV1 show significant decreases in open circuit voltage and fill factor. PERC experiences only a slight change, maintaining better long-term stability. PERC remains stable with minimal changes in FF.

Based on the specific batches of modules investigated in this study, preliminary results indicate that two different TOPCon modules from different manufacturers exhibit unexpectedly higher levels of power degradation in comparison to the reference PERC modules.

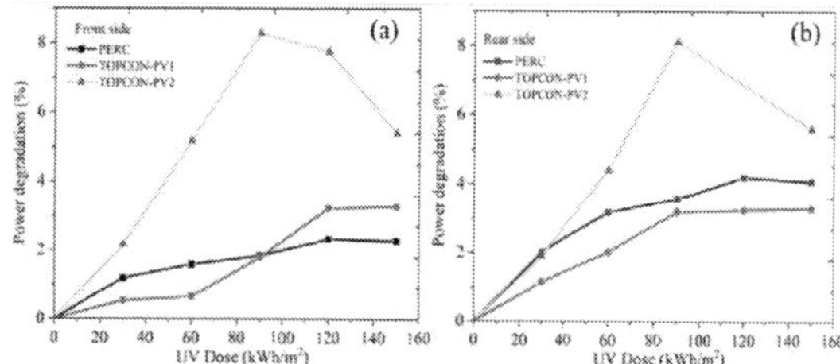

Fig.1: Continuous UV aging of TOPCON PV modules: (a) front side and (b) rear side power degradation.

Fig. 2 illustrates the power degradation of TOPCON-PV3, TOPCON-PV4, and TOPCON-PV5 modules under UV exposure and different storage conditions.

- TOPCon-PV5 shows the highest degradation (~13%) after cumulative UV doses and specific storage periods, with noticeable spikes after "UV60 + Storage" and intermediate light soaking and storage intervals.

- TOPCon-PV4 exhibits rapid initial degradation (~10%) at low UV doses (UV15) and storage conditions, but the degradation rate stabilizes after 20 kWh UV exposure.

- TOPCon-PV3 shows the least degradation and maintains stability even with extended UV doses, indicating better resistance to long-term UV stress compared to the other variants.

- Storage conditions (notably after UV exposure) significantly influence power degradation, as seen with TOPCon-PV5 experiencing sharp spikes during the storage periods (e.g., Storage 2d, Storage +1d).

- Light soaking stability (LS) tests (LS 26h, LS 20 kWh) indicate minimal additional degradation for TOPCon-PV3, highlighting its robust design or materials compared to the others.

Fig. 3 illustrates the electroluminescence (EL) images of TOPCon and PERC PV modules before and after the 150 kWh/m² UV test. TOPCon modules exhibit a surprisingly high frequency of dark and white check patterns in contrast to minor changes in PERC modules. This behaviour is similar to the reported study [12]. The combination of electrical and EL studies suggests potential performance and reliability issues with the specific batches of TopCon modules that were investigated. These observations at the very least warrant further investigation into the cause of these potential causes of

instabilities in TopCon modules, specifically after extended UV exposure.

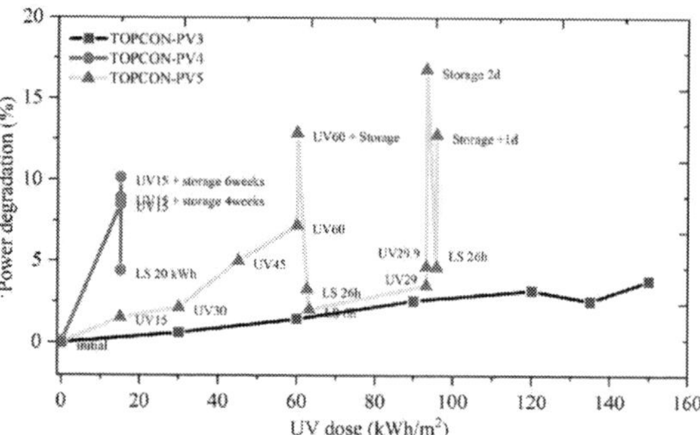

Fig. 2: Effect of UV exposure, dark storage, and light soaking on TOPCON PV modules

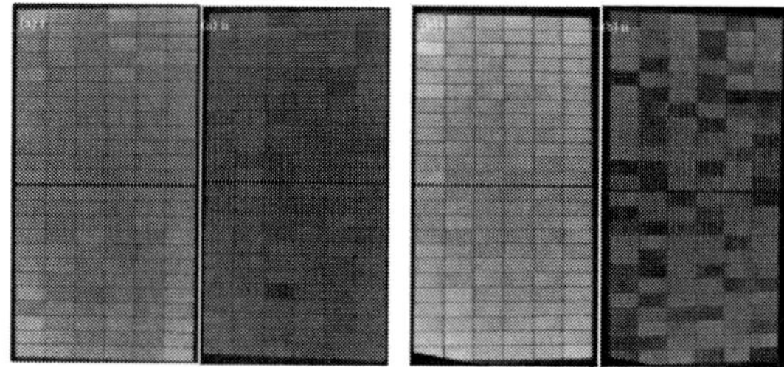

Fig. 3: Representative EL images of (a) PERC, and (b) TOPCON solar PV modules investigated in this study

Fig. 4 depicts the significant UV fluorescence (UVF) features that were observed in TOPCon modules, particularly along the cell edges and multibusbars. This observation suggests that, in addition to the possible degradation of TOPCon cell characteristics, interconnection and soldering defects may contribute to power degradation of new generation TOPCon modules. The fluorescence from both modules is not the same, indicating the BOM difference.

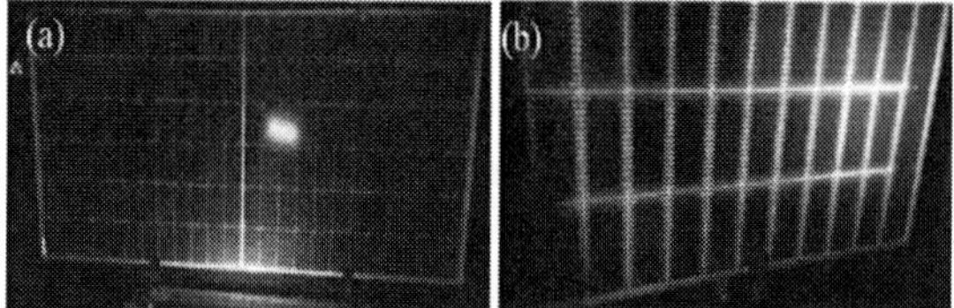

Fig. 4: Representative UVF images of (a) PERC and (b) TOPCON modules investigated in this study.

IV. CONCLUSIONS

The study on a limited batch of TOPCon PV modules raises concerns about its increased vulnerable to UV-induced degradation. In comparison to reference PERC modules, power losses in some TOPCon modules considered in this study reached 8–16.5% (especially when combined with dark storage), while others stayed within the range of only ~2% degradation like PERC modules. Various characterization techniques reveal distinct degradation features in some TOPCon modules, including a checkerboard pattern in EL imaging and UV fluorescence along cell edges and soldering points, abnormalities that were less prominent in reference PERC modules. These findings revealed potential risks that are associated with TOPCon technology. Further insights show:

- IV results: TOPCon exhibits stronger UV sensitivity, with a significant impact on Voc and FF.

- Front vs rear sides: degradation behavior is similar.

- Stability variation: The variation in fluorescence observed in UV-F imaging is strongly influenced by the manufacturer type and the quality of the BOM.

- Instability trends: continuous degradation under UV, sharp losses in dark storage, and partial recovery after light soaking in some modules.

The study emphasizes the need for interlaboratory reliability testing and deeper investigation into the mechanisms behind fluorescence, checkerboard EL patterns, and potential instability in TOPCon modules to improve their long-term reliability.

REFERENCES

[1] B. Adothu, S. Kumar, J.J. John, G. Oreski, G. Mathiak, B. Jäckel, V. Alberts, J. Bin Jahangir, M.A. Alam, R. Gottschalg, Comprehensive review on performance, reliability, and roadmap of c-Si PV modules in desert climates: A proposal for improved testing standard, Progress in Photovoltaics: Research and Applications 32 (2024) 495–527. https://doi.org/10.1002/PIP.3827.

[2] International Technology Roadmap for Photovoltaic (ITRPV)-2025, 16th Edition, 2025. https://www.vdma.eu/international-technology-roadmap-photovoltaic (accessed August 26, 2025).

[3] F.T. Thome, P. Meßmer, S. Mack, E. Schnabel, F. Schindler, W. Kwapil, M.C. Schubert, UV-Induced Degradation of Industrial PERC, TOPCon, and HJT Solar Cells: The Next Big Reliability Challenge?, Solar RRL 8 (2024). https://doi.org/10.1002/SOLR.202400628.

[4] M.Q. Khokhar, H. Yousuf, S. Jeong, S. Kim, X. Fan, Y. Kim, S.K. Dhungel, J. Yi, A Review on p-Type Tunnel Oxide Passivated Contact (TOPCon) Solar Cell, Transactions on Electrical and Electronic Materials 24 (2023) 169–177. https://doi.org/10.1007/S42341-023-00433-Z.

[5] M.U. Khan, C. Sen, M. Pollard, T. Huang, M. Gao, R. Lv, Y. Yu, X. Wu, H. Wang, X. Wang, B. Hoex, UV-induced degradation in TOPCon solar cells: Hydrogen dynamics and impact of UV wavelength, Solar Energy Materials and Solar Cells 294 (2026) 113895. https://doi.org/10.1016/J.SOLMAT.2025.113895.

[6] Baloji Adothu, Sagarika Kumar, Bengt Jaeckel, Neha Lyka Muttumthala, Z. Shekason, David Daßler, Kaushal Chapaneri, Prashanth Gabbadi, Yogesh Kumar, Ahmad Alheloo, Ali Almheiri, Jim Joseph John, Gerhard Mathiak, Vivian Alberts, Ralph Gottschalg, Identification and Investigation of Materials Degradation in Photovoltaic Modules from Middle East Hot Desert, in: 40th European Photovoltaic Solar Energy Conference and Exhibition (EU PVSEC 2023), 2023: pp. 001–004. https://doi.org/10.4229/EUPVSEC2023/3AV.2.29.

[7] Baloji Adothu;, Sagarika Kumar;, Swathi Sreekuttan;, Zahra Faiyaz Shekason;, A. Alheloo;, A. Almheiri;, Jim Joseph John;, Gerhard Mathiak;, Bengt Jaeckel;, Ralph Gottschalg;, Vivian Alberts, Discoloration Effect on Performance of PV Modules Installed in Middle East Hot Desert, in: 2023 Middle East and North Africa Solar Conference (MENA-SC), Dubai, United Arab Emirates, 2023: pp. 1–4. https://doi.org/10.1109/MENA-SC54044.2023.10374527.

[8] Bengt Jaeckel, David Daßler, Matthias Pander, Jim Joseph John, Sagarika Kumar, Baloji Adothu, Mission profile concept for PV modules: use case – middle east deserts vs temperate European climate, EPJ Photovoltaics 14 (2023) 1–10. https://doi.org/https://doi.org/10.1051/epjpv/2023030.

[9] B. Adothu, J.J. John, G. Mathiak, V. Alberts, B. Jäckel, R. Gottschalg, N.S. Shiradkar, A.A. Abdallah, J. Lopez Garcia, M. Salvador, B. Hoex, H.A. Kazem, M.A. Alam, Development of PV Module Hot Desert Test Cycle Protocol Extended Failure Modes and Effective Analysis, in: 41st European Photovoltaic Solar Energy Conference and Exhibit (EU PVSEC 2024)Ion, 2024: pp. 1–8. https://doi.org/10.4229/EUPVSEC2024/3BO.15.4.

[10] B. Adothu, S. Pamir Aly, A. Seentakath Puthiyapurayil, K. Chapaneri, J. Joseph John, G. Mathiak, V. Alberts, Investigation of PV module degradation in fixed and single-axis tracker in hot desert climate, in: 41st EUPVSEC, 2024. abstract submitted (accessed February 5, 2024).

[11] B. Adothu, G. Mathiak, S.P. Aly, A. Alheloo, A. Almheiri, V. Alberts, B. Jäckel, R. Gottschalg, N.S. Shiradkar, A.A. Abdallah, J.L. Garcia, M. Salvador, B. Hoex, J.J. John, H.A. Kazem, M.A. Alam, Extended Failure Mode and Effects Analysis for Development of

Hot Desert Test Cycle Proposal, Progress in Photovoltaics: Research and Applications 33 (2024). https://doi.org/https://doi.org/10.1002/pip.3862.

[12] P. Gebhardt, U. Kräling, E. Fokuhl, I. Hädrich, D. Philipp, Reliability of Commercial TOPCon PV Modules—An Extensive Comparative Study, Progress in Photovoltaics: Research and Applications 0 (2024) 1–9. https://doi.org/10.1002/PIP.3868.

10.4229/EUPVSEC2025/3DO.16.6
020229-005

Recent Findings on Glass-Breakage Issues: From Factory Production Oversight, On-Site Inspection and Laboratory Testing Results

Thomas Weber[*,1], Moritz Heiser, Abdullah Abu Sayed[1,2], Roman Joziak, Eduardo Tellez Rodriguez[1], Nattapark Pongthanacharoenkul[1], Sören Rindert[1], Benjamin Lippke[1], Craig Wong[1], Steven Xuereb[1] Mahyar Nezhad[3], Don Cowan[3], Matthew Lu[4], Claudia Buerhop-Lutz, Ian Marius Peters

kiwa

The empire strikes back — but it's overwhelmed by the sheer force of real-world impacts.

Recent Findings on Glass-Breakage Issues:
From Factory Production Oversight, On-Site Inspection and Laboratory Testing Results

3DO.19.2

Thomas Weber[**,1], Moritz Heiser, Abdullah Abu Sayed[1,2], Roman Joziak, Eduardo Tellez Rodriguez[1], Nattapark Pongthanacharoenkul[1], Sören Rindert[1], Benjamin Lippke[1], Craig Wong[1], Steven Xuereb[1] Mahyar Nezhad[3], Don Cowan[3], Matthew Lu[4], Claudia Buerhop-Lutz, Ian Marius Peters

kiwa

Trusted Experts Worldwide
Wherever and Whenever You Need Us

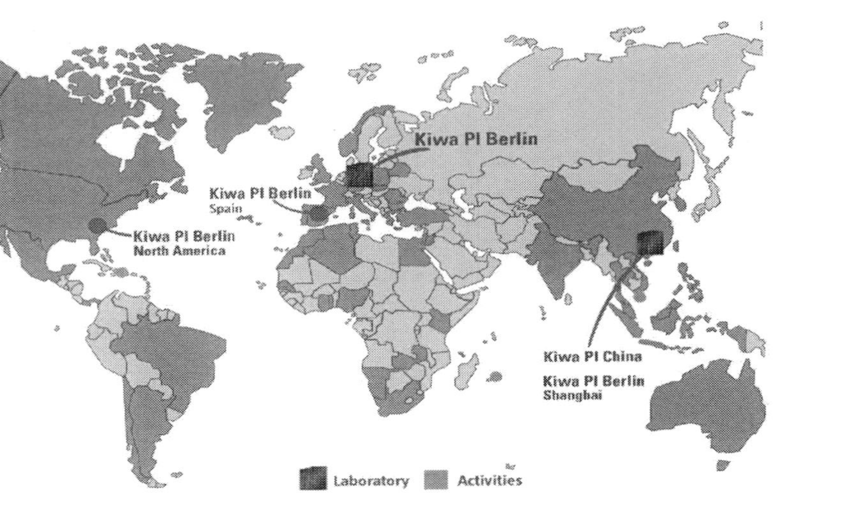

Key PV Services Around the World

From roofs on industrial buildings in central Europe to utility plants in desert regions, our experts are there for you.

- Audits
- Factory Work
- Owners Engineering
- Root Cause Analysis and Claims
- Laboratory

Glass / Glass Modules are Prevalent and Glass is Getting Thinner

Market

- Ca. 700 GW of glass/glass (G/G) modules have been already produced and deployed; current G/G market share: ~60 %

Contribution of Kiwa

- Conducted around 20 projects in the last 5 years

- For some projects, we observed breakage rates of < 0.1 %; < 3 %; and even < 20 %

- On an inspection rate of < 0.1 to 100 %

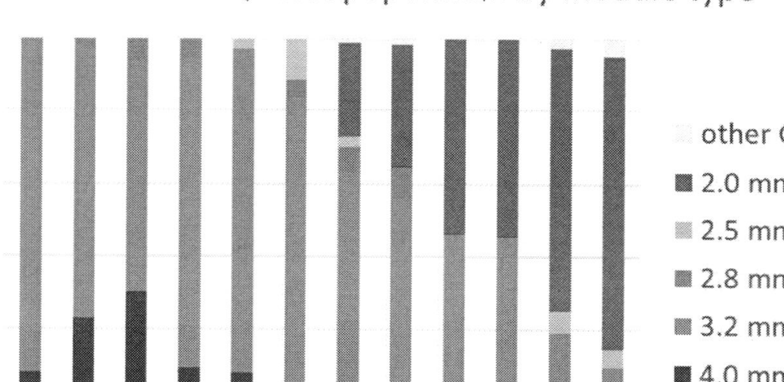

1) Glassbreakage occurred with introduction of 2 mm G//G modules

2) Outlook: The big headaches are still ahead of us.

[1] KIWA PVEL, 2025 PV Module Reliability Scorecard
[2] Savannah Bennett et al.: USING CONVOLUTIONAL NEURAL NETWORKS TO DETECT IN-FIELD PV MODULE GLASS CRACKS, IEEE JOURNAL OF PHOTOVOLTAICS, submitted 2025
[3] ITRPV, "2025 International Technology Roadmap for Photovoltaic (ITRPV), March 2025
[4] Thomas Weber, "Glass breakage—A growing phenomenon in large-scale PV," 20 Nov. 2023. Accessed: 1 Dec. 2023. [Online]. Available: https://www.pv-magazine.com/webinars/glass-breakage-a-growing-phenomenon-in-large-scale-pv/

kiwa

Analysis of Fracture Patterns

What does it look like?

- Breakage pattern
- Point of origin
  - Impact vs. bending break
  - Thermal or mechanical induced
  - Origination at fixation point or jb
- Laminat: „Edge-Pinch" [7]

Problems

- Frame covered edge
- Superimposed by secondary breakage

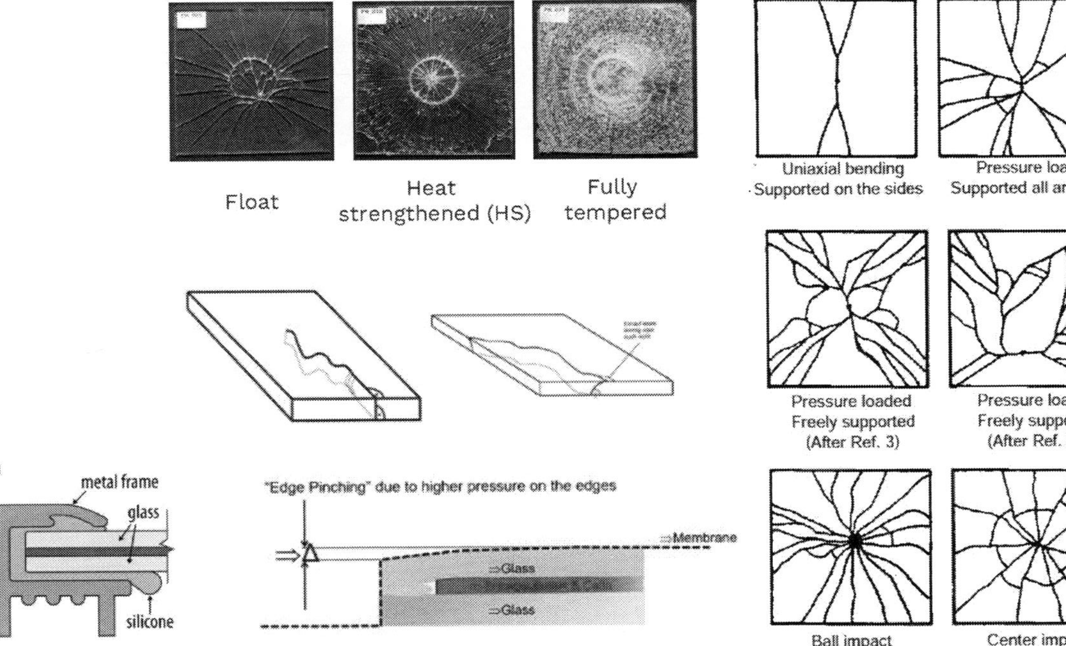

[5] George D. Quinn; Fractography of Ceramics and Glasses
[6] Ekkehard Wagner, "Glasschäden„, 5. Auflage, 2020
[7] Ashley Gaulding, 3CP.2.1 , EUPVSEC Wien 2024
[8] Tim Silverman, at al.; "Tough Break: Many Factors Make Glass Breakage More Likely", 2024

Analysis of Fracture Patterns

What does it look like?

- Breakage pattern
- Point of origin
  - Impact vs. bending break
  - Thermal or mechanical induced
  - Origination at fixation point or jb
- Laminat: „Edge-Pinch" [6]

Problems

- Frame covered edge
- Superimposed by secondary breakage

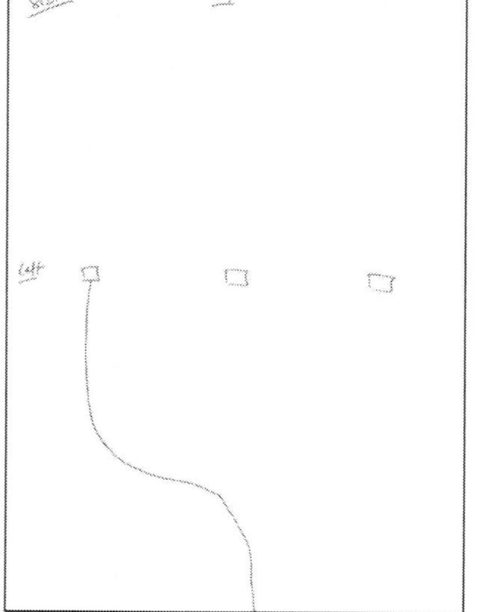

Analysis of Fracture Patterns

What does it look like?

- Breakage pattern
- Point of origin
  - Impact vs. bending break
  - Thermal or mechanical induced
  - Origination at fixation point or jb
- Laminat: „Edge-Pinch" [6]

Problems

- Frame covered edge
- Superimposed by secondary breakage

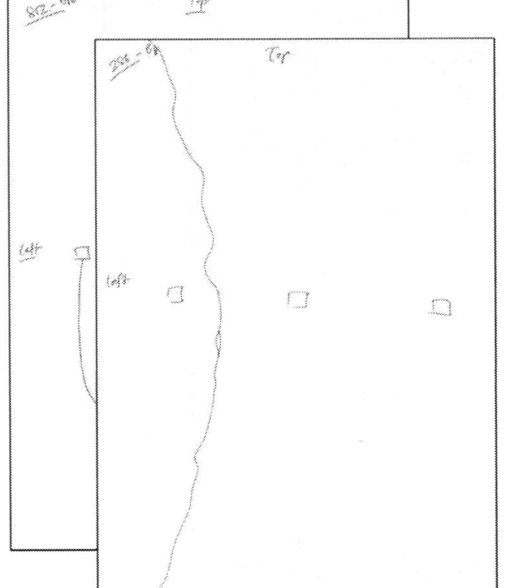

Analysis of Fracture Patterns

What does it look like?

- Breakage pattern
- Point of origin
  - Impact vs. bending break
  - Thermal or mechanical induced
  - Origination at fixation point or jb
- Laminat: „Edge-Pinch" [6]

Problems

- Frame covered edge
- Superimposed by secondary breakage

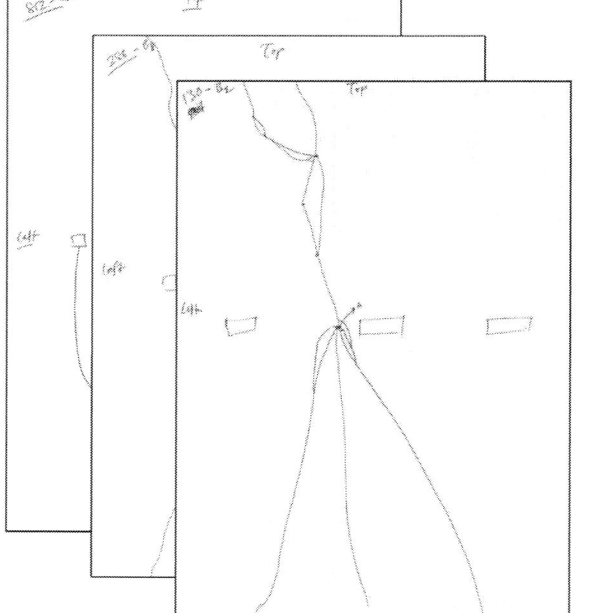

Analysis of Fracture Patterns

What does it look like?

- Breakage pattern
- Point of origin
  - Impact vs. bending break
  - Thermal or mechanical induced
  - Origination at fixation point or jb
- Laminat: „Edge-Pinch" [6]

Problems

- Frame covered edge
- Superimposed by secondary breakage

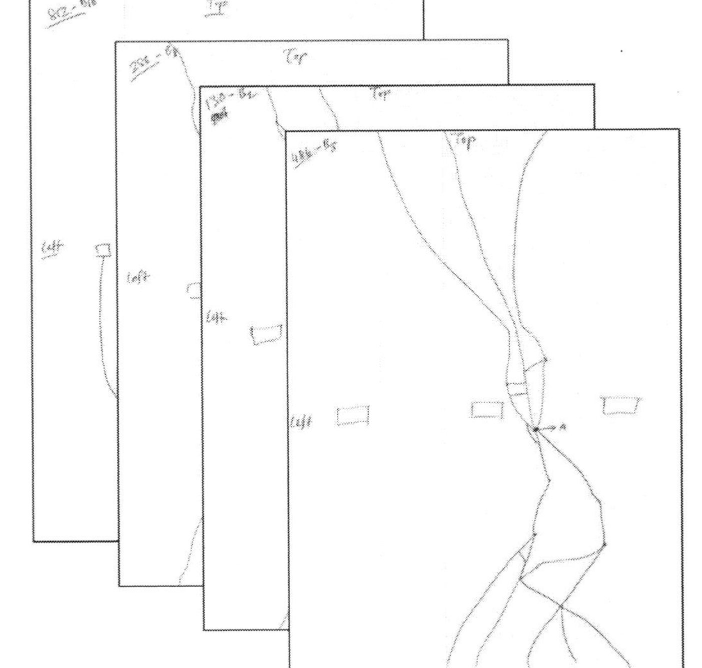

Analysis of Fracture Patterns

What does it look like?

- Breakage pattern
- Point of origin
  - Impact vs. bending break
  - Thermal or mechanical induced
  - Origination at fixation point or jb
- Laminat: „Edge-Pinch" [6]

Problems

- Frame covered edge
- Superimposed by secondary breakage

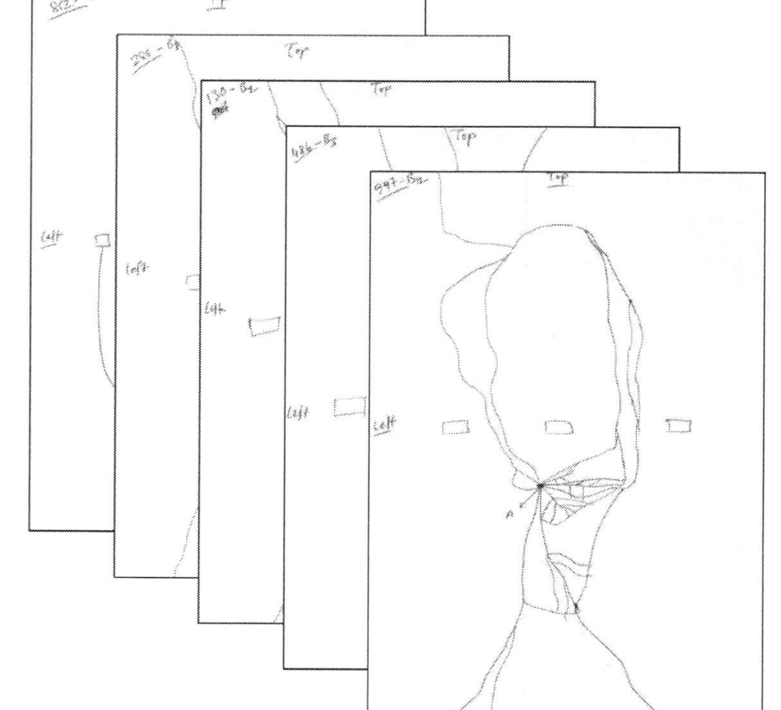

[6] Ekkehard Wagner, "Glasschäden.,, 5. Auflage, 2020

020230-010

Analysis of Fracture Patterns

What does it look like?

- Breakage pattern
- Point of origin
  - Impact vs. bending break
  - Thermal or mechanical induced
  - Origination at fixation point or jb
- Laminat: „Edge-Pinch" [6]

Problems

- Frame covered edge
- Superimposed by secondary breakage

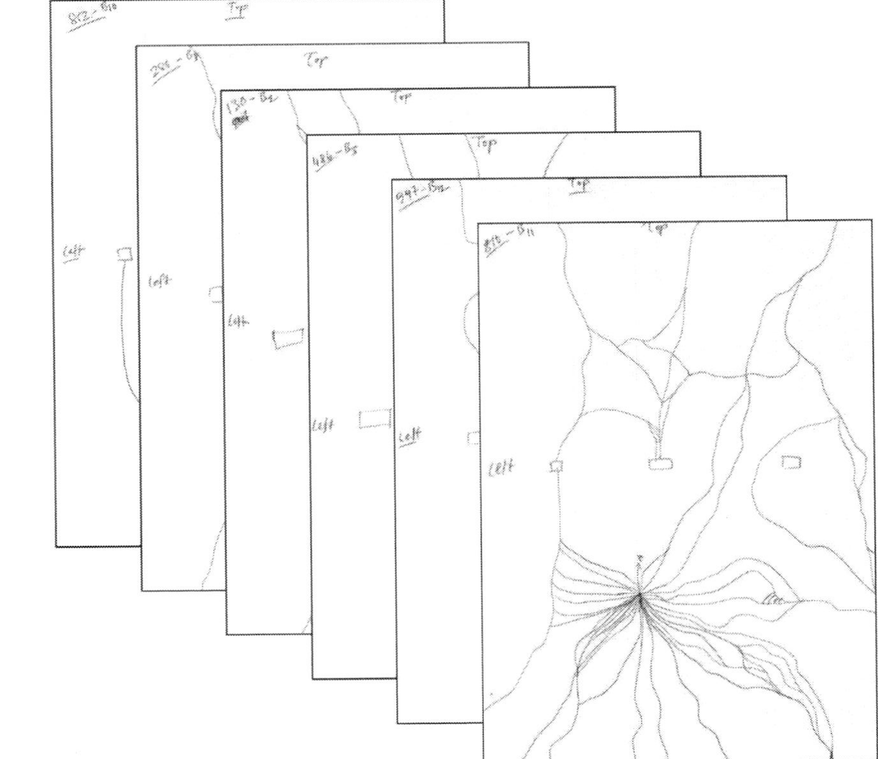

[6] Ekkehard Wagner, "Glasschäden„, 5. Auflage, 2020

020230-011

Analysis of Fracture Patterns

What does it look like?

- Breakage pattern
- Point of origin
  - Impact vs. bending break
  - Thermal or mechanical induced
  - Origination at fixation point or jb
- Laminat: „Edge-Pinch" [6]

Problems

- Frame covered edge
- Superimposed by secondary breakage

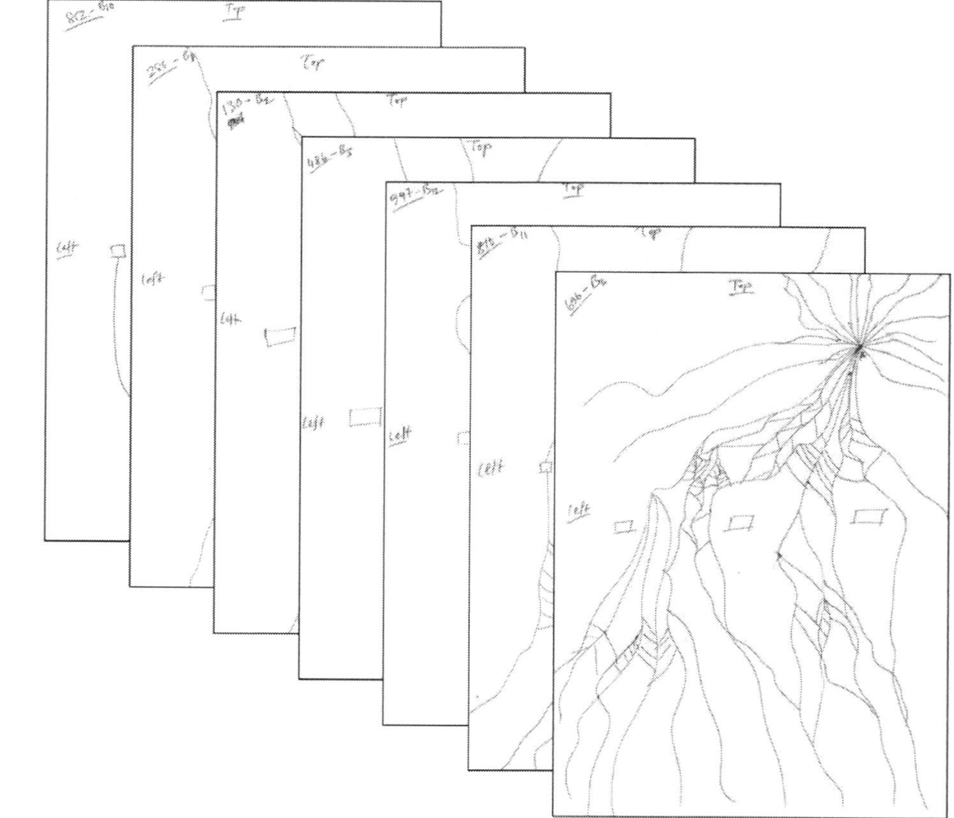

020230-012

Tempered Glass and Shelling

Zones of residual stress in prestressed glass

a) Thickness matters: compressive stress zone protects only 20 % of thickness

- Surface cracks may sneak in quietly, (called subcritical growth). But once they cross the line, the glass goes out with a bang.

b) Development of shelling at the breakage edges, if the glass is bended

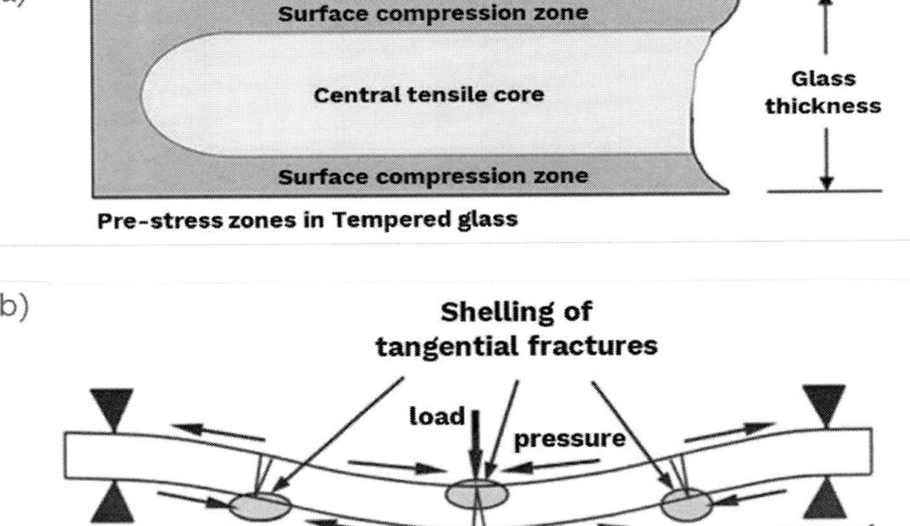

Intervention in a Projects Timeline

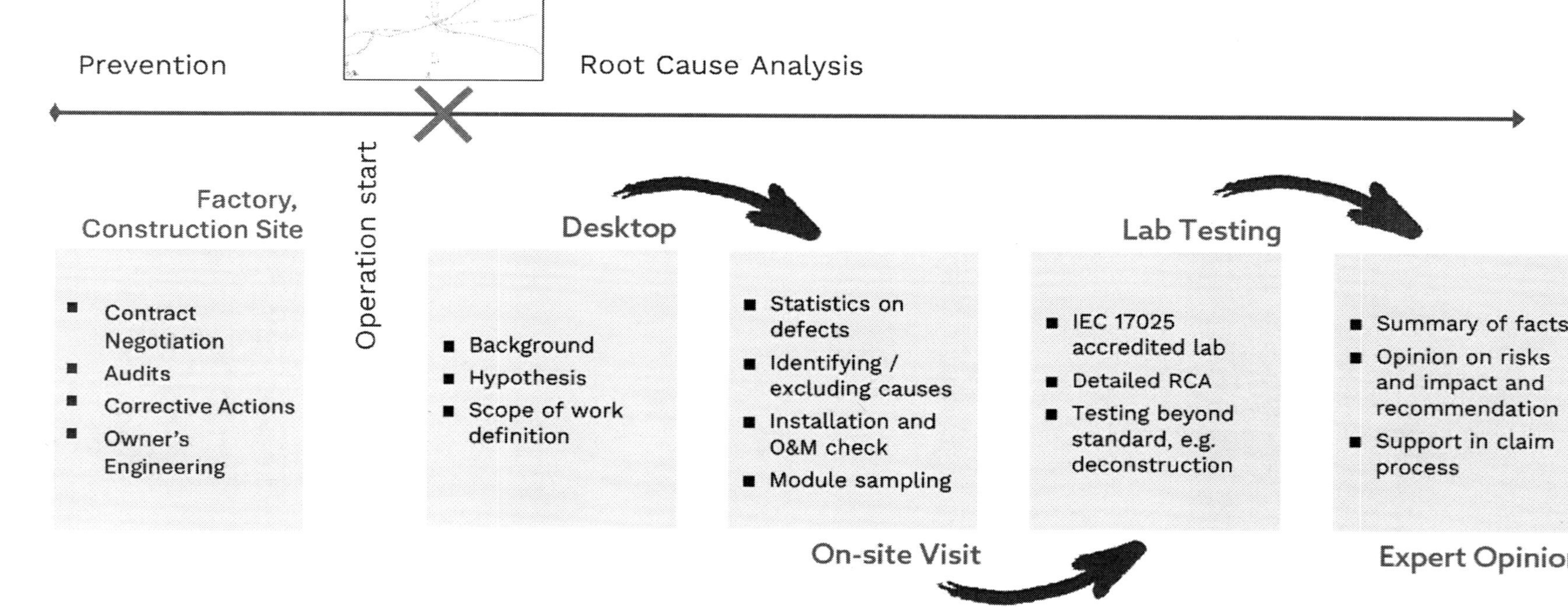

[3] George D. Quinn, Fractography of Ceramics and Glasses
[4] Ekkehard Wagner, Glasschaden, 5. Auflage, 2020
[6] Ashley Gaulding, 3CP.2.1, EUPVSEC Wien

Results
Selection of Found Issues

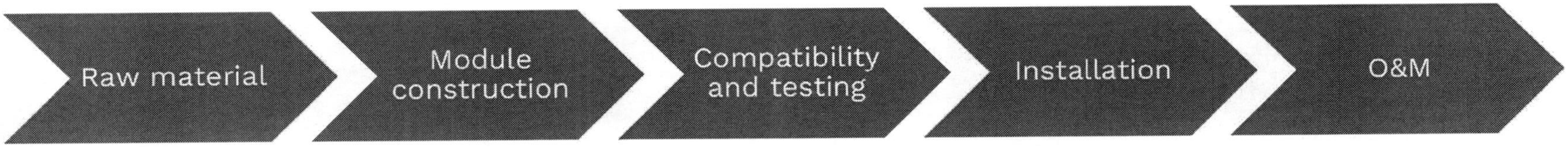

Results
Thickness and Inhomogeneity of Surface Compression

Thickness

- Glass thickness not as expected:
  tolerance of +/-0.2 mm is too big,
  it should be tightened to **-0**/+0.2 mm (-50 %)

Inhomogeneity of Surface Compression

Inhomogeneous, but heat-strengthened to tempered glass

- Surface compression on 2 mm rear side glass:
  -64 to -117 N/mm^2 determined over four modules

- Scalp, ASTM C1279-13 (2019)
  Standard Test Method for Non-Destructive Photoelastic Measurement […] in Glass

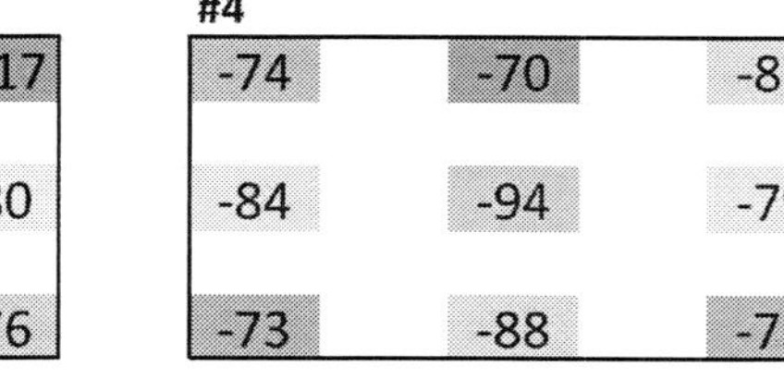

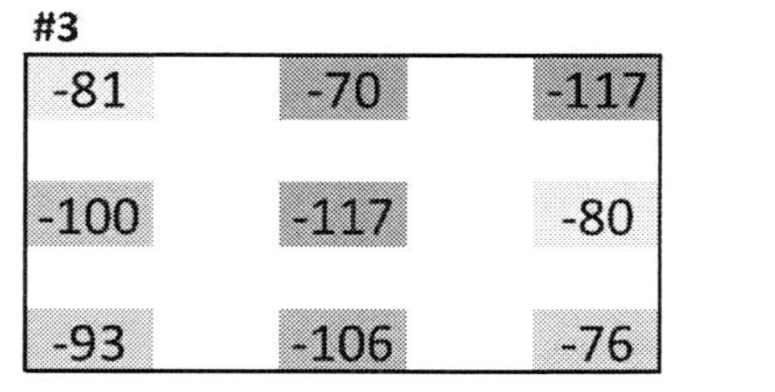

#1

-72	-76	-86
-111	-80	-89
-80	-64	-91

#2

-111	-82	-119
-111	-110	-105
-108	-117	-103

#3

-81	-70	-117
-100	-117	-80
-93	-106	-76

#4

-74	-70	-87
-84	-94	-79
-73	-88	-73

Results
Module Construction and Production Quality

PV Module Manufacturing **Quality Report**

- Published annual by Kiwa
- Data from all factory activities
  - Factory audits
  - Production oversights
  - **Pre-shipment inspections (PSI)**
- Analysis, trends and conclusions

www.kiwa.com/
pvqualityreport

Results
Module Construction and Production Quality

PV Module Manufacturing **Quality Report**

The distribution of defects identified during Pre-shipment inspection (PSI)

- Directly impacting glass breakage risk
  - Glass damage
  - Frame assembly
  - Curing

Preventive action need criteria!

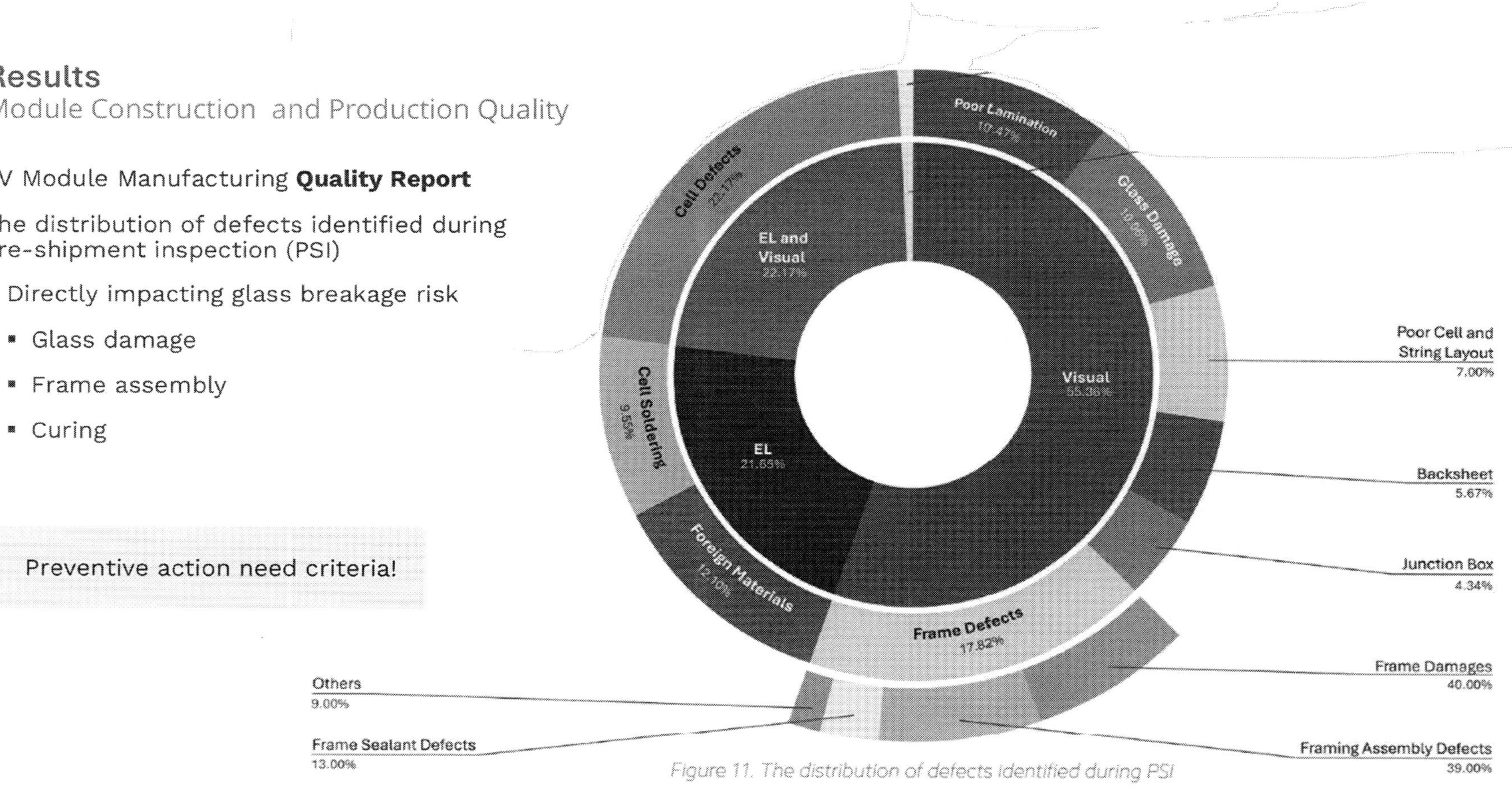

Figure 11. The distribution of defects identified during PSI

020230-018

Results
Cross Section Cut Findings

Cross-section-cut analysis

- To check hidden quality

Preventive action need criteria!

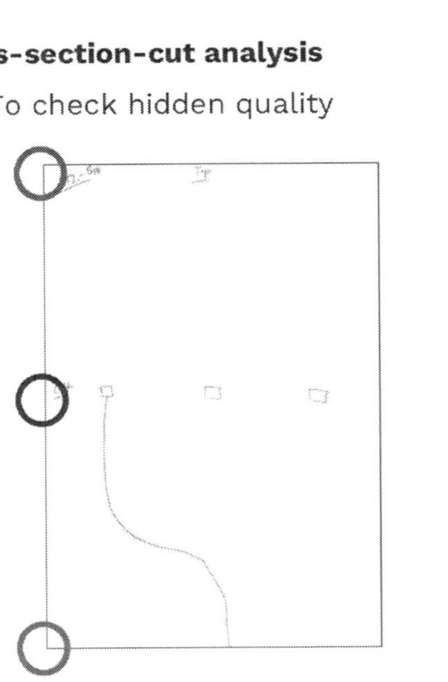

Silicone (or gap) thickness @ long side

Results
Mechanical Load Testing

Under construction / clamp and grounding

- SML-Test acc. IEC 61215 MQT 16

Test	Result
3600 Pa, 15 Nm, **A) with grounding plate**	Fail
3600 Pa, 15 Nm, **B) no grounding plate**	Pass

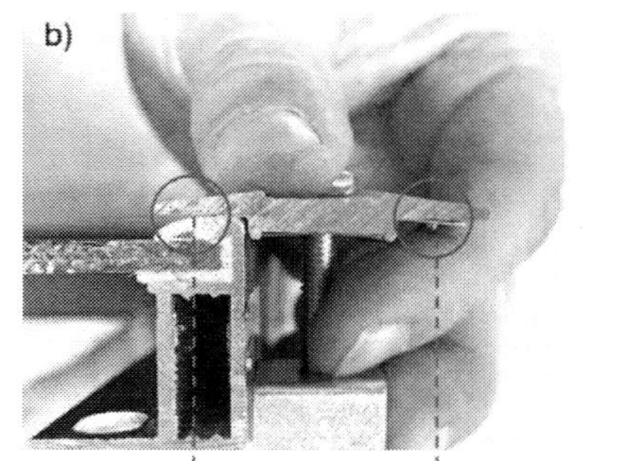

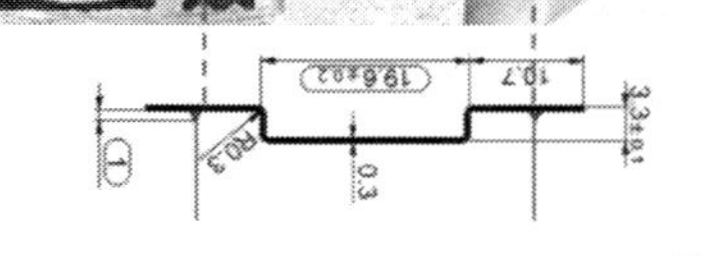

Mounting matters:
torques, distances, design must be correct.

[8] Pascal Romer et al., "How to Mount PV Modules: the Effect of Different Clamping Configuration on Mechanical Stresses in PV Modules, EU PVSEC 2024

Results
Mounting System Improvements Tested

Incompatibility Between Module and/ or Mounting Support

- 7 cases, mean breakage rate ~7 %
- RCA:
  - Missing support: module rail too short with module mounting at 400 mm
  - Too weak module (frame, glass, …)
- Tested solution: with additional support, modules passed standard testing

The industry is currently lacking in testing and understanding.

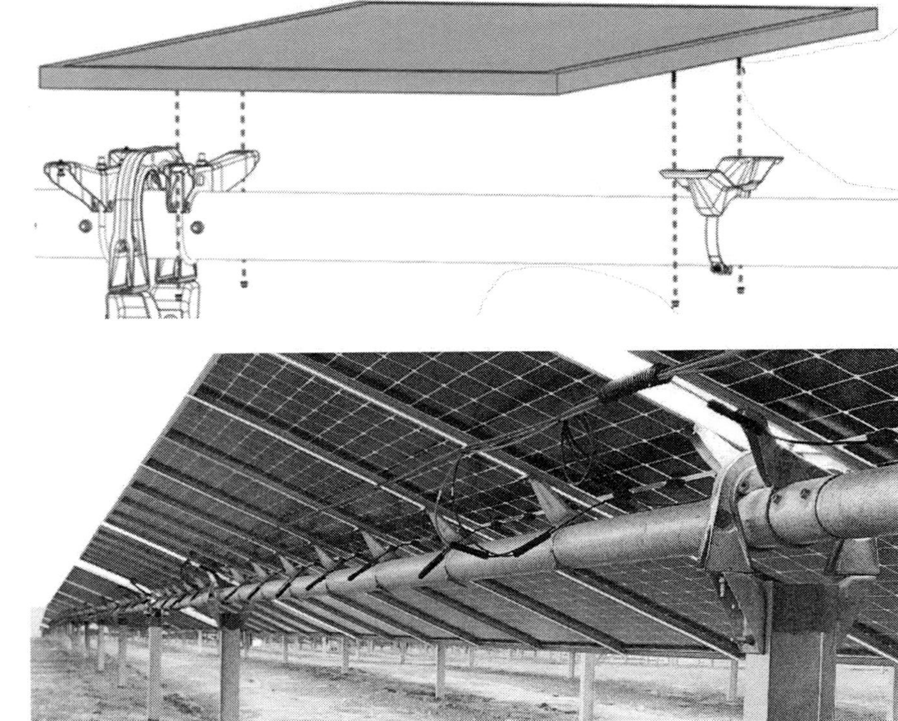

Results
"Impacts" from O&M are a factor

On-site investigation results and laboratory validation: 5 cases

- 6 to 27 % of the broken modules show **clear signs of impact**, but high (proven) uncertainty in that number

- Proved thrown stones and mud (all); cleaning device defect (case E)

Details matter:
Clear(er) statistcs after microscopic validation.
Should we shoot the rear side?

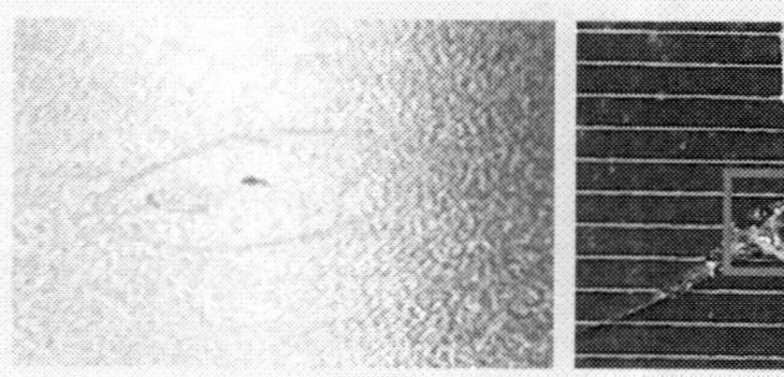

kiwa

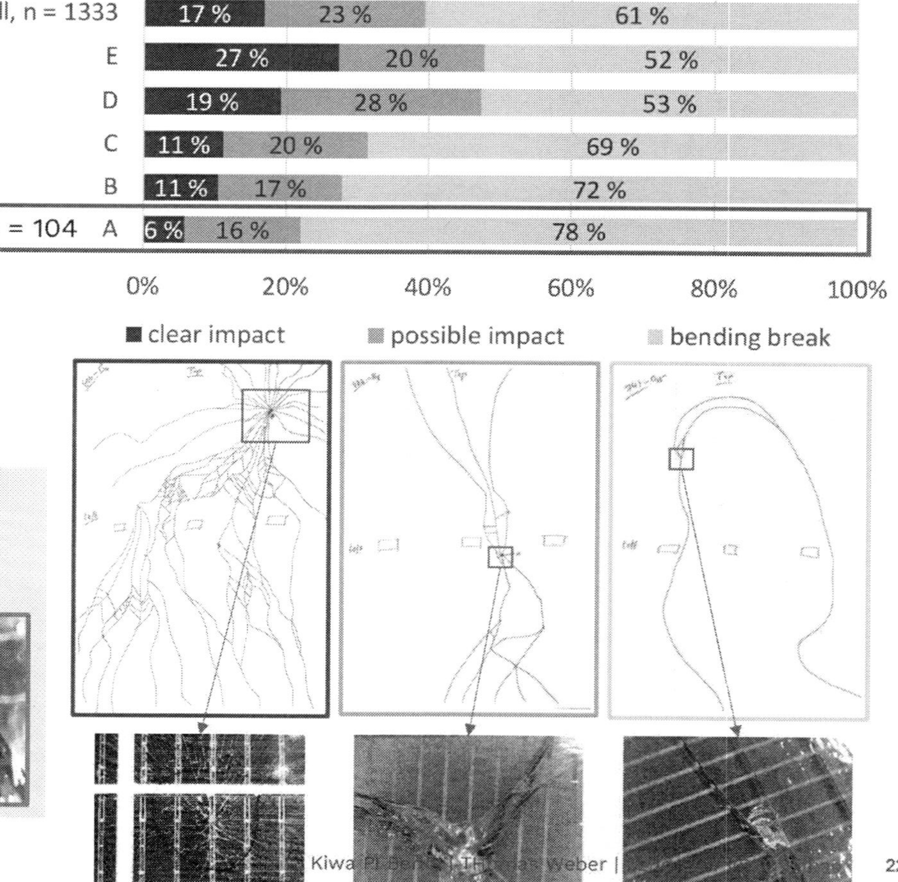

22

Conclusion

- **Stone Impact**
  O&M teams need to be sensitized to the risk.

- **Module & Installation Quality**
  Construction and mounting practices should
  at least follow the installation guide.

- **Glass has Become a Load Bearing Element**
  Design processes are lacking

- **Need for more Testing**
  Current methods (IEC: hail, SML/DML) failed
  to prevent breakage.

- **Urgent Need for New Standards**
  Practical MSA criteria and test protocols for
  production are needed, approval, and
  lifetime testing. Strength verification of PV
  glass as required in the construction
  industry?!

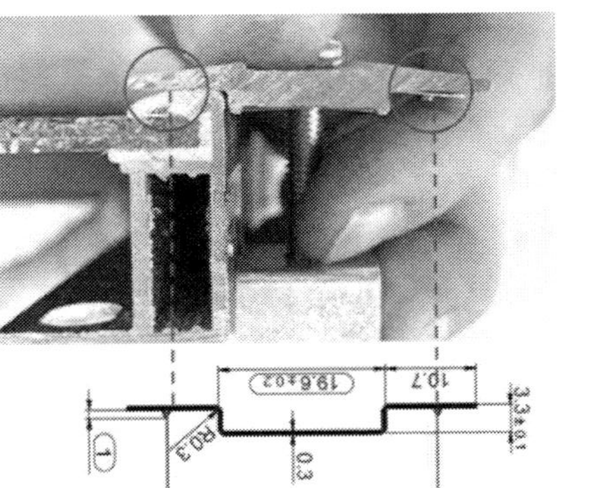

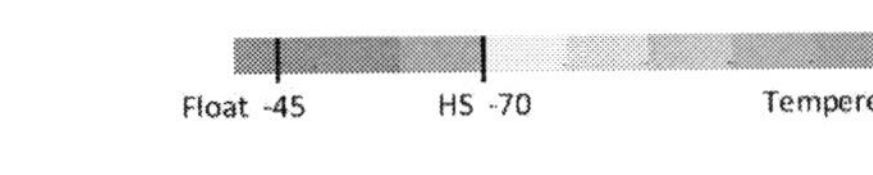

Conclusion

- **Stone Impact**
  O&M teams need to be sensitized to the risk.

- **Module & Installation Quality**
  Construction and mounting practices should at least follow the installation guide.

- **Glass has Become a Load Bearing Element**
  Design processes are lacking

- **Need for more Testing**
  Current methods (IEC: hail, SML/DML) failed to prevent breakage.

- **Urgent Need for New Standards**
  Practical MSA criteria and test protocols for production are needed, approval, and lifetime testing. Strength verification of PV glass as required in the construction industry?!

Thank you – Questions ?

UNDERSTANDING GLASS BREAKAGE IN FIELD-OPERATED PV MODULES: LEARNINGS FROM INHOMOGENEOUS MECHANICAL LOAD TESTS

Jochen Markert, Aditya Girish Belawadi, Enzo Job, Pascal Romer, Ingrid Haedrich, Daniel Philipp
Fraunhofer Institute for Solar Energy Systems ISE, Heidenhofstr. 2, 79110 Freiburg, Germany

ABSTRACT: A significant increase in glass breakages in photovoltaic (PV) power plants has been observed in recent years, particularly in glass/glass (G/G) modules with thin (~2 mm) glass and large areas (>2.5 m²). These failures often occur within months of field deployment and affect various mounting configurations, including framed and unframed modules on tracked or fixed sub-structures. Traditional causes, such as severe weather or faulty installation, can largely be excluded. Furthermore, even modules that passed the mechanical load (ML) tests during certification according to IEC 61215 are currently failing in the field. Laboratory tests and field observations reveal distinct fracture patterns, suggesting fundamentally different triggering mechanisms. Field fractures are often characterized by long, single-running cracks, originating within the surface, with no clear connection to glass edges. In contrast, laboratory tests under homogeneous load scenarios typically show chaotic crack patterns originating at clamp positions due to stress concentrations. The reduced mechanical stability of thinner glass, particularly with lower surface pre-stress, is assumed to be one key factor, while other factors as for example the influence of more realistic load profiles remain unclear. This study investigates the mechanical failure behavior of G/G and glass/backsheet (G/B) modules under homogeneous and inhomogeneous load profiles and sets them into context to the currently observed breakages in the field. Results show that G/G modules consistently exhibit lower failure loads compared to G/B modules in the respective mounting configuration replicating a 1P tracker setup. However, G/G and G/B modules demonstrate a distinct mechanical response to specific inhomogeneous load profiles, with failure loads converging under increasingly inhomogeneous conditions. Based on the laboratory findings, field fractures are hypothesized to result from sustained, low-intensity loads. Contributing factors may include sagging-induced tensile stress or low-energy impacts, such as stone-strikes during grass mowing.
The findings highlight the limitations of current ML tests, which fail to replicate real-world load conditions. Further research is needed to refine laboratory tests, integrate cyclic loads, and investigate defect formation and aging effects. Such future efforts will be essential for identifying root causes and guiding the development of more robust module designs and maintenance practices to mitigate future failures.
Keywords: PV modules, glass breakage, inhomogeneous loads, mechanical loads

1 INTRODUCTION

A significant increase in glass breakages in photovoltaic (PV) power plants has been observed in recent years [1–3]. This issue affects various module types, including both, framed and unframed modules, as well as those mounted on tracked or permanently installed sub-structures. Traditional root causes, such as severe weather events or faulty installation practices, which have historically contributed to glass breakages [4–6], can largely be excluded in these cases. Notably, all reported incidents share a common factor: Tthe affected modules feature a double-glass design with approximately 2 mm thick glass, an area often exceeding 2.5 m² and the failures are typically observed within just a few months of field deployment. Furthermore, even modules that passed the mechanical load (ML) tests during certification according to IEC 61215 are currently failing in the field.

Our findings to date suggest that the root cause is linked to fundamental challenges associated with the ongoing industry trend toward larger modules and thinner glass [7]. Specifically, the reduced mechanical stability of thinner glass is a key concern. This is partly attributed to the typically lower surface pre-stress in 2 mm glass compared to the 3.2 mm glass in conventional glass/backsheet modules caused by technical limitations during the tempering process for thin glass [8].

While the root causes of cracks originating at module edges are often easier to identify and more frequently reproducible in laboratory tests, field observations increasingly reveal fractures characterized by single, long-propagating cracks (Fig. 1, top). These cracks are typically observed in the rear glass pane, often with no or only single connections to the glass edge and without a clearly identifiable crack origin. For simplicity, we will refer to these incidents as "field fractures" throughout this publication. By contrast, laboratory tests of similar modules typically produce more chaotic fracture patterns affecting both front and rear panes, with numerous cracks originating at the clamp positions (Fig. 1, bottom).

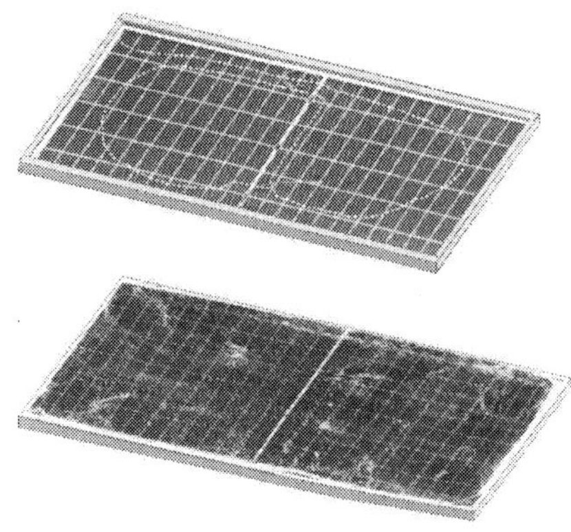

Fig. 1: Typical breakage patterns with no clear origins in rear glass of glass/glass (G/G) modules observed in the field (top) and in the lab (bottom).

The fact that established homogeneous load tests cannot reproduce these field fracture patterns suggests that other triggering mechanisms are responsible for the glass breakage. Romer et al. used finite-element modeling (FEM) to examine how load distributions on modules differ under realistic conditions such as snow or wind from varying directions [9] (compare Fig. 2). This study aims to experimentally reproduce such inhomogeneous load profiles to provide a preliminary insight into their influence on the mechanical failure behavior of G/G and glass/backsheet (G/B) modules. The results of the ML tests are analyzed in the context of field-observed breakage patterns, with the aim of ruling out specific failure mechanisms and narrowing down the root causes that contribute to the observed fractures in the field.

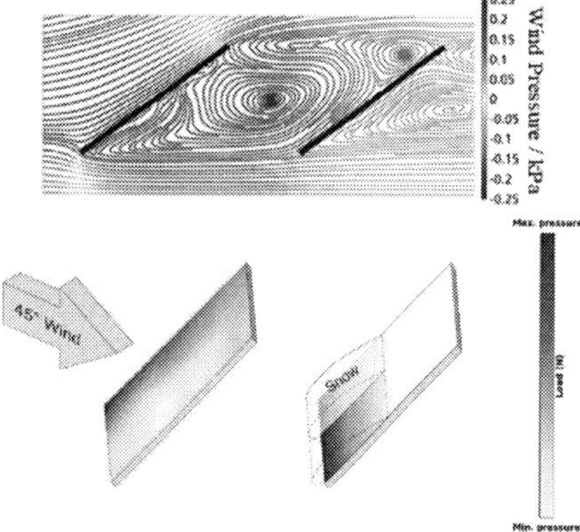

Fig. 2: Top: Side view of a computational fluid dynamics (CFD) simulation of the wind load distribution with frontal wind on inclined module structures by Romer et al. [9]; Bottom: Resulting wind load profiles from a 45 ° cross wind determined by FEM simulations (left) and snow load accumulating on the lower edge (right).

2 METHODOLOGY

2.1 Samples

Two module types, G/G and G/B, from the same manufacturer are tested. According to the datasheets, the basic module designs, including frame height (30 mm) and module dimensions (compare Fig. 3), are identical. Consequently, the only variable parameter is the laminate design. The G/B design featured a front pane with 3.2 mm thickness, while the G/G modules featured front and rear panes with 2 mm each. Furthermore, the surface pre-stress was measured with a scattered light polariscope (SCALP) and showed values in the range of thermally toughened glass (TTG) according to EN 12150-1 [10] for the 3.2 mm glass (<-110 MPa) and between heat-strengthened glass (HSG) according to EN 1863-1 [11] and TTG for the 2 mm glass (around -80 MPa).

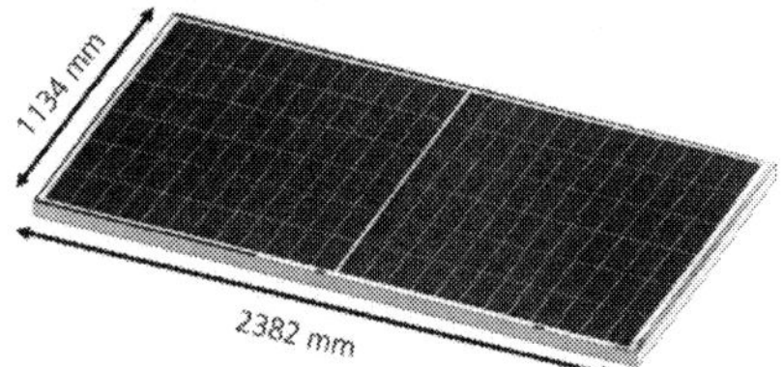

Fig. 3: Appearance and dimensions of the modules used for testing. 2382×1134×30mm

2.2 Test Specifications

The experiments were designed following a test-to-fail approach applying pressure conditions (no suction). Different load profiles including homogeneous and inhomogeneous loads are applied as illustrated in Fig. 4. To account for variability in the results, which is expected due to the probabilistic nature of glass breakage, three modules were tested for homogeneous load scenarios and four modules for inhomogeneous load scenarios. For the homogeneous load profile, a load ramp with 50 Pa/s is applied. For the inhomogeneous load cases, the loads at the cylinder(s) with the highest individual load is increased in 50 N steps, with a holding time of 30 s at each load level to ensure equilibrium conditions. This holding time is necessary because changes in load on individual cylinders can affect the overall load distribution across the module surface, which must be compensated by readjusting the remaining cylinders according to the load distribution calculated from FEM simulations (see Fig. 4). Load levels in homogeneous scenarios can be readily characterized using force per unit area specifications. However, for inhomogeneous load distributions, such characterization might lead to misinterpretation of results. Therefore, absolute force values were utilized to describe the specific load distribution patterns, ensuring accurate representation of the experimental conditions. The homogeneous distribution is used as a reference and corresponds to the load application as typically applied during laboratory ML tests according to IEC 61215-2. The load profile for front wind from 45° is simulated using CFD in combination with FEM. The distribution in the case of snow load is defined based on the standard IEC 62938, a standard that aims to test the attachment of the frame to the module during snow loads on inclined setups by applying an inhomogeneous distribution of snow on one half of the modules [12].

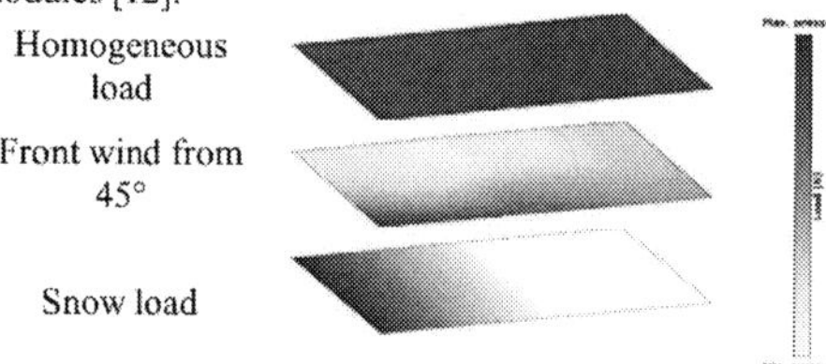

Fig. 4: Load distribution of the three investigated profiles: homogeneous (top), cross wind (middle) and snow load (bottom).

For the test approach a relatively unstable, but nevertheless widely used configuration for utility modules was used. It is further referred to as tracker setup (Fig. 5, top and bottom, blue clamps). It reflects the assembly of modules in a 1P single-axis tracked system, which is often used in large power plants and open-field systems. The module clamps with a width of 50 mm are set centrally with a distance of 200 mm from the module center and fixed with 15 Nm torque, which is accompanied by large, freely overhanging module areas and an overall increased vulnerability to deformation compared to other mounting situations as e.g. in typical fixed tilt setups (Fig. 5, bottom, light grey clamps). To evaluate the deformation of each module, the deflection was recorded on the module corner, where the highest deflection is expected, using a laser sensor. For the G/B type the experiments are complemented by additional FEM simulations for the specific load profiles.

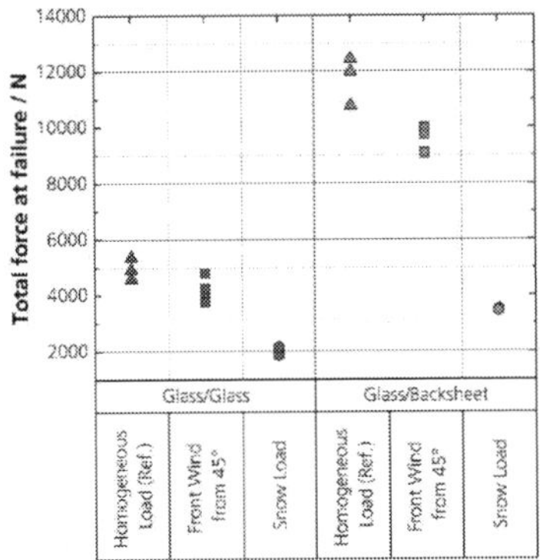

Fig. 5: Top: Tracker setup on the ML test stand; Bottom: Module with sketched clamping position for tracker setup with clamp spacing = 400 mm (blue) and standard configuration with clamping at 20 % of the long module side (light grey).

3   RESULTS

Fig. 6 illustrates the total failure force for the specific load distributions of each module during the single ML tests. The G/G design consistently exhibits lower failure loads compared to the G/B modules, with the largest difference observed under the homogeneous load scenario. In this case, the average failure load of the G/B design is 136% higher than that of the G/G design. As the load distribution becomes increasingly inhomogeneous, the concentration of loads in specific areas leads to higher localized stresses, resulting in a general decrease in absolute failure loads for both module types. However, the failure loads of the G/B modules decrease more rapidly, converging towards those of the G/G modules during the inhomogeneous configurations. Specifically, under the crosswind scenario, the G/B modules exhibit a failure load 124% higher than that of the G/G modules, while under the snow load scenario, the failure load is approximately 75% higher.

Fig. 6: The total force at failure on the G/G and G/B modules during ML tests with homogeneous (reference) and inhomogeneous loads until failure in pressure direction.

Fig. 7 presents the deflection at the module corner as a function of the total applied force for one representative module per test. A notable observation is the significantly different deformation behavior between the G/G and G/B modules across all tested load configurations. This difference is most pronounced under the homogeneous load scenario and becomes less distinct as the inhomogeneity of the applied load increases.

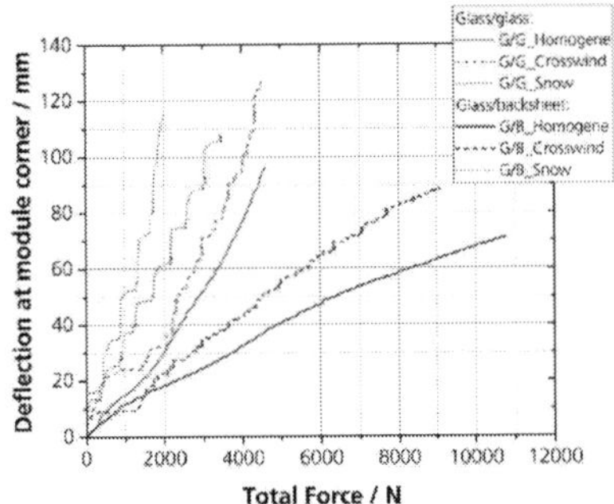

Fig. 7: Deflection at module corner vs. total applied force of the modules under different load profiles.

Looking at the deformation behavior of the modules during the homogeneous load test, the G/G modules exhibit bending predominantly along the long side of the module, while the short side remains largely undeformed (Fig. 8, top left). In contrast, G/B modules under a comparable surface load show initial deformation across the module surface along the short side, which seems to stabilize the module and effectively prevents the deformation along the long side during increased load levels (Fig. 8, bottom left).

Fig. 8: Deformation behavior of G/G modules (top) and G/B modules (bottom) with an absolute applied force of ~5000 N homogeneous load (left) and ~2000 N snow load (right).

A similar deformation behavior is observed under the cross-wind load profile, although the difference of G/B and G/G is less pronounced. Under snow-load conditions, the deformation pattern of G/B converges to that of G/G modules, with bending occurring predominantly along the long side of the module (Fig. 8, right). With this load distribution, the G/B module does not exhibit initial bending along the short edge allowing the modules to deform with a bending along the long side, similar to the G/G design.

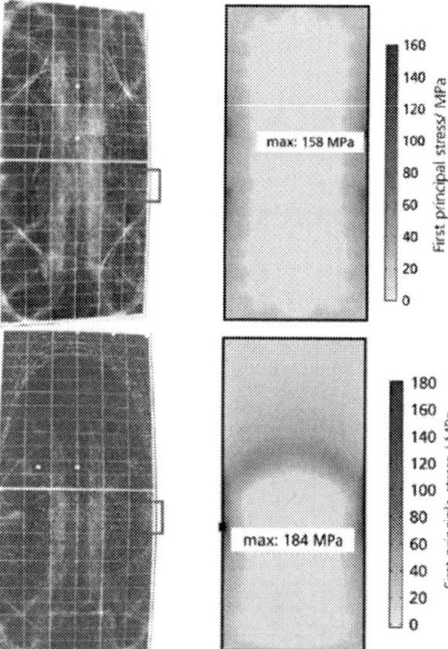

Fig. 9: Left: G/B module after failure under homogeneous- (top) and snow load (bottom) with breakage origins marked in red; Right: Corresponding distribution of first principal stress in the front glass at total force at failure of around 12000 N (top) and 3800 N (bottom).

Fig. 9 shows representative breakage patterns from the G/B modules for the homogeneous and the snow load scenario on the left and corresponding FEM simulations of the first principal stress in the front glass for the load distribution at 12000 N (homogeneous) 3800 N (snow load) total force on the right. The failure pattern in the cross-wind scenario matches closely with the homogeneous case and is therefore not shown. Due to the surface pre-stress in the TTG range according to EN 12150-1 [10], the fracture pattern appears fine grained over the entire surface in all three scenarios. The breakage origins in both scenarios match with the location of highest first principal stress of the FEM simulations at the clamp positions. Furthermore, the fracture pattern observed during snow load aligns well to the stress distribution derived from FEM, indicating that crack lines tend to follow the stress fields within the glass. The appearance of fractures on front and rear side of the G/G modules was similar, indicating comparable stress distributions in the two panes. However, the absolute stress according to FEM is higher in the front glass. Fig. 10 shows the general breakage patterns during homogeneous and snow load only in the rear glass due to better traceability of the crack lines. The crack origins are observed at one clamp position similar to the G/B modules. The crack distribution and density aligns with the load distribution, so that the module half where no load was applied in the snow load scenario shows significantly less cracks than the loaded half.

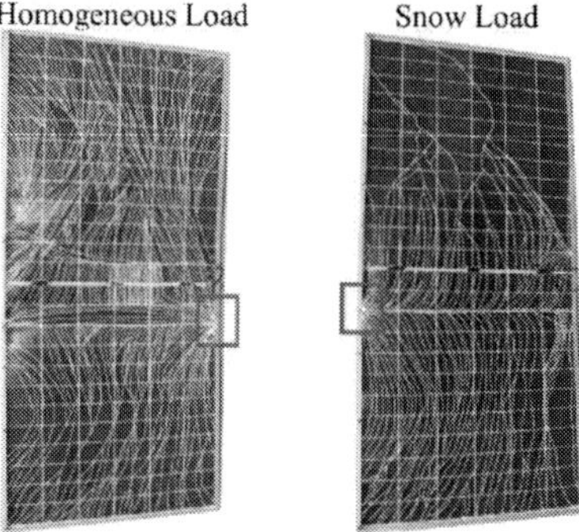

Fig. 10: Breakage pattern with main crack line orientation traced (white dashed) from rear glass of the G/G modules during homogeneous (left) and snow load (right); Crack origins marked with a red square.

4 DISCUSSION AND CONCLUSION

The significant difference in failure loads between G/G and G/B modules in the homogeneous case can most likely be attributed to their distinct deformation behavior under specific surface load distributions. In the G/G module, the first principal stress increases more rapidly at the clamp positions due to bending along the longer side. In contrast, the G/B module deforms initially by bending along the short side and subsequently stabilizes as schematically shown in Fig. 11. The primary factor influencing the different deformation behaviors is assumed to be a more rigid response of the G/G laminate compared to G/B during the initial loading phase. However, this needs further investigation with FEM simulations to be able to draw clearer conclusions. The deformation becomes more similar applying inhomogeneous loads, because less pressure is initially applied in the center, thereby preventing a bending of the G/B laminate along the short side during low loads. This leads to a less pronounced difference in failure loads with increasing inhomogeneity.

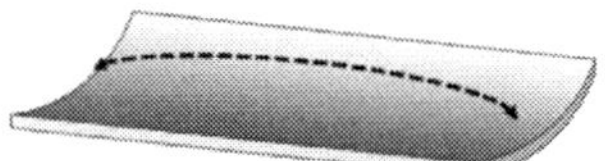

Fig. 11: Schematic deformation behavior of G/B module during homogeneous load application.

Another factor believed to contribute to the overall lower failure loads of G/G modules is the reduced surface pre-stress of the module glass. This reduction decreases the critical first principal stress needed to induce breakage and is assumed to be a significant parameter dominating the observed breakage behavior under snow load.

When comparing the fracture behavior of G/G and G/B modules under inhomogeneous load scenarios to standard ML tests with homogeneous loads, a key observation is that the critical failure regions, where maximum first principal stress concentrates, are consistently located at clamp positions. This appears to be largely independent of the test setup. For highly unstable setups as examined in this study, this results in a more rapid increase in first principal stress, and a resulting reduction of total force at failure, which is assumed to be different for more stable mounting setups. In addition, the concentration of failure loads in specific areas leads to higher crack densities in the corresponding regions of the module and cracks tend to follow the stress distribution in the glass.

Based on observations from laboratory ML tests – both homogeneous and inhomogeneous – several key conclusions can be drawn with regard to the field fractures as explained in section 1:

Crack origins:

Fractures observed during laboratory tests typically originate near clamp positions at the glass edge, attributed to stress concentrations induced by surface loading. Inhomogeneous loads may therefore represent a significant contributing factor to breakages in the field that initiate at clamp positions. However, field fracture patterns often differ remarkably, exhibiting long-running cracks with only a single, or in some cases no, connection to a glass edge, and lacking other distinct points of origin. This discrepancy complicates the identification of specific root causes and strongly suggest that fundamentally distinct mechanisms underlie fracture formation in field conditions compared to laboratory settings in such cases.

Similar failure patterns, characterized by single, long-running crack lines, have been reported by E. Wagner for laminated glass with heat-strengthened glass and are referred to as "surface pressure fractures." [13]. This source suggests that crack origins in such cases are often challenging to identify but are typically initiated at surface defects. ISO 1288-1 highlights that the tensile strength of glass panes decreases with increasing dimensions, attributed to the enhanced probability of critical surface defects being present in larger surface areas [14], which further supports the hypothesis of module dimensions approaching critical limits. This effect could be particularly critical for thin glass with reduced surface pre-stress, as the pre-stressed surface layer in thermally tempered glass typically constitutes around 20% of the total glass thickness [13]. In thinner glass, even shallow defects could reach critical dimensions, increasing the likelihood of failure.

Crack distribution and density:

Crack patterns observed in laboratory tests typically appear chaotic, with significantly higher crack densities in regions subjected to high surface loads and fewer cracks with larger unbroken pieces in areas with lower loads.

In contrast, field fractures are characterized by long, single, well-coordinated oval-shaped crack patterns. This suggests that the loads involved are generally homogeneous and may not result from particularly high total loads but rather from lower, sustained loads and an initiation point within the surface. A common phenomenon in fielded modules is the sagging of laminates between frames, which exerts a constant, homogeneous, low-intensity tensile stress on the rear pane (compare Fig. 12). Multiple parameters could potentially contribute to this phenomenon, including the self-weight of large-scale laminate modules and compressive stresses induced by thermal expansion of the framing, e.g. due to seasonal changes. This sustained stress is thought to increase the susceptibility of the rear pane to surface defects, contributing to the observed field fractures.

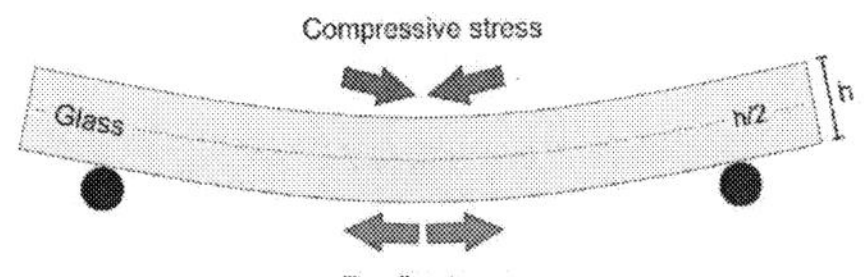

Fig. 12: Stresses developing on each side of a G/G laminate resulting from deformation induced by a surface pressure.

Fig. 13 illustrates a comparison between a typical fracture pattern documented from field observations in the rear glass (left) and the isobaric distribution of first principal stresses in the rear pane while sagging as determined through an FEM simulation (right). The simulation results demonstrate the stress pattern that develops when the laminate structure experiences gravitational deformation. The propagation paths of cracks exhibit a tendency to follow the stress isobars within the rear glass. This correlation, particularly in the presence of point defects, may offer a mechanistic explanation for the characteristic crack patterns observed in field installations.

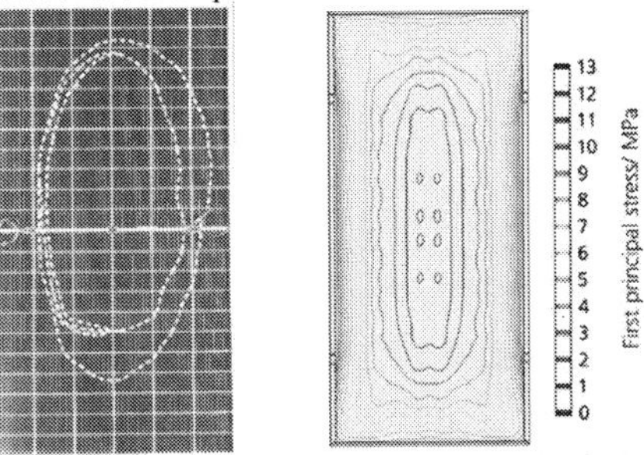

Fig. 13: Left: Breakage pattern observed in the field in the rear glass; Right: FEM simulation first principal stress in a module rear glass during sagging.

Breakage/triggering mechanisms:

As previously discussed, laboratory testing with both homogeneous and inhomogeneous loads reveal that the glass edge at clamping positions constitutes the primary vulnerability due to stress concentration during surface load application. The initiation of this failure mechanism is highly dependent on the absolute load magnitude, surface load distribution, and mounting configuration. Additionally, module design parameters demonstrate significant influence on the deformation response under various loading scenarios.

In contrast, field observations of rear glass breakages suggest that fracture initiation in modules typically originates at surface defects. Current analyses of fractured module glass indicate that, in some instances, low-intensity impacts from stones possibly ejected during vegetation maintenance activities may contribute to failures. However, alternative causative factors, including micro-defects introduced during the glass manufacturing process, remain a plausible hypothesis at this stage of investigation. Generally, a strong correlation with defect depth is anticipated. Furthermore, prolonged exposure to relatively low surface loads may induce progressive degradation mechanisms or exacerbate pre-existing surface defects, thereby compromising the overall mechanical integrity of the glass components over extended time.

5 SUMMARY AND OUTLOOK

A preliminary analysis of G/G and G/B modules was conducted to evaluate their mechanical response to various inhomogeneous stress profiles. The results revealed a higher fracture probability for G/G modules. However, under more inhomogeneous loading scenarios, the G/B design exhibited a more comparable behavior, likely due to reduced stabilization caused by changing deformation patterns. The resulting breakage patterns consistently showed crack origins at the clamp positions but failed to replicate the long, oval-shaped crack lines observed in field fractures. This highlights significant differences in the triggering mechanisms between laboratory and field scenarios. Nevertheless, several key conclusions regarding the factors that play a role in the currently observed field fractures can be drawn.

The observed fracture patterns suggest substantially lower loads in the field and initiation through surface defects. In some cases, the root cause of field fractures is likely attributable to low-intensity impacts, such as stone striking during vegetation maintenance. However, in other instances, the origins of the fractures remain unclear, and production-specific issues cannot be ruled out. Additionally, the role of crack propagation and the influence of long-term loads on the stability of glass with pre-existing defects require further investigation.

The results of this initial study on the influence of inhomogeneous loads in a specific experimental setup revealed design-dependent deformation behaviors, resulting in highly variable failure loads. These findings establish a preliminary foundation for future investigations into the effects of inhomogeneous load testing across diverse mounting configurations and module designs. Further comprehensive FEM analyses on G/G module behavior are required. Implementation of inhomogeneous load testing protocols could potentially address the currently observed discrepancies between field failures and successful certification according to IEC 61215. Additionally, qualification methodologies for modules intended for specific applications, such as customized mounting structures or unique operational environments, should be considered. To develop testing protocols with greater real-world relevance, additional research is necessary to replicate field load profiles more accurately, including the incorporation of cyclic loads characteristic for wind-induced stresses.

To gain a deeper understanding of the breakage mechanisms involved in the field more extensive investigations are required, particularly on the impact of defect depth and other surface characteristics. Additionally, greater attention should be given to maintenance techniques applied in specific fields and the load scenarios they impose on modules. It appears that multiple factors seem to contribute to the currently observed failures, with two of the major issues being the application of thin glass with low surface pre-stress and dimensions approaching 3 m^2. This situation warrants further research to identify definitive root causes, allowing the industry to respond effectively. Potential solutions could include both, the development of adjusted module designs and the avoidance of specific external loads caused by maintenance practices.

These efforts combined might be necessary to mitigate future field fractures and therefore reduce the general risk for large module replacements.

6 ACKNOWLEDGEMENTS

This work was funded by the Federal Ministry for Economic Affairs and Energy (BMWE) under grant number 03EE1131A as part of the research project "Similar". The authors gratefully acknowledge this funding which made this research possible. We would like to express our sincere appreciation to all colleagues and partners who contributed to this study through their expertise, technical support, and valuable discussions.

7 REFERENCES

[1] Chris Crowell, *Solar module glass is 'spontaneously breaking' in the field.* [Online]. Available: https://solarbuildermag.com/featured/solar-module-glass-is-spontaneously-breaking-in-the-field/ (accessed: Oct. 16 2024).

[2] Ryan Kennedy, *Spontaneous glass breakage on solar panels on the rise.* [Online]. Available: https://www.pv-magazine.com/2024/06/24/spontaneous-glass-breakage-on-solar-panels-on-the-rise/ (accessed: Oct. 16 2024).

[3] Lisa McDonald, *Solar panel breakage on the rise as glass thickness decreases and hail severity increases.* [Online]. Available: https://ceramics.org/ceramic-tech-today/solar-panel-breakage-on-the-rise-as-glass-thickness-decreases-and-hail-severity-increases/ (accessed: Oct. 16 2024).

[4] P. Sinha and A. Wade, "Assessment of Leaching Tests for Evaluating Potential Environmental Impacts of PV Module Field Breakage," *IEEE J. Photovoltaics*, vol. 5, no. 6, pp. 1710–1714, 2015, doi: 10.1109/JPHOTOV.2015.2479459.

[5] A. Sinha *et al.*, "Glass/glass photovoltaic module reliability and degradation: a review," *J. Phys. D: Appl. Phys.*, vol. 54, no. 41, p. 413002, 2021, doi: 10.1088/1361-6463/ac1462.

[6] M. Aghaei *et al.*, "Review of degradation and failure phenomena in photovoltaic modules," *Renewable and Sustainable Energy Reviews*, vol. 159, p. 112160, 2022, doi: 10.1016/j.rser.2022.112160.

[7] ITRPV, "International Technology Roadmap for Photovoltaic (ITRPV): 2022 Results," 2023.

[8] B.-W. Fan, K.-Q. Zhu, Q. Shi, T. Sun, N.-Y. Yuan, and J.-N. Ding, "Effect of glass thickness on temperature gradient and stress distribution during glass tempering," *Journal of Non-Crystalline Solids*, vol. 437, pp. 72–79, 2016, doi: 10.1016/j.jnoncrysol.2016.01.008.

[9] P. Romer, K. B. Pethani, and A. J. Beinert, "Effect of inhomogeneous loads on the mechanics of PV modules," *Prog. Photovolt: Res. Appl.*, vol. 32, no. 2, pp. 84–101, 2024, doi: 10.1002/pip.3738.

[10] *DIN EN 12150-1: Glas im Bauwesen – Thermisch vorgespanntes Kalknatron-Einscheiben-Sicherheitsglas: Teil 1: Definition und Beschreibung*, Deutsches Institut für Normung e. V., Berlin, 2019.

[11] *DIN EN 1863-1: Glas im Bauwesen – Teilvorgespanntes Kalknatronglas: Teil 1: Definition und Beschreibung; Deutsche Fassung 1863-1:2011*, Deutsches Institut für Normung e. V., Berlin, 2011.

[12] *Photovoltaic (PV) modules - Non-uniform snow load testing,* IEC 62938:2020, International Electrotechnical Commission (IEC), Geneva, Switzerland, 2020.

[13] E. Wagner, *Glasschäden: Oberflächenbeschädigungen, Glasbrüche in Theorie und Praxis,* 5th ed. Stuttgart: Fraunhofer IRB Verlag, 2020.

[14] *DIN EN 1288-1: Bestimmung der Biegefestigkeit von Glas: Teil 1: Grundlagen,* Deutsches Institut für Normung e. V., Berlin, Sep. 2000.

DETERMINING THE GLASS STRENGTH OF SOLAR GLASS - TEST AND EVALUATION METHODS

Hannah Reichart[1], Matthias Pander[2], Ruth Kasper[1]

[1] TH Köln - University of Applied Sciences, Faculty of Civil Engineering and Environmental Technology, Cologne Germany

[2] Fraunhofer Center for Silicon Photovoltaics (CSP), Halle (Saale), Germany

Motivation

- Glass-glass PV modules are reaching a new high and a continued upward trend

- Increase in module dimensions up to 3 m²

- Decrease of glass thickness from 3.2 mm to 2 mm – 1.6 mm

- Glass breakage of PV-Modules more likely

Research question: How can the strength of solar glass $\leq$ 2 mm be accurately determined?

Methodology

The material glass

- Brittle material behavior

- Theoretical material strength of glass is very high

- Actual strength depends on the condition of the surface

- Probabilistic approach is required to determine the characteristic strength f_k of glass

- A minimum of 30 equal specimen is required

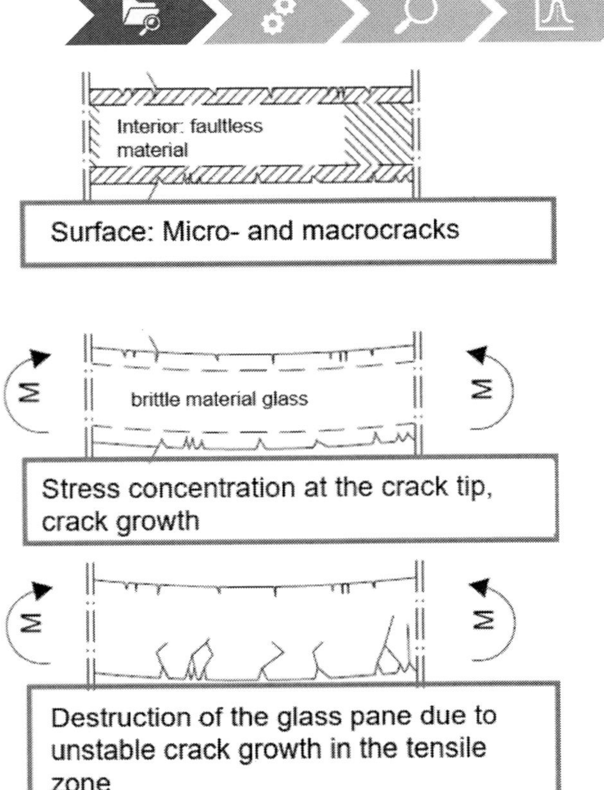

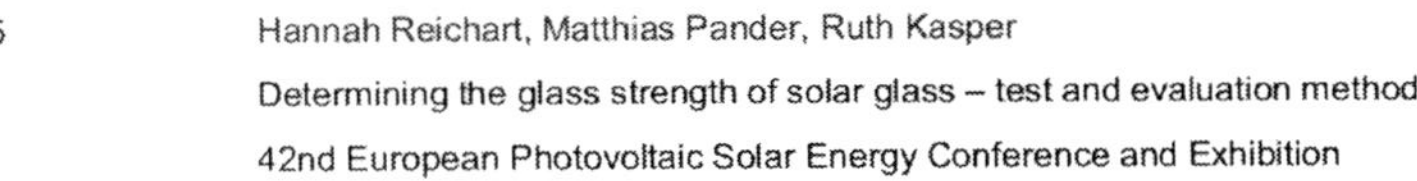

Fraunhofer CSP

Technology Arts Sciences TH Köln

020232-004

Determining the glass strength in the building sector

- EN 1288-3 standardizes tests for pane thicknesses of 3 mm to 19 mm

- Glass dimensions 360 mm x 1100 mm

- Calculation of the breaking stress using linear beam theory, assuming the deformations remain sufficiently small

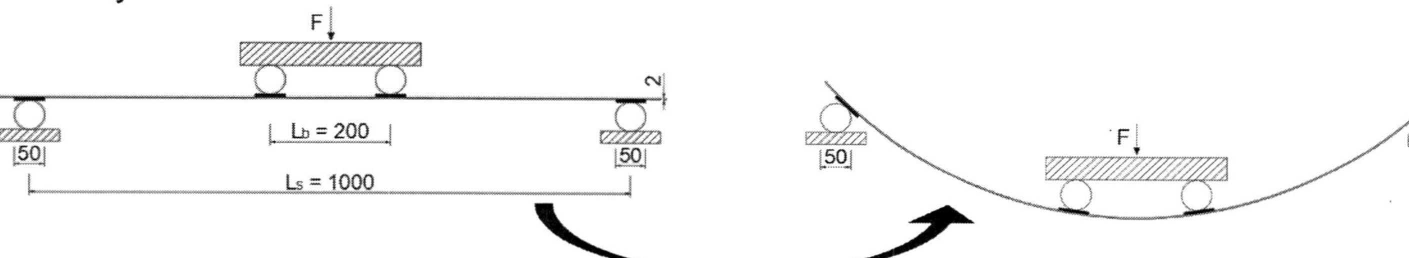

Problem: When testing panes ≤ 2 mm very large deformations occurs
→ Pane slips off the support rollers before reaching maximum load
→ Significant geometric nonlinear effects occur

EN 1288-3 does not apply to thin glass!

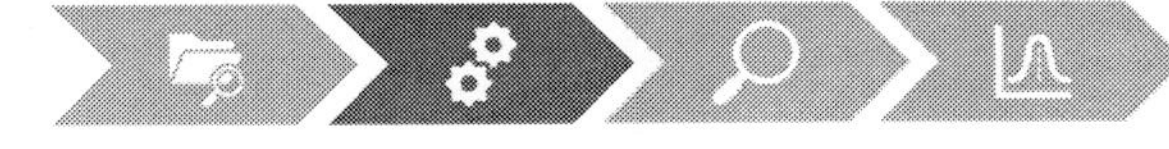

Adjustment of the test setup

- Reduction of the support spacing L_s from 1000 mm to 700 mm

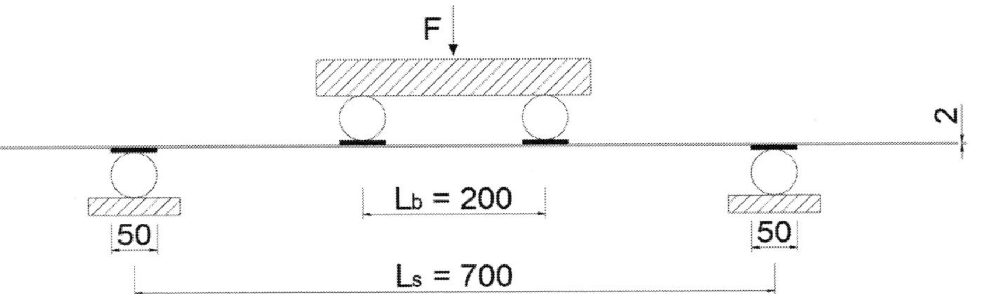

Due to nonlinear effects and membrane stresses, development of a new evaluation method is necessary!

25.09.2025

Hannah Reichart, Matthias Pander, Ruth Kasper

Determining the glass strength of solar glass – test and evaluation methods

6

42nd European Photovoltaic Solar Energy Conference and Exhibition

Fraunhofer CSP

Technology Arts Sciences TH Köln

020232-006

Numerical simulation and parameter study

- Numerical investigation with FEM solid simulation using ANSYS mechanical

- Consideration of various parameters, including glass E-modulus, roller friction, glass Poisson's ratio, and pane thickness

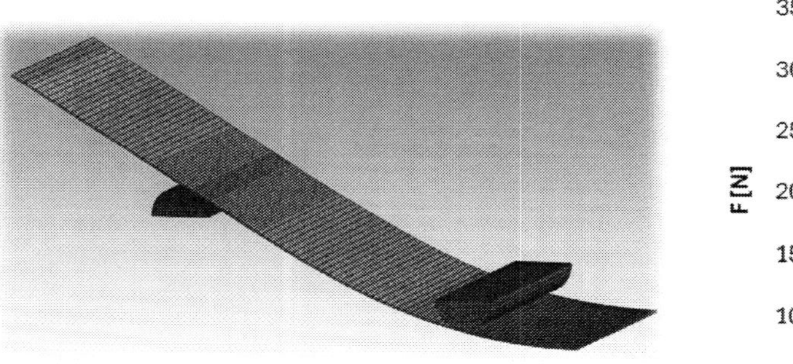

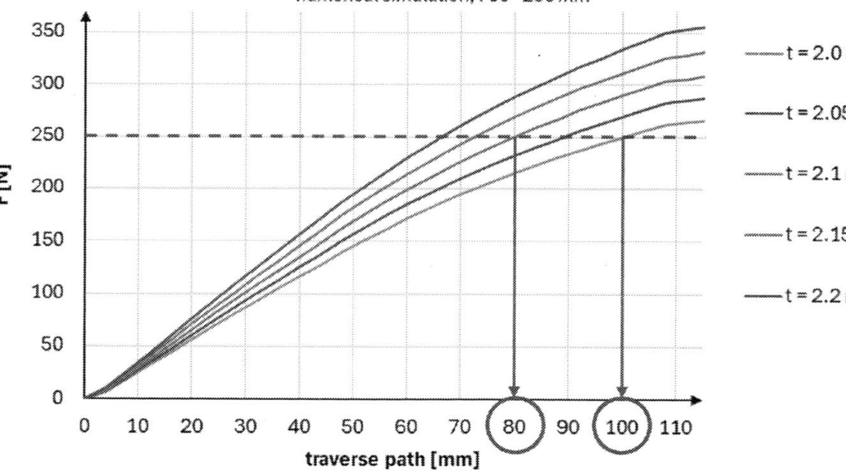

The significant influencing parameter is the glass thickness.

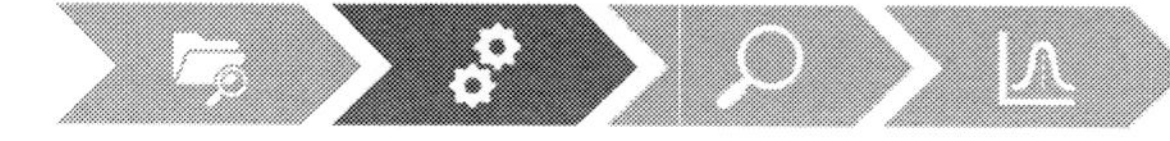

Verification of the numerical model through experiments

- Deformation and strain measurement
- Nonlinearity clearly visible

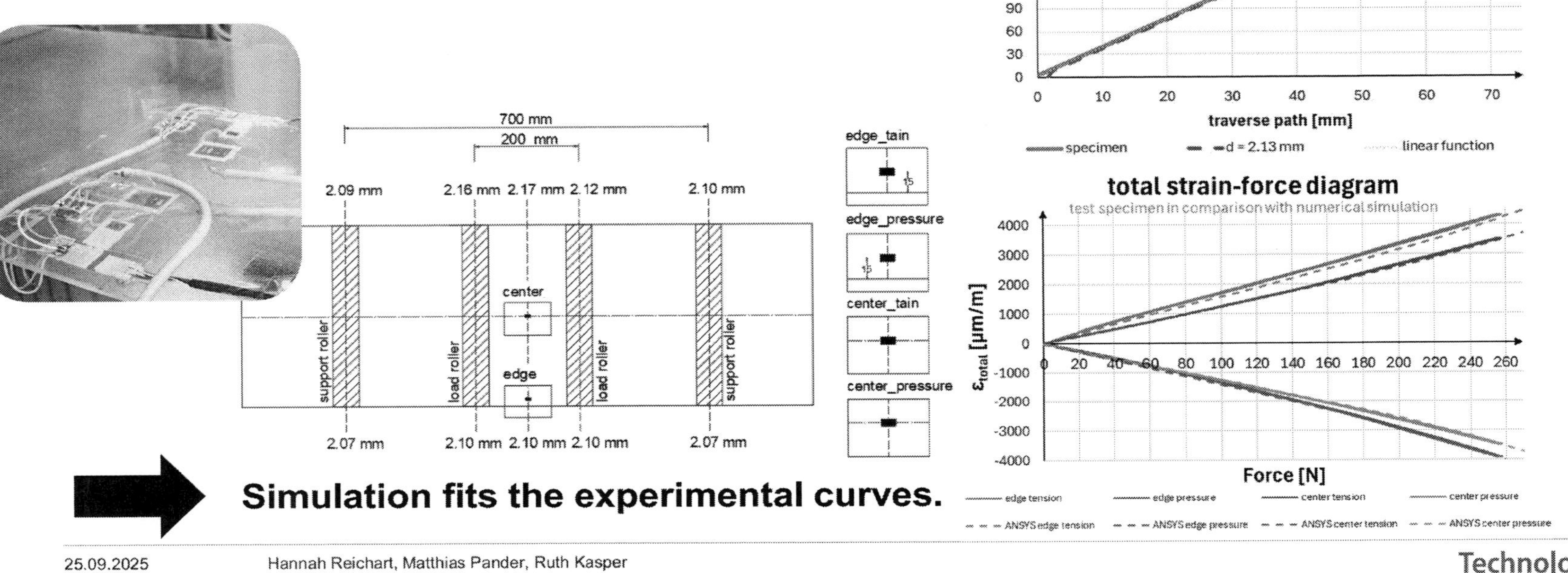

Simulation fits the experimental curves.

Fraunhofer CSP

Technology
Arts Sciences
TH Köln

Test setup

- Material strength test were carried out at two Locations: Frauenhofer CSP Halle and TH Köln
- Total of 128 panes of different qualities of Glasmanufaktur Brandenburg (GMB)
- Additionally optical surface pre-stress measurement using SCALP

Serie	Location	Annealed solar glass	Thermally prestressed solar glass	Thermally prestressed with AR-coating
1	TH Köln	18 panes	23 panes	26 panes (AR - coating on tensile side)
2	CSP Halle	11 panes	10 panes	10 panes (AR-coating on tensile side)
3	TH Köln	-	14 panes	17 panes (8 AR-coating on tensile side/ 9 AR-coating on compression side)

Hannah Reichart, Matthias Pander, Ruth Kasper
Determining the glass strength of solar glass – test and evaluation methods

Fraunhofer CSP

Technology
Arts Sciences
TH Köln

020232-009

25.09.2025

Hannah Reichart, Matthias Pander, Ruth Kasper

Determining the glass strength of solar glass – test and evaluation methods

42nd European Photovoltaic Solar Energy Conference and Exhibition

10

Fraunhofer CSP

Technology Arts Sciences TH Köln

020232-010

Evaluation Method for material strength

- Determination of the breaking stress using numerically determined curves

3. Consideration of the fracture origin across the width of the pane

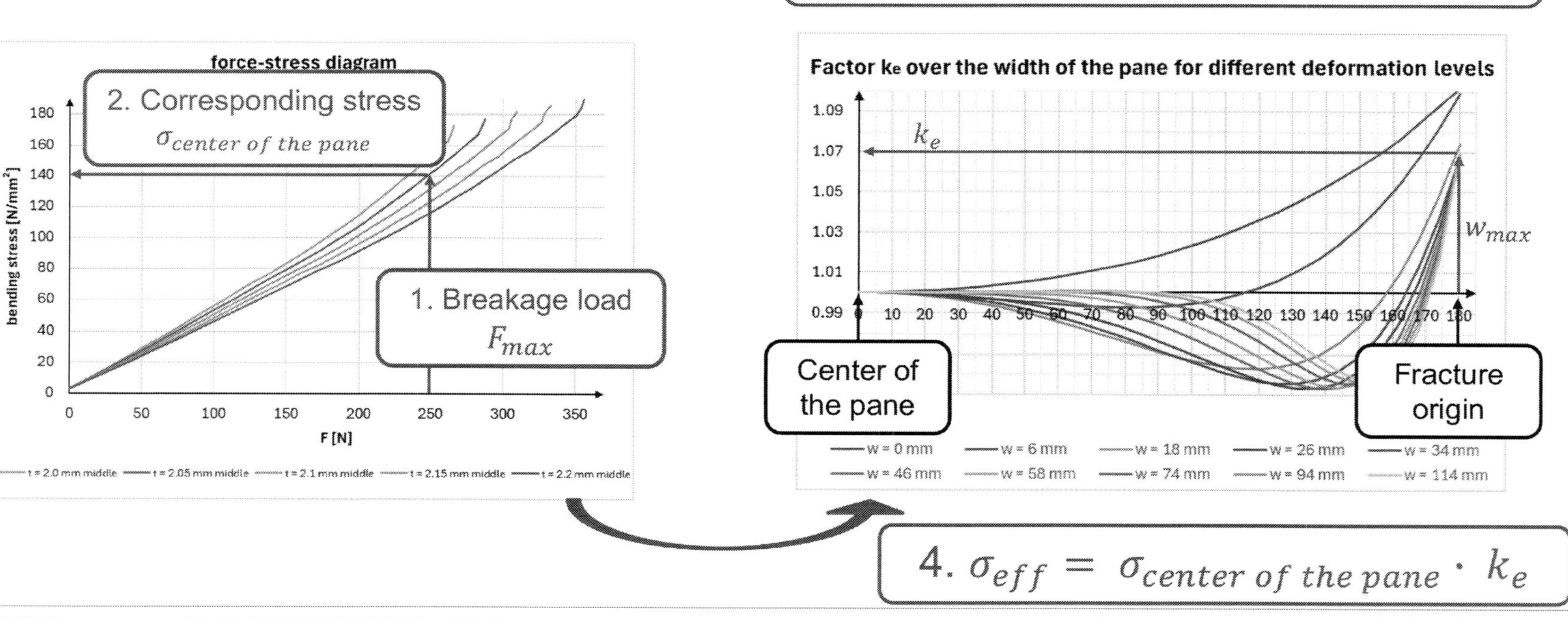

Evaluation and statistical analysis

- Characteristic strength corresponds to the 5% quantile value with a confidence level of 95%
- Lognormal and Weibull distribution was used

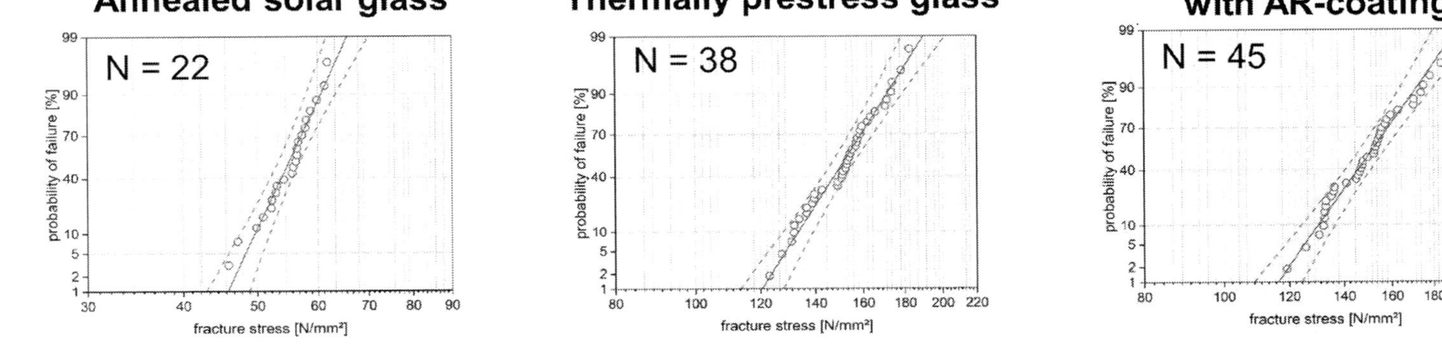

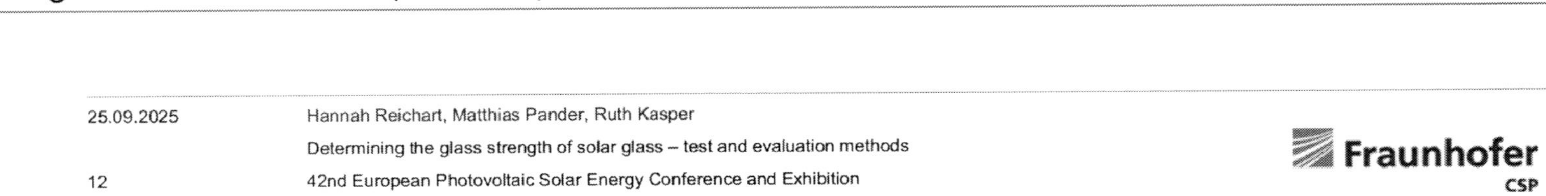

	Annealed solar glass	Thermally prestress glass	Thermally prestress with AR-coating
f_k Weibull	47 (**44** … 51)	122 (**113** … 132)	119 (**110** … 129)
f_k Lognormal	48 (**46** … 50)	129 (**123** … 132)	127 (**121** … 133)

Hannah Reichart, Matthias Pander, Ruth Kasper

Determining the glass strength of solar glass – test and evaluation methods

42nd European Photovoltaic Solar Energy Conference and Exhibition

Fraunhofer CSP

Technology
Arts Sciences
TH Köln

020232-012

Conclusion

- Determining the strength of glass ≤ 2 mm with adapted four point bending test setup possible

- Due to nonlinear effects and membrane stresses, evaluation according to EN 1288-3 is not suitable; instead, evaluation via FEM simulation is required.

- Tested glass of GMB reached characteristic strength of:
  - Annealed glass f_k = 44 N/mm²
  - Thermally prestressed glass f_k = 123 N/mm²
  - Thermally prestressed with AR-coating f_k = 121 N/mm²

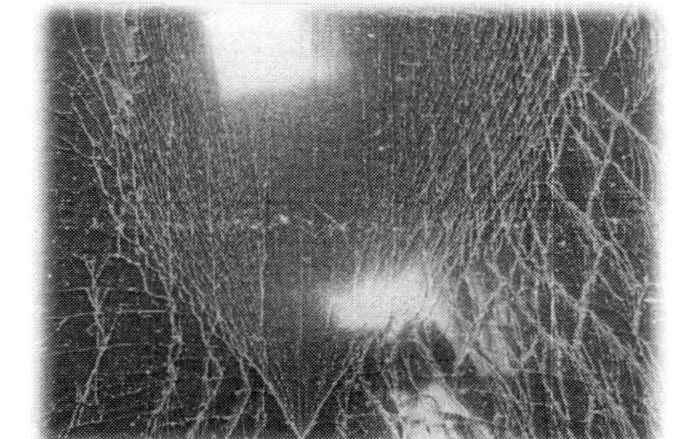

Outlook

- Verified material strength data are necessary for a reliable static design of PV-modules instead of load testing according to IEC 61215

Thank you for your attention!

Contact:

Hannah Reichart
TH Köln -
University of Applied Sciences
hannah_sophie.reichart@th-koeln.de

Matthias Pander
Fraunhofer Center for Silicon
Photovoltaics (CSP)
matthias.pander@csp.fraunhofer.de

Ruth Kasper
TH Köln –
University of Applied Sciences
ruth.kasper@th-koeln.de

The Paper has been selected by the Committee of the EU PVSEC 2025 for submission to the journal "Progress in Photovoltaics"

Acknowledgement:

 Federal Ministry for Economic Affairs and Energy

This publication was funded by the Federal Ministry for Economic Affairs and Energy in the project Green Solar Modules under grant number 00EE1161A and 03EE1161B. The findings herein reflect the work, and are solely the responsibility, of the authors. We would also like to thank Glasmanufaktur Brandenburg, our project partner, for providing the test specimens.

This presentation was selected by the Sc. Committee of the EU PVSEC 2025 for submission of a full paper to one of the EU PVSEC's collaborating peer-reviewed journals.

Reliability studies of UV downshifting encapsulants after Damp-Heat and UV weathering

Jishnu Ramachandran Nair[1,2], Marius Lüdemann[1,2], Paul-Tiberiu Miclea[1], Kai Zhang[3], Kaining Ding[3], Andreas Lambertz[3], Ralph Gottschalg[1,2], Robert Heidrich[1,2], and Anton Mordvinkin[1]

[1]Fraunhofer Center for Silicon Photovoltaics (CSP), Otto-Eißfeldt-Str. 12, 06120 Halle, Germany,
[2] Anhalt University of Applied Sciences, Köthen, Sachsen-Anhalt, 06366, Germany
[3] IMD-3 Photovoltaics, Forschungszentrum Jülich GmbH, Jülich, Germany
Corresponding Author: anton.mordvinkin@csp.fraunhofer.de,
First authors: jishnu.ramachandran.nair@imws.fraunhofer.de, marius.luedemann@imws.fraunhofer.de

ABSTRACT: A rigorous degradation analysis of emerging encapsulants containing UV downshifters (DS) was conducted. The encapsulants are based on ethylene vinyl-acetate copolymer (EVA) and a three-layered system, composed of 2 EVAs flanking a polyolefin elastomer (POE) layer, so-called EPE. The UV-downshifting EVA and EPE were exposed to 1000 h damp-heat (DH), 120 kWh UV, and combined DH and UV (100 kWh) accelerated weathering tests and analyzed using a multi-faceted analytical approach. The UV-vis spectroscopy showed degradation of the UV downshifter after the accelerated aging, which was especially pronounced after the UV exposure. The findings were supported by the 2D fluorescence spectroscopy, which also suggested severe changes in the mode of action of the UV downshifter. The changed mode of action led to the reduction in the conversion efficiency by 2 orders of magnitude and shift of the excitation wavelength towards higher values, thus significantly worsening the original functionality. For the first time, encapsulants with UV downshifters were analyzed using pyrolysis-gas-chromatography (Py-GCMS), and the changes of the presumable UV downshifter signal could be directly correlated to the UV-vis and fluorescence spectroscopy results as well as degradation of antioxidant and hindered amine light stabilizer. Building up on the provided results, the degradation analysis will be continued with the encapsulants extracted from the aged minimodules, correlating the material and module degradation. This comprehensive characterization provides insights into the degradation behavior of DS encapsulants under accelerated aging conditions, contributing to a deeper understanding of DS material reliability needed for its PV integration and enabling the development of more robust and efficient PV modules.

Keywords: Downshifting , degradation, reliability

1 Introduction

UV downshifting (DS) encapsulants is an emerging class of active encapsulants that, apart from their typical properties directed to the cell protection against environmental factors, can enhance photovoltaic performance and cell protection by converting high-energy ultraviolet photons into lower-energy visible light . While module-level studies confirm the benefits of DS films, material-level investigations, particularly regarding long-term performance and weathering, require further exploration, especially concerning the stability of the DS materials in encapsulants themselves. Babics et al. [3] recently investigated the performance and reliability of PV modules made with co-extruded encapsulant containing a UV down-shifting compound, showing vulnerability towards photooxidation.

However, molecular details on the DS-encapsulants degradation are still missing. This study aspires to close the gap between the deterioration of the DS effect and relevant material changes causing it. To this end, the DS EVA and EPE encapsulants, aged according to typical accelerated weathering protocols for PV modules, will be rigorously analyzed. For the first time, the disappearance of the DS effect will be linked to the additive degradation (DS itself and stabilizing additives). Accompanying chemical and microstructural changes in the polymer matrix will be likewise scrutinized. The contribution given is highly relevant to facilitate the design of emerging DS encapsulants, whose reliability is not well understood yet. The study will provide insights into the enhancement of the encapsulant and hence module reliability.

2 Materials and Methods

The study aims to pinpoint the degradation mechanism of emerging EVA and EPE encapsulants containing UV downshifting moieties during UV and damp-heat (DH) accelerated aging. In particular, the factors leading to the degradation of the UV downshifting effect will be scrutinized. To this end, plain films as well as minimodules, based on the encapsulants, having different configurations (double glass, lightweight with a polymeric front sheet) modulating the moisture and oxygen ingress, will be weathered. The degradation behavior will be assessed by a variety of methods, enabling tracking the additive and polymer degradation. In the first iteration, the encapsulants will undergo 1000 h of the DH, 120 kWh of the UV exposure, and 1000 h at combined DH and UV conditions. The damp heat was conducted under standard conditions of 85°C and 85% relative humidity. The UV exposure was performed using a mercury light tube with a UV intensity of approximately 70 W/m2 between 320 and 400 nm, chamber temperature of around 25°C and no humidity control. The combined DH and UV weathering was carried out at 85°C, 60% relative humidity, and about 100 W/m2 UV irradiance between 300 and 400 nm. The degradation will be compared for the plain films and the films extracted from the minimodules to assess the importance of the module microclimate. Also, the material and module degradation will be correlated.

3 Results and Discussion

3.1 UV- Vis Spectroscopy

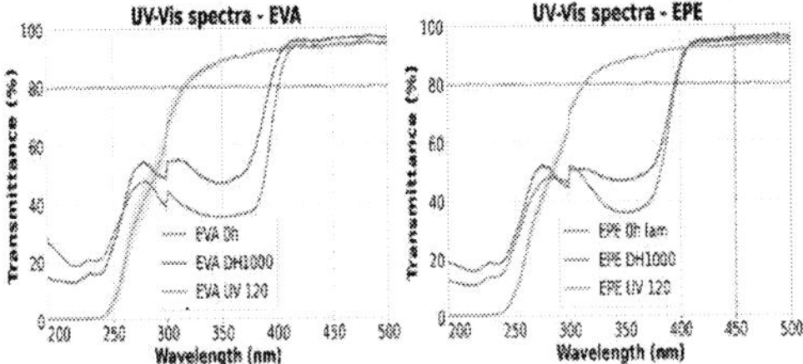

Figure 1: UV- Vis spectra of EVA (left) and EPE (right) films showing drastic changes for UV aged films

UV-Vis spectroscopy data featured a pronounced (but not complete) absorption below 400 nm in both EVA and EPE The accelerated aging (especially the UV exposure) reduced the absorption (increased the transmittance) in the UVA and UVB regions, which can be due to degradation of the UV absorbing [3] or/and UV downshifting species. The PyGCMS results below narrowed it down to the sole degradation of UV downshifters. No reduction in transmittance due to the chromophore formation was observed.

3.2 Fluorescence Spectroscopy

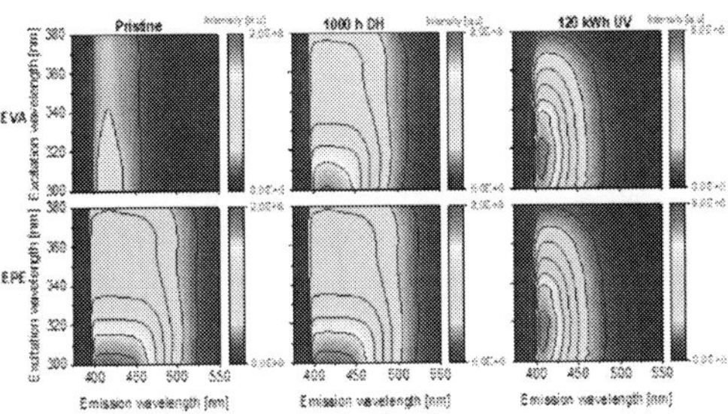

Figure 2 : 2D-fluorescence spectra for EVA (top) and EPE (bottom) in the pristine state (left) and after DH (middle) and UV (right) aging.

2D fluorescence spectroscopy was employed to analyze the changes in the mode of action of the UV downshifters. The EPE encapsulant exhibits a more pronounced fluorescence in the pristine state compared to EVA. Both show a maximum in the excitation wavelength below 300 nm. After DH, either no changes or some elevation in the fluorescence intensity could be observed. The elevation can be explained by the heterogeneous distribution of the UV downshifting species. Remarkable changes occurred after the UV exposure. First, the fluorescence intensity dropped by 2 orders of magnitude. Second, the maximum of the excitation wavelength shifted to higher values, which suggests that the UV downshifter underwent chemical conversion.

3.3 Fluorescence lifetime

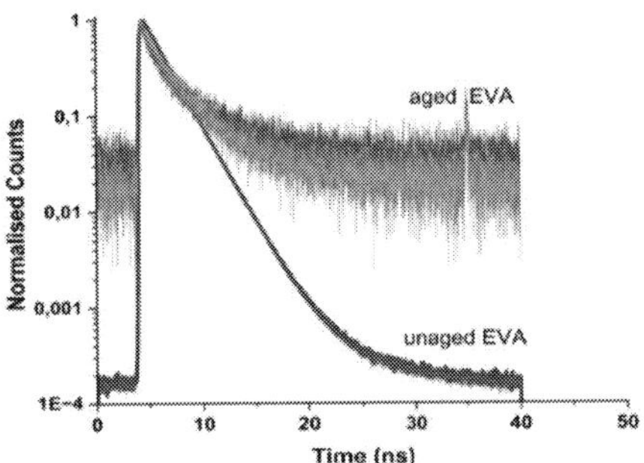

Figure 2 Fluoresence decay plots for aged and unaged EVA

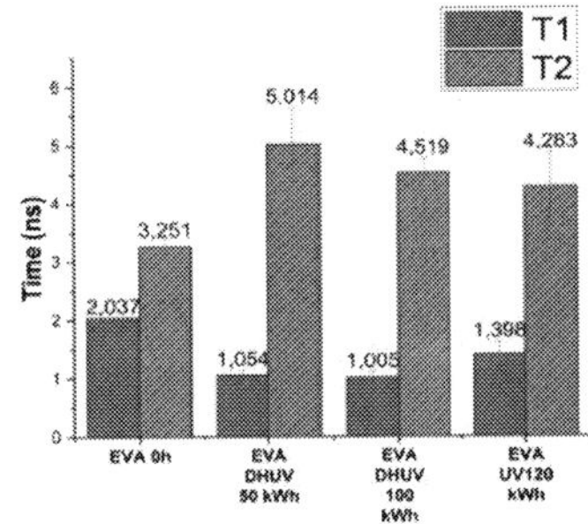

Figure 4 Decay components as T1 and T2 after exponential decay fits .

Fluorescence lifetime plots showed a significant change after the combined DH and UV weathering. The decays were fitted to a biexponential function, yielding characteristic lifetimes T1 and T2. After weathering, the faster component T1 became comparatively faster to unaged sample. It points to the possibility of fluorescence quenching and creation of new non radiative pathways [6]. On the other hand, the increase in the slower component T2 hints towards new fluorophore activity [6]. Further investigations are needed to provide more insights into chemical transformations.

3.4 Pyrolysis-Gas Chromatography-Mass Spectrometry

Pyrolysis-Gas Chromatography-Mass Spectrometry (PY-GCMS) was employed to provide the qualitative and semi-quantitative analysis of the EVA and EPE films in the pristine and aged state. The exact description of the measurement method can be found in [4]. The analysis showed that the films include crosslinking additives (peroxide and accelerator), different types of adhesion promoters, antioxidant, plasticizers, hindered amine light stabilizer (HALS) and its fragments, and one additive unknown to the NIST library, which can be presumably a UV downshifter. No UV absorbers were found, suggesting that the above reduction in absorbance detected by UV-vis spectroscopy can be completely related to the UV downshifter degradation. shows intensities of the selected additives which can especially contribute to the long-term stability against the DH and UV: antioxidant, HALS and its fragment, presumable UV downshifter. The intensities were obtained in the pristine and aged state and compared after normalizing to the sample mass. It allowed one to track the relative changes.

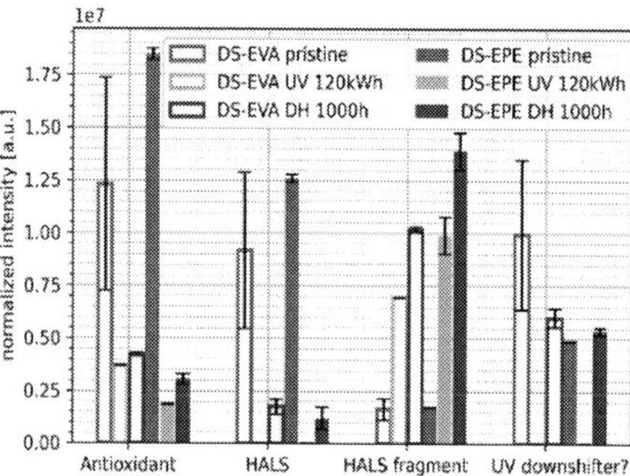

Figure 5 Normalized intensity of additives quantified by PY-GCMS (DS-EVA UV 120kWh: single determination, remaining: double determination)

The antioxidant content in EVA and EPE decreased more during UV weathering than during DH weathering. The same result can be seen for the HALS, which was already completely depleted after 120 kWh of the UV weathering. In [5], it was shown that the HALS can degrade under both UV and DH conditions. During aging, large HALS molecules fragmented into smaller ones, which stay active and continue protecting the polymer [5]. The presumable UV downshifter showed little change in concentration after DH but completely disappeared after the UV exposure.

This observation agrees with the above fluorescence data and supports the hypothesis of the additive being a UV downshifter. However, the additive nature must be still elucidated, e.g. based on its mass spectrum. Further, organic UV downshifters are known to be vulnerable against photooxidation (UV+O2)[2]. Therefore, the depletion of the antioxidant and HALS can have a negative impact on its stability.

4 Conclusion

This study successfully demonstrated that the degradation of organic UV downshifters can be effectively tracked using combination of methods like py GCMS and Fluorescence lifetime and spectroscopy. It revealed that HALS and antioxidants are consumed in parallel, offering protection against photo-oxidation. The role of additional additives in enhancing the stability of the downshifter needs further investigation along with fluorphore mechanisms. These findings highlight the importance of formulations of downshifting encapsulants for the reliability and long-term performance of PV modules.

5 References

[1] T. Trupke, M. A. Green, and P. Würfel, "Improving solar cell efficiencies by down-conversion of high-energy photons," Jul. 28, 2002, American Institute of Physics.

[2] M. Babics et al., "Performance and reliability of PV modules made with co-extruded encapsulant containing UV down-shifting compound." 2024.

[3] V. Fiandra, L. Sannino, C. Andreozzi, G. Flaminio, and M. Pellegrino, "New PV encapsulants: assessment of change in optical and thermal properties and chemical degradation after UV aging," Dec. 23, 2023, Elsevier BV. doi: 10.1016/j.polymdegradstab.2023.110643.

[4] Heidrich, Robert, Anton Mordvinkin, and Ralph Gottschalg. "Quantification of UV protecting additives in ethylene-vinyl acetate copolymer encapsulants for photovoltaic modules with pyrolysis-gas chromatography-mass spectrometry." Polymer Testing 118 (2023): 107913.

[5] Heidrich, Robert, et al. " From Performance Measurements to Molecular Level Characterization: Exploring the Differences between Ultraviolet and Damp Heat Weathering of Photovoltaics Modules." Solar RRL 8.10 (2024): 2400144.

[6] Tunstall Garcia, H. (2025). Design and Characterisation of Hybrid Organic-Inorganic Materials for Luminescence Downshifting Devices [Apollo - University of Cambridge Repository]. https://doi.org/10.17863/CAM.117427

Festina Lente! The Impact of Lamination Duration on Encapsulant Stability

<u>Nikolina Pervan</u>, Jutta Geier, Christian Veas, Gernot Oreski

Polymer Competence Center Leoben GmbH, 8700 Leoben, Austria
Chair of Materials Science and Testing of Polymers, Montanuniversität Leoben, Leoben, Austria

42nd EUPVSEC, Bilbao, Spain, 22 – 26. September 2025.

It is all about encapsulants!

PCCL Polymer Competence Center Leoben

- **Adhesion**
- **Protection**
- **Light transmission**
- **Aesthetic**

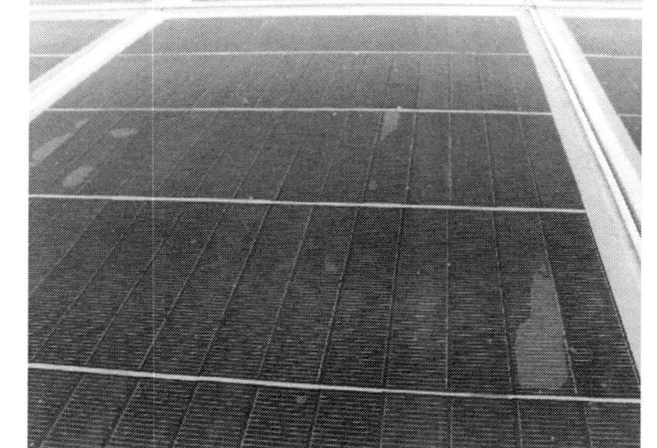

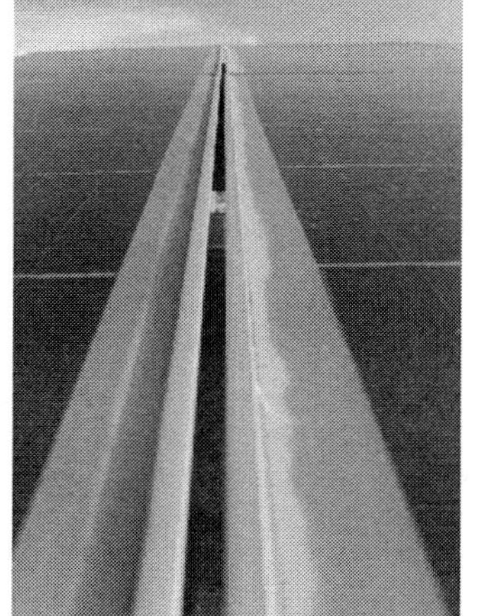

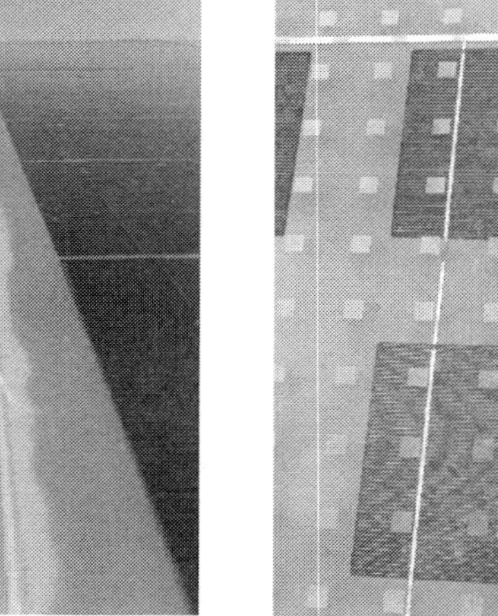

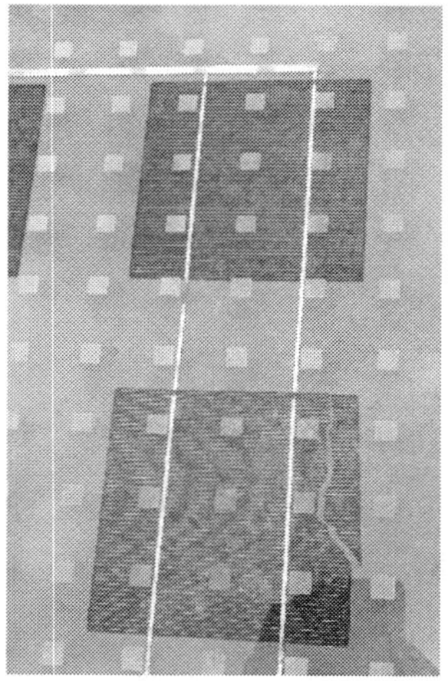

- Most commonly used encapsulants:
  - **EVA** (ethylene vinyl acetate)
  - Polyolefin (**POE** – crosslinking, **TPO** – non-crosslinking)
  - **EPE** (coextruded EVA-polyolefin-EVA)

Different polymer chemical and physical structures behind the same name – different material behaviour!!!

K. Aitola, et al., Encapsulation of commercial and emerging solar cells with focus on perovskite solar cells, Solar Energy, Vol 237, 2022.

Encapsulant's processing history

PCCL Polymer Competence Center Leoben

Encapsulant production process

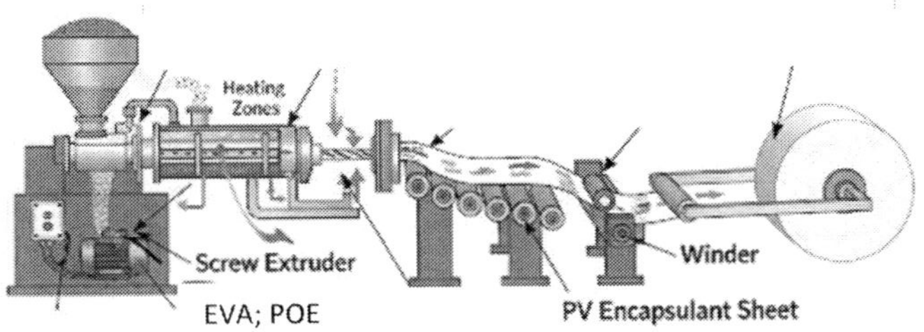

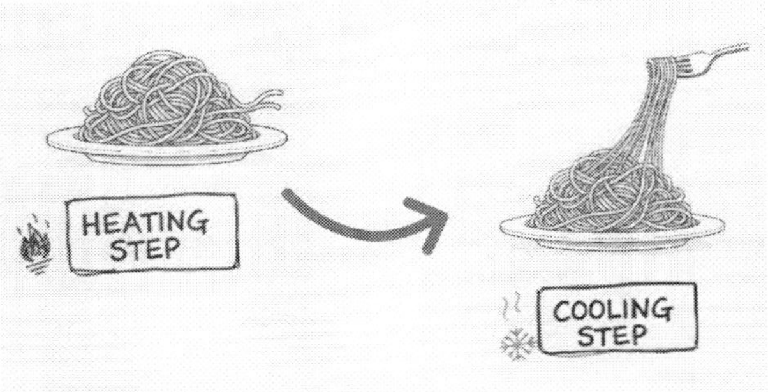

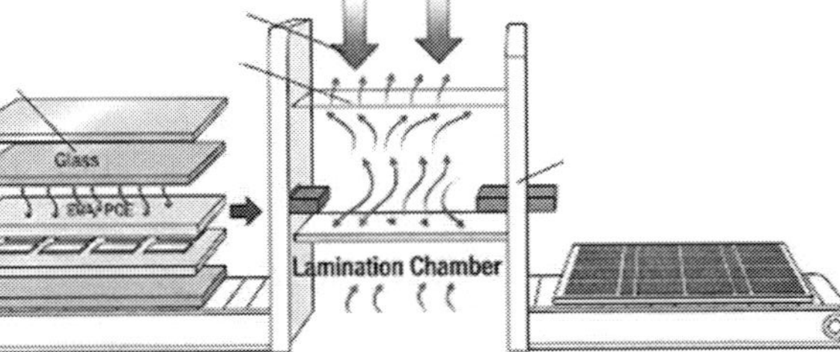

Extrusion + forming R2R process: orientation created – machine direction (MD)

PV module lamination process

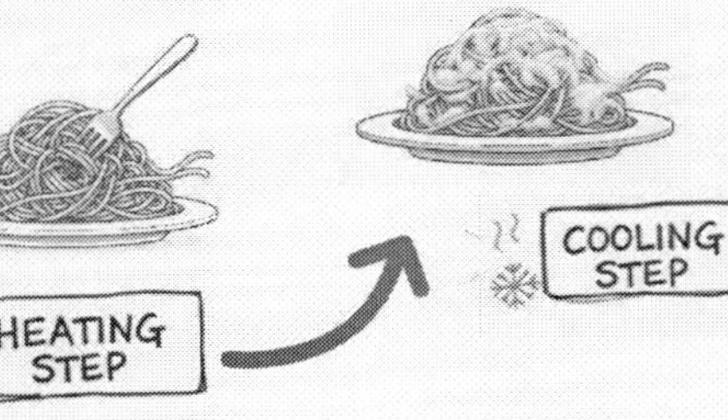

Lamination – 1 step process: MD orientation removed (vacuum); new orientation created (lamination)

Introduced stress in PV module:

- interconnection failure
- cell fragmentation
- interlayer delamination
- backsheet dislocation and deformation

Image created using AI tool „Gemini 2.5 Flash".

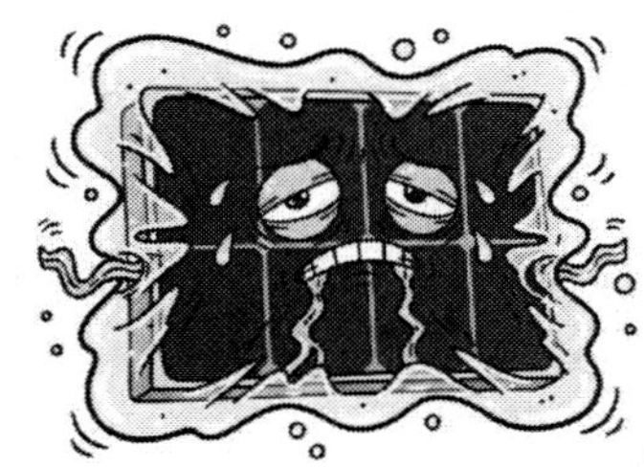

Images created using AI tool „Gemini 2.5 Flash"

26.09.2025

www.pccl.at

020234-004

Experimental work – encapsulant types

Encapsulant type	Polymer type (FTIR-ATR analysis)	Crosslinking type (TDS)
EVA	ethylene vinyl acetate	peroxides
POE-1	ethylene α-olefin	peroxides
POE-2	ethylene α-olefin	peroxides
TPO	ethylene ethyl acrylate	non-crosslinking
EPE-1	2x ethylene vinyl acetate (P?)	peroxides (EVA)
EPE-2	2x ethylene vinyl acetate (P?)	peroxides

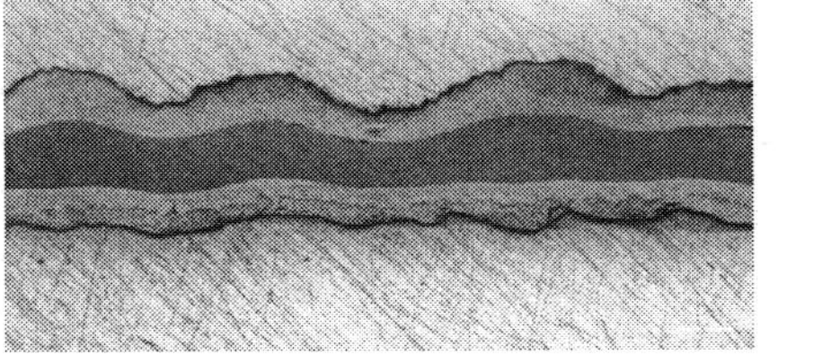
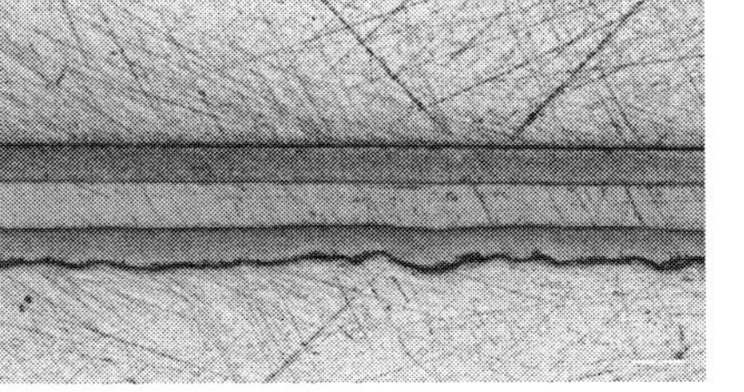

EPE (EVA – polyolefin – EVA) same name tag – different encapsulants

020234-005

Experimental work – encapsulant lamination and characterisation

LAMINATION

- 2 encapsulant layers per lamination
- 20 x 20 cm² size
- Stack: glass / Teflon / encapsulant / Teflon / encapsulant / Teflon / glass

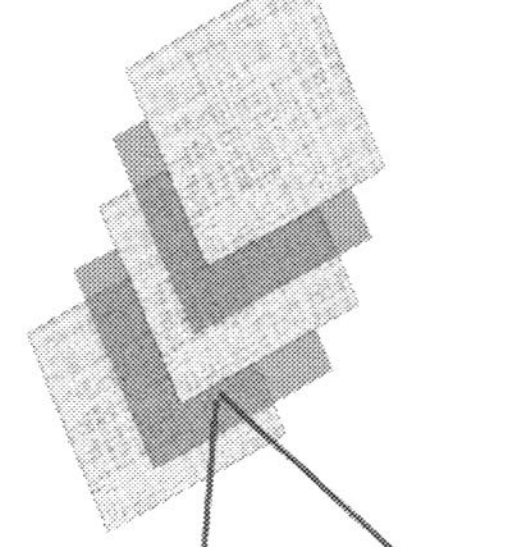

Lamination times

- **0** min – **non-laminated** – production history
- **2** and **5** min – short lamination times
- **10**, **12** and **15** min – industrial standards
- **20** and **30** min – extended lamination time
- *Lamination temperature – from TDS and from DSC*

Degree of curing – DSC (IEC 62788-1-6:2017)

- Determination of degree of curing for crosslinking encapsulants according to:
  - **Residual enthalpy** (crosslinking process)
  - **Melt/freeze (MF) method** (crystallization peak)

Coefficient of thermal expansion (CTE) – Digital image correlation (DIC) (20 °C to 140 °C)

- Determination of thermomechanical properties:
  - **Non-laminated encapsulant** vs. **laminated samples** (lamination duration impact)

DSC is commonly used to measure degree of curing in crosslinking encapsulants with peroxides, but determining lamination time for non-crosslinking types remains challenging. **Can we see which lamination time is optimal for both encapsulant types from the thermomechanical behaviour?**

020234-006

Images created using AI tool „Gemini 2.5 Flash"

www.pccl.at

020234-007

DSC – facts about encapsulants

PCCL
Polymer Competence Center Leoben

- **TPO** as non-crosslinking encapsulant is excluded from the calculations
- **EPE-1** - polyolefin component is a non-crosslinking type - T_m and Tc are the same for all lamination times
- **EPE-2** - polyolefin is a crosslinking type – 2nd crystallization peak present for lamination times above 12 minutes – *due to the presence of 2nd crystallization peak excluded from the MF method calculations*

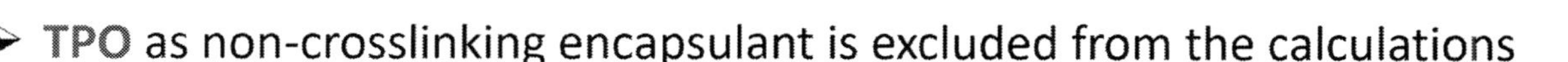

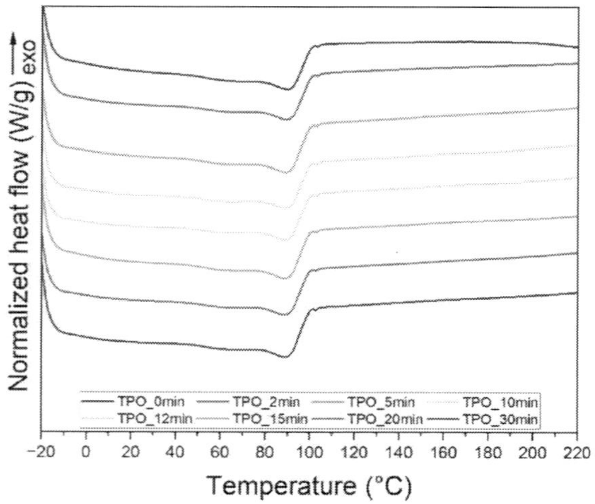

TPO – 2nd heating curves

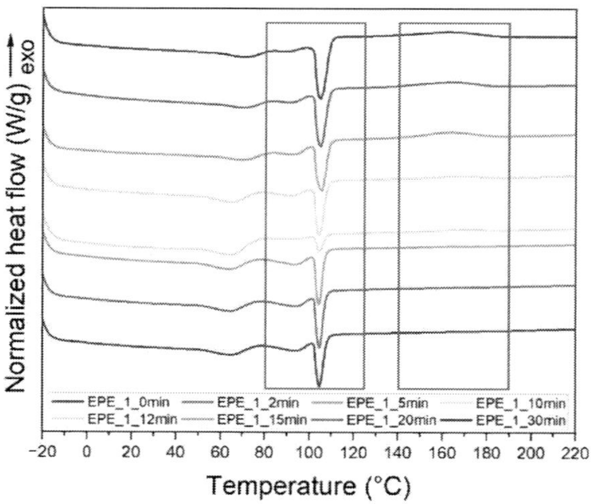

EPE-1 – 2nd heating curves

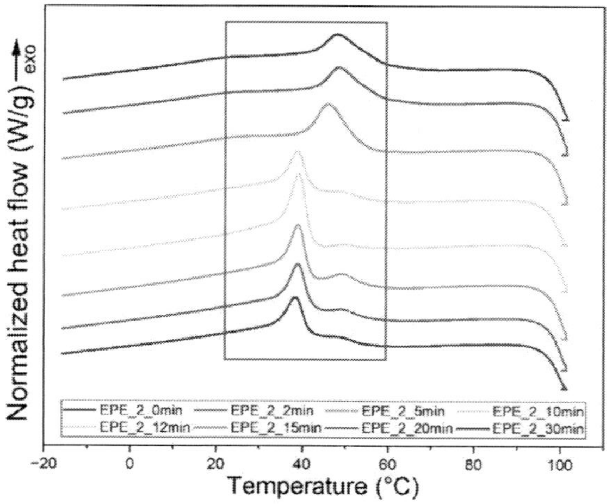

EPE-2 – 1st cooling curves

DSC – curing degrees according to residual enthalpy and melt/freeze (MF) method

PCCL
Polymer Competence Center Leoben

- Curing degrees calculated from residual enthalpy and MF methods differ
- Both DSC methods may not deliver reliable results for EPE - the same issue is expected from Soxhlet method!
- Unreliable results due to the unknown data:
  - Are all layers crosslinking?
  - What is the thickness distribution of the layers?
- All of the methods depend on weight – results can be over/under estimated

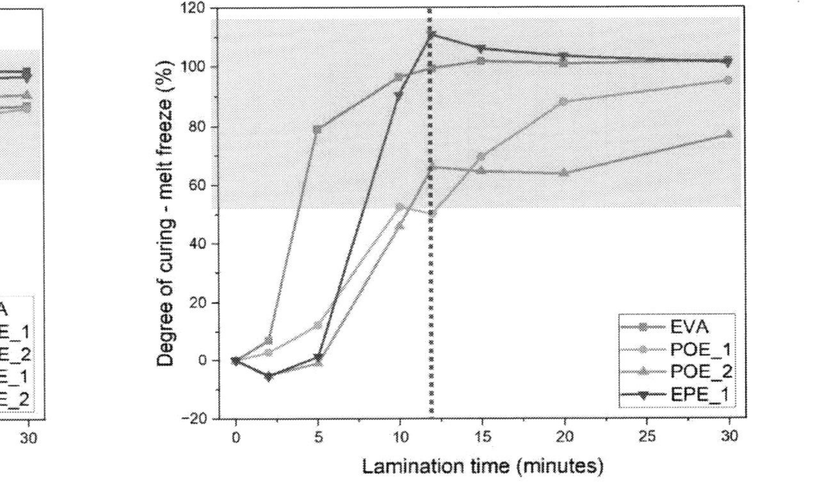

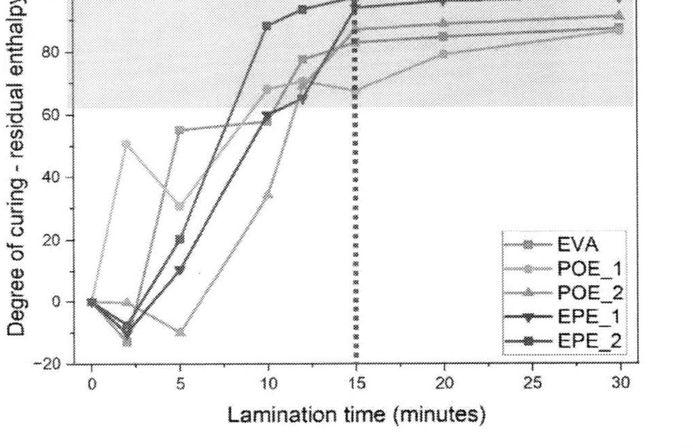

020234-009

Non-laminated encapsulants vs. 30 minutes laminated encapsulants – CTE

PCCL
Polymer Competence Center Leoben

Inherited behaviour - stress during the lamination

Thermomechanical behaviour/stress during lifetime

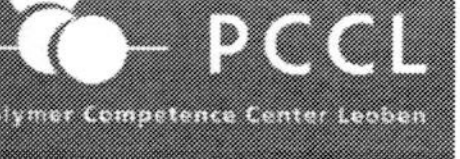

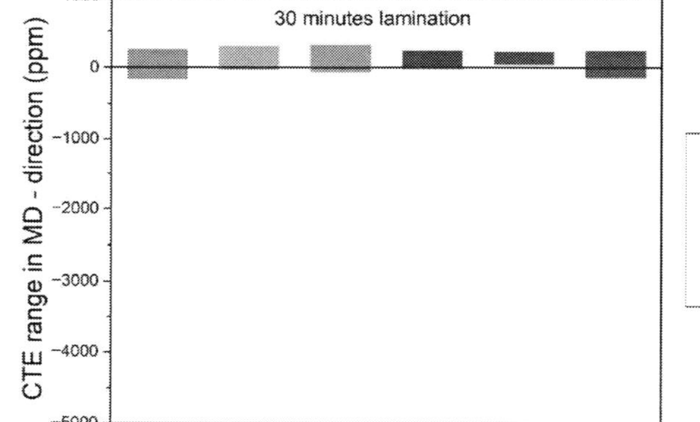

- **Negative CTE values** represent **shrinkage** of **non-laminated encapsulant** in the **MD direction**:
  - POE-1, **TPO** and **EPE-1** - high; EVA – medium; POE-2 and **EPE-2** – low shrinkage
  - Material orientation and extrusion processing conditions are the reason for shrinkage of encapsulant
- Non-crosslinking polyolefins in **TPO** and **EPE-1** exhibit high shrinkage for non-laminated state, but have lowest CTE value range after 30 minutes lamination
- Interestingly, **EPE-2** is characterised by an increase of CTE values range after the lamination

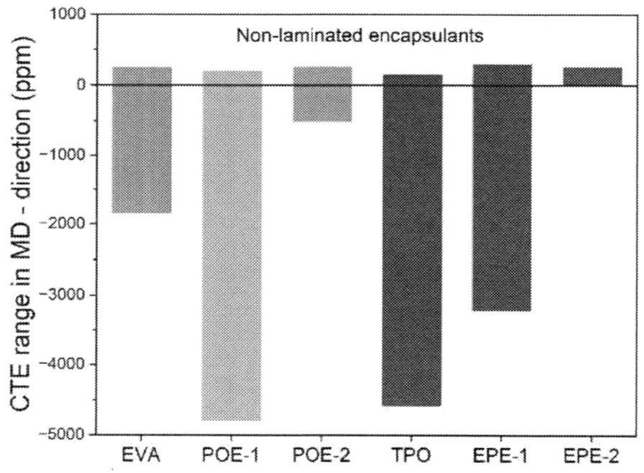

Results of CTE – for all lamination times – TPO and EPE-2

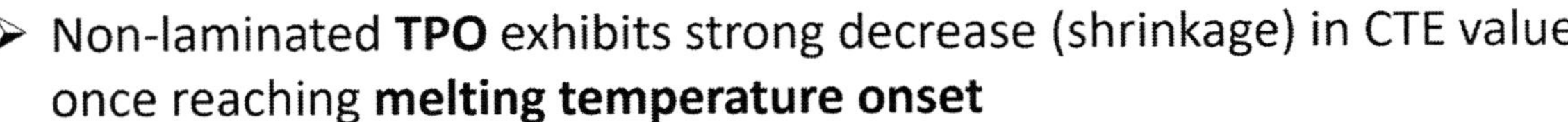

- Non-laminated **TPO** exhibits strong decrease (shrinkage) in CTE values once reaching **melting temperature onset**

- **High CTE values** for **0**, **2** (and **5**) minutes of TPO, EVA, (POE-1 and EPE-1) laminated samples is a sign of too short lamination times for polymer chains reorientation

- **EPE-2** and **POE-2** have **lower CTE values for 0 and 2 min** samples compared to the rest of encapsulants

  - **How does the extrusion process differ for these samples?**

- All encapsulants reached "final" CTE values by 10 minutes of lamination duration – time needed for **chain reorientation** ((non-)crosslinking) and **polymer network creation** (crosslinking)

- Higher degrees of curing (according to DSC) do not impact CTE values of encapsulants significantly

020234-011

Encapsulant before and after CTE measurement

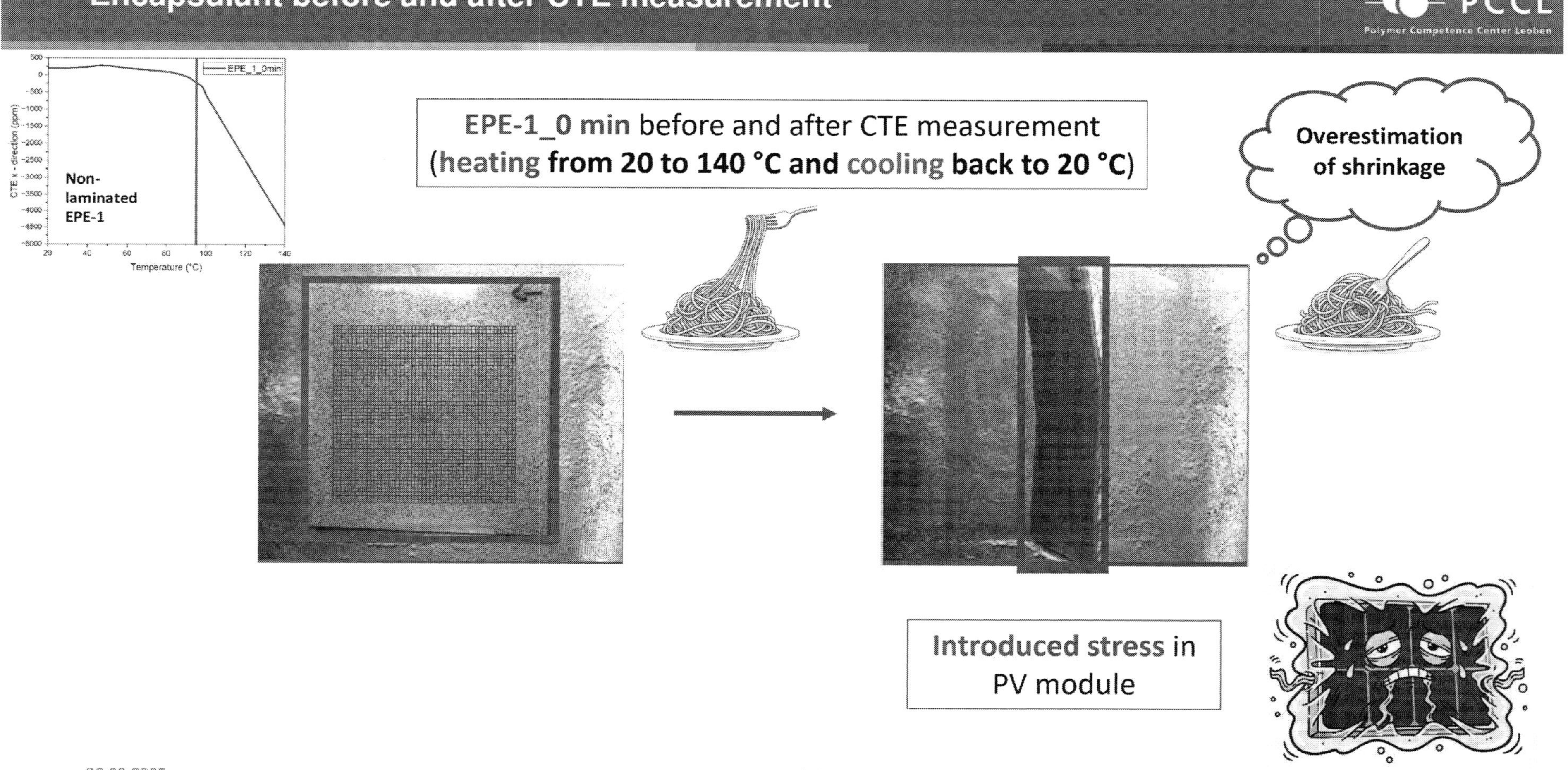

PCCL
Polymer Competence Center Leoben

Non-laminated encapsulants can shrink significantly during the vacuum step in lamination process due to the inherited polymer chain orientation from the extrusion process - this can cause various issues from interconnection failures, cell fragmentation and delamination especially for emerging and thin film technologies perovskites, CIGS, tandem.

Too short lamination time may affect **early life PV module failure** for encapsulants with high shrinkage.

Laminating for at least 10 minutes (5 minutes for TPO) will reset the material's processing history and reorient polymer chains. However, this does not eliminate thermomechanical stress caused by the high, temperature-dependent CTE of encapsulants that is still present in PV modules during service.

Impact???

Images created using AI tool „Gemini 2.5 Flash"

26.09.2025

www.pccl.at

13

020234-013

Conclusions and outlook

➢ Different polymer properties behind the same name

➢ Calculations of degree of curing from residual enthalpy and melt/freeze method – inapplicable for new EPE encapsulants

➢ All samples reached "final" thermomechanical properties by 10 minutes of lamination duration – including non-crosslinking types

How does the extrusion process differ for encapsulants?

Image created using AI tool „Gemini 2.5 Flash".
26.09.2025

www.pccl.at

14

020234-014

Acknowledgment

This work was conducted as part of the Solar Era Net Project "DELIGHT", which is supported under the umbrella of SOLAR-ERA.NET Cofund by Austrian Research Promotion Agency (FFG, contract number FO999897443), Swiss Federal Office of Energy (SFOE, contract number SI/502501-01) and Flanders Innovation and Entrepreneurship (VLAIO, contract number HBC.2022.0406). SOLAR-ERA.NET is supported by the European Commission within the EU Framework Programme for Research and Innovation HORIZON 2020 (Cofund ERA-NET Action, N° 691664).

This work was conducted as part of the Austrian "e!MISSION.at – Energy Mission Austria" project "PV Industriefassade" (FFG No. FO999915062) funded by the Austrian Climate and Energy Fund and the Austrian Research Promotion Agency (FFG).

020234-015

PCCL
Polymer Competence Center Leoben

Image created using AI tool „Gemini 2.5 Flash".
26.09.2025

www.pccl.at

020234-016

POTENTIAL OF DECIMETER-RESOLUTION GROUND ALBEDO DATA FOR BIFACIAL PHOTOVOLTAICS

Niklas Blum, Bijan Nouri, Yann Fabel, Stefan Wilbert

Deutsches Zentrum für Luft- und Raumfahrt e.V. (DLR)

Agenda

- Motivation

- Approach

- Case study

- Conclusion

Niklas Blum, Bijan Nouri et al., DLR Institute of Solar Research, 22.09.2025

020235-002

Motivation
Relevance of albedo information for bifacial PV

- Performance models for bifacial PV plants can exhibit notable deviations

- Inaccurate ground albedo contributes a considerable part to uncertainty

- Variations of ground albedo are frequent in PV plants:
    - temporally as vegetation recovers from construction works and seasonal changes
    - spatially with different surface types present in a PV plant:
        - Different rock types
        - Sand
        - vegetation of different type, height and stage
        - …

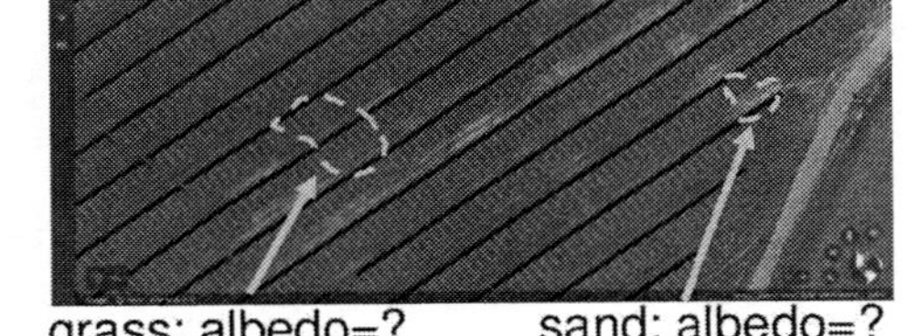

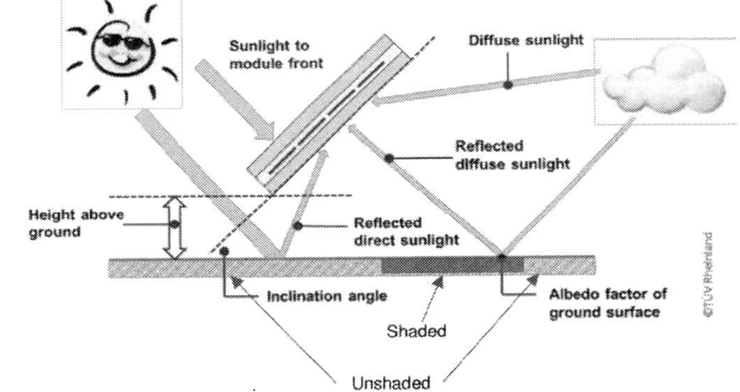

Niklas Blum, Bijan Nouri et al., DLR Institute of Solar Research, 22.09.2025

020235-003

Motivation
Relevance of albedo information for bifacial PV

- **Uncertainty in albedo information affects all phases of a PV project…**
  - Yield prediction before construction
    - Bankability affected
    - Sub-optimal design selected
  - Acceptance testing
    - Economic loss if guaranteed performance not met
  - Tracker control
    - Contribution of rear-side irradiance over-simplified
    - Sub-optimal performance under certain conditions
  - Fault detection
    - Differences between inverters, PV strings partly obscured

Image source: https://commons.wikimedia.org/wiki/File:Suntrix_Horizontal_Single_Axis_tracker_with_Tilted_Modules.JPG

Niklas Blum, Bijan Nouri et al., DLR Institute of Solar Research, 22.09.2025

020235-004

Motivation
State-of-the-art albedo data sources

- Ground measurements
  - Point-wise
  - High cost
  - Practical difficulty to find large unshaded space
  - IEC 61724-1 Class A one or more measurement positions depending on plant size

- Alternative: Remotely sensed
  - MODIS
    - 500 m x 500 m resolution (footprint in image)
  - Sentinel, Landsat and other open access systems
    - Up to 10 m x 10 m resolution (footprint in image)
  - → To coarse to distinguish PV rows from ground

- This study: Centimeter-resolution albedo from aerial images (case study, footprint in image)

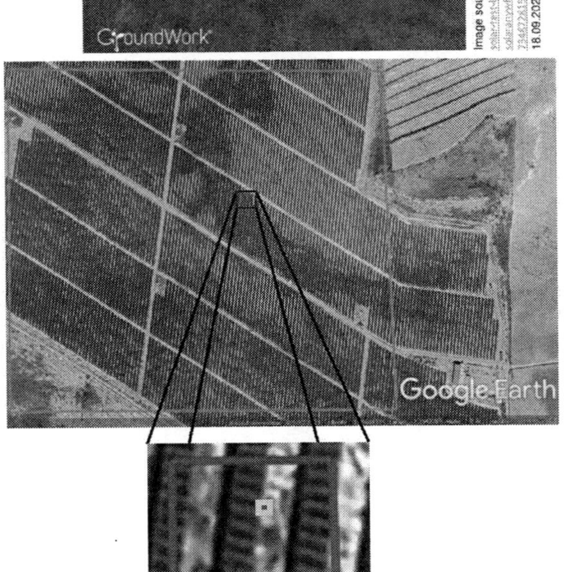

Niklas Blum, Bijan Nouri et al., DLR Institute of Solar Research, 22.09.2025

020235-005

Approach
Centimeter-resolution ground albedo

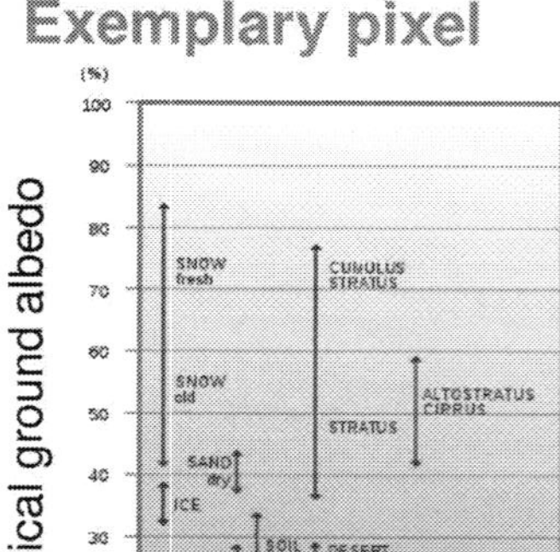

Image taken at PSA. The research site Plataforma Solar de Almería (PSA) is owned and operated by the Spanish CIEMAT

- Commercial satellite constellations show potential beyond state of the art
  - Multispectral reflectance data: panchromatic, R, G, B, NIR, …
  - Fine ground sampling distances (GSD) of 30 cm (15 cm with super-resolution techniques)

- Fine resolution allows to characterize surface in detail
  - Built surfaces, shadows, unshaded ground
  - Surface types: Green/dry vegetation, sand, rock, snow, concrete

- Ground albedo can be calculated from the reflectance information of unshaded ground pixels
  - Radiometric relationship between pixel reflectance and broadband albedo
  - Surface classification and typical albedo per surface type

Exemplary pixel

Niklas Blum, Bijan Nouri et al., DLR Institute of Solar Research, 22.09.2025

020235-006

Approach
Current case study

Image source: Bayerische Vermessungsverwaltung GeoBasis-DE / BKG 2018 – Daten verändert, Copernicus Sentinel 2 der Europäischen Union, Datenbezug 2018, verarbeitet durch das Bundesamt für Kartographie und Geodäsie (BKG).

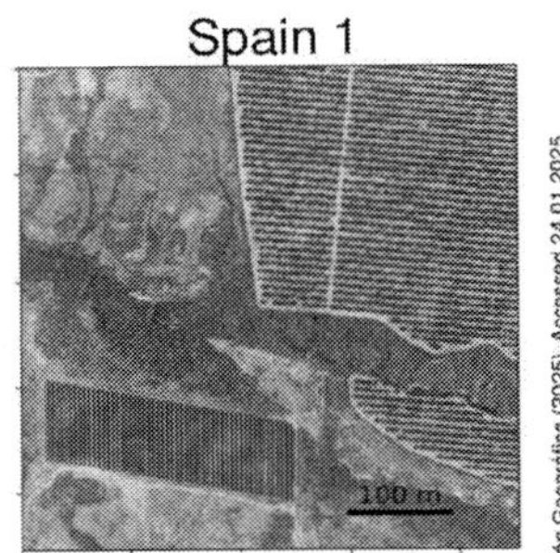

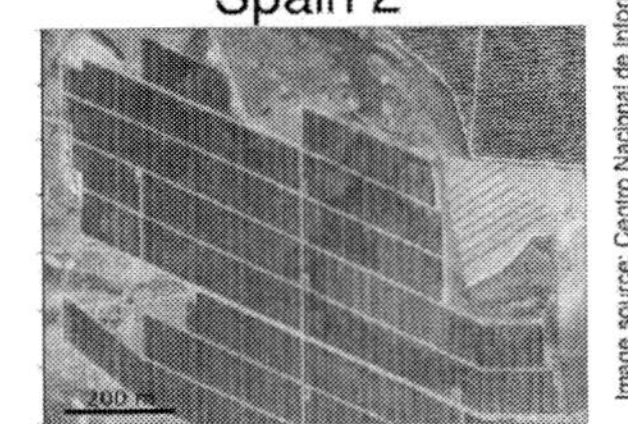

Image source: Centro Nacional de Información Geográfica (2025). Accessed 24.01.2025. fototeca.cnig.es/fototeca/

- 3 exemplary PV plants in southern Germany and Spain selected

- Aerial images with ground sampling distances (GSD) of 20-22 cm represent satellite images
  - → Similar GSD to Worldview-3 (GSD 15-30 cm)
  - → No atmospheric correction required

Niklas Blum, Bijan Nouri et al., DLR Institute of Solar Research, 22.09.2025

020235-007

Approach
Current case study

- PV modules segmented
- Shades of PV modules calculated from PV module positions and solar geometry
- PV and shades masked
- Masked areas filled (inpainting) with information from surrounding pixels

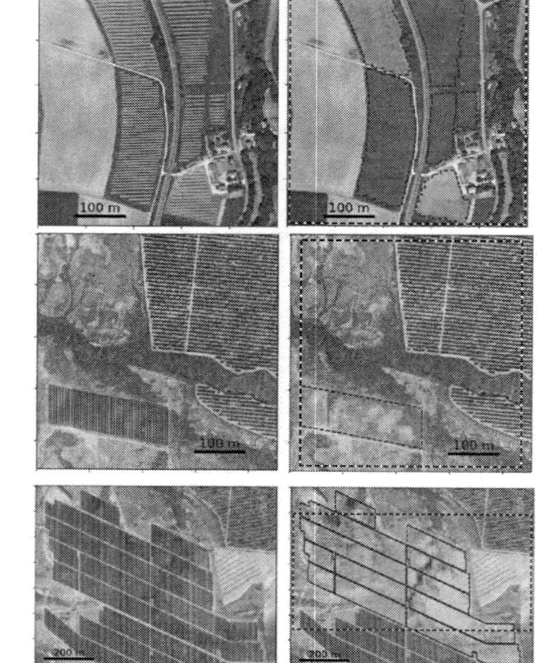

Niklas Blum, Bijan Nouri et al., DLR Institute of Solar Research, 22.09.2025

020235-008

Approach
Current case study

- Ground albedo estimated as linear function of R, G, B intensities' weighted average

- Estimation calibrated using pixels with known surface type and corresponding ground albedo (literature)

- Resulting albedo maps exhibit plausible distributions of albedo values with variations related to
  - Agricultural activity
  - Height profile,
  - Soil and vegetation properties

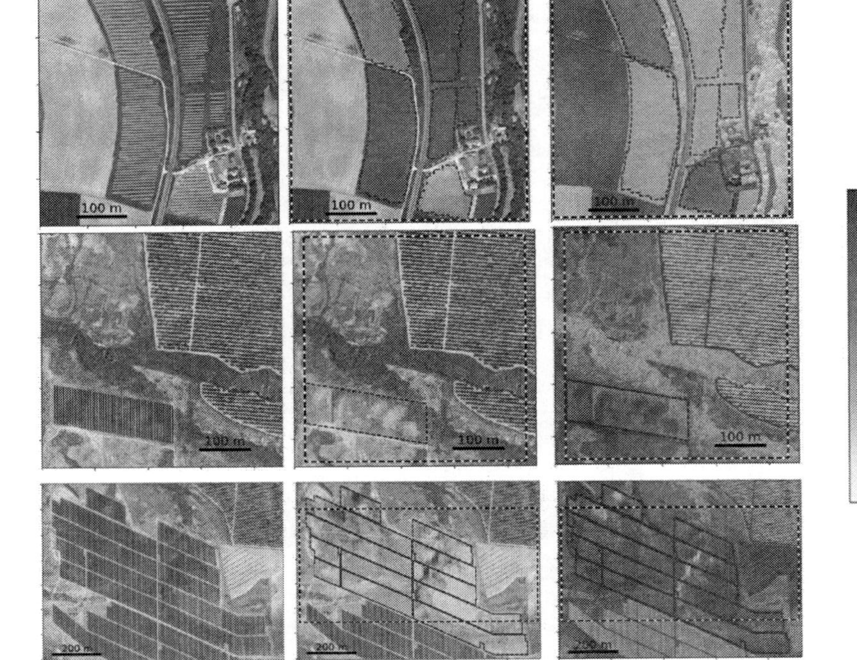

Niklas Blum, Bijan Nouri et al., DLR Institute of Solar Research, 22.09.2025

Approach
Current case study

- Albedo information from aerial images used as input for annual PV yield simulations using PVWatts

- Temporal variation of ground albedo neglected for simplicity

- 3 scenarios evaluated
  - High-resolution ('**HR**') albedo: Representative albedo calculated over PV plant footprint using HR albedo map
  - **'Ground measurement'**: 5 sampling points defined which represent bins between $0^{th} - 20^{th}$, $20^{th} - 40^{th}$, …, $80^{th} - 100^{th}$ percentiles of the albedo distribution in the HR albedo map
  - **'MODIS'** albedo: HR albedo map averaged over imaginary 500 m x 500 m pixels, **including PV and shades**

- HR albedo used as reference in the following

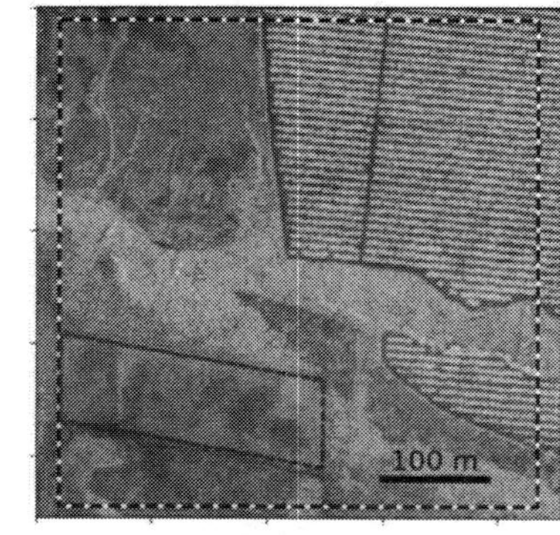
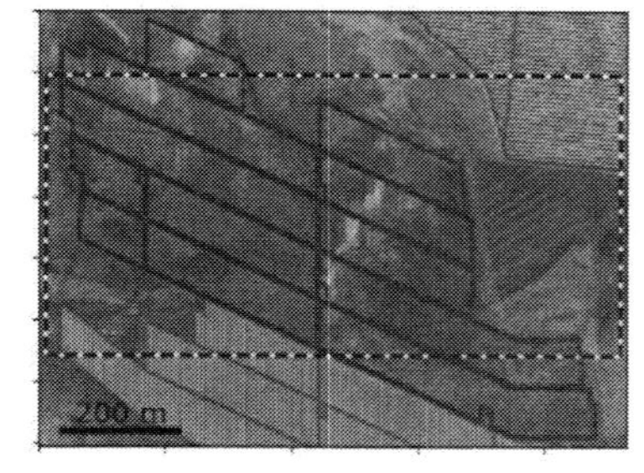

Niklas Blum, Bijan Nouri et al., DLR Institute of Solar Research, 22.09.2025

020235-010

Study results

- 'MODIS' albedo deviates notably from 'HR' albedo
  - Seinsheim: overestimation by 0.041 → nearby dry plowed fields
  - Tabernas 1: strong underestimation by 0.072 → dark green olive grove nearby
  - Tabernas 2: strong underestimation by 0.098 → dark PV
- 'Ground measurement'
  - Significant variation of the ground albedo in all plants
  - Accordingly representative measurement depends strongly selection of measurement point
- Shortcomings of both state-of-the-art methods:
  - Systematic deviations
  - No resolution of spatial variations

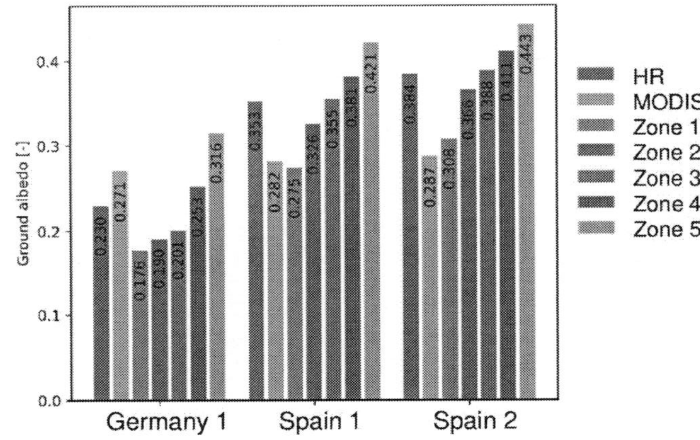

Study results
Annual yields

- Ground measurement
  - Predicted PV production deviates by -1.6% to 2.1%
- 'MODIS'
  - Predicted PV production deviates by 1%, -1.4 and -1.9%

- Deviations will be more pronounced in other practically relevant evaluations:
  - Production in shorter time scales
  - Production in morning and evening hours
  - Production of individual inverter strings

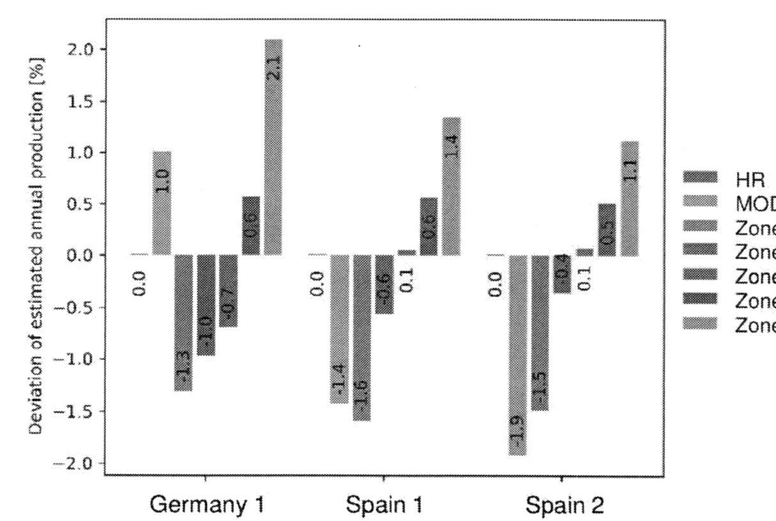

Niklas Blum, Bijan Nouri et al., DLR Institute of Solar Research, 22.09.2025

020235-012

Conclusion

- State-of-the-art approaches to determine ground albedo have shortcomings
  - Practical and cost restrictions (e.g. ground measurements)
  - Systematic deviations
  - Resolution of spatial variations
- Potential of highly-resolved ground albedo exemplified in a case study
  - Able to determine ground albedo within PV plants
  - Above-mentioned shortcomings avoided
- Error in annual yield prediction of ±2% may be avoided
  - Even stronger effects for individual inverters/PV strings and at shorter timescales expected

Niklas Blum, Bijan Nouri et al., DLR Institute of Solar Research, 22.09.2025

020235-013

Outlook

Image source: https://doi.org/10.3390/app10208482

Image taken at PSA. The research site Plataforma Solar de Almería (PSA) is owned and operated by the Spanish CIEMAT

- Current case study is preliminary – research activity is ongoing
- Aerial data being replaced with satellite data (WorldView, Pleiades, …)
- Combination under development of satellite albedo with ground data from:
  - Albedometer
  - Rear-side irradiance measurements
  - Ground-facing cameras
- Temporal update for seasonal effects under development
- Broader validation campaign planned

Niklas Blum, Bijan Nouri et al., DLR Institute of Solar Research, 22.09.2025

020235-014

DLR
THANK YOU FOR YOUR
ATTENTION!
QUESTIONS?
NIKLAS.BLUM@DLR.DE
BIJAN.NOURI@DLR.DE

020235-015

Method for the determination of spectral responsivity of digital solar irradiance sensors

David Hinken[*,1], Sebastian Denke[1], Karsten Bothe[1] and Rolf Brendel[1,2]

[1]Institute for Solar Energy Research in Hamelin, Emmerthal, GERMANY
[2]Institute for Solid State Physics, Leibniz Universität Hannover, Hannover, GERMANY

Digital solar irradiance sensors

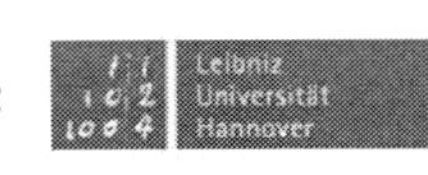

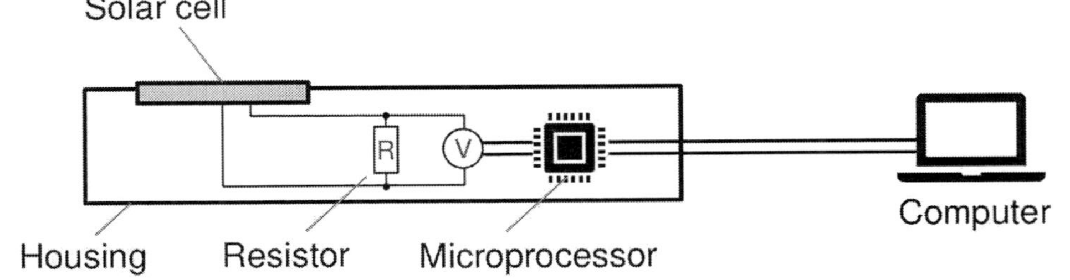

- Typical structure:
  1. Solar cell with shunt resistor
  2. Analog-digital conversion with microprocessor (also provides digital interface)

- Microprocessor converts voltage V (in mV) to irradiance G_{dig} (in W/m²) using a **calibration factor**

- Different types of solar irradiance sensors available, many with a Modbus interface

- Calibration of these sensors required!

020236-002

Calibration of digital irradiance sensors

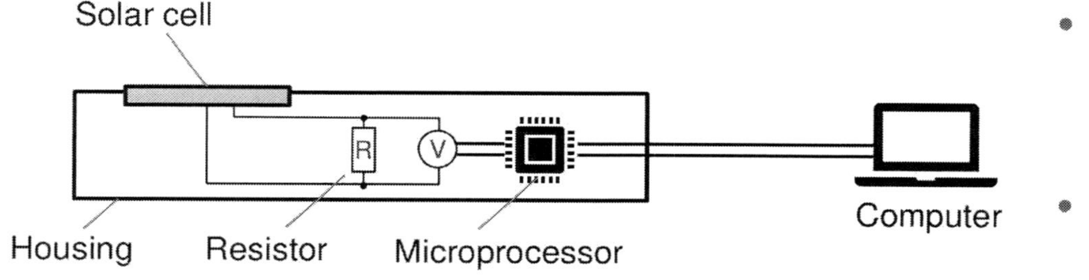

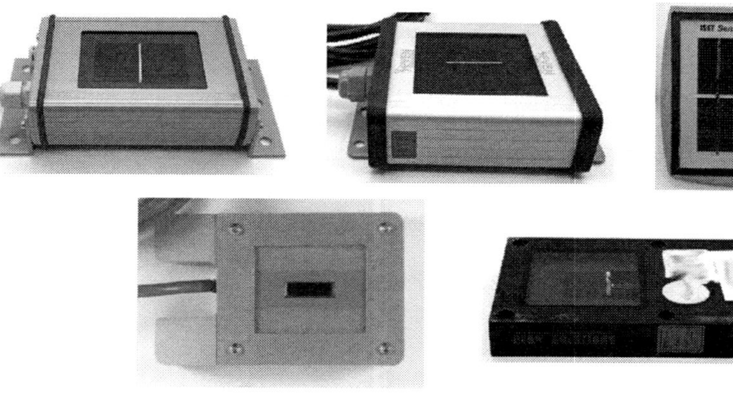

- PV system monitoring standard IEC 61724-1 demands regular calibration of irradiance sensors

- Calibration requirements:

  - **Fulfillment of IEC 60904-2**

  - Reference spectrum IEC 60904-3 ($\rightarrow$ AM1.5G)

  - Resolution <1 W/m^2

  - Measurement uncertainty $\leq$ 3%

Requirements of IEC 60904-2

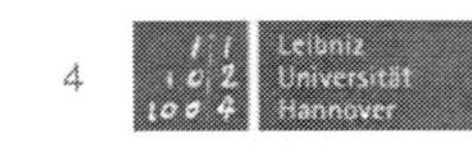

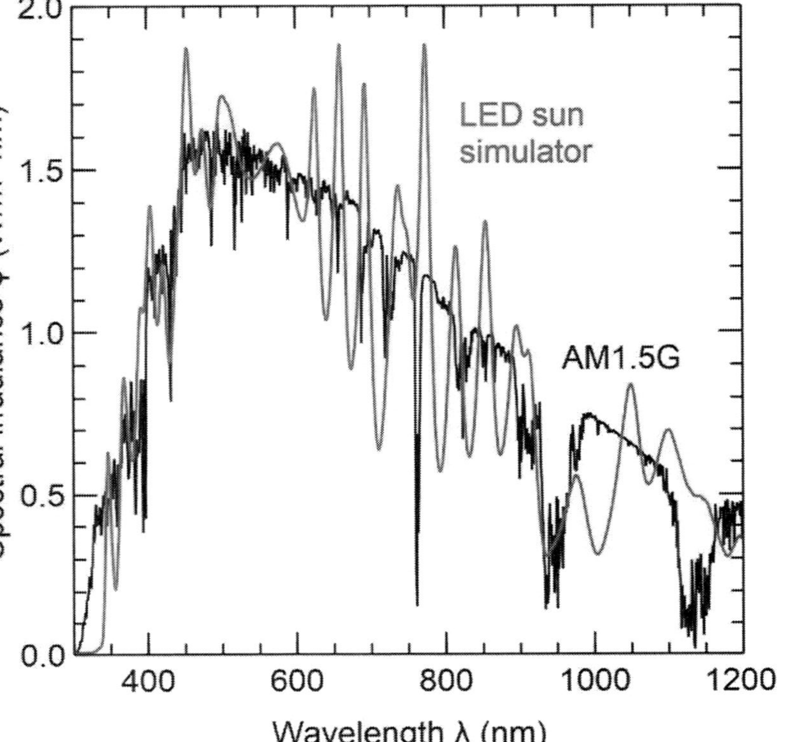

- **IEC 60904-2:** The spectral responsivity (SR/EQE) of each device has to be measured.

- Background: Tabulated reference spectrum cannot be exactly reproduced within a sun simulator

- Calculation of **spectral mismatch factor** requires determination of the spectral responsivity (SR_{smpl})

$$MM = \frac{\int d\lambda\ \varphi_{\mathrm{ref}}(\lambda)SR_{\mathrm{ref}}(\lambda) \int d\lambda\ \varphi_{\mathrm{meas}}(\lambda)SR_{\mathrm{smpl}}(\lambda)}{\int d\lambda\ \varphi_{\mathrm{meas}}(\lambda)SR_{\mathrm{ref}}(\lambda) \int d\lambda\ \varphi_{\mathrm{ref}}(\lambda)SR_{\mathrm{smpl}}(\lambda)}$$

020236-004

Determination of spectral responsivity

- **IEC60904-2:** The spectral responsivity (SR/EQE) of each device has to be measured.

- Traditional DSR/SR requires **current as measurand** and does not work with digital units

- Only option: Open sensor, disconnect electronics and shunt resistor, add a direct wire connection to solar cell

- Not feasible for customer sensors → We need something new!

DSR/SR measurement facility at ISFH CalTeC

020236-005

Use LED sun simulator for *SR* determination

Close-up picture of LED array

IV measurement facility at ISFH CalTeC

- Continuous spectrum produced by several LEDs of different color (350 nm to 1200 nm)

- Homogenization optics overlap all LED outputs on the measurement field

- **Idea:** Use spectral variations to determine the spectral responsivity

020236-006

Method 1: „Single-LED"

Green LEDs on

Red LEDs on

IV measurement facility during SR_{dig} determination

- Single-LED uses one LED channel after the other. For each channel:

  1. Measure short-circuit current I_{scref} of a calibrated solar cell

  2. Get irradiance G_{dig} (W/m²) of sensor (digital)

  3. Calculate spectral responsivity:
     $$SR_{\mathrm{dig}} = SR_{\mathrm{ref}} / I_{\mathrm{scref}} \cdot P_{\mathrm{dig}}$$

- SR_{dig} is digital spectral responsivity, quantitiy is dimensionless

020236-007

Method 2: „Multi-SR"

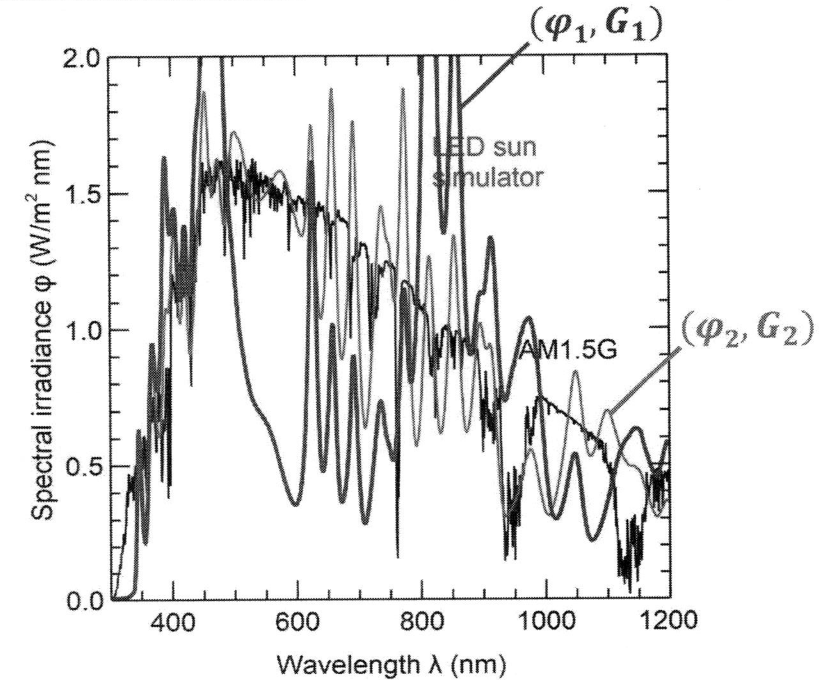

- Multi-SR [1] uses all channels at the same time but with variations:

  1. Measure resulting spectra $\varphi_i(\lambda)$ with a calibrated spectrometer

  2. Get digital output G_{dig} (W/m²) of sensor

  3. Utilize equation

  $$G_i = \int d\lambda\, \varphi_i\, SR_{dig}$$

  and a least-square regression to determine SR_{dig}

- We use 50 different broadband spectra

[1] Hinken et al. (2023), Sol. RRL, 7: 2300240.
https://doi.org/10.1002/solr.202300240

020236-008

Testing on two solar irradiance sensors

Sensor 1: Si-RS485TC-T-MB
(IMT Technology)

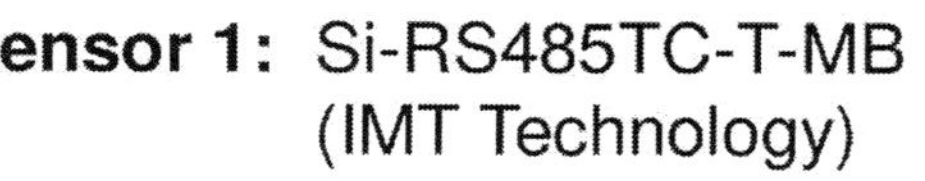

Sensor 2: 3S-IS with Modbus RTU
(Seven Sensor)

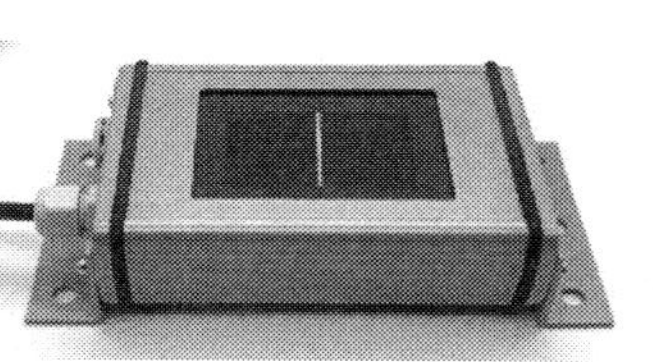

- Testing with two solar irradiance sensors

- Apply both methods

020236-009

Resulting curves of both methods

Sensor 1: Si-RS485TC-T-MB
(IMT Technology)

Sensor 2: 3S-IS with Modbus RTU
(Seven Sensor)

- Curves of both methods are consistent and have expected shape

- Validation with reference method still required

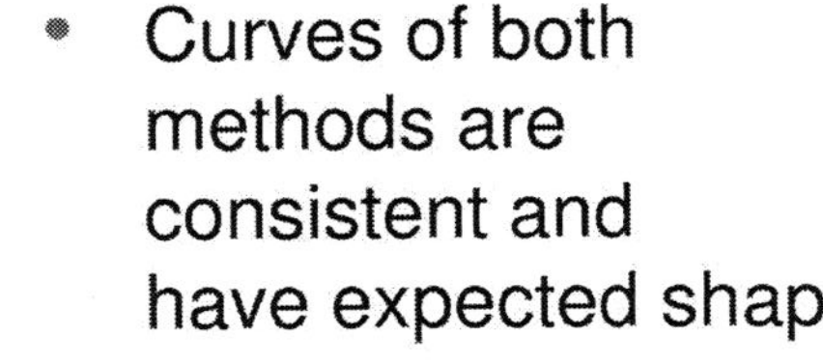

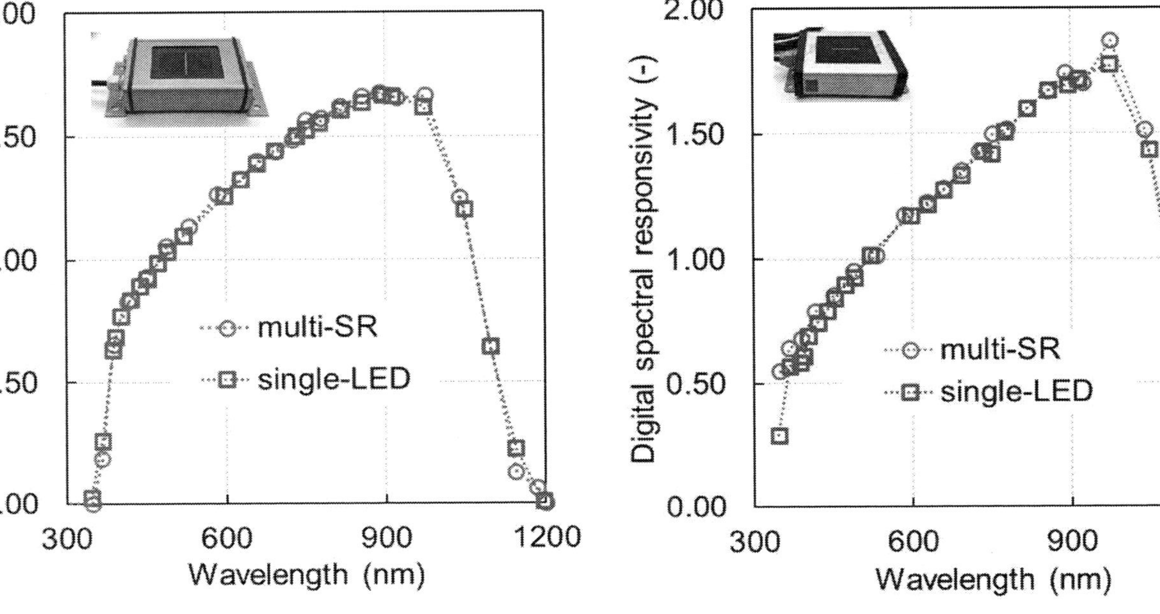

020236-010

Comparison with DSR/SR measurement facility

Sensor 1: Si-RS485TC-T-MB (IMT Technology)

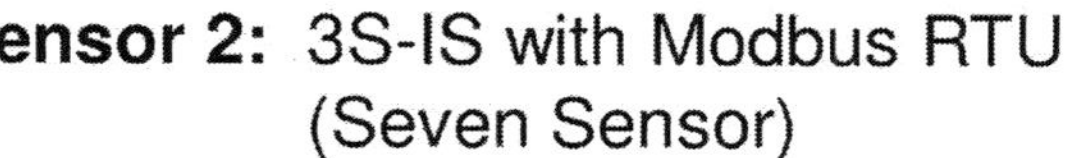

Sensor 2: 3S-IS with Modbus RTU (Seven Sensor)

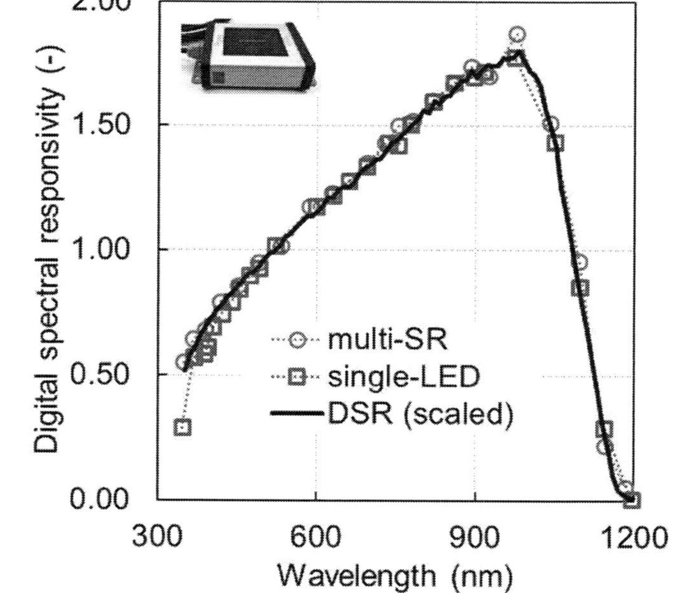

- We opened sensors, removed electronics and shunt and attached direct wire

- Consistent to curve from reference method (solid black line)

020236-011

Comparison of spectral mismatch factors

Sensor 1: Si-RS485TC-T-MB
(IMT Technology)

Sensor 2: 3S-IS with Modbus RTU
(Seven Sensor)

- Calculation of spectral mismatch factor (MM) using:

  1. Class A++ sun simulator spectrum

  2. WPVS reference solar cell

- Max. deviation in MM factor to reference method (DSR/SR) is 0.12%

Sensor 1

	MM	Dev.
single-LED	1.0030	0.00%
multi-SR	1.0038	0.08%
DSR/SR	1.0030	

Sensor 2

	MM	Dev.
single-LED	1.0029	0.12%
multi-SR	1.0018	0.01%
DSR/SR	1.0017	

$$MM = \frac{\int d\lambda\, \varphi_{\mathrm{ref}}(\lambda) SR_{\mathrm{ref}}(\lambda) \int d\lambda\, \varphi_{\mathrm{meas}}(\lambda) SR_{\mathrm{dig}}(\lambda)}{\int d\lambda\, \varphi_{\mathrm{meas}}(\lambda) SR_{\mathrm{ref}}(\lambda) \int d\lambda\, \varphi_{\mathrm{ref}}(\lambda) SR_{\mathrm{dig}}(\lambda)}$$

020236-012

12

Leibniz Universität Hannover

Comparison table

	Single-LED	Multi-SR	DSR/SR (with modified sensor)
Directly applicable to digital irradiance sensors	Yes	Yes	No
Reference	Calibrated solar cell	Calibrated spectrometer	Calibrated solar cell
Measurement time	5 minutes	5 minutes	1 hour
Can be integrated in IV measurement facility?	Yes	Yes	No, separate facility required
Technical complexity?	Low	Low	High ($\rightarrow$ lock-in technique required)
Components commercially available?	Yes	Yes	No ($\rightarrow$ transimpedance-amplifier)
Wavelength resolution	Low, LEDs with narrow spectrum required	Higher	Highest
Working point (excess charge carrier density)	Extremely low or bias-variations required	Same working conditions	Bias-variations required

020236-013

Conclusion

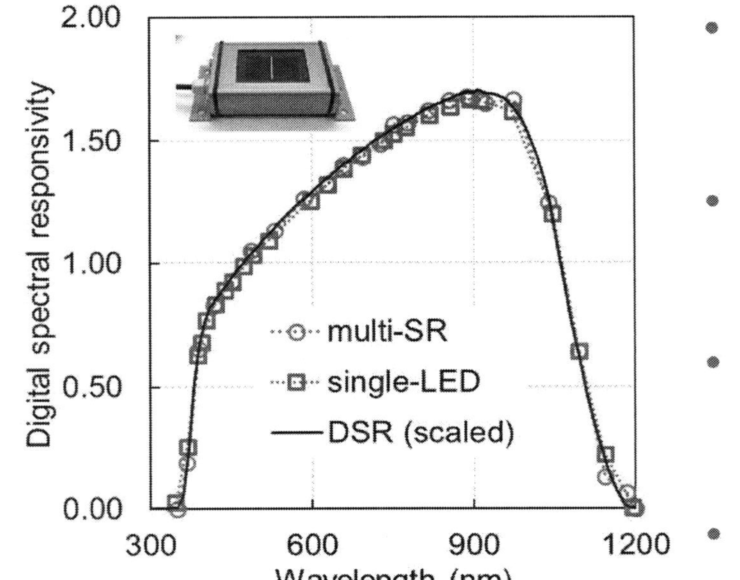

- Introduced two methods for the determination of the spectral responsivity of digital irradiance sensors

- Tests and validation successful!

- Calibration of digital irradiance sensors now available at ISFH CalTeC with a measurement uncertainty of 1.0% (k=2)

- Contact us: sensors@caltec.isfh.de

020236-014

Acknowledgments

This work was funded by the **state of Lower Saxony**

and the **project SOLiD-PV** (24GRD04), which has received funding from the **European Partnership on Metrology** (Funder ID: 10.13039/100019599), co-financed from the European Union's Horizon Europe Research and Innovation Programme and by the Participating States.

EUROPEAN PARTNERSHIP • Co-funded by the European Union • METROLOGY PARTNERSHIP • EURAMET

CUTTING-EDGE GENERATIVE AI FOR INTRA-HOUR SOLAR FORECASTING

Yann Fabel, Dominik Schnaus, Bijan Nouri, Stefan Wilbert, Niklas Blum, Luis F. Zarzalejo, Julia Kowalski, Robert Pitz-Paal

EUPVSEC 2025

22th of September 2025, Bilbao, Spain

Agenda

- Introduction
- Generative Forecasting Approach
- Ramp Event Prediction
- Conclusion & Outlook

DLR
MOTIVATION
Yann Fabel, DLR, EUPVSEC 2025

Motivation

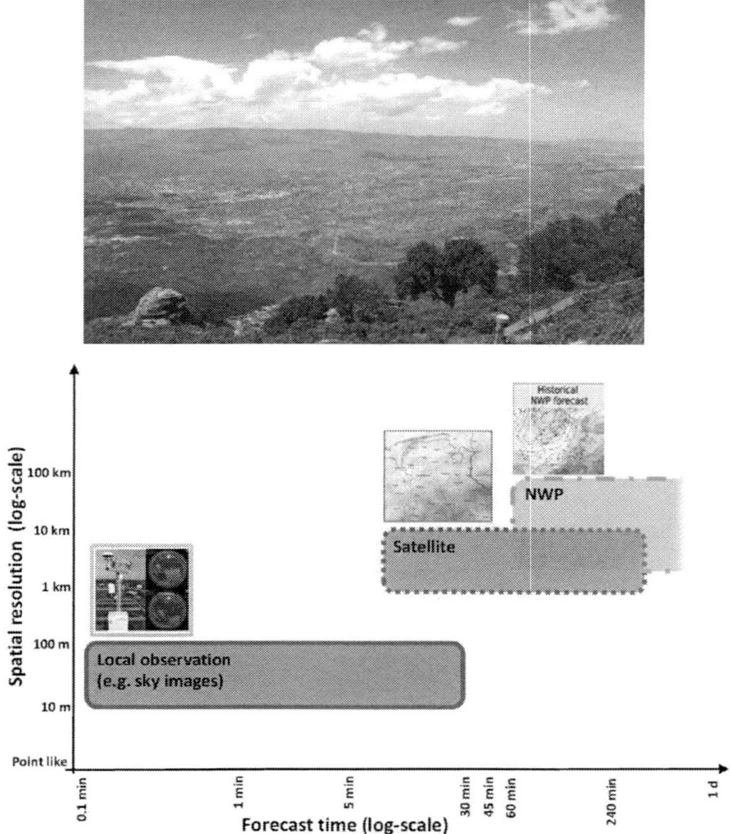

Why forecasting solar irradiance?

- Predict expected energy yield of PV power plants
- Anticipate local short-term fluctuations caused by cloud passages (ramp events)

Challenges by ramp events

- Local power output variability
- Potential risk of grid instabilities at high solar penetration

Benefits of intra-hour forecasting

- Better situational awareness for plant and grid operators
- Reduced storage requirements
- Improved market trading strategies
- More efficient operation of CST plants

Requirements

- High-resolution cloud information in space and time
  → All-Sky-Imagers

Yann Fabel, DLR, EUPVSEC 2025

Motivation
Ramp Events

- Typically no evaluation of predicting the variability of solar irradiance
- Common forecasting metrics (e.g., RMSE, MAE, MBE) represent an average error of the target quantity (e.g., GHI)
  - Good measure to assess expected energy yield (integration of irradiance over time)
  - No information on variability within the forecast
- Definition Ramp Event [1]:

$$\frac{|\Delta GHI|}{\Delta t} > \tau \Longrightarrow Ramp$$

$$t: \ if\ \exists\ Ramp\ in\ [t - tw/2, t + tw/2] \Longrightarrow Ramp\ Event\ at\ t$$

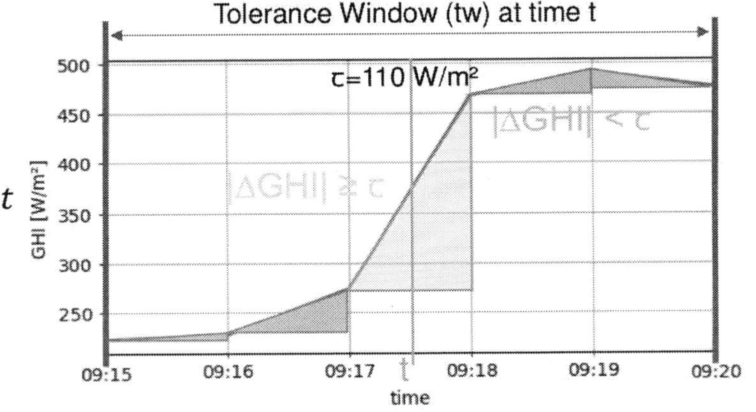

Limitations of State-of-the-Art Models

- State-of-the-Art direct data-driven models are often optimized on RMSE [2, 3, 4]

Fabel et al. [4]

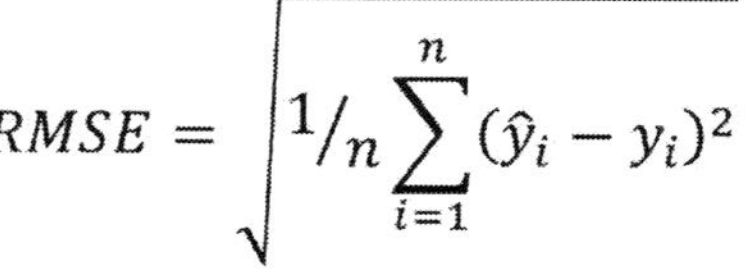
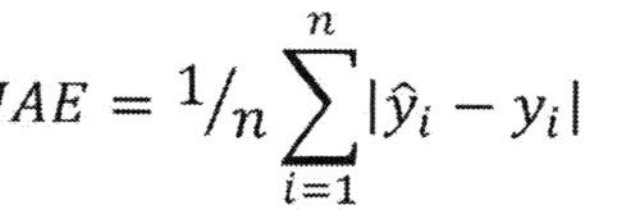

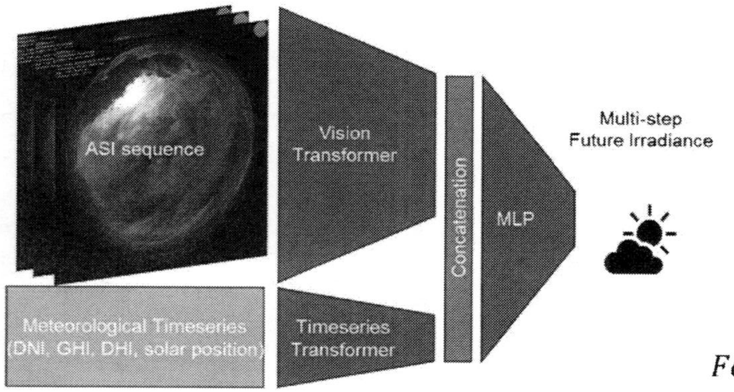

$$RMSE = \sqrt{1/n \sum_{i=1}^{n} (\hat{y}_i - y_i)^2}$$

$$MAE = 1/n \sum_{i=1}^{n} |\hat{y}_i - y_i|$$

$$MBE = 1/n \sum_{i=1}^{n} \hat{y}_i - y_i$$

$$Forecast\ Skill = 1 - \frac{RMSE_{model}}{RMSE_{persistence}}$$

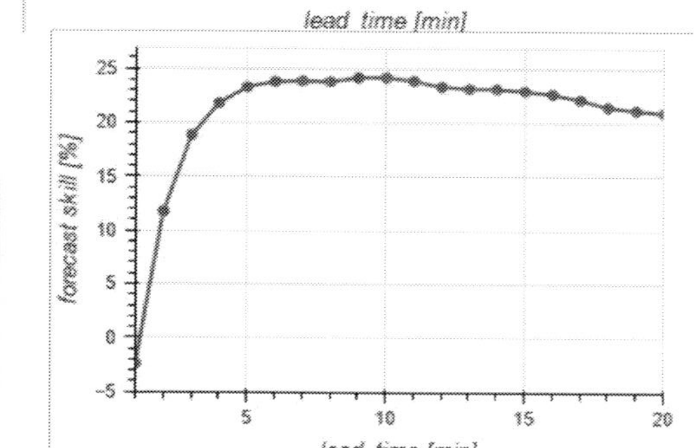

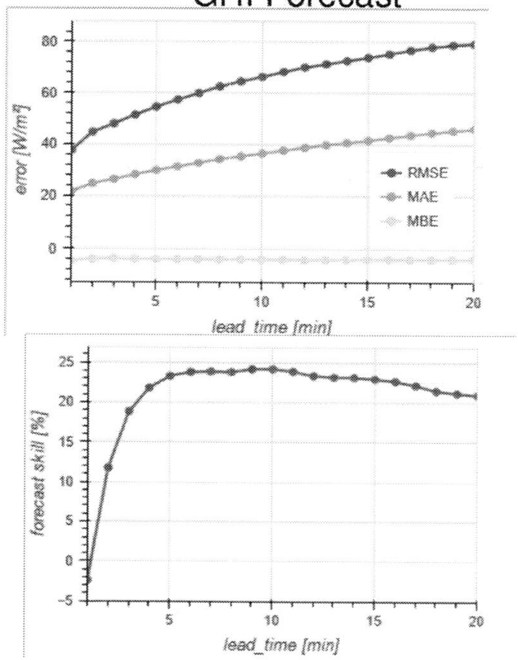

- Strong performance on standard error metrics, but ramp events remain undetected due to overly smoothed forecast curves (see later slides)
- How can we circumvent smoothing of the forecast curve?

DLR
GENERATIVE FORECASTING
APPROACH
Yann Fabel, DLR, EUPVSEC 2025

Generative Forecasting Model Architecture

- **Video Prediction (VP):**
  - Given a sequence of M past images the next N images are predicted
  - Multiple future scenarios can be generated from the same input sequence by sampling from Gaussian noise
    → Measure for uncertainty

- **Regressor/Classifier:**
  - Given individual predicted future frames a second model (e.g. CNN) is used to derive the desired target quantity
  - Trained separately on real images
  - E.g., a model predicts ramp events or GHI corresponding to the predicted sky image

020237-008

Video Prediction Models
Train and Test setup

- Two different generative models were tested
  - SkyGPT [5]: Adaptation of the VideoGPT [6] model combined with PhyCells [7]
  - Ours: Adaptation of the DiT model [8] (diffusion-based transformer)
- Training
  - Both models were trained on selected camera data from CIEMAT's PSA (Almería, Spain)
  - SkyGPT model trained with the same hyperparameter configuration as in the original publication
- Testing
  - Evaluation on separate benchmark dataset defined in All-Sky Imager-based forecasting study [9]
  - 28 selected days from a single camera at PSA representing diverse sky conditions
  - 4 image samples per model were generated for each lead time

	SkyGPT	DiT
Image res	64x64	128x128
Temporal res.	2min	1min
Forecast horizon	15min	30min
Auto-Encoder	VQ-VAE [6]	Pretrained VAE [9]

Video Prediction Evaluation
Examplary Results – Single Sample, Selected Lead Times

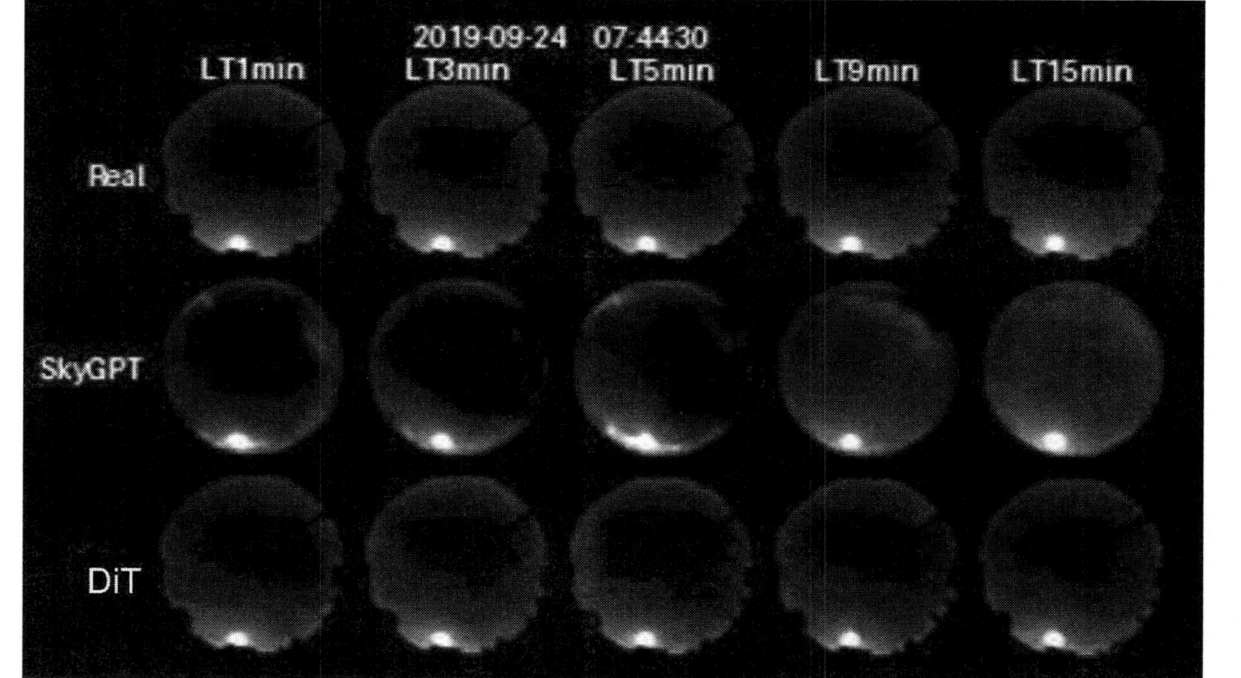

→ A lot of „halluzinations" even for clear sky conditions

Video Prediction Evaluation
Examplary Results – Single Sample, Selected Lead Times

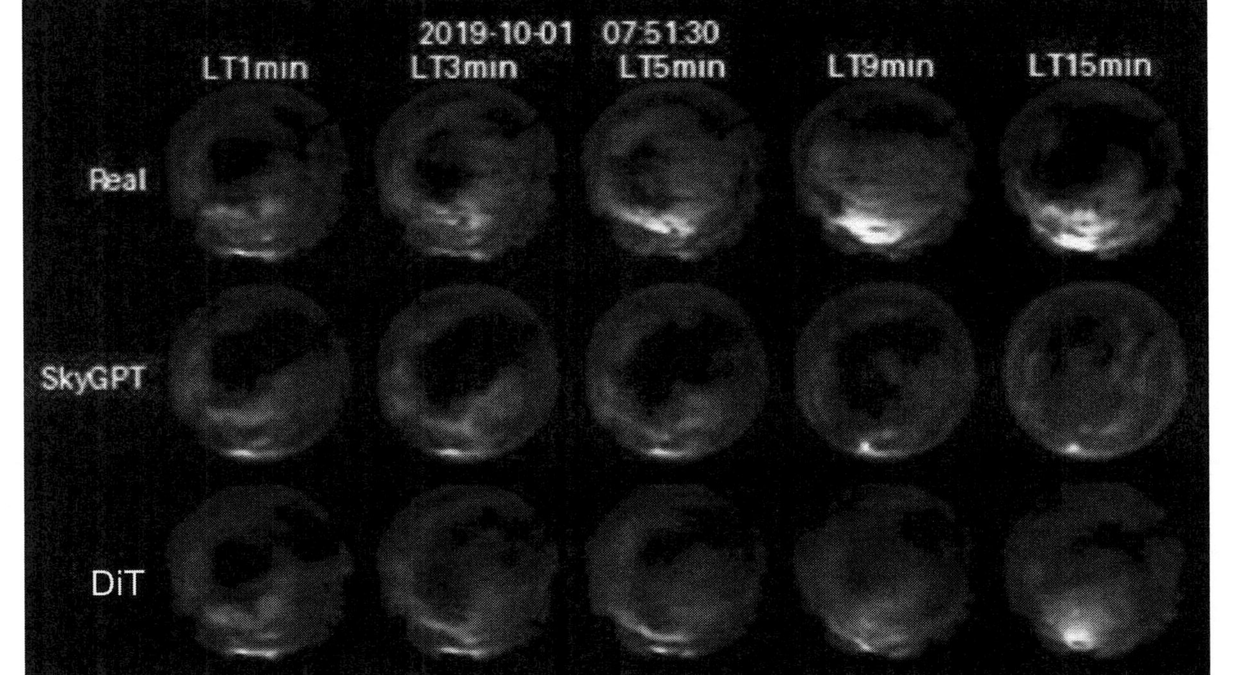

→ Strong deviations in terms of cloud coverage for larger lead times

Video Prediction Evaluation
Quantitative Results

- **Evaluation of predicted sky image frames**
  - Image data range: [0, 255]
  - Lead-time specific calculation averaged over all generated future scenarios

- **Image-wise pixel metrics**
  - Mean Absolute Error (MAE)$\downarrow$:
    - Average error per pixel
  - Peak Signal-to-Noise Ratio (PSNR)$\uparrow$:
    - Ratio of maximum possible signal to error in decibels (measure of fidelity)
  - Structural Similarity Index (SSIM)$\uparrow$:
    - Measure for perceptual similarity (capturing sharpness and structure)

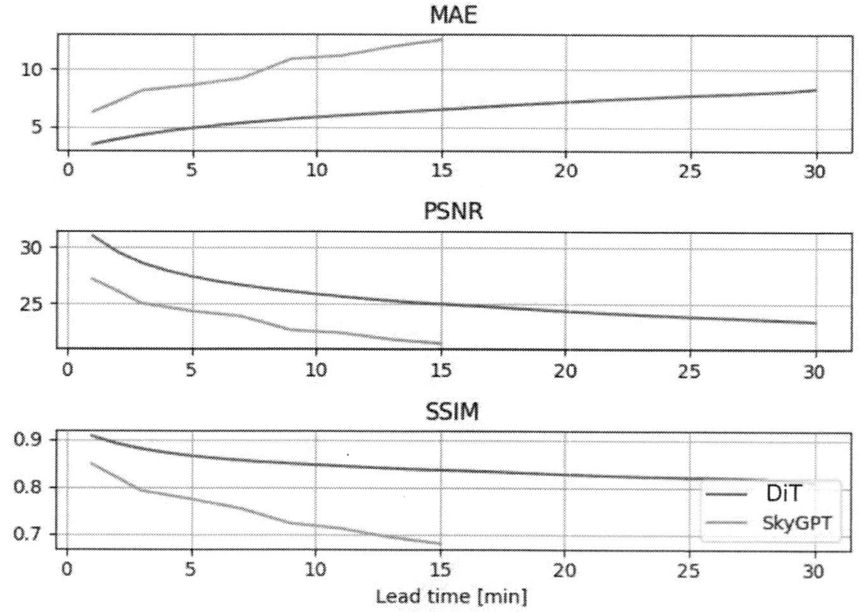

→ Better performance of DiT model in terms of image quality

DLR
RAMP EVENT PREDICTION
Yann Fabel, DLR, EUPVSEC 2025

Ramp Event Prediction

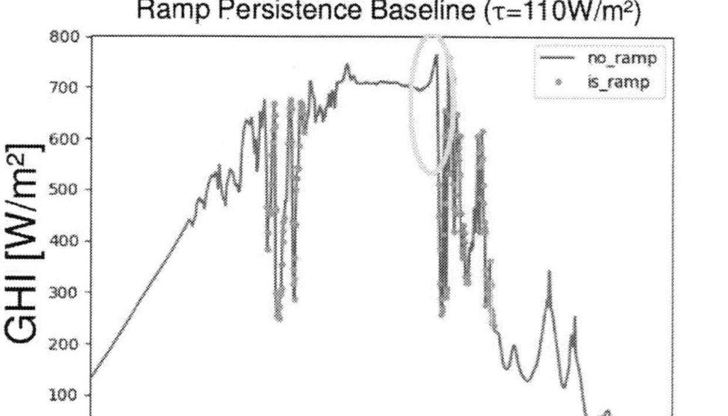

- <u>Ramp Classifier</u>
  - CNN predicts likelihood of ramp event (RE) based on corresponding image
  - Ground truth $y_t = \begin{cases} 1 \ \ if \ \exists \ ramp \ in \ [t-3, t+3] \\ \quad 0 \ \ otherwise \end{cases}$
  - **Trained on real sky images**
  - **Evaluated on synthetic images** from generative model to obtain ramp event prediction

- <u>Baseline model</u>: Ramp Persistence
  - If a ramp was observed in the measured irradiance curve in the last T=30min a ramp is expected in the next T minutes too
  - Independent of sky images

Yann Fabel, DLR, EUPVSEC 2025

Ramp Event Prediction Evaluation

- Video prediction models generate K=4 samples (images) for all lead times for each forecast
- Predicted RE from average probability of ramp classifier over all samples
- Observed RE by measured ramp within tolerance window (tw=10min)
- Low classifier threshold (TH=0.3) chosen to prioritize recall
- Evaluation of classification metrics over lead times

$$accuracy = \frac{TP + TN}{TP + FN + FP + TN}$$

$$precision = \frac{TP}{TP + FP}$$

$$f1 = 2 \times \frac{precision \times recall}{precision + recall}$$

$$recall = \frac{TP}{TP + FN}$$

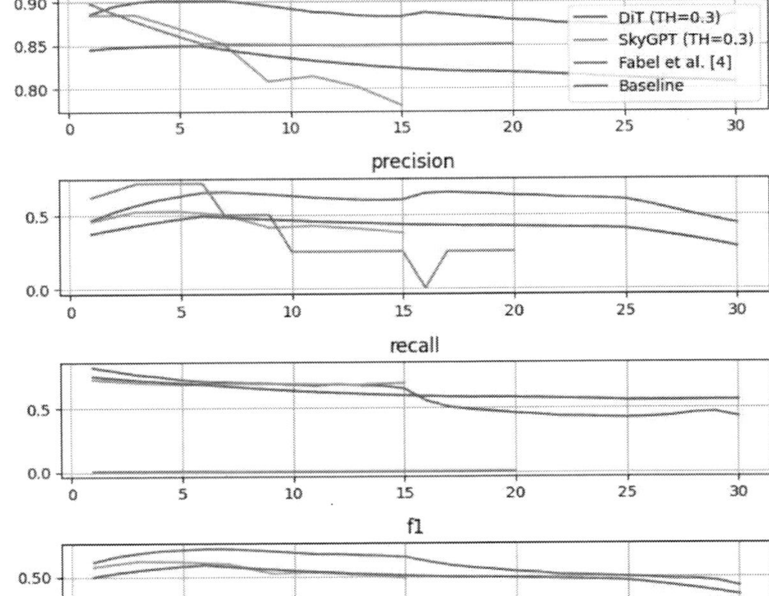

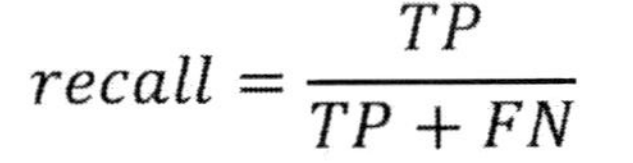

020237-015

Conclusion

- Summary:
  - Low RMSE does not guarantee realistic representation of irradiance variability (e.g., ramp events)
  - Generative, image-based modeling of cloud dynamics offers a promising alternative to capture short-term variability
  - Current video prediction models for ASI still struggle at longer horizons (inconsistencies and physically unrealistic cloud scenes)
  - But generated images remain useful for detecting ramp events
- Outlook
  - Enhance ASI-based video prediction
    - Focus training on highly variable cloud conditions
    - Leverage advances in generative video modeling (e.g., noise warping, motion conditioning)
  - Combine multiple perspectives to learn better cloud representations

References

1. Nouri et al. 2024, **Ramp Rate Metric Suitable for Solar Forecasting**, DOI: 10.1002/solr.202400468

2. Sun et al., **Solar PV output prediction from video streams using convolutional neural networks**, DOI: 10.1039/c7ee03420b

3. Paletta et al. 2021, **Benchmarking of deep learning irradiance forecasting models from sky images - An in-depth analysis**, DOI: 10.1016/j.solener.2021.05.056

4. Fabel et al. 2023, **Combining deep learning and physical models: a benchmark study on all-sky imagerbased solar nowcasting systems**

5. Nie et al. 2024, **SkyGPT: Probabilistic ultra-short-term solar forecasting using synthetic sky images from physics-constrained VideoGPT**, DOI: 10.1016/j.adapen.2024.100172

6. Yan et al. 2021, **VideoGPT: Video Generation using VQ-VAE and Transformers**, DOI: 10.48550/ARXIV.2104.10157

7. LeGuen et al. 2020, **Disentangling Physical Dynamics From Unknown Factors for Unsupervised Video Prediction**, DOI: 10.1109/cvpr42600.2020.01149

8. Pebbles et al. 2022, **Scalable Diffusion Models with Transformers**, DOI: 10.48550/ARXIV.2212.09748

9. Blattmann et. al 2023, **Stable video diffusion: Scaling latent video diffusion models to large datasets**, DOI: 10.48550/ARXIV.2311.15127

AuSeSol AI (Grant number 67KI21007A)

Gefördert durch:

Bundesministerium
für Umwelt, Klimaschutz, Naturschutz
und nukleare Sicherheit

aufgrund eines Beschlusses
des Deutschen Bundestages

DLR

THANK YOU FOR YOUR ATTENTION!
QUESTIONS? YANN.FABEL@DLR.DE

Yann Fabel, DLR, EUPVSEO 2025

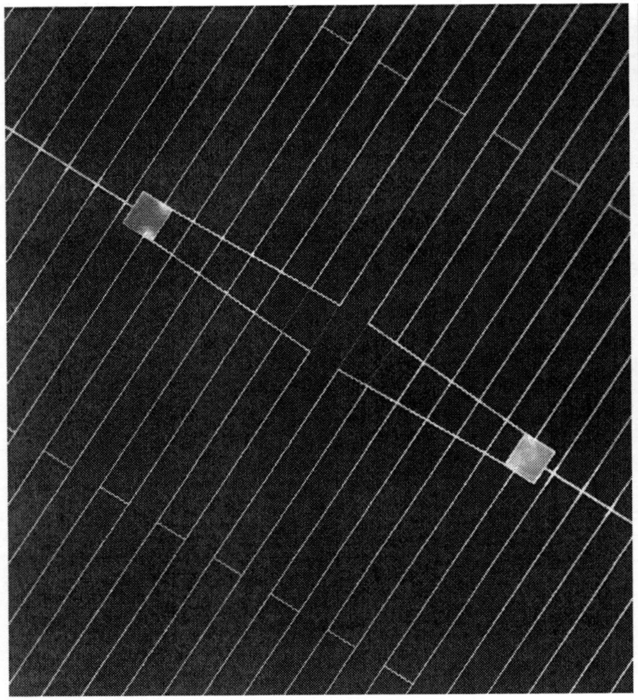

Baptiste Schubnel, Jelena Simeunovic, Corentin Tissier, Pierre-Jean Alet and **Rafael Carrillo**

EUPVSEC, 22.09.2025

INTEGRATING SATELLITE IMAGERY AND GNNS FOR IMPROVING DAY-AHEAD IRRADIANCE FORECASTING

SUPERNOVA

Co-funded by
the European Union

:: csem

MOTIVATION

- Intraday and day-ahead solar forecasts are crucial for control, trading, and group balance management
- CSEM developed an intraday solution based on a network of ground sensors
  - It works well during the day, but accuracy drops in the morning due to limited data
- **Motivation:** improve early-morning and extend solution to day-ahead predictions
- **Problem:** day-ahead forecasts require broader spatial and temporal context
  - Satellite images provide this context but **how to fuse with ground data?**

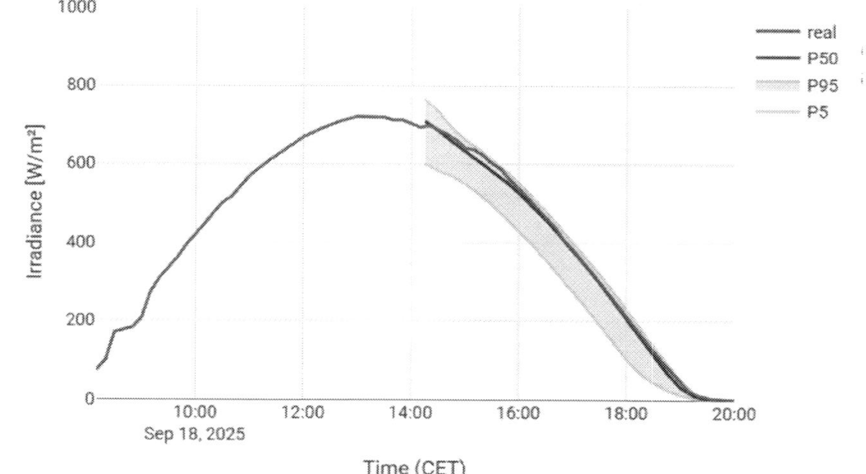

:: csem

020238-002

LIMITATIONS OF EXISTING DATA-FUSION APPROACHES

- **Very short-term:**
  - All sky imagers + ground-based measurements
  - Mainly developed for single location or small area
- **Intraday:**
  - Satellite-derived data or ground-based observations
  - Successful spatio-temporal approaches from only ground-based network of sensors but no wide spatial context
- **Day-ahead:**
  - Spatio-temporal models that exploit image pixel location and ground-based data developed for single site
  - Do not exploit intra image – network correlation and inter-correlations between multiple locations

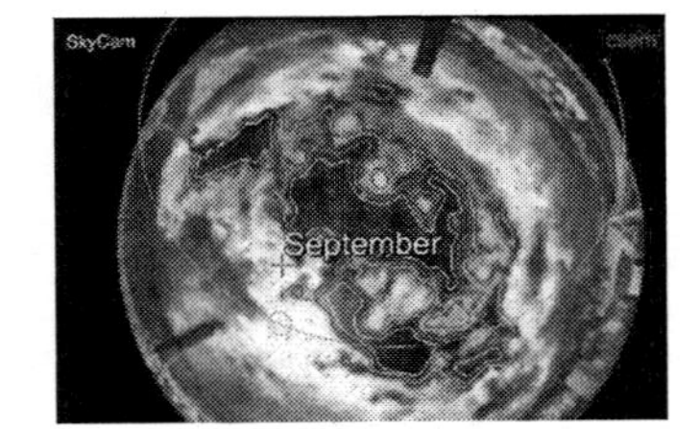
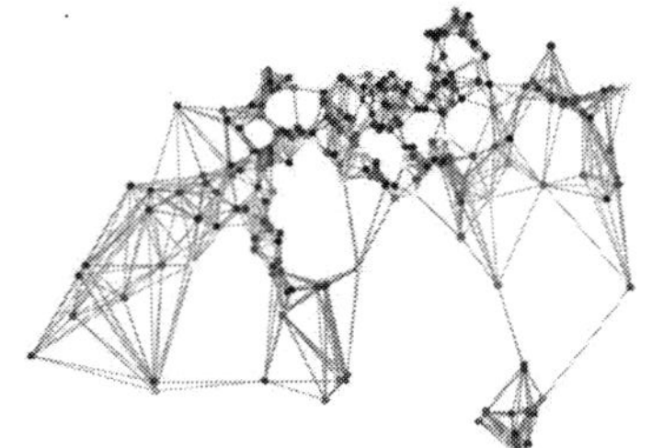
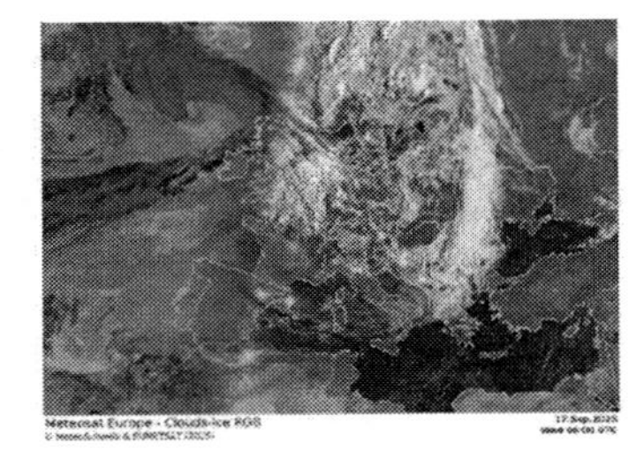

:: csem

3 SolarCrossFormer

SOLARCROSSFORMER: DAY-AHEAD FORECASTING

- Improved day-ahead solar irradiance forecasting by multi-modal information fusion
- **Inputs:**
  - Satellite imagery (visual + infrared)
  - Time-series from a network of ground-based meteorological stations
- **Key idea:** Graph Neural Networks (GNNs) to model:
  - Intra-modal correlations (between ground sensors, between pixels)
  - Inter-modal correlations (between satellite and ground sensors)

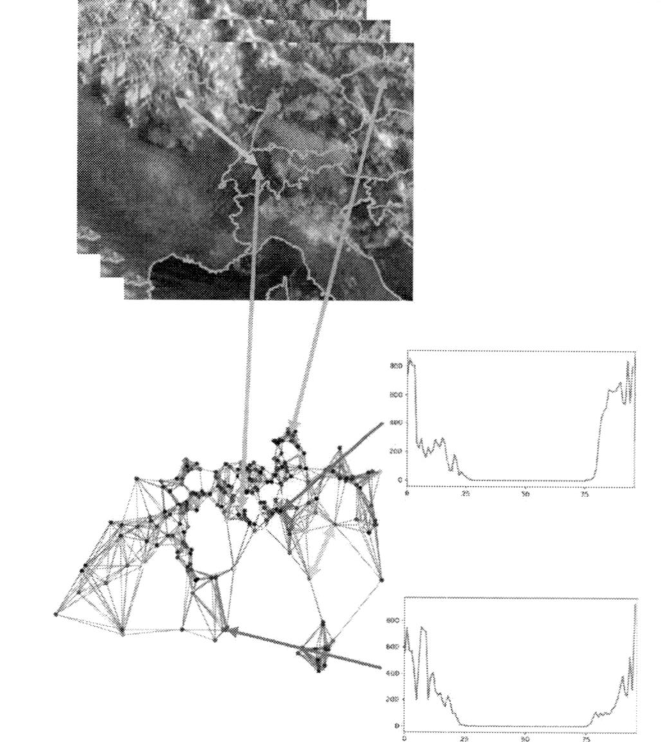

:: csem

ARCHITECTURE

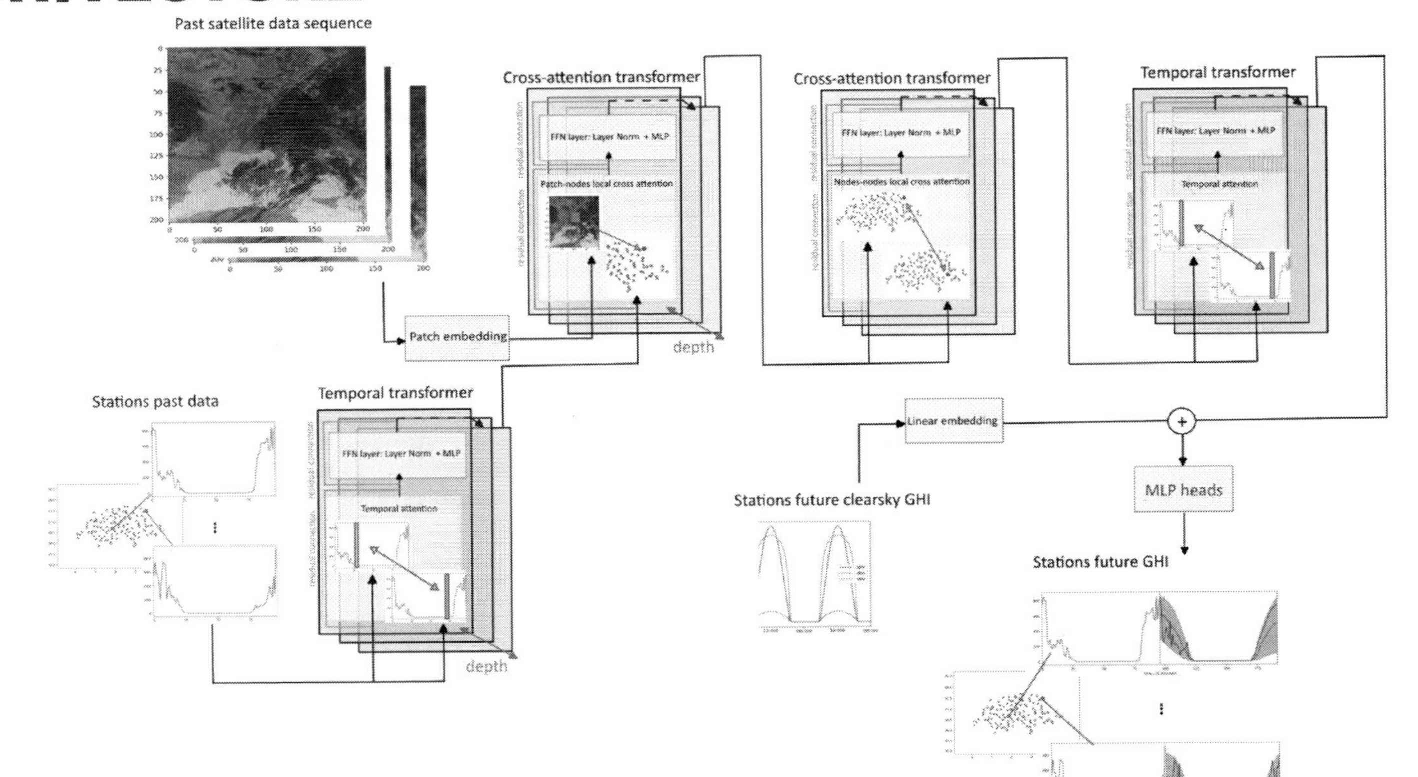

B. Schubnel et al., "SolarCrossFormer: Improving day-ahead Solar Irradiance Forecasting by Integrating Satellite Imagery and Ground Sensors," submitted to IEEE TSE, 2025. arXiv:2509.15827.

5 SolarCrossFormer

:: csem

TRAINING

- Pin-ball loss function used in training to output quantile forecasts
  - Median value (50% quant.)
  - Upper bound (95% quant.)
  - Lower bound (5% quant.)
- Dynamic masking strategy for training
  - Random masking of a percentage of node's data and image pixels per batch
  - It enables the forecast of GHI at locations where no local observations are available

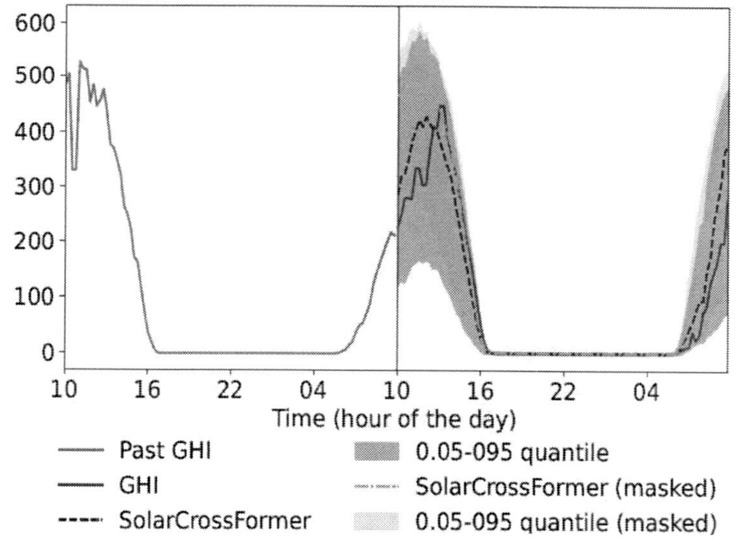

:: CSem

020238-006

INPUT DATA

- Satellite data from EUMETSAT MSG-4
  - Visual and infrared channels: IR039, IR087, IR108 and VIS006
- Time-series from MeteoSwiss automatic measurement network
  - GHI, DNI, DHI, outside temperature, wind speed and direction, pressure and RH
- Time-series and images with a temporal resolution of 15 minutes
- 9 years of data in total (2016-2024)
  - Training set: 8 years (2016-2023)
  - Evaluation set: 1 year (2024)

Covered area by input satellite image

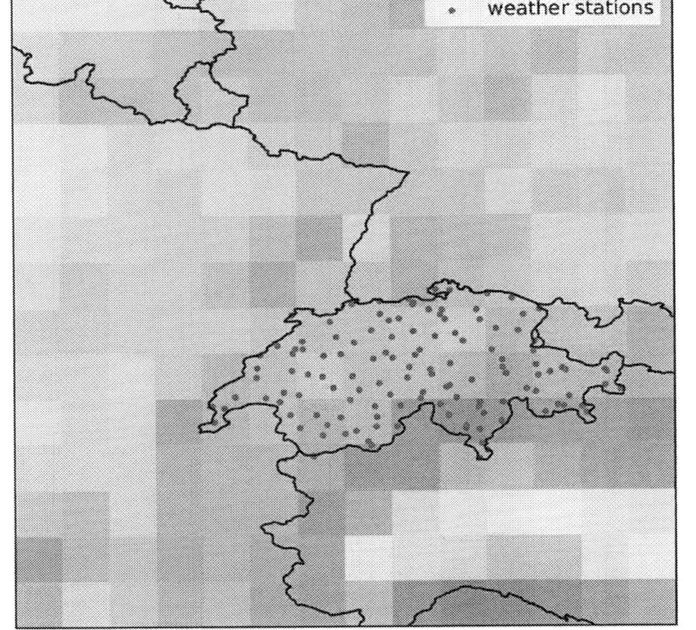

:: csem

7 SolarCrossFormer

COMPARISON AGAINST OTHER DL MODELS

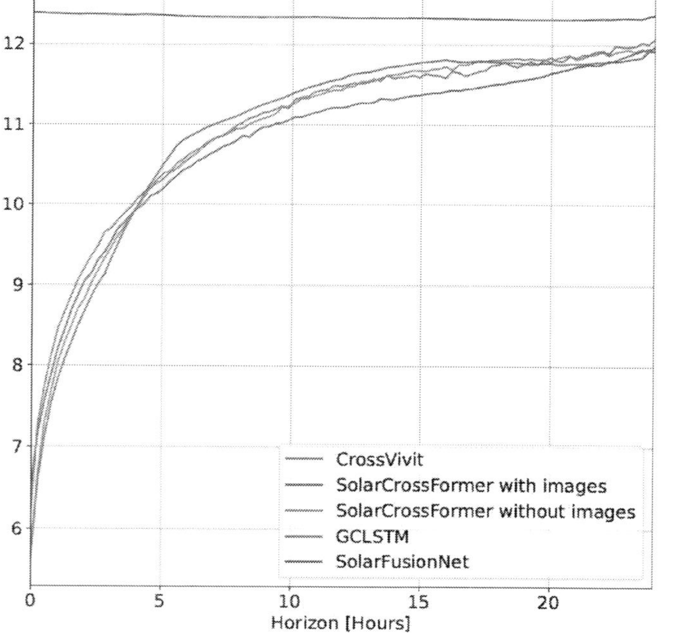

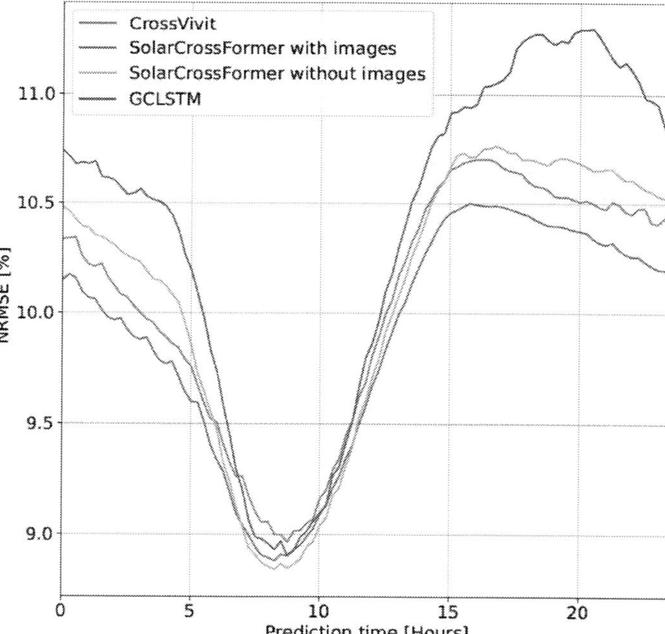

:: csem

SEASONAL ERROR

- SolarCrossFormer outperforms other models in summer, spring and autumn

- During winter, models with only ground data outperform models that use satellite data

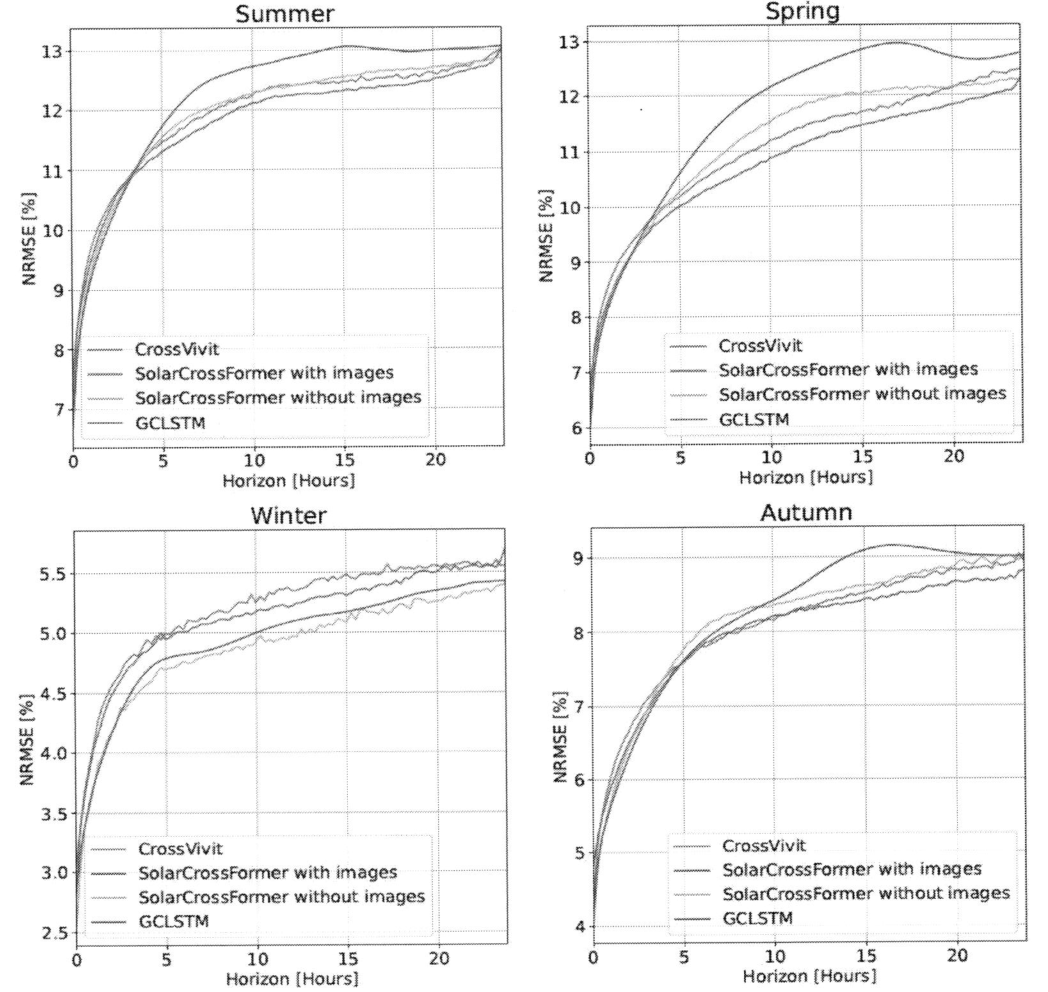

020238-009

COMPARISON AGAINST NWP-BASED FORECASTS

NMAE vs forecasting horizon

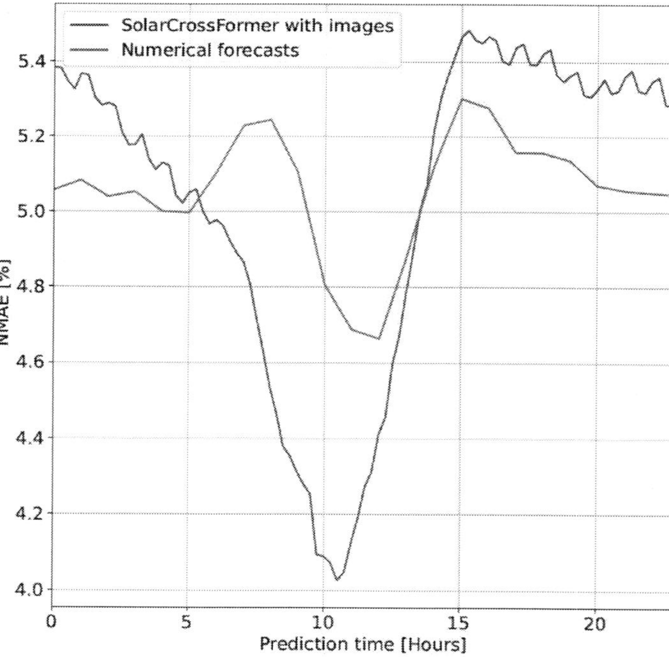

NMAE vs prediction time

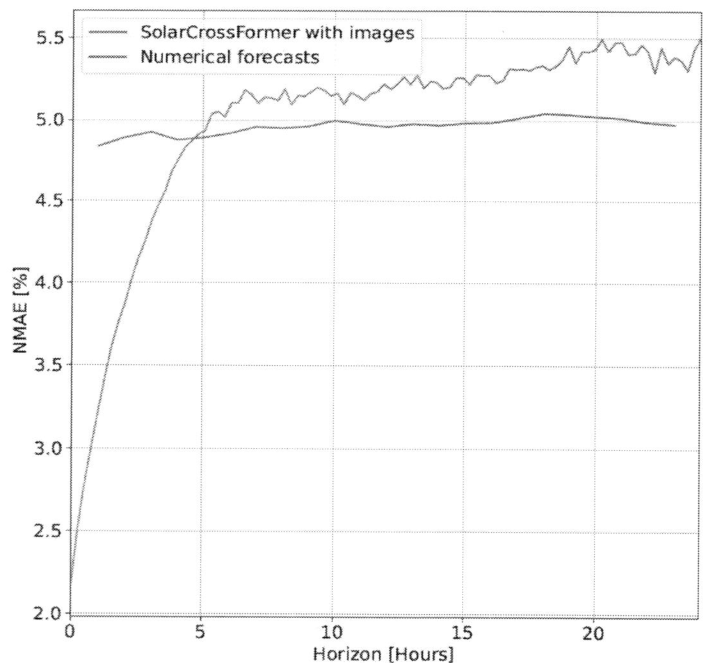

10 SolarCrossFormer

:: CSem

FORECAST AT UNSEEN LOCATIONS

- Test at 5 unseen locations
  - Two within Switzerland
  - Three outside

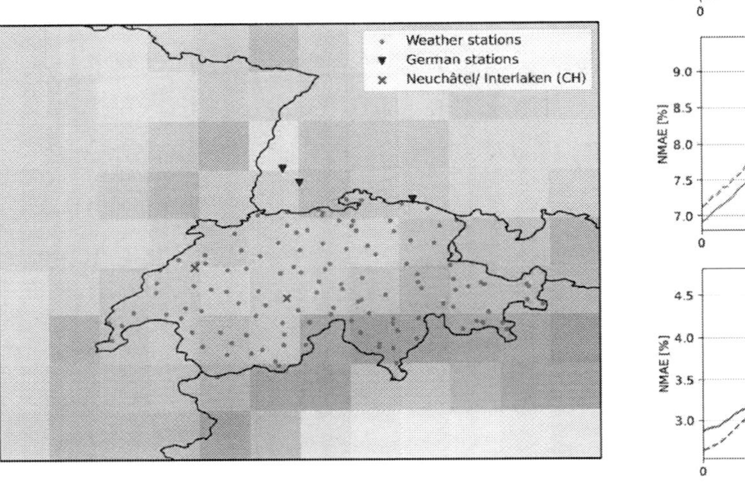

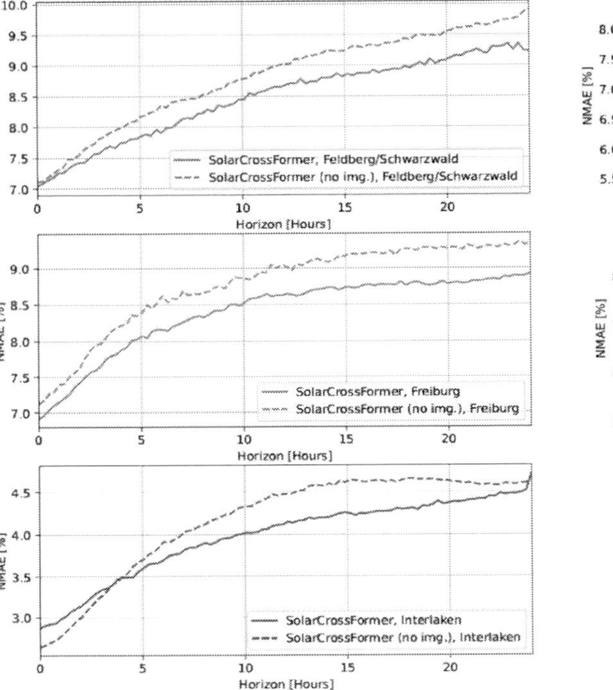

:: csem

IMPACT OF LOCAL OBSERVATIONS ON FORECAST ACCURACY

- **SolarCrossformer remains robust**, but performance slightly degrades without local inputs
  - When ground measurements are available, the model captures local irradiance variations more effectively
  - In the absence of local data, the model relies on spatial context from satellite imagery and nearby stations
- Highlights the **importance of sensor network density**

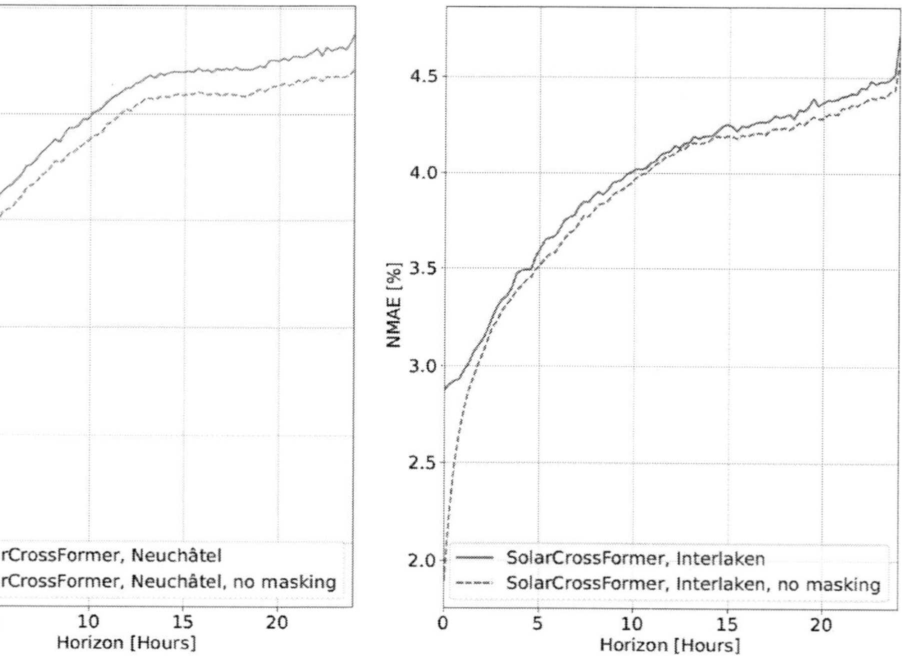

:: CSem

CONCLUSIONS

- **SolarCrossformer** yields probabilistic forecasts of irradiance for horizons up to 24h ahead with a temporal resolution of 15 minutes

- It uses advanced GNN to learn the **multi-modal data relations**

- **Robust and flexible:** works at new locations without retraining or historical data

- **Accurate:** outperforms state-of-the-art models and commercial NWP solutions across Switzerland

- **Scalable:** can forecast for any site using only coordinates, satellite, and network data

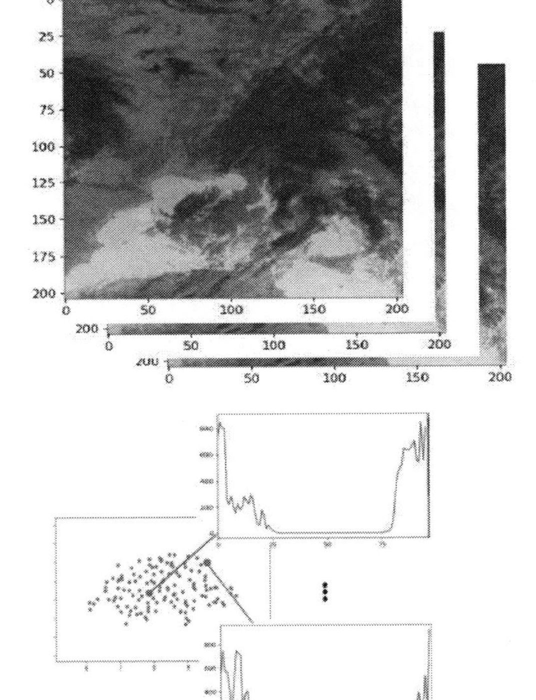

:: csem

020238-013

Rafael Carrillo
Expert, Digital Energy Solutions
rafael.carrillo@csem.ch
+41 32 720 5389
Co-funded by the European Union under Horizon Europe Agreement No 101146883. Views and opinions expressed are however those of the author(s) only and do not necessarily reflect those of the European Union or CINEA. Neither the European Union nor the granting authority can be held responsible for them.
:: csem

ENHANCING INTRA-HOUR SOLAR IRRADIANCE FORECASTING FOR SOLAR APPLICATIONS: A BLENDED MODEL OF SATELLITE, SKY IMAGER AND PERSISTENCE

Bijan Nouri, Jorge Lezaca, Yann Fabel, Annette Hammer, Niklas Blum, Stefan Wilbert

Bijan Nouri, DLR, EUPVSec 2025

020239-001

Agenda

- Motivation
- Methodology
  - Forecasting systems
  - Blending methods
  - Used datasets
- Results
  - General benchmark forecasts
  - Influence of prevailing sky conditions
  - Spatial influence
- Conclusion

020239-002

Motivation

- Solar irradiance variabilities in space and time on the local scale occur due to cloud passing

- Forecasting could make it possible to anticipate changes

- Accuracy of forecasts is crucial for their applicability

- Complementary Methods
  - Local observations (e.g. sky cameras and radiometers) offer high temporal and spatial resolution, but have limited spatial coverage and a short forecast horizon.
  - Satellites provide broad coverage and an extended forecast horizon, but have a coarser resolution.

- A hybrid model that blends local and satellite forecasts to produce robust, high-resolution, intra-hour local forecasts.

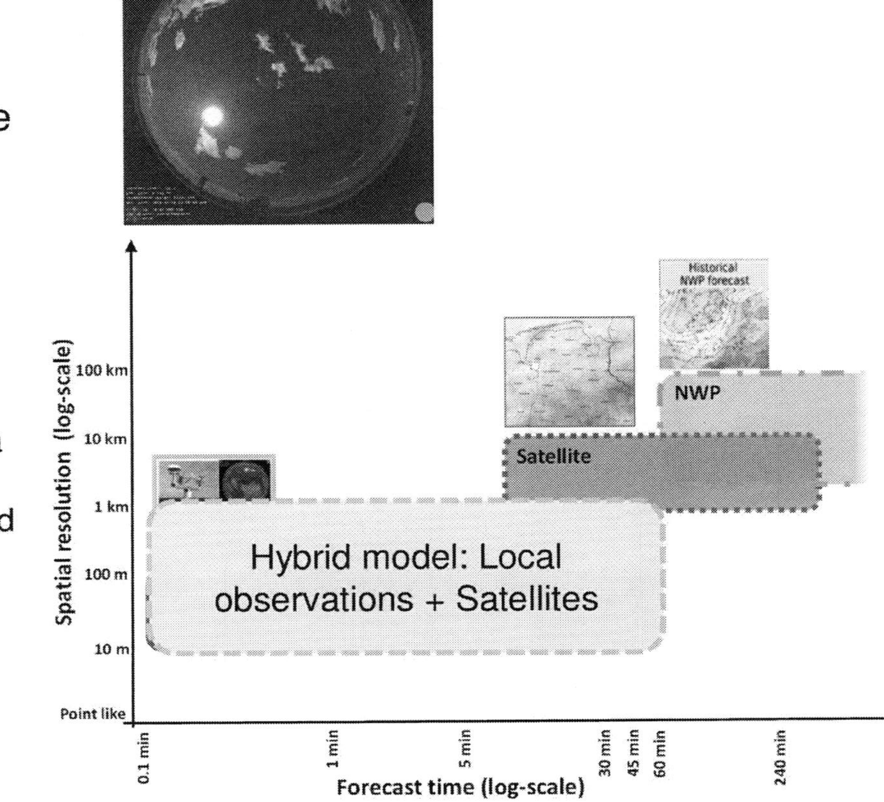

Bijan Nouri, DLR, EUPVSec 2025

020239-003

Forecasting systems

Meteosat based forecasts

All sky imager (ASI) based forecast

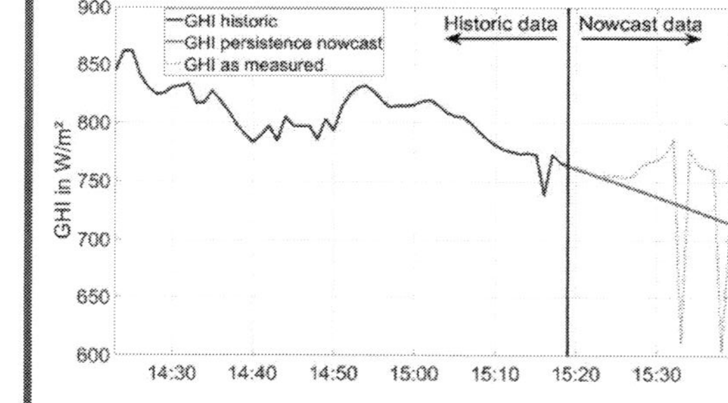

Persistence forecast

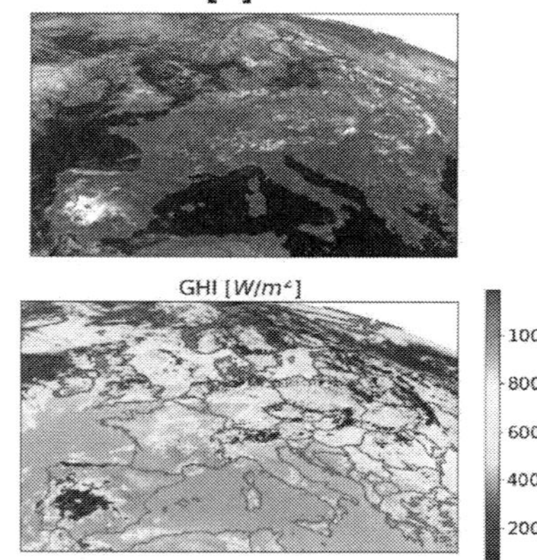

Heliosat method [1]

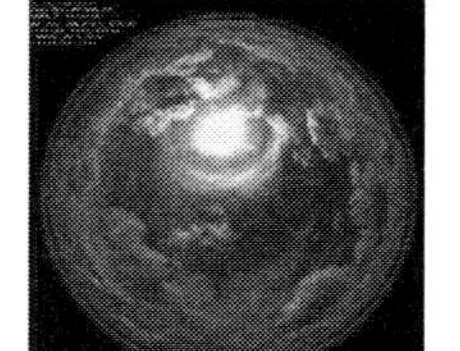

Deep learning transformer method [2]

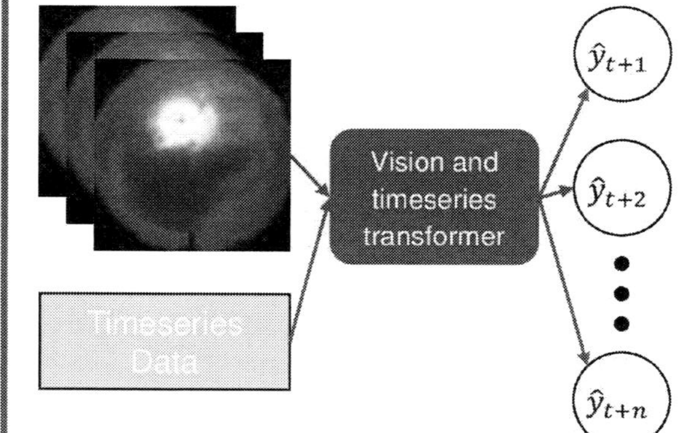

Scaled persistence method [3]

- Horizon ~6h
- Spatial resolution ~ 2km
- Temporal resolution and update rate 15 min

- Horizon 1h
- Temporal resolution 1 min
- Update rate 30 s
- Model trained on data set in southern Spain
- >3000000 data points distributed over 7 years

- Update rate 1 min

Bijan Nouri, DLR, EUPVSec 2025

020239-004

Blending methods

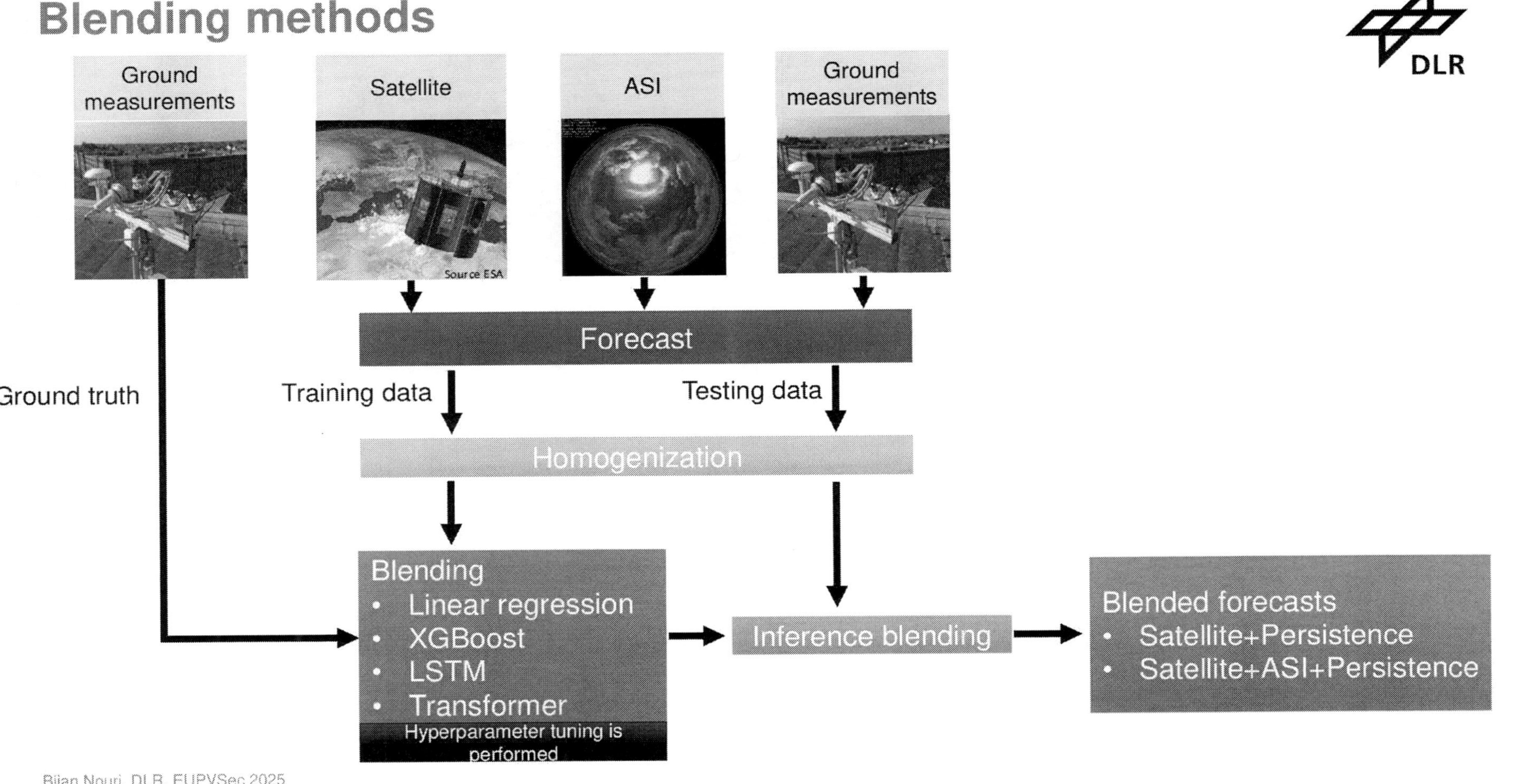

Bijan Nouri, DLR, EUPVSec 2025

020239-005

Used datasets

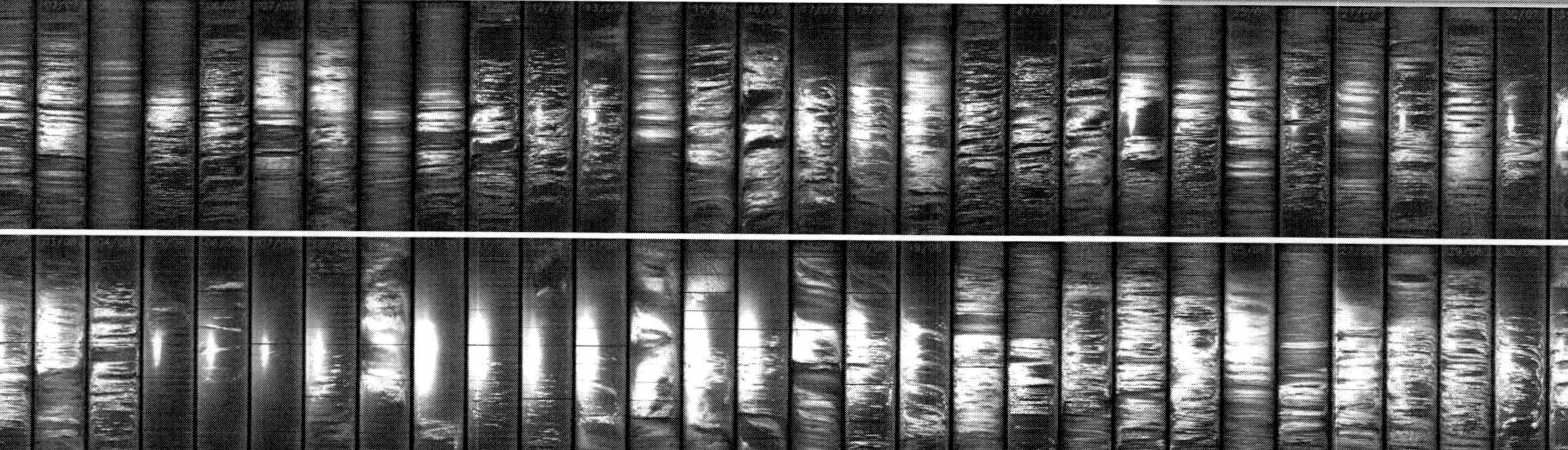

- Site: Oldenburg (Germany)
  - OLDON station of Eye2Sky Network [4]
  - 53°8′46.96′′N / 8°13′2.41′′E
- Used data
  - Training/Validation: July 2020
    (50373 datapoints)
  - Testing: August 2020
    (45163 datapoints)

	July	August
$\overline{GHI}$	321.7 W/m²	358.1 W/m²
Max GHI	972.3 W/m²	840.0 W/m²
$\overline{DHI}$	192.1 W/m²	166.7 W/m²
Max DHI	505.4 W/m²	442.1 W/m²
$\overline{DNI}$	209.9 W/m²	323.5 W/m²
Max DNI	876.4 W/m²	847.7 W/m²

Bijan Nouri, DLR, EUPVSec 2025

020239-006

General benchmark forecasts

$$RMSE = \sqrt{\frac{1}{n}\sum_{i=1}^{n}(\hat{y}_i - y_i)^2} \qquad MAE = \frac{1}{n}\sum_{i=1}^{n}|\hat{y}_i - y_i| \qquad Skill\ score = 1 - \frac{error_{model}}{error_{persistence}}$$

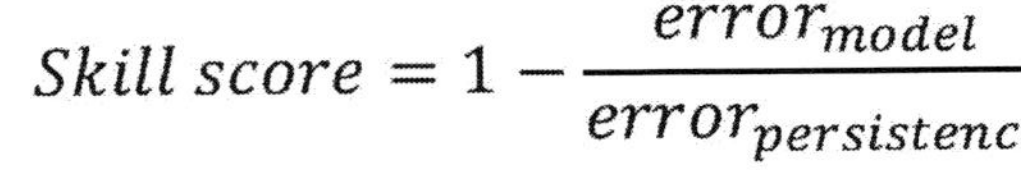

	Satellite+ASI+Persistence			
Error metric	LR	XGBoost	LSTM	Transfor-mer
RMSE	121.8	120.8	119.7	120.4
[W/m²] ↓	±16.9	±17.2	±17.4	±17.2
MAE	77.6	80.3	78.1	79.5
[W/m²] ↓	±14.2	±14.9	±14.5	±14.6
MBE	-1.7	-5.5	-2.8	-1.8
[W/m²] ↓	±1.6	±1.5	±3.0	±5.1
Skill Score	0.24	0.25	0.26	0.26
(RMSE) ↑	±0.04	±0.02	±0.01	±0.02
Skill Score	0.17	0.14	0.17	0.15
(MAE) ↑	±0.03	±0.04	±0.03	±0.05

Averaged results over all lead times (± std)

Bijan Nouri, DLR, EUPVSec 2025

020239-007

Influence of prevailing sky conditions

- Mostly/almost clear sky with high clear sky index
  - 27% of the dataset
  - Low variability
  - Average cloud coverage ≈ 11%
  - Average clear sky index ≈ 0.94
- Partly cloudy with intermediate clear sky index
  - 25% of the dataset
  - High/intermediate variability
  - average cloud coverage ≈ 53%
  - average clear sky index ≈ 0.57
- Almost/mostly overcast with low clear sky index
  - 48% of the dataset
  - Intermediate/low variability
  - average cloud coverage ≈ 85%
  - average clear sky index ≈ 0.08

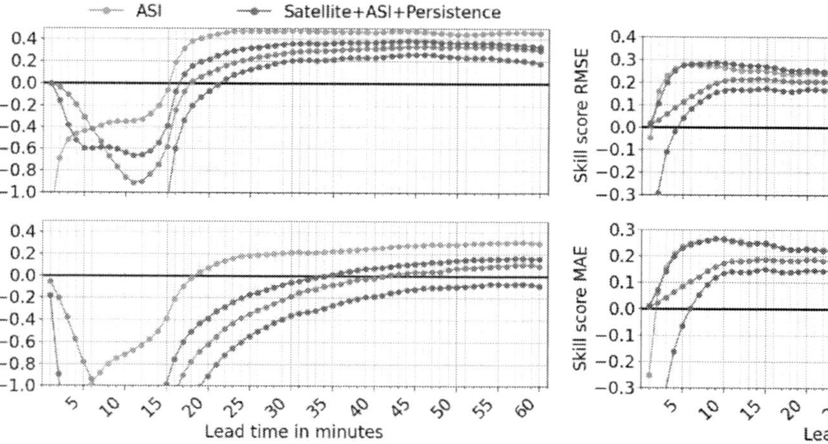

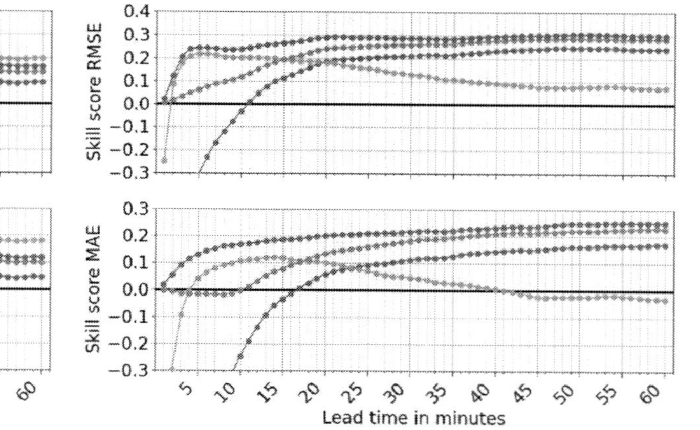

Bijan Nouri, DLR, EUPVSec 2025

020239-008

Spatial influence

- Benchmark OLDON hybrid forecast against satellite forecasts at 3 additional sites
  - OLDON hybrid forecast remains unchanged.
  - Use site-specific satellite forecasts for comparison.
  - Sites are part of the Eye2Sky network with reference sensors.

$$Skill\ score = 1 - \frac{error_{Hybrid_{OLDON}@site(n)}}{error_{Satellite_{site(n)}}}$$

	Hybrid OLDON@OLCLO (Baseline: Satellite OLCLO)	Hybrid OLDON@OLUOL (Baseline: Satellite OLUOL)	Hybrid OLDON@OLJET (Baseline: Satellite OLJET)
Skill Score (RMSE) ↑	0.09±0.04	0.04±0.02	-0.01±0.06
Skill Score (MAE) ↑	0.14±0.03	0.07±0.02	0.05±0.03

Averaged results over all lead times (± std)

Bijan Nouri, DLR, EUPVSec 2025

020239-009

Conclusion

- Intra-Hour Boost: Ground measurements significantly enhance site-specific satellite forecasts in the intra-hour range.

- Hybrid Superiority: Satellite+ASI+Persistence model delivers lowest error metrics with top skill scores (RMSE: 0.24±0.04, MAE: 0.17±0.03).

- Cross-Climate Success: ASI, trained in desert climate, performs well in temperate regions.

- Short-Term Strength: ASI excels in short lead times and partly cloudy conditions, enhancing hybrid performance.

- Spatial Reach: Hybrid forecast shows a positive impact up to ~4 km away from the origin.

- Future Focus: Strong for overall irradiance, less for ramp events; generative ASI models to be explored.

Bijan Nouri, DLR, EUPVSec 2025

020239-010

References

1. Hammer, A., Kühnert, J., Weinreich, K., & Lorenz, E. (2015). Short-term forecasting of surface solar irradiance based on Meteosat-SEVIRI data using a nighttime cloud index. Remote Sensing, 7(7), 9070-9090.

2. Fabel, Y., Nouri, B., Wilbert, S., Blum, N., Schnaus, D., Triebel, R., ... & Pitz-Paal, R. (2024). Combining Deep Learning and Physical Models: A Benchmark Study on All-Sky Imager-Based Solar Nowcasting Systems. Solar RRL, 8(4), 2300808.

3. Chu, Y., Li, M., Coimbra, C. F., Feng, D., & Wang, H. (2021). Intra-hour irradiance forecasting techniques for solar power integration: A review. Iscience, 24(10).

4. Schmidt, T., Stührenberg, J., Blum, N., Lezaca, J., Hammer, A., Wilbert, S., ... & Vogt, T. (2025). Eye2Sky–a network of all-sky imager and meteorological measurement stations for high resolution nowcasting of solar irradiance. *Meteorologische Zeitschrift, 34*(1), 35-55.

THANK YOU FOR YOUR ATTENTION!
QUESTIONS?
BIJAN.NOURI@DLR.DE
DLR
Bijan Nouri, DLR, EUPVSec 2025

020239-012

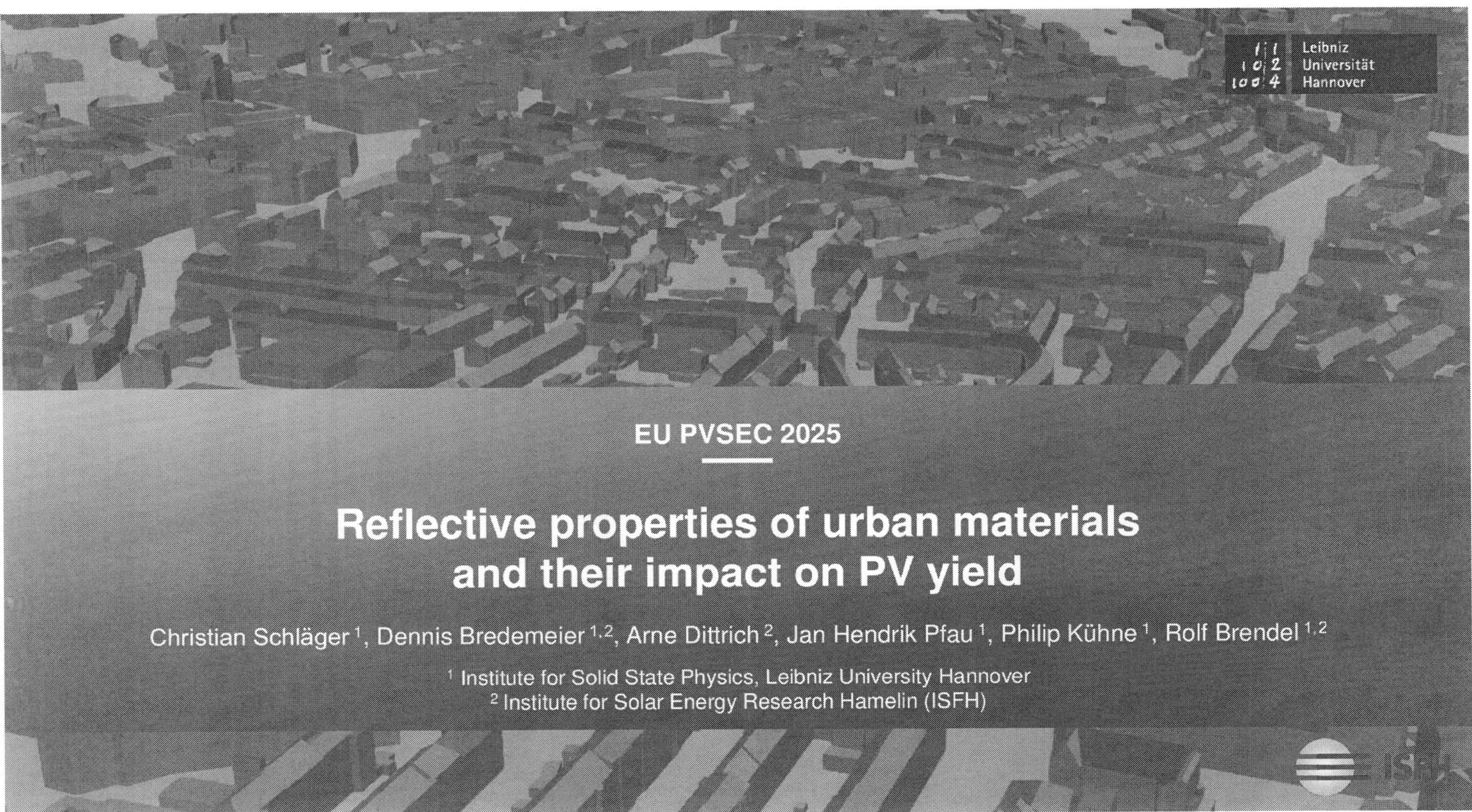

Leibniz
Universität
Hannover
EU PVSEC 2025
Reflective properties of urban materials
and their impact on PV yield
Christian Schläger [1], Dennis Bredemeier [1,2], Arne Dittrich [2], Jan Hendrik Pfau [1], Philip Kühne [1], Rolf Brendel [1,2]
[1] Institute for Solid State Physics, Leibniz University Hannover
[2] Institute for Solar Energy Research Hamelin (ISFH)
ISFH

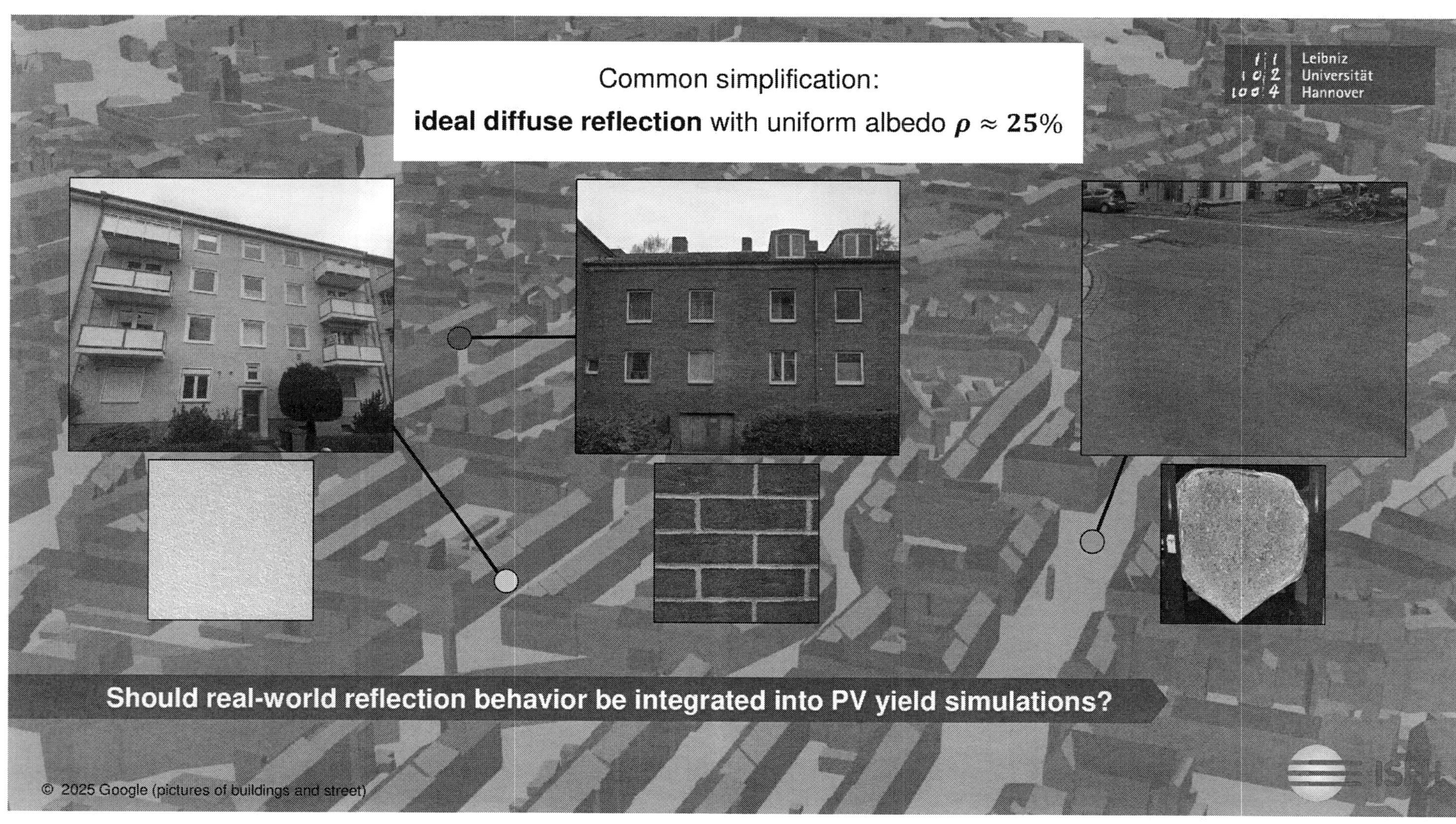
Leibniz
Universität
Hannover
Common simplification:
ideal diffuse reflection with uniform albedo $\rho \approx 25\%$
Should real-world reflection behavior be integrated into PV yield simulations?
© 2025 Google (pictures of buildings and street)

Experimental setup

Leibniz Universität Hannover

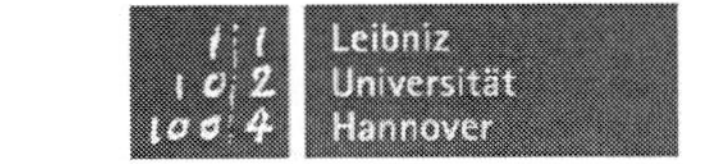

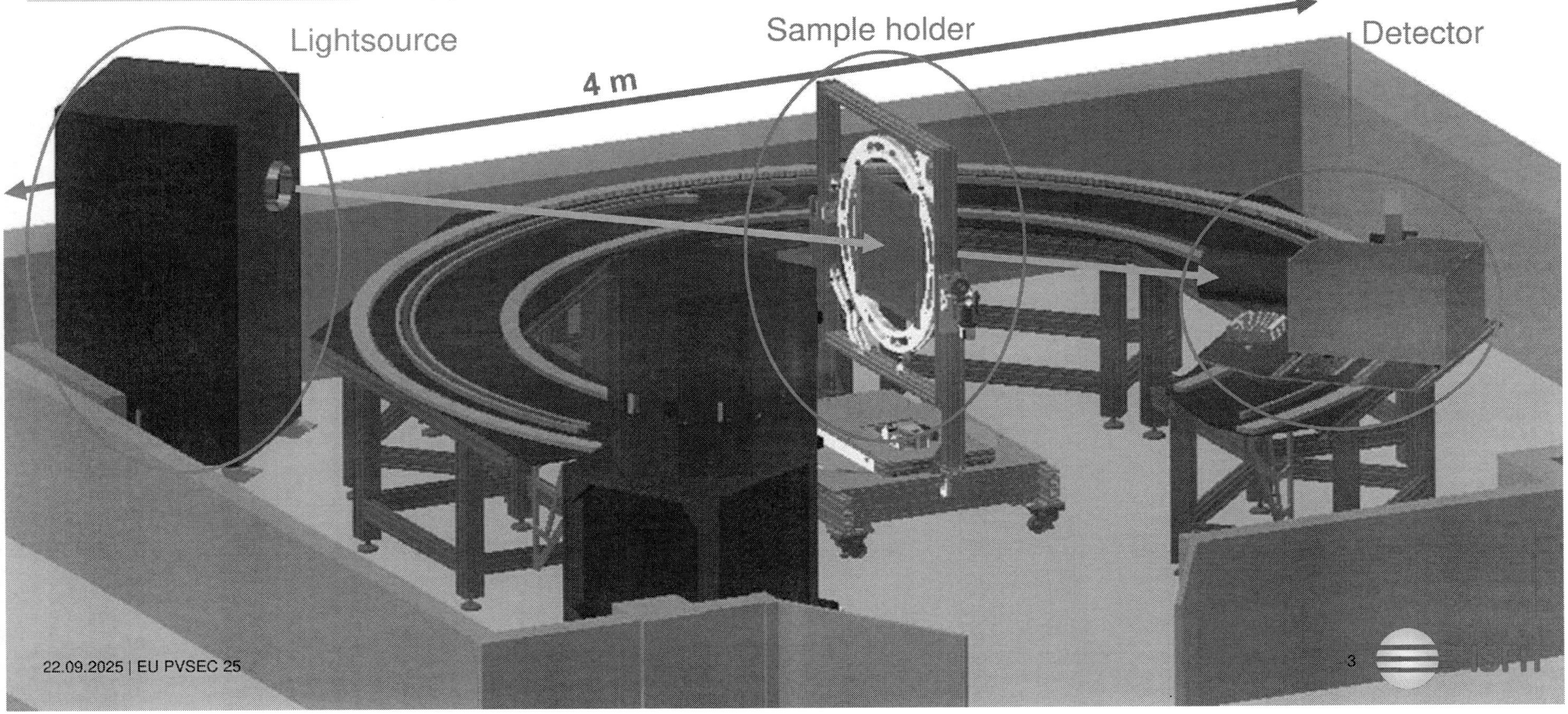

Experimental setup

020240-004

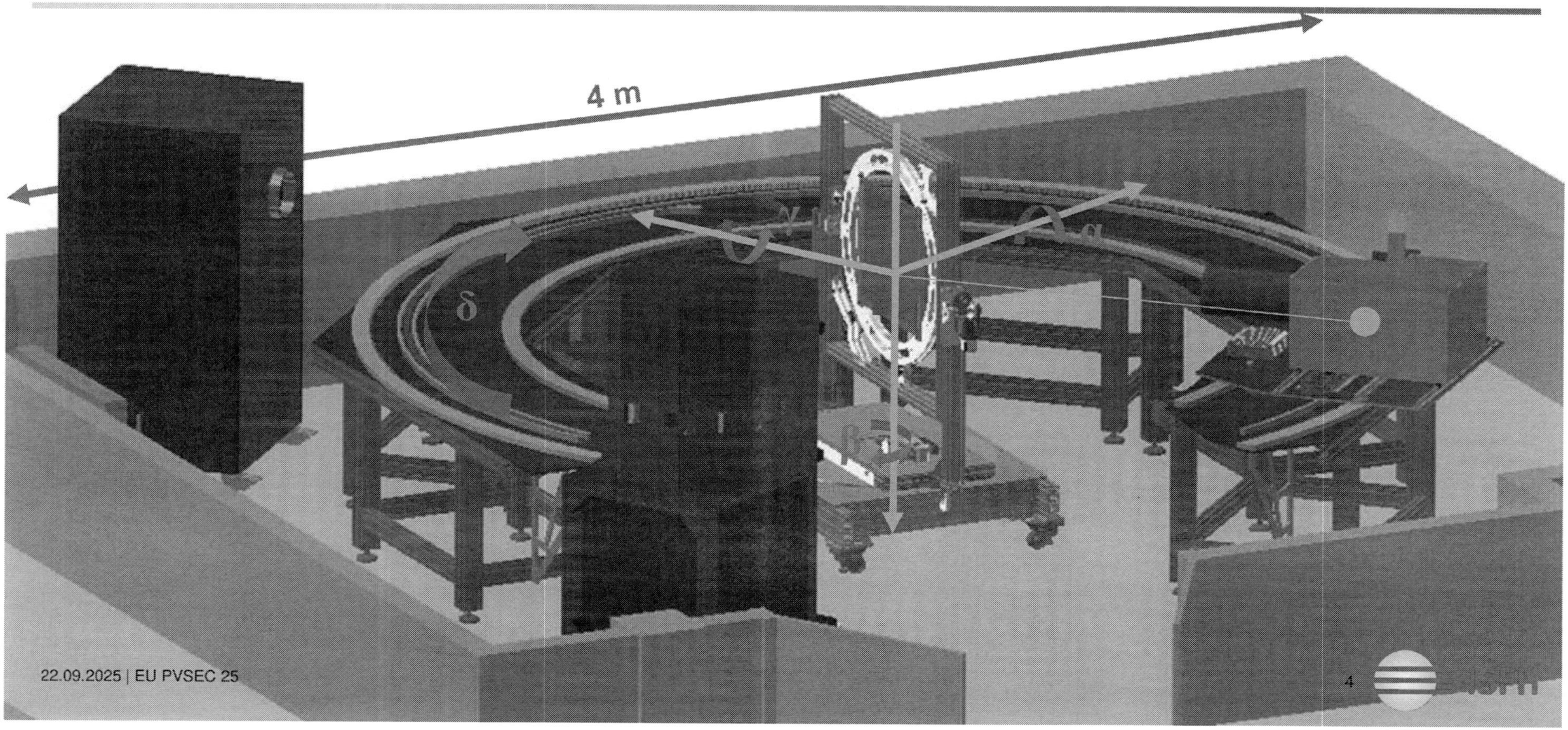

<u>B</u>idirectional <u>R</u>eflectance <u>D</u>istribution <u>F</u>unction

$$\text{BRDF} = \frac{\text{Radiance}}{\text{Irradiance}}$$

$$f_r(\vec{\omega}_{in}, \vec{\omega}_{out}, \lambda) = \frac{dL_r}{dE}$$

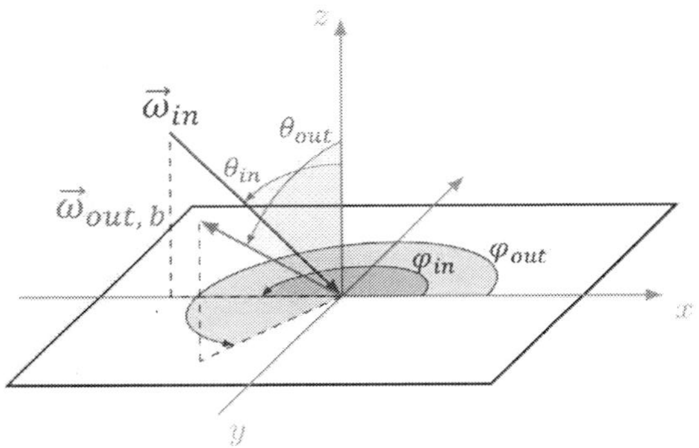

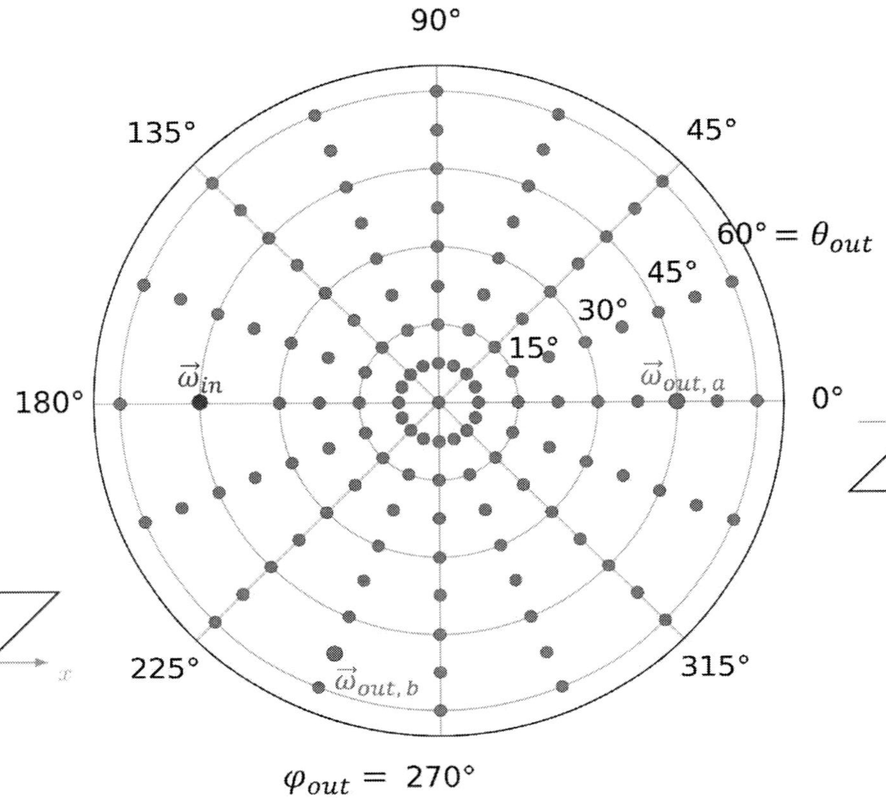

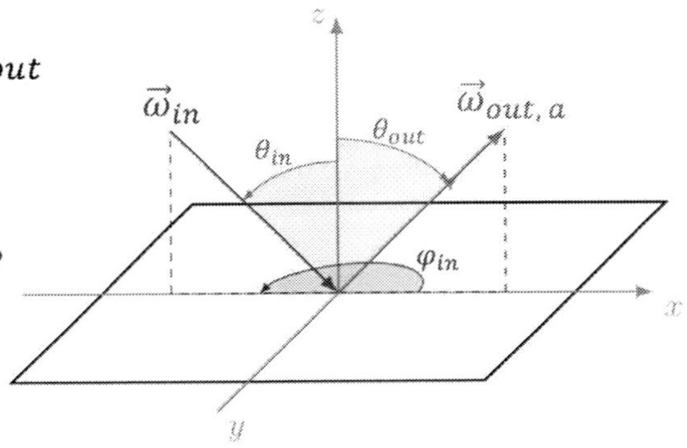

5

ISFH

020240-005

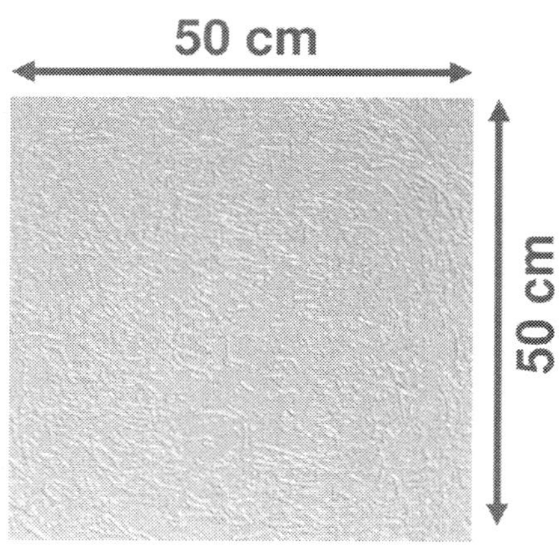

Plaster (light-blue)

020240-006

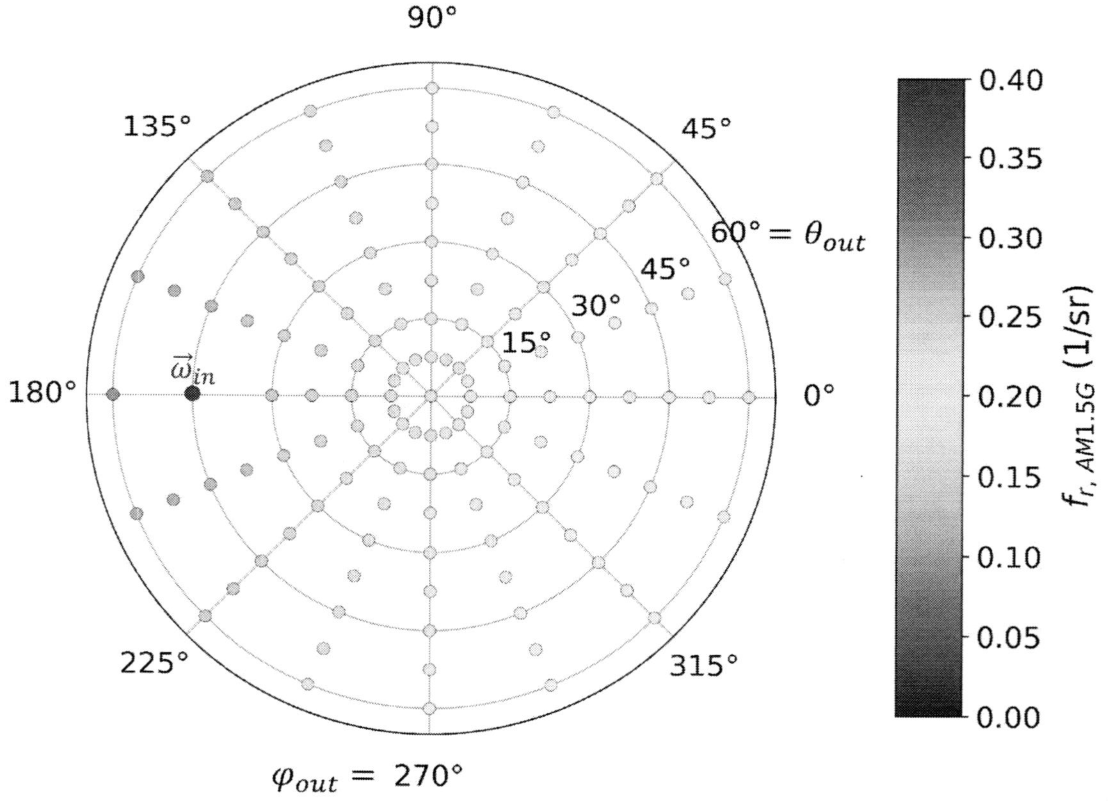

Plaster (light-blue)

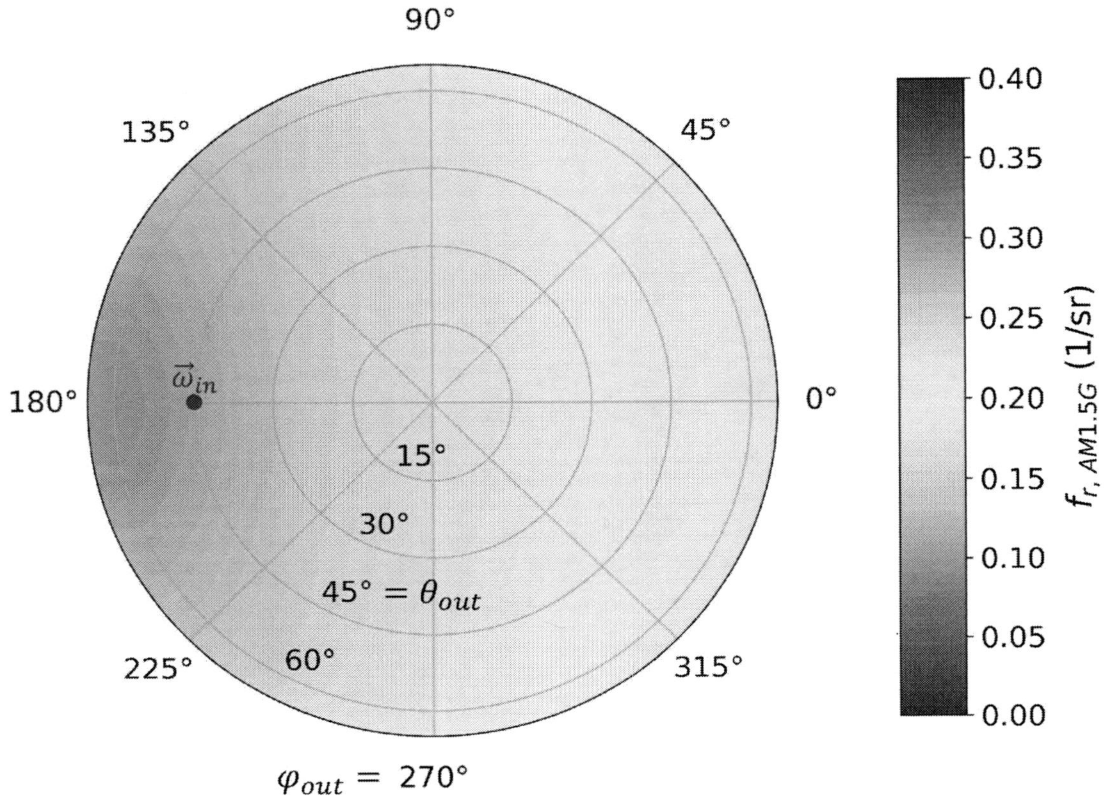

Clinker brick slips (red-brown)

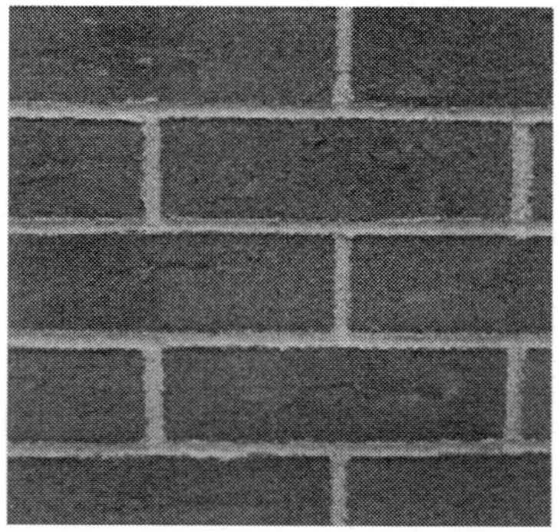

Clinker brick slips
(red-brown)

ISFH

020240-008

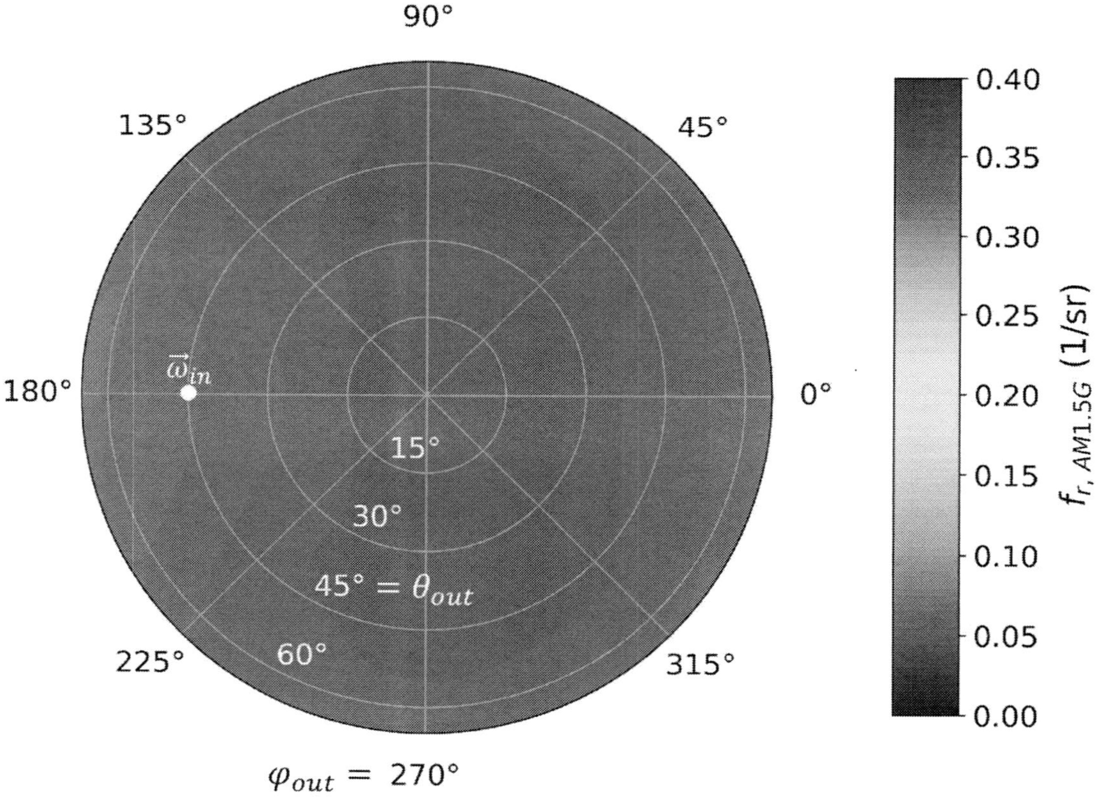

Asphalt (worn)

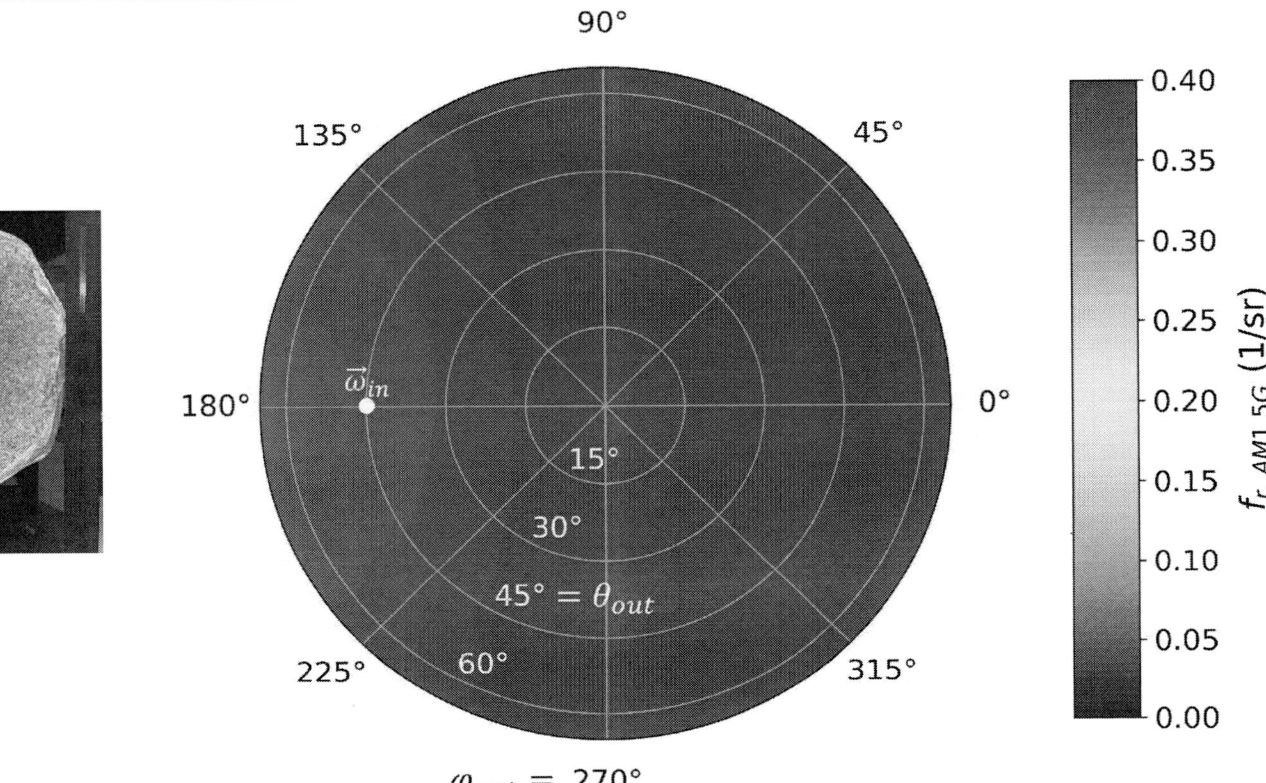

Asphalt
(worn)

020240-009

Leibniz Universität Hannover

ISFH

Energy-preserving Oren-Nayar reflection (EON)

Measured BRDF for Plaster (light-blue):

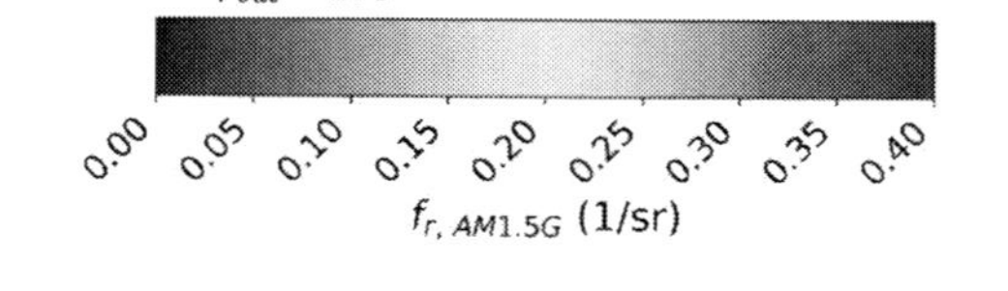

Ideal diffuse reflection:

$$f_r(\vec{\omega}_{in}, \vec{\omega}_{out}) = const. = \frac{\rho}{\pi}$$

$$\rho = 0.73$$

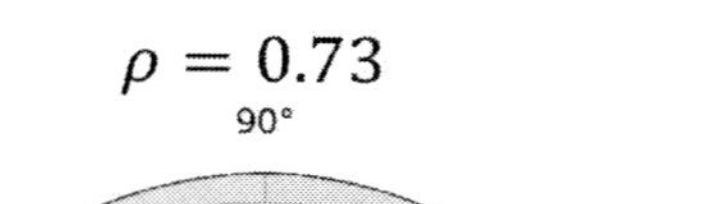

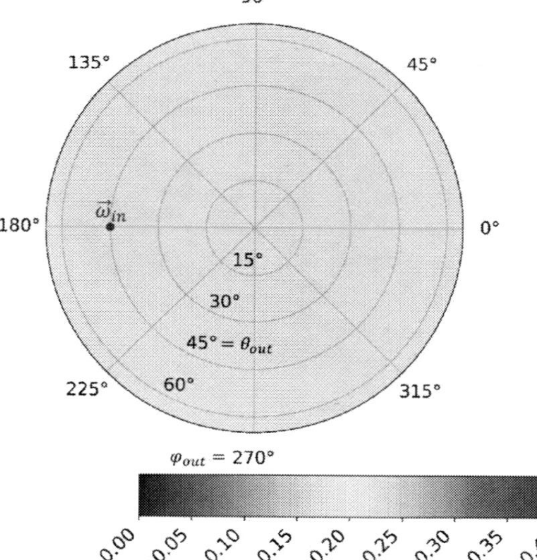

Energy-preserving Oren-Nayar reflection: [2]

$$f_r(\vec{\omega}_{in}, \vec{\omega}_{out}) = \frac{\rho}{\pi}(A + B\frac{s}{t}) + f_{ms}(\vec{\omega}_{in}, \vec{\omega}_{out})$$

Ideal diffuse term: $\quad A = \dfrac{1}{1 + (\frac{1}{2} - \frac{2}{3\pi})\,r}$

Non-diffuse term: $\quad B = A \cdot r$

Compensation term (multi-scattering events)

Roughness r: mixing ratio of (diffuse term) / (non-diffuse term)

[2] Portsmouth et al. 2025, J. Comput. Graph. Tech. 14(1)

020240-010

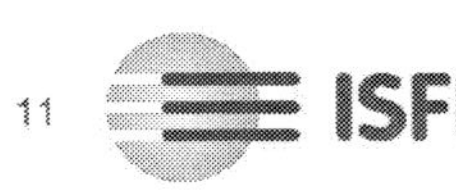

Energy-preserving Oren-Nayar reflection (EON)

Measured BRDF for Plaster (light-blue):

Ideal diffuse reflection:

$$f_r(\vec{\omega}_{in}, \vec{\omega}_{out}) = const. = \frac{\rho}{\pi}$$

$$\rho = 0.73$$

Energy-preserving Oren-Nayar reflection: [2]

$$f_r(\vec{\omega}_{in}, \vec{\omega}_{out}) = \frac{\rho}{\pi}\left(A + B\frac{s}{t}\right) + f_{ms}(\vec{\omega}_{in}, \vec{\omega}_{out})$$

$$\rho = 0.73 \quad r = 0.38$$

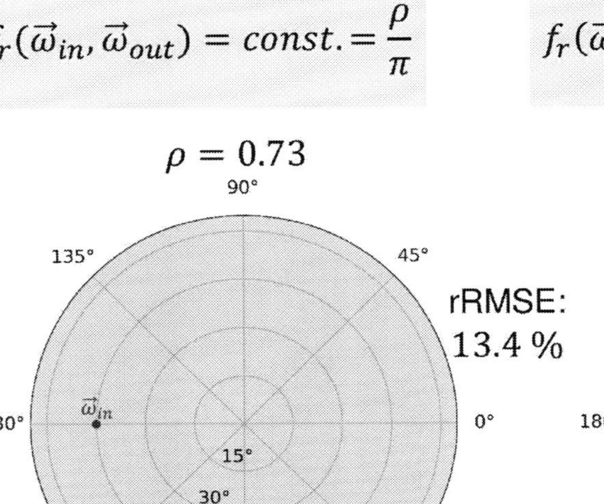

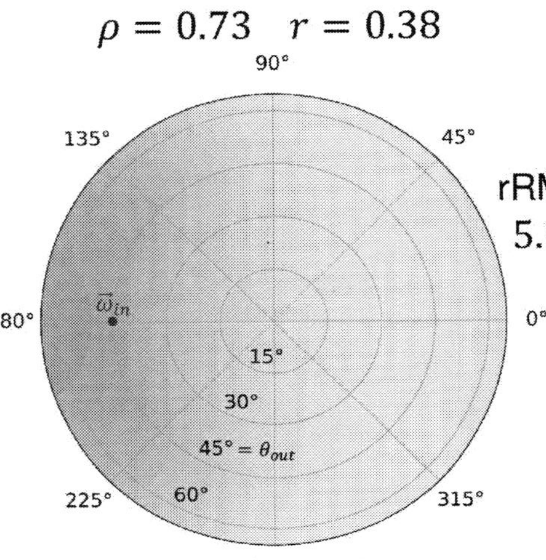

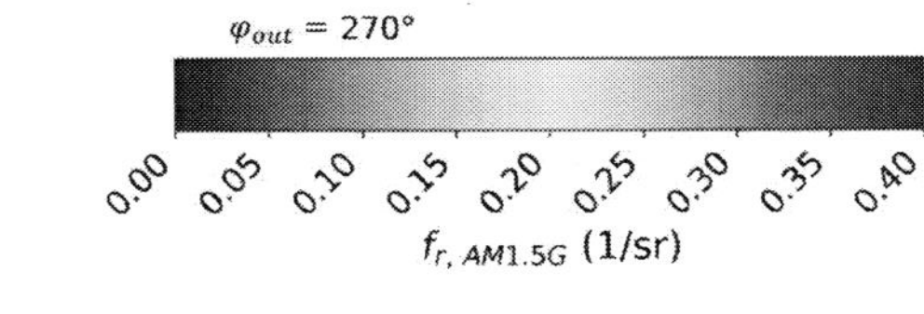

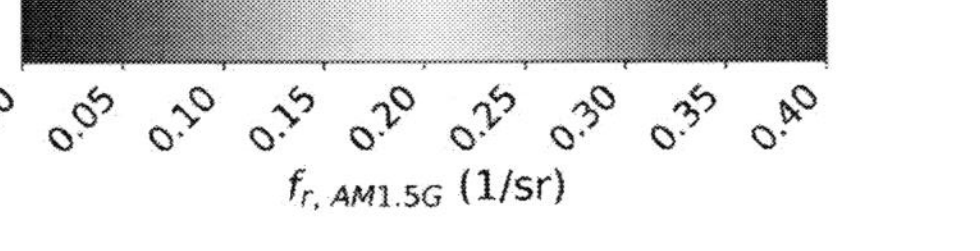

[2] Portsmouth et al. 2025, J. Comput. Graph. Tech. 14(1)

11

020240-011

Albedo vs. roughness

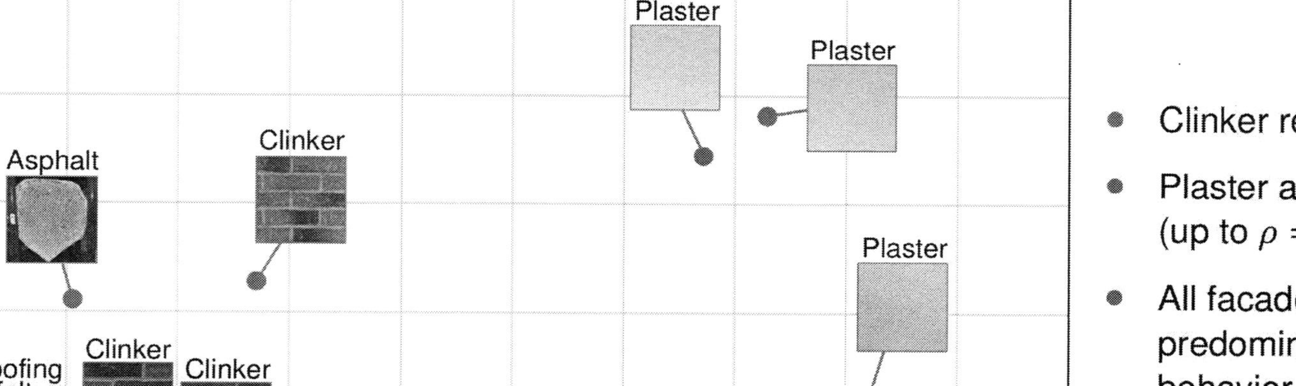

- Clinker region around $\rho \approx 0.25$

- Plaster achieves higher albedos (up to $\rho = 0.82$ for white plaster)

- All facade materials show predominantly diffuse reflection behavior $r \leq 0.4$

020240-012

Material labeling

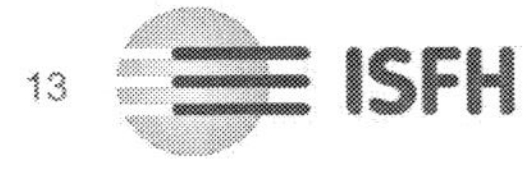

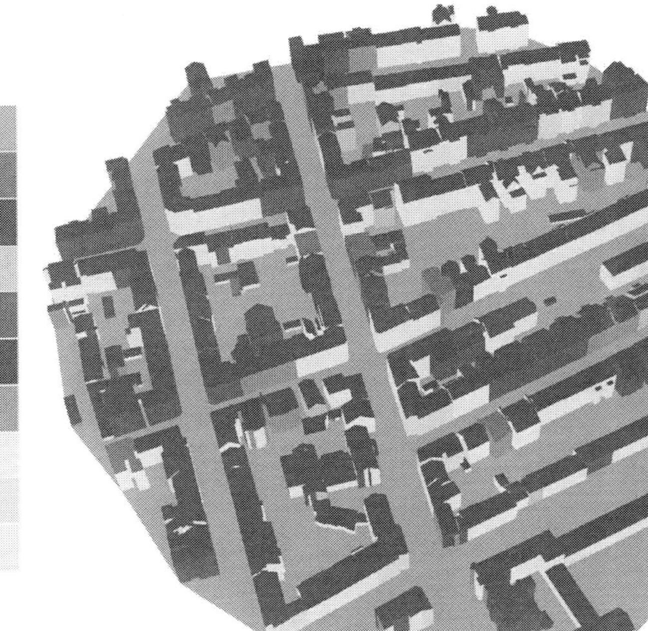

- Residential area with a radius of 200 meters in Hannover (Germany)

- Building geometry is derived from LoD2 data [3]

- Facade and roof material information are provided using images from Google Street View & Google Maps API and human categorization

- Ground is set to asphalt

Three simulation scenarios

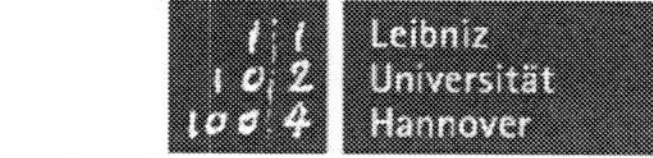

Ref.
ideal diffuse reflection
uniform $\rho = 25\,\%$

SA
ideal diffuse reflection
surface-specific ρ

EON
Energy-preserving Oren-Nayar
surface-specific ρ and r

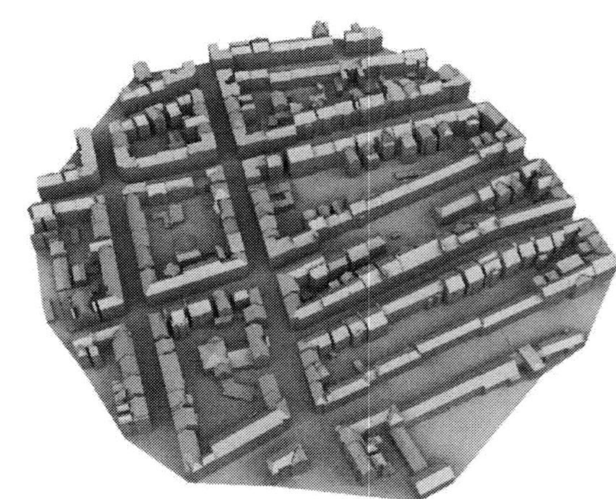
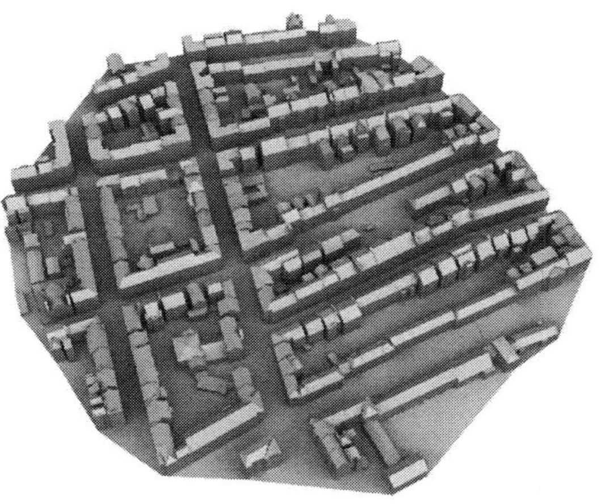
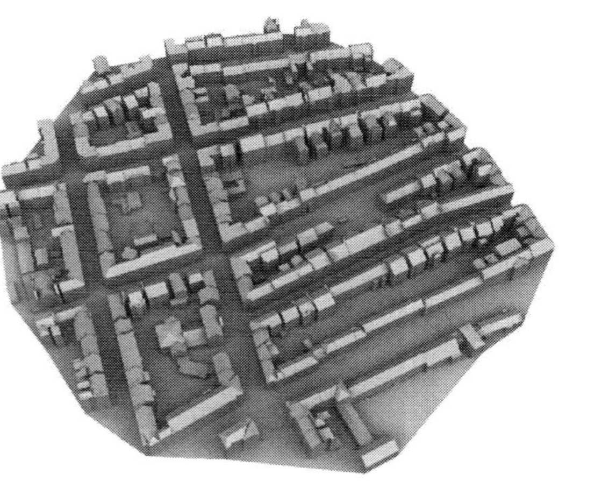

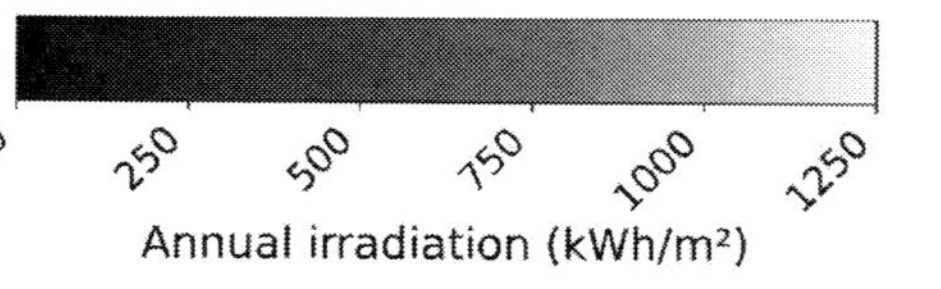

020240-014

Impact of albedo

Impact of albedo
SA – Ref.

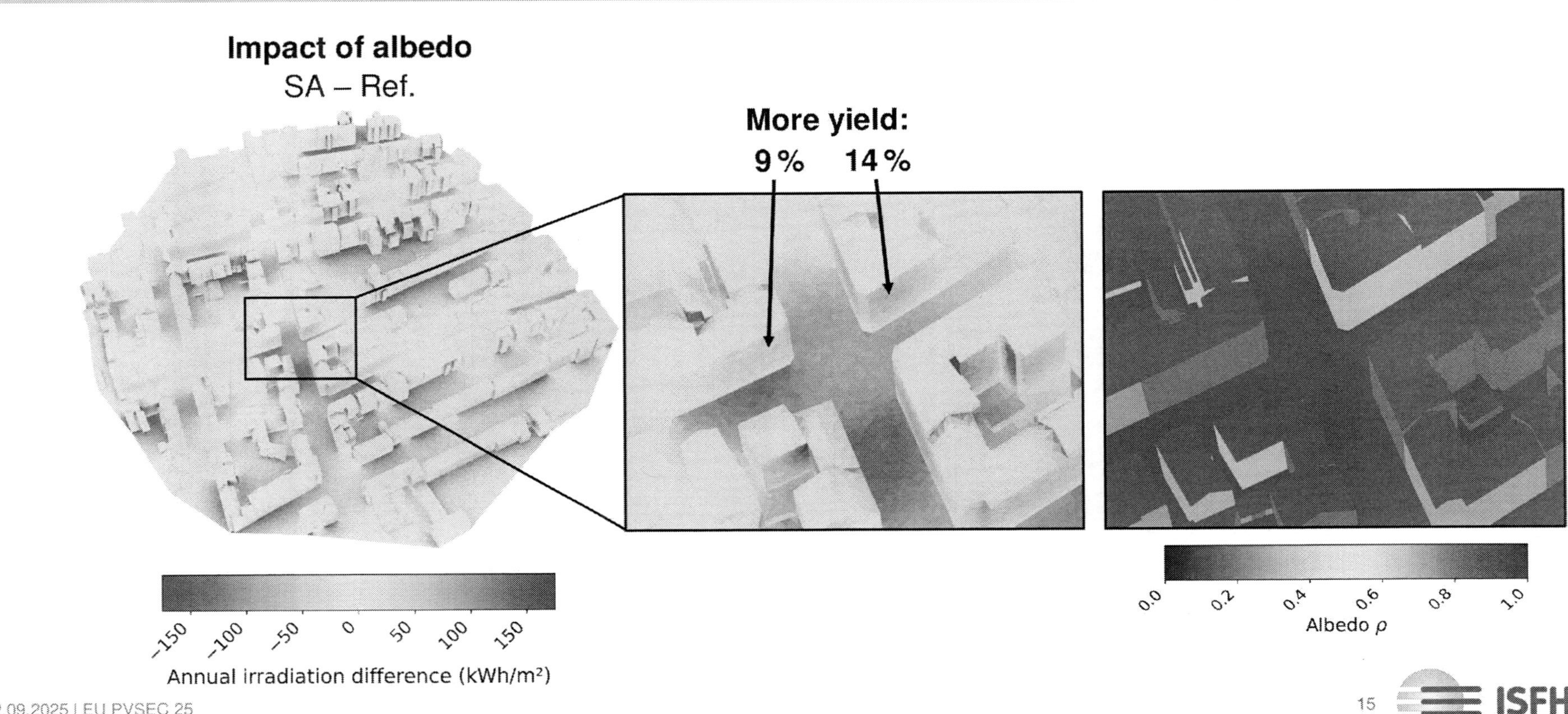

ISFH

Impact of directionality

Leibniz
Universität
Hannover

Impact of albedo
SA – Ref.

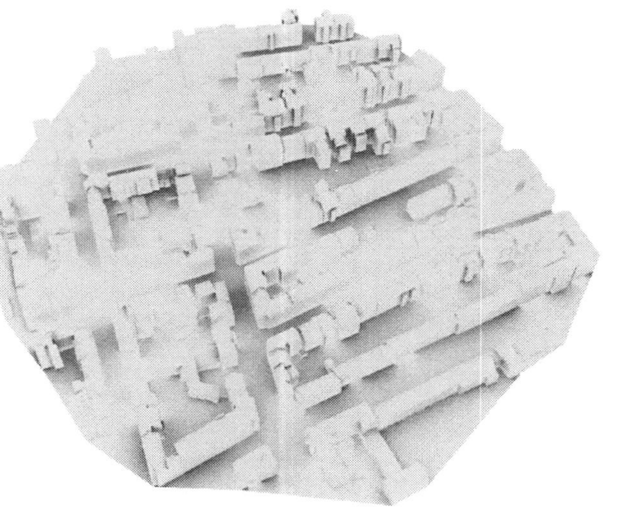

Impact of directionality
EON – SA

ISFH

020240-016

Impact of directionality

Impact of albedo
SA – Ref.

Impact of directionality
EON – SA

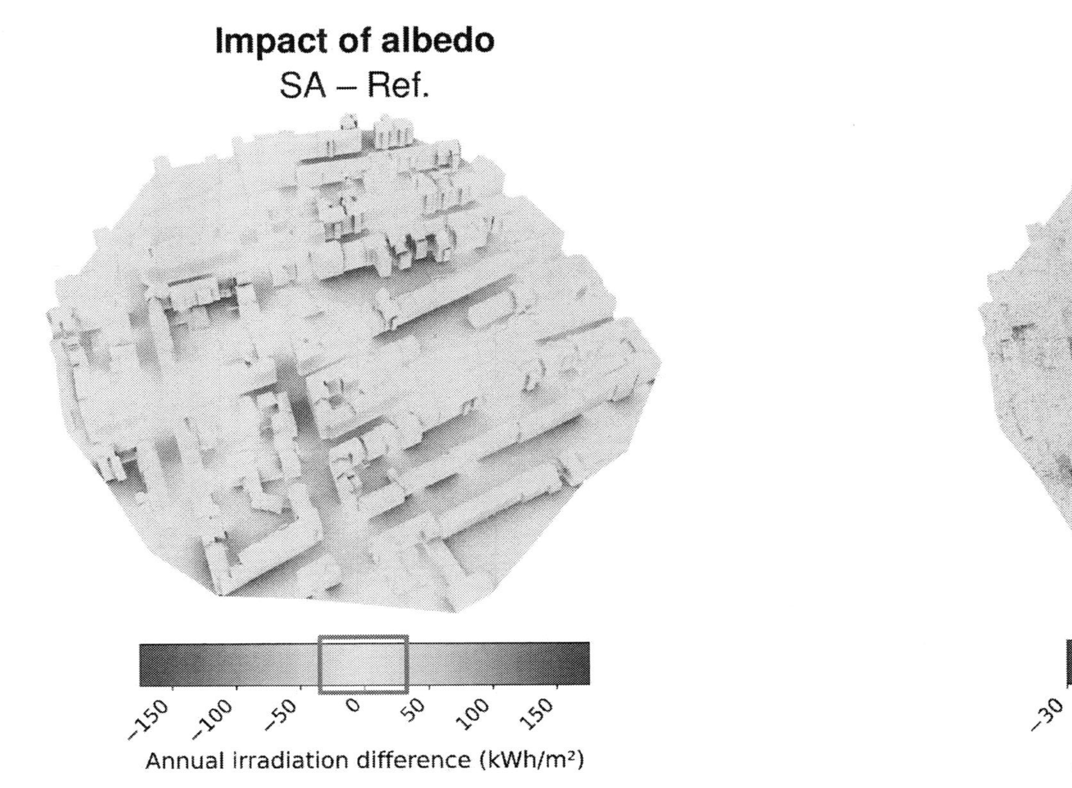

020240-017

Key take aways

- Reflection modeling has a significant impact on irradiation results

- Impact of albedo is an order of magnitude higher than impact of directionality

  - Impact of albedo $\rho \approx \pm 100$ kWh/m² (e.g. **14 %** more irradiation on some south-facing facades)

  - Impact of roughness $r \approx \pm 10$ kWh/m²

Should real-world reflection behavior be integrated into PV yield simulations?

▶ Surface-specific albedos should be integrated.

▶ Simplification of ideal diffuse reflection is justified.

18

020240-018

Thank you!

Contact

Christian Schläger

Research Associate
Institute of Solid State Physics
Department of Solar Energy

schlaeger@solar.uni-hannover.de

Funding

UNDERSTANDING SHORT-TERM PV POWER VARIABILITY
BASED ON SOLARGIS TIME SERIES DATA AND SIMULATIONS

Martin Opatovsky, Marta Pelfort Ojer, Juraj Betak, Konstantin Rosina
Solargis (Bratislava, Slovakia)
Corresponding author: martin.opatovsky@solargis.com; +421 2 4319 1708

ABSTRACT: This study analyzes the variability of PV power plant output (PVOUT) and Global Horizontal Irradiance (GHI) at both 15-minute and 1-minute temporal resolutions. The PVOUT data is calculated using the detailed Solargis PV simulator. The variability is expressed through the occurrence of ramps in the GHI and PVOUT data, and the ramps are categorized based on their severity. The results highlight that 15-minute GHI data may underestimate high-severity variability events observed in the 1-minute data, especially in tropical, temperate, and continental climates. In moderate latitudes we observe seasonal and diurnal patterns in the GHI and PVOUT ramps, suggesting that single-value variability metrics are insufficient for feasibility analysis of PV projects. To better capture the impact of high-severity events and allow for a more nuanced assessment of variability risk, we propose the Root Mean Square Ramp (RMSR) as a new metric. The findings emphasize the importance of high temporal resolution data and advanced PV simulation for accurate variability assessment, particularly for high criticality PV projects, while keeping the computationally and analytically simpler single-value metrics for prefeasibility analysis.
Keywords: Solar resource variability, PV power variability, Sub-hourly variability, Short-term variability

1 INTRODUCTION

Variability of solar resource has been investigated in multiple studies in the past [1], including our recent contribution on global spatial patterns of the short-term variability of GLOBAL horizontal irradiance (GHI), presented at the EU PVSEC 2024 [2]. However, the variability of GHI is only an approximate measure of a PV power plant's output (PVOUT) variability, and the link between them is non-trivial [3]. From a practical point of view, the variability of the on-grid PV generation is highly relevant. It can affect the PV project revenues and drives the requirements for countermeasures at the plant or grid level to ensure the reliability and stability of the distribution system.

In this work, we examine the short-term variability of GHI and PVOUT across different geographies and climate conditions to determine the optimal measures to assess the variability of on-grid PV power plants. We focus on PVOUT ramps, a sudden increase or decrease of PVOUT over defined time and set threshold [4]. Power ramps create challenges for plant and grid operators that are typically addressed with infrastructure improvements, compensation with fossil-fueled power sources, or short-term storage technologies. We utilize PVOUT simulations in Solargis PV simulator with different input data:

1. Satellite-derived time series with 15-minute temporal resolution
2. Synthetic time series with 1-minute temporal resolution

Based on the simulated data, the variability is assessed using the number of ramps over a certain threshold. Furthermore, the statistics based on the simulated PVOUT are compared with the equivalent statistics calculated from satellite-based GHI data with 15-minute and 1-minute time resolution.

The study analyzes the variability calculated from the different source data, and compares the results in order to determine the accuracy and efficiency of the different data and approaches. Ultimately it proposes optimal approaches for assessing the variability of on-grid PV projects in different development stages or projects with different criticality.

2 METHODOLOGY

2.1 Source GHI data

We use Solargis Time Series data of GHI in 15-minute time resolution over the past 5 complete calendar years (2020 - 2024). Although the 15-minute data from a satellite-based solar model may underestimate the variability observed in a real PV power plant [2], this data can be used as an optimistic estimate of the expected variability.

Furthermore we use synthetically generated 1-minute time series data. This data is generated from 10- or 15-minute GHI, DNI, clear-sky GHI (GHIc) and clear-sky DNI (DNIc) satellite data using a Solargis proprietary multi-scale hierarchical approach. This method provides 1-minute data with similar variability to that of 1-minute GHI and DNI observations and, at the same time, is consistent with the satellite-based GHI and DNI inputs. The synthetic generator has been created to reproduce the long-term statistical properties of the 1-minute GHI and DNI data, especially the likelihood of extreme GHI values caused by over-irradiance or cloud enhancement events, typical of highly variable sky conditions.

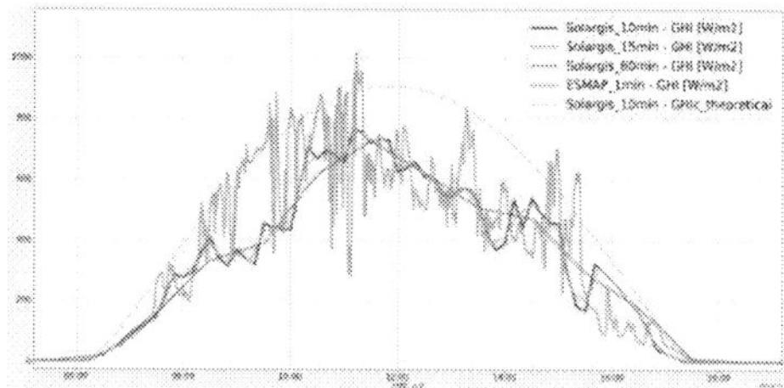

Figure 1: Comparison of GHI time series of different temporal resolutions for a location in Central Highlands, Vietnam; 1-minute derived from ground data measured from ESMAP solar meteorological stations network, station VNCEH [5], [6]. 10-minute, 15-minute and hourly derived from Solargis Time Series

The variability observed in the 1-minute data is significantly higher than that observed in 15-minute data as shown in the example in Figure 1 above. 1-minute data is conceptually analogous to point measurements (e.g.

from a pyranometer), whereas 15-minute satellite-derived data represent spatially averaged solar irradiance over an area of approximately 3×3 km. Although the PVOUT variability of a large PV power plant will be in practice lower than the variability of the 1-minute GHI due to the spatial smoothing effect [7], the 1-minute data can be used as a conservative estimate to establish the upper boundary of the expected variability.

The input data was generated for 8 locations (see Table I) in different geographies. The locations were selected to cover various geographies, climate zones [8], and short-term variability of GHI according to [2].

Table I: Locations used in the study

Site name	Latitude	Longitude	Average annual count of GHI ramps >300 W/m^2	Climate zone
Penang, Malaysia	5.358	100.302	240.4	Af
Wagga, Australia	-35.158	147.457	418.0	Bsk/Cfa
San Sebastian, Spain	43.308	-2.039	153.0	Cfb
Boulder, USA	40.125	-105.237	344.4	Bsk
Jaipur, India	26.809	75.862	198.2	Bsh
Helios, South Africa	-30.501	19.561	178.6	BWk
Petrolina, Brazil	-9.068	-40.319	557.8	Bsh
Kishinev, Moldova	47.001	28.816	135.8	Dfb

2.2 PV Simulation

PVOUT time series was calculated from the source GHI data using the Solargis PV simulator (available in the Solargis Evaluate web application). The Solargis PV simulator provides highly accurate PVOUT through the use of real-world model simulation scenes, ray-tracing for irradiance calculation, and standardized PV component models. Irradiance calculation, performed per cell, evaluates both the front and rear side of the PV module using backward ray tracing. The system designer in the Evaluate application enables real-world modeling of the simulation scene and all shading objects (including terrain) quickly and accurately for systems of up to 500 MWp size. These two features allow for accurate calculation of shading conditions at each time step [9]. System losses, in both optical and electrical simulation, are estimated using validated models (such as for soiling, angular reflection, or inverter performance) and best-practice estimates (such as unavailability and auxiliary system losses), to accurately reflect operating conditions [10]. The simulator can ingest input data with up to 1-minute time resolution, allowing for analysis of high frequency transient events necessary for this study, provided the input data is of sufficient quality.

The same PV power plant was modelled and simulated for each of the 8 locations. Its main features are given in Table II.

Table II: Parameters of the simulated PV power plant

Power plant layout	Rectangular Relative row spacing of 2 (regular) 500,406 m^2 area
DC installed capacity	51.7 MWp
AC installed capacity	42 MWp
DC:AC ratio	1.23
PV modules	Monofacial, half-cut cell, 555 Wp
PV module mounting	Fixed tilt, optimal angle for maximizing in-plane irradiance at the site
Inverters	Centralized, 4.2 MW AC
DC cable losses	2 %
AC cable losses	1 %

2.3 Calculation of ramps

Four types of input data are evaluated in this study:
1. GHI time series with 15-minute time resolution.
2. GHI time series with 1-minute time resolution,
3. PVOUT time series with 15-minute time resolution
4. PVOUT time series with 1-minute time resolution.

Ramps are calculated from all time series as the difference between the consecutive time slots of the dataset. The calculated ramps are then categorized by their severity.

The PVOUT ramp thresholds are set based on the impact on the grid. Globally, a very common grid limit for the PVOUT is ±10% of the installed capacity per minute [11]. This value is taken as the basic threshold for a PVOUT ramp to be studied. Furthermore, as we observed significantly larger ramps in the datasets which may pose significantly larger operational issues, we distinguish Low, Medium, High category PVOUT ramps with linearly scaled thresholds. The thresholds for GHI ramp classifications are set equivalently, considering the Standard Test Conditions (STC) irradiance value of 1,000 W/m^2 instead of the installed capacity of the power plant. To enable comparison, the same thresholds are used for investigation of 15-minute and 1-minute datasets. All thresholds are summarized in Table III below.

Table III: Categorization of ramps used in the study

Ramp category	Description	GHI threshold [W/m^2]	PVOUT threshold [kW]
No ramp	Normal variability, slight changes in irradiance	< 100	0 - 4,200 (< 10% installed capacity)
Low	Typical of moving cumulus clouds	100 - 200	4,200 - 8,400 (10 - 20% installed capacity)
Medium	Rapid transitions between cloud cover and clear sky	200 - 300	8,400 - 12,600 (20 - 30% installed capacity)
High	Sharp irradiance drop/spike	> 300	> 12,600 (> 30% installed capacity)

The division of ramps in GHI and PVOUT dataset by the thresholds is illustrated in Figure 2 below.

Furthermore, to compare ramps between the 15-minute and 1-minute datasets, the occurrence of ramps is calculated as the proportion of time slots with ramps relative to the total number of time slots. This normalization is necessary because the 1-minute datasets contain 15 times more time slots, and hence 15 times more opportunities for ramps. By scaling the number of ramps in this way, it becomes possible to compare ramp rates between different time resolutions.

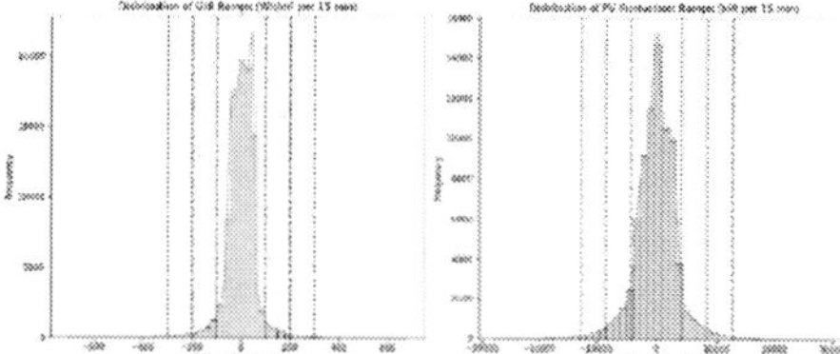

Figure 2: Distribution of GHI (left) and PVOUT (right) ramps in the 15-minute datasets from Boulder site, and their division by the thresholds (vertical dashed lines)

3   RESULTS

The variability of the GHI data with 15-minute time resolution has been analyzed in the previous work [2] and is available in the Solargis Prospect web application. This is therefore taken as the default data, and compared with the variability calculated from the other analyzed datasets, in order to compare the different indicators and advise which are best suited for different design objectives.

The analysis presented below is therefore structured in two steps: 1) comparison of variability between 15-minute and 1-minute data, and 2) comparison of variability between PVOUT and GHI data.

3.1 Variability in 15-minute and 1-minute data

The differences in the occurrence of categorized ramps in the 15-minute and 1-minute datasets for all sites are shown in Figure 3. The occurrence of low ramps is higher in all 15-minute datasets, as changes of at least 100 W/m^2 are not uncommon within 15 minutes (but rare within 1 minute).

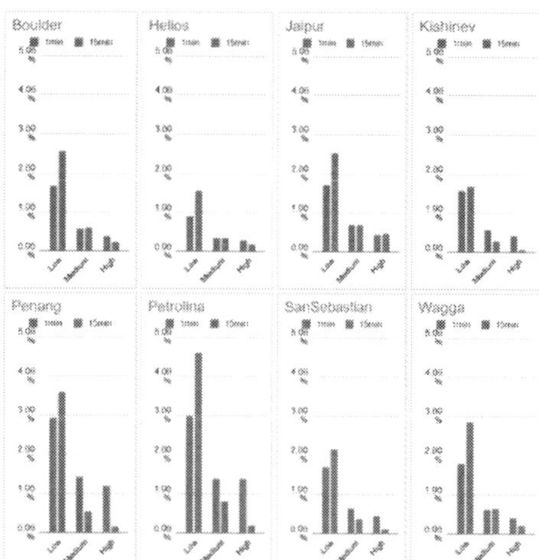

Figure 3: Comparison of occurrence of categorized ramps between 15-minute and 1-minute GHI data for all eight studied sites

The occurrence of medium and high ramps is higher in the 1-minute data, as expected. Specifically, the sites close to the Equator (Penang, Petrolina) but also sites in the temperate/continental climate (Kishinev, San Sebastian)

see significantly higher occurrence of these ramps. This indicates variability assessed based on 1-minute data includes proportionally more severe events than the 15-minute data. Note that the Petrolina site, while strictly in dry climate, appears to be strongly affected by the surrounding tropical climate regions.

As the two datasets set the boundaries of the real expected variability at the PV power plant output, the 15-minute data appears to underestimate the more significant variability events in almost all geographies. In arid regions further from Equator (Boulder, Helios, Jaipur, Wagga), occurrence of medium and high ramps in the two datasets is more similar, suggesting a better representation of the real variability by the 15-minute data. These observations can be explained by the nature of the different climates - in arid regions the cloud cover typically does not change as quickly as in temperate or tropical climates.

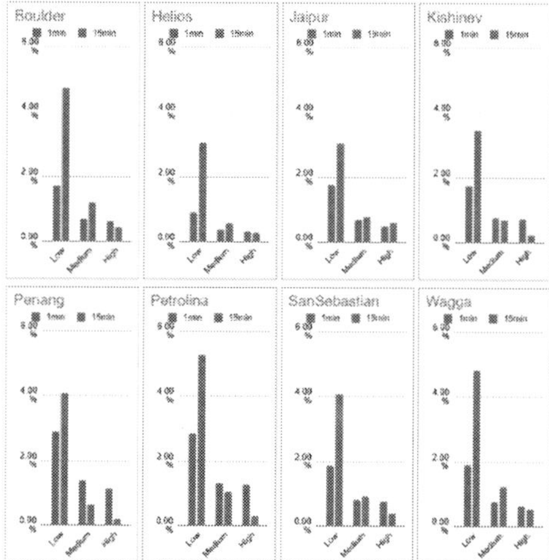

Figure 4: Comparison of occurrence of categorized ramps between 15-minute and 1-minute PVOUT data for all eight studied sites

Considering the same comparison with the PVOUT data shown in Figure 4 above, we observe similar patterns as in the GHI data. However, the occurrence of ramps is higher in the 15-minute dataset. This is most likely due to the effect of PV module temperature, which during GHI ramp events does not vary as quickly as GHI [12], and hence acts as a dampener on the PVOUT signal, and clipping which reduces the size of the PVOUT ramps compared to GHI ramps (see further analysis below). This effect is again more pronounced in the arid regions.

3.2 Variability in GHI and PVOUT data

In the second part we compare the GHI and PVOUT ramps to determine suitability of GHI ramps as an indicator of PVOUT ramps, and investigate diurnal and seasonal patterns. For this analysis we use scatter plots - samples from Boulder and Penang sites are shown in Figure 5 below.

From the plots a clear difference between equatorial (Penang) and mid-latitude sites is obvious, driven by the seasonal patterns of solar radiation. To investigate this pattern further, we plot monthly scatter plots for the Boulder site, shown in Figure 6. These show a higher range of GHI ramp values during the summer half of the year (approx. April to September) than in the winter half of the year (approx. October to March), caused by higher values of GHI during the summer half. The PVOUT ramp values change in the same manner, but with a smaller change which can be attributed to the effect of temperature (higher temperatures lead to lower PVOUT due to temperature derating of PV modules and inverters). In the result, the best fit line of the monthly scatter plots changes slope seasonally, with higher slope (larger PVOUT ramps relative to GHI ramps) in the winter half of the year. In the yearly scatter plot this gives rise to the scattered appearance with no clear single relationship between the GHI and PVOUT ramps in the mid-latitude sites. The same pattern as in Boulder is observed for Helios (see Figure 8) and Wagga sites with the expected flip in the winter-summer seasons due to the northern-southern hemisphere difference.

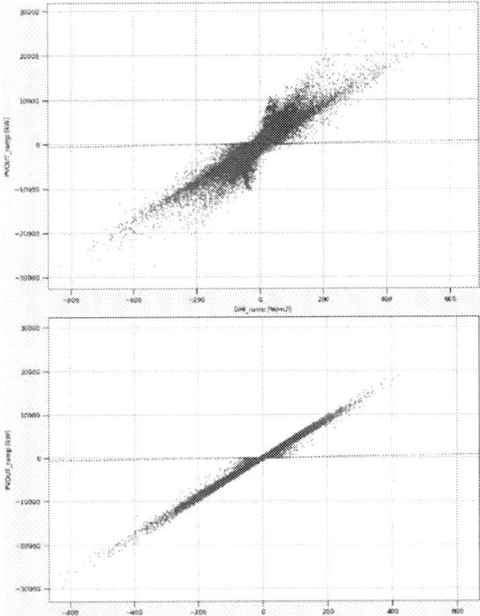

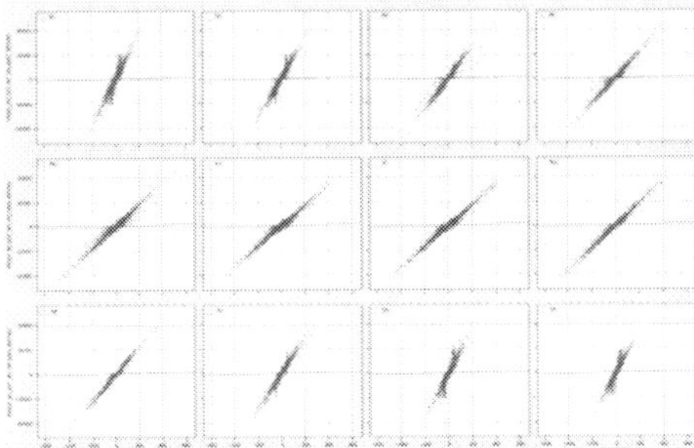

Figure 5: Scatter plots of GHI ramps vs PVOUT ramps (both 15-minute data) for Boulder (top) and Penang (bottom) sites

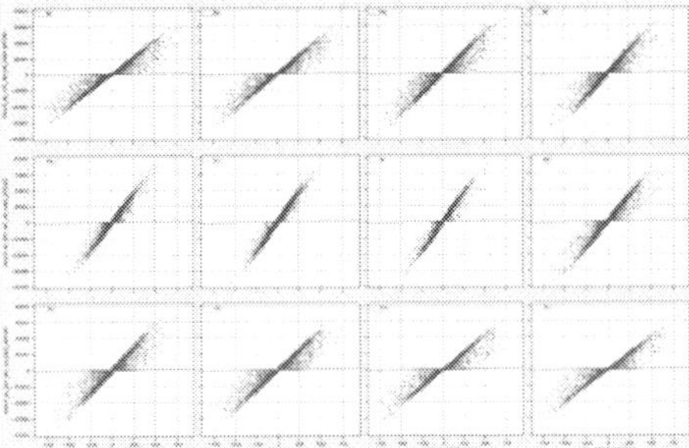

Figure 6: Monthly scatter plots of GHI ramps vs PVOUT ramps (15-minute data) for Boulder site

Furthermore, during the winter half of the year, a pattern can be observed in the morning and evening (defined for simplicity as Sun elevation angle under 20 degrees). In these periods, PVOUT ramps are disproportionately large compared to GHI ramps, as seen in Figure 7 compared with Figure 6. This effect is likely caused by inter-row shading at low sun angles and temperature derating of PV components. It highlights the importance of good plant layout and its detailed analysis in the design stage, as it can affect the variability experienced by the power plant.

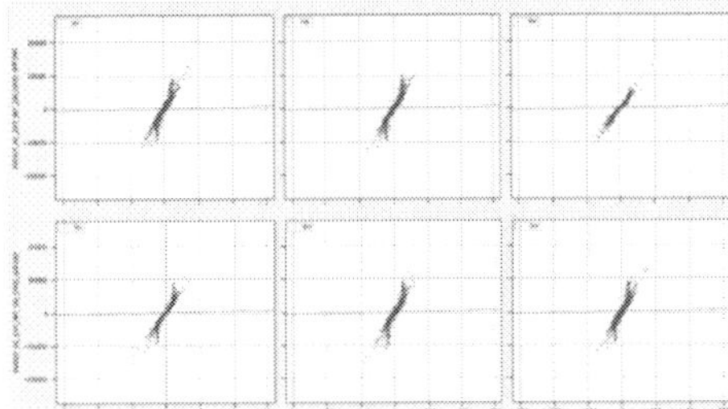

Figure 7: Monthly (top: Jan - Mar, bottom: Oct - Dec) scatter plots of GHI ramps vs PVOUT ramps (15-minute data) for Boulder site for Sun elevation angle smaller than 20 degrees

Analyzing the 1-minute data, Figure 8 illustrates inverter clipping of AC PVOUT visible as point clusters between the best-fit line and horizontal zero. This indicates GHI ramps with disproportionally small PVOUT ramps. The use of 1-minute data for PV simulation allows for a more accurate modeling of the inverter clipping losses, as documented in [13], [14]. Compared to Figure 6, Figure 8 shows that 1-minute data captures a significantly wider range of GHI and PVOUT ramps, both in magnitude (noting the different axis ranges) and combinations. This highlights the importance of high temporal resolution data for analyzing the full spectrum of possible scenarios in the most critical applications. Optimizing the DC:AC ratio in the power plant design will also affect the PVOUT variability experienced by the power plant.

Figure 8: Monthly scatter plots of GHI ramps vs PVOUT ramps (1-minute data) for Helios site

4 DISCUSSION

The results shows that the global variability dataset created in [2], while a useful proxy metric for the expected variability, does not capture the full scope of variability events (ramps) that a PV power plant can experience. Comparison of 15-minute and 1-minute data shows that the 1-minute datasets capture more high-severity variability (events with larger ramps), especially in tropical, temperate, and continental climates where the clouds can be expected to change more rapidly. The difference between the variability observed in the 15-minute and 1-minute PVOUT datasets is smaller than in the case of GHI data, however, the difference in the high-severity events remains.

To address the relative importance of the high-severity events while maintaining a practical approach that is computationally and analytically simple we propose a new metric - the Root Mean Square Ramp (RMSR). This metric is calculated as the root mean square of the calculated ramps, either in PVOUT or GHI data. PVOUT RMSR is normalized (denoted nRMSR) to the installed capacity of the power plant as ramp size scales with installed capacity. This metric emphasizes the high-severity variability, which is not considered in the original metric of count of GHI ramps over a certain threshold (300 W/m² in Solargis Prospect).

The nRMSR calculated from 15-minute and 1-minute PVOUT datasets together with the old metric for comparison are shown in Figure 9 below. The figure highlights important differences in the variability metrics for some sites. While the original metric may overstate the variability risk at the Petrolina site, the simple count of ramps obscures high-severity events at sites like Kishinev and San Sebastian. The nRMSR at these sites shows variability risk comparable to sites like Boulder or Wagga with much higher average GHI (and hence higher risk of large ramps).

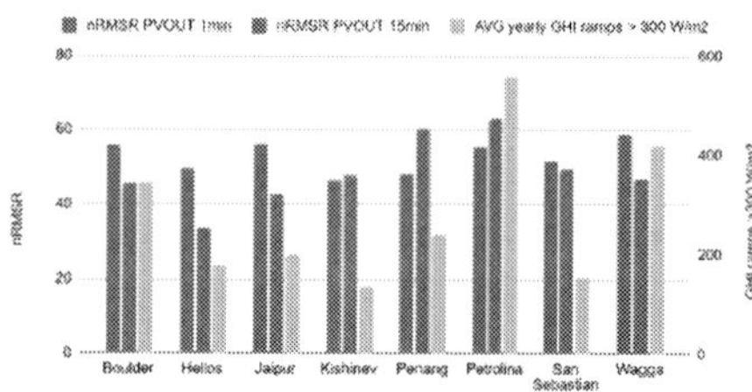

Figure 9: nRMSR (left axis) and count of GHI ramps over 300 W/m² (yellow, right axis) as different metrics of variability

Analyzing the relationship between the ramps in GHI and PVOUT data, seasonal and diurnal patterns emerge for all sites apart from the ones close to the Equator (Penang, Petrolina). This indicates that any metric that takes a single value per site, while useful in the prefeasibility stage, should not be used later in the design process, as it can obscure important nuances in the expected variability. The strong seasonal patterns of variability also suggest that seasonally adjusted response (at the level of a PV power plant, or the whole grid) may be an advantageous approach. Moreover, these results highlight the advantages in using high temporal resolution data in the design of the PV power plant, as design choices such as row spacing and DC:AC ratio will have, among others, effect on the variability of the PVOUT.

5 CONCLUSION

This study analyzed variability in GHI and PVOUT datasets with 15-minute and 1-minute temporal resolution at 8 sites in different climates and geographies. The results indicate that the variability of PV projects in the prefeasibility stage can be assessed using simple variability metrics, optimally ones which consider the severity of the observed ramps. To this end, the study proposes Root Mean Square Ramp (RMSR) as a metric

considering the size of the ramp. However, to assess variability of PV projects in the feasibility stage and especially high criticality projects (e.g. projects with large installed capacity or located in poorly interconnected grids), time series analysis is recommended, although this may not be necessary in all world regions. The analysis can be improved by utilizing high temporal resolution data for conservative variability estimates and, if an advanced PV simulator is available, PVOUT data to reflect the effects of parameters other than GHI on the final PV power plant output variability.

Further work in this scope should focus on analyzing more sites in different geographies and more varied PV power plant layout. Worldwide analysis via geospatial data processing of high temporal resolution data and/or PVOUT data should also be carried out, to analyze regional patterns of variability, and contrast them with the patterns described in [2].

6 REFERENCES

[1] M. Sengupta *et al.*, *Best Practices Handbook for the Collection and Use of Solar Resource Data for Solar Energy Applications: Fourth Edition*, 4th ed. IEA PVPS Task 16, 2024. Accessed: Jan. 28, 2025. [Online]. Available: https://iea-pvps.org/key-topics/best-practices-handbook-for-the-collection-and-use-of-solar-resource-data-for-solar-energy-applications-fourth-edition/

[2] J. Betak, M. Opatovsky, K. Rosina, and M. Suri, "Global Patterns of Solar Resource Short-Term Variability Based on Solargis Time Series Data," in *41st European Photovoltaic Solar Energy Conference and Exhibition*, Vienna, Austria: WIP-Munich, Nov. 2024, pp. 020387-001-020387-005. doi: 10.4229/EUPVSEC2024/4CO.8.5.

[3] K. Lappalainen, G. C. Wang, and J. Kleissl, "Estimation of the largest expected photovoltaic power ramp rates," *Applied Energy*, vol. 278, p. 115636, Nov. 2020, doi: 10.1016/j.apenergy.2020.115636.

[4] J. Zhang, X. Zhu, Y. Xie, G. Chen, and S. Liu, "Detection and Prediction of Wind and Solar Photovoltaic Power Ramp Events Based on Data-Driven Methods: A Critical Review," *Energies*, vol. 18, no. 13, p. 3290, Jan. 2025, doi: 10.3390/en18133290.

[5] World Bank Group, "Vietnam - Solar Radiation Measurement Data - ENERGYDATA.INFO." https://energydata.info/dataset/vietnam-solar-radiation-measurement-data, 2017. Accessed: Sept. 03, 2024. [CSV]. Available: https://energydata.info/dataset/vietnam-solar-radiation-measurement-data

[6] World Bank Group, "Global Solar Atlas." Accessed: Jan. 20, 2024. [Online]. Available: https://globalsolaratlas.info/map?c=12.7535,107.87 61,8&s=12.7535,107.8761&m=solar

[7] J. Remund, C. Calhau, L. Perret, and D. Marcel, "Characterization of the spatio-temporal variations and ramp rates of solar radiation and PV," IEA PVPS Task 14, IEA-PVPS T14-05:2015, Aug. 2015. Accessed: Sept. 15, 2025. [Online]. Available: https://iea-pvps.org/wp-content/uploads/2020/01/Characterization_of_the_s patio-

temporal_variations_and_ramp_rates_of_solar_radi
ation_and_PV.pdf

[8] H. E. Beck, N. E. Zimmermann, T. R. McVicar, N. Vergopolan, A. Berg, and E. F. Wood, "Present and future Köppen-Geiger climate classification maps at 1-km resolution," *Sci Data*, vol. 5, no. 1, p. 180214, Oct. 2018, doi: 10.1038/sdata.2018.214.

[9] L. Dvonc, P. Orosi, T. Cebecauer, and B. Schnierer, "Implementation of Ray Tracing Rendering Technique for Improved Solar Radiation Modeling of Bifacial PV Modules," WCPEC-8, 2022. Accessed: Sept. 08, 2023. [Online]. Available: https://userarea.eupvsec.org/proceedings/WCPEC-8/4BV.4.28/

[10] L. Helienek *et al.*, "Uncertainties in PV Power Simulation Chain," in *2023 IEEE 50th Photovoltaic Specialists Conference (PVSC)*, IEEE, June 2023, pp. 1–6. doi: 10.1109/PVSC48320.2023.10359583.

[11] J. Schaible *et al.*, "Application of nowcasting to reduce the impact of irradiance ramps on PV power plants," *EPJ Photovolt.*, vol. 15, p. 15, 2024, doi: 10.1051/epjpv/2024009.

[12] J. Barry *et al.*, "Dynamic model of photovoltaic module temperature as a function of atmospheric conditions," in *Advances in Science and Research*, Copernicus GmbH, July 2020, pp. 165–173. doi: 10.5194/asr-17-165-2020.

[13] J. Rusnak, B. Schnierer, M. Suri, M. Opatovsky, and G. Srinivasan, "Impact of Time Resolution of Solar and Meteorological Data on Clipping Losses and Energy Yield Simulation," in *Proceedings of the 40th European Photovoltaic Solar Energy Conference and Exhibition in Lisbon, Portugal*, Lisbon, Portugal, Sept. 2023, pp. 020493-001-020493–010. doi: 10.4229/EUPVSEC2023/5CO.6.2.

[14] J. Rusnak, B. Schnierer, and M. Suri, "The importance of sub-hourly input data in PV systems simulation using satellite-based solar model data," presented at the 2024 European PVPMC Workshop, Copenhagen, Denmark, Aug. 21, 2024. Accessed: Nov. 15, 2024. [Online]. Available: https://www.sandia.gov/app/uploads/sites/243/dlm_uploads/2024/09/Rusnak_2.pdf

SOLARGIS

Short-Term Variability of PV Power Output Based on Simulations with Solargis Time Series Data

Martin Opatovsky, **Marta Pelfort Ojer**, Juraj Betak, Konstantin Rosina

Solargis, Slovakia

© 2025 Solargis

020242-001

Context – our work at EUPVSEC 2024

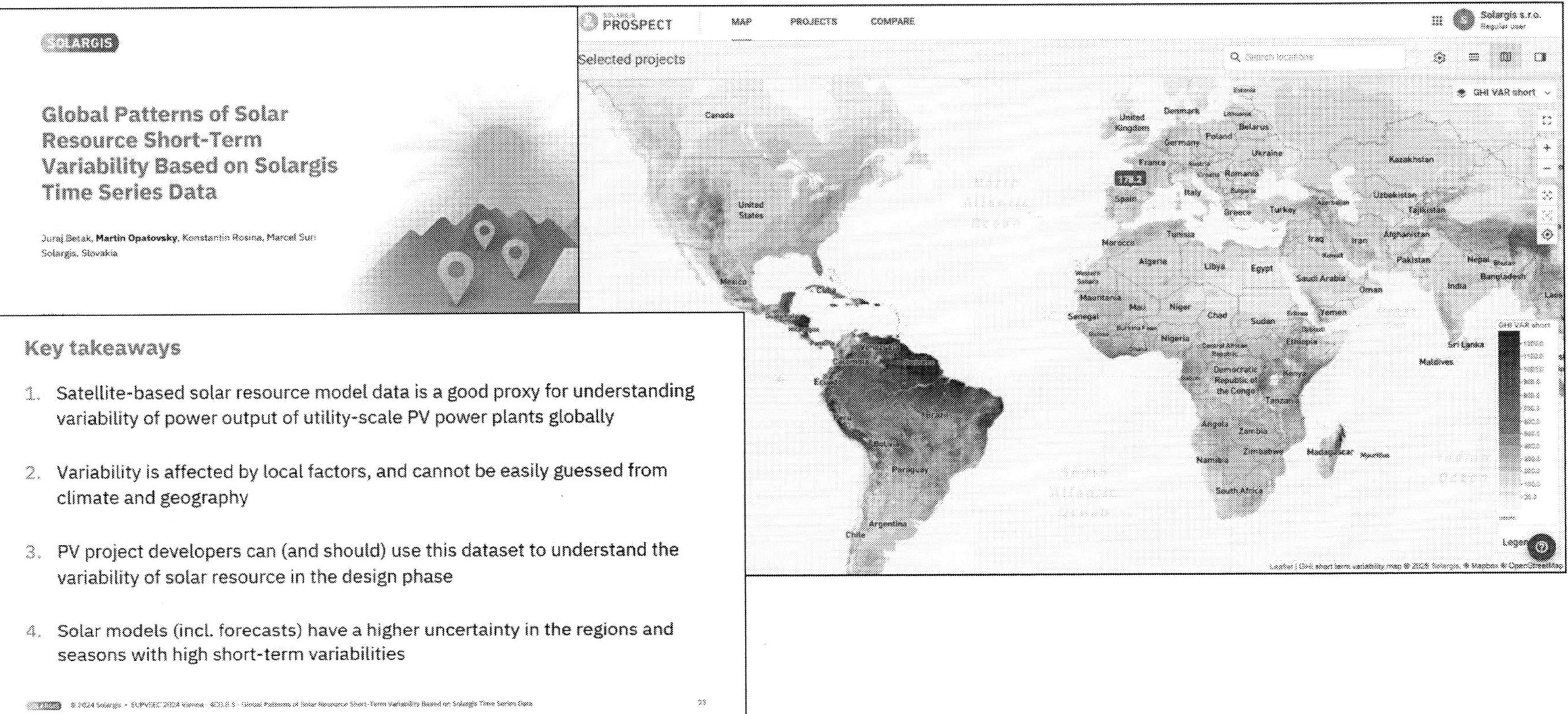

The challenge

Power Ramps

Sudden increases or decreases in PV output create operational challenges for plant and grid operators.

Grid Stability

Variability affects project revenues and requires countermeasures to ensure distribution system reliability.

Storage Needs

Power ramps typically require short-term storage technologies to maintain grid stability.

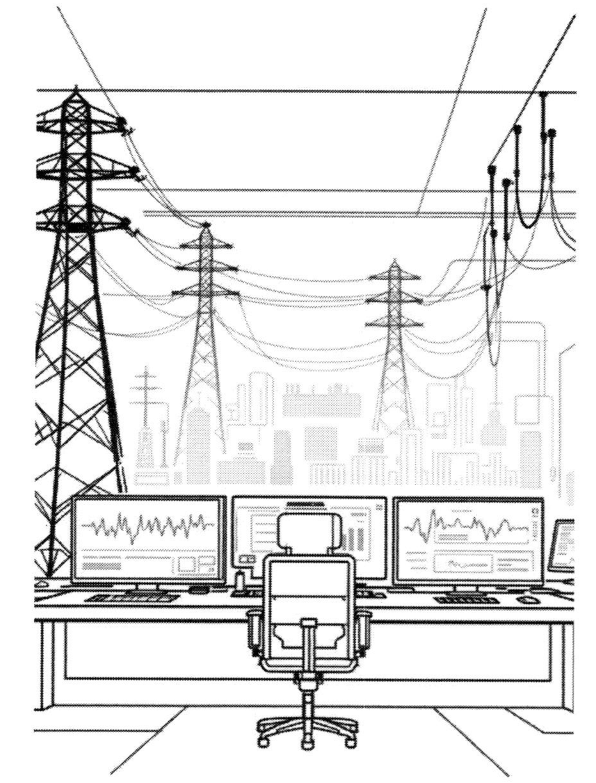

Practical applications

Project development

Use variability metrics during site assessment and system design to optimize plant configuration and storage requirements.

Grid integration

Inform grid operators about expected ramp rates to ensure adequate response capabilities and system stability.

Storage sizing

Determine optimal battery capacity and response times based on location-specific variability patterns.

Methodology

Data preparation
- 8 global locations in different climates and different variability based on our previous work
- Satellite-derived 15-minute and synthetic 1-minute GHI time series data

PV Simulation
- PVOUT calculation using Solargis PV simulator (Solargis Evaluate) with ray-tracing and real-world modelling

Ramp analysis
- Calculate ramps as differences between consecutive time slots in time series data
- Classify ramps according to severity based on set thresholds

Metrics proposal
- Proposes optimal approaches for assessing the variability of on-grid PV projects in different development stages or projects with different criticality.

020242-005

Studied locations

Location	Climate	Avg. annual count of GHI ramps > 300 W/m^2
Penang, Malaysia	Tropical	240.4
Wagga, Australia	Semi-arid	418.0
San Sebastian, Spain	Oceanic	153.0
Boulder, USA	Semi-arid	344.4
Jaipur, India	Hot semi-arid	198.2
Helios, South Africa	Desert	178.6
Petrolina, Brazil	Hot semi-arid (surrounded by tropical)	557.8
Kishinev, Moldova	Continental	135.8

Eight locations selected to cover diverse geographies, climate zones, and GHI variability patterns.

Simulated PV power plant

51.7 MWp

DC installed capacity

42 MWp

AC installed capacity

1.23

DC:AC ratio

Fixed tilt

Optimum angle for maximization of in-plane irradiance

500,000 m²

Plant area

Monofacial modules

Central inverters

PV power plant modelled in Solargis Evaluate, simulated with Solargis Evaluate PV simulator

020242-007

Ramp classification system

- Single ramp classification **applied to both GHI and PVOUT ramps**
- To enable **comparison of 1-minute and 15-minute data** ramp occurrence calculated as **proportion** of **time slots with ramps** relative to the **total number of time slots**

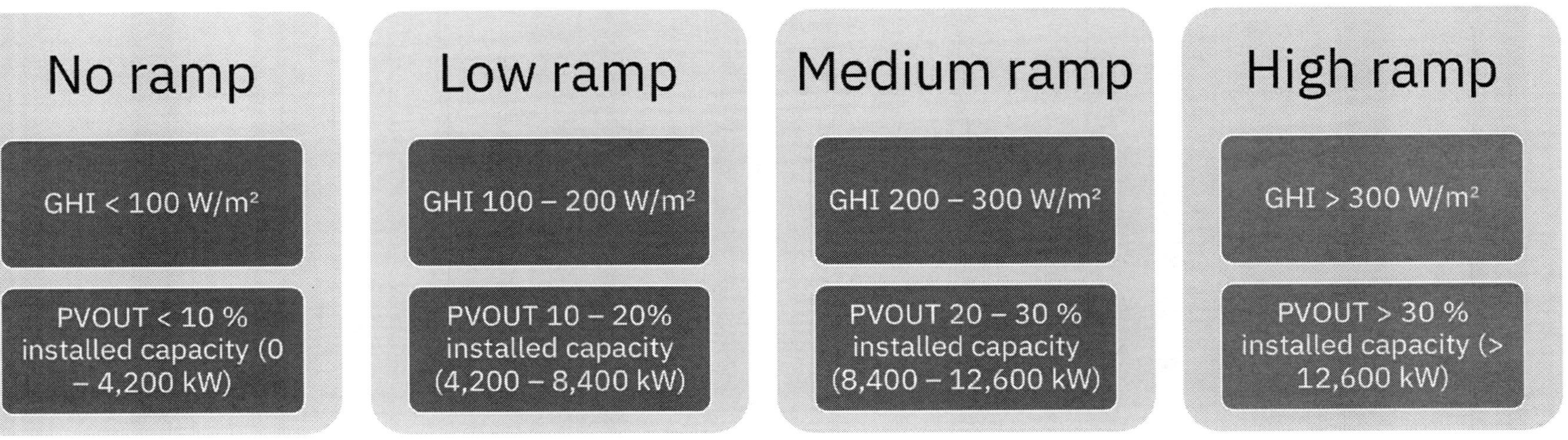

Ramp analysis

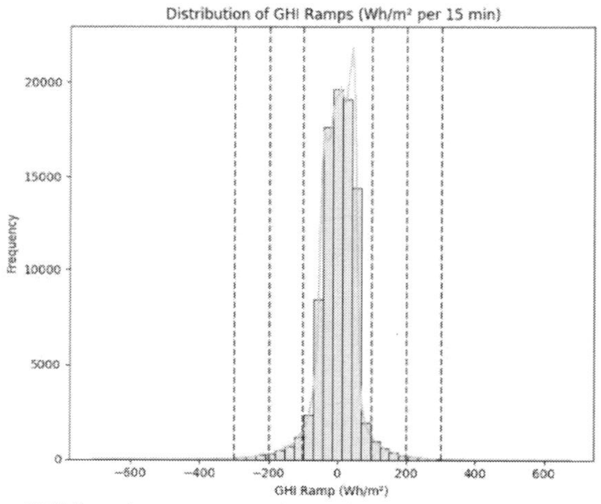

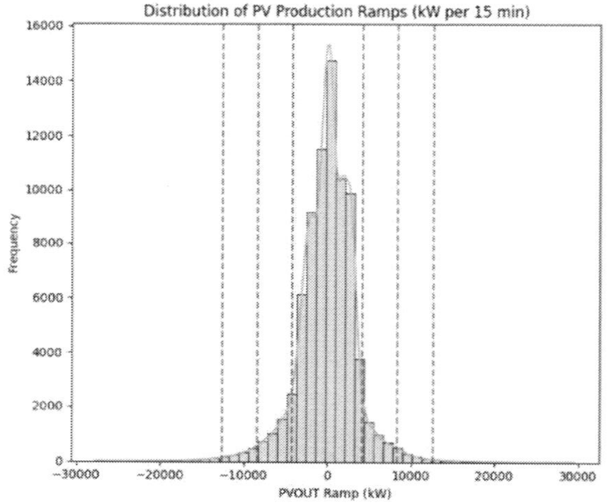

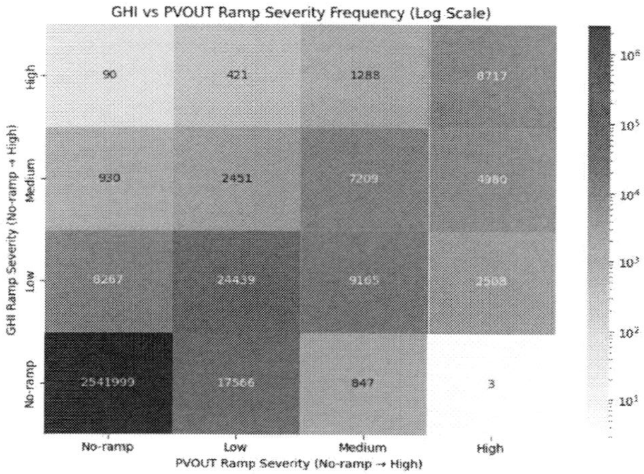

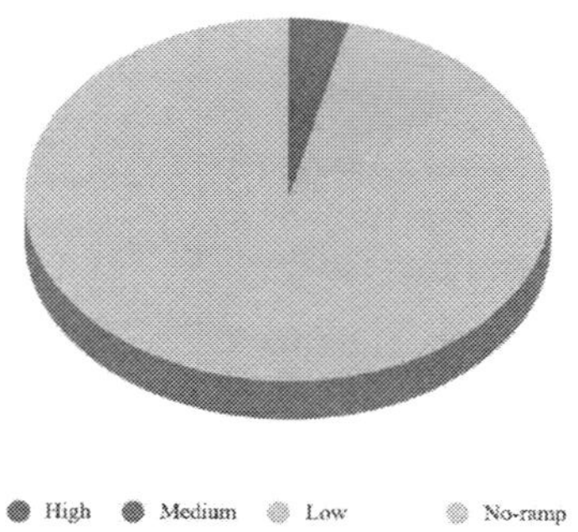

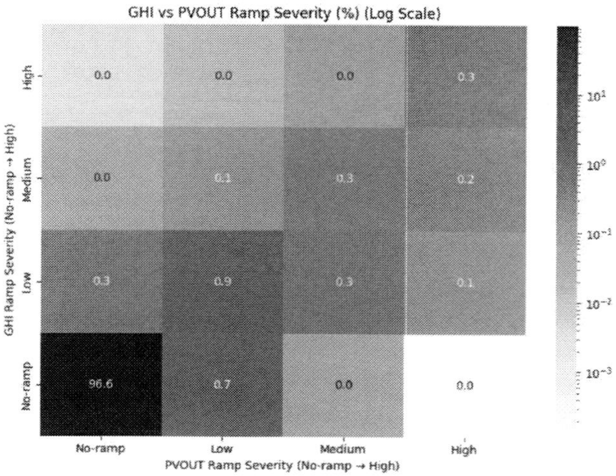

SOLARGIS © 2025 Solargis • EUPVSEC 2025 Bilbao - 4AO.9 - Short-Term Variability of PV Power Output Based on Simulations with Sola

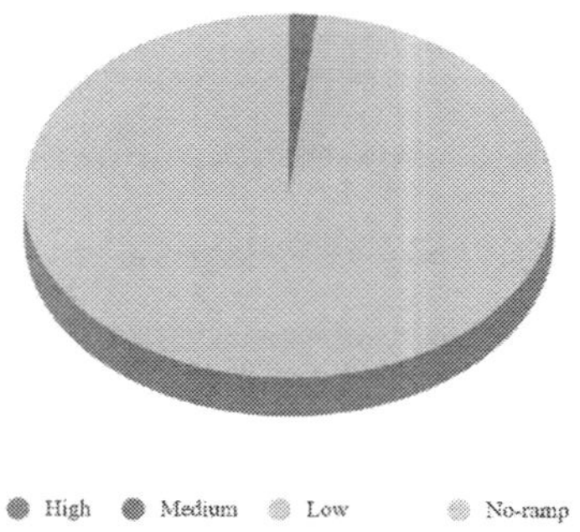

Ramp analysis

Occurrence of ramps in GHI data

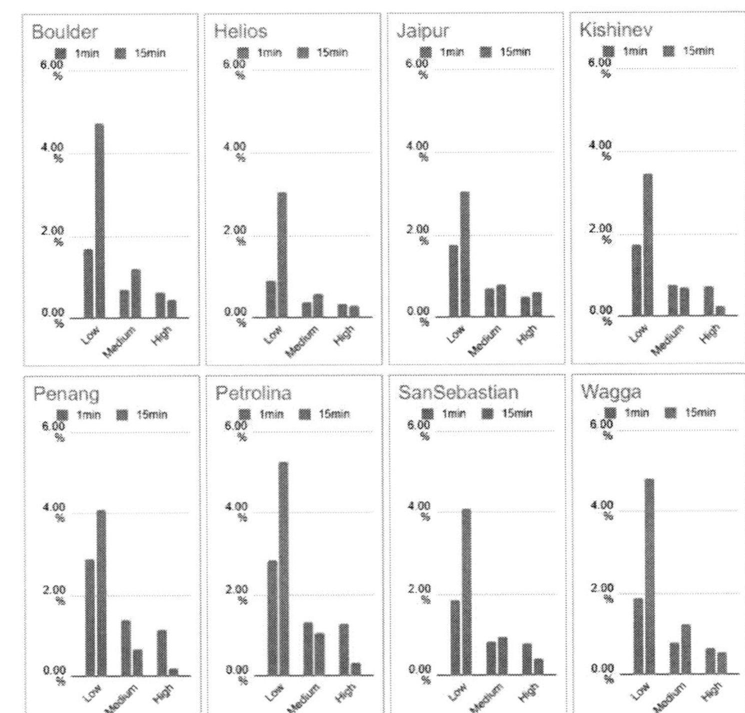

Occurrence of ramps in PVOUT data

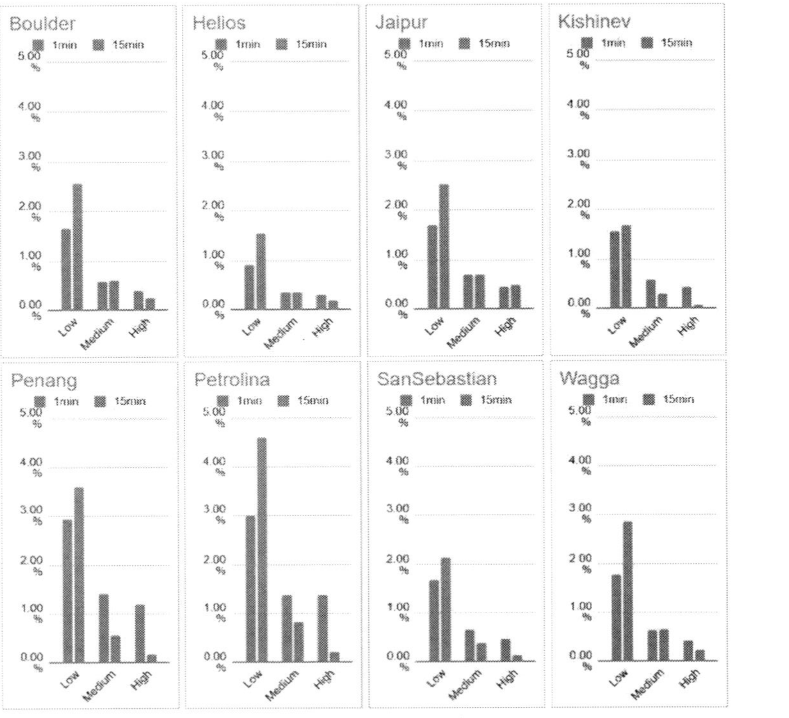

15min vs 1 min PVOUT

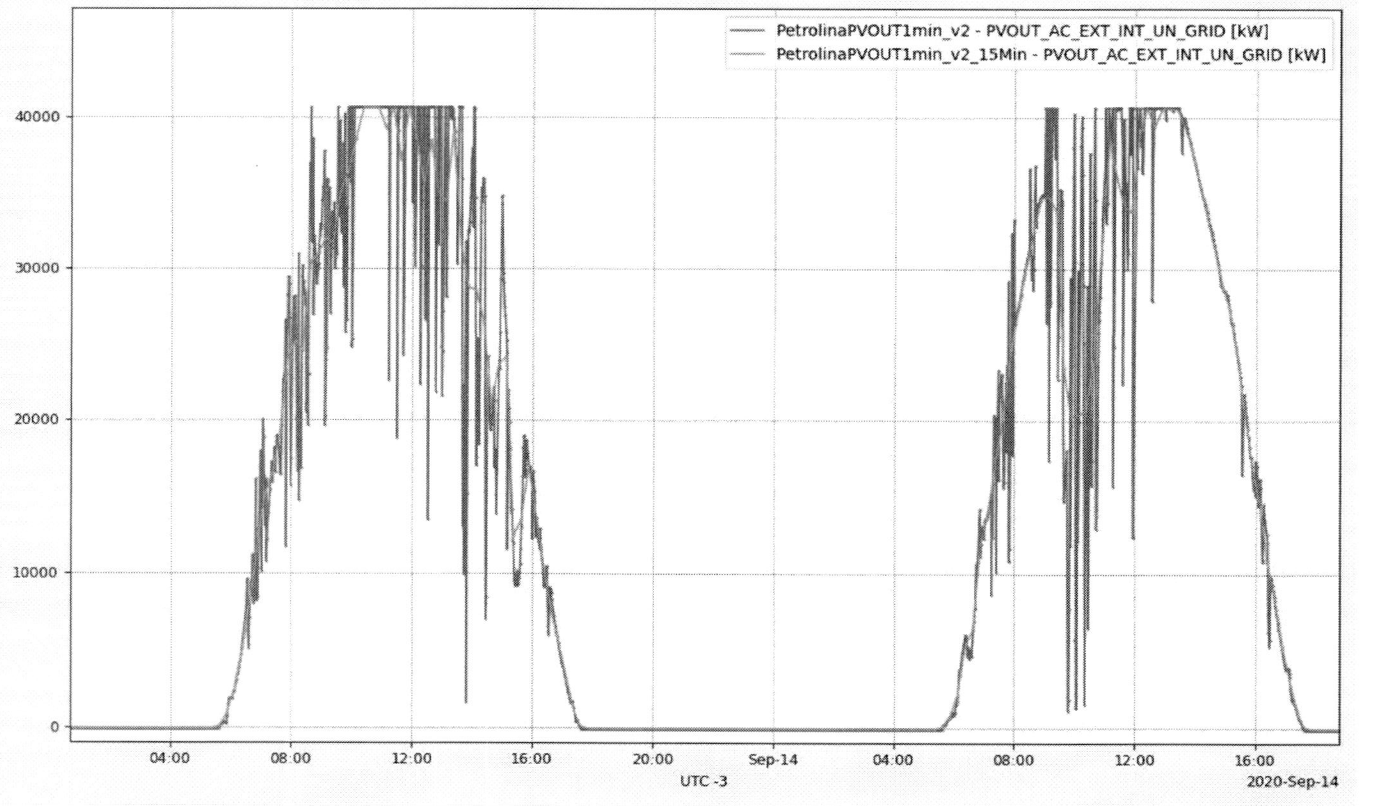

SOLARGIS © 2025 Solargis • EUPVSEC 2025 Bilbao - 4AO.9 - Short-Term Variability of PV Power Output Based on Simulations with Solargis Time Series Data

Ramp analysis

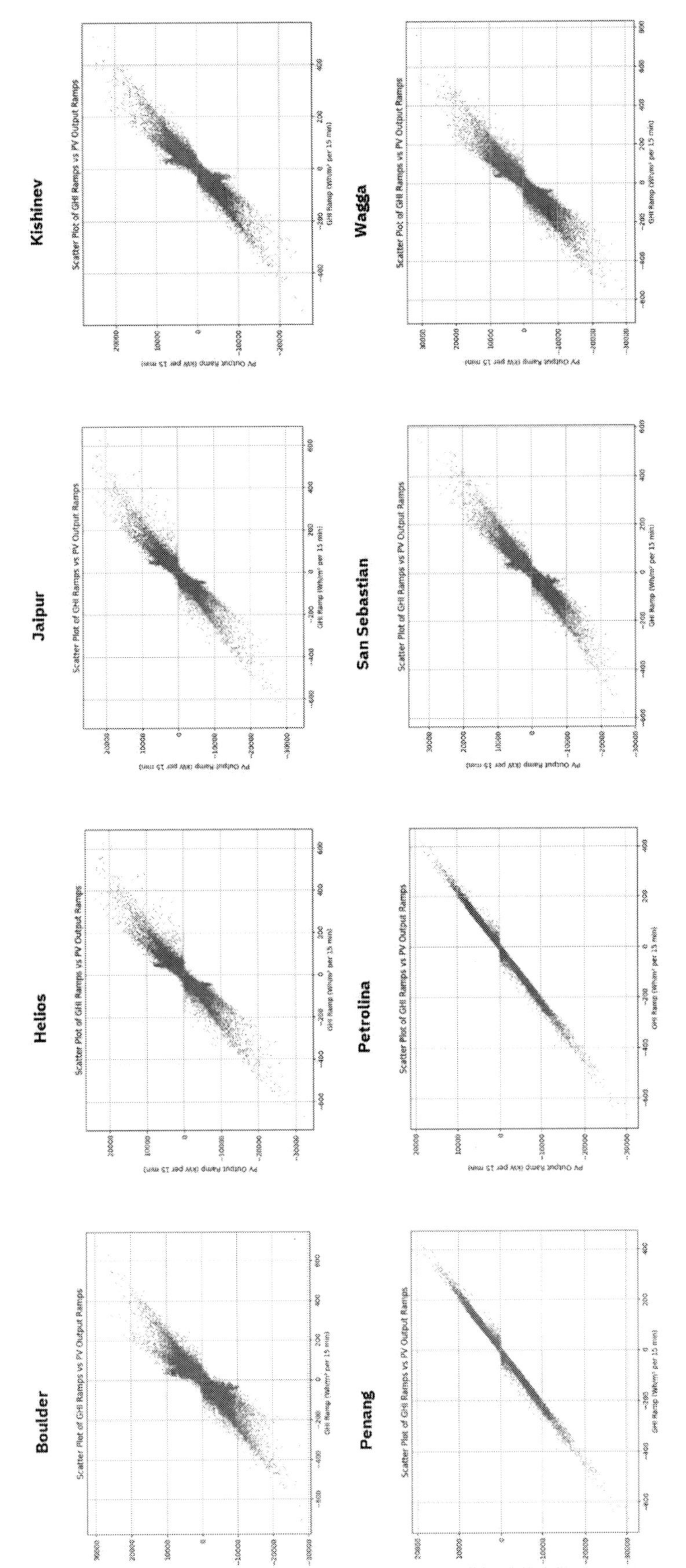

020242-012

SOLARGIS © 2025 Solargis • EUPVSEC 2025 Bilbao - 4AO.9 - Short-Term Variability of PV Power Output Based on Simulations with Solargis Time Series Data

GHI and PVOUT ramp relationship

Seasonal variations

- Higher GHI ramps in summer result in lower slope relationships between GHI and PVOUT variability.

Temperature and shading

- Morning and evening hours show proportionally larger PVOUT ramps due to lower temperatures and inter-row shading

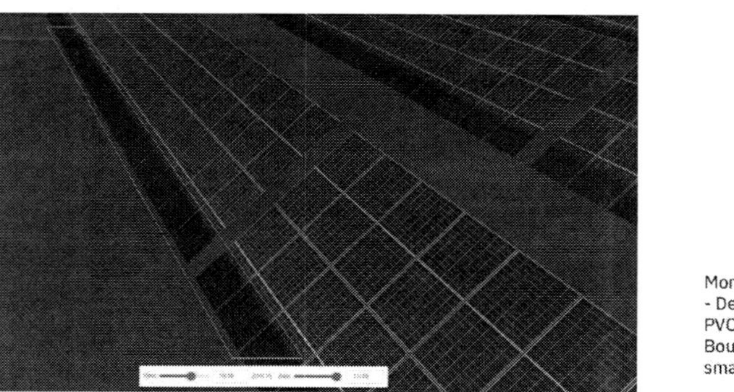

Monthly scatter plots of GHI ramps vs PVOUT ramps (15-minute data) for Boulder site

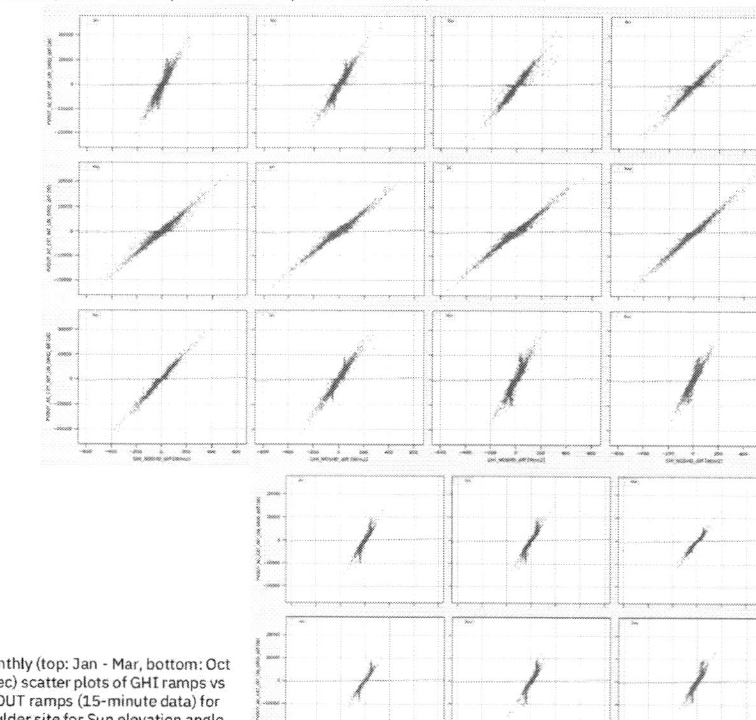

Monthly (top: Jan - Mar, bottom: Oct - Dec) scatter plots of GHI ramps vs PVOUT ramps (15-minute data) for Boulder site for Sun elevation angle smaller than 20 degrees

15-minute and 1-minute data – clipping effects

1-minute fidelity

- High-resolution simulation accurately captures clipping losses during peak irradiance periods.

Grid impact

- Clipping results in proportionally smaller PVOUT ramps compared to GHI ramps

Design implications

- DC:AC ratio optimization affects variability of power plant output

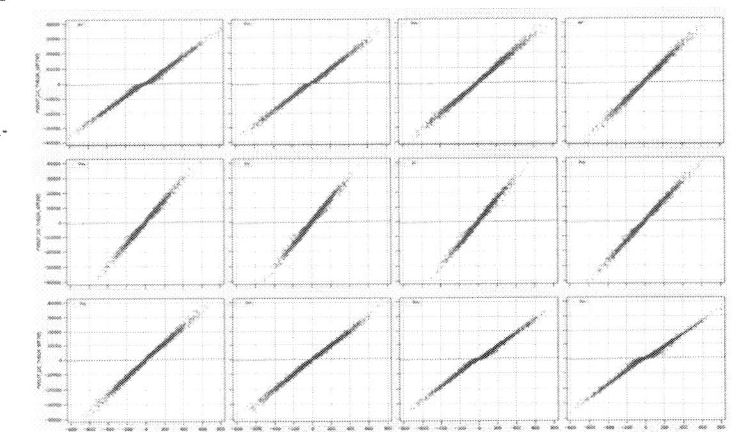

Monthly scatter plots of GHI ramps vs **AC PVOUT ramps** (1-minute data) for Helios site

Monthly scatter plots of GHI ramps vs **DC PVOUT ramps** (1-minute data) for Helios site

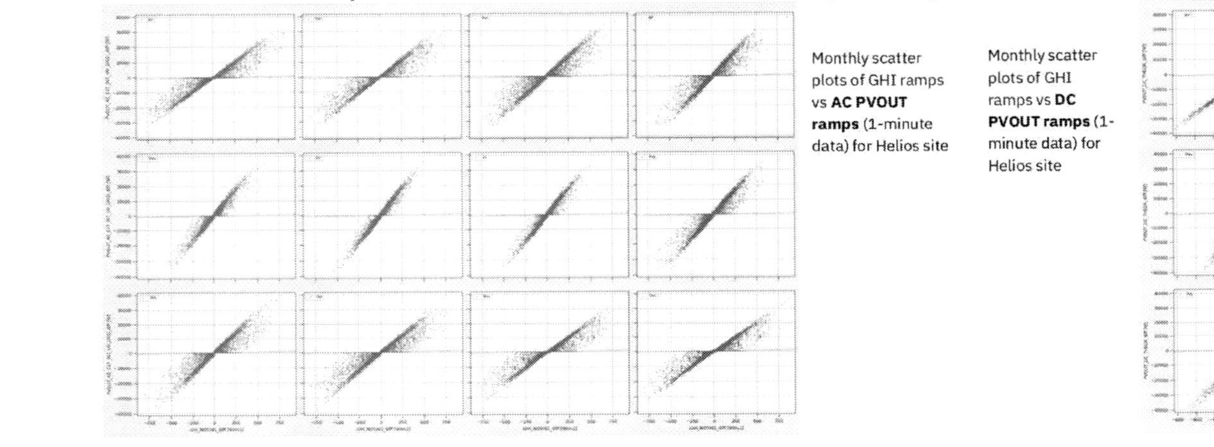

020242-014

Ramp analysis - RMSR

- To account for ramp severity, we propose a **new metric - Root Mean Square Ramp (RMSR)**

- RMSR quantifies site-specific variability by **weighting larger power ramps** more heavily and **normalizing** by **plant capacity (nRMSR)**, enabling direct comparison of grid-integration challenges across sites

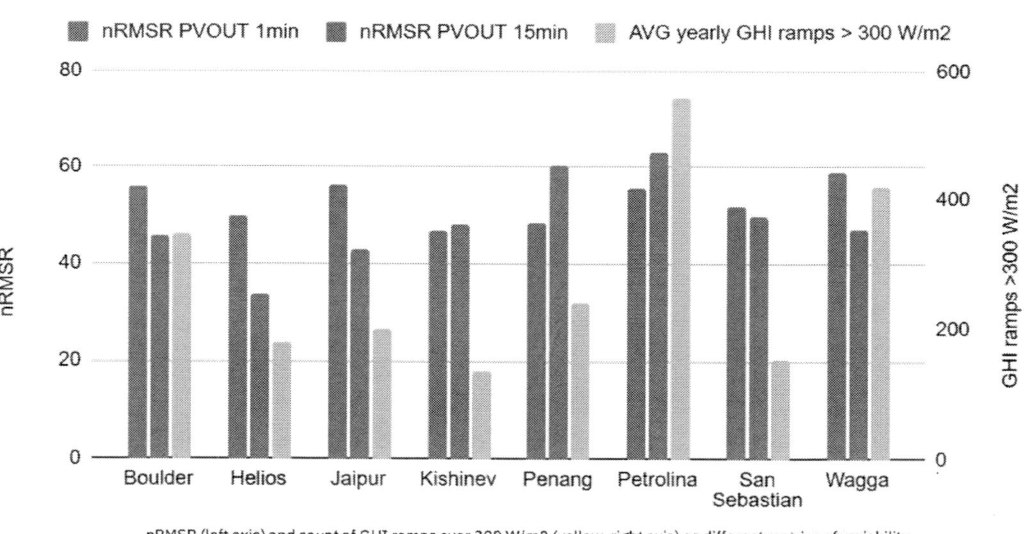

nRMSR (left axis) and count of GHI ramps over 300 W/m2 (yellow, right axis) as different metrics of variability

020242-015

15-minute vs 1-minute variability

Higher resolution = more severe events

- 1-minute data captures proportionally more medium and high category ramps than 15-minute data.

Geographic patterns

- Equatorial and temperate sites show higher 1-minute variability. Arid regions see slower changes.

Realistic boundaries

- 15-minute data provides slight underestimation, 1-minute data provides conservative upper boundary.

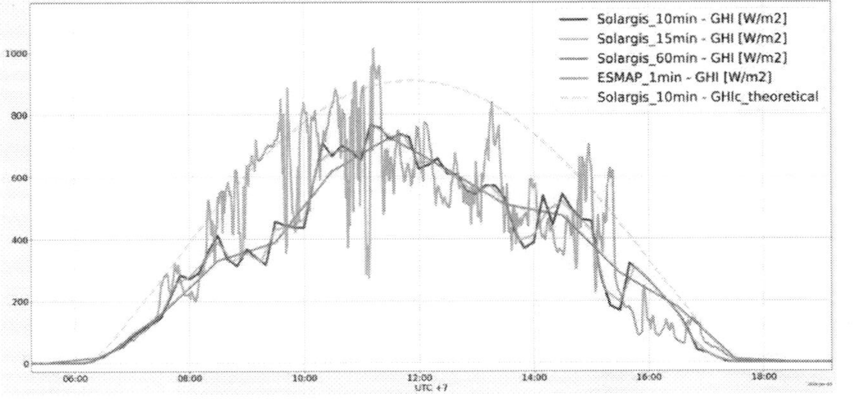

020242-016

Conclusions

- For **pre-feasibility** studies, **simple metrics** can be sufficient, but they should account for the **ramp size**, not only the count. **RMSR** is a good candidate

- For **feasibility** and high criticality projects, **Time Series** analysis is necessary, ideally with **1min resolution** data and **PV simulator** that captures the behavior of the plant.

- **Seasonal and diurnal variability** suggests that flexibility at the plant and grid level should be considered in **system design.**

Thank you

Marta Pelfort Ojer

Head of Customer Support, Solargis, Slovakia

solargis.com

© 2025 Solargis

ACCELERATING PHOTOVOLTAIC SYSTEM SIMULATIONS
VIA STATISTICAL DATA AGGREGATION

Adrián Blanco Aguiar [1], Brais González Rodríguez [2, 3], María Martínez Barbeito [1],
Miguel Sánchez de León Peque [1]
[1] ieco.io
Tomás A. Alonso, 189, 36208 Vigo, Pontevedra, Spain
[2] Department of Statistics and Operations Research and SiDOR Research Group, University of Vigo
[3] Research collaborator at CITMAga
Corresponding author: Miguel Sánchez de León Peque, +34 639 835 484, peque@ieco.io

ABSTRACT: Accurate energy yield assessments (EYAs) for photovoltaic (PV) systems are critical for their financial viability, yet simulating the non-linear effects of partial shading over a full year remains computationally prohibitive. High-fidelity models, essential for capturing these mismatch losses, create a significant bottleneck in the rapid design and optimization of PV projects. This ieco.io work introduces a novel data-centric framework to accelerate annual PV simulations by applying statistical aggregation, reducing the input dataset of operating conditions while preserving the high-resolution information necessary for accurate shading analysis. We propose and evaluate two methods based on k-means clustering, with results clearly demonstrating the superiority of one approach. A key advantage of this method is its tunability, enabling substantial reductions in simulation time while introducing only minimal, controllable error, thereby outperforming standard module-level simulations in both speed and accuracy. Importantly, when quantifying annual shading-induced power losses, the method drastically reduces computational overhead with negligible impact on accuracy, contrasting sharply with the significant underestimation of losses inherent to the module-level approach. This framework offers engineers a powerful and flexible tool for fast, reliable energy yield assessments without compromising simulation fidelity.
Keywords: data aggregation, photovoltaic systems, partial shading, clustering, simulation acceleration

1 INTRODUCTION

The widespread adoption of photovoltaic (PV) technology is crucial for the global transition to sustainable energy. Accurate energy yield assessments (EYAs) are fundamental to this adoption, underpinning both the financial viability and the design of PV projects [1]. However, real-world conditions (particularly partial shading from obstructions such as buildings or clouds) can cause significant performance degradation due to non-linear electrical mismatch losses [2]. While high-fidelity simulations at the cell or submodule level can accurately capture these effects, they are computationally intensive, creating a substantial bottleneck for the annual performance analyses required for reliable EYAs. An annual simulation involves processing thousands of time steps, and the computational cost of detailed models renders tasks such as rapid design iteration and large-scale optimization impractical.

To address this challenge, ieco.io researchers have explored various acceleration strategies. One common approach is to reduce the input data by using clustering algorithms, such as k-means [3], to generate a set of "representative days" from a full year's weather data [4, 5]. Other methods focus on simplifying the physical model itself, employing techniques like Model Order Reduction (MOR) [6] or replacing it entirely with machine learning (ML) surrogate models [7]. While effective, existing "representative day" methods often aggregate 24-hour data profiles before clustering, a process that smooths out the instantaneous variations in sun position and irradiance. This loss of temporal resolution is critical, as the effects of partial shading are highly sensitive to the moment-to-moment geometry of the sun, array, and shading objects.

This ieco.io work introduces a novel framework that accelerates simulations by applying statistical aggregation directly to the instantaneous operating conditions, thereby preserving the high-resolution data necessary for accurate shading analysis. We present and evaluate two distinct methods: StraightForward Aggregation (SFA), which applies k-means [3] clustering directly to the multi-dimensional space of sun irradiance, elevation, and azimuth; and Hierarchical Hourly Aggregation (HHA), which first segregates data by hour of the day before clustering. A key contribution of this work is the tunability of the SFA method, allowing users to explicitly define the desired data reduction percentage and predictably control the trade-off between simulation speed and accuracy. This study demonstrates that this data-centric approach provides a more robust and predictable performance improvement across various scenarios compared to simply using a less detailed physical model.

The work is structured as follows: Section 2 describes the PV system scenarios used for testing. Section 3 establishes the baseline simulation framework and justifies the use of a submodule-level model as the benchmark for both accuracy and computational cost. Section 4 details the proposed SFA and HHA methods, presenting a rigorous performance analysis of their accuracy and speed, particularly for quantifying annual shading losses. Finally, Section 5 summarizes the key findings and concludes the work.

2 SIMULATION SCENARIOS

To evaluate the performance of the methods introduced in this work, we consider various PV system scenarios, summarized in Table I. These scenarios range in size from small systems, typical of residential installations, to larger commercial-scale systems. The shading objects are chosen to cast partial shading on the modules.

10.4229/EUPVSEC2025/4AO.9.5

Senario ID	Tilt (°)	Azimuth (°)	Obstrucion(s)	Parameters (dist/height [m], x-range)
1 Module (small residential)				
1M_T20_A0_1IW	20	0	1 infinite wall	1.2 / 1.35
1M_T0_A50_1IW	0	50	1 infinite wall	1.2 / 1.35
1M_T30_A-10_1C	30	-10	1 chimney	2 / 2, [3, 4]
1M_T30_A-10_2C	30	-10	2 chimneys	#1: 1.5 / 2, [-5, -4] #2: 2 / 2, [3, 4]
8 Modules (4 series, 2 parallel, medium residential)				
8M_T20_A0_1IW	0	0	1 infinite wall	1.2 / 1.35
8M_T20_A50_1IW	0	50	1 infinite wall	4 / 2
8M_T20_A0_2W	0	0	2 walls	#1: 1.2 / 1.35, [-7, -2] #2: 1.2 / 1.35, [2, 7]
8M_T30_A-10_1C	30	-10	1 chimney	2 / 2, [3, 4]
8M_T30_A-10_2C	30	-10	2 chimneys	#1: 1.5 / 2, [-5, -4] #2: 2 / 2, [3, 4]
16 Modules (4 series, 4 parallel, large residential)				
16M_T30_A-10_1C	30	-10	1 chimney	2 / 2, [3, 4]
16M_T30_A-10_2C	30	-10	2 chimneys	#1: 1.5 / 2, [-5, -4] #2: 2 / 2, [3, 4]
64 Modules (8 series, 8 parallel, commercial)				
64M_T0_A0_1B	0	0	1 box	1 / 2, [3, 6]
64M_T0_A0_1B1C	0	0	Box and chimney	Box: 1 / 2, [3, 6] Chimney: 1 / 2, [-4, -3]

Table I: Simulation scenarios considered.

The simulations are performed using the JA Solar JAM72_S20_440 module [8], which features a twin half-cut cell architecture [9]. The module consists of three submodules connected in series. Each submodule, in turn, is composed of two parallel-connected half-submodules, each containing 24 cells in series. Figure 2.1 provides a schematic of the module architecture used in this work.

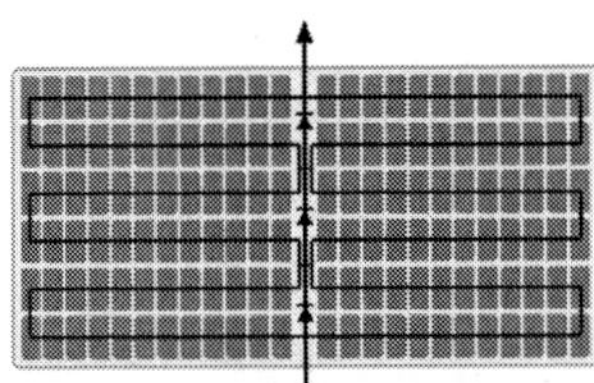

Figure 2.1: Module architecture used in simulations.

Furthermore, inverter effects are disregarded to simplify the analysis, under the assumption that the inverter can operate ideally under all conditions. Hourly meteorological data for Madrid, Spain, obtained from the Photovoltaic Geographical Information System (PVGIS) [10], are used as input for the simulations.

3 SIMULATION METHODS

To assess the power output of a PV system, we employ a custom Python simulation framework [11] developed at ieco.io built upon the pvlib library [12]. This community-developed, open-source toolbox provides the functions and classes necessary to model PV system performance. The simulation first computes the system's current-voltage (I-V) curve, from which the power output is determined by identifying the maximum power point (MPP).

To model the I-V curve of a cell, module, or array, we use the single-diode model as implemented in pvlib. This model describes the I-V curve by representing the PV device with a simple equivalent circuit [13].

Our simulation framework supports multiple methods for computing PV system power output. Since this work focuses on partial shading, a cell-level simulation is the most accurate approach, as it explicitly models the electrical mismatch between individual cells.

However, this method is computationally intensive for large systems. It requires calculating the I-V curve for each cell and then aggregating these curves while accounting for mismatches due to shading and the effects of bypass diodes. The high computational cost motivates the adoption of faster, albeit less precise, methods.

One such alternative is a submodule-level simulation. This approach applies the single-diode model to each submodule as a whole, calculating an aggregate I-V curve that incorporates the effects of shading across that submodule. These submodule curves are then combined, taking bypass diodes into account. This method provides a good approximation of the power output while requiring significantly fewer computational resources. For these reasons, we use the submodule-level simulation as a benchmark method to evaluate the performance of the novel approaches introduced in this paper.

Finally, we consider a module-level method that disregards the mismatch caused by partial shading. In the following section, the performance of all three approaches (cell-, submodule-, and module-level) is evaluated under these partial shading scenarios, and compared with a simpler approach that does not consider shading.

3.1 Simulation methods comparison

The precision of the simulation methods described above depends on their level of granularity. Less detailed methods tend to overestimate the system's power output, as they do not account for the electrical mismatch losses caused by partial shading.

To illustrate this behavior, we present the simulated power output from the different methods for a specific scenario: a single-module system shaded by two chimneys (Scenario 1M_T30_A-10_2C in Table 2.1) on November 3rd.

We show the results in Figure 3.1, which plots the MPP in Watts as a function of the hour of the day (from 06:00 to 19:00). We represent each simulation method by a different color: the ideal, unshaded case (red), the module-level simulation (orange), the submodule-level simulation (blue), and the cell-level simulation (green).

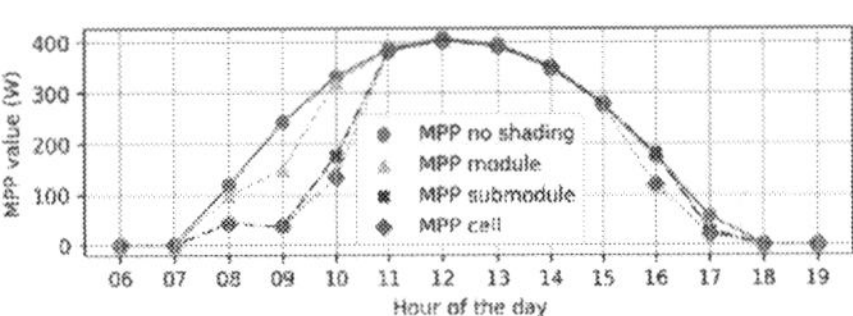

Figure 3.1: MPP output on November 3rd for different simulation methods.

As established above, less detailed simulation methods overestimate the system's power output because they neglect the mismatch losses caused by partial shading. To quantify the accuracy of the different methods presented in this work, we compute the error using

$$RelativeError = \frac{\sum |MPP_{newmethod} - MPP_{referencemethod}|}{\sum MPP_{referencemethod}} \quad (1)$$

The summation in this equation is performed over all

MPP values in the evaluation period. This provides a scale-independent metric for the relative error.

To evaluate the long-term performance, we will also use

$$RelativeDifference = \frac{\sum(MPP_{newmethod} - MPP_{referencemethod})}{\sum MPP_{referencemethod}} = \frac{\sum MPP_{newmethod}}{\sum MPP_{referencemethod}} - 1 \quad ,(2)$$

which calculates the relative difference in annual energy yield between any two methods being compared.

Figure 3.2 displays the distribution of the relative difference in annual energy yield for each simulation method, calculated with (2) using the ideal (unshaded) simulation as the reference. Each boxplot [14] in the figure summarizes the results across all the scenarios described previously.

It is important to note that the relative difference computed with (2) and the relative error computed with (1) generally differ. However, since the less detailed methods consistently overestimate power output, these two values are equal in magnitude but opposite in sign in this context. This motivates using the negative value to explicitly express the overestimation by the less detailed methods.

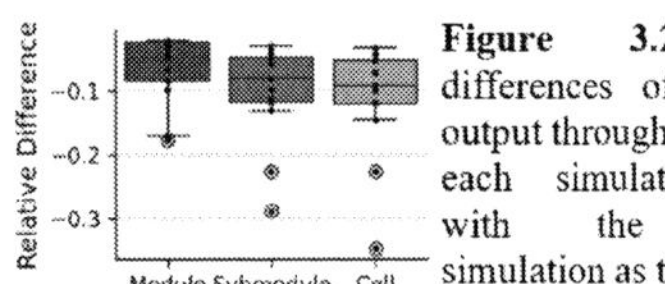

Figure 3.2: Yearly differences of the power output throughout a year for each simulation method with the unshaded simulation as the reference.

The results show a clear trend: as the model detail increases, the estimated annual energy yield decreases. This reduction, which quantifies the estimated power loss from partial shading, reaches up to 30% for the cell-level simulation in scenarios with significant mismatch.

However, this precision comes at a high computational cost. To quantify this trade-off, we compare the execution times of the methods by calculating a relative time metric, analogous to (1), as

$$RelativeTime = \frac{time_{newmethod} - time_{referencemethod}}{time_{referencemethod}}. \quad (3)$$

We present in Figure 3.3 the relative execution times for each simulation method, calculated with (3) using the unshaded simulation as the reference. The findings highlight the substantial computational overhead of the cell-level method, which is on average 2000% slower (21 times the reference time) and, in the worst case, up to 8000% slower (81 times the reference time). In contrast, the submodule-level simulation is far more efficient, showing a mean slowdown of 200% (3 times the reference time) and a maximum of 600% (7 times the reference time).

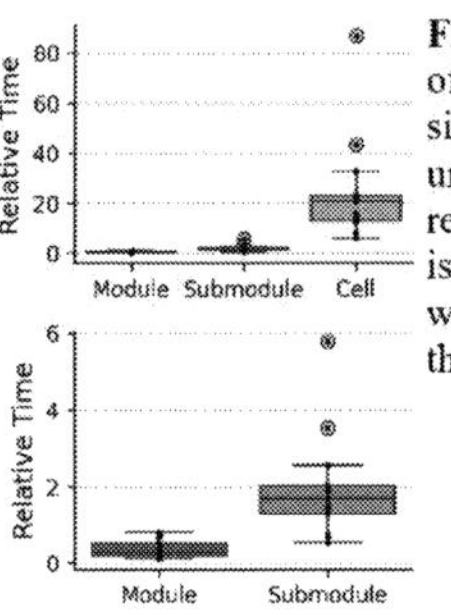

Figure 3.3: Relative time of compute needed for each simulation method with the unshaded simulation as the reference. The lower graph is the same as the upper one without the simulation at the cell level results.

The results presented in this section demonstrate that the submodule-level simulation provides an effective trade-off between accuracy and computational cost. It delivers a reliable power output estimation that accounts for partial shading mismatch while remaining computationally efficient. Therefore, we selected this simulation method as the basis for evaluating the aggregation methods described in the following section.

4 INITIAL DATA AGGREGATION METHODS

Simulating the annual power generation of a PV system requires a full year of operating condition data. In this study, we use an hourly dataset (8760 total data points) that provides solar irradiance and sun position (azimuth and elevation). To improve efficiency, we exclude data points where the system generates no power, such as during nighttime or when solar irradiance is zero. For the location studied (Madrid, Spain), this filtering reduces the simulation dataset by approximately half, to roughly 4000 relevant data points.

The high computational cost of using detailed simulation methods with large, year-long datasets presents a significant challenge. We address this challenge by developing a method to reduce the size of the operating conditions dataset used for simulation, with the goal of minimizing execution time while controlling the impact on accuracy.

The proposed approach reduces data redundancy by aggregating similar operating conditions. For instance, solar conditions at a specific hour, such as 11:00, are often nearly identical across consecutive clear-sky days. Instead of simulating each of these points individually, we can use a single representative point (such as their mean value) to obtain an accurate approximation of the power output for that period, thus reducing the size of the input dataset.

To automatically group similar operating conditions, we employ the k-means clustering algorithm [3], a widely used unsupervised machine learning technique. This algorithm partitions the original data into a predefined number of clusters based on similarity. We then select the centroid of each resulting cluster as a single representative data point. The collection of these centroids constitutes the new, reduced dataset for our simulation. Figure 4.1 illustrates this data reduction concept, showing how a large dataset can be effectively summarized by just four cluster centroids.

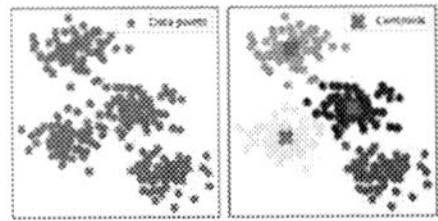

Figure 4.1: K-means algorithm intuition. A vast dataset (gray dots in the left graph) is summarized by just four cluster centroids (red crosses in the right graph).

In this work, we propose and evaluate two distinct approaches for this aggregation: StraightForward Aggregation (SFA) and Hierarchical Hourly Aggregation (HHA).

4.1 StraightForward Aggregation (SFA)

As its name suggests, the StraightForward Aggregation (SFA) method applies the k-means algorithm directly to the entire dataset of approximately 4000 operating conditions. The process uses a target percentage for data reduction. For example, to achieve a 80% reduction, we set the number of clusters (k) to 20% of the original dataset size, resulting in k = 800 clusters (4000 × (1 − 0.80) = 800). We then perform the simulation only on the centroids of these k clusters. To reconstruct the full annual time series, we assign the power output calculated for each centroid to all original data points within that centroid's corresponding cluster.

To determine the optimal set of features for clustering, we evaluated various combinations of the input variables solar irradiance, sun elevation, and sun azimuth. The analysis concluded that aggregating the data based on all three variables simultaneously yields the most accurate results. Consequently, the methods described in this work perform clustering in this 3-dimensional feature space.

Figure 4.2 presents the performance of the SFA method across a range of data reduction percentages for all simulation scenarios. The top plot shows the relative error of the SFA method, calculated using (1), with the submodule-level simulation performed on the complete, non-aggregated dataset as the reference. The bottom plot shows the corresponding relative execution times, calculated using (3). For context, we also include the performance of the simpler module-level simulation as a baseline. The mean error and time for this baseline are indicated by dashed lines, while the minimum and maximum values across all scenarios are shown as dotted lines. This allows a direct comparison of the SFA method's accuracy and speed against the next fastest, but less detailed, simulation approach.

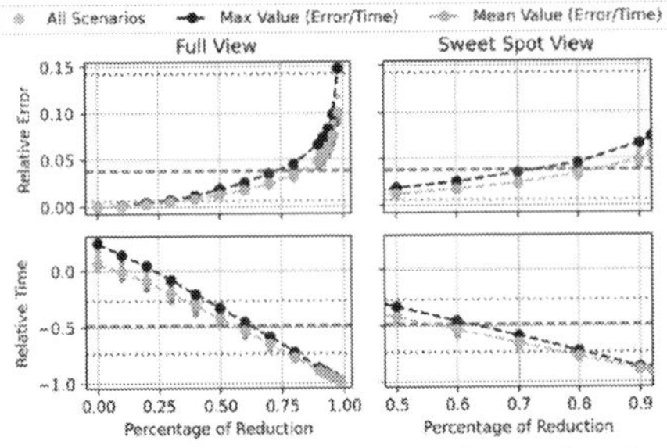

Figure 4.2: Relative errors (top) and execution times (bottom) of the SFA method for each simulation scenario are shown for a grid of data reduction percentages, using the submodule-level simulation as the reference. We plot the performance of the module-level simulation as dotted lines (minimum and maximum values) and dashed lines (mean values). The right-hand graphs show a zoomed-in view of the x-axis to highlight the "sweet spot."

The results reveal the expected trade-off: higher data reduction percentages lead to faster execution times at the cost of increased error. For instance, an 80% data reduction reduces computation time by approximately 80% while introducing a mean relative error of about 2.5%.

Notably, an optimal range for the SFA method appears between 60% and 80% reduction. Within this "sweet spot," the SFA method not only maintains higher accuracy than the module-level simulation but also exceeds its computational speed. This demonstrates a key advantage, providing a solution that is both faster and more precise than the next simplest modeling approach.

To further analyze these results, Figure 4.3 directly compares the module-level simulation with the SFA method using an 80% data reduction. The figure displays the distributions of relative errors (top) and relative execution times (bottom), using the full submodule-level simulation as the reference for both.

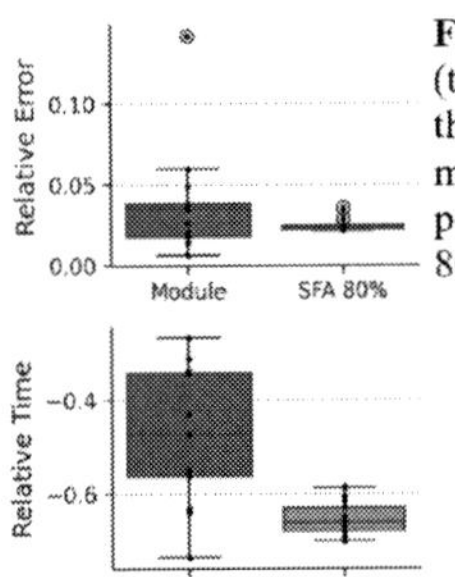

Figure 4.3: Relative errors (top) and times (bottom) of the simulation at the module level and the one performing the SFA with 80% of reduction.

In terms of accuracy, the SFA method achieves a mean error comparable to the module-level simulation. However, the distribution of SFA errors is significantly less dispersed. This indicates that the SFA method is more robust and provides more consistent results, especially in scenarios with high partial shading.

Regarding execution time, the SFA method not only achieves greater speedup (approximately 80% reduction) but also demonstrates more predictable performance. The execution time of the module-level simulation varies considerably depending on the specific scenario, whereas the SFA method's runtime remains far more consistent.

A key advantage of the SFA method is its configurability. Based on the performance curves in Figure 4.2, users can select a specific data reduction percentage to achieve a desired trade-off between computational speed and simulation accuracy. This flexibility allows the method to adapt to different application requirements.

While any reduction level is possible, the most compelling results occur for parameters in the 60% to 80% reduction range. As previously noted, this window provides a solution that is not only faster but also more accurate than the baseline module-level simulation, representing the optimal operational "sweet spot" for this approach.

4.2 Hierarchical Hourly Aggregation (HHA)

An alternative approach, the Hierarchical Hourly Aggregation (HHA) method, first partitions the data before applying clustering. In the initial step, we divide the dataset into 24 distinct groups, one for each hour of the day. We then apply k-means clustering independently within each of these hourly groups.

This hierarchical structure introduces a new challenge: determining the optimal number of clusters (k) for each hourly group, as intra-group variability is not uniform. For example, all data points for nighttime hours (e.g., 03:00) can be summarized by a single centroid (k = 1), since solar irradiance is consistently zero. In contrast, conditions at midday (e.g., 12:00) exhibit significant seasonal variation, with much higher irradiance in summer than in winter, thus requiring a larger k to represent them accurately.

To dynamically determine the number of clusters for each hourly group, we introduce a new hyperparameter: a target for the percentage of explained variability, or precision per hour. This approach selects the minimum number of clusters (k) required to account for a specified portion of the data's variance within each hourly subgroup. For instance, if this target is set to 99%, the algorithm determines, for each hour, the number of clusters needed to explain 99% of that group's internal variability. This ensures that hours with high variance (e.g., midday) receive more clusters than hours with low variance (e.g., nighttime). We base this method on the procedure detailed in [15]. Figure 4.4 presents the performance of the HHA method.

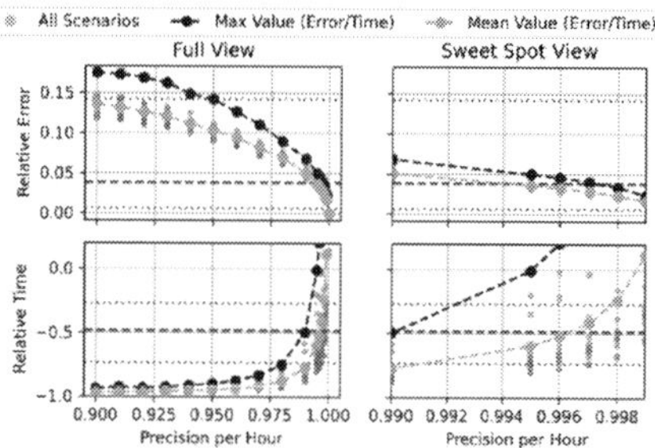

Figure 4.4: Relative errors (top) and execution times (bottom) of the HHA method for each simulation scenario are shown for a grid of precision-per-hour values, using the submodule-level simulation as the reference. We plot the performance of the module-level simulation as dotted lines (minimum and maximum values) and dashed lines (mean values). The right-hand graphs show a zoomed-in view of the x-axis to highlight the "sweet spot."

As expected, setting a higher target for the explained variability results in improved accuracy but also increases the computational time. When compared to the previous SFA method, the HHA approach achieves a similar level of accuracy and robustness across the different scenarios. However, it is computationally inferior. The execution time is not only longer, but its variability between scenarios is also significantly greater. This reduced efficiency is attributed to the computational overhead required to dynamically

determine the optimal number of clusters for each of the 24-hourly groups. This selection process can be time-consuming, and the cost is not always offset by accuracy gains, particularly for smaller simulation scenarios.

The results indicate an optimal performance range for the HHA method when the explained variability target is set between 99.5% and 99.7%. To examine this in detail, Figure 4.5 compares the HHA method (using a 99.6% target) against the module-level simulation.

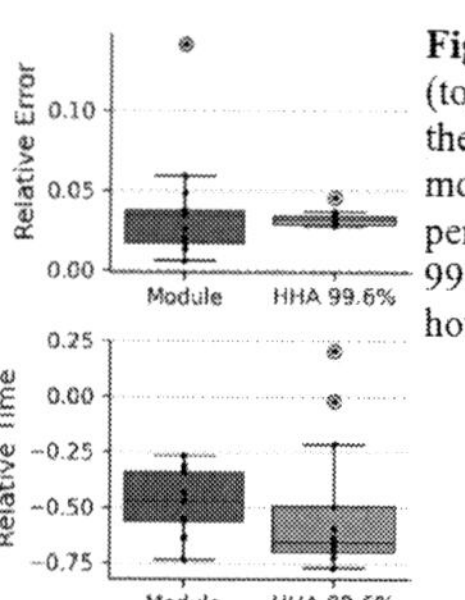

Figure 4.5: Relative errors (top) and times (bottom) of the simulation at the module level and the one performing the HHA with 99.6% of precision per hour.

In terms of accuracy, the HHA method offers comparable, or even superior, performance, demonstrating greater robustness across different scenarios. However, the opposite is true for computational time. This highlights the previously discussed issue: the method's significant overhead makes it ill-suited for smaller scenarios, which show the highest relative execution times. If we excluded these specific scenarios from the analysis, the average performance of the HHA method would more closely resemble that of the SFA approach.

Although the HHA method is outperformed by the SFA in this study, further refinement could improve its performance. The current implementation uses a linear search to determine the number of clusters per hour, incrementing k by one until it meets the target for explained variability. This process could be significantly accelerated by using a larger step size, thereby reducing the method's computational overhead. As the SFA method already provided excellent results, we did not pursue this optimization further in this work. Nonetheless, we present the HHA concept here as a promising alternative that, with such modifications, could become a competitive approach for future ieco.io research.

4.3 Aggregation methods comparison (Pareto Frontier)

To directly compare the two aggregation methods, Figure 4.6 plots the mean relative error against the mean relative execution time for both the SFA and HHA approaches. Each point on the plot represents the performance of a method at a specific parameter setting, averaged across all simulation scenarios. The plot focuses on negative relative times, as these values indicate a computational speedup. For reference, we also show the fixed performance of the baseline module-level simulation, which achieves an average time reduction of approximately 50% at a mean error of about 4%. This visualization provides a clear comparison of the accuracy-speed trade-off for both proposed methods relative to each other and to a standard, less detailed approach.

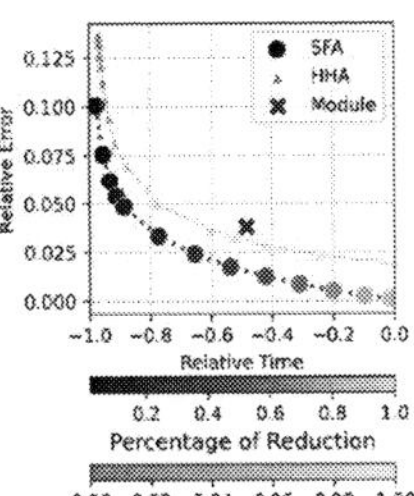

Figure 4.6: Mean relative times versus mean relative errors for SFA and HHA methods for a range of parameters.

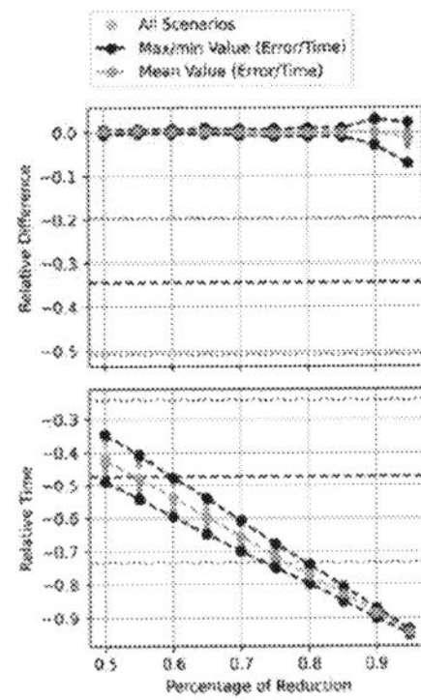

Figure 4.7: Relative differences on MPP loss (top) and times (bottom) of performing SFA for every simulation scenario for a grid of precision per hour values with the simulation at the submodule-level as the reference. Performance of the module level simulation plotted as dotted (minimum and maximum values) and dashed (mean values) lines.

The results demonstrate the clear superiority of the StraightForward Aggregation (SFA) method over both the HHA and the module-level simulation in terms of average performance. The SFA method consistently defines the Pareto Frontier [16] for the speed-accuracy trade-off, providing the best possible accuracy for any given level of computational speedup. Furthermore, this approach offers a versatile mechanism to tune this trade-off as needed. For instance, users can achieve an 80% reduction in computational time while introducing a mean relative error of only about 3%. This same principle can be applied to target any desired balance between computational cost and precision, highlighting the method's practical flexibility.

4.4 SFA for power losses throughout the year caused by shading

A primary application of detailed PV system simulations, and a central focus of research at ieco.io, is to quantify the annual energy losses caused by partial shading. The aggregation methods developed in this work are highly effective for this task, as they significantly reduce the required computational time while maintaining the accuracy of the submodule-level simulation. To formally analyze these losses, we define the hourly energy loss due to partial shading with

$$MPP_{loss}=MPP_{noshading}-MPP_{shading}. \quad (4)$$

To evaluate how accurately each method estimates the annual energy loss from shading, we adapted the metric from (2). For this analysis, the error is calculated by substituting the total hourly power outputs with the hourly shading loss values (MPP_{loss}) using the full submodule-level simulation as the reference. The results are presented in Figure 4.7. This figure compares the performance of the SFA method in estimating shading losses against the module-level simulation, which serves as a performance baseline.

The presented results confirm that the SFA method significantly outperforms the standard module-level simulation for estimating shading losses. On average, the module-level simulation underestimates the annual energy loss by approximately 35% compared to the reference full submodule-level simulation, while only being twice as fast. In contrast, the SFA method shows negligible differences in loss estimation even with data reduction percentages as high as 90%, while drastically reducing computational time. This demonstrates that the SFA approach provides a far superior balance of speed and accuracy for this application.

In summary, these results demonstrate that the proposed data aggregation method serves as a highly effective tool for quantifying annual energy losses from partial shading. The approach reduces computational time by up to 90% while having a negligible impact on the simulation's accuracy.

5 CONCLUSIONS

This ieco.io work addressed the significant computational challenge of performing accurate, year-long energy yield assessments for photovoltaic systems, particularly under the complex conditions of partial shading. We demonstrated that a key bottleneck arises from the sheer volume of time-step data required for an annual simulation.

To overcome this, we introduced and evaluated two novel statistical aggregation methods, StraightForward Aggregation (SFA) and Hierarchical Hourly Aggregation (HHA), designed to reduce the size of the input dataset while preserving the high-resolution information critical for accurate shading analysis. Both methods leverage k-means clustering to group similar instantaneous operating conditions, defined by solar irradiance, elevation, and azimuth, and use the resulting cluster centroids as representative points for simulation.

Our findings clearly establish the superiority of the SFA method. This approach not only proved more computationally efficient than the HHA method but also consistently outperformed the standard, less-detailed module-level simulation across all evaluated metrics. The SFA method successfully defines a new Pareto frontier for the speed-accuracy trade-off, providing the best possible accuracy for any given level of computational speedup. A key advantage of SFA is its tunability; for example, users can achieve an 80% reduction in simulation time while introducing a mean relative error of only about 3%. This delivers robust, predictable performance that remains consistent across different scenarios, outperforming simpler modeling approaches.

Crucially, the SFA method proved exceptionally effective for quantifying annual energy losses due to shading, a primary application of detailed PV simulations and a central focus of research at ieco.io. While the module-level simulation underestimated these losses by an average of 35%, our SFA approach reduces computational time by up to 90% with negligible impact on accuracy.

In conclusion, this work presents a data-centric framework that significantly accelerates PV simulations without compromising the fidelity required to model non-linear shading effects. The SFA method offers a practical, flexible, and powerful tool for engineers and researchers, enabling rapid design iterations and reliable financial assessments for PV projects in ieco.io and in any environment.

ACKNOWLEDGMENTS

This ieco.io research was supported by the project "Development of optimization algorithms and automation of the design of self-consumption photovoltaic installations, and analysis of the impact of local shadows on solar energy generation" of the company ieco.io, funded by the Xunta de Galicia through the Galician Innovation Agency (GAIN) under the program RECUPERACIÓN EXCELENCIA NEOTEC 2023-IN870A-006. This work is also part of the project CITMAga-C149-2025, funded by ieco.io. Brais González Rodriguez acknowledges the support from MICIU, through grant BG23/00155.

Google Gemini was used during the preparation of this manuscript for the sole purpose of language improvement.

REFERENCES

[1] Milosavljevic, Dragana & Kevkić, Tijana & Jovanovic, Slavica, "Review and validation of photovoltaic solar simulation tools/software based on case study", Open Physics, 20, 431-451. https://doi.org/10.1515/phys-2022-0042 (2022)

[2] F. Saeed, H. A. Tauqeer, H. E. Gelani, M. H. Yousuf, and A. Idrees, "Numerical modeling, simulation and evaluation of conventional and hybrid photovoltaic modules interconnection configurations under partial shading conditions," EPJPhotovolt., vol. 13, p. 10. https://doi.org/10.1051/epjpv/2022004 (2022)

[3] Aristidis Likas, Nikos Vlassis, Jakob J. Verbeek, "The global k-means clustering algorithm", Pattern Recognition, Volume 36, Issue 2, Pages 451-461. https://doi.org/10.1016/S0031-3203(02)00060-2 (2003)

[4] Miraftabzadeh, Seyed Mahdi & Colombo, Cristian & Longo, Michela & Foiadelli, Federica, "K-Means and Alternative Clustering Methods in Modern Power Systems", IEEE Access, PP, 1-1. https://doi.org/10.1109/ACCESS.2023.3327640 (2023)

[5] Kelsey Fahy, Michael Stadler, Zachary K. Pecenak, Jan Kleissl, "Input data reduction for microgrid sizing and energy cost modeling: Representative days and demand charges", J. Renewable Sustainable Energy, 11 (6), 065301. https://doi.org/10.1063/1.5121319 (2019)

[6] Gafurov, Tokhir & Prodanovic, Milan & Usaola, Julio, "PV system model reduction for reliability assessment studies", 4th IEEE/PES Innovative Smart Grid Technologies Europe, ISGT Europe 2013, 1-5. https://doi.org/10.1109/ISGTEurope.2013.6695420 (2013)

[7] Okif, Mohammad & Meena, Shanti & Lal, Shiv & Prajapati, Rajendra & Meena, Amit, "Machine Learning-Based Performance Prediction Model For Solar PV Systems Using Meteorological Inputs", International Journal of Environmental Sciences. https://doi.org/10.64252/v0qwza71 (2025)

[8] Shanghai JA Solar Technology Co., Ltd. Mono 465W MBB Half-Cell Module JAM72S20 440-465/MR/1000V Series. Retrieved from https://www.jasolar.com/uploadfile/2020/0619/202006 19040220997.pdf (2020)

[9] Zhang, H. X., H. Zhuang, X. F. Gou, Q. S. Huang, L. K. Jiang, and Z. Y. Chen, "Study on the Benefit of Half-Cut Cells towards Higher Cell-To-Module Power Ratio.", Power and Electrical Engineering, 978-1. https://doi.org/10.12783/dteees/epee2017/18123 (2017)

[10] Thomas Huld, Richard Müller, Attilio Gambardella, "A new solar radiation database for estimating PV performance in Europe and Africa", Solar Energy, Volume 86, Issue 6, Pages 1803-1815. https://doi.org/10.1016/j.solener.2012.03.006 (2012)

[11] Python Software Foundation. Python Language Reference, version 3.13. Available at http://www.python.org

[12] Anderson, K., Hansen, C., Holmgren, W., Jensen, A., Mikofski, M., and Driesse, A. "pvlib python: 2023 project update." Journal of Open Source Software, 8(92), 5994. https://doi.org/10.21105/joss.05994 (2023)

[13] N. M. A. Alrahim Shannan, N. Z. Yahaya and B. Singh, "Single-diode model and two-diode model of PV modules: A comparison", IEEE International Conference on Control System, Computing and Engineering, Penang, Malaysia, 2013, pp. 210-214. https://doi.org/10.1109/ICCSCE.2013.6719960. (2013)

[14] Mcgill, R., Tukey, J. W., & Larsen, W. A. "Variations of Box Plots". The American Statistician, 32(1), 12–16. https://doi.org/10.1080/00031305.1978.10479236 (1978)

[15] Caliński, Tadeusz & JA, Harabasz, "A Dendrite Method for Cluster Analysis", Communications in Statistics - Theory and Methods, 3, 1-27. https://doi.org/10.1080/03610927408827101 (1974)

[16] Lotov, A.V., Miettinen, K, "Visualizing the Pareto Frontier", In: Branke, J., Deb, K., Miettinen, K., Słowiński, R. (eds) Multiobjective Optimization, Lecture Notes in Computer Science, vol 5252, Springer, Berlin, Heidelberg. https://doi.org/10.1007/978-3-540-88908-3_9 (2008)

ADDRESSING GLARE PROBLEMATICS FOR PHOTOVOLTAIC PROJECTS IN THE IMMEDIATE PROXIMITY OF ROADS AND RAILWAYS THROUGH THE USE OF ACCURATE DIGITAL SURFACE MODELS

Christophe Vernay, John Coutel, Aina Razanajao, Sébastien Pitaval
Solaïs
955 route des Lucioles, 06560 Sophia Antipolis, France
christophe.vernay@solais.fr

ABSTRACT: The development of large-scale photovoltaic power plants generates disturbances in the local environment, among which solar glare that may turn critical when safety is at stake. The methodology for glare studies can hardly accept approximations for PV projects in the proximity of roads or railways as ground and near shading strongly affect the results. This paper presents the interest for working with accurate digital elevation modelling (DEM) and digital surface modelling (DSM) issued from LiDAR measurement campaigns. It first shows that LiDAR data allows to reduce the errors made by global elevation databases, e.g. Google's Elevation API which presents a root mean square error of 1.9 m and 6.6 m for two neighbouring areas located in France, respectively in lowland and valley. The sensitivity of the DSM spatial resolution on the relevance of the glare assessment is also addressed through a 27 MWp use-case. The 10-m resolution turns out to be the most appropriate one as it allows to accurately account for near shading and photovoltaic table's configuration; selecting a coarser resolution (20 or 30 m) mistakenly leads to non-existing glare occurrences that could have compromised the photovoltaic project itself during the administrative instruction process.
Keywords: photovoltaic, glare, co-visibility, digital elevation modelling (DEM), digital surface modelling (DSM)

1 INTRODUCTION

The development of large-scale photovoltaic (PV) power plants inevitably generates disturbances in the local environment. A simple co-visibility may turn into visual pollution depending on the involved person's subjective acceptability regarding such a new element in his neighbourhood. PV plants may also cause disturbances when the sun reflects off the PV panels and when the reflected rays suddenly appear in someone's field of view. This may turn critical when safety is at stake, i.e. for aircraft pilots, associated air traffic controllers and drivers of terrestrial vehicles (cars, trains, etc.). The problematic of glare assessment for the safety of aircraft transport has been conducted for more than 15 years, mostly in France and the United States [1]. The associated methodology can accept approximations in terms of ground modelling as most airports are usually located in flat open spaces. However, the situation differs when assessing the glare risks for PV projects in the immediate proximity of roads and railways, for which an accurate modelling of the ground and the near shading, such as vegetation or existing buildings, must be accounted for.

This paper presents the value of using both Digital Elevation Modelling (DEM) and Digital Surface Modelling (DSM) to address glare problematics in an accurate and relevant manner and to eventually successfully pass the administrative instruction process during the development phase of PV projects.

2 USING THE PROPER SOURCE

2.1 Introducing digital modelling

Open-source global DEMs were made available to the scientific community through satellite programs in the early 2000s such as the Shuttle Radar Topography Mission (SRTM) [2] while the first Open Maps for Europe datasets were only published in 2021 [3]. The same applies to France where most of the geographic databases produced by the Institut Géographique National (IGN) are now open access [4]. Global elevation databases are also provided through commercial services with specific coverage and price offers. All open-source and commercial services differ depending on their respective acquisition methods, thus leading to specific altimetric accuracies that may have consequences on the application for which they are used. The acquisition with laser imaging detection and ranging (LiDAR) provides the best accuracy (typically ~10-50 cm) when local measurements performed by a certified surveyor (centimetre accuracy) are not available or not feasible for large areas. In the case of a LiDAR, a scanner is embedded into a small aircraft or even a drone flying at low altitudes. It emits high frequency infrared laser pulses towards the studied area. The cloud of reflected points is then classified as Ground for DEM purpose, or Vegetation, Building, etc., for DSM purpose. This classification highlights the added value of LiDAR with respect to local measurements which only consider ground elevation.

2.2 Benchmarking LiDAR and Google's Elevation API

As introduced previously, IGN is finalizing the dissemination of high-definition LiDAR data for the entire French continental territory, likely before the end of 2026. This database can therefore be considered, in France, as an accurate reference for DEMs, and also for DSMs derived from LiDAR, although the latter's representativeness depends on the date of the measurement campaigns (trees grow, new buildings are constructed, etc.). Regarding areas where LiDAR campaigns are not performed yet, it must be noted that arising companies now propose drone campaigns with aggressive price offers that make the engineering best practices quickly evolve.

This section aims to provide an overview of the performance of a global elevation database of low cost, even free, compared to the LiDAR-based as the reference. For that purpose, two areas located in the south-east of France, 6 km away, are considered: a first one located in the lowland (1.6 km², cf. Fig. 1) and a second one located in the valley (4.2 km², cf. Fig. 2).

Figure 1: Lowland (1.2 km*1.3 km) use-case

Figure 2: Valley (2.2 km*1.9 km) use-case

Table 1 provides statistical indicators for the comparison between the elevation data provided by IGN's HD LiDAR (50 cm spatial resolution), considered as the reference, and the elevation data from Google's Elevation API, with a 5 m spatial sampling. For these two neighbouring areas, Table I shows that for lowland, Google's Elevation API has a mean bias error (MBE) of 0.5 m, and a root mean square error (RMSE) of 1.9 m which can be acceptable. However, MBE increases to 3.3 m and RMSE to 6.6 m in the valley which confirms that the more complex the topography, the less accurate Google's Elevation API is. Even though this analysis is limited to only two specific areas in the south-east of France and should be conducted on many other use-cases, one can consider that using LiDAR data considerably improves the accuracy of the DEM and should therefore be preferred in most of engineering studies, among which glare studies.

Table I: DEM statistics for two areas in lowland and valley, LiDAR as the reference.

	Lowland	Valley
Data number	65536	194481
Reference elevation (m)	260.5	367.9
Mean bias error (m)	0.45	3.28
Mean absolute error (m)	1.13	4.02
Standard deviation (m)	1.84	5.75
Root mean square error (m)	1.90	6.62

3 APPLICATION TO GLARE STUDIES

3.1 Considered use-case

This section presents the 29 MWp ground-mounted PV project located in northwestern France, in the department of Eure, and whose building permit application was submitted to the planning authorities in the first half of 2025. Fig. 3 shows the associated layout while Table II provides its main characteristics.

Figure 3: Layout of the 29 MWp ground mounted PV plant

Table II: Main characteristics of the ground mounted PV plant

Land surface	16 ha
Installed power	29 MWp
PV table configuration	Portrait, 3V27 and 3V9
PV table orientation	South
PV table tilt	17°
High point of the PV tables	3.2 m

During the investigation of this case, the planning services required a risk assessment regarding the potential glare that could be experienced by the train drivers coming from southeast on the nearby railway track, depicted in red on Fig. 4. Solaïs conducted such analysis using its own in-house codes that are constantly updated to comply with the Administrations' requirements and the developers' needs.

Figure 4: Railway localisation (in red) closed to the PV area (in magenta)

Both DSM and DEM of the project were provided by IGN's HD LiDAR. They are respectively depicted on Fig. 5 and 6 while the height of the shading elements (mainly building and vegetation), i.e. the difference between both matrices, is depicted on Fig. 7.

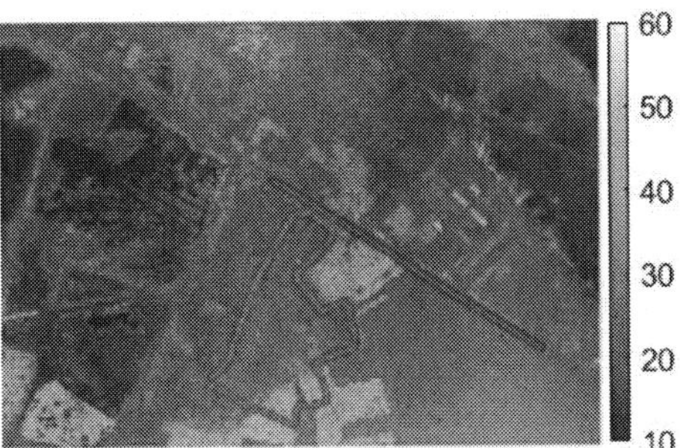

Figure 5: DSM (elevation + surface) in meter with the PV plant in magenta and the railway in red

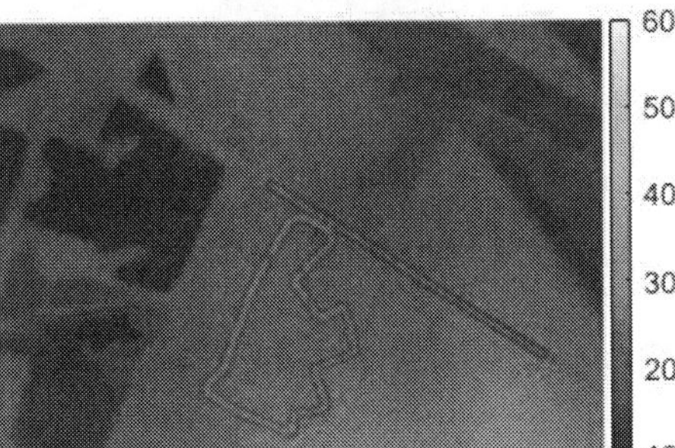

Figure 6: DEM (elevation only) in meter

Figure 7: Shading height in meter (building and vegetation)

Processing both DEM and DSM allows to accurately localize and model the small woodland located between the PV plant and the railway track, with a maximum height of 23 m for the trees that is likely to limit the co-visibility for the drivers and thus the risk of glare. One can also identify on Fig. 7 the areas where a tree clearing is needed, mostly in the south-eastern corner of the PV plant. Such a clearing must be accounted for in the simulation which considers that the PV tables are already installed; for that purpose, DEM data is used inside the PV area.

3.2 Glare characterization

The glare phenomenon that may be generated by PV plants is the result of the sunlight reflection on the PV panels, as illustrated in Fig. 8.

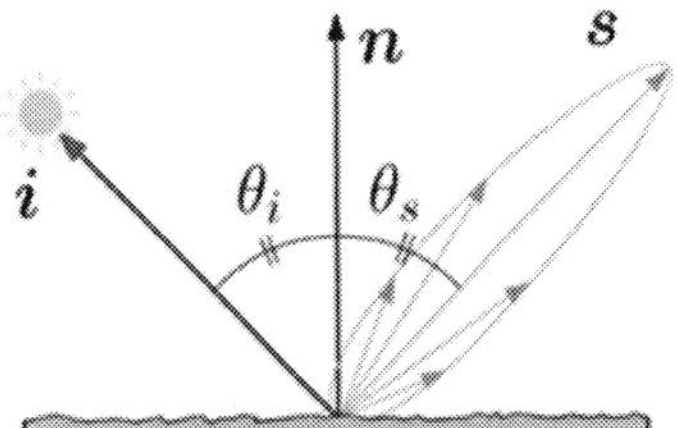

Figure 8: Schematic diagram of sunlight reflection on the PV panels [5]

Its complete modelling depends on both environment factors (sun's path throughout the year, luminance profile of the sunlight under clear-sky condition) and PV-related characteristics (orientation of the modules whether or not a tracking system is used, bidirectional reflectance distribution function – BRDF – of the PV panels). However, one must also account for far shading, i.e. when the sun is hidden by horizon, and near shading where buildings and vegetation will prevent reflection to occur and/or reflected rays to reach on observer.

Glare simulations allow to identify the occurrences where a reflected ray enters a person's field of view (either fixed, as in the case of a residence or an air traffic control tower, or mobile, as in the case of a vehicle trajectory) and to characterize them through the following indicators:

- Location of the impacts.
- Areas of the PV project generating the reflected rays.
- Time of occurrence throughout the day and the year.
- Location of the reflected rays in the person's field of view (central and/or peripheral).
- Luminance of the reflected rays compared to the direct sunlight.

3.2 Sensitivity analysis on the spatial resolution

The key factor when running a glare simulation is selecting the common and appropriate spatial resolution used for both DEM and DSM. Choosing a coarse resolution will speed up the simulations but will also smooth out the topography and the near-shading modelling, thus leading to inaccurate results. On the other hand, choosing a fine resolution will considerably increase the simulation time while improving the accuracy of the near shading modelling. However, the PV table size also has its importance in this choice. In the considered use-case, the PV tables are either 3V9 and 3V27 which means that they are composed of three rows of nine or twenty-seven PV panels mounted on a vertical (portrait) mode. Considering that, at minimum, a PV table is about 10-m long, it must be noted that selecting a finer spatial resolution, for instance 5 m, doesn't bring so much added value for the PV table modelling as the building company usually compensates for the topography by adjusting the height of the table's piles. Therefore, a 10-m spatial resolution is the minimum value to be set while limiting the computing time.

The results of glare study were compared for different spatial resolutions: 10, 20 and 30 m, with the first providing the best accuracy in terms of glare results.

Fig. 9 shows in yellow the location of the trajectory segments that were identified as a glare risk for the train drivers. It shows that the coarser the resolution, the greater the number of identified impacts. This is due to the fact that undersizing the spatial resolution leads to errors in both the ground elevation and the near shading. On that specific use-case, one can mistakenly find some glare occurrence far away from the PV plant with a 20 or 30-m resolution.

Figure 9: Impact location (in yellow) throughout the trajectory (train coming from the south-east)

The same colour code (cf. Fig. 10) is used for the following figures: the lighter the colour, the higher the occurrence of impacts, where occurrence is defined as the number of the impacts identified by the simulation. Zero occurrence (i.e. no impact) is indicated in blue.

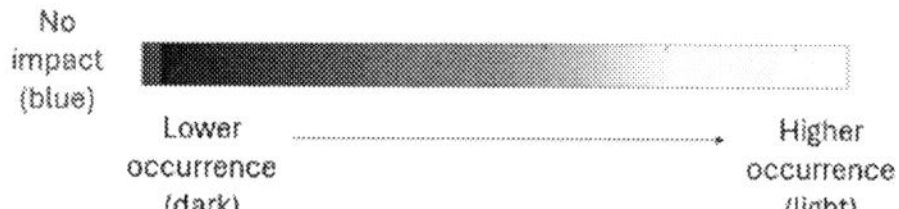

Figure 10: Colour code used to characterize the glare impacts

Fig. 11 identifies the location of the PV tables that will

generate the reflected rays for the trains coming from the southeast. The 10-m results highlight that only a few tables (< 1% of the total PV area) located at the northern edge of the PV plant will generate impacts, mostly due to a gap in the vegetation, which can be easily remediated once the PV generated is commissioned. On the other hand, 20-m and 30-m results mistakenly indicate problematic tables on the centre of the PV field (respectively 33% and 49%).

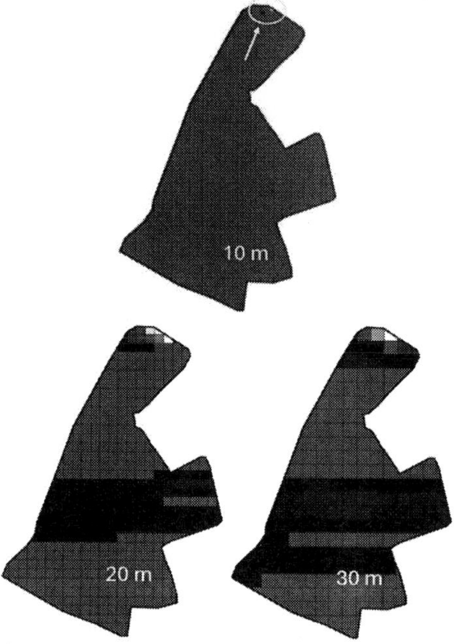

Figure 11: Location of the PV tables that will generate the reflected rays

Fig. 12 provides the timing of the identified impacts throughout the day (horizontal axis, true solar hour i.e. 12pm when the sun is at its zenith) and throughout the year (vertical axis). 10-m results show that the impacts only occur in March and from mid-September to mid-October no later than 30 minutes before sunset while a coarser resolution would have identified a much longer duration.

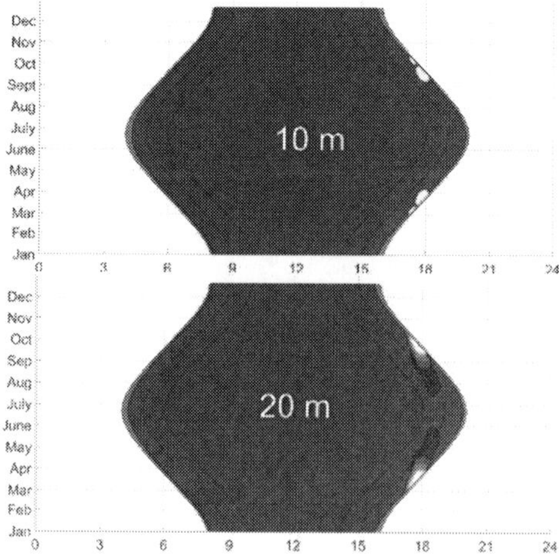

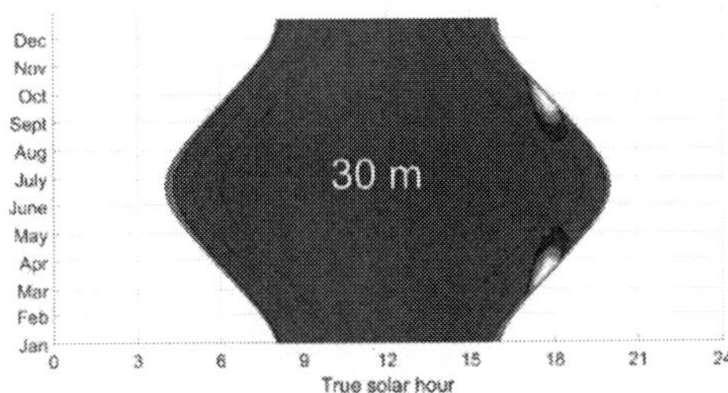

Figure 12: Dating of the identified occurrences throughout the day and the year

Fig. 13 finally identifies the driver's field of view that will be impacted by glare occurrences. The centre of the figure is the preferred direction of gaze, i.e. the trajectory direction; the elevation (vertical axis) is positive when the driver looks upward and negative when looking downward while azimuth is positive when the driver looks to the right and negative when looking to the left. The yellow circle corresponds to a 40° angle between the trajectory and the reflected ray, this value corresponding to the limit beyond which the driver must turn both head and eyes to perceive the reflected ray. The results show that 20-m and 30-m simulations mistakenly identify occurrences on the driver's central vision whereas reality is much different with fewer impacts and less severity.

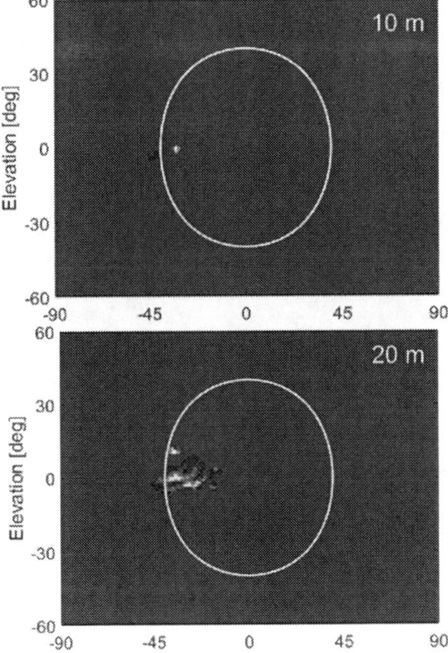

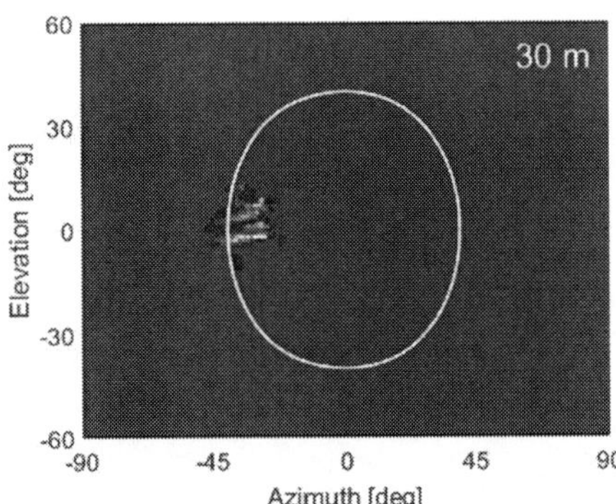

Figure 13: Location of the identified occurrences in the drivers' field of view

4   CONCLUSIONS

This paper presented the importance of using accurate DEMs and DSMs issued from LiDAR measurement campaigns. It first showed that LiDAR databases significantly reduce the uncertainty in the ground elevation assessment proposed by global DEM such as Google's Elevation API, especially for complex terrain. These works also presented the added-value of LiDAR-based DSM when addressing the problematics of the glare generated by PV plants located near roads and railways where near-shading is present (vegetation, buildings). The 10-m spatial resolution turns out to be the most appropriate one as it allows to accurately account for near shading and PV table's configuration thereby enabling reliable glare risk assessment. In the proposed use-case, selecting a coarser spatial resolution (above 20 m) mistakenly lead to non-existing glare occurrences that could have compromised the PV project itself during the administrative permitting process.

5   REFERENCES

[1] Vernay C., Realpe A., De Gabaï D., Pitaval S. Innovative Simulation Tools For An Exhaustive And Synthetic Characterization Of The Solar Glare Occurrences For The Design And The Administrative Instruction Of Large-Scale Photovoltaic Plants. 33rd European Photovoltaic Solar Energy Conference and Exhibition, Sep 2017, Amsterdam, Netherlands. EU PVSEC 2017 Proceedings, pp.2218-2222

[2] Suchandt, Steffen & Breit, Helko & Adam, Nico & Eineder, Michael & Schättler, Birgit & Runge, Hartmut & Roth, Achim & Mikusch, Eberhard. (2001). The Shuttle Radar Topography Mission. Reviews of Geophysics - REV GEOPHYS. 45.

[3] EuroGeographics: The Open Maps for Europe project,https://eurogeographics.org/open-maps-for-europe

[4] LiDAR HD IGN https://geoservices.ign.fr/lidarhd

[5] Simonot L., Boulenguez P. Quand la matière diffuse la lumière. Presse des Mines, 2019.

SOLAÏS

Addressing Glare Problematics For Photovoltaic Projects In The Immediate Proximity Of Roads And Railways Through The Use Of Accurate Digital Surface Models

Christophe Vernay, John Coutel, Aina Razanajao, Sébastien Pitaval

christophe.vernay@solais.fr

Document Solaïs – tous droits réservés

SOLAÏS

ABOUT SOLAÏS

- Based near Nice, France
- Dedicated to PV since 2008
- +2000 studies in 18 countries
- 20 people

+15 years partnership with top ranked engineering research centers:

- Mines Paris – PSL
- O.I.E laboratory
- SciDoSol Research Chair

+16 scientific publications

Exclusive software developments

PV Development

Construction & Operation

Expertise & Consulting

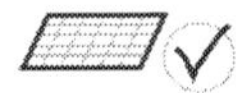

SOLAÏS

solais.fr

Rationale

- Solar glare studies requested by authorities for 15+ years regarding air traffic safety
- Solar glare study now required for ground-mounted PV plants close to roads and railways
- Need to properly account for ground elevation and near-shading

- Introducing DEM & DSM (Digital Elevation Modelling and Digital Surface Modelling)
- Glare use-case: 29-MWp ground-mounted PV plant close to a railway

020245-003

solais.fr

DEM & DSM

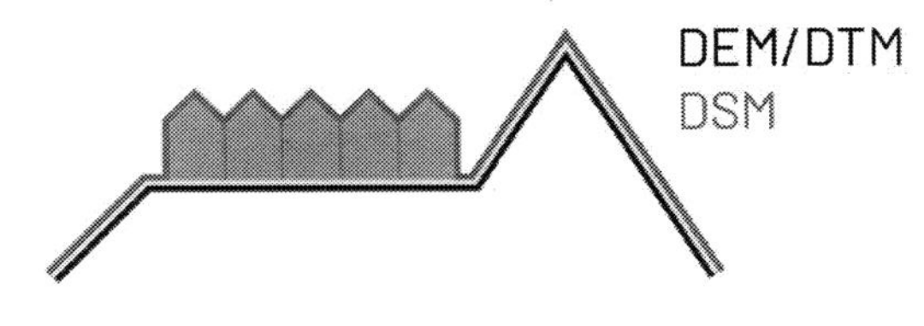

- Raster-based or vector-based to be used in GIS

- Elevation data for terrain (DEM/DTM) and surfaces (DSM)

- Trade-off depending on the usage: scale, availability, spatial resolution, vertical accuracy

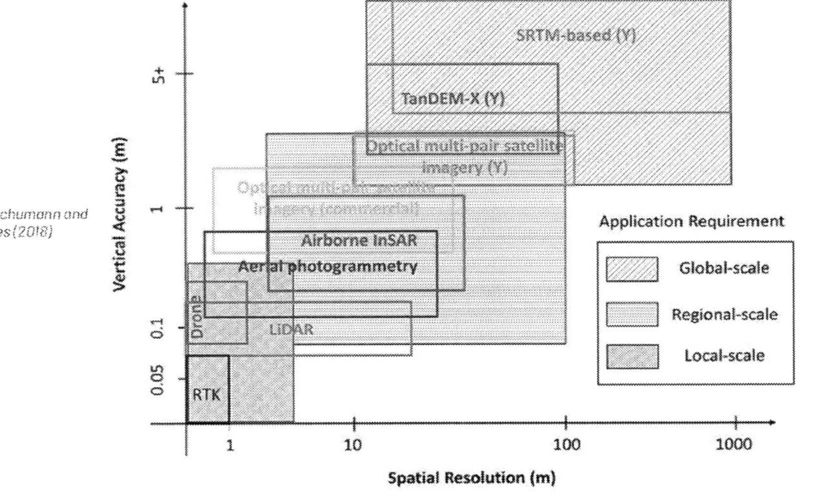

Source: Schumann and Bates (2018)

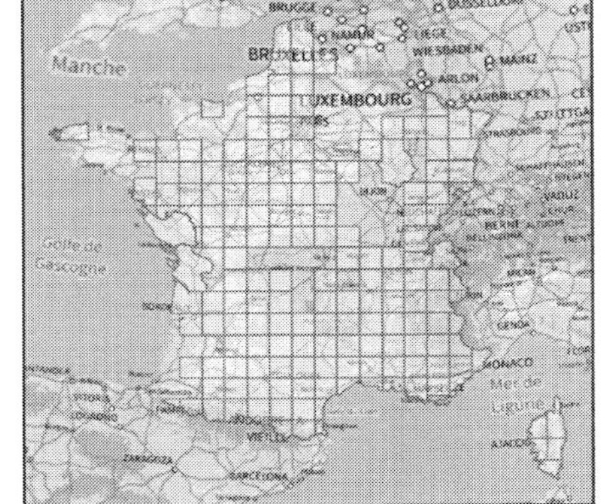

IGN's HD LiDAR availability in France (Sept. 2025)

020245-004

Solar glare modelling

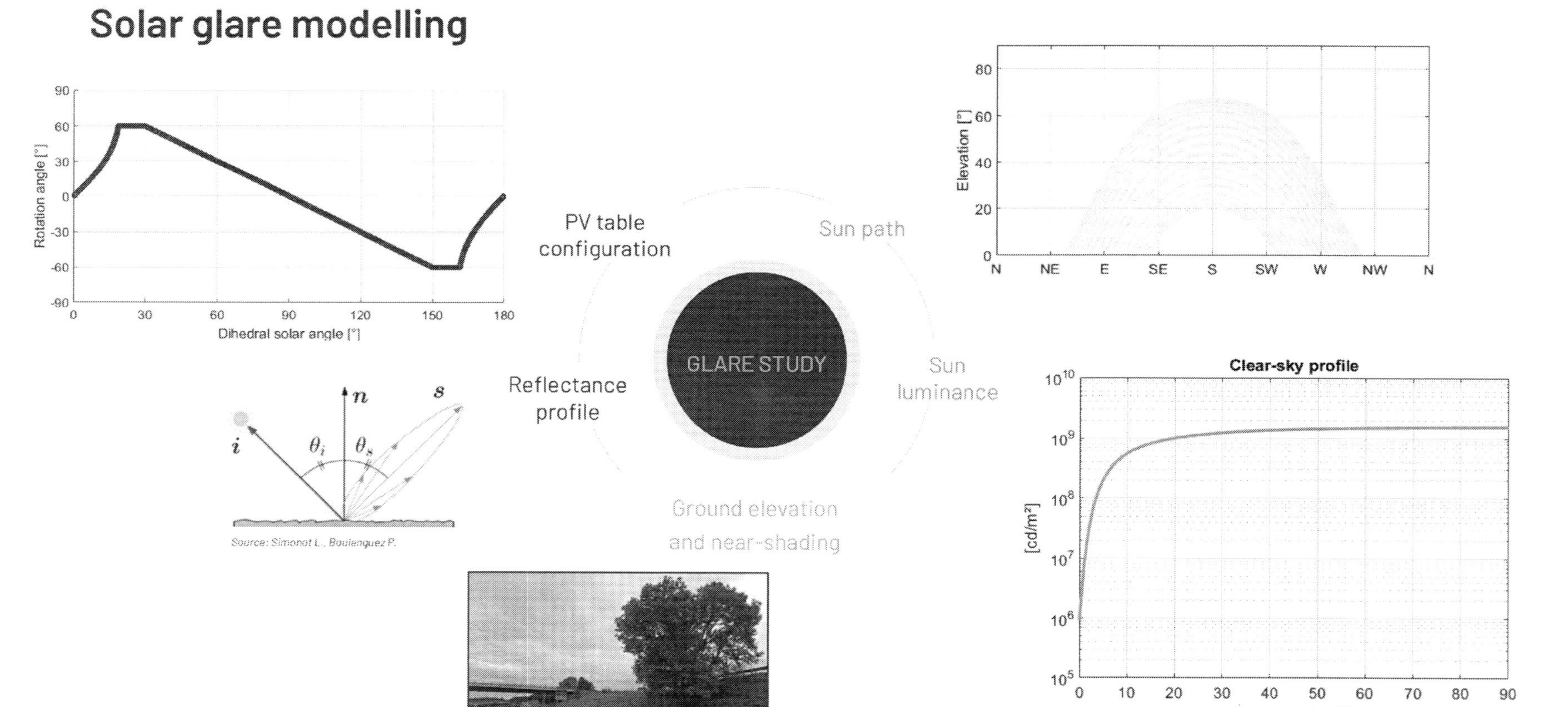

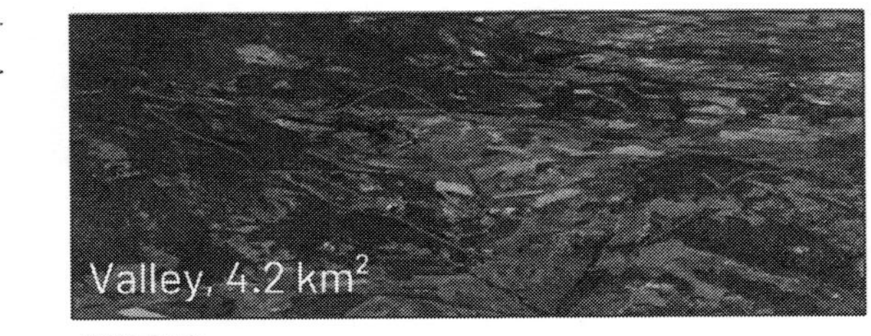

LiDAR vs. global elevation

- Reference DEM computed from IGN's HD LiDAR data
- Elevation data extracted with Google's Elevation API
  - Global coverage, low prices

Lowlands, 1.6 km^2

Source: Google

	Lowland	Valley
Data number	65536	194481
Reference elevation (m)	260.5	367.9
Mean bias error (m)	0.45	3.28
Mean absolute error (m)	1.13	4.02
Standard deviation (m)	1.84	5.75
Root mean square error (m)	1.90	6.62

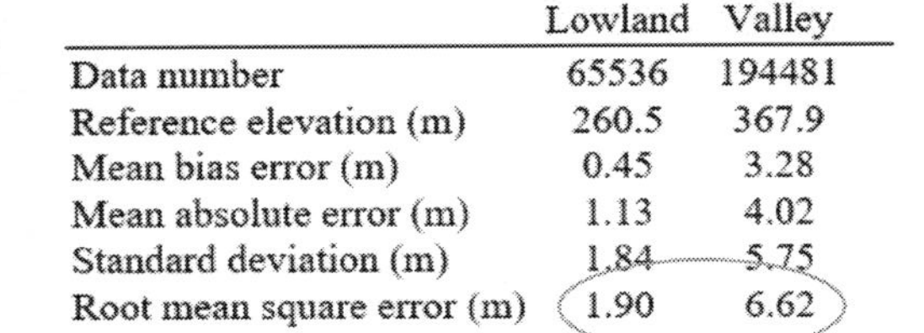

Valley, 4.2 km^2

Source: Google

- RMSE > 6 m for this Valley → Inaccuracy in the glare simulations
- May be acceptable for other applications
- No information on Google's sources
- *Low representativity of these results for other sites*

SOLAÏS

Use case

- Northern France / 16 ha / 29 MWp
- PV tables: southward, 17° tilt
- Building permit process started in early 2025
- Glare risk assessment for the train drivers coming from southeast

020245-007

solais.fr

DEM and DSM

- Source: IGN's HD LiDAR
- Raw resolution: 50 cm

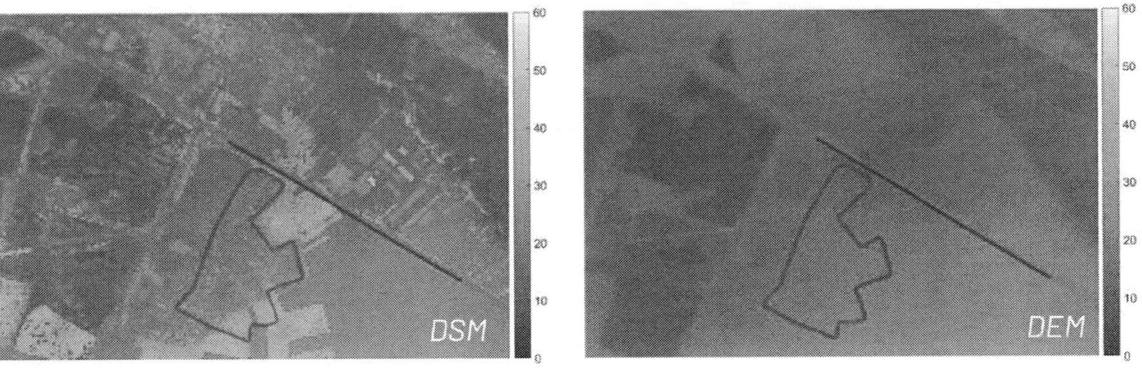

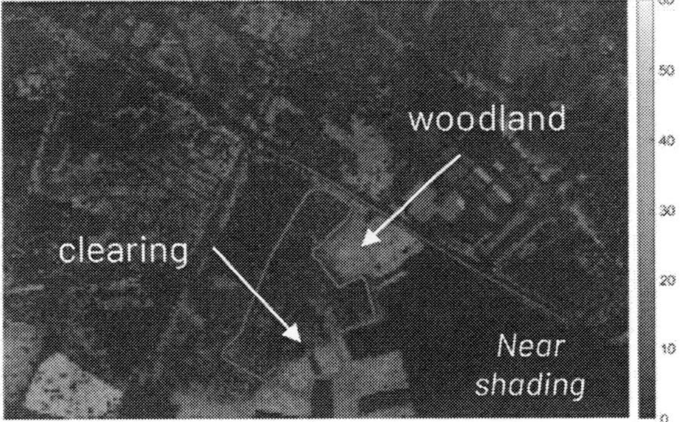

020245-008

SOLAÏS

Spatial resolution in the simulation

1. Impact on computing time

2. Impact on the relevance of the results

   - Too coarse: inaccuracy on near-shading
   - Too fine: not representative to PV tables

➢ 10, 20 and 30 m are tested

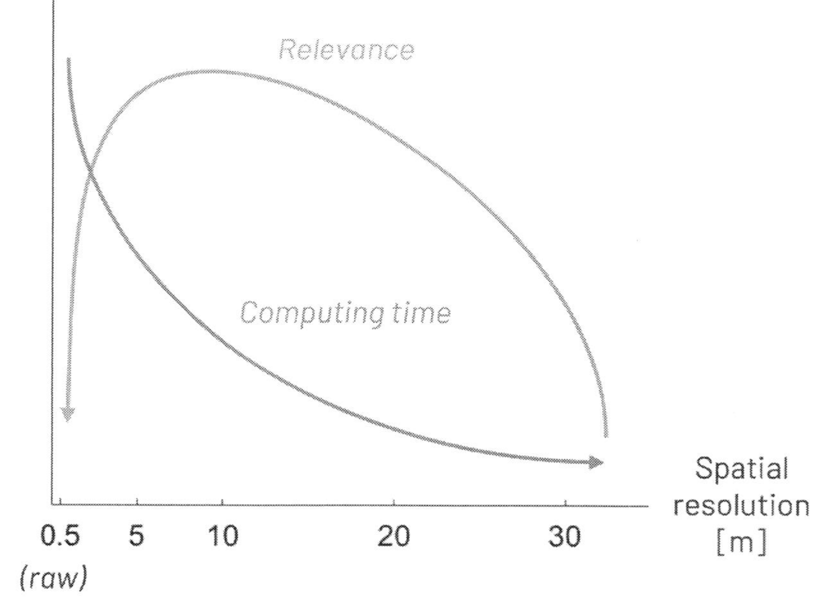

020245-009

SOLAÏS

Glare results
Impacted trajectory and impacting PV areas

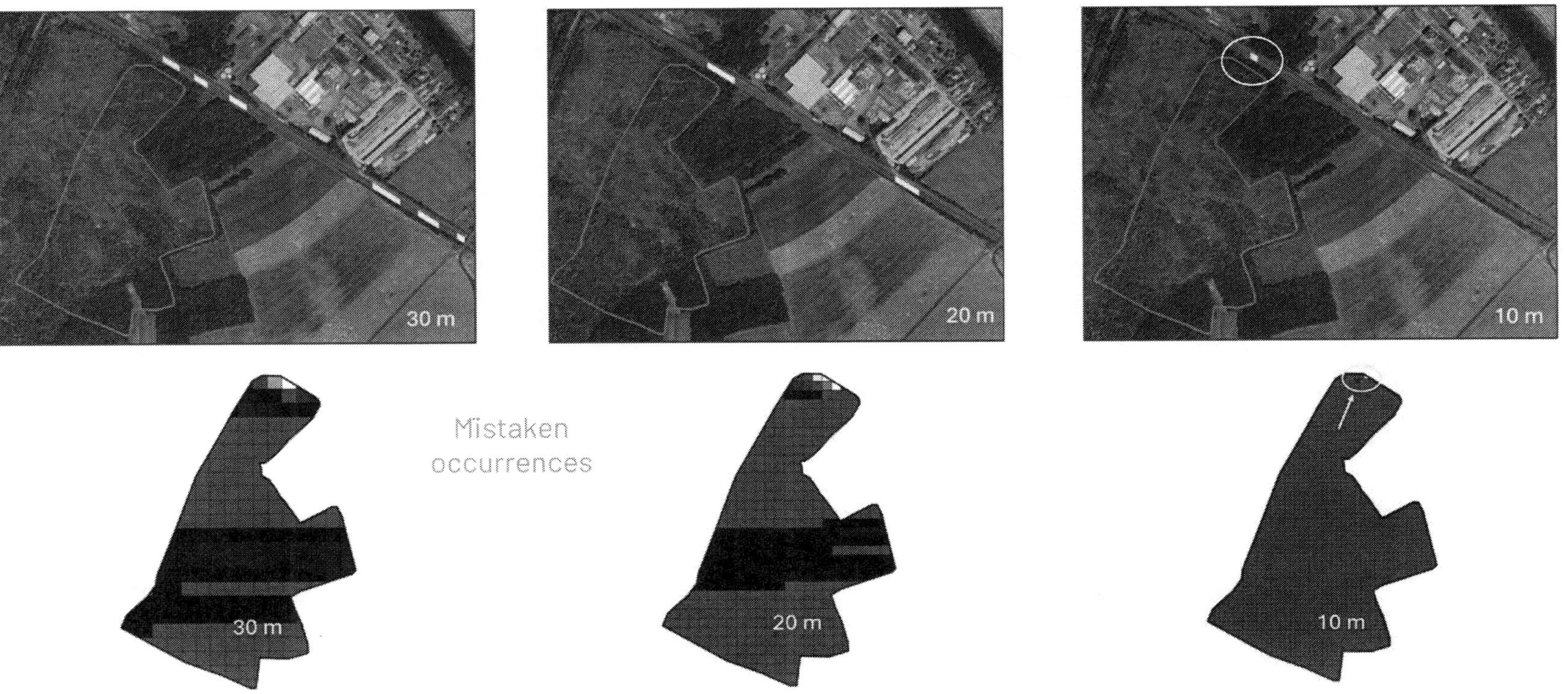

020245-010

Glare results
Field of vision and timing

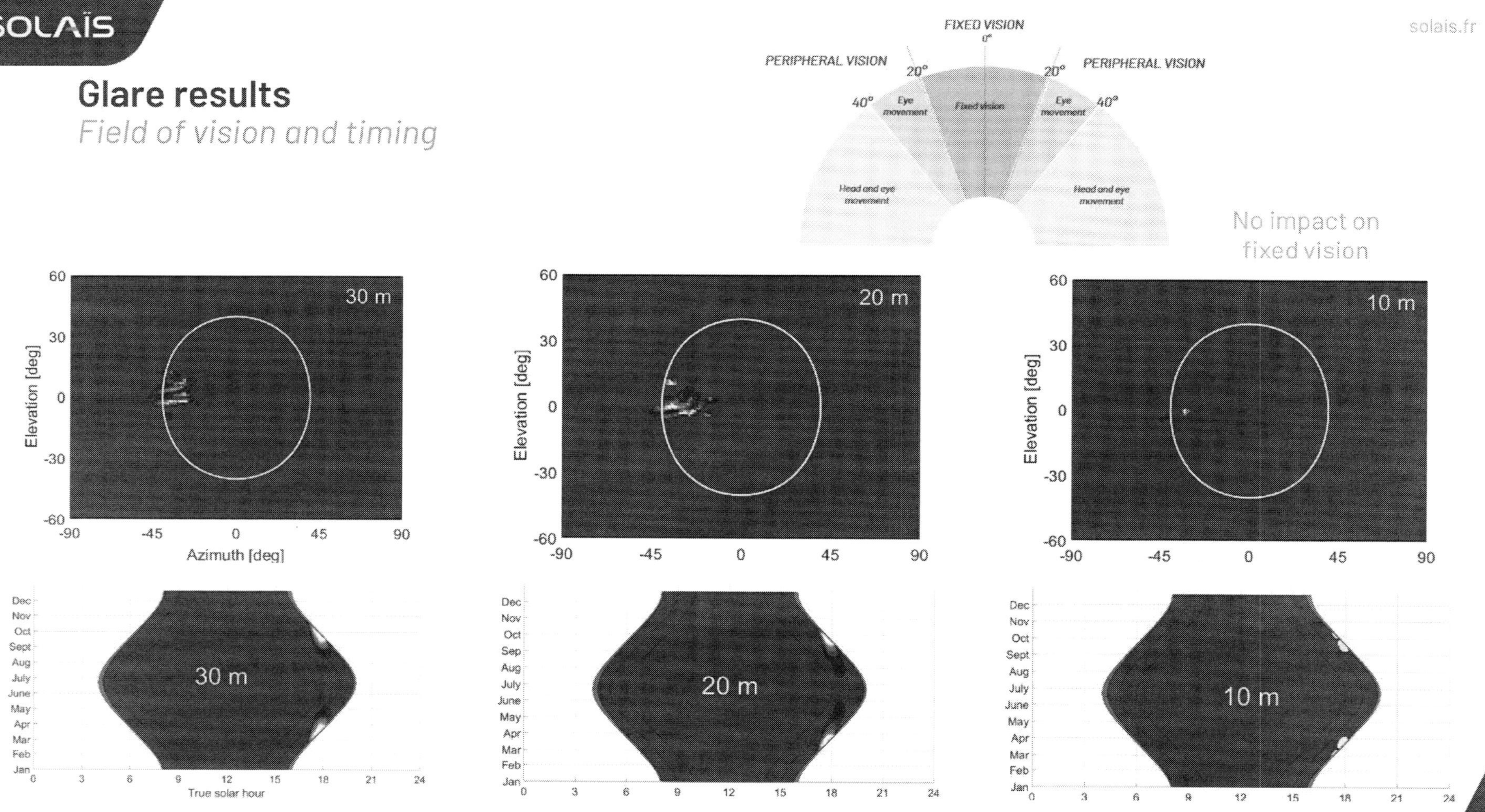

SOLAÏS

solais.fr

Conclusion

- Glare studies to be conducted in the PV development process
- Importance of working with accurate DEM and DSM
- 5–10 m resolution is preferred to mitigate the risk for mistaken occurrences

Thank you! Any questions?

solais.fr

SOLAÏS

PV Expertise & Consulting

Ecolucioles Bat. A1 – 955 route des Lucioles
06560 Valbonne – France

Contact : christophe.vernay@solais.fr

020245-013

This presentation was selected by the Sc. Committee of the EU PVSEC 2025 for submission of a full paper to one of the EU PVSEC's collaborating peer-reviewed journals.

MICRO-CONCENTRATOR PHOTOVOLTAICS FOR DEEP SPACE MISSIONS: OVERCOMING LILT CHALLENGES WITH HIGH-SPECIFIC-POWER SOLAR ARRAYS

Guido Vallerotto[1], Anderson Bermudez-Garcia[2], Gerald Siefer[3], Maike Wiesenfarth[3], Almudena Garcia-Sanchez[1], Ignacio Antón[1], Carsten Baur[4], Pier Luigi Coz[4] and César Domínguez[1]

[1] Instituto de Energía Solar, Universidad Politécnica de Madrid, Madrid, Spain
[2] R&D Solar Generators and Mechanisms, Thales Alenia Space, Cannes, France
[3] Division Photovoltaics, Fraunhofer Institute for Solar Energy Systems ISE, Freiburg, Germany
[4] Solar Generators Section, European Space Agency, Noordwijk, Netherlands

ABSTRACT: Exploration of the outer solar system is one of the European Space Agency (ESA) top scientific priorities, as defined in the Voyage 2050 program. Micro-concentrator photovoltaics (micro-CPV) are gaining attention as a viable approach to power spacecrafts operating in deep space, where conventional solar arrays may suffer severe drops in performance due to low-intensity, low-temperature (LILT) conditions. This study reports on the design, development, and testing of two novel micro-CPV solar panel architectures optimized for maximizing specific power beyond Mars orbit and for being compatible with the standard 5° angular accuracy of spacecraft attitude control: first, a silicone-on-glass (SoG) Fresnel microlens array and, second, a catadioptric concentrator that combines refraction with total internal reflection (TIR). Optical simulations indicate that the Fresnel concept delivers higher efficiency and lower mass, while the catadioptric design offers superior angular tolerance and alignment stability. Initial Fresnel prototypes were fabricated and characterized, achieving 83–85% optical efficiency, +/-5° acceptance angle, +/-1.5 mm focal distance tolerance and excellent uniformity across the 72 lenses in the array. These findings confirm both the feasibility and manufacturability of micro-CPV technology, which is expected to surpass the specific power of conventional cell-interconnected-cover (CIC) arrays for the next large scientific missions of ESA to the outer solar system.

Keywords: concentrator photovoltaics (CPV), low intensity low temperature (LILT), Fresnel lens concentrator, catadioptric concentrator.

1 INTRODUCTION

Exploration of the outer solar system is one of the European Space Agency (ESA) top scientific priorities, as defined in the Voyage 2050 program. Missions to the icy moons of Jupiter and Saturn to investigate the habitability and to find signs of past or present life are one of the main themes of the program. Going further than 4 astronomical units (AU), the low light intensity and low irradiance (LILT) conditions represent a critical challenge for deep space missions, as the state-of-the-art space qualified multi-junction (MJ) solar cells can exhibit serious performance degradation under these LILT conditions due to majority carrier barriers [1], forcing oversized and heavier solar arrays.

Concentrator photovoltaics (CPV) has the potential to mitigate this effect by increasing the effective irradiance on the cells, thereby raising operating temperature, reducing semiconductor area, and improving radiation shielding. Previous missions, such as NASA's Deep Space 1 (SCARLET array) [2–4], validated CPV in space but relied on bulky optics with limited compactness.

Micro-concentrator photovoltaics (micro-CPV), using sub-mm cells and moderate concentration ratios (10X–100X), have recently emerged as a transformative approach. Theoretical estimates show that micro-CPV systems can exceed 350 W/kg [5,6], compared to 100–200 W/kg of conventional cover-interconnect-cell (CIC) technology [7]. This work presents two micro-CPV architectures tailored for ESA deep-space missions to Jupiter and Saturn: a refractive Fresnel microlens array and a catadioptric design combining refraction and total internal reflection (TIR).

2 MODULE ARCHITECTURE

The proposed module architecture replaces the conventional CIC layers on a honeycomb substrate with a micro-CPV assembly consisting of a matrix of sub-millimeter solar cells coupled to an optical concentrator array. This approach ensures compatibility with standard deployment systems while enabling a fair comparison in terms of specific power.

Key design requirements were established to guarantee suitability for deep-space missions:

- Maximization of specific power (W/kg) at the end of life (EOL) under Jupiter and Saturn irradiance levels (3% and 1% of the AM0 spectrum, respectively).
- Angular tolerance of at least ±5° to accommodate typical spacecraft attitude control.
- Total thickness below 5 mm to remain compatible with existing solar array wings.
- Resilience against thermal cycling, radiation, high-energy particles, and micrometeoroid impact.

Following a trade-off analysis of different optical candidates, two refractive concepts were selected for development: a silicone-on-glass (SoG) Fresnel microlens array and a catadioptric unit combining refraction and TIR. The Fresnel design benefits from low weight, thin profile, high optical efficiency, and extensive flight heritage. The catadioptric system, although more complex, offers improved angular tolerance and enhanced alignment robustness. Figure 1 shows a scheme of the two proposed architectures.

10.4229/EUPVSEC2025/4AP.1.3
020246-001

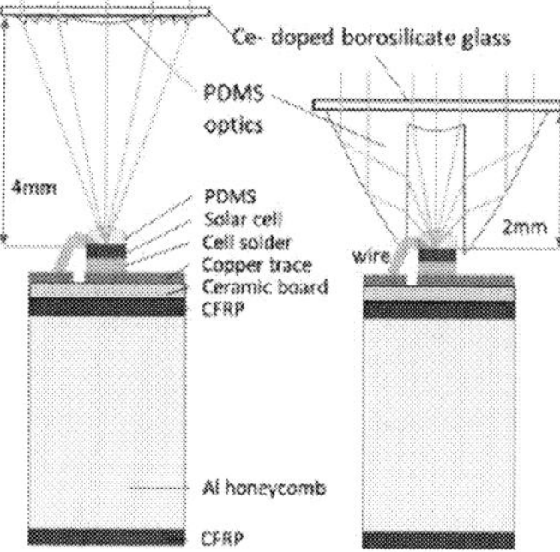

Figure 1: Scheme of the proposed structure of the two architectures presented in this work. The Fresnel version on the left and the catadioptric on the right.

The materials for both concentrator designs were selected from space-qualified options. Schott 0787 cerium-doped borosilicate glass was chosen as the cover glass, while Dowsil (Dow Corning) DC 93-500 silicone was adopted as the moldable material to form the refractive surfaces. Both materials feature extensive flight heritage and long-term reliability in space applications.

3 OPTICAL DESIGN

The optical aperture of both architectures was defined in close connection with the optimization of the solar cell dimensions. Space-qualified triple and quadruple junction (3J and 4J) devices of different sub-millimeter sizes were characterized under LILT conditions in a cryostat with two main objectives: to evaluate efficiency losses caused by edge recombination in cells with high perimeter-to-area ratios under low irradiance, and to determine the minimum operating temperature required to avoid degradation due to majority carrier barrier effects. The results showed that a cell diameter of 0.8 mm (0.5 mm² active area) represents the optimal compromise: small enough to reduce semiconductor mass and maximize specific power, large enough to limit perimeter related recombination losses. Regarding temperature, –137 °C was identified as the lowest point at which cells operating under low irradiance (~14 W/m²) remain unaffected by majority carrier barrier effects. Considering an environmental temperature below -150 °C we estimate that an effective concentration of 10X is sufficient to raise the cell operating temperature near this limit. Assuming a realistic optical efficiency of approximately 80%, this corresponds to a geometrical concentration of 12X and an optical aperture area of ~6 mm². To avoid the aperture losses typically associated with circular optics the optical array has been designed with hexagonal lenses with 1.52 mm diameter of the circumscribed circumference.

3.1 Design optimization

The two designs were modeled and optimized for the maximum efficiency and angular tolerance using a commercial 3D ray-tracing software. For the Fresnel architecture the main optimization parameters are the height of the Fresnel facets and the focal distance of the lens (*i.e.* the f-number) while for the catadioptric the aperture of the inner cavity. Considering the mentioned design constraints for the Fresnel lens the focal distance

was set to the maximum value of 4 mm to maximize the efficiency and the facets height to 50 μm based on mold manufacturers' feedback and a trade-off between minimizing tip rounding losses and reducing lens volume and weight.

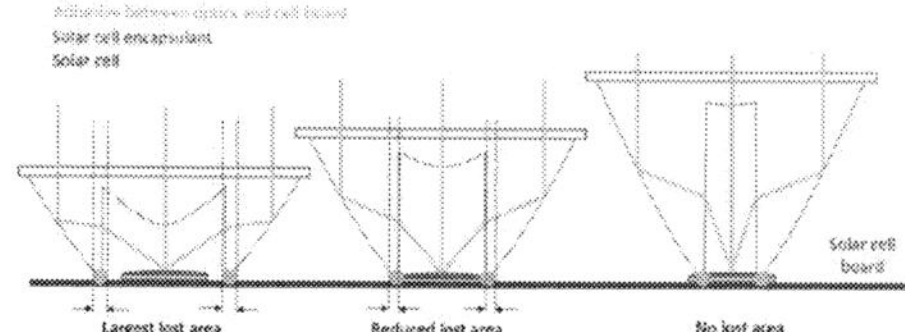

Figure 2: Sketches of three possible configurations of the catadioptric architecture. Note that the figure is not in scale and it is purely qualitative.

For the catadioptric the nominal design matches the solar cell diameter to the cavity aperture (Figure 2, center). Increasing the aperture results in a shorter, more compact system, but rays incident on the peaks are lost (Figure 2, left). Decreasing the aperture recovers these rays but increases the volume, the weight and the absorption losses resulting from an increased optical path length (Figure 2, right). Seven apertures, from 0.7 mm to 0.9 mm, were simulated to evaluate the sensitivity of acceptance angle and optical efficiency and 0.9 mm resulted to be the optimum solution.

On the optimized design Two simulation sets were conducted for each optical architecture:

1. **Operational condition simulations:** Using the refractive index of DC 93-500 silicone at -190 °C and a 1% AM0 spectrum to emulate deep-space LILT conditions.

2. **Room temperature simulations:** Based on the refractive index at 25 °C, to predict the performance of prototypes to be tested under laboratory conditions (using the Helios 3198 CPV solar simulator available at the Solar Energy Institute [8]).

The first set serves to validate the suitability of each design for deep-space applications. However, given that initial prototypes will be fabricated and tested at room temperature, the second set is critical for assessing expected performance in upcoming experimental campaigns.

It is important to note that LILT-condition simulations assume an idealized optic geometry (*i.e.*, the nominal profile derived from design procedure), without accounting for deformations due to thermal contraction. In reality, the optics will be manufactured at room temperature and subsequently experience severe temperature changes in space. As such, the mold must be pre-compensated to account for expected shrinkage and ensure that the operational profile matches the design.

To evaluate this, a preliminary finite element modeling (FEM) simulation was performed on the Fresnel lens geometry. The results indicate that, in the absence of mold compensation, efficiency losses at -190 °C may become significant.

Figure 3 summarizes the key outcomes of the ray-tracing simulations. Note that the simulation model include spectral material properties, Fresnel reflection, and non-ideality caused by the manufacturing process (*i.e.* draft angles for mold release and rounding of tips and valley of the lens profile).

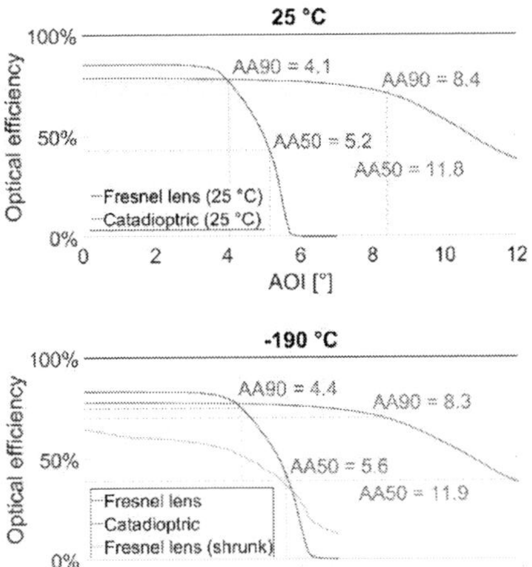

Figure 3: Graph showing the optical efficiency as a function of the angle of incidence (AOI) for the Fresnel lens and the catadioptric at room temperature (up) and at -190 °C (bottom). In yellow, the optical efficiency for Fresnel lens at -190 °C if no mold compensation is made.

The blue and red curves correspond to the optical efficiency versus angle of incidence (AOI) for the Fresnel and catadioptric designs, respectively. The upper plot shows results at room temperature, while the lower refers to –190 °C. At normal incidence, the Fresnel lens achieves higher efficiency thanks to lower absorption, but beyond ±4° the catadioptric outperform the Fresnel lens. As anticipated, when considering ideal geometries, at both room (upper graph) and cryogenic (bottom graph) temperatures the curves overlap closely, indicating that with appropriate mold compensation the optical performance at LILT should remain similar to that at ambient conditions.

The figure also reports the acceptance angles for the 90% and the 50% of the maximum power (AA90 and AA50, respectively) for both configurations. The yellow curve in Figure 3 (bottom) represents the Fresnel profile after thermal shrinkage at –190 °C, simulated via FEM. In this case, even under perfect alignment, the efficiency decreases from ~85% to ~65%.

Due to its more complex optical path and bulkier geometry, the catadioptric system is expected to experience comparable or greater efficiency losses at cryogenic temperatures, although dedicated FEM simulations are still required to quantify them. Overall, the results highlight that mold compensation is an essential design measure to ensure reliable optical performance in deep-space environments

4 MANUFACTURING AND CHARACTERIZATION

The first prototypes of the Fresnel microlens array were manufactured using the Dow Corning DC 93-500 silicone directly molded onto Schott 0787 borosilicate substrates with 150 µm thickness. The mold was produced via precision micromachining, ensuring groove depths of 50 µm with controlled surface quality. A degassing step was applied before curing to eliminate trapped air bubbles, and curing was carried out under vacuum conditions.

The mold designed consists of an array of 8×9 individual lenses arranged on a 20x20 mm² tile, corresponding to a total of 72 optical units.

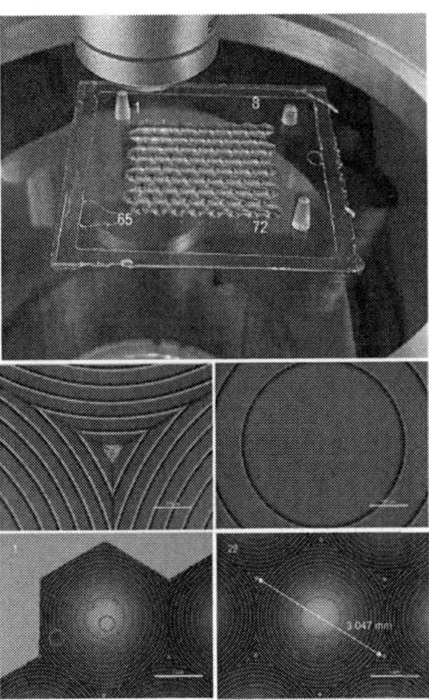

Figure 4: (Up) Photograph of the first manufactured prototype of the Fresnel architecture. (Bottom) photographs taken with an optical microscope of one lens of the manufactured prototype.

Figure 4 show a photograph of the manufactured array on the left and some sample pictures taken with an optical microscope on the right. Microscopic inspection of the cured arrays confirmed accurate reproduction of the mold geometry across most of the surface, with only minor imperfections at the edges. These defects have negligible impact on the overall optical performance, as confirmed by subsequent characterization.

Optical characterization was carried out using the solar simulator Helios 3198 for CPV modules [8], which provides collimated and spectrally matched AM0-like illumination. The array was mounted on a high-precision automated three axis moving platform, allowing fine control of both lateral displacement and cell-to-lens distance. In addition, the optical setup is mounted over an automated rotary stage allowing the cell-lens system to rotate with respect to the direction of the collimated light source.

Figure 5 shows a scheme and a photograph of the experimental setup. The measurement procedure is as follow: first, the current generated by the bare solar cell is measured. Then, the cell is moved behind each lens composing the array, and the current is measured individually for each lens. Finally, knowing the lens aperture it is possible to calculate the optical efficiency of each lens using the formula:

$$\eta_{opti} = \frac{\dfrac{I_{sc,lens}}{I_{sc,bare}}}{\dfrac{A_{lens}}{A_{cell}}} = \frac{X_{eff}}{X_{geo}} \qquad (1)$$

where $I_{sc,lens}$ and $I_{sc,bare}$ are the currents generated by the solar cell with and without optics, respectively. A_{lens} and A_{cell} are the aperture area of the lens and the solar cell. Therefore, the first ratio represents the effective concentration (X_{eff}), that is the increase in the effective irradiance over the solar cell, and the second ratio represents the geometrical concentration (X_{geo}).

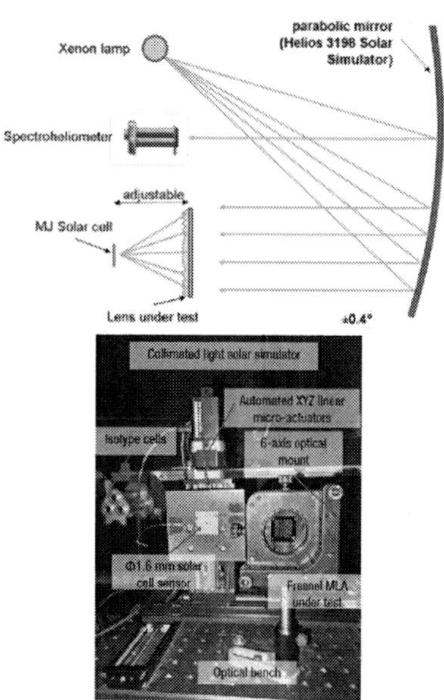

Figure 5: (Up) Scheme of the solar simulator Helios 3198. (Right) Photograph of the automated three-axis moving platform used to align solar sensor and optics during characterization.

Solar cells with a nominal lens aperture of 0.5 mm² were not available at the time of the measurement campaign. Therefore, to evaluate the performance of the optics at the nominal geometrical concentration (*i.e.*, 12X), a copper mask with a 0.8 mm diameter pinhole was used to reduce the sensor active area and characterize the optical system.

Two main issues arose. First, it was impossible to precisely measure the exact aperture area of the pinhole. Second, a light sensor with such a small active surface is highly sensitive to minor defects on the collimating mirror surface. While these defects are negligible when using a larger sensor, since the light is integrated over a wider aperture, they can produce significant variations in measured irradiance when using a smaller sensor, where even millimetric displacements can affect the result.

To minimize these sources of uncertainty, the optical array was scanned using a larger solar cell (2.3 mm diameter), and the photocurrent was measured at 72 positions corresponding to each lens in the array. The same scan was then repeated with the solar cell masked by the 0.8 mm pinhole. By dividing the average photocurrent obtained with the bare and masked cell, the effective ratio between the solar cell aperture and the pinhole aperture was estimated. Subsequently, the reference current used to calculate X_{eff} in Equation (1) was determined by dividing the photocurrent of the 2.3 mm solar cell (less sensitive to mirror imperfections) by this ratio.

With this method, the calculated efficiency becomes independent of the pinhole aperture, while the influence of surface defects is mitigated by using a sensor whose size remains only slightly smaller than the lens aperture.

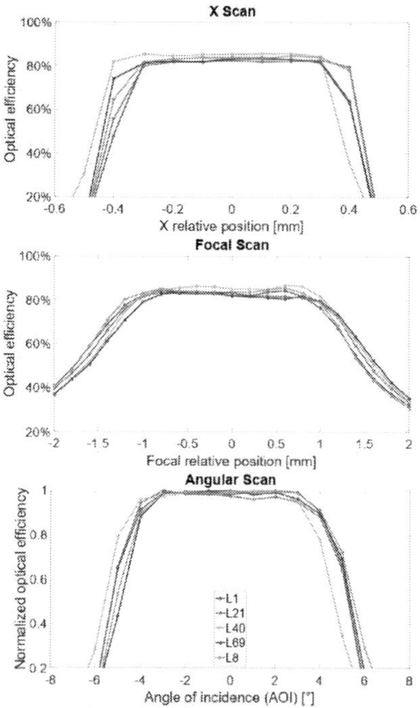

Figure 6: Characterization results of the five randomly selected lenses. X scan is in the direction parallel to the lens plane. Focal scan is in the direction perpendicular to the lens plane and the angular scan is obtained by rotating the whole system with respect to the collimating mirror.

Due to the time-consuming iterative procedure required to correctly align the solar cell and the optics, only five randomly chosen lenses of the array were fully characterized.

Figure 6 shows the results of the characterization. The measured optical efficiency of 83–85% is in close agreement with the ray-tracing predictions. Alignment tolerance was investigated by intentionally offsetting the lens array with respect to the detector: lateral displacements up to ±0.3 mm and axial displacements up to ±1 mm caused negligible efficiency demonstrating robust alignment margins for integration at module level loss (see Figure 6 up and center). Finally, the acceptance angle measured at 50% efficiency (AA50) is approximately ±5° (Figure 6, bottom), perfectly matching with simulation results. Note that the five measured lenses show highly similar performance suggesting a good uniformity of the quality of the lenses composing the array.

In order to know the optical quality of all the lenses composing the array a larger solar cell of 1.6 mm diameter is used to ease the alignment procedure. Because of the lower geometrical concentration (~3X) the absolute efficiency value measured with this cell is not representative of the system but may be used to assess the uniformity of the quality of the lenses. Figure 7 shows the optical efficiency of the 72 measured lenses normalized with the maximum value.

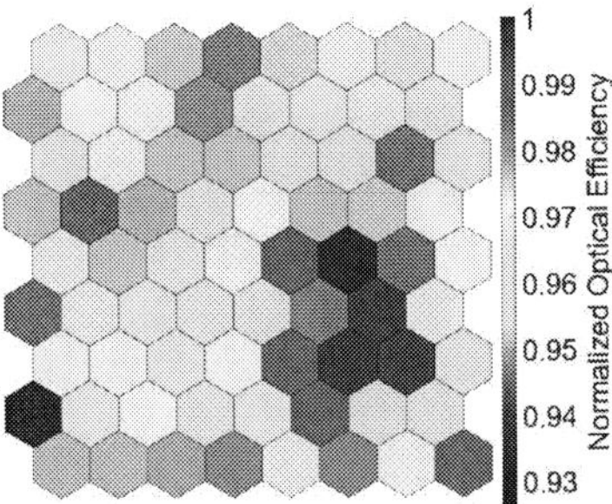

Figure 7: Normalized optical efficiency measured for the 72 lenses composing the first manufactured array. A colormap is used to show the efficiency of each lens together with its position within the array.

It can be noted that there is good consistency among the lenses composing the array (standard deviation equal to 1.2%). However, from this map, it is evident that a higher efficiency region is concentrated in the lower-right part of the array. Further work is needed to determine whether this is a measurement artifact or a real pattern, and if confirmed, to identify its underlying cause.

Although only Fresnel microlens arrays were fabricated at this stage, the catadioptric concept is following a similar development path, with future prototypes expected to provide a direct comparison between both designs.

7 CONCLUSIONS

This study reports the design, fabrication, and initial validation of two micro-concentrator photovoltaic (micro-CPV) concepts tailored for deep-space applications. Targeting the combined challenges of low irradiance and cryogenic environments beyond 4 AU, the results highlight micro-CPV as a promising high-specific-power solution for future missions.

Two optical approaches were proposed, which were optimized for maximizing specific power beyond Mars orbit and for being compatible with the standard 5° angular accuracy of spacecraft attitude control: a Fresnel microlens array and a catadioptric system, both built with space-qualified materials. Ray-tracing simulation modeling was used to optimize both optical designs showing that the Fresnel architecture achieves higher efficiency and lower mass at normal incidence, whereas the catadioptric design offers broader angular tolerance and stronger alignment robustness.

The first Fresnel array prototype was successfully manufactured and characterized. The resulting optical efficiencies at the nominal geometrical concentration of 12X is in the range of 83–85%, +/-5° acceptance angle, +/-1.5 mm focal distance tolerance and excellent uniformity across the 72 lenses in the array, closely matching simulations and confirming the design's manufacturability. These findings confirm both the feasibility and manufacturability of micro-CPV technology.

Overall, the work positions micro-CPV as a competitive alternative to conventional cover-interconnect-cell (CIC) technology, with the potential to surpass the specific power of conventional cell-interconnected-cover (CIC) arrays. Future efforts will address full module integration, thermal management, and in-orbit validation, consolidating micro-CPV as an enabling option for upcoming ESA deep-space missions.

A full paper with an extended dissertation of this work is currently under revision in the journal RRL Solar.

REFERENCES

[1] R. Hoheisel *et al.*, "Low temperature effects in photovoltaic devices for deep space missions," in *2015 IEEE 42nd Photovoltaic Specialist Conference (PVSC)*, 2015, pp. 1–5, doi: 10.1109/PVSC.2015.7355666.

[2] J. J. Wachholz *et al.*, "SCARLET I: Mechanization Solutions for Deployable Concentrator Optics Integrated with Rigid Array Technology." 1996.

[3] D. M. Murphy *et al.*, "SCARLET development, fabrication, and testing for the Deep Space 1 spacecraft," in *IECEC-97 Proceedings of the Thirty-Second Intersociety Energy Conversion Engineering Conference*, 1997, vol. 4, pp. 2237–2245, doi: 10.1109/IECEC.1997.658216.

[4] D. M. Murphy, "The Scarlet Solar Array: Technology Validation and Flight Results." AEC-Able Engineering Co., Inc, Pasadena, CA, 2000, [Online]. Available: http://www.aec-able.com.

[5] J. S. Price *et al.*, "High-Concentration Planar Microtracking Photovoltaic System Exceeding 30% Efficiency," *Nat. Energy*, vol. 2, no. 8, p. 17113, 2017, doi: 10.1038/nenergy.2017.113.

[6] L. Li *et al.*, "Highly-integrated Hybrid Micro-Concentrating Photovoltaics," in *2018 IEEE 7th World Conference on Photovoltaic Energy Conversion (WCPEC)*, 2018, pp. 1655–1657, doi: 10.1109/PVSC.2018.8547904.

[7] C. J. Ruud *et al.*, "Microcell concentrating photovoltaics for space," *Joule*, vol. 7, no. 6, pp. 1093–1098, 2023, doi: 10.1016/j.joule.2023.04.004.

[8] C. Dominguez *et al.*, "Solar simulator for indoor characterization of large area high-concentration PV modules," in *2008 33rd IEEE Photovolatic Specialists Conference*, San Diego, CA, USA, May 2008, pp. 1–5, doi: 10.1109/PVSC.2008.4922739.

Micro-concentrator photovoltaics for deep space missions: overcoming LILT challenges with high-specific-power solar arrays

Guido Vallerotto
Almudena Garcia-Sanchez
Ignacio Antón
César Domínguez

Anderson Bermudez-Garcia

Gerald Siefer
Maike Wiesenfarth

Carsten Baur
Pier Luigi Coz

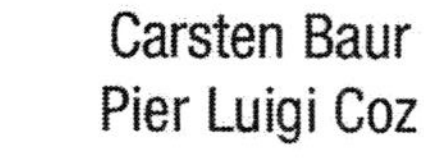

020247-001

Context

Powering up large-class European Space Agency (ESA) deep space missions up to mid-21st century (2035-2050)

Moons of the giant planets

- Liquid water

- Source of energy

- Chemical elements

Enceladus – credit: ESA

1

020247-002

Context

Powering up large-class European Space Agency (ESA) deep space missions up to mid-21st century (2035-2050)

Moons of the giant

planets

- Liquid water

- Source of energy

- Chemical elements

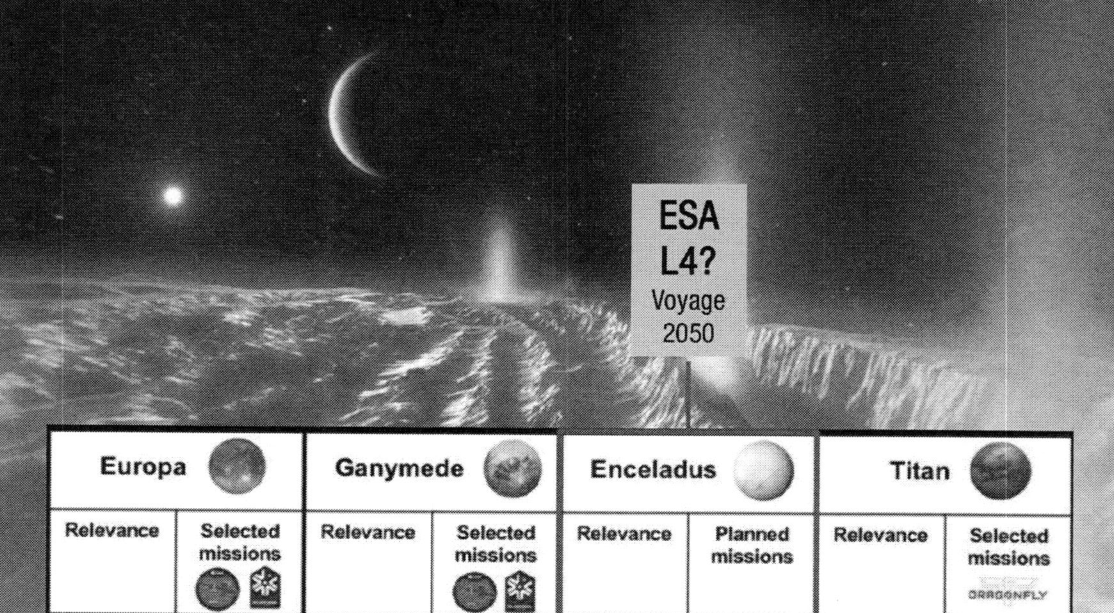

Enceladus – credit: ESA

020247-003

Challenges of LILT conditions

- ## What is the main challenge for deep space missions (> 4 AU)?

  - Extremely low light intensity and temperature (LILT) → 1-3% AM0, < -150°

JUICE spacecraft features **85 m²** of solar arrays (3J solar cells) delivering only **800-850 W** in the proximity of **Jupiter**

In **Saturn**, for the same delivered power the solar array should be approximately **250 m²**

020247-004

Challenges of LILT conditions

- **What is the main challenge for deep space missions (> 4 AU)?**

  – Extremely low light intensity and temperature (LILT) → 1-3% AM0, < -150°

Efficiency drop of state-of-the-art 3J/4J cells at low T

⬇

Concentrator Photovoltaic (CPV) technology can potentially mitigate this effect by increasing the effective irradiance reaching the cell

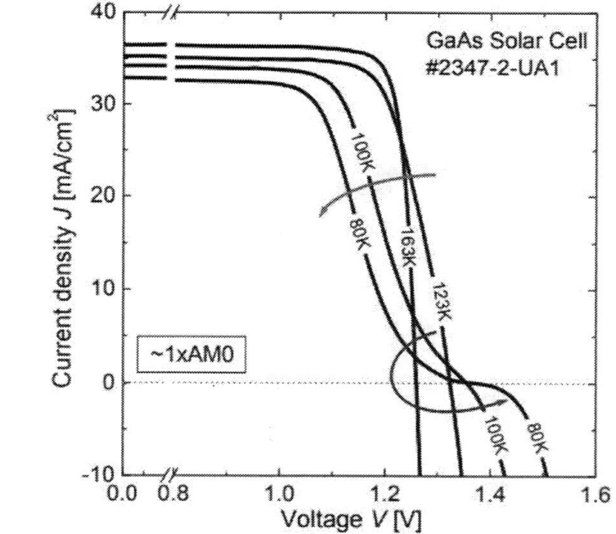

Hoheisel, "Low temperature effects in photovoltaic devices for deep space missions," in *2015 IEEE 42nd Photovoltaic Specialist Conference*

POLITÉCNICA

020247-005

CPV space heritage

- ## Has CPV technology been tested in space?

  - In 1994 the **PASP Plus experiment** was launched: 16 cell modules flying for 1 year.

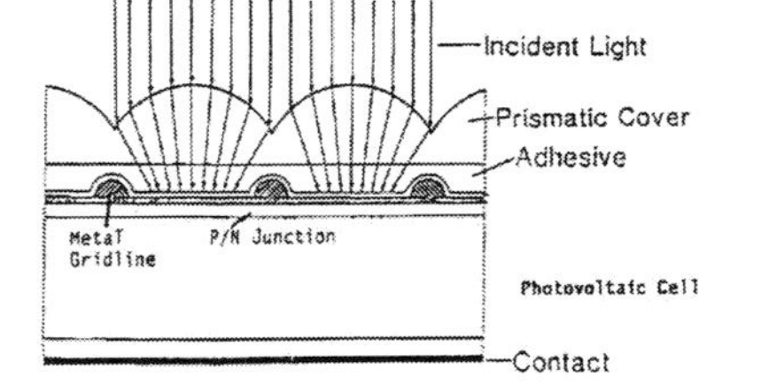

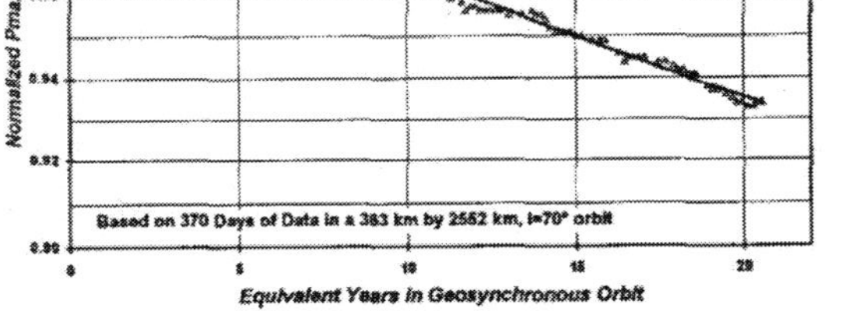

- High performance (efficiency 20% AMO)

- Lowest degradation (7% in one year) than any other **bare** solar cell technology

POLITÉCNICA

4

020247-006

Requirements for deep space missions

- **What are the requirements of a solar array for deep space missions?**

High specific power (W/kg)

Low stowed volume (m³/W)

Mitigation of LILT conditions

Conventional CPV

Bulky optics

High focal distance and volume

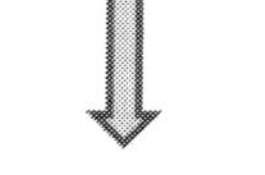

Micro-CPV

Reduced dust / particle radiation damage

High EOL efficiency

High voltage for SEP

Potential benefits of micro-CPV

INSTITUTO DE ENERGÍA SOLAR

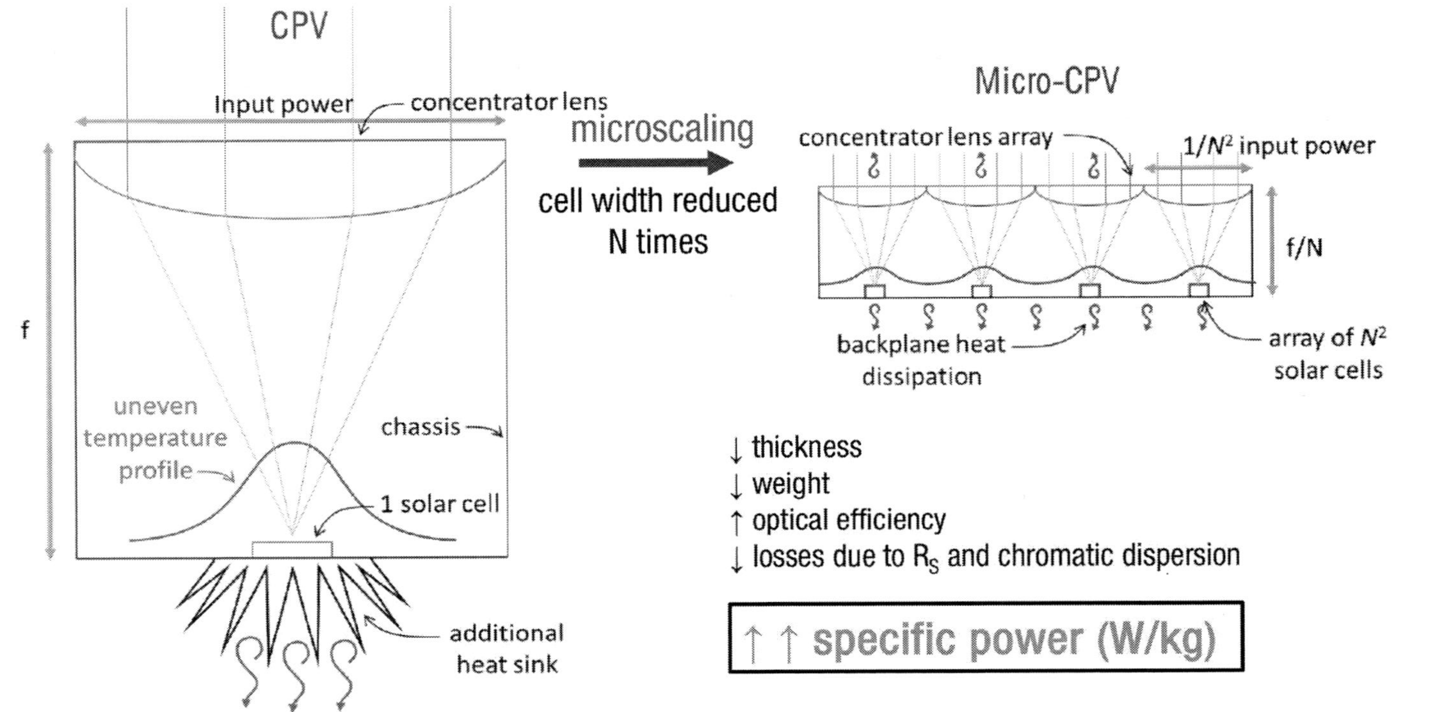

POLITÉCNICA

020247-008

Micro-CPV space heritage

- **Pioneers of micro-CPV for space:**

  – US Naval Research Laboratory / Semprius: 30% eff., 14X, >5° AA

  – JAXA: 2.3 & 3X refractive μ-CPV on SHARP's InGaP/GaAs/Ge 3J cells

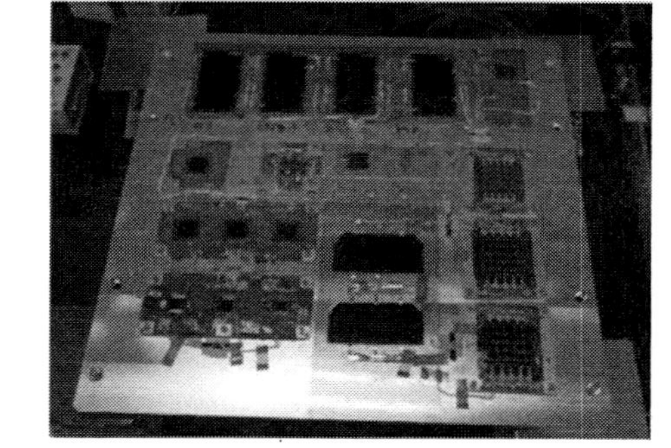

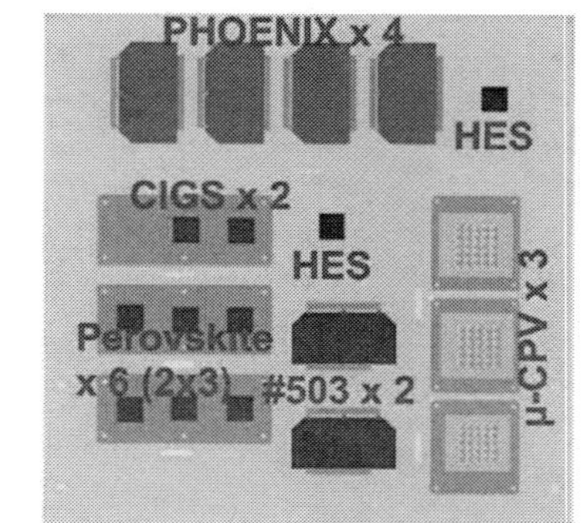

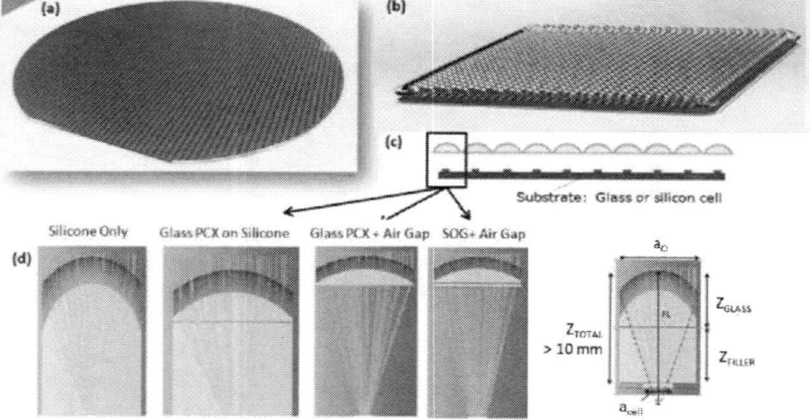

A new European endeavor

Proof-of-concept CPV module optimized for missions to Jupiter, Saturn and beyond

Objectives:

- 10X concentrator with moderate angular tolerance ($>5°$) and low thickness

- Compatible with existing solar array wing architectures

- Able to avoid LILT performance drop

8

020247-010

Proposed architectures

Immersed two-stage

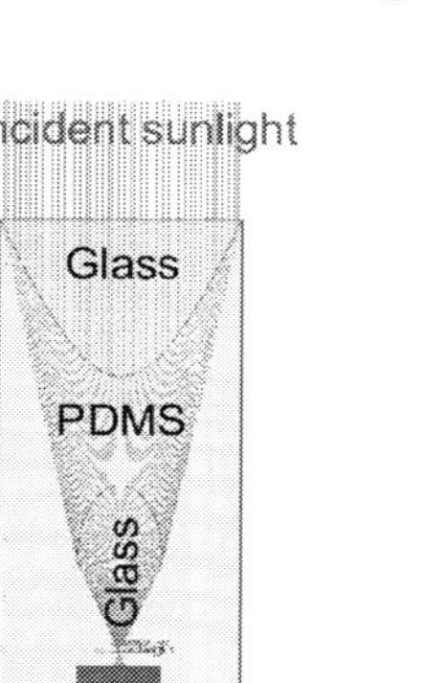

Catadioptric

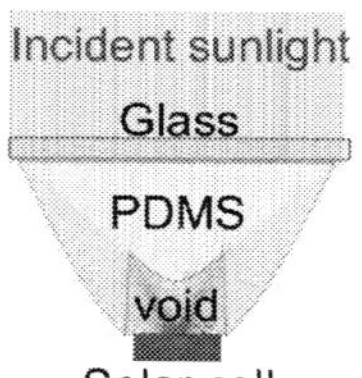

Fresnel lens

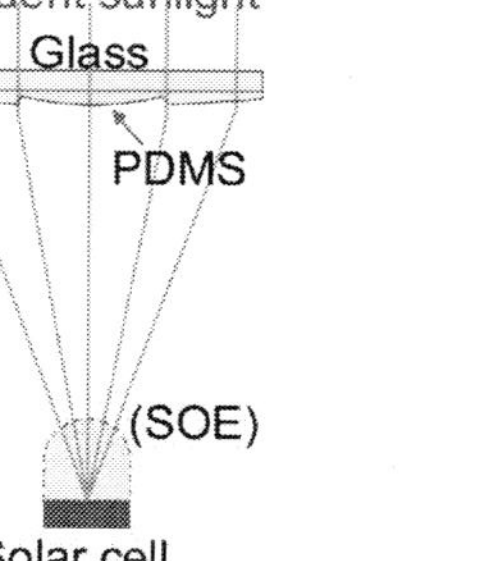

Aspheric lens

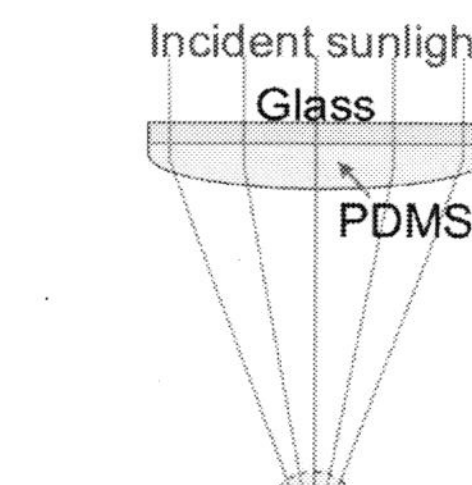

POLITÉCNICA

Proposed architectures

INSTITUTO DE ENERGÍA SOLAR

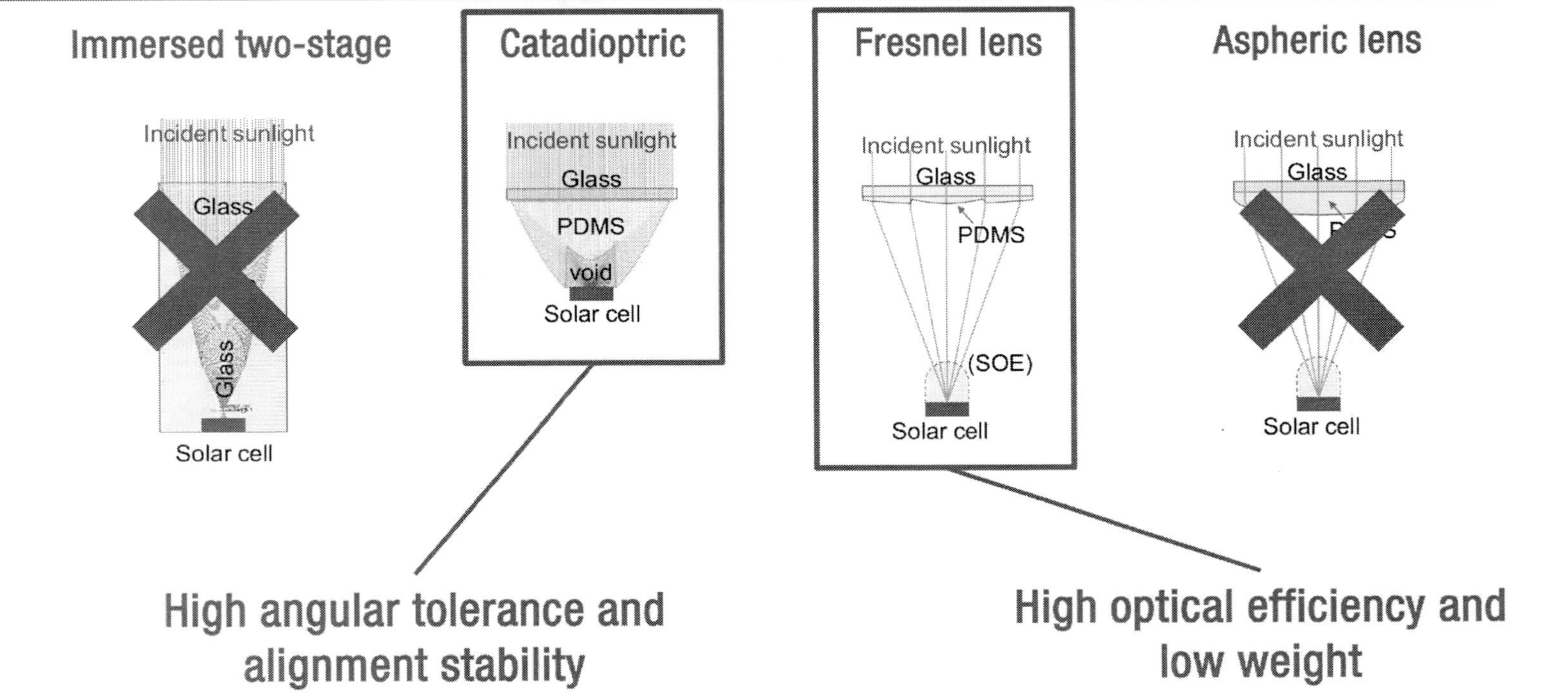

020247-012

Proposed architectures

Conventional cell-interconnect-cover (CIC) on honeycomb technology

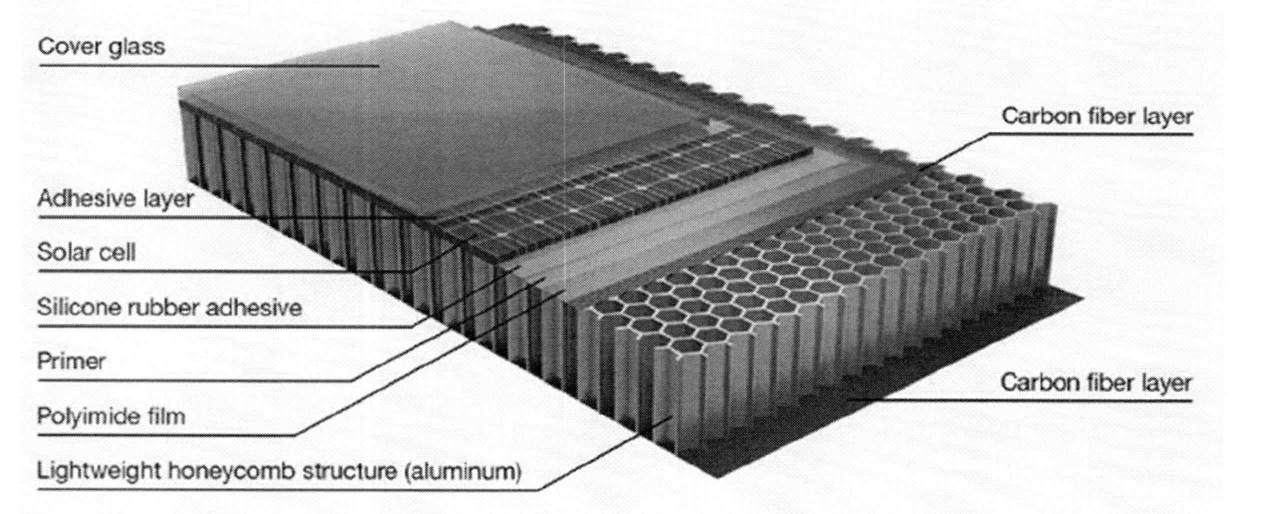

020247-013

Proposed architectures

Conventional cell-interconnect-cover (CIC) on honeycomb technology

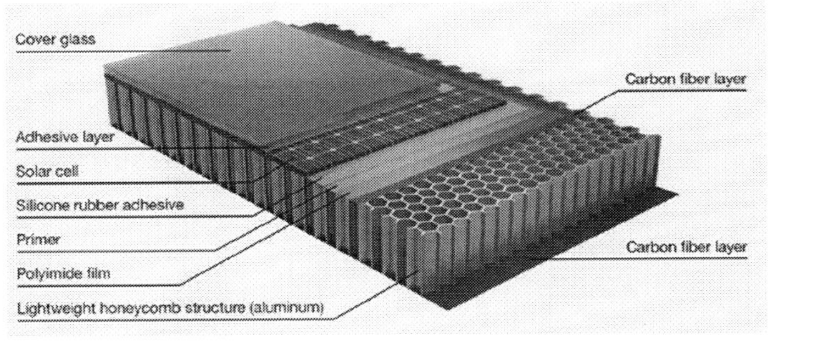

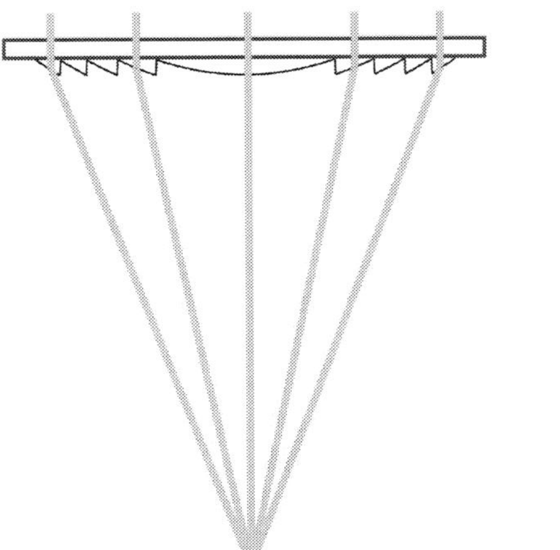

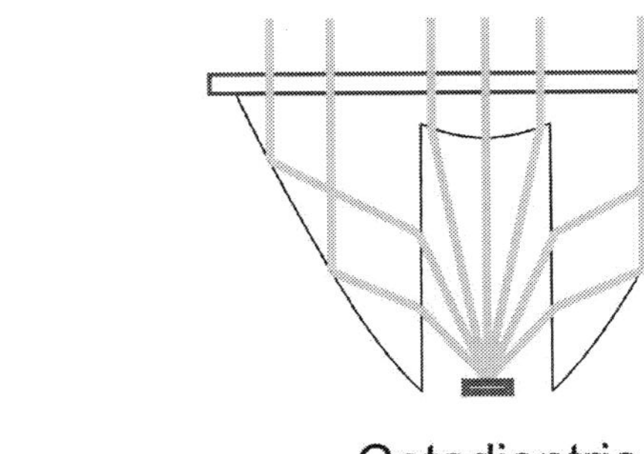

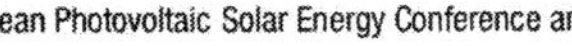

Fresnel

Catadioptric

Proposed architectures

INSTITUTO DE ENERGÍA SOLAR

Conventional cell-interconnect-cover (CIC) on honeycomb technology

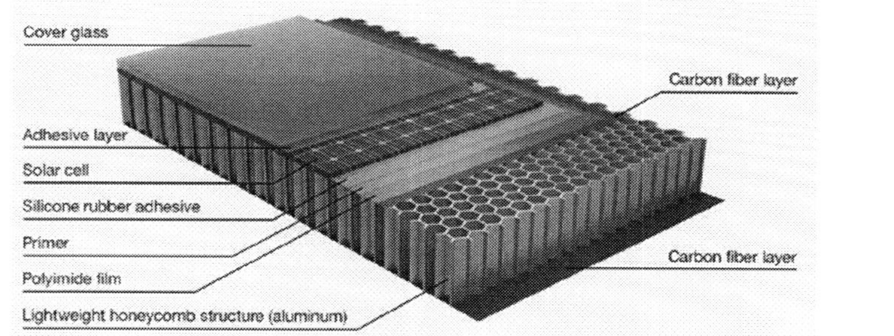

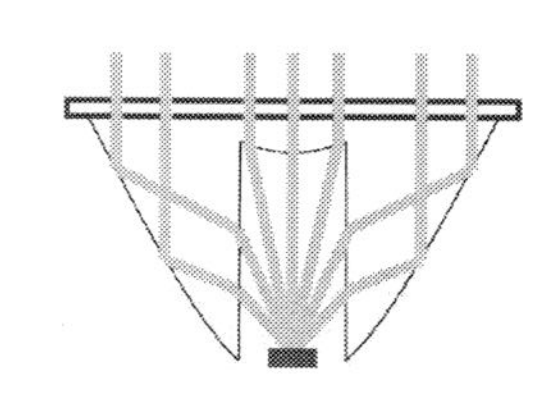

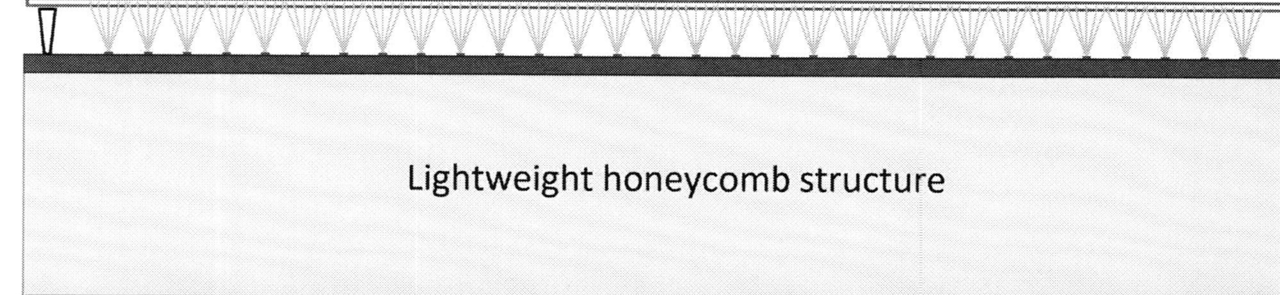

POLITÉCNICA

020247-015

Work carried out

- Material selection

- Space qualified solar cell characterization at LILT conditions

- Optimization of the optical designs by means of ray-tracing simulation

- Manufacturing of the optical arrays prototypes (only Fresnel)

- Manufacturing of solar cell board

- Experimental characterization of the optical arrays prototypes (only Fresnel)

- Manufacturing and characterization of 4J solar cell envisaged for the project.

Optical design: constraints and specifications

INSTITUTO DE ENERGÍA SOLAR

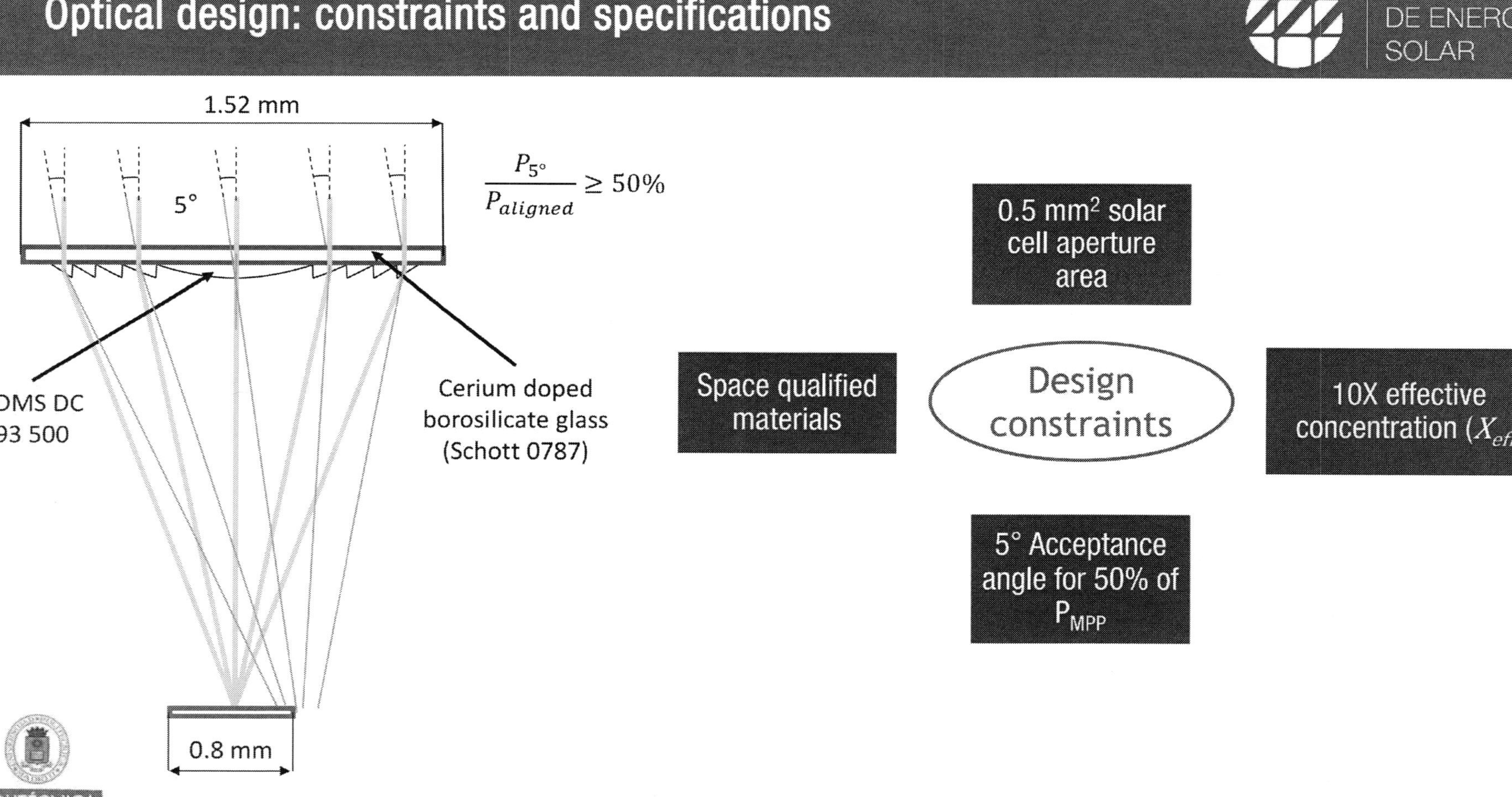

Optical design: modeling results

INSTITUTO DE ENERGÍA SOLAR

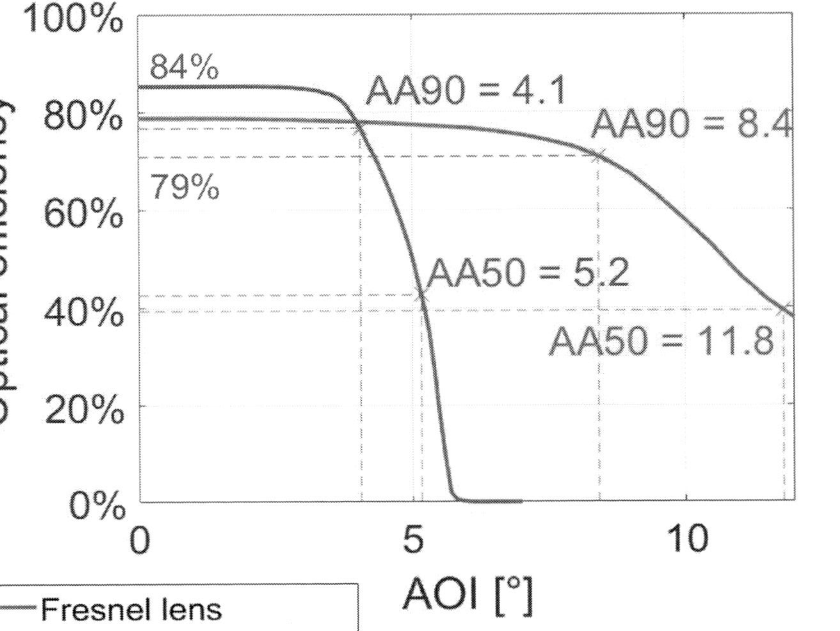

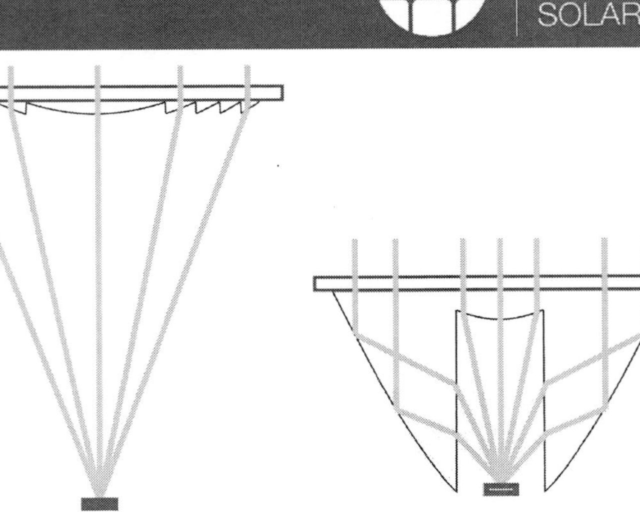

$$\eta_{opti} = \frac{P_{cell}}{P_{lens}}$$

POLITÉCNICA

Experimental characterization: optics

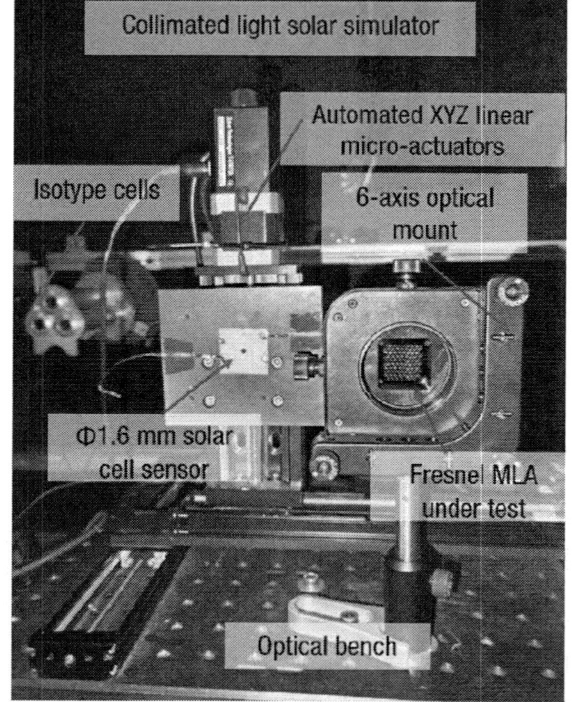

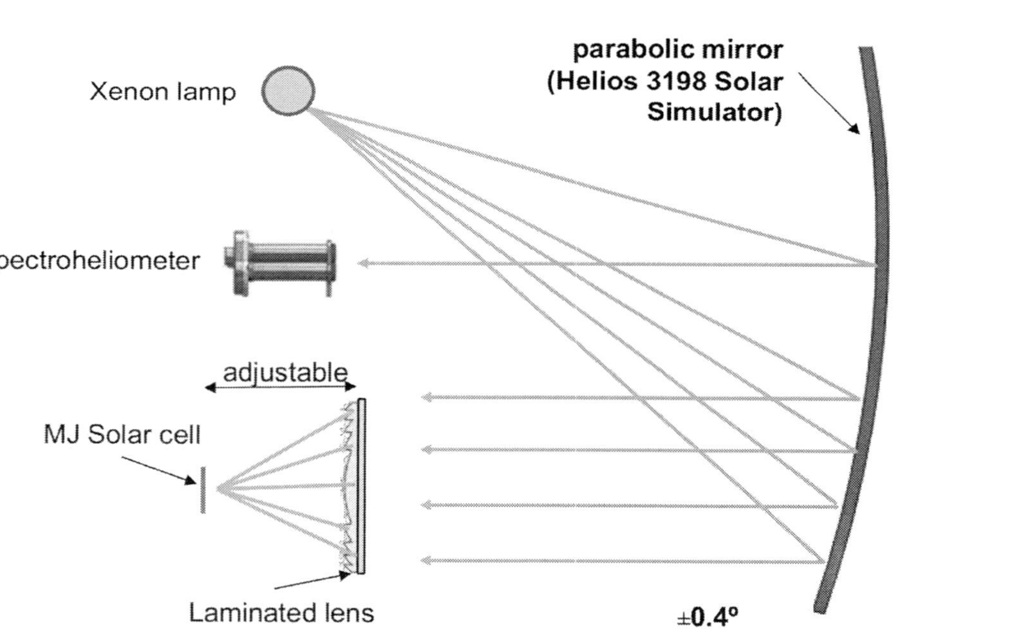

Experimental characterization: optics

INSTITUTO DE ENERGÍA SOLAR

Five randomly chosen lenses fully characterized:

- Optical efficiency: 83-85%

- Horizontal positioning tolerance: ±0.3 mm

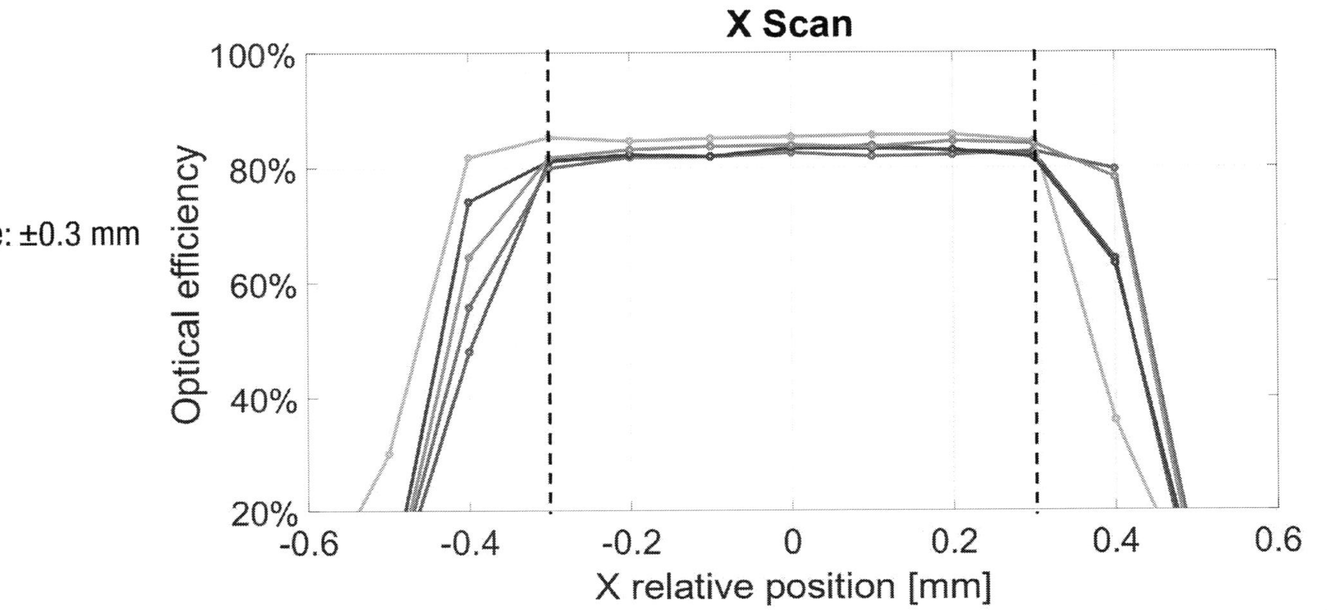

POLITÉCNICA

Experimental characterization: optics

Five randomly chosen lenses fully characterized:

- Optical efficiency: 83-85%
- Horizontal positioning tolerance: ±0.3 mm
- Focal distance tolerance: ±1 mm

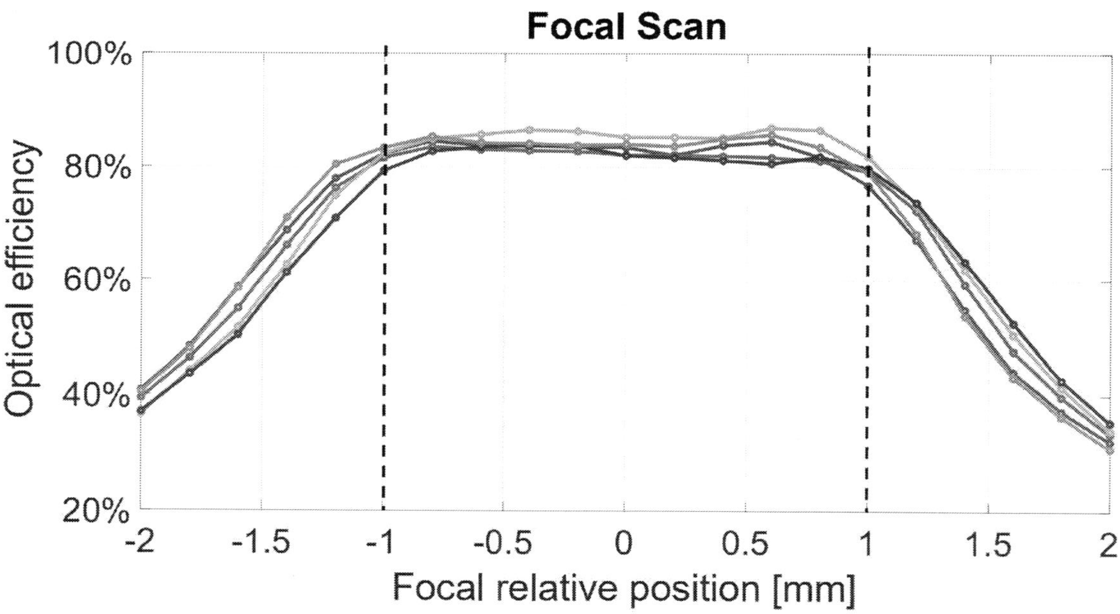

Experimental characterization: optics

Five randomly chosen lenses fully characterized:

- Optical efficiency: 83-85%

- Horizontal positioning tolerance: ±0.3 mm

- Focal distance tolerance: ±1 mm

- Acceptance angle: 5° AA50, 4° AA90

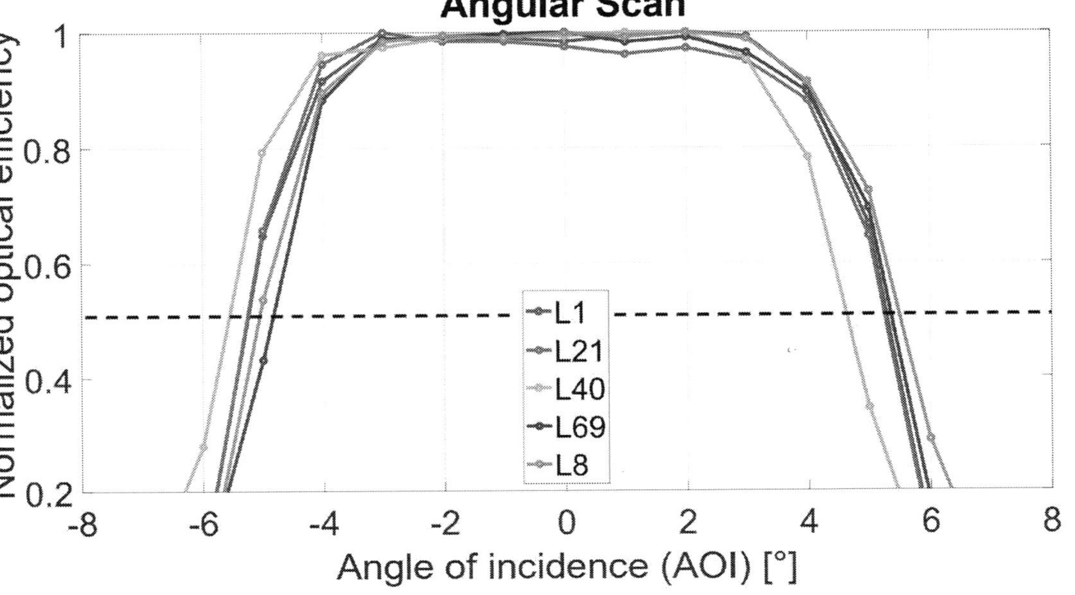

Experimental characterization: optics

Five randomly chosen lenses fully characterized:

- Optical efficiency: 83-85%
- Horizontal positioning tolerance: ±0.3 mm
- Focal distance tolerance: ±1 mm
- Acceptance angle: 4° AA50, 5° AA90
- Good match between different lenses

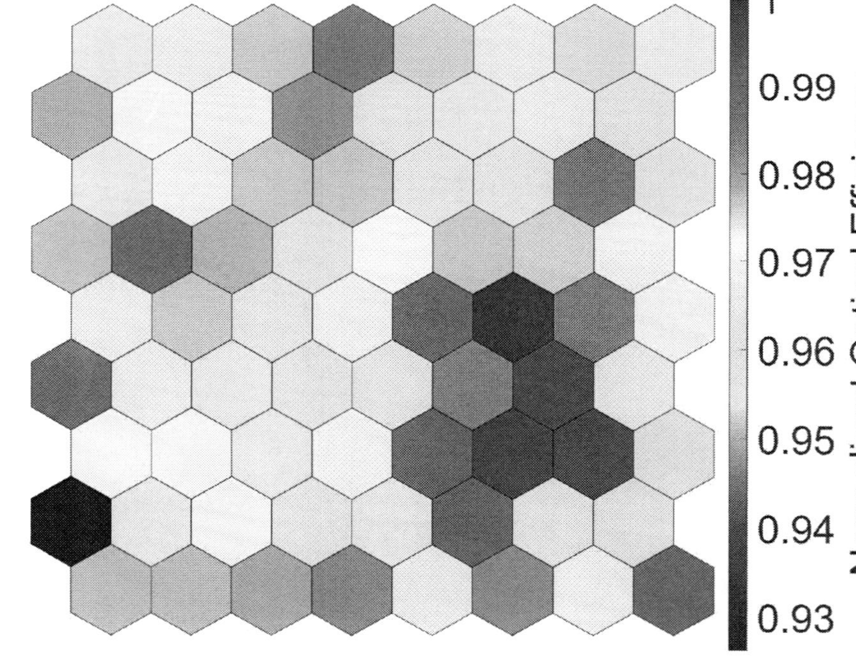

Conclusions

- The study confirms that micro-CPV technology may be a mission enabler for large-class deep space mission

- Two complementary optical architectures were investigated:

  - Fresnel microlens arrays
    - High optical efficiency (85%)
    - Low weight
    - **High specific power (W/kg)**

  - Catadioptric system
    - High angular tolerance
    - Good alignment stability
    - **Medium specific power (W/kg) (higher than CIC)**

- Successfully manufactured and characterized the first Fresnel architecture prototype:

  - Optical efficiency: 84%
  - Acceptance angle for 50% of P_{MPP}: 5°

Future work

INSTITUTO
DE ENERGÍA
SOLAR

- Manufacturing and characterization

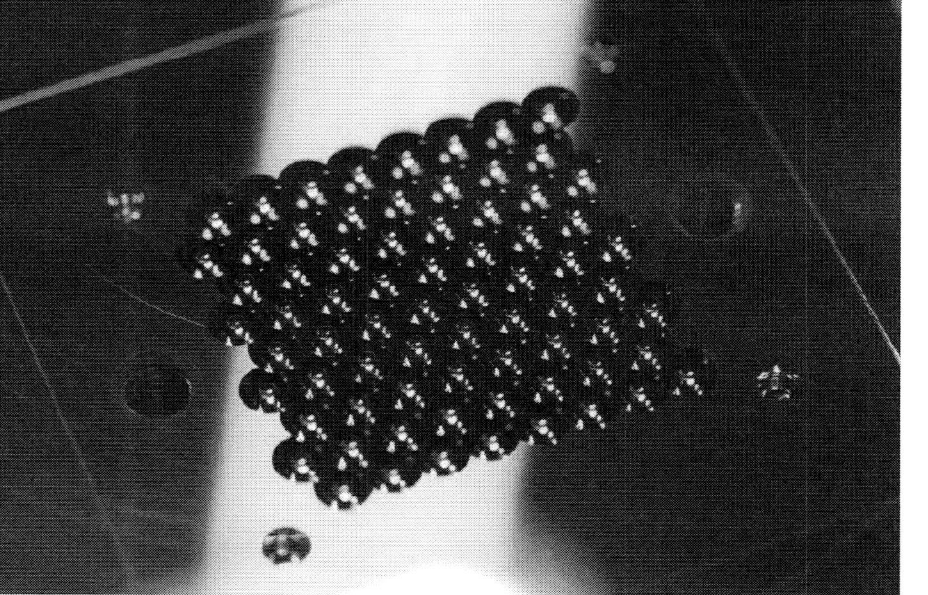

POLITÉCNICA

Future work

- Manufacturing and characterization of the catadioptric architecture

- Full module integration

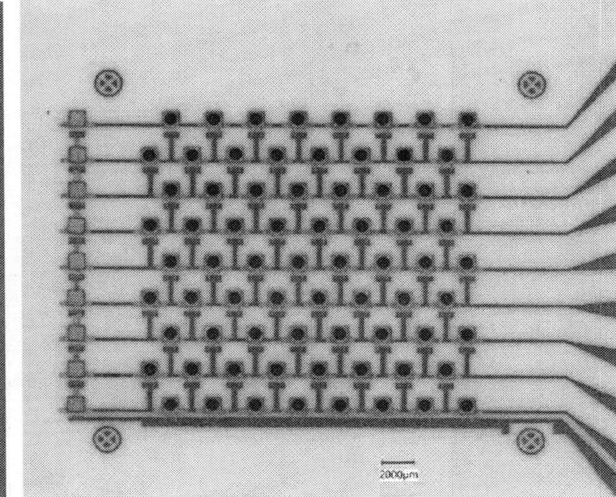

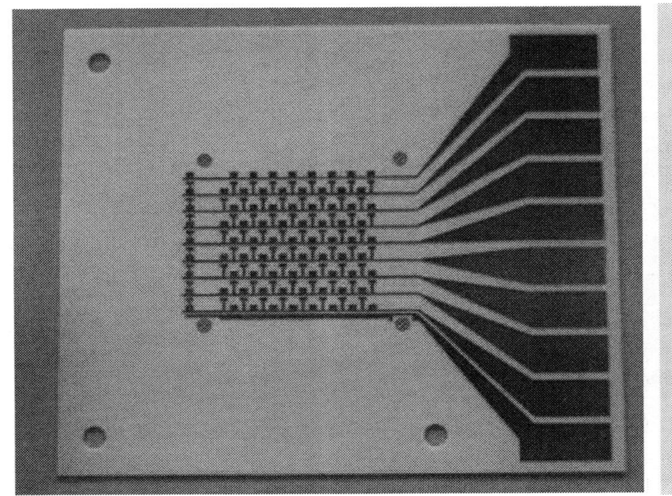

020247-026

Future work

- Manufacturing and characterization of the catadioptric architecture

- Full module integration

- Thermal management strategies

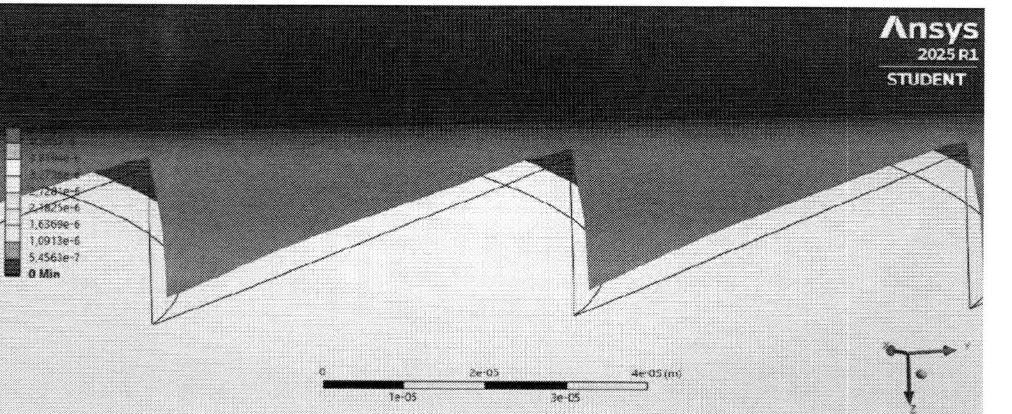

020247-027

17

Future work

- Manufacturing and characterization of the catadioptric architecture

- Full module integration

- Thermal management strategies

- In orbit demonstration

POLITÉCNICA

Thank you for your attention

Dr. Guido Vallerotto

Happy to take your questions

This work has been supported by the European Space Agency's Technology Development Activity "Concentrator Systems as Mission Enablers for Deep Space Missions", under ESA Contract No. 4000141821/23/NL/Mgu. UPM authors acknowledge support by grant MICROBEAM ref. PID2021-127810OB-I00, funded by MCIN/AEI/10.13039/501100011033 "ERDF A way of making Europe".

We gratefully acknowledge the support of these institutions:

Experimental Investigation of
Colored BIPV/T Systems for Wood-Framed Roofs

Anna-Maria Sigounis[1], Andreas Athienitis[2]
1 - PhD Candidate, 2 - Professor

Building, Civil and Environmental Engineering Department, Concordia University, Montréal, Canada

23 September 2025

| Introduction | Methodology | Results | Conclusion |

Canada & Quebec

Total consumption by energy type in Quebec, 2020

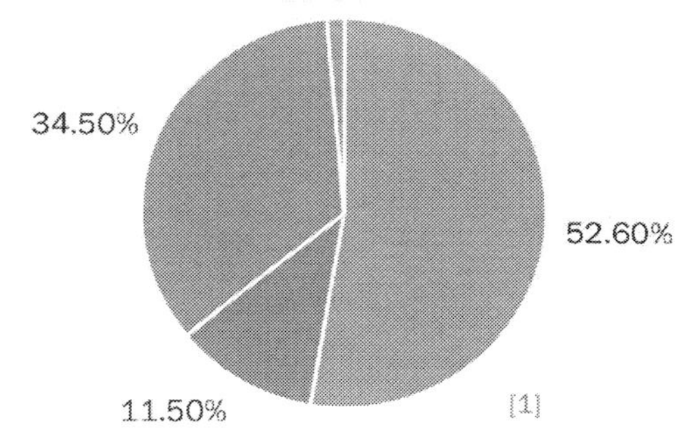

source: www.cer-rec.gc.ca

source: hydro quebec

Canadian Residential building stock

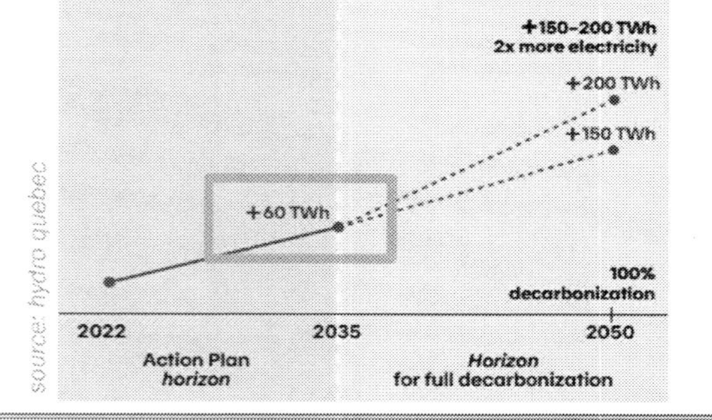

■ Single-detached ■ Semi-detached ■ Apartments ■ Mobile homes

- Pitched roofs are one of the most common roof typologies in low-rise residential dwellings

- Have greater sun exposure and account for a large share of the total building envelope area.

Projected trajectory of electricity demand by 2050

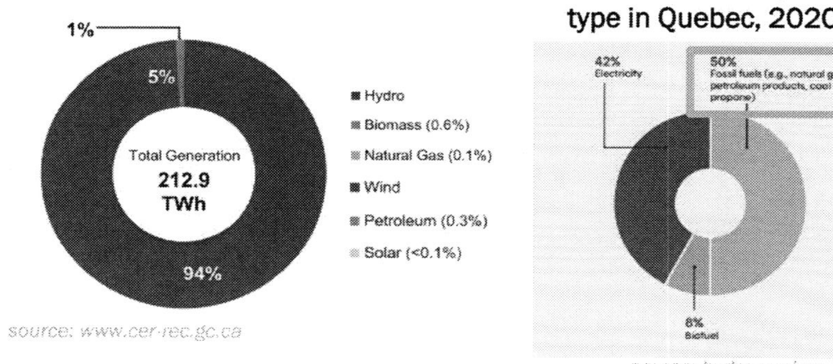

[1] Statistics Canada, "Census Profile, 2021 Census of Population."

020248-002

| Introduction | Methodology | Results | Conclusion |

Building Integrated PV

BIPV/T

Heated air can be used for:

1. pre-heating ventilation air
2. source-side of ASHP
3. water-heating though HE

Colored PV

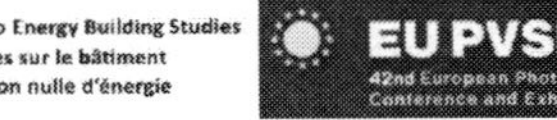
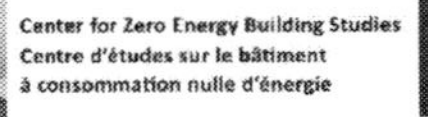

- Offer greater design flexibility
- Higher cost than standard PV
- Reduced electrical efficiency due to coloring
- Color layers can raise PV temperatures
- Uncertain applied performance due to limited research

Objectives

Experimental evaluation • Modelling guidelines • Design & installation strategies

020248-003

Introduction | **Methodology** | Results | Conclusion

BIPV/T Experimental Prototype

- Dimensions: 1.34m x 2.08m

- Two PV modules connected in series

- The PV framing system transforms standard frameless PV modules into solar tiles for sloping roofs.

- Air channel beneath the PV modules has a varying height of 45 - 55 mm

- Custom-made wooden manifold connects the BIPV/T outlet with the air collector

- Two PV colors were tested:

Terracotta

Grey

Concordia UNIVERSITY — Center for Zero Energy Building Studies / Centre d'études sur le bâtiment à consommation nulle d'énergie — EU PVSEC 2025 — 42nd European Photovoltaic Solar Energy Conference and Exhibition

020248-004

Introduction | **Methodology** | Results | Conclusion

Solar Simulator Laboratory

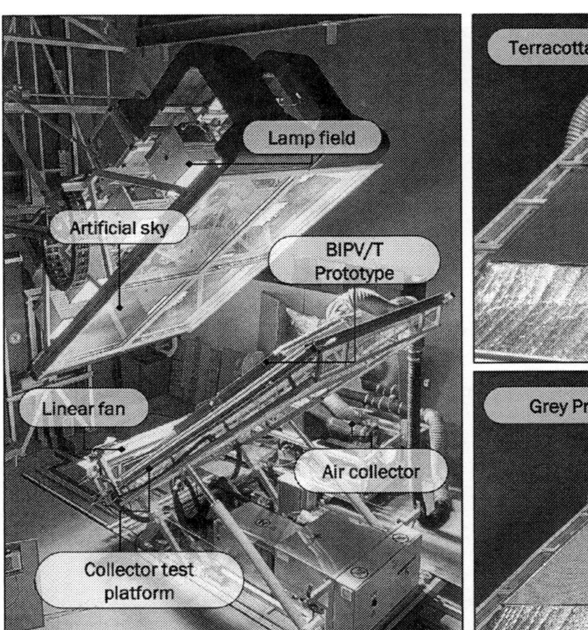

Indoor steady state solar simulator

Lamp Field

- 8 metal halide lamps
- 500 - 1200 W/m^2
- Artificial sky removes the effect of the infrared radiation

Collector test platform

- Can be adjusted 0 - 90°
- Linear, variable-speed fan
- X-Y scanner with pyranometer and anemometer
- Air collector attached to BIPV/T outlet

Cases studied (Testing Sessions)

PV Color	Positions	Irradiance Levels	Wind Speeds	Mass flow rates
Terracotta	Horizontal (0°)	~1086 W/m^2	2.68 m/s	380 kg/h [1.49m/s]
				200 kg/h [0.78m/s]
				120 kg/h [0.47m/s]
Grey	Inclined (40°)	~836 W/m^2	1.43 m/s	Natural Ventilation: 0 kg/h

Introduction | Methodology | Results | Conclusion

Testing Procedure

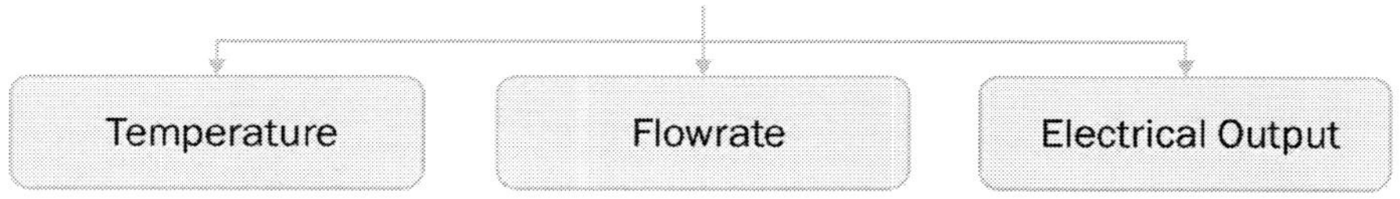

Measurements

- Temperature
- Flowrate
- Electrical Output

Sensor Placement

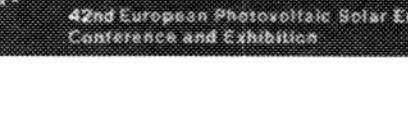

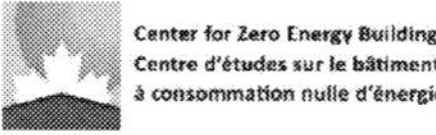

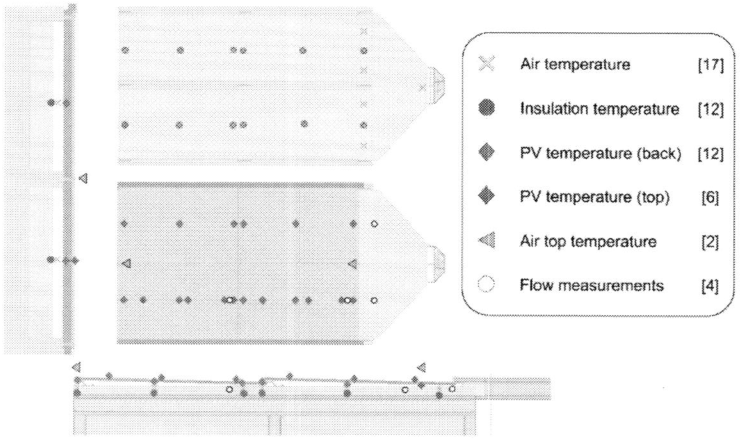

Per Test Session

Concordia UNIVERSITY

Center for Zero Energy Building Studies
Centre d'études sur le bâtiment
à consommation nulle d'énergie

EU PVSEC 2025
42nd European Photovoltaic Solar Energy
Conference and Exhibition

020248-006

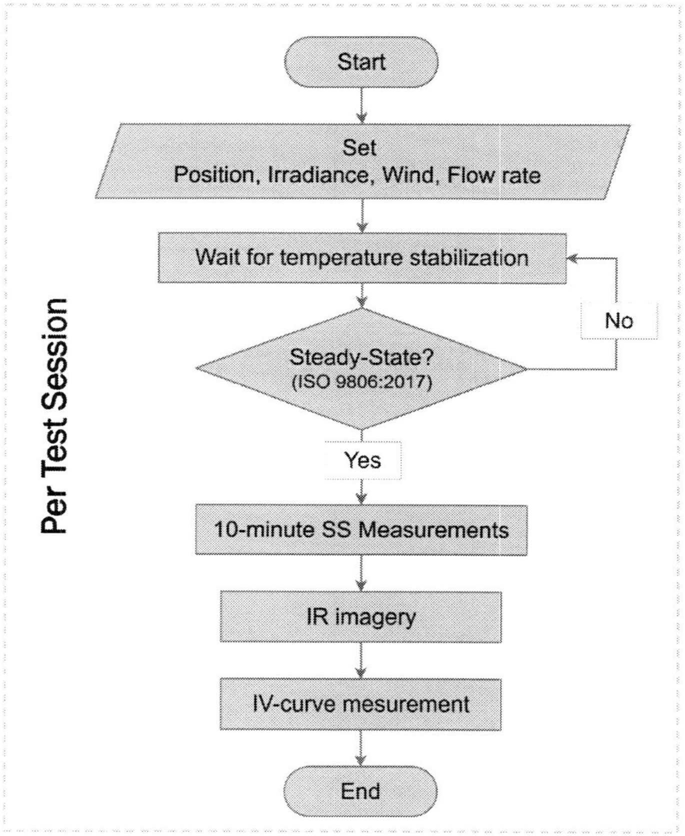

Convective Heat Transfer Analysis

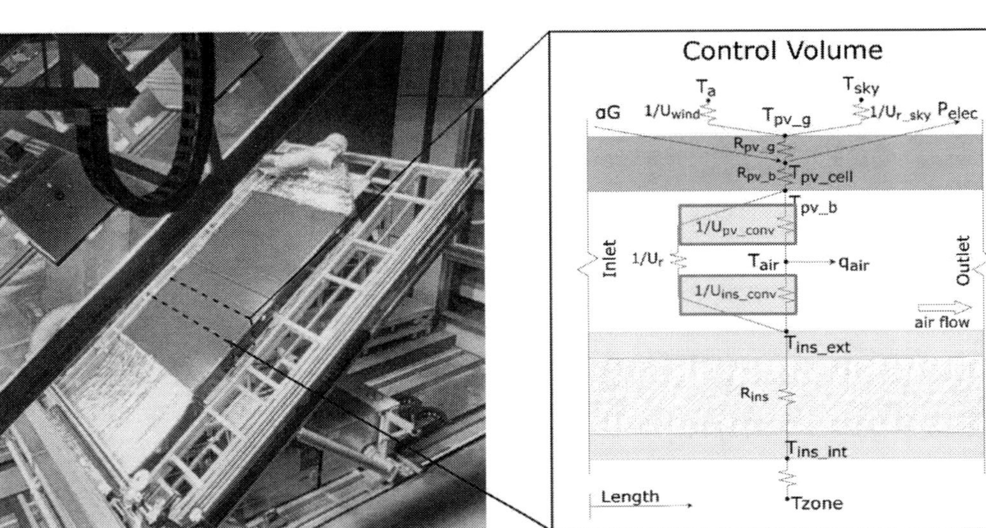

Energy balance of the BIPV/T in the form of a thermal network

The convective heat transfer coefficients (**CHTC**) and Nusselt numbers (**Nu**) within the air channel were derived through conducting an **energy balance**

Average CHTC & Nu

$$\dot{m} \cdot c_p \cdot \Delta T = CHTC \cdot (T_{PV} + T_{ins} - 2\overline{T_{air}}) \cdot A$$

$$Nu = \frac{CHTC \cdot D_h}{k}$$

m : mass flow rate (kg/s),
ΔT : temperature difference between the inlet and outlet (°C),
TPV, Tins, Tair : temperatures of the PV, insulation, air (°C),
A : area of the BIPV/T (m²),
Dh : hydraulic diameter (m)

Thermal and Electrical Performance

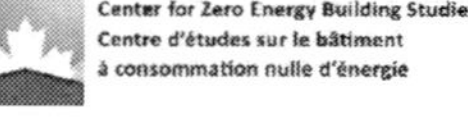

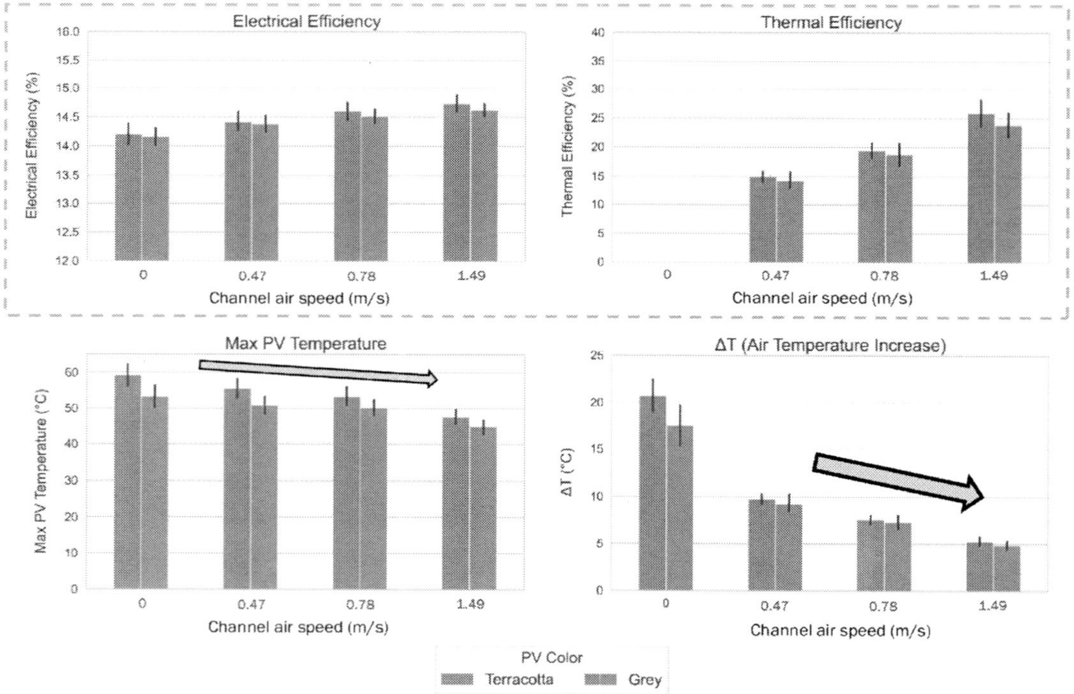

System Performance Overview

Efficiencies	Terracotta	Grey
Thermal (%)	28.2	26.6
Electrical (%)	14.9	14.5

Effect of Airflow Rate

- Increasing airflow (0.47 to 1.49 m/s) reduced ΔT by 4.4 °C
- PV temperature reductions with mechanical ventilation (−13 °C for terracotta, −10.3 °C for grey)

Impact of Color on Performance

- Grey panels showed lower electrical and thermal efficiencies
- Up to 6.2 °C difference in PV temperature

020248-008

Introduction   Methodology   Results   Conclusion

Temperature Distribution

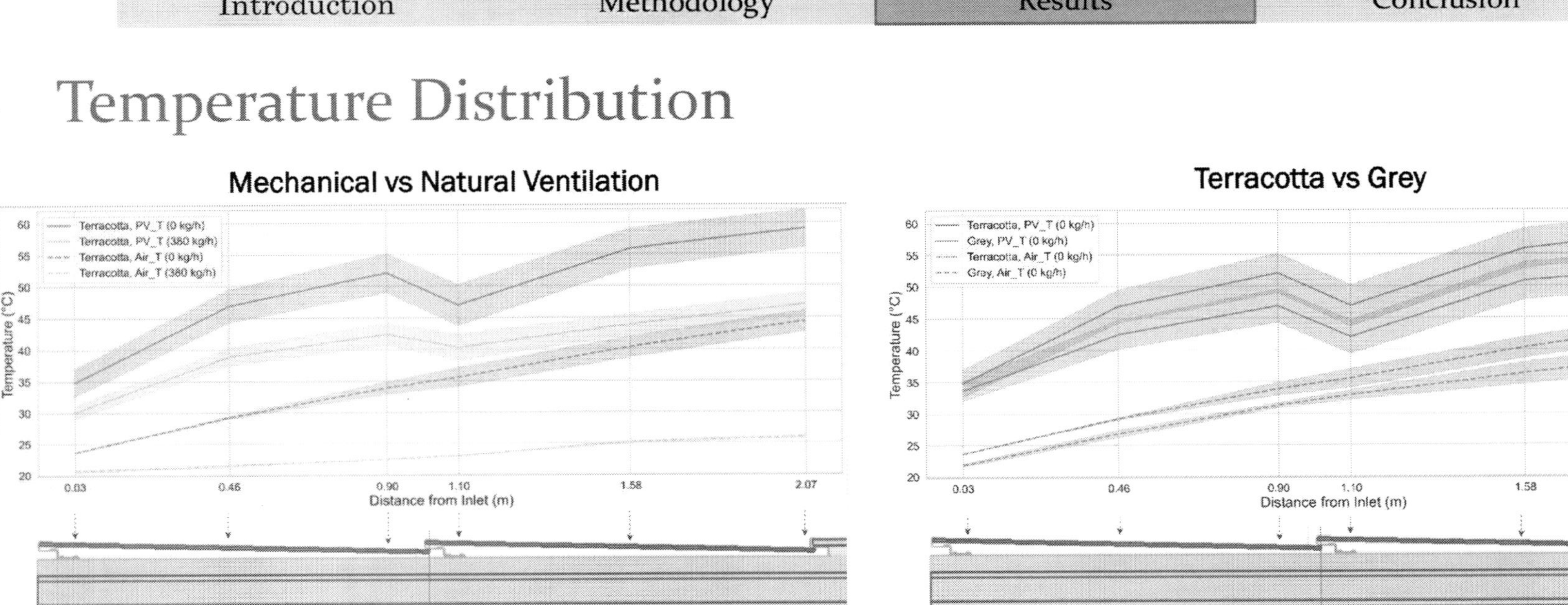

Mechanical vs Natural Ventilation

Terracotta vs Grey

UNIVERSITÉ Concordia UNIVERSITY
Center for Zero Energy Building Studies
Centre d'études sur le bâtiment à consommation nulle d'énergie
EU PVSEC 2025
42nd European Photovoltaic Solar Energy Conference and Exhibition

020248-009

Introduction | Methodology | **Results** | Conclusion

Temperature Distribution

Mechanical vs Natural Ventilation

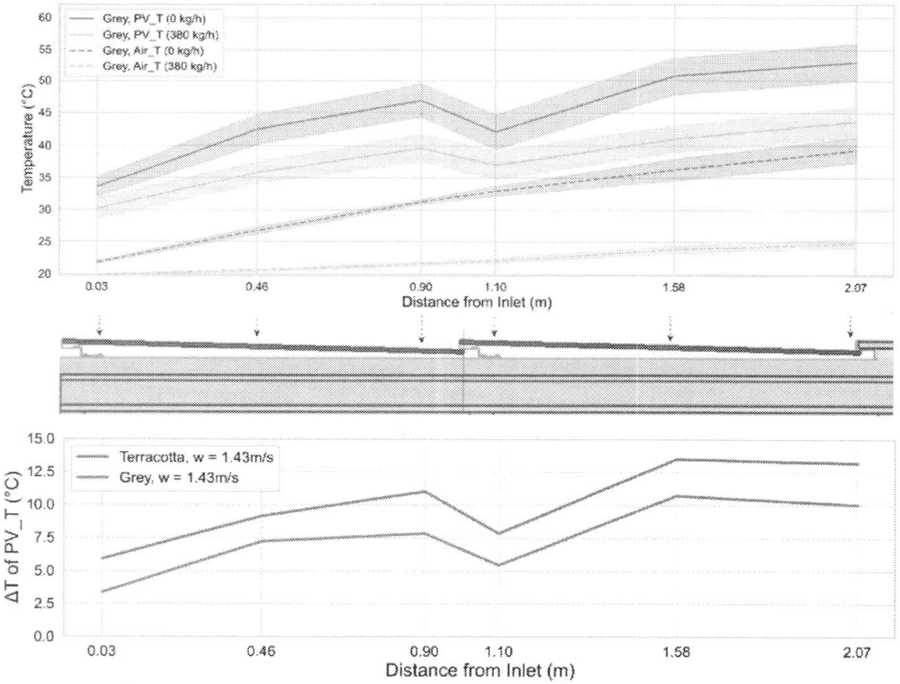

Terracotta vs Grey

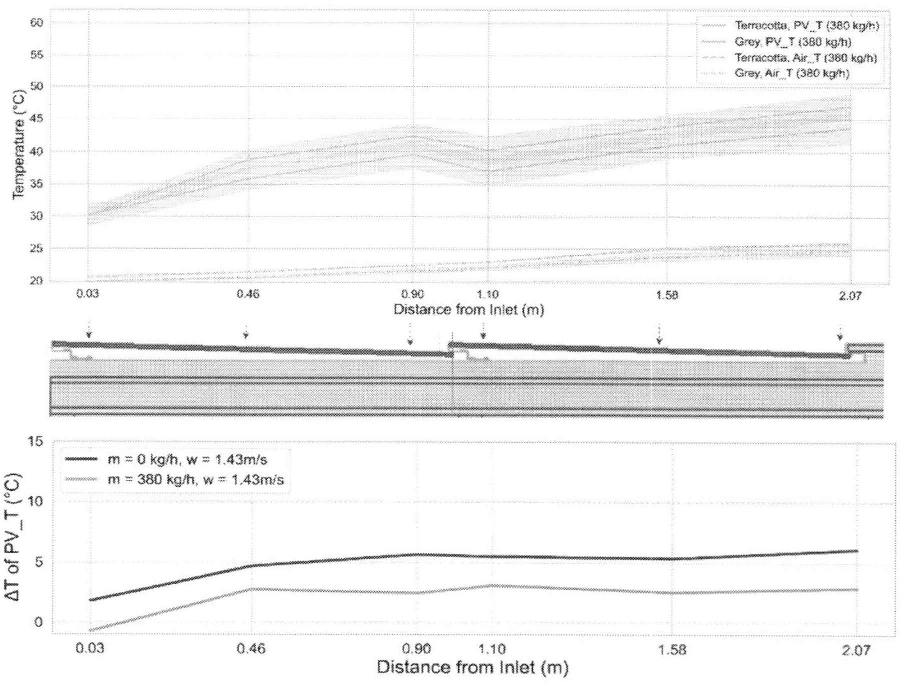

Introduction	Methodology	Results	Conclusion

Convective Heat Transfer Analysis

Average Nu (Overall)

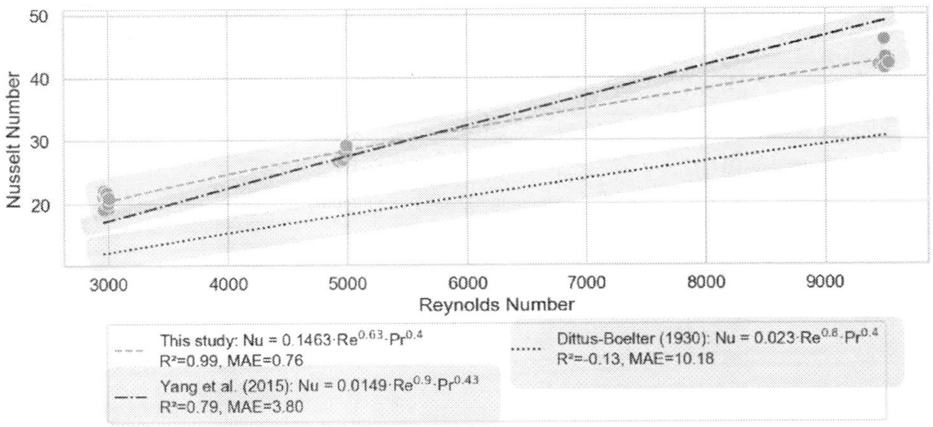

$$Nu = 0.146Re^{0.63}Pr^{0.4} \qquad \text{for} \quad 3000 < Re < 10000$$

Nu (PV & Insulation side)

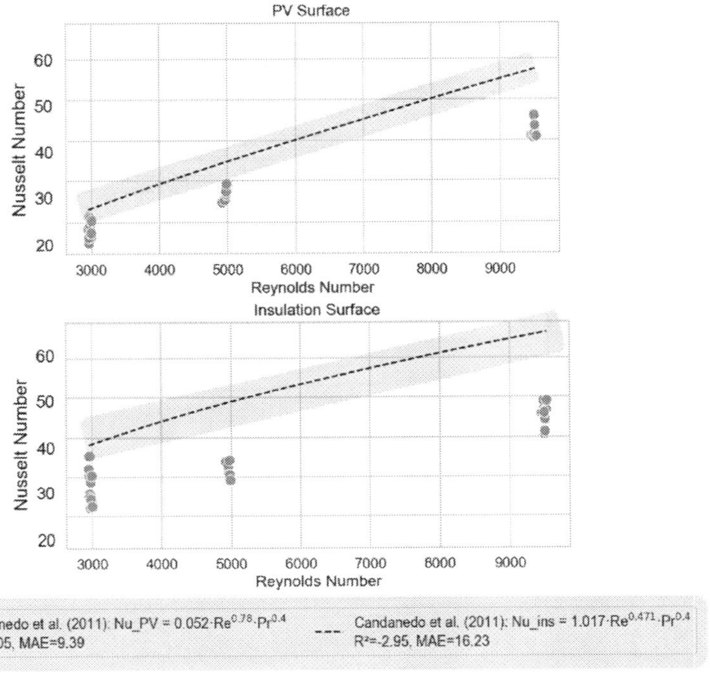

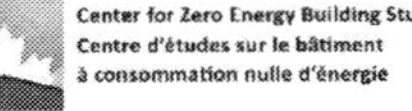

Concordia University · Center for Zero Energy Building Studies / Centre d'études sur le bâtiment à consommation nulle d'énergie · EU PVSEC 2025

Experimental Investigation of Colored BIPV/T Systems for Wood-Framed Roofs

| Introduction | Methodology | Results | Conclusion |

Limitations & Next Steps

Limitations

- Other coloring technologies, may have different impacts; further testing needed

- Laboratory conditions do not fully replicate real-world conditions (wind or solar spectrum)

- Fully developed flow conditions may not have been reached due to reduced prototype scale

Outdoor Full-scale Installation

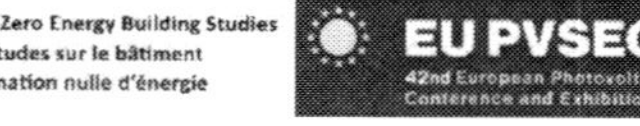
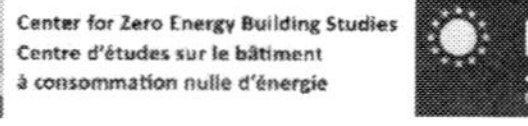
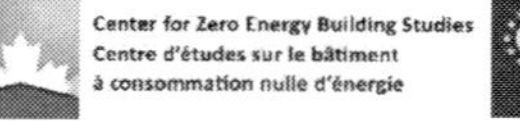

Three full scale systems
- Two "solar shingle" systems and one curtain wall
- 12 modules per system (2 columns x 6 rows)

020248-012

Introduction Methodology Results **Conclusion**

Conclusions

This study investigated the performance of colored BIPV/T systems through experimental testing under controlled laboratory conditions.

- Addition of mechanical ventilation reduced PV temperature by up to **13°C** for the terracotta PV and **10.3°C** for the grey

- Terracotta modules exhibited higher temperatures than the grey, attributed to the higher reflectance of the grey

- Thermal efficiencies 12.5 - 28.6% with the terracotta achieving slightly higher thermal and electrical efficiencies

Acknowledgements

Financial support was received by a Natural Sciences and Engineering Research Council of Canada **(NSERC)/Hydro-Québec Industrial Research Chair** and an **NSERC Postgraduate Scholarship – Doctoral**

Thank you to **Dr. Jiwu Rao, Gia-Khanh PHI** and **Yearim Yang** for their assistance with the experimental procedure & setup.

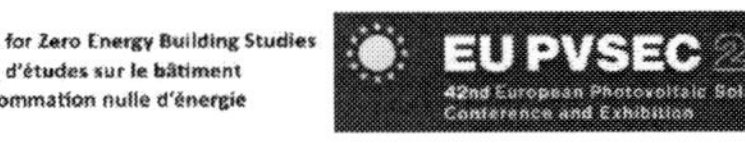

Thank you!

Questions?

Contact Information

Anna-Maria Sigounis, PhD candidate

Centre for Zero Energy Building Studies (CZEBS)
Concordia University, Montréal, Canada

sigounisan@gmail.com

www.linkedin.com/in/ann
a-maria-sigounis

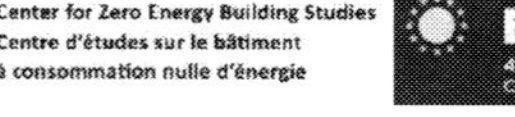
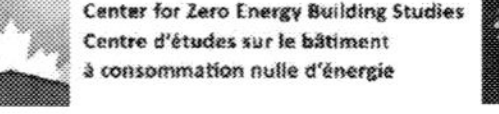

020248-014

How to Perform Accurate Colour Measurements for BIPV Module Glass Covers:
an IEA PVPS Task 15 Round-Robin Measurement Campaign

M. Babin, G.C. Eder, T. Friesen, M. Pelle, G. Gonnella, F. Leonforte, Y. Voronko, H.R. Wilson, S. Thorsteinsson, L. Maturi, N. Aste, C. Del Pero, J. Halme, J.-T. Kim, S. Santamaría Fernández, A.-M. Sigounis, H. Ge, G. Friesen, F. Frontini

Technology Collaboration Programme
by iea

020249-001

Challenges for coloured BIPV

BIPV requires visual integration
→ demand for coloured BIPV

Colour matching of existing materials
→ challenge of different surfaces

Reproducability of coloured BIPV modules
→ production monitoring (quality control)

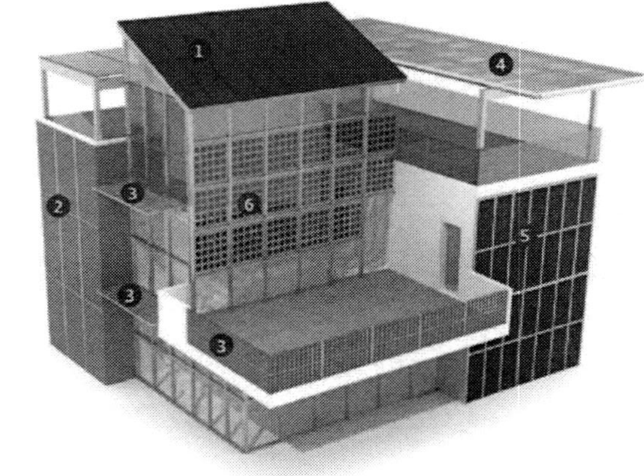

© Fraunhofer ISE

020249-002

IEA PVPS Task 15

IEA PVPS Task 15
"Enabling Framework for the Development of BIPV"

- Market barriers and opportunities
- Digitalisation, training, stakeholder involvement
- Long-term behaviour and reliability
- Pre-normative research

> 60 active experts from > 15 countries

Activity B4
"Performance modelling and characterization of coloured BIPV"

PVPS

3

Background – how to measure colours

Spectral reflectance

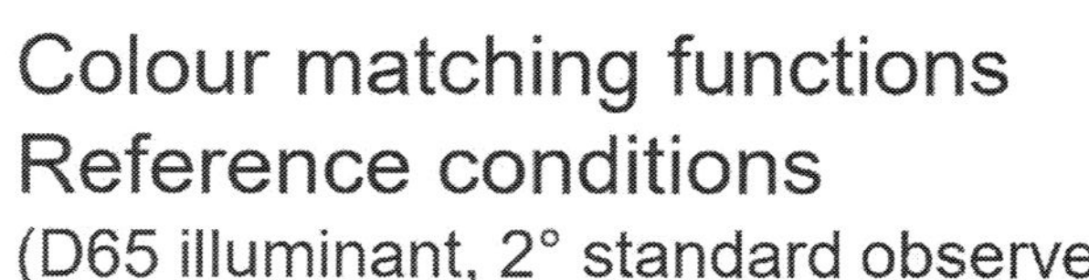

Colour matching functions
Reference conditions
(D65 illuminant, 2° standard observer)

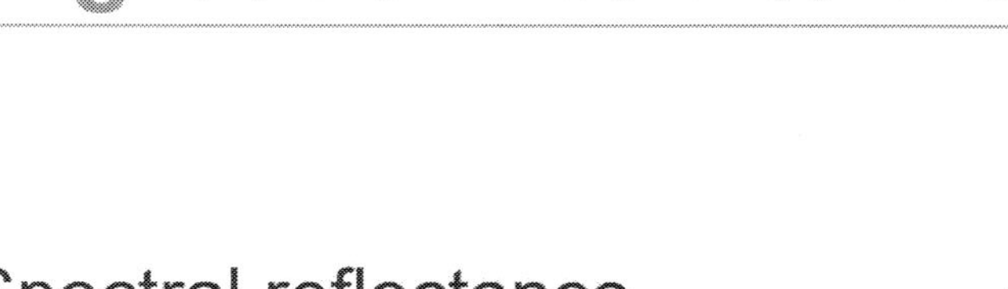

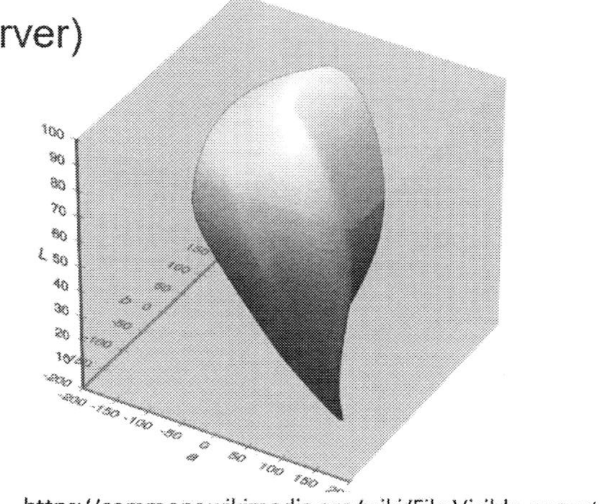

Colour coordinates
(CIELAB colour space)

https://commons.wikimedia.org/wiki/File:Visible_gamut_
within_CIELAB_color_space_D65_whitepoint_mesh.png

PVPS

020249-004

Approach – colour measurement instruments

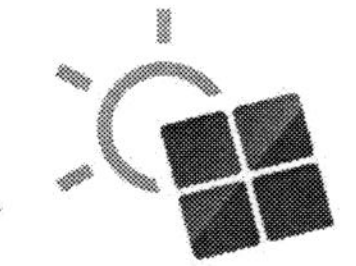

Spectrometers – different collection optics

- Integrating sphere (with/without specular reflections)
- Backscatter probe
- Multi-angle array

Colourimeters – different manufacturers and designs

- Spectrometer-based with integrating sphere
  (with/without specular reflections)
- Camera-based

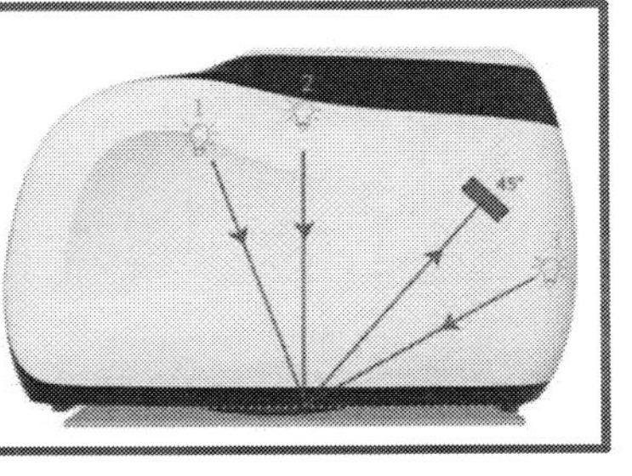

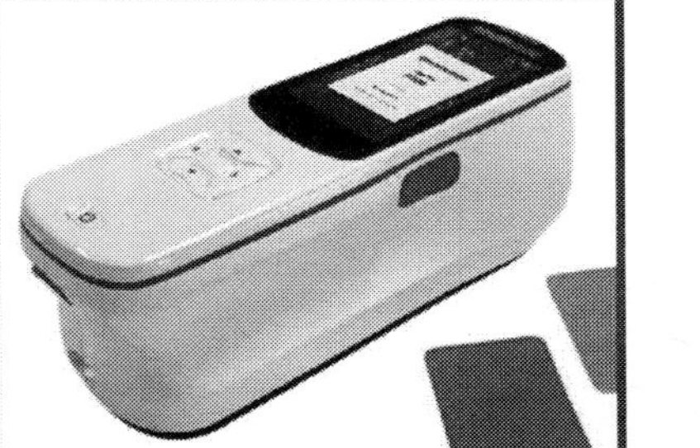
© spectrology.com

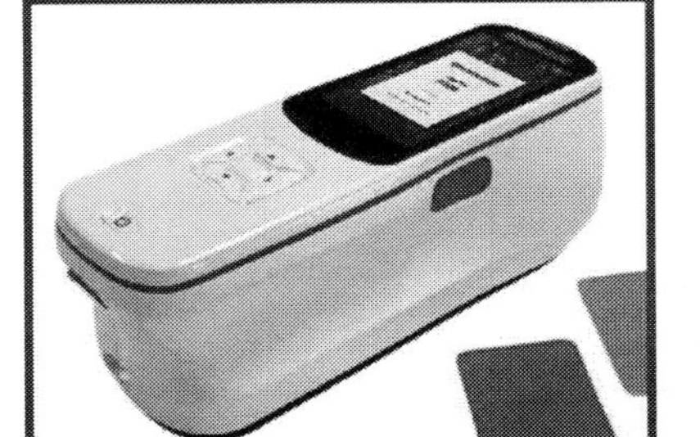
© datacolor.com

© colorix.com

Effect of different glass surfaces (modules)

020249-006

Effect of different glass surfaces (modules)

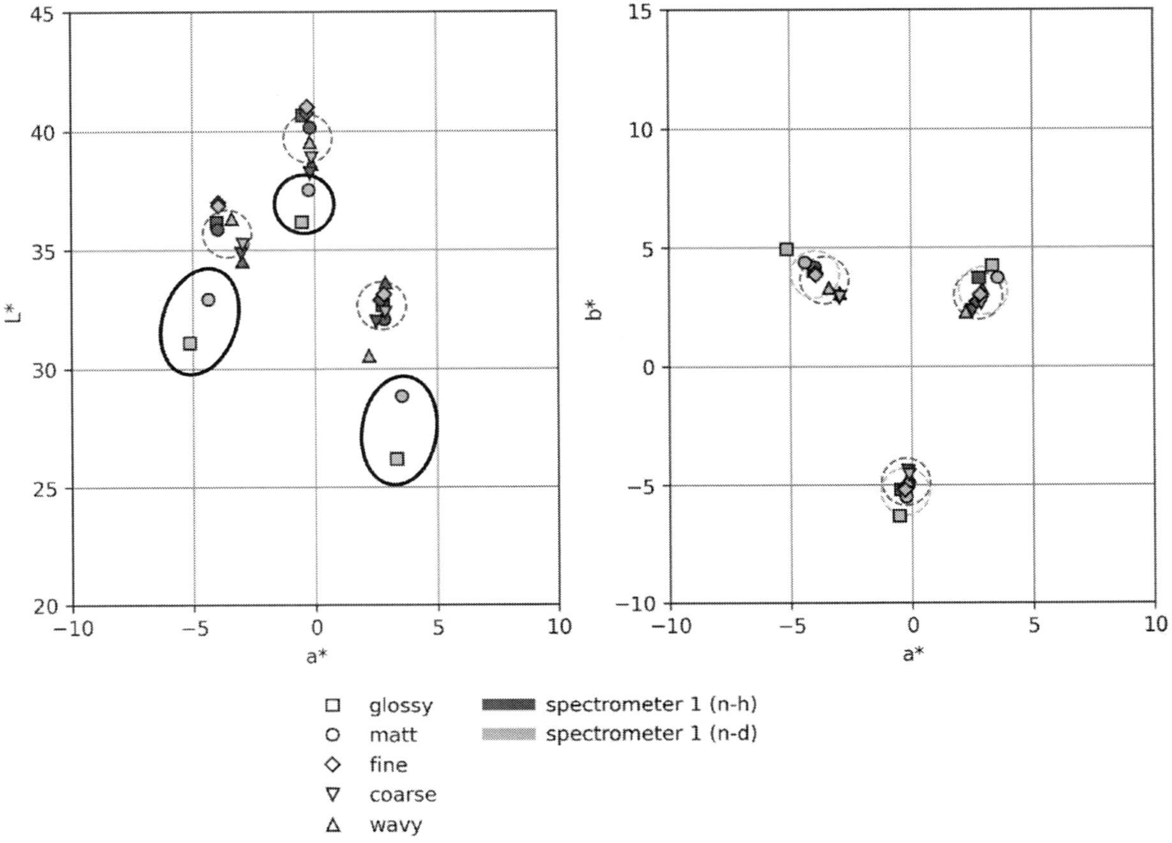

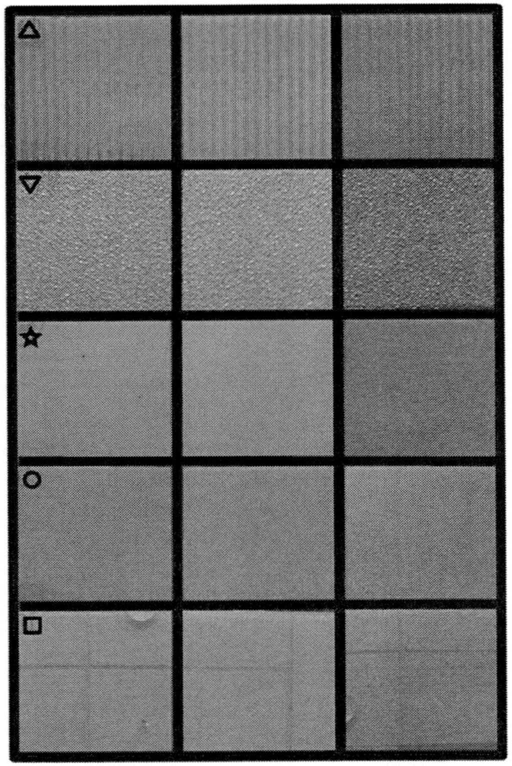

7

Effect of different glass surfaces (modules)

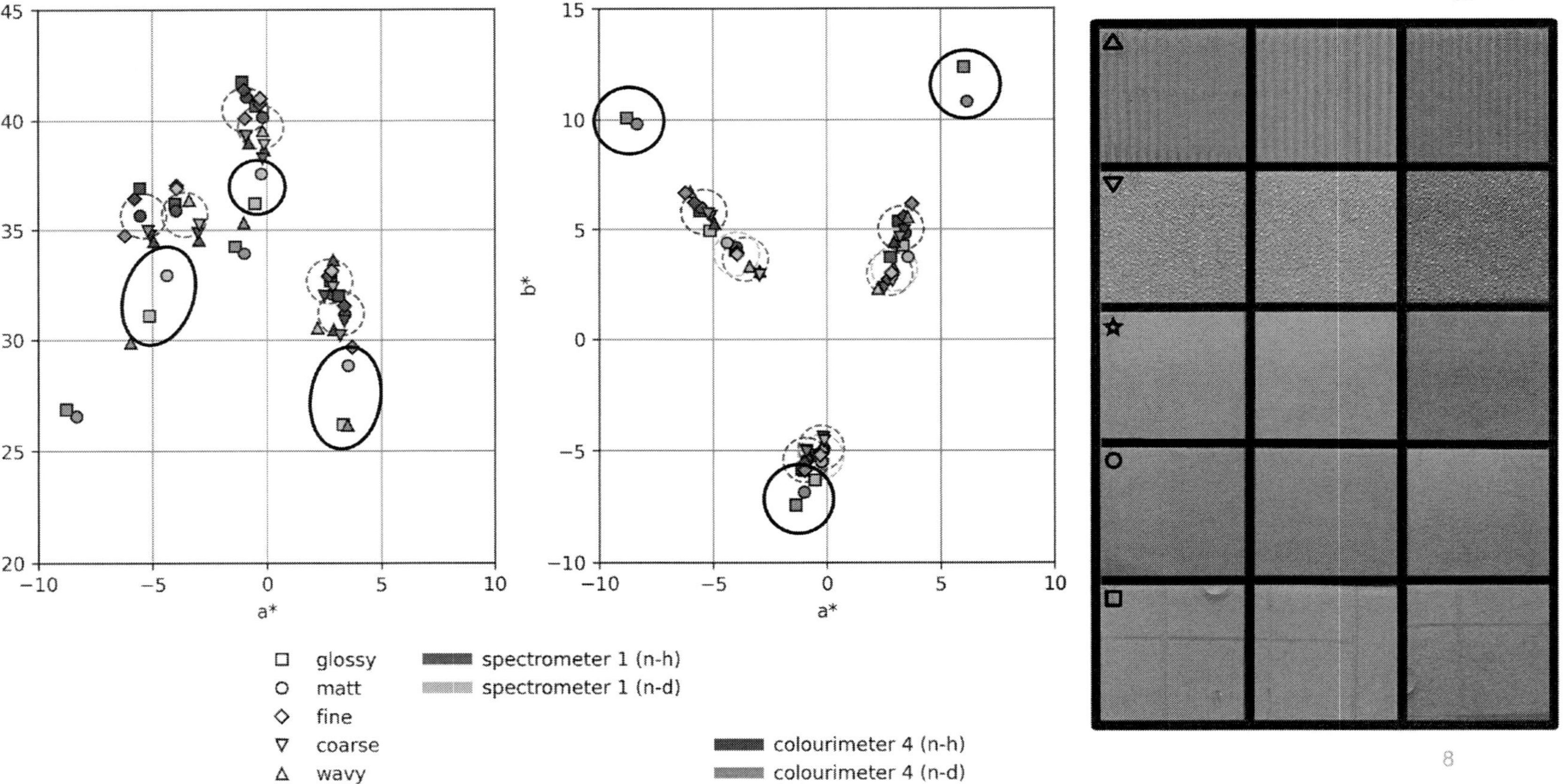

020249-008

8

Effect of different glass surfaces (modules)

PVPS

9

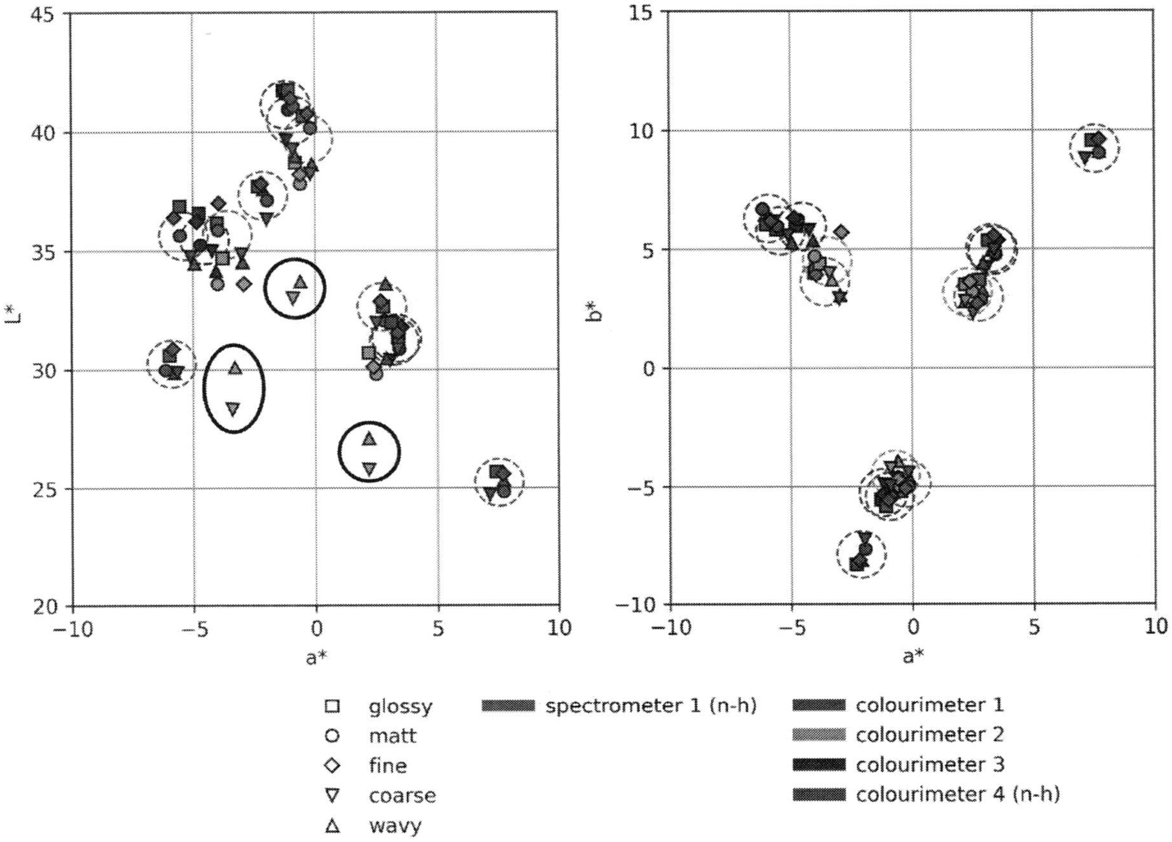

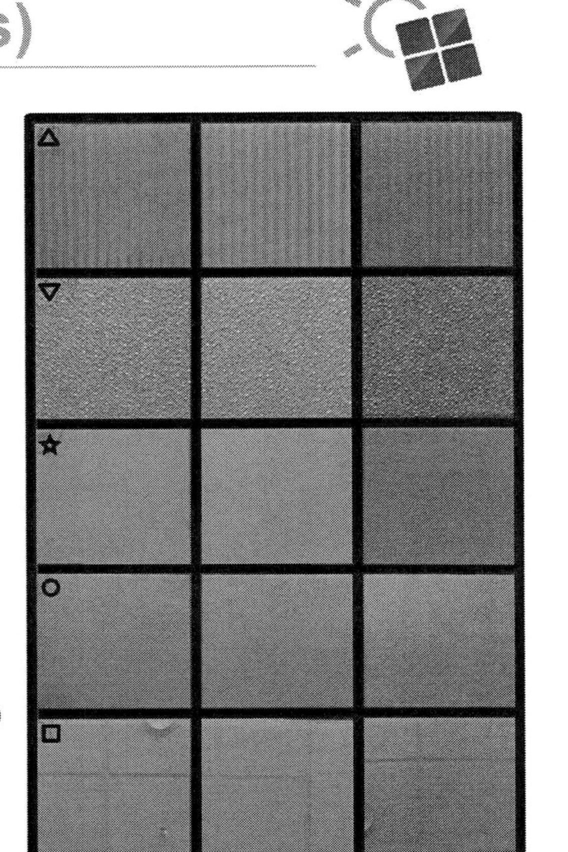

Effect of different glass surfaces (modules)

Effect of different glass surfaces (modules)

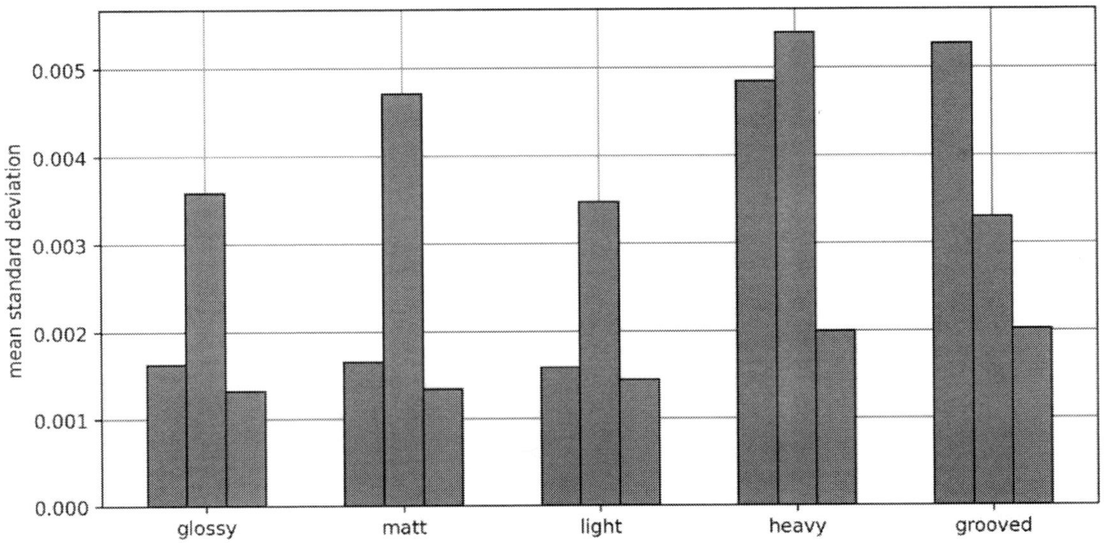

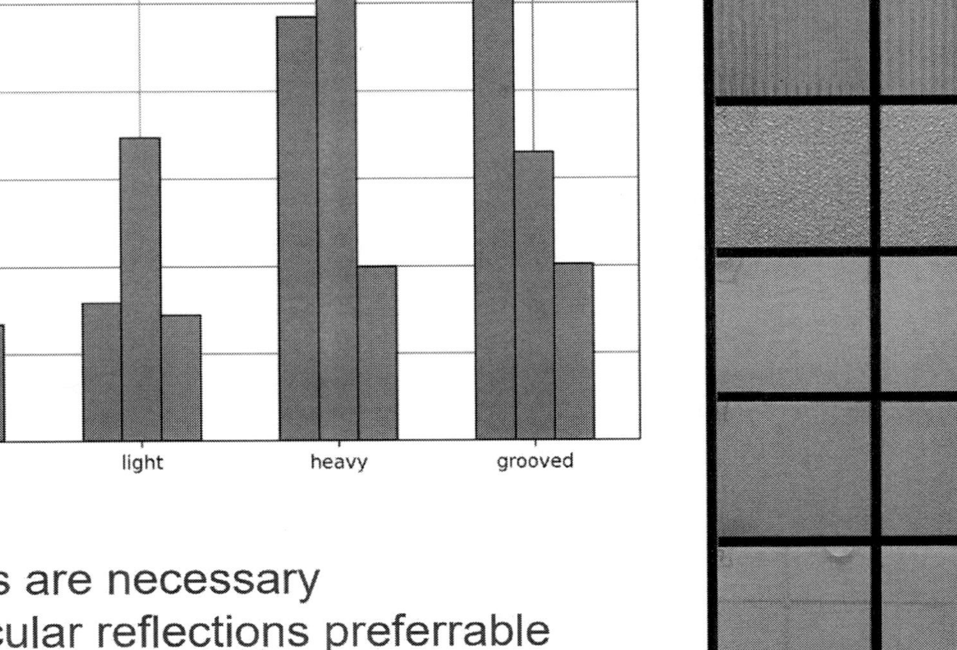

Learnings:
- Integrating optics are necessary
- Inclusion of specular reflections preferrable
- Higher uncertainty for textured glass

11

020249-011

Comparing measurements on modules and glass

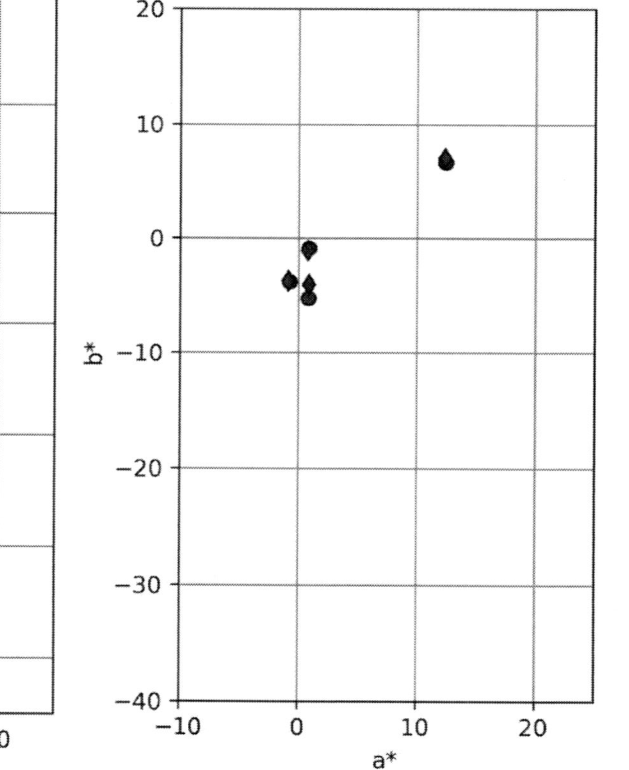

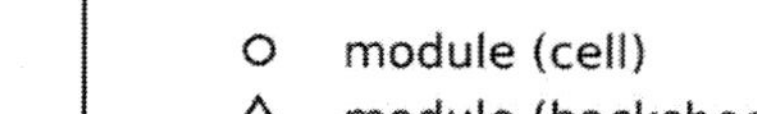

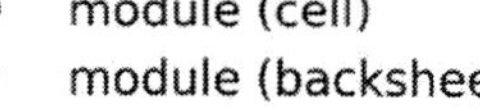

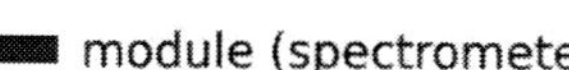

020249-012

Comparing measurements on modules and glass

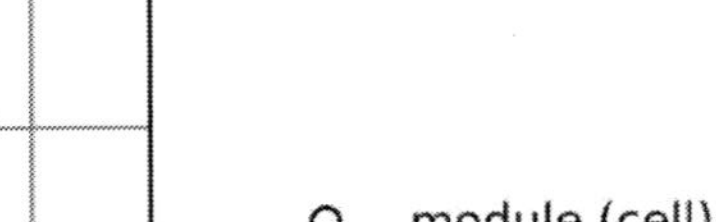

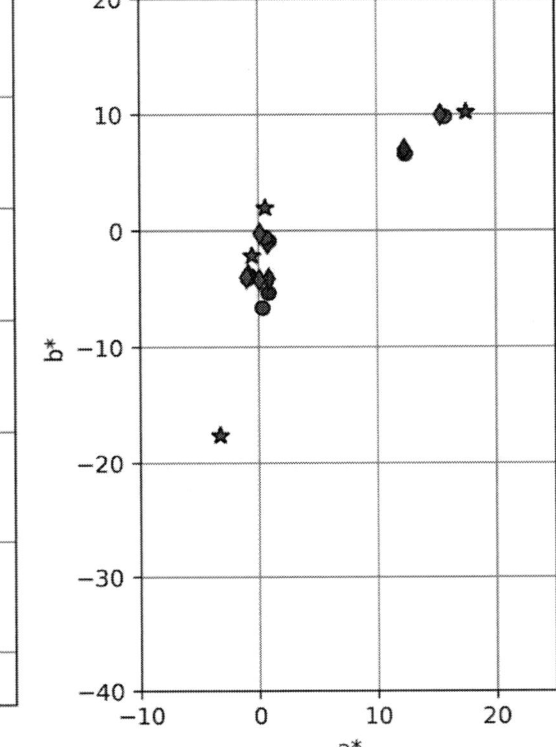

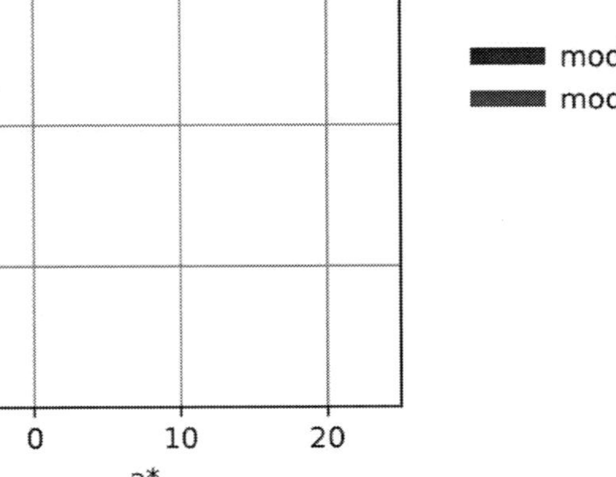

020249-013

Comparing measurements on modules and glass

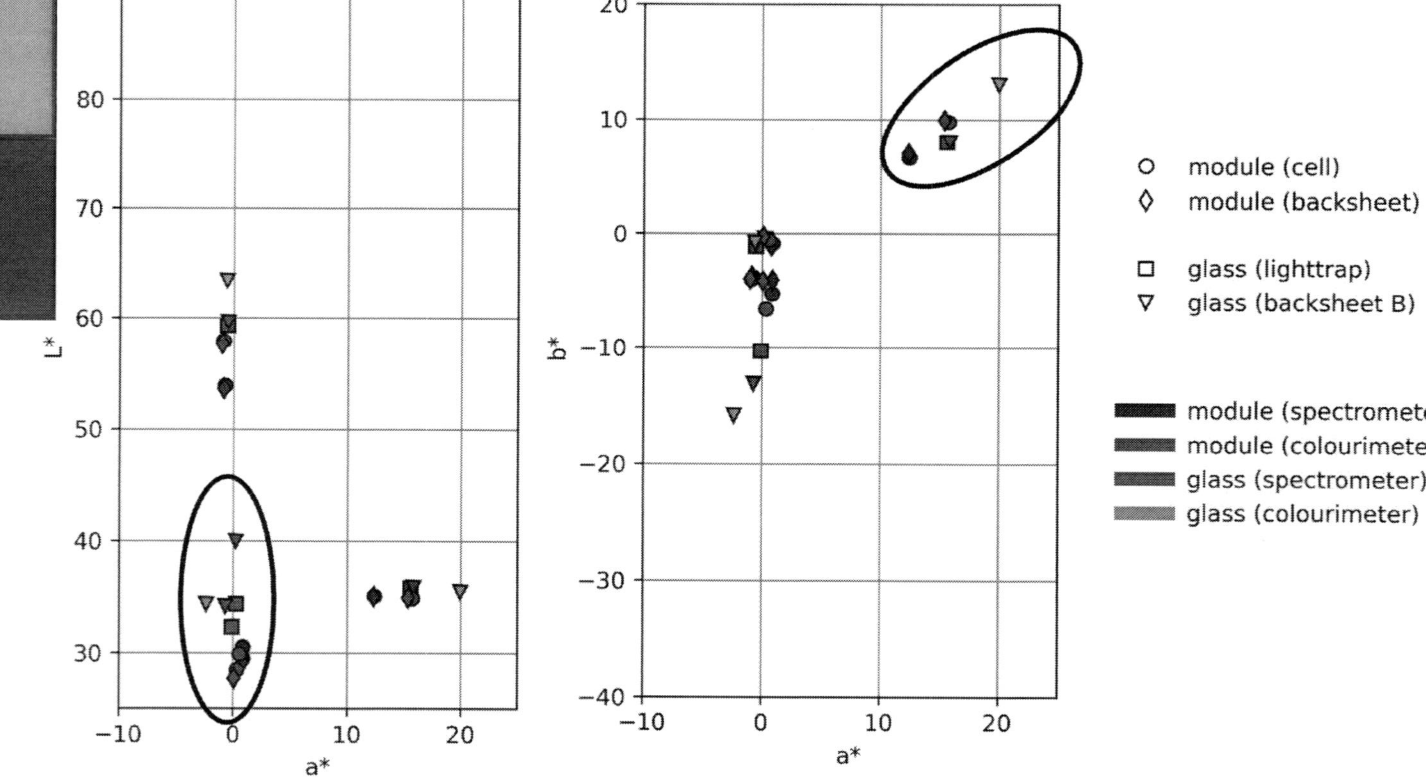

Comparing measurements on modules and glass

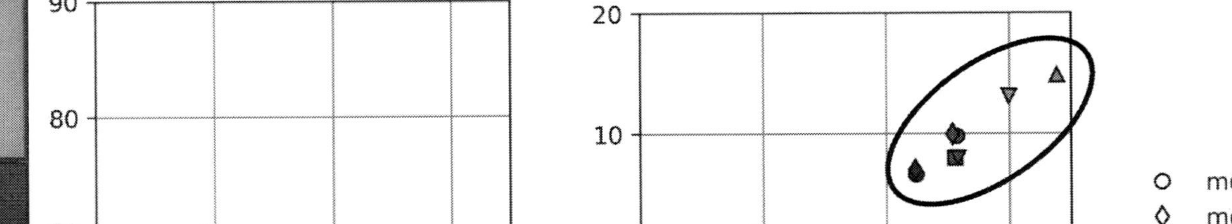

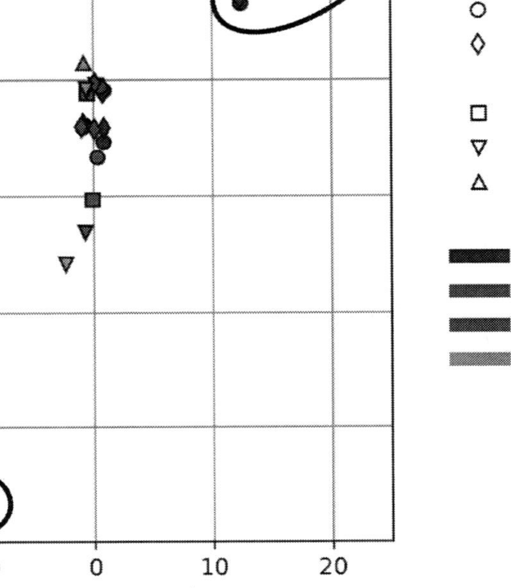

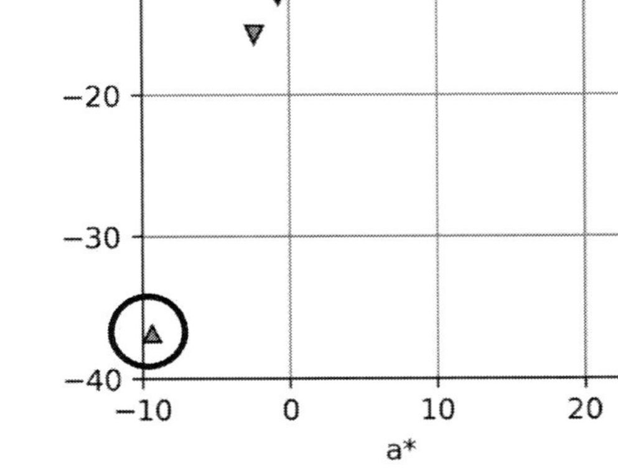

020249-015

Comparing measurements on modules and glass

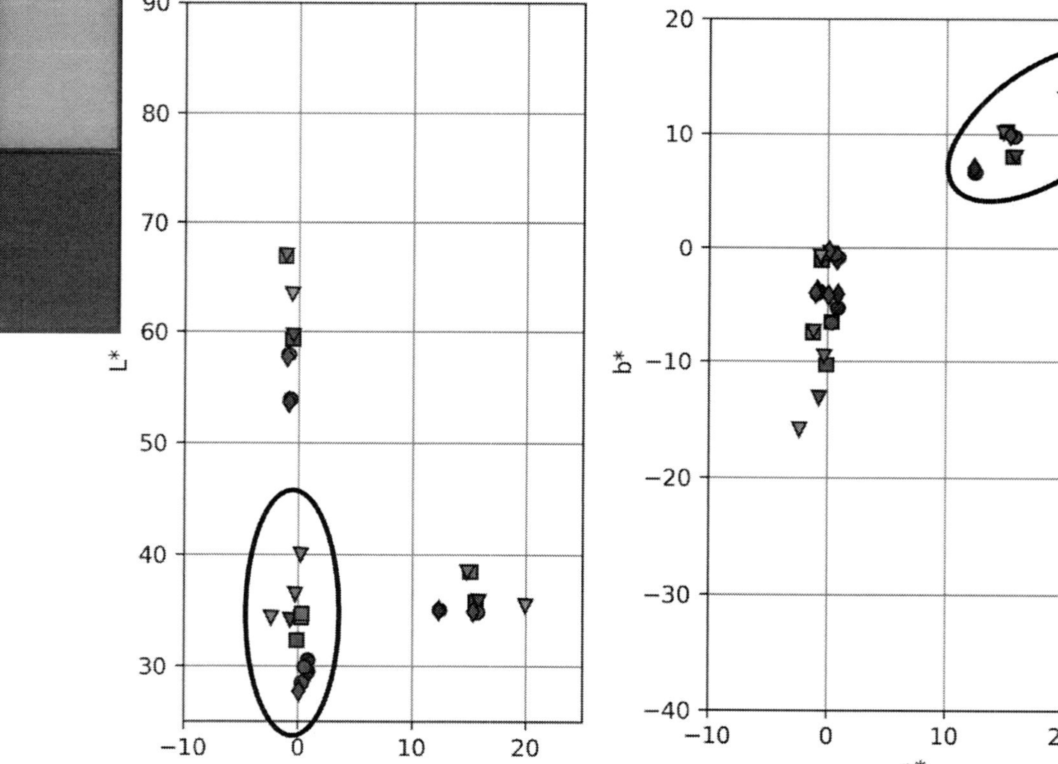

020249-016

Spectral transmittance of coloured glass

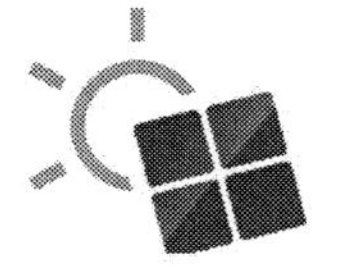

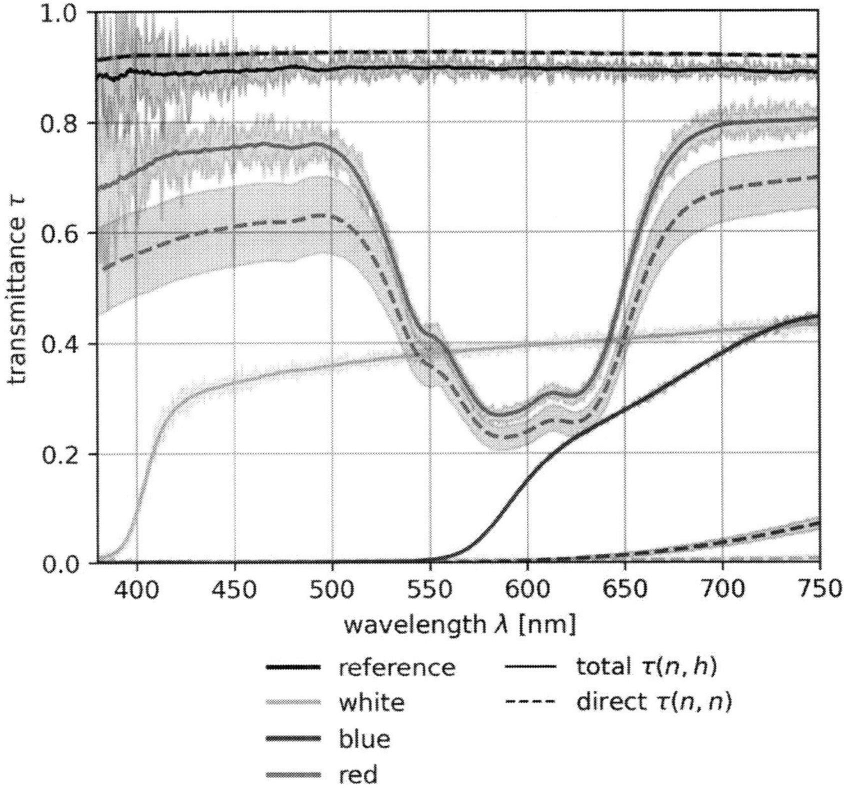

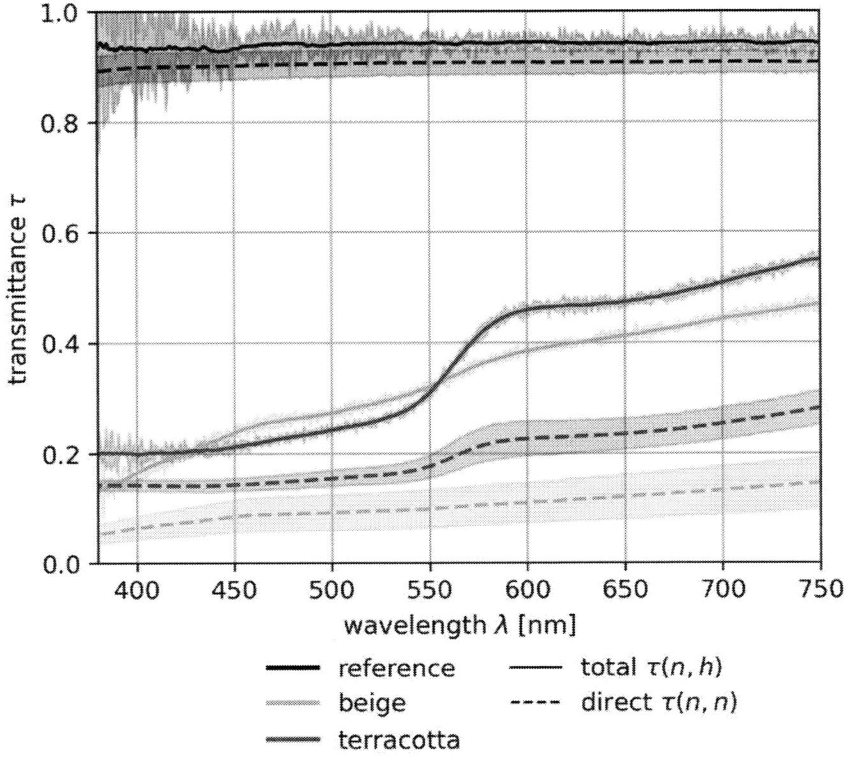

020249-017

Summary

Specular reflection components matter

→ Hemispherical measurements advisable
→ Textured glass increases measurement uncertainty

Significant differences between instruments

→ Differences in collection optics
→ Often designed for matt surfaces

Scattering strongly influences transmittance measurements

Conclusions & Next steps

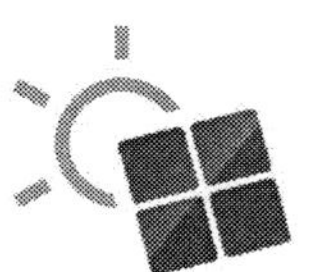

Colour measurements on glazed (BI)PV modules are non-trivial!

Sources of disagreement between instruments:

- Integrating optics
- Aperture sizes

Correlation between glass and module measurements:

- Sample set with different print intensities and textures
- Involvement of additional laboratories and methods

PVPS

020249-019

www.iea-pvps.org

Starting in October
1st IEA PVPS Task 15
Blind Modelling Intercomparison

Open to all PV system modellers!

Thank you to…
… all participants in activity B4!
… the respective funding bodies!
… you for listening!

Markus Babin, Task 15
marbab@dtu.dk

Technology Collaboration Programme
by iea

PREDICTING LIGHT SCATTER IN STRUCTURAL COLORED BIPV MODULES AND TEXTURED GLASS USING RADIANCE

Nanna L. Andersen[1], Markus Babin[1], Jan Svatos[1], Karlis Petersons[2], Leif Yde[2], Jan F. Stensborg[2], Catarina G. Ferreira[3,4], Ananta Paul[3,5], Jani Lamminaho[3,5], Joel D. Cox[3,4,6], MortenMadsen[3,5], Peter B. Poulsen[1], and Sune Thorsteinsson[1]

[1] DTU Electro, Technical University of Denmark, Roskilde, Denmark
[2] Stensborg A/S, 4000 Roskilde, Denmark
[3] SDU Climate Cluster, University of Southern Denmark, Odense 5230, Denmark
[4] POLIMA, University of Southern Denmark, 5230 Odense M, Denmark
[5] CAPE, University of Southern Denmark, Mads Clausen Institute, 6400 Sønderborg, Denmark
[6] Danish Institute for Advanced Study, University of Southern Denmark, 5230 Odense M, Denmark
Email: nalan@dtu.dk

ABSTRACT: This work investigates the use of ray-tracing simulations to support the design of colored Building-Integrated Photovoltaic (BIPV) modules. Aesthetic integration of BIPV often requires color. To minimize angular dependency in structural colored BIPV modules, texture can be applied. Predicting the optical appearance of such modules is challenging, typically requiring iterative fabrication and measurement. To overcome this, the ray-tracing software Radiance is evaluated for simulating light scattering in textured BIPV components and modules. Simulations were compared with Bidirectional Reflection Distribution Function (BRDF) measurements of textured front glasses and foils, both before and after EVA encapsulation. Simulations showed promising results for individual components but revealed limitations in reproducing multilayer behavior. Encapsulation was found to strongly influence light scattering, highlighting the need for full-stack analysis. Radiance demonstrates potential as a design tool in colored BIPV, though further analysis is needed to assess the possibility for accurate module-level predictions.
Keywords: BIPV, modelling, appearance, ray-tracing

1 INTRODUCTION & MOTIVATION

Improving the aesthetics of modules is an important part of Building-Integrated Photovoltaics (BIPV). To make them an appealing solution, we need the possibility of adding color, which can be achieved using various methods [1]. One option being structural coloration. Structural colors, relying on constructive interference effects, offer high light transmission but are typically strongly angular dependent, meaning the module appearance changes based on light incidence and viewing angle.

In the ColorFoil project the aim is to produce colored BIPV modules using a colored interlayer based on structural coloration. The structural coloration is obtained by a stack of thin dielectric layers that interfere with the incoming light [2-3]. To mitigate the angular dependency of the coloration, the colored interlayered is textured, scattering the light in different directions.

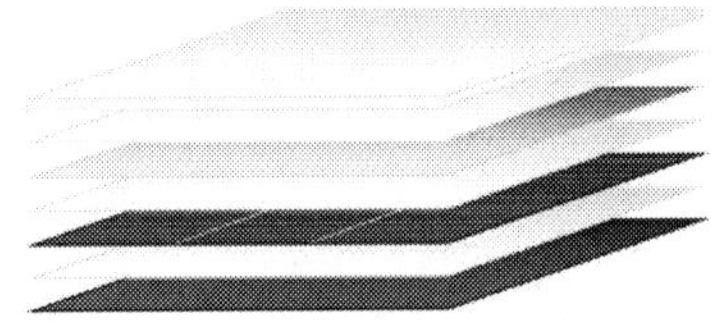

Figure 1: BIPV module stack for ColorFoil. From the top the layers are: Front glass, encapsulant, Colored + textured foil, encapsulant, PV cell, encapsulant, backsheet.

Evaluating the performance of the textures and predicting the final appearance of the full module stack can be difficult, in most cases requiring manufacturing and measuring of all samples. Leading to a trial-and-error testing for all changes of the color or texture design. This work aims to investigate how the ray-tracing based software Radiance [4] can be used in the design process of BIPV modules.

In this work the ray-tracing simulation tool will be used to simulate how light is scattered by different textures within the PV module. The simulations will be validated using bidirectional reflectance distribution function measurements of constructed PV components and modules including differently textured foils and front glasses.

2 METHODS

2.1 Simulations

In order to consider the angular dependency in our simulations we need to use 3D raytracing. A popular tool for this is Radiance, which is software developed to analyze and visualize lightning in design. In Radiance you define a system or scene consisting of a set of materials, objects and light sources. Radiance contains several functions to analyze or visualize the defined system, one of them simulating and returning the Bidirectional Reflection Distribution Function (BRDF) [5-6]. The BRDF describes how a material reflects incoming light at different incidence and viewing angles.

2.2 Experiments

The selection of samples consists of two differently textured glasses: A standard PV front glass and a satinated front glass, and three differently textured interlayer foils. The interlayer foils do not contain the dielectric stack, but instead a thin layer of gold is sputtered onto the textures to assess how they scatter the light.

To evaluate the performance of the Radiance simulations, the BRDF of all samples is measured using a setup that consists of a collimated light source, a moveable sensor connected to a spectrometer and a sample holder capable of rotating around one axis. This setup is capable of producing inplane BRDF measurements. A detailed description can be found in [7]. Recently an upgrade was made to this system, replacing the 1-axis rotating sample holder with a robot arm, enabling full hemispherical BRDF measurements [8]. Examples of both BRDF measurements will be presented in this work. BRDF measurements of the textured foils have been performed before and after EVA encapsulation to assess the changes in the BRDF as the foils are imbedded in BIPV modules.

To be able to replicate the textured surfaces of the samples in Radiance, 3D scans of the sample surfaces were performed using an optical 3D profiling microscope (Sensorfar S neox) [9]. At this point the surface of three of the samples have been characterized, consisting of the two textured glasses and one of the textured foils, as indicated in Table I.

Table I: Samples and experimental measurements

	BRDF	Surface scan
Standard PV Glass	Hemispherical	X
Satinated Glass	Hemispherical	X
Textured Foil 1	Inplane	X
Textured Foil 2	Inplane	-
Textured Foil 3	Inplane	-
Foil 1 + EVA	Inplane	-

3 RESULTS AND ANALYSIS

3.1 Textured Front Glasses

Figure 2 shows hemispherical BRDF measurements of the two textured glass samples for one incident angle, indicated by the black arrow. For the standard PV glass specular peaks from the glass surface can be seen, although of low magnitude compared to plain glass. While for the satinated glass sample, no specular peak is observed and low BRDF values are spread over the entire hemisphere.

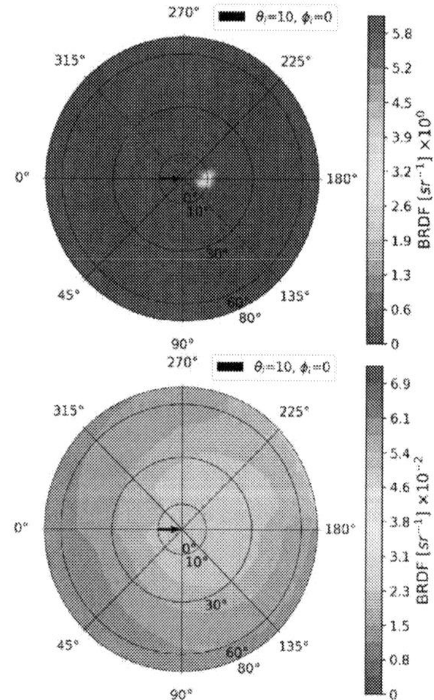

Figure 2: BRDF measurements of standard PV glass (top) and satinated glass (bottom) [7].

A big part of the explanation for the differences in

BRDF of the two samples arises from the difference in surface textures. Figure 3 shows the 3D surface scans of the two glasses. The 1x1 mm surface scan of the standard PV glass shows very smooth surface topology with low height gradients, reducing the strength of the specular reflections. The surface scan of the satinated sample shows a high surface variation over an even smaller area of 0.25x0.25 mm.

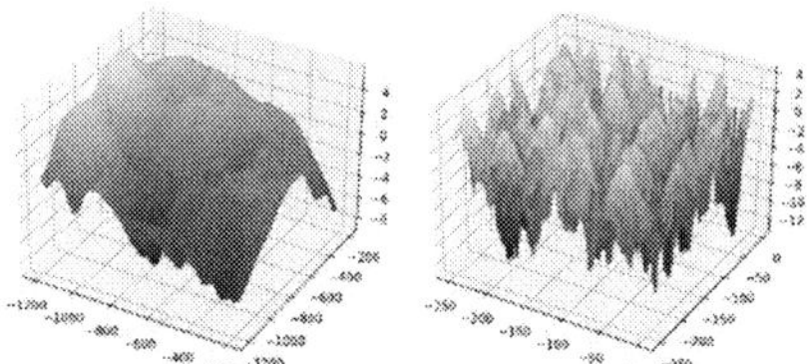

Figure 3: 3D surface scans in μm of standard PV glass (top) and satinated glass (bottom).

Figure 4 shows the simulation results of the implementation of the two textures in Radiance as dielectric surfaces with a refractive index of 1.5 and transmission coefficients 0.96. Compared to the measurements, the overall distribution with the specular reflection for the standard PV glass is captured well, though with a slightly higher magnitude. For the satinated glass sample the simulation shows less scattering and higher specular and near specular reflections than what is seen in the measurements. As the samples are only modelled as surfaces in Radiance, any potential subsurface reflections are not captured in the simulation, which could be a potential explanation for the observed differences between measured and simulated results for the satinated sample.

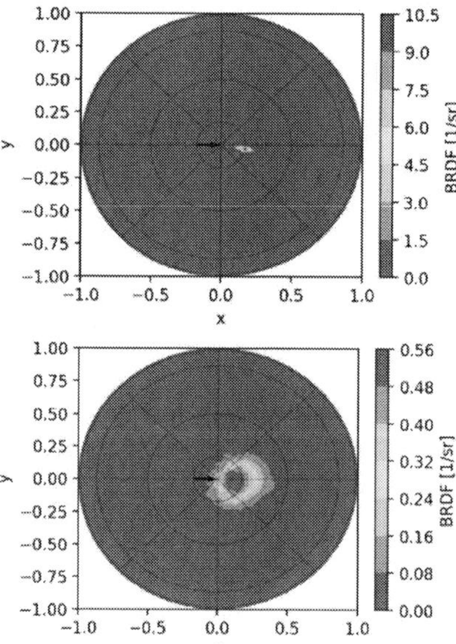

Figure 4: BRDF simulations of standard PV glass (top) and satinated glass (bottom).

3.2 Textured Foils and Multiple Layers

Figure 5 shows the inplane BRDF measurements of the three textured foils. In the top graph the foils are measured as they are and in the bottom graph is the same measurement but after encapsulation in EVA. Comparing the two graphs, it is clear to see how the differently textured foils scatter the light and how the scattering changes after EVA encapsulation, more for some than for others. For example, the orange graph - Foil 2 - shows wide scattering before encapsulation that seems to not be present after encapsulated in the EVA. Meanwhile Foil 3 seems to not change much after encapsulation. This emphasizes the need for looking at the full BIPV module stack when evaluating the performance of the textured foils.

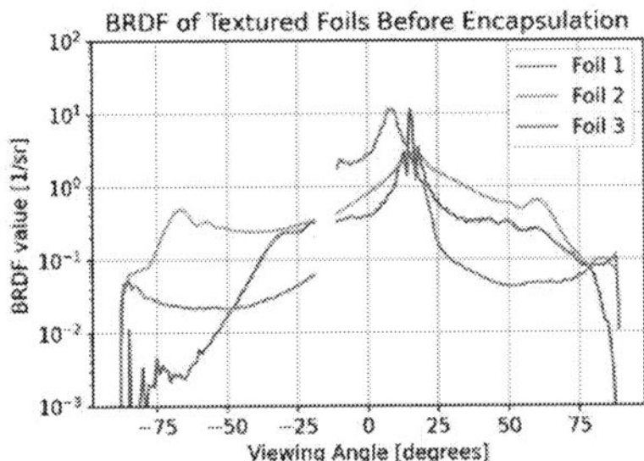

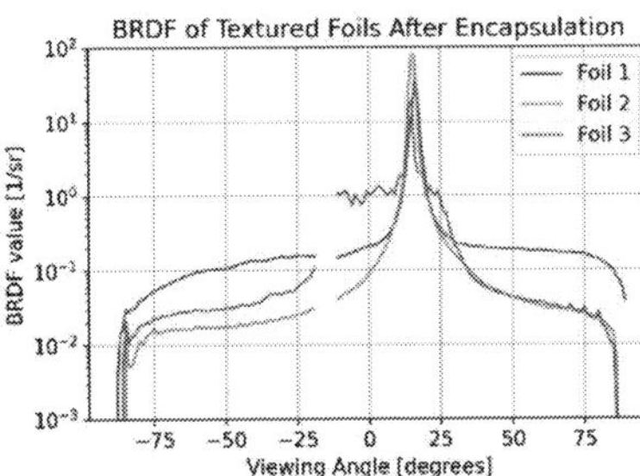

Figure 5: BRDF measurements of the textured foils, before (top) and after (bottom) EVA encapsulation.

Figure 6 shows the simulations and BRDF measurements of Foil 1 before and after encapsulation. For the foil before encapsulation, we see a high level of agreement between the measured and simulated BRDF results.

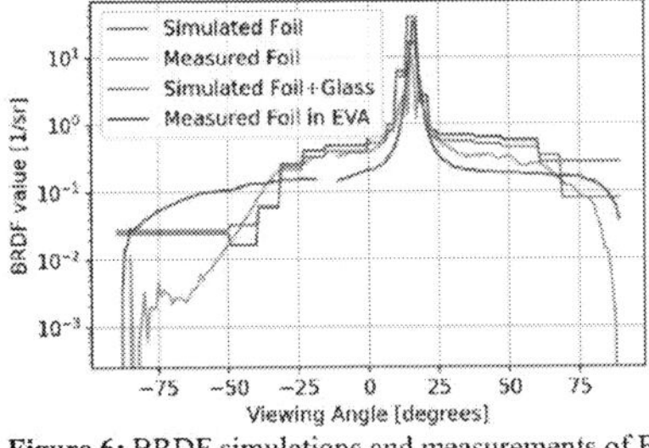

Figure 6: BRDF simulations and measurements of Foil 1 before and after encapsulation.

When considering multiple layers simulations, the foil is first simulated as encapsulated in a dielectric material as a representation of the EVA encapsulation. For this composition Radiance is not able to return sensible simulation results, indicating that how the materials are modelled in Radiance does not capture the behavior of the BIPV stack. The results shown in Figure 6 are instead the simulation results of Foil 1 embedded in a simplified version of the dielectric, designed for representing normal glass but avoiding simulating internal reflections. Here the simulation returns reasonable results but with high similarity to the results of the foil without encapsulation.

4 CONCLUSIONS & FUTURE WORK

Simulations and measurements of BIPV modules with textured elements have been performed of both individual components and of a multilayer stack representing the full BIPV module. Results for the individual components seem promising, while for the multilayer simulations, Radiance struggles to capture all effects at play. The BRDF measurements of the foils before and after EVA encapsulation highlights the need for full stack simulations to predict the final BIPV design. It is possible that Radiance could be one step in a chain of tools to predict final BIPV designs, though further work is needed to fully evaluate the potential of Radiance for BIPV module design simulations.

5 ACKNOWLEDGEMENTS

This work was funded by EUDP as part of the "ColorFoil" project under grant 64022-1027.

6 REFERENCES

[1] A. Borja Block, J. Escarre Palou, M. Courtant, A. Virtuani, G. Cattaneo, M. Roten, H.Y. Li, M. Despeisse, A. Hessler-Wyser, U. Desai et al., Energy and Buildings 314 (2024)

[2] C. Ferreira, I. Vyalih, J. Lamminaho, M. Babin, N. Andersen, P. Poulsen, S. Thorsteinsson, K. Petersons, J. Cox, M. Madsen (2024)

[3] B. Blasi, T. Kroyer, T. Kuhn, O. Hohn, IEEE Journal of Photovoltaics 11, 1305 – 1311 (2021)

[4] Radiance, https://www.radiance-online.org/, accessed 25-09-2025

[5] G. Ward, M. Kurt, N. Bonneel, Reducing Anisotropic BSDF Measurement to Common Practice (2014)

[6] D. Geisler-Moroder, E.S. Lee, G.J. Ward, B. Bueno, L.O. Grobe, T. Wang, B. Deroisy, H.R. Wilson, Tech. rep., IEA SHC Task 61 (2021)

[7] M. Babin, S. Thorsteinsson, M.L. Jakobsen, S.V. Spataru, 12, 1314 – 1318 (2022)

[8] J. Svatos, Mater Thesis, DTU, (2024)

[9] CMM-014-Sensofar, DOI: 10.57735/13866, accessed 25-09-2025

EPFL
PV-lab
IMT NEUCHÂTEL
:: csem

INSTITUT
POLYTECHNIQUE
DE PARIS

Modeling Partial Shading at the Cell Level on Photovoltaic Modules

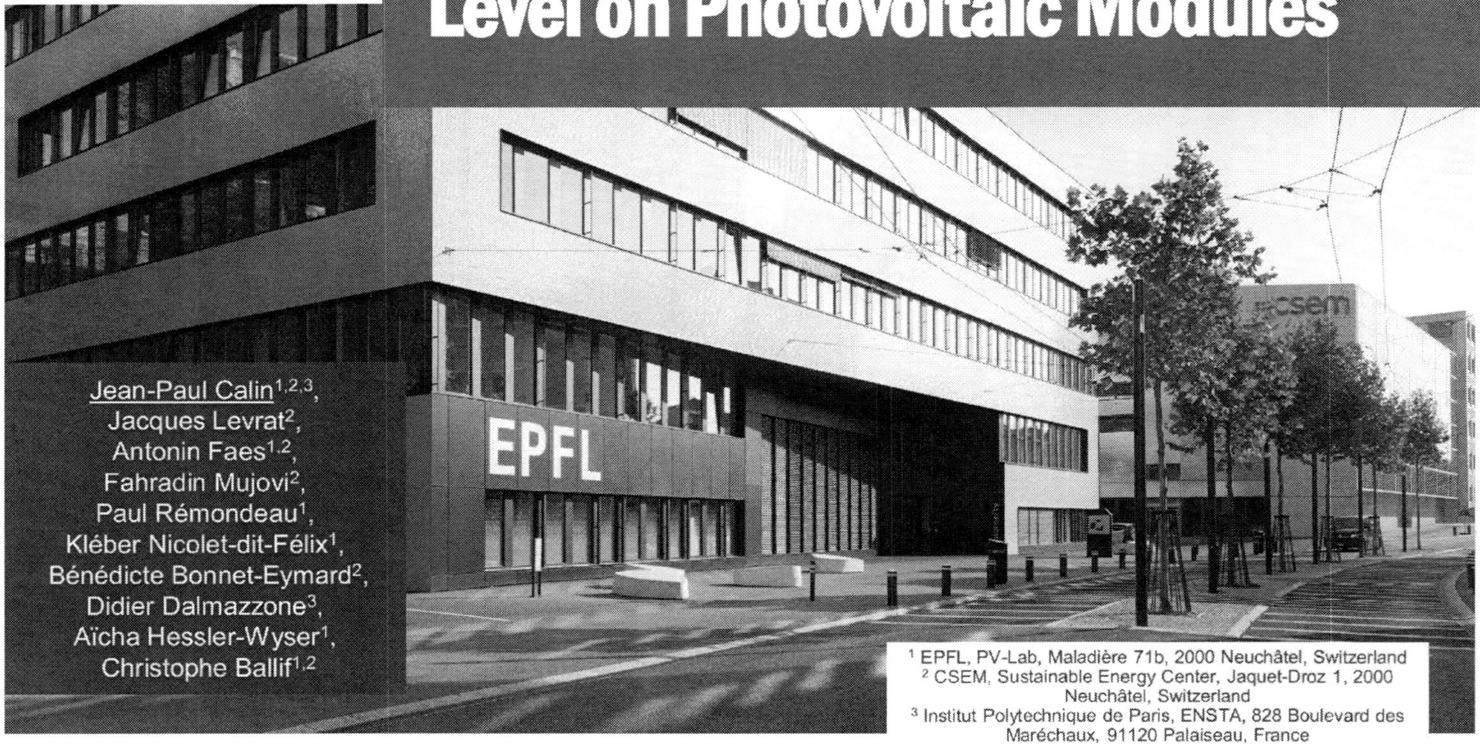

Jean-Paul Calin[1,2,3],
Jacques Levrat[2],
Antonin Faes[1,2],
Fahradin Mujovi[2],
Paul Rémondeau[1],
Kléber Nicolet-dit-Félix[1],
Bénédicte Bonnet-Eymard[2],
Didier Dalmazzone[3],
Aïcha Hessler-Wyser[1],
Christophe Ballif[1,2]

[1] EPFL, PV-Lab, Maladière 71b, 2000 Neuchâtel, Switzerland
[2] CSEM, Sustainable Energy Center, Jaquet-Droz 1, 2000 Neuchâtel, Switzerland
[3] Institut Polytechnique de Paris, ENSTA, 828 Boulevard des Maréchaux, 91120 Palaiseau, France

020251-001

Introduction

EPFL
PV-lab
IMT NEUCHATEL
:: csem
INSTITUT POLYTECHNIQUE DE PARIS

- PV expanding in sectors like buildings, infrastructure, transportation, and agriculture
- Shadows may be thinner than submodules or even individual cells
- Shading losses reduce performance sharply, are nonlinear and configuration-dependent
- Near shading is modeled in state-of-the art software
- PVsyst: linear and electrical shading [1]
  - I-V curve based on sub-module

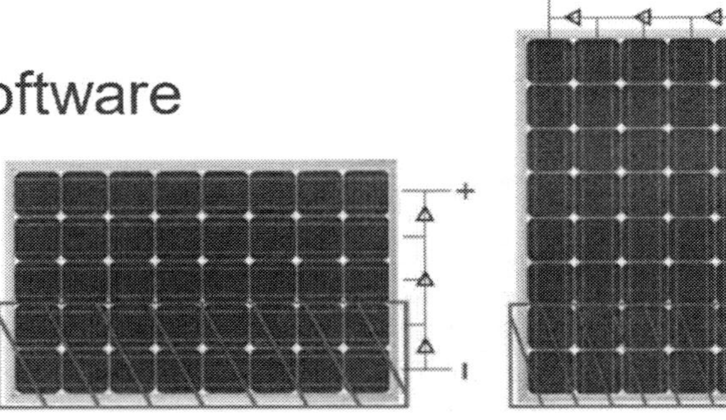

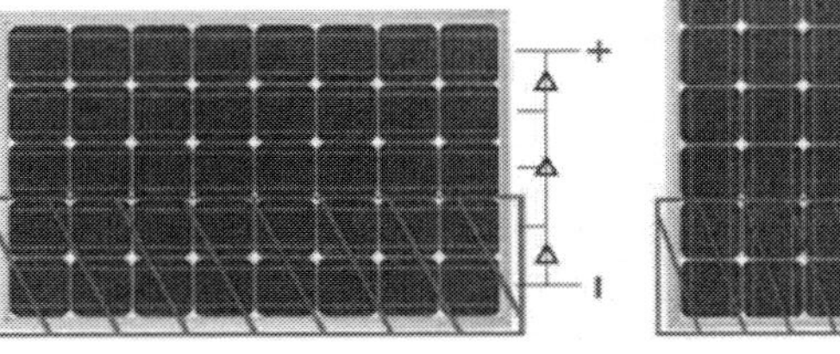

[1] A. Mermoud, "PVSYST: a user-friendly software for PV-systems simulation," in *Twelfth European Photovoltaic Solar Energy Conference: proceedings of the International Conference*, 1994.

020251-002

Introduction

- Near shading modeling approach:

  - Project shadow on sub-module (or cells in our case)

  - Check points for shadow intersection

  - Calculate irradiance or IV curve

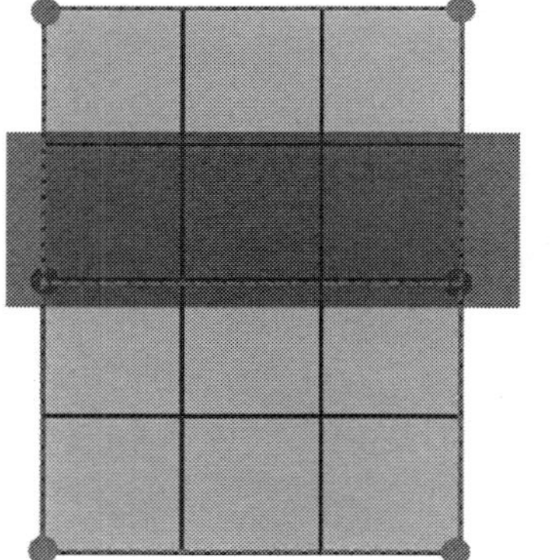

Experimental Setup

- Installed a chimney-like structure in front of BIPV roof tile modules

- Captured images of the shadow throughout the day

- Monitored I-V curves, power, irradiance, and temperature

Method: Vertex Projection

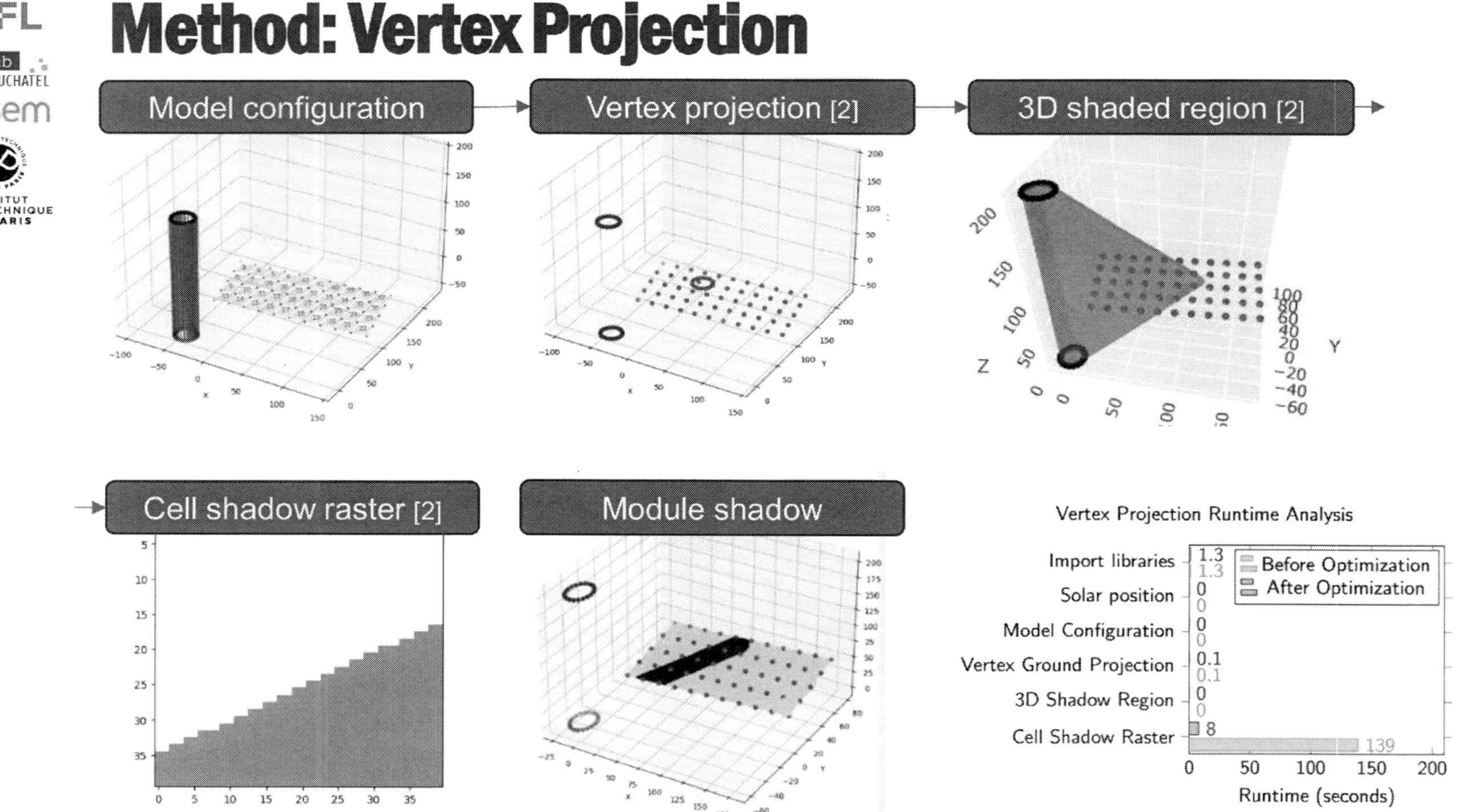

[2] B. A. de Sá, T. Dezuo, and D. Ohf, "Shadow Modelling Algorithm for Photovoltaic Systems: Extended Analysis and Simulation," *J. Control Autom. Electr. Syst.*, vol. 33, no. 5, pp. 1507–1518, Oct. 2022, doi: 10.1007/s40313-022-00905-2.

Method: Ray Tracing

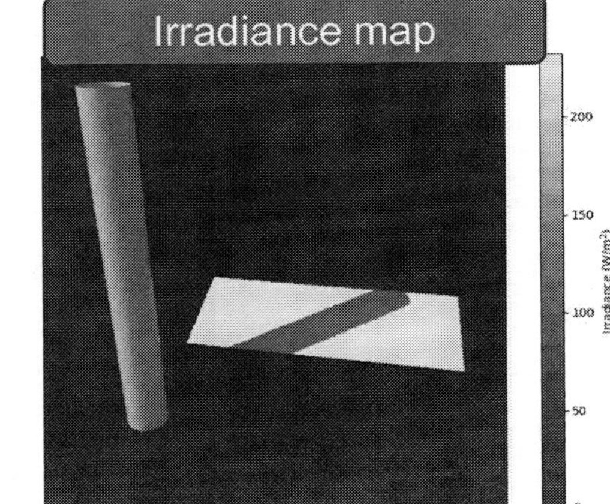

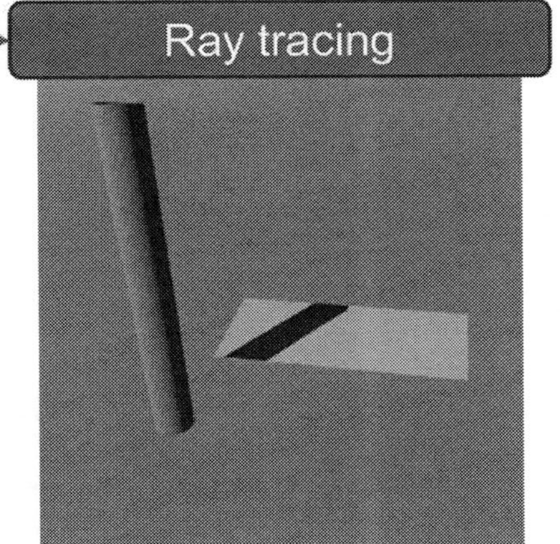

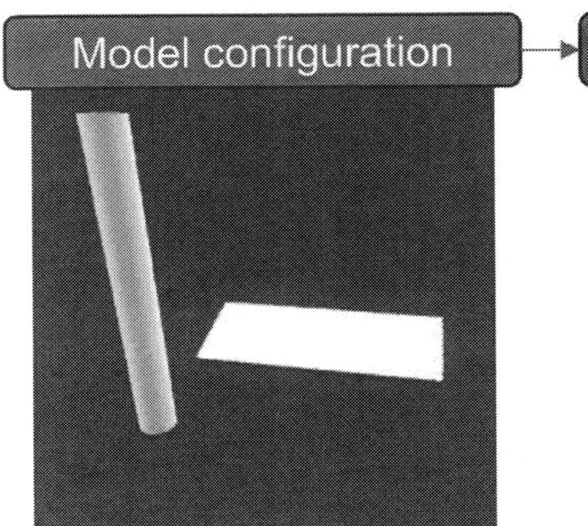

- Implemented using Radiance engine [3]

- Runtime optimized to 2.5 seconds per solar position using Radiance data structures

- Simple model configuration → fast shadow position
  - More accurate irradiance simulation possible with detailed model configuration [4]

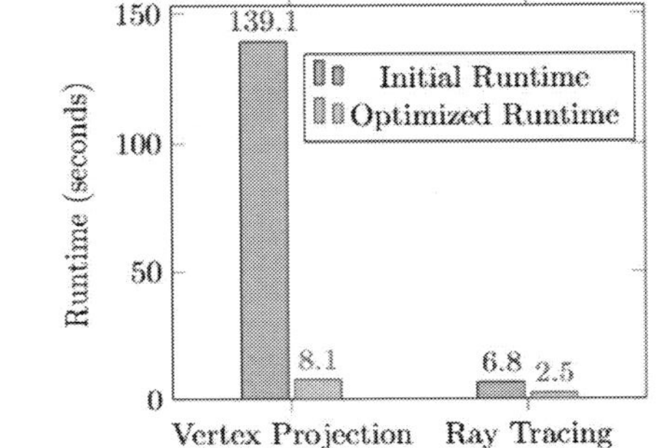

[3] G. W. Larson and R. Shakespeare, *Rendering with Radiance: the art and science of lighting visualization.* Morgan Kaufmann Publishers Inc., 1998.
[4] M. A. Mikofski, M. Lynn, J. Byrne, M. Hamer, A. Neubert, and J. Newmiller, "Accurate Performance Predictions of Large PV Systems with Shading using Submodule Mismatch Calculation," in *2018 IEEE 7th World Conference on Photovoltaic Energy Conversion (WCPEC) (A Joint Conference of 45th IEEE PVSC, 28th PVSEC & 34th EU PVSEC)*, Jun. 2018, pp. 3635–3639. doi: 10.1109/PVSC.2018.8547323.

Method: Check Points for Shadow Intersection

EPFL
PV-lab
IMT NEUCHÂTEL
:: csem
INSTITUT POLYTECHNIQUE DE PARIS

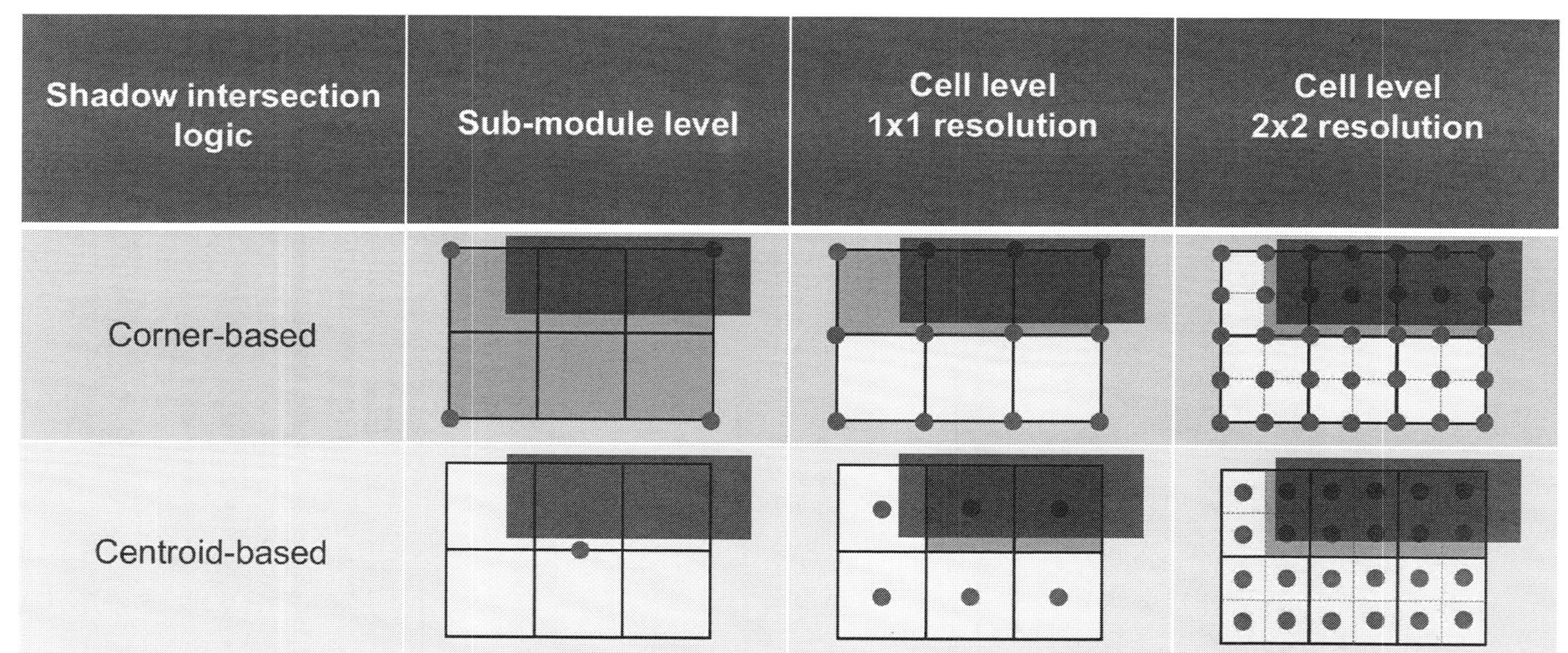

- Goal: to investigate strategies to model thinner shadows
  - Potential to improve accuracy by checking more points

020251-007

Method: Check Points for Shadow Intersection

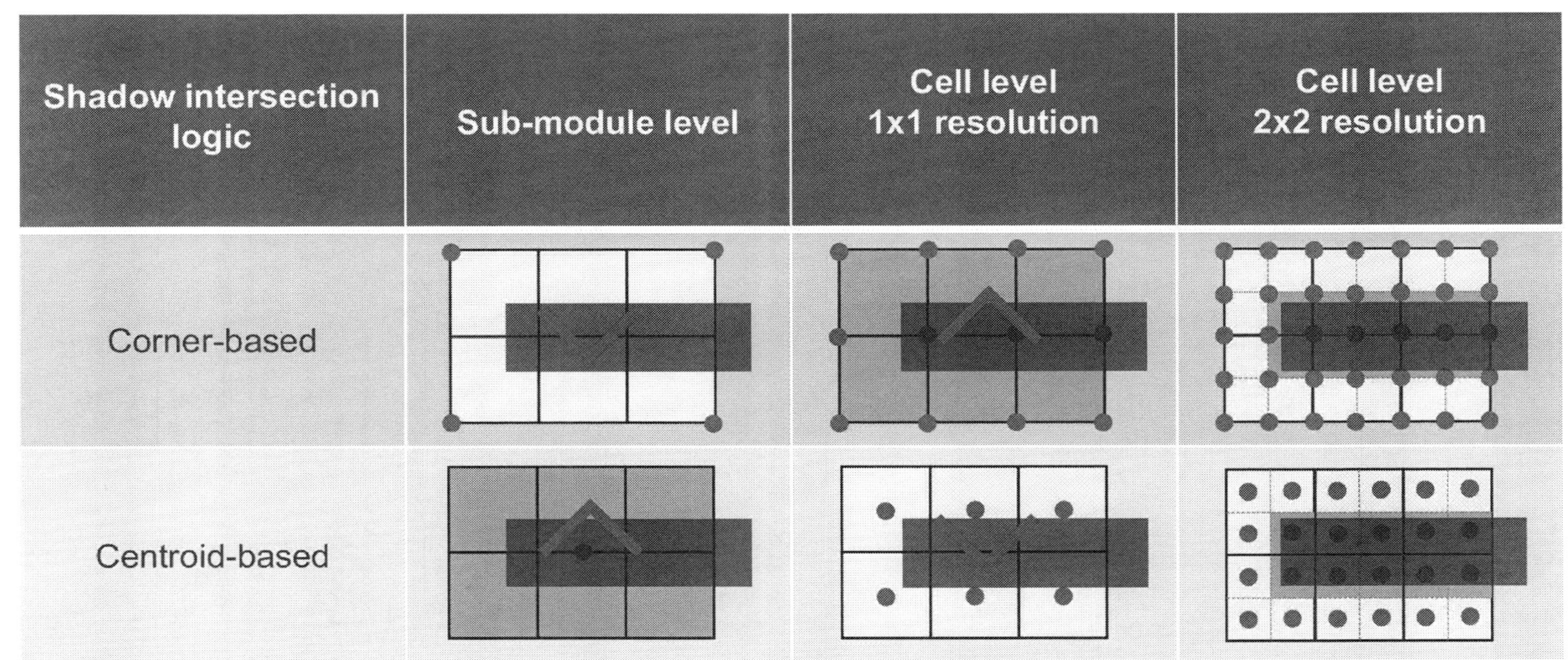

- Limitation of point sampling: some shadows will trick the algorithm
  - Checking more points takes more time. How to choose wisely?

Method: Irradiance Model

Quantity	Equation	Number
Global plane-of-array (POA) irradiance	$G_{POA} = G_{beam} + G_{sky} + G_{ground}$ [5]	(1)
Direct (beam) POA irradiance	$G_{beam} = DNI \cdot \cos(\theta)$	(2)
Diffuse sky POA irradiance	$G_{sky} = DHI \cdot \dfrac{1+\cos(\beta)}{2}$ [6]	(3)
Diffuse ground-reflected POA irradiance	$G_{ground} = GHI \cdot \rho \cdot \dfrac{1-\cos(\beta)}{2}$ [5]	(4)
Cell effective irradiance	$G_{cell} = G_{beam} * (1 - \chi) + G_{sky} + G_{ground}$	(5)

- θ: angle of incidence
- β: module tilt angle
- ρ: ground surface albedo
- χ: cell shaded fraction

- DNI: direct normal irradiance
- DHI: diffuse horizontal irradiance
- GHI: global horizontal irradiance

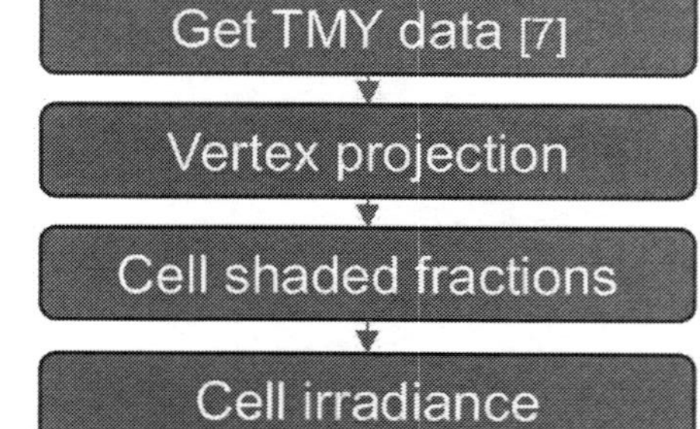

[5] P. G. Loutzenhiser, H. Manz, C. Felsmann, P. A. Strachan, T. Frank, and G. M. Maxwell, "Empirical validation of models to compute solar irradiance on inclined surfaces for building energy simulation," *Sol. Energy*, vol. 81, no. 2, pp. 254–267, Feb. 2007, doi: 10.1016/j.solener.2006.03.009.
[6] H. C. Hottel and B. B. Woertz, "The Performance of Flat-Plate Solar-Heat Collectors," *Trans. Am. Soc. Mech. Eng.*, vol. 64, no. 2, pp. 91–103, Dec. 2022, doi: 10.1115/1.4018980.
[7] Martinez, A., PVGIS Photovoltaic Geographical Information System, European Commission, Ispra, 2025, JRC142887.

Results: Shadow Validation

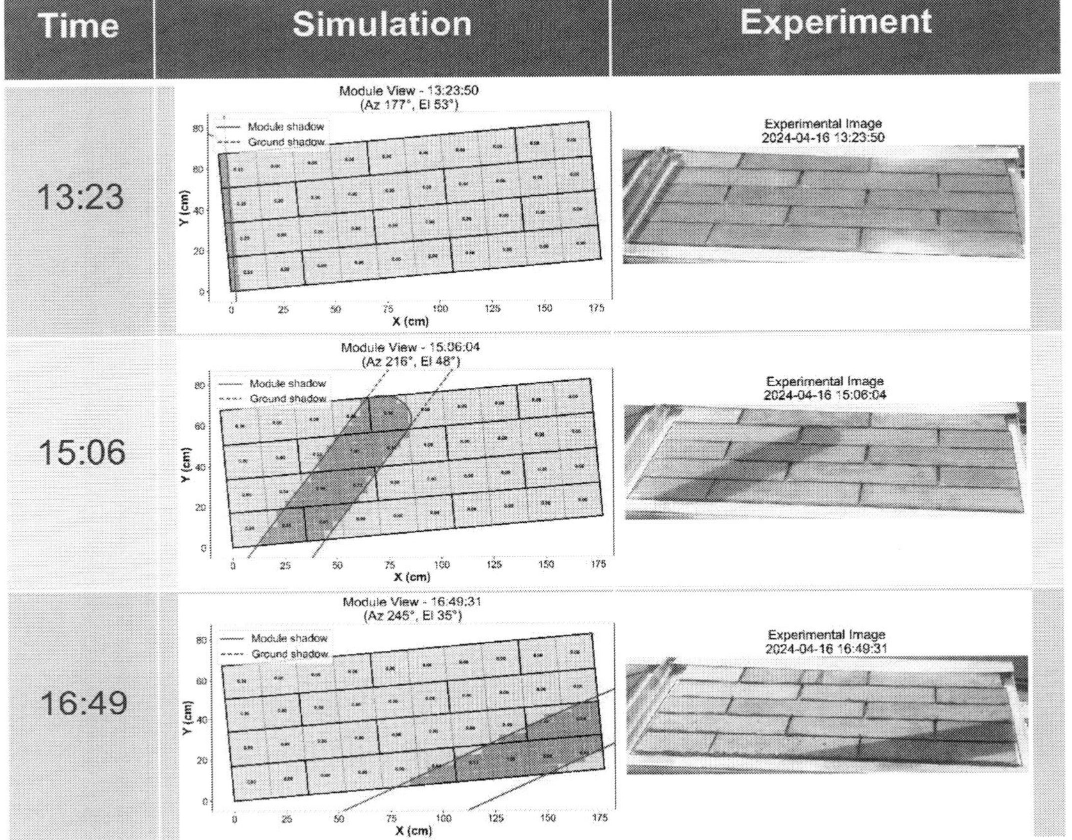

- Shadow positions validated against experiment

Results: Shaded Fractions

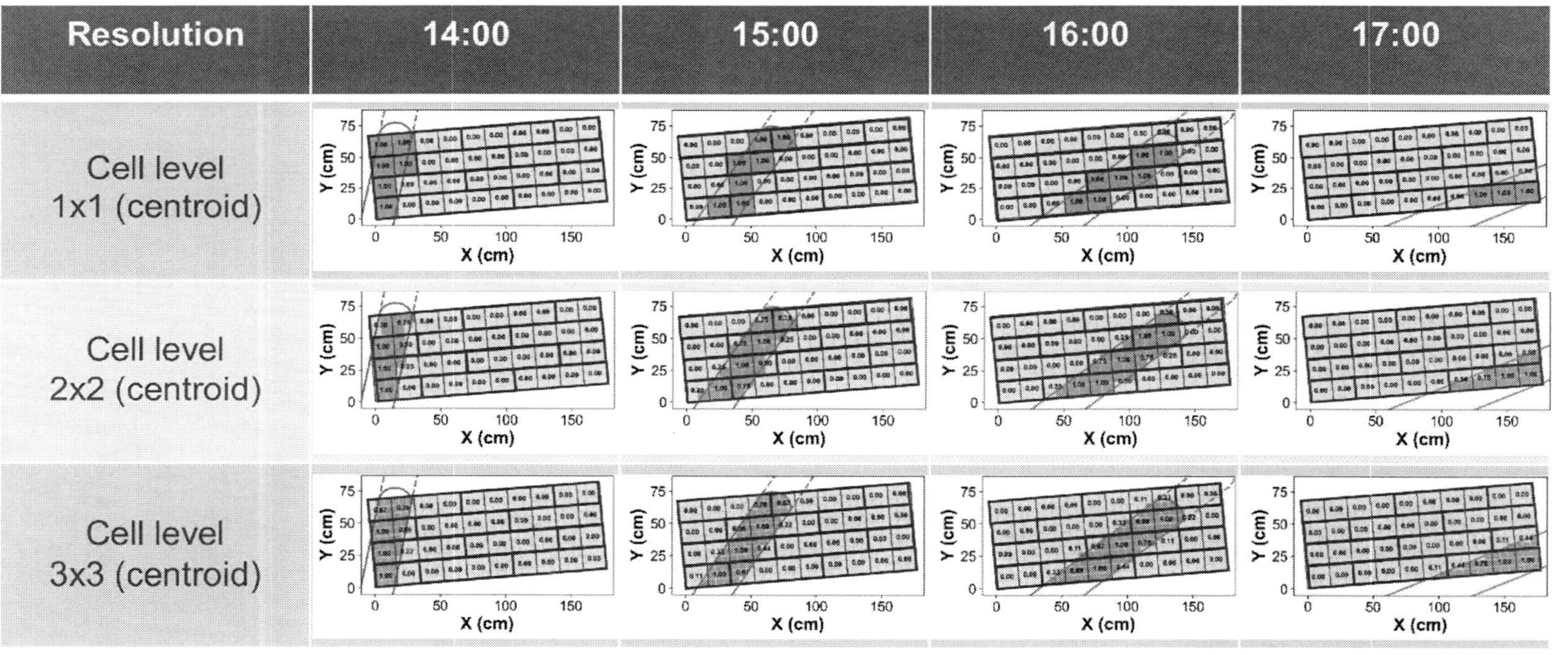

- 1x1 cell level resolution: shaded fraction is 0 or 1
- Higher resolutions: cell shaded fraction can be estimated more precisely

Results: Daily Irradiance & Irradiance Loss

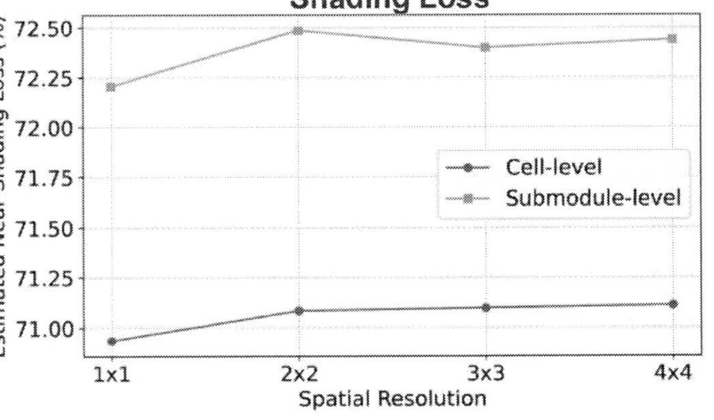

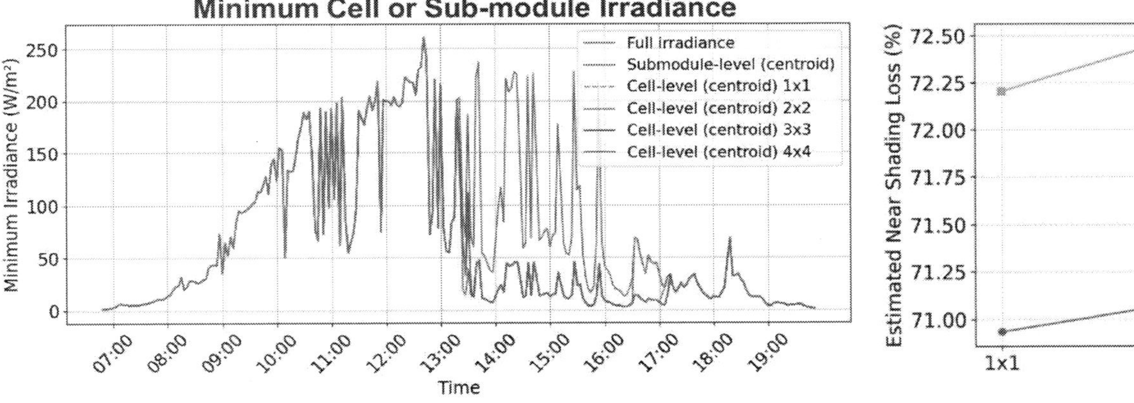

- Data from April 16 at 3-minute intervals
  - No shading in the morning, shadow events in the afternoon between 13:21 and 17:12
- Submodule-level approach sometimes over-estimates or under-estimates shading losses during partial shading events
  - Over-estimated losses at 13:27, by over 45 W/m²
  - Under-estimated losses at 16:34, by over 60 W/m²

- Potential gain in accuracy of 1% for given shadow configuration
- Model converges at 2x2 resolution and above for the given shadow size
  - Thinner shadows: model may converge at higher resolutions, potentially more accuracy gain

Results: Annual Simulation Runtime

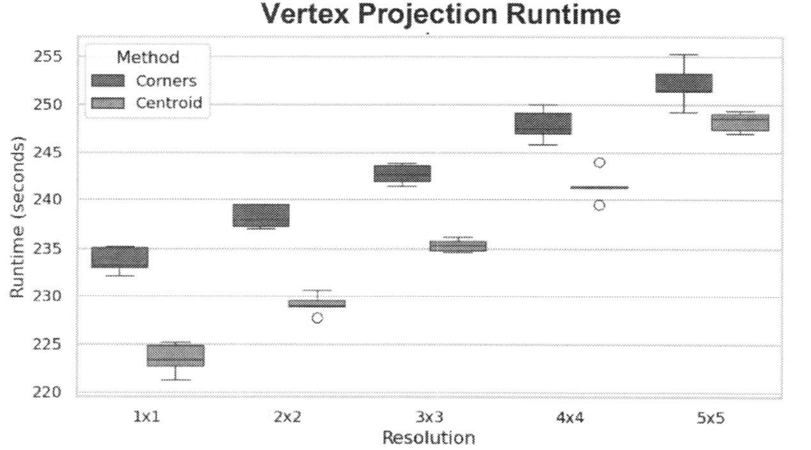

- Around 4 minutes on the lab desktop (64 GB RAM)

- Scales linearly with resolution

020251-013

EPFL
PV-lab
IMT NEUCHÂTEL
:: csem
INSTITUT POLYTECHNIQUE DE PARIS

Conclusion & Outlook

- Near shading simulation at cell level: TMY data, vertex projection, cell shading fractions, cell effective irradiance
  - Two shadow modeling approaches: vertex projection and ray tracing. Validated shadow positions experimentally
  - Compared strategies for selecting points to check for shadow intersection
- Potential to improve the accuracy of irradiance losses with more points
  - 1% less annual irradiance loss at cell level in the experimental configuration
- Tradeoff: computation time
  - Vertex projection runtime: optimized to around 4 minutes for 1-year hourly simulation, scales linearly with resolution
- Future work: investigate impact of shadow and cell sizes on optimal resolution

020251-014

This research was funded by the European Union's Horizon Europe, Innovation Actions programme under grant agreement No 101136112 (Increase Project), No 101136094 (Sphinx Project), and No 101172767 (Empower project). This work has received funding from the Swiss State Secretariat of Education, Research and Innovation (SERI).

Metallization & Interconnection
WORKSHOP 2025
for Solar Cells   13TH EDITION
October 20 & 21, Berlin, Germany
www.miworkshop.info
Registration is open! – early bird until
September 29
Berlin (Germany) – hosted by HZB
Website and program: https://miworkshop.info/
Proceedings in IEEE Journal of Photovoltaics
Sponsors :: csem Dow GORDA Henkel MONDRAGON ASSEMBLY 晶银新材

MARKET POTENTIAL OF BUILDING-INTEGRATED PHOTOVOLTAICS: A GRANULAR ANALYSIS OF THE EUROPEAN BUILDING STOCK

Juan Ignacio Martinez[2], Julien Van Overstraeten[2], Philippe Macé[1], José María Vega de Seoane[2], Elina Bosch[1], Mélodie de l'Épine[3]
[1]Becquerel Institute, Brussels (Belgium) [2]Becquerel Institute España, San Sebastián (Spain), [3]Becquerel Institute France, Lyon (France)
j.martinez@becquerelinstitute.eu, j.vanoverstraeten@becquerelinstitute.eu, p.mace@becquerelinstitute.org

ABSTRACT: Building-Integrated Photovoltaics (BIPV) has gained relevance as it offers a unique solution fulfilling the role of a construction element and an energy generation device. This study aims to assess the market potential for BIPV in Europe up to 2050, covering multiple building typologies within the European building stock, for roofs and façades, under two different growth scenarios. The methodology follows a multi-step approach that is divided into two distinct sections: The first section estimates the 'technical potential' for PV on buildings, considering architectural and solar suitability. The second section, the 'specific market potential' quantifies the Total Addressable Market and Serviceable Addressable Market for BIPV, reflecting its intrinsic constraint that installations occur during new construction and renovation, and models adoption dynamics using the Diffusion of Innovations model. Through its scenarios, the project highlights the importance of regulation and higher renovation activity to unlock the potential for BIPV. Overall, BIPV can significantly contribute to Europe's energy transition, with rooftops representing most of the potential, while façades contribute selectively where architectural integration and visibility are prioritised.

Keywords: PV, Building-Integrated, Market Potential, Technical Potential

1 INTRODUCTION

This paper estimates the European BIPV market potential up to 2050 using a supply-side approach considering different building typologies. Two growth scenarios reflecting different renovation activity levels map distinct uptake pathways across roofs and façades.

The technical potential is first calculated from the gross European roof and façade area and by applying architectural and solar suitability factors.

The specific market potential is then calculated. The Total Addressable Market (TAM) limits the market to installations during new construction and renovation. The Serviceable Addressable Market (SAM) considers market and regulatory factors for BIPV and uses the Diffusion of Innovations theory to model adoption dynamics under the scenarios.

2 METHODOLOGY

The aim of this study is to assess the market potential for Building-Integrated Photovoltaics (BIPV) in Europe up to 2050, for both roofs and façades, under two different growth scenarios. Because BIPV is integrated into the building envelope, installations occur during new construction or renovation, so annual uptake depends on the rate of new construction and renovation. The assessment follows a multi-step process divided into two distinct sections. The first section involves estimating the technical potential of PV in buildings, using a supply-side approach, considering architectural differences in each building type, construction period and country. At each stage, the scope is progressively narrowed using suitability considerations for integration and scenario assumptions for market uptake to provide a more realistic estimation. The second section develops different deployment scenarios based on the Diffusion of Innovations model [1], in order to understand and analyse the adoption trends of BIPV deployment over time.

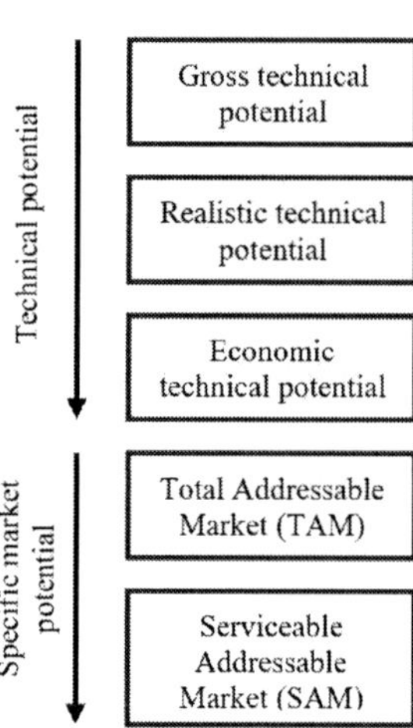

Figure 1 – Methodology approach flowchart

2.1 Technical potential

The Gross technical potential by 2050 represents all available roof and façade surfaces in the EU + Switzerland and UK, using available data for 2020, and adding new constructions and renovations obtained from [2] up to 2050. At this stage, it does not distinguish between BIPV and BAPV. Constructed floor surfaces are derived from the EU Building Stock Observatory (BSO) [3, 4] and are then converted to roof and façade areas using TABULA-EPISCOPE ratios by country, building use and construction period [5]. Two scenarios are introduced here. The 'Renovation wave' scenario considers a significant increase in building renovations, while the 'No renovation wave' scenario is a business-as-usual case, with no major increase in renovations. Renovation rates in the 'Renovation wave' scenario were taken from [2], while in the 'No renovation wave' scenario, rates reported by the European Commission [6] were used and projected to 2050 based on the work by Sandberg [7]. Renovation rates in both scenarios varied according to country and sector (residential, non-residential). Table I presents the average renovation rates used in both scenarios

Table I – Average renovation rates in Europe 2020-2050

	No renovation wave	Renovation wave
Residential buildings	1.1-1.19	2.51-2.67
Non-residential buildings	1.64-1.72	2.51-2.66

The Realistic technical potential considers 'architecturally' suitable areas only. It accounts for obstacles, windows, sharp corners and other inaccessible areas on the building envelope, which are excluded. For roofs, only 60% of the available area was considered usable, based on [8]. For façades, this factor considers areas with insufficient space for PV modules, obstacles, etc. It is approximately 35% that is subtracted from the initial surface [9]. Window areas are excluded for façades, with BIPV windows not considered in the scope of this project. Architectural suitability ratios are applied as shown in Table II.

Due to the lack of available information about the architectural suitability for different building typologies, no distinction was made between them when applying these ratios.

The economic technical potential is then obtained by only including areas which receive sufficient solar radiation. Because of the complexity of urbanized areas, with neighbouring buildings, vegetation and nearby objects being possible sources of shading, this was achieved using a solar suitability ratio. For roofs, this ratio considers unfavourable orientation, inclination and shading from surrounding elements. It was taken from [8]. For façades, the solar suitability is highly dependent on building height, distance from other buildings and orientation [10]. Chatzipoulka found that the sky view factor (SVF) can be used as a predictor to estimate solar irradiation on building façades [11]. The SVF is a measure of the portion of the sky visible from a given point on the building surface. Due to lack of available information about the solar suitability in different building typologies, the building typology was not considered when applying the solar suitability ratio. The solar suitability ratio was computed by country, considering the repartition of cities, suburbs and rural areas, which affect the average SVF. Using the relationship between the SVF and the solar irradiation on façades, suitability ratios ranged from 14 to 33%, with an average of 27%.

Table II – Architectural and solar suitability ratios

	Façade	Roof
Architectural suitability	~ 65%	60%
Solar suitability	~ 27%	~ 56%
Window exclusion	~ 30%	

2.2 Specific market potential

The Total Addressable Market (TAM) refers to the maximum market potential of BIPV. It includes only the areas arising from new construction and renovations between 2024 and 2050, reflecting the natural limitation that BIPV is installed during integration windows rather than as stand-alone retrofits.

The Serviceable Addressable Market (SAM) refers to the portion of the TAM that can realistically be accessed given market and regulatory conditions. Two suitability dimensions are applied to the TAM:

(1) Regulatory suitability factor: Reflects the impact of regulations, policies and incentives to determine the share of the TAM that would actually be covered by PV.

(2) Market suitability factor: Considers the competitiveness and market dynamics of BIPV to determine the share of PV installations on buildings that could be BIPV (and not BAPV).

Table III – Average SAM market and regulatory factors 2024-2050

	Façade	Roof
Regulatory suitability	3-17%	60-90%
Market suitability	85-96%	10-50%

Both factors vary by country, year, surface type, and building typology. The Diffusion of Innovations model is implemented at this stage to assess the possible evolution of BIPV deployment up to 2050. BIPV historical capacity, as well as short-term forecasts made by Becquerel Institute, were used to model the growth rate for BIPV adoption for both scenarios. The analysis is segmented into residential and non-residential buildings and further divided by roofs and façades, producing annual and cumulative trajectories under both scenarios.

Finally, the area values were converted to capacity (GW), differentiating between roof and façade surfaces because of the specific requirements and characteristics of the types of BIPV installed in them. The ITRPV 2024 report [12], as well as case studies from multiple BIPV projects were used to estimate the evolution of the power density for BIPV until 2050. The type of cell technology, projected module efficiency, share of semi-transparent modules, and semi-transparency level were considered to make a robust estimation of the potential capacity that BIPV can represent in Europe.

Table IV – Power density values (W/m^2)

	Façade	Roof
2025	141.3	202.6
2030	145.7	208.8
2040	151.6	216.6
2050	157.1	223.6

3 RESULTS

3.1 Technical potential

The European gross technical potential for BIPV amounted to approximately 64 000 km^2 in 2024 as shown in Figure 3. This value increases significantly when taken to 2050 because of renovations and new constructions. In the end, after reductions from the realistic and economic technical potential, only around 12% of the gross technical potential is considered viable for BIPV, which amounts to 16 416 km^2.

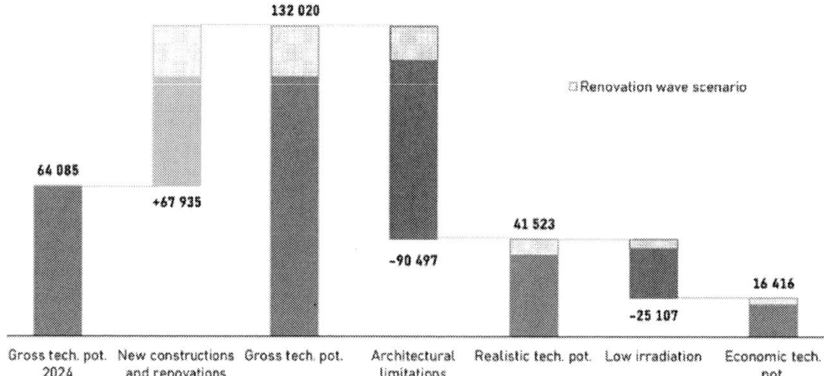

Figure 3 – Technical potential for BIPV in Europe (km²)

Figure 2 shows the distribution of the BIPV market potential in the residential and non-residential sectors, as well as for the surface type, roof or façade. 67% of the potential for PV on buildings comes from the residential sector. Façades are over 2/3 of the gross potential, which is a large share, but makes sense considering that buildings usually have a greater vertical area than roof area.

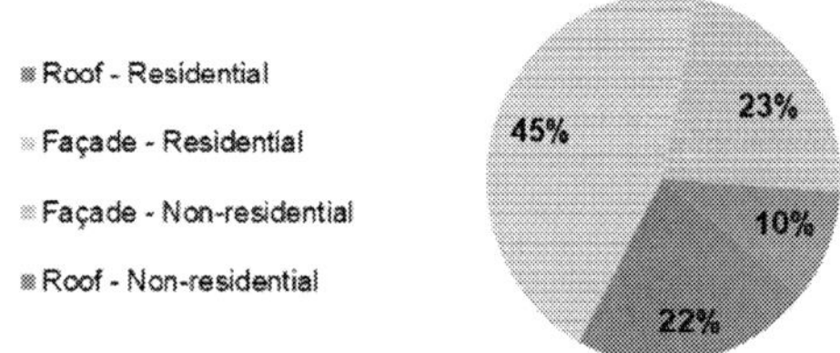

Figure 2 – Share of façade and roof gross technical potential in 2024 for residential and non-residential buildings

3.2 Specific market potential

The installation of BIPV takes place only when a building is being renovated or constructed. So, we assume the BIPV market potential to be limited by the number of renovations and new constructions that take place. An increase in building renovations would mean an increase in the potential of BIPV installations. By considering this, the total addressable market (TAM) represents the maximum possible potential market BIPV could reach in Europe.

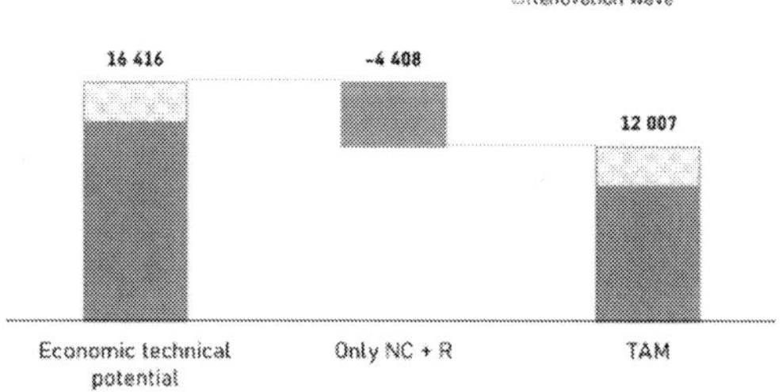

Figure 4 – BIPV total addressable market by 2050 (km²)

Figure 5 shows the share of the BIPV market potential in the residential and non-residential sectors, as well as the type of surface, roof or façade. Compared to Figure 2, the

potential for façades has been reduced notably in the TAM because architectural limitations and low irradiation were more significant in façades than roofs. The increase in renovation rates in the Renovation wave scenario target the residential sector in particular, that is why the share of residential BIPV potential is larger in this scenario. The distribution between roofs and façades is not directly impacted by the scenarios, that is why it stays roughly the same in both cases.

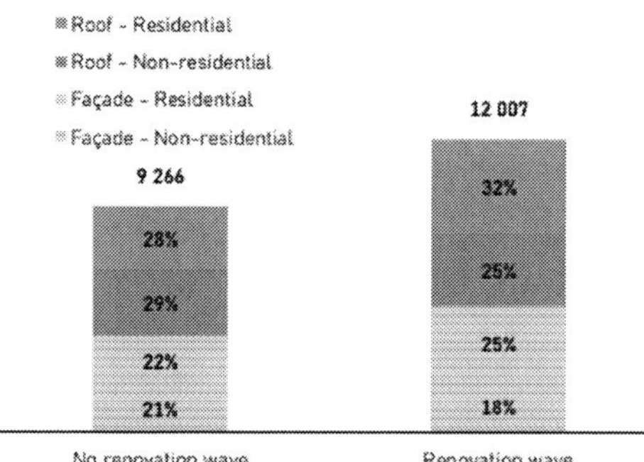

Figure 5 – Distribution of TAM potential by 2050 (km²)

The serviceable addressable market (SAM) represents the potential for BIPV by considering its regulatory suitability and competition from BAPV. The diffusion of innovations (S-curve) model was used to represent the way in which the BIPV market would grow, providing an annual and cumulative potential from 2024 to 2050.

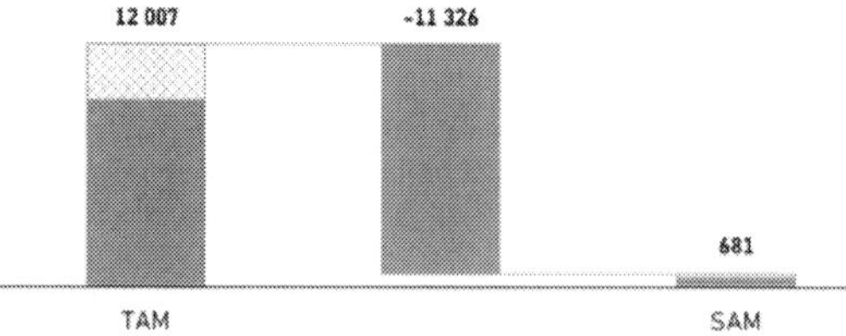

Figure 6 – BIPV serviceable addressable market by 2050 (km²)

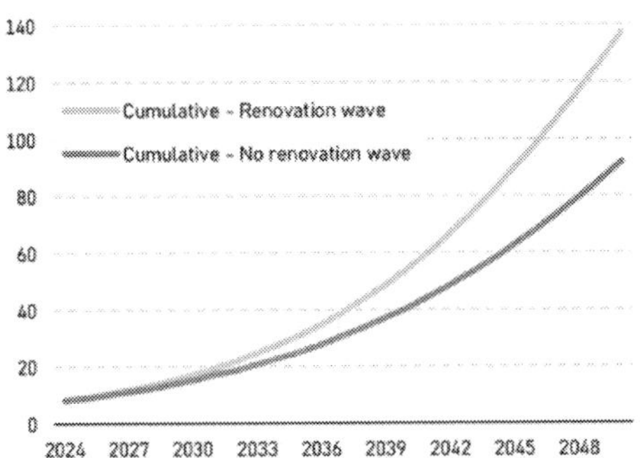
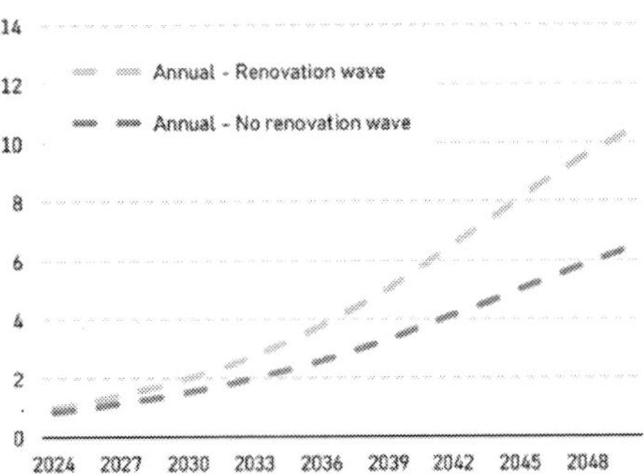

Figure 7 – BIPV cumulative (left) and annual (right) serviceable addressable market by 2050 (GW)

As shown in Figure 6, the serviceable addressable market for BIPV is much lower than the total addressable market, due to the aforementioned regulatory and market factors, as well as the adoption trends from the S-curve model. Figure 8 shows that over 85% of the potential for BIPV comes from roofs, even though in the TAM, the façade and roof shares were closer to each other. This is because, especially in the residential sector, the energy needs for most buildings will be met by rooftop PV, which reduces the attractiveness of investing in a BIPV façade. As illustrated in Figure 7, the S-curve has not reached a plateau by 2050 in either scenario, indicating that the peak annual BIPV installations have not been reached. In other words, market saturation will not be achieved by 2050.

design-oriented niche where visibility, architectural integration, and urban context favour BIPV solutions. A sustained increase in renovation activity is key for unlocking a larger share of the potential, since BIPV adoption aligns with building renovations and new construction cycles. The adoption trends modelled in both scenarios show that BIPV will not reach market saturation by 2050. Annual BIPV installations will continue to rise beyond mid-century as products mature, standards improve, and policy support strengthens. Overall, BIPV is positioned to play a significant role in the energy transition, led by roofs at scale, complemented by façade applications where architectural value is central, and enabled by an acceleration of building renovations.

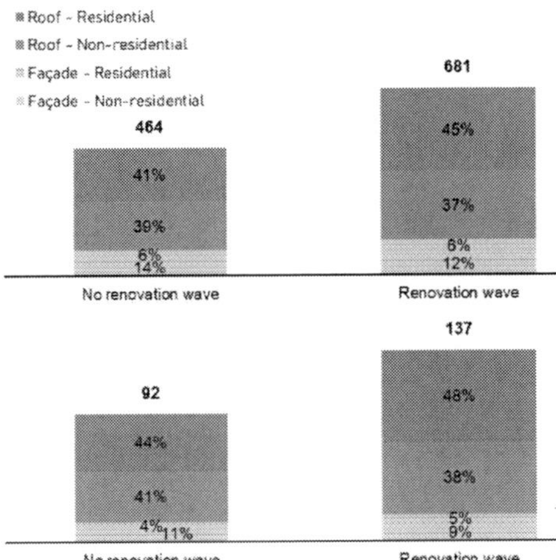

Figure 8 – Distribution of SAM potential in km² (top) and GW (bottom)

4   CONCLUSIONS

This study finds that the technical potential of PV on buildings is significant, with façades offering a large and underused surface. Even after conservative exclusions and constraints, the total addressable market for BIPV is noteworthy, with a balanced contribution by sector and surface type. The serviceable addressable market remains notable, with around 100 GW of market potential in both scenarios. Within the SAM, roofs account for most of the realizable opportunity, while façades remain a focused,

Table V – Summary of serviceable addressable market for BIPV (GW)

	Renovation wave		No renovation wave	
	2030	2050	2030	2050
Cumulative				
Roof-residential	7	65.3	6.1	40.4
Roof-non-residential	7.8	52.6	6.9	37.5
Façade-residential	1	6.5	0.9	4.1
Façade-non-residential	1.3	12.6	1.2	9.7
Total	17.1	137	15.1	91.7
Annual				
Roof-residential	0.8	5.6	0.6	3.1
Roof-non-residential	0.9	3.4	0.7	2.4
Façade-residential	0.1	0.5	0.1	0.3
Façade-non-residential	0.2	0.8	0.1	0.7
Total	2	10.4	1.5	6.4

5   REFERENCES

[1]   E. M. Rogers, Diffusion of innovations, 1982.

[2]   A. L. C. B. S. F. A. T. K. M. C. L. T. D. a. A. T. Damgaard, «Background data collection

and life cycle assessment for construction and demolition waste (CDW) management,» 2022.

[3]   European Commission, «EU Building Stock Observatory,» 2024.

[4]   D. B. S. Pezzutto, «Deliverable 3.2: Static building stock analysis. MODERATE PROJECT,» 2023.

[5]   T. S. Loga, «TABULA building typologies in 20 European countries,» 2016.

[6]   European Commission, «Comprehensive study of building energy renovation activities and the uptake of nearly zero-energy buildings in the EU – Final report,» Publications Office, 2019.

[7]   N. H.-R. Sandberg, «Dynamic building stock modelling: Application to 11 European countries to support the energy efficiency and retrofit ambitions of the EU,» 2016.

[8]   K. K. I. J.-W. A. T. N. a. S. S. Bodis, «A high-resolution geospatial assessment of the rooftop solar photovoltaic potential in the European Union. RENEWABLE and SUSTAINABLE ENERGY REVIEWS, ISSN 1364-0321, 114, 2019, p. 109309, JRC113070,» 2019.

[9]   X. L. Lu, «Estimating the photovoltaic potential of building facades and roofs using,» 2021.

[10]   Z. Z. A. Mohammad, «Techno-economic BIPV evaluation method in urban areas,» 2019.

[11]   R. C. C. Chatzipoulka, «Sky view factor as predictor of solar availability on building,» 2018.

[12]   VDMA, «International Technology Roadmap for Photovoltaics (ITRPV),» 2024.

6   FUNDING

SEAMLESS-PV - Development of advanced manufacturing equipment and processes aimed at the seamless integration of multifunctional PV solutions, enabling the deployment of IPV sectors, is a Horizon Europe Innovation Action started in January 2023 that will continue through December 2026. Grant N°101096126

Scuola universitaria professionale della Svizzera italiana
Dipartimento ambiente costruzioni e design
Istituto sostenibilità applicata all'ambiente costruito

TU/e EINDHOVEN UNIVERSITY OF TECHNOLOGY

1

SUPSI

Photovoltaics in the Built Environment:

An Overview of Timely Topics for Research and Development

42nd EUPVSEC Conference, Bilbao

Prof. Dr. Francesco Frontini,
Director ISAAC-SUPSI, Switzerland

Prof.dr. Angèle Reinders,
Eindhoven University of Technology, The Netherlands

Left: Omicron Headquarter, Middle: Wienerberger , residential BIPV, Right: La Cartosa Island

020253-001

Building Integrated Photovoltaics

❖ High variety of BIPV applications available

❖ For each of these applications, multiple BIPV products exist on the market, with their own specifications and their own effect on buildings' visual appearance, architectural design and technical construction features.

❖ In the segment of residential buildings, cold roofs are the most common BIPV installations.

❖ In the segment of commercial buildings, façade BIPV systems are much more common, as well as BIPV skylights.

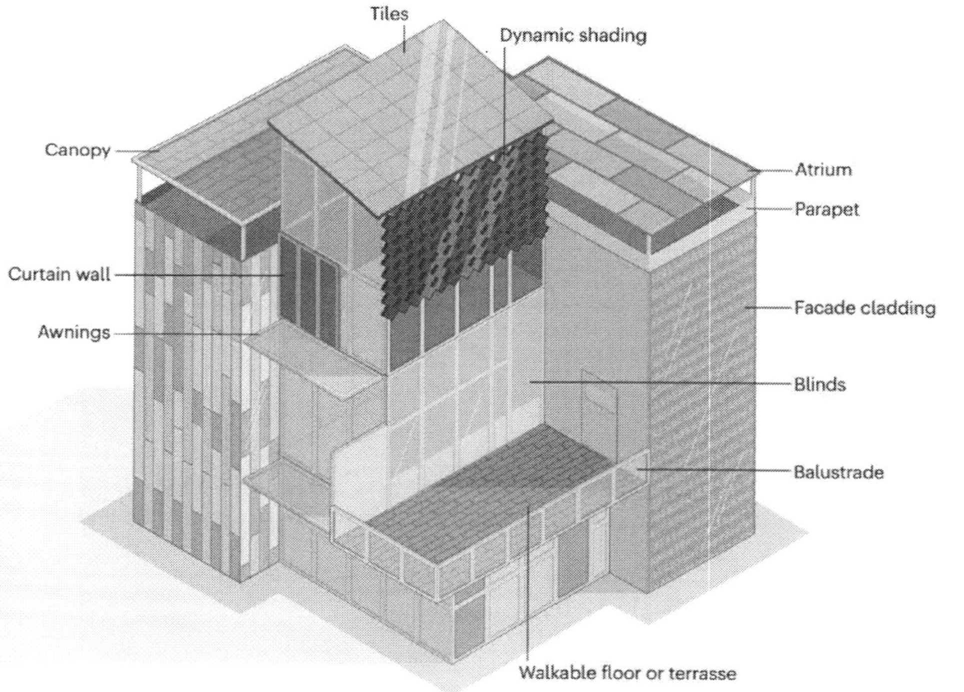

Source: Faes, A. *et al.* Building-integrated photovoltaics. *Nat. Rev. Clean Technol.* 1, 333–350 (2025).

Elaborated from IEA PVPS Task 15.

IEA
PVPS

European BIPV market history: still difficult to assess

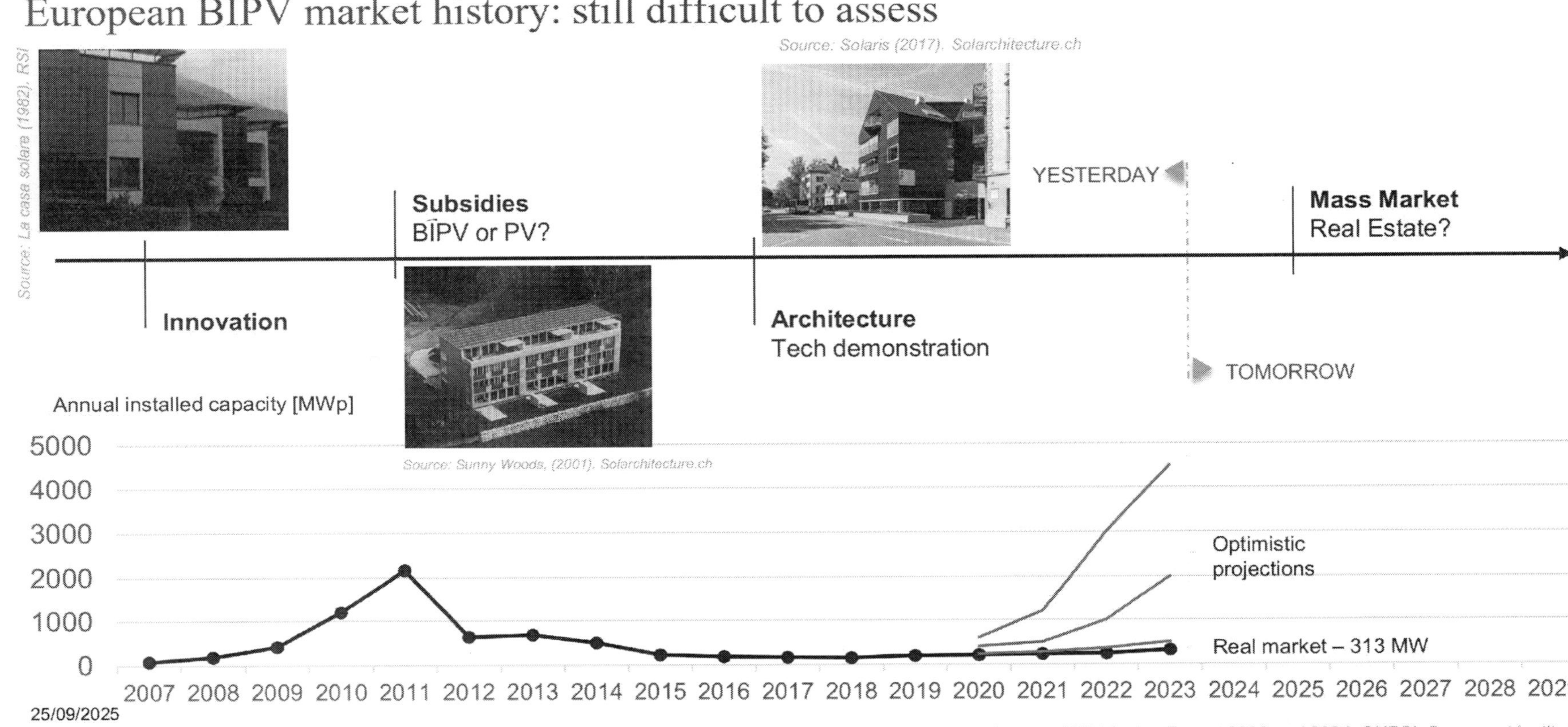

European BIPV market segmentation

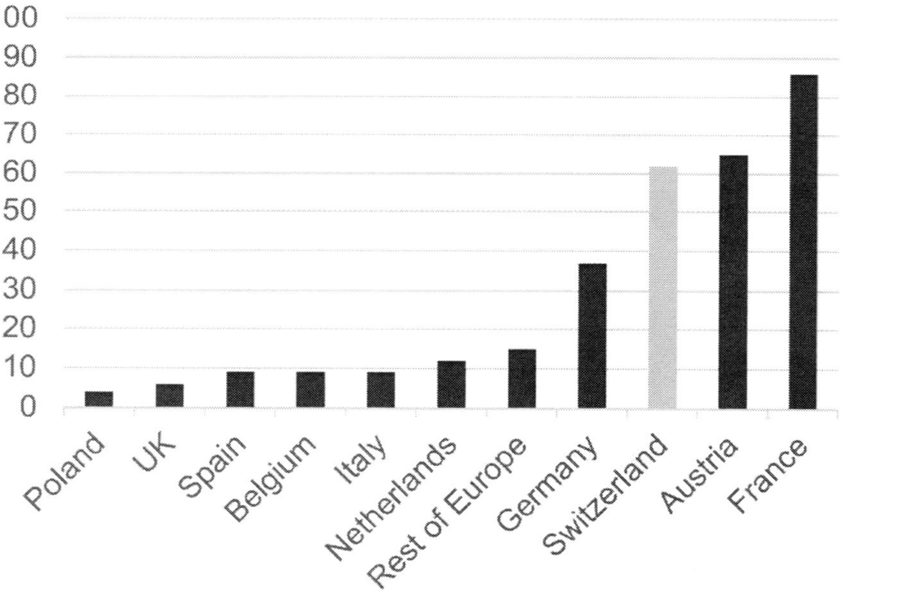

- **France**: mainly residential and commercial BIPV applications
- **Austria**: the BIPV market followed the exceptional growth of PV market in 2023
- **Switzerland:** current incentives for integrated PV systems and bonus for the tilt angle >75°
- **Germany**: traditionally on of the main markets for BIPV in Europe
- **Netherlands**: after slowing down due to the public reputation (fire safety incidents), the trust is buing rebuilt and the market is expected to grow again
- **Italy**: the residential sector accounts for a big part. No supporting schemes
- **Belgium**: 2023 has seen the closure of a regional PV support scheme, resulting in a significative growth
- **Spain**: around 1% of residential and commercial PV systems is estimated to be BIPV

Source: BIPV Status Report 2024. Becquerel Institute.

Special Issue: Photovoltaics in the built environment

(1) La Certosa Island, (2) eV-Chalet, (3) Väla Gård, (4) Sol'CH, (5) Wienerberger, (6) Omicron Headquarter, (7) Social housing apartments, (8) Solsmaragden Office, (9) Solarix – Headquarter Kuijpers, (10) Soltech manufacturing plant (11) Polis, (12) Franklin, (13) Novartis Pavillion.

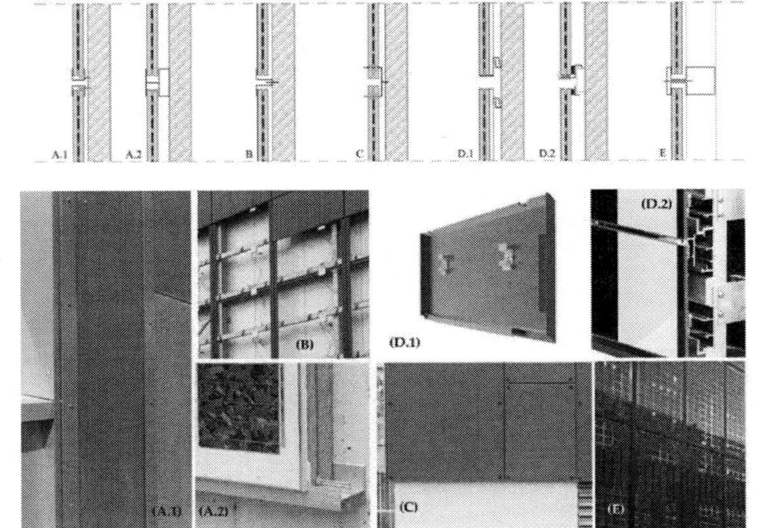

Four different families of fixing solutions are presented: A1 linear frame screwed on site (Source picture: Sunage), A2 continuous clamping (picture source: PIZ), B individual/point clamping (picture source: 3S), C point fixing with drilled holes (picture source: Sunage), D1 Adhesive vertical rail with hooks (picture source: Schweizer), D2 Adhesive self-weight system with safety mechanical retention (picture source: Gasser GFT), and E continuous post-and-rail façade system (picture source: Onyx)

Source: P. Bonomo et al., Comprehensive review and state of play in the use of photovoltaics in buildings

Special Issue on PV in the Built Environment

- SI of scientific journal **Energy and Buildings**, with impact factor 6.6
- Timeline collection and reviewing of manuscripts: 2024
- Weblink: Energy and Buildings | Photovoltaics in the Built Environment | ScienceDirect.com by Elsevier
- Scope:

Special issue

Photovoltaics in the Built Environment

Last update 15 April 2024

In the past decade photovoltaics (PV) has become a mature, efficient and feasible sustainable energy technology essential for the energy transition in the built environment. Within these developments photovoltaics in the built environment cover PV systems, PV modules and new PV technologies and their innovative applications in building envelops, urban infrastructures for energy and transport, and in the public space, also called Building Added Photovoltaics (BAPV), Building Integrated Photovoltaics (BIPV), and photovoltaics integrated in urban landscapes.

Guest Editors:

Dr Angèle Reinders
Eindhoven University of Technology, the Netherlands

Dr Francesco Frontini
University of Applied Sciences and Arts of Southern Switzerland (SUPSI)

- **26 papers accepted at a 30% acceptance rate**

Analysis of authors and countries

Authors involved: 130 authors from Europe, CI

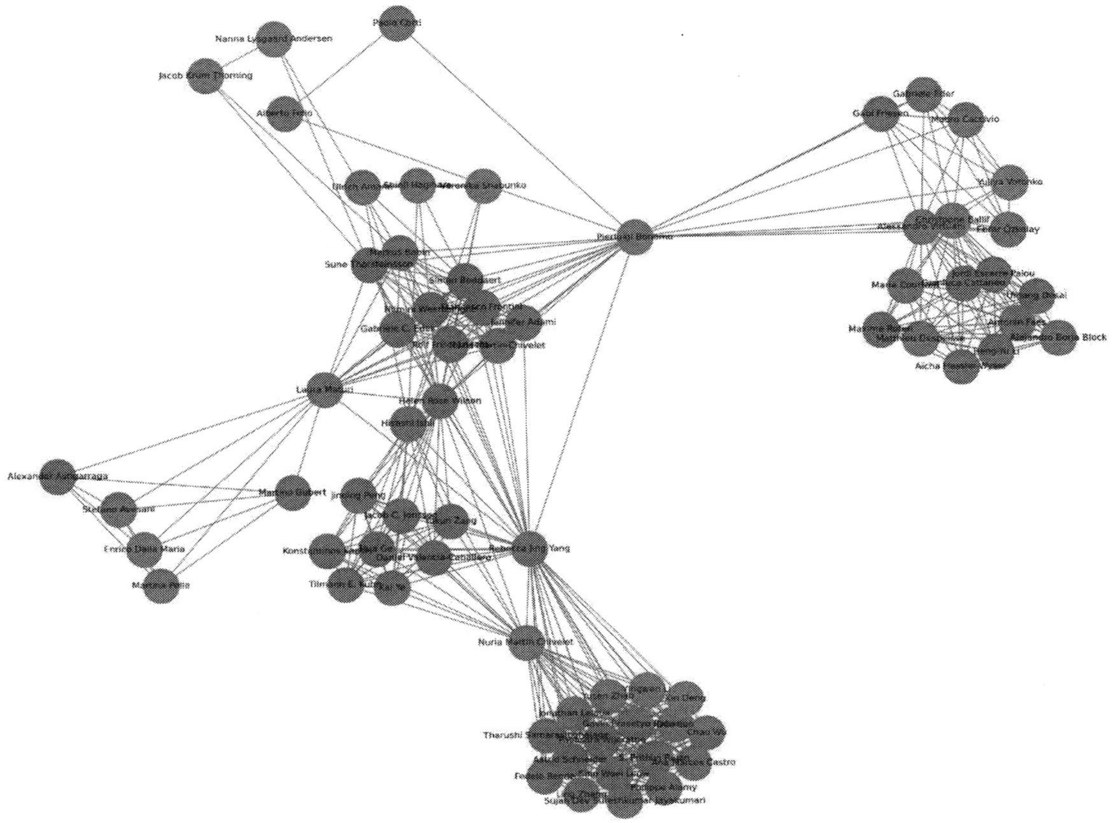

Analysis of collaboration network

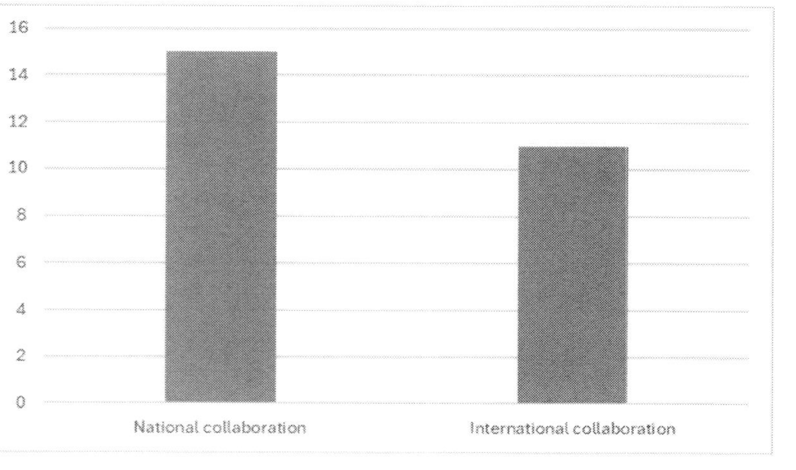

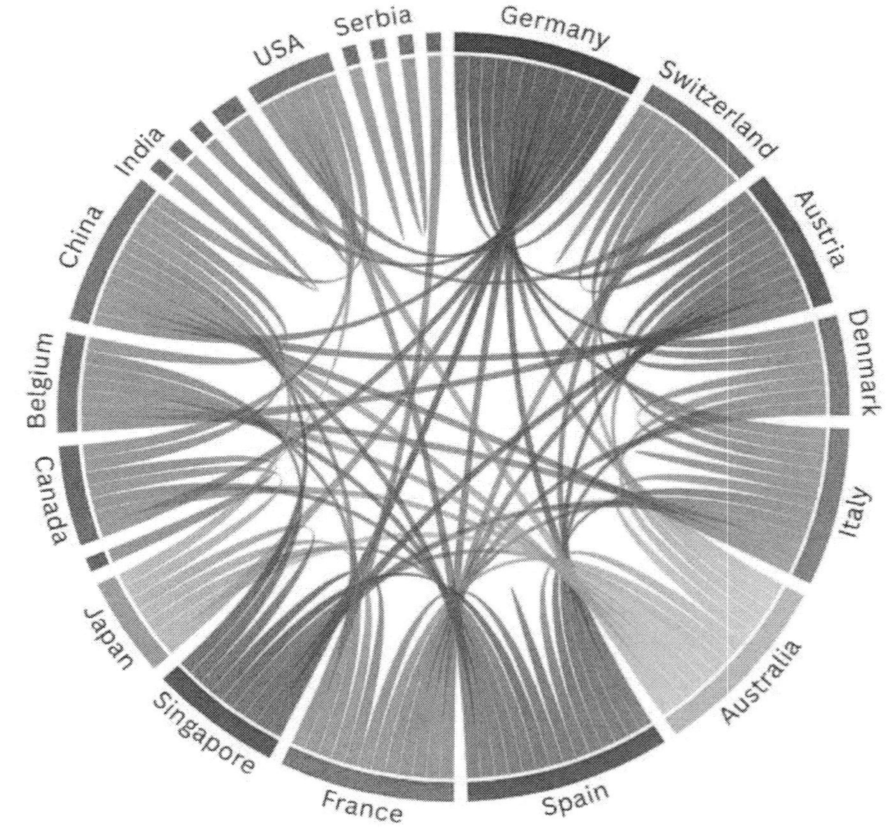

SUPSI TU/e PV in the built environment - 42nd EUPVSEC, Bilbao

Analysis of research themes
with some examples of papers

Hafsa Fares at al. *A methodology for assessing environmental impact of building integrated PV in low carbon footprint electricity generation context*

Christian Popp et al. *Prospective life cycle analysis of a BIPV façade – Life cycle assessment of greenhouse gas emissions using future projections for a case study*

P. Bonomo et al., *Comprehensive review and state of play in the use of photovoltaics in buildings*

Ha Eun Yoon et al., *Research on the virtual design and implementation of colored glass for BIPV*

Alejandro Borja Block et al., *Colouring solutions for building integrated photovoltaic modules: A review*

Helen Rose Wilson et al., *Multi-dimensional evaluation of BIPV installations: Development of a tool to assess the performance as building component and electricity generator*

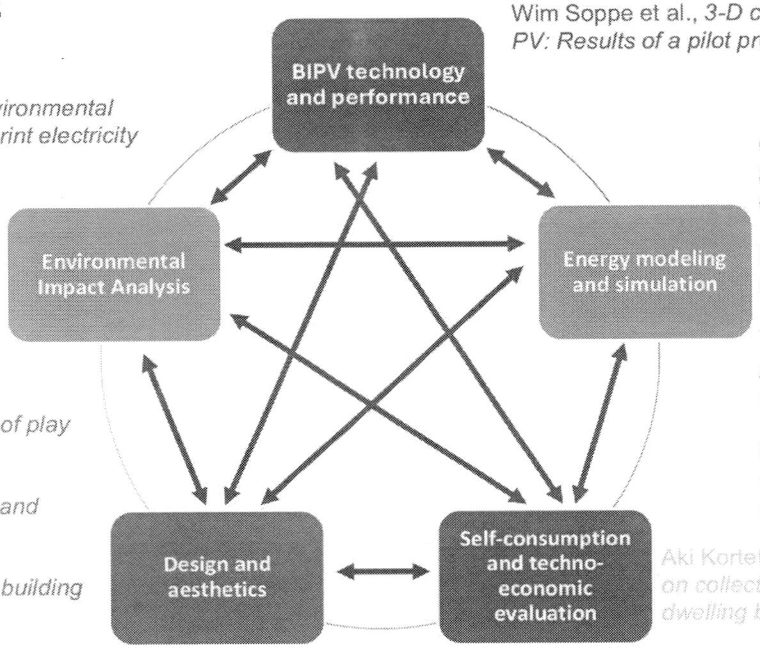

25/09/2025

Helen Rose Wilson et al. *Component-based SHGC determination of BIPV glazing for product comparison* 9

Marios C. Phocas et al., *Concept analysis of an adaptive building envelope with thin-film photovoltaic modules*

Wim Soppe et al., *3-D curved composite façade elements with PV: Results of a pilot project*

Gianni Di Giovanni et al. *Exploiting building information modeling and machine learning for optimizing rooftop photovoltaic systems*

Rebecca Jing Yang et al., *Digitalising BIPV energy simulation: A cross tool investigation*

Tamás Soha et al. *City-scale analysis of PV potential and visibility in heritage environment using GIS and LiDAR*

Stefani Peratikou, Alexandros G. Charalambides, *Short-term PV energy yield predictions within city neighborhoods for optimum grid management*

Aki Kortetmäki at al., *The impact of metering methods on collective self-consumption: Insights from multi-dwelling buildings in Finland*

M.T. Miranda, et al., *Analysis of photovoltaic self-consumption as a function of the demand profile in detached houses*

020253-009

Theme 1: BIPV technology and performance

Integration of solar panels in façades is **still too little applied** nowadays due to the **limitations in design options.**

- Façade PV elements can be **varied in color and size** but still have a flat surface and fix dimensions → difficulties especially in **retrofit.**
- **Performance assessment** and **standardization** needed to demonstrate the impact and contribution of multi-fuctional BIPV element/system: **SHGC, Temperature** behavior and performances, **impact** of mounting system
- Dynamic facades with multi-purpose, i.e. shading of indoor space, can yield more benefit

Customizable solutions

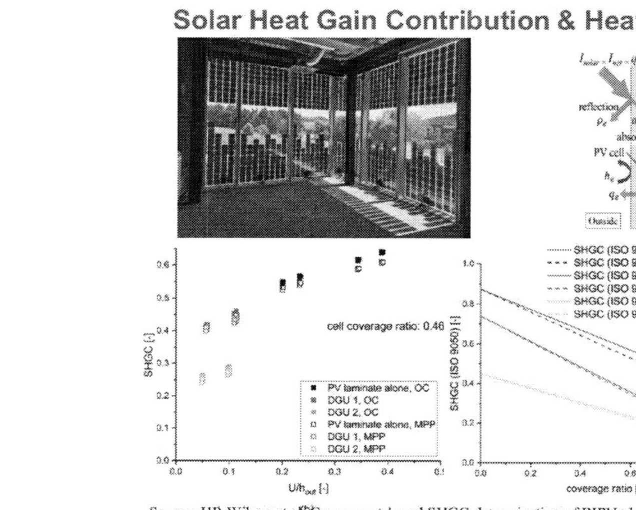

Source: Soppe et.al. 3-D curved composite façade elements with PV: Results of a pilot project

Solar Heat Gain Contribution & Heat Transfer

Source: HR Wilson et al. Component-based SHGC determination of BIPV glazing for product comparison

Hisashi et al. International inter-laboratory comparison of solar heat gain coefficient of building-integrated photovoltaic modules - results of tests with or without power generation and tests with PV cell coverage ratios

Dynamic facade concept with multi-purposes

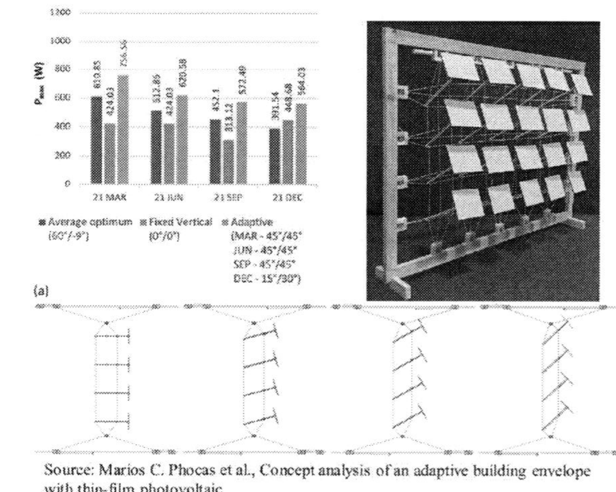

Source: Marios C. Phocas et al., Concept analysis of an adaptive building envelope with thin-film photovoltaic

Theme 2: Energy modeling and simulation

From **city model** to **digital tool** to better assess the PV in building performances, considering multiple aspects of PV and buildings

1. City-scale analysis of PV potential and visibility in heritage environments
2. Exploiting BIM, digitalization and machine learning for rooftop PV optimization and complex BIPV projects: need of more accurate models
3. Yield analysis of a BIPV façade prototype strongly influenced by module layering (i.e. colors) and type of facades system (i.e. ventilation)

PV potential of roof areas and to assess the visibility of solar panels in urban areas.

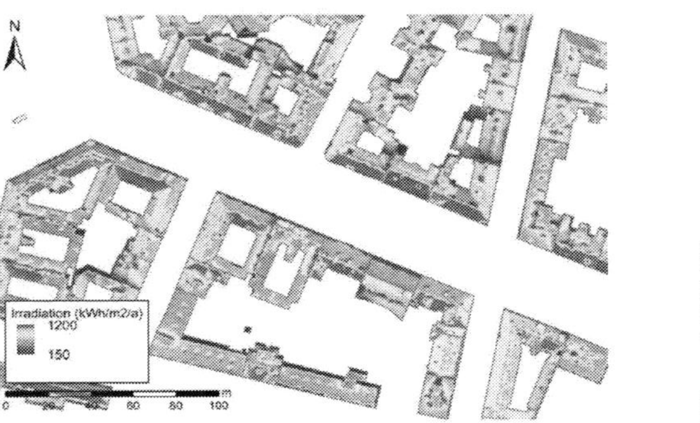

Source: Soha et al, City-scale analysis of PV potential and visibility in heritage environment using GIS and LiDAR

25/09/2025

DIGITALIZATION as opportunity to proper manage complex BIPV projects

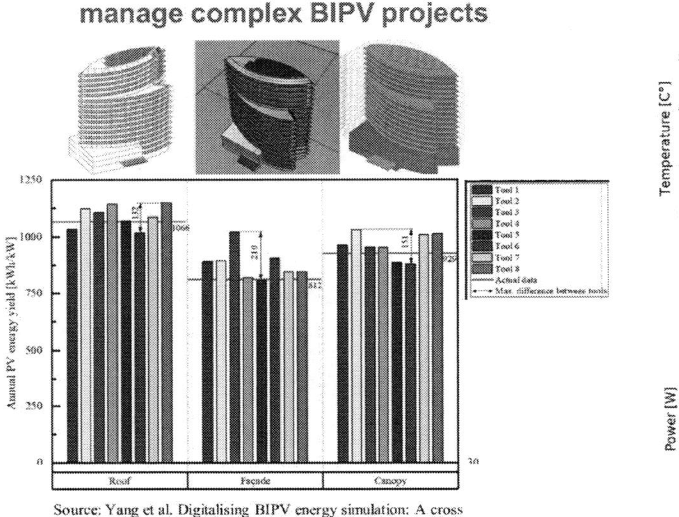

Source: Yang et al. Digitalising BIPV energy simulation: A cross tool investigation

Color impact on temperature & Power generation

West facade

Source: Babin et al. Yield analysis of a BIPV façade prototype installation

Theme 3: Self-consumption and techno-economic evaluation

Techno-economic evaluations are covering **energy performance and related financial aspects** of PV systems. In many **countries self-consumption** has become an incentive for PV system installations with the aim to **mitigate emissions** associated with fossil fuels, increase **financial benefits**, or **balance local low voltage grids**, which is strongly related to techno-economic evaluations.

- **Five papers** on this topic in this SI present about
    - Self-consumption and self-sufficiency at a neighborhood level and in individual dwellings
    - Techno-economic evaluations of PV on facades
    - Workflow to support cost-benefits comparison of BIPV project

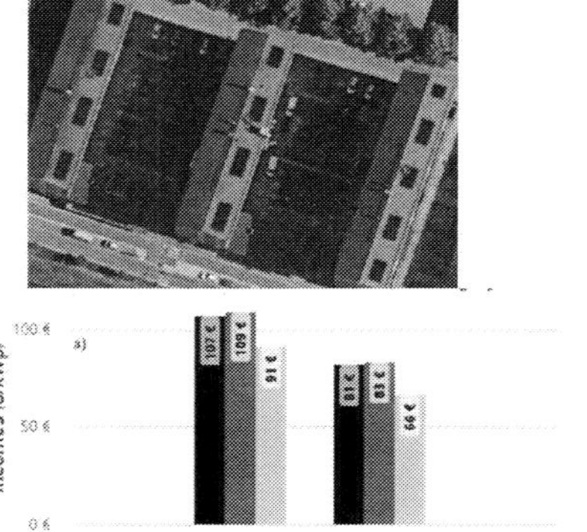

Remote sensing for techno-economic assessments

Irene Del Hierro López et al., Photovoltaic self-sufficiency potential at a district scale in Madrid. A scalable methodology

Energy communities and self-consumption

Aki Kortetmäki et al., The impact of metering methods on collective self-consumption: Insights from multi-dwelling buildings in Finland,

Electricity pricing and PV

W.L. Schram et al., PV on façades: A financial, technical and environmental assessment

Theme 4: Design and aesthetics

As a building product, BIPV must meet different expectations regarding **design, form, and dimensions** for a variety of **building archetypes** as well as **performance requirements**: such as mechanical or safety requirements but also energy saving, water tightness, etc.

Eight papers on this topic in this SI present about

- **Interdisciplinary methods** to assess existing designs of BIPV in buildings or to be used during design processes
- **Design features of PV modules** such as coloring and curvature
- **Design of** buildings and/or products required for PV installations

Conclusions: Design features such as color techniques, printing and curvature are highly customizable, and analysis methods also seem to be available, but with a strong focus on energy performance, however limited reporting on actual design of buildings with integrated PV systems

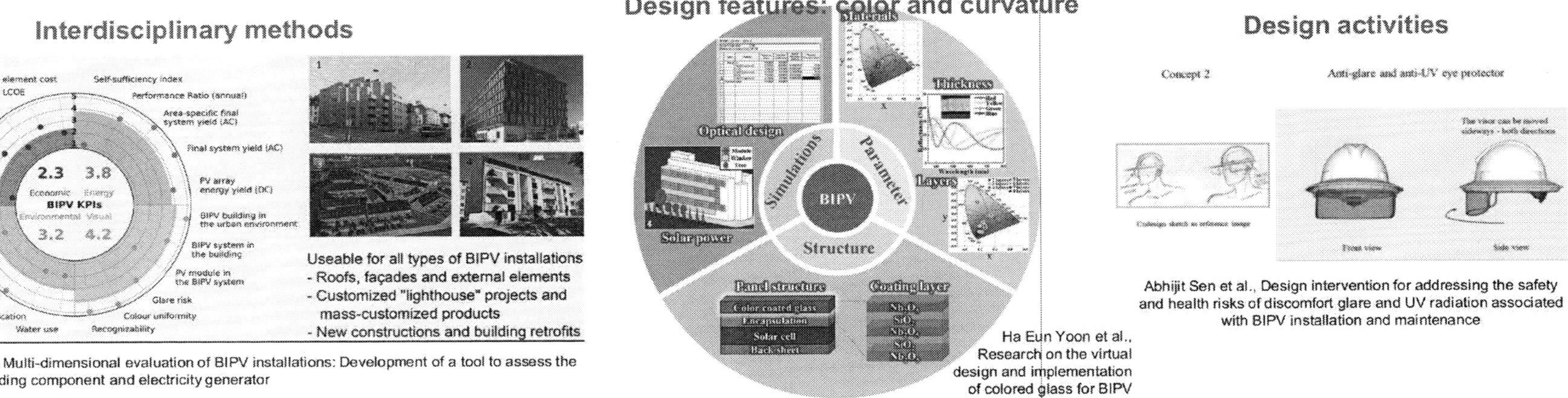

Interdisciplinary methods

Gabriele Eder et al., Multi-dimensional evaluation of BIPV installations: Development of a tool to assess the performance as building component and electricity generator

Design features: color and curvature

Ha Eun Yoon et al., Research on the virtual design and implementation of colored glass for BIPV

Design activities

Abhijit Sen et al., Design intervention for addressing the safety and health risks of discomfort glare and UV radiation associated with BIPV installation and maintenance

Theme 5: Environmental Impact Analysis

Environmental impact analysis of PV systems including BIPV is strongly founded on **life cycle analysis methodology**
Three papers on this topic in this SI present about
- LCA methods for BIPV in a **low emission electricity system** and **as compared with building materials (without PV)**
- **Prospective LCA** for BIPV, the term prospective LCA describes an analysis that models a system at a future point in time
- Integration of environmental impact in technical-economic studies of BIPV by means of an **emission factor for CO$_2$ resulting from LCA**

Conclusion: Prospective LCA approaches are required that take into account future changes of PV manufacturing and electricity mix

BIPV emissions in a low emission electricity system

Prospective LCA for BIPV

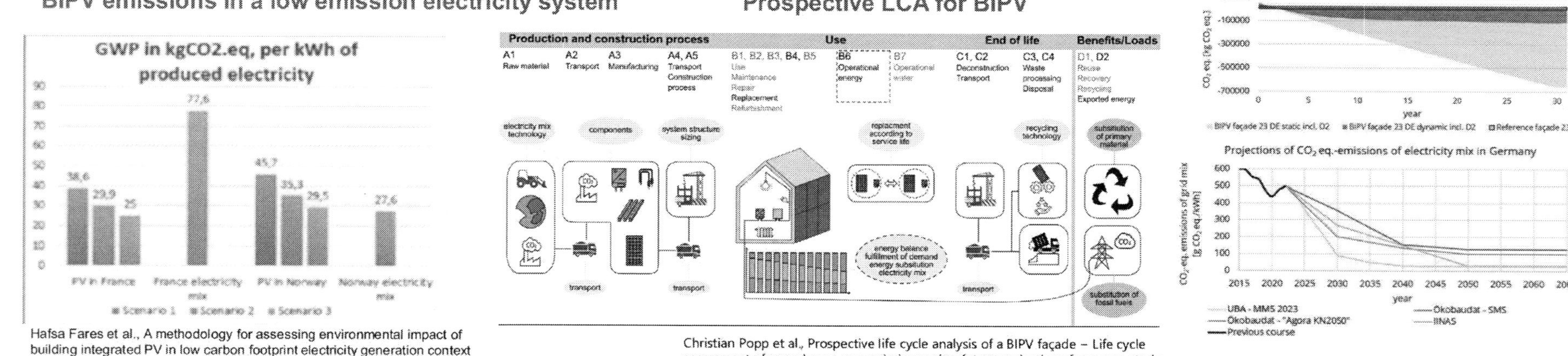

Hafsa Fares et al., A methodology for assessing environmental impact of building integrated PV in low carbon footprint electricity generation context

Christian Popp et al., Prospective life cycle analysis of a BIPV façade – Life cycle assessment of greenhouse gas emissions using future projections for a case study

SUPSI TU/e PV in the built environment - 42nd EUPVSEC, Bilbao

Conclusions and recommendations

BIPV is becoming a mature technology:
- **In the past**, main focus on **new products** development to address market needs
- **Today** different technologies are available to make BIPV products attractive to architect and construction company

Different digital tools available to control the technology from large scale (city level) to detailed energy output:
- How to follow product innovations is a challenge and new physical based approaches are need to be further investigated and implemented
- BIM and ML approaches can support decision making
- Standardization is needed to properly define the scope in the built environment (SHGC, Reliability, Performance, Designing,…)

BIPV is complex due to needs of **multiple stakeholders** and their interest in **different KPIs**, but also:
- Large interest from PV manufactures and scientists
- Economy of BIPV system is still a major concern due to the complexity of most of the project. Customizable tools are needed to demonstrate the sustainability and economic feasibility of BIPV
- Prospective LCA approaches are required that take into account future changes of PV manufacturing and electricity mix and to demonstrate BIPV competitiveness in respect to conventional passive solution (no PV)

Acknowledgements

- Prof.dr. Angèle Reinders, main editor and our co-authors Pierluigi Bonomo and Roel C.G.M. Loonen

- Paolo Corti, SUPSI, for providing data from BIPV Status Rerport

- Matte Cadei, SUPSI, for supporting with diagrams and pictures preparation

- All authors and co-authors of papers in the Special Issues

Do not miss today:

- *13:30 -15:00 Parallel session: Unlocking the Potential of Integrated Photovoltaic Systems - European R&D Approach (Room 1B) in collaboration with* IEA PVPS **Seamless-PV**

- *15:15: 4BV.4: the Poster session on BIPV this afternoon*
- *17:00-18:30: 4BO.5: PV-Products for Buildings (Auditorium 1)*

25/09/2025

Scuola universitaria professionale della Svizzera italiana
Dipartimento ambiente costruzioni e design
Istituto sostenibilità applicata all'ambiente costruito

TU/e EINDHOVEN UNIVERSITY OF TECHNOLOGY

SUPSI

Thanks for your attention!

Email: francesco.frontini@supsi.ch and a.h.m.e.reinders@tue.nl
Please check our **Special Issue** of Energy & Buildings on **Photovoltaics in the Built Environment**
https://www.sciencedirect.com/special-issue/10SL29QN11V

25/09/2025

ADVANCING BIPV: SHINGLED HJT TRCHNOLOGY FOR HIGH-EFFICIENCY AND AESTHETIC SOLAR INTEGRATION

G. Gonnella[1], A. de Gruijter[1], J. Veirman[1], M. Pelle[1], L. Maturi[1], D. Moser[2], L. Fialho[1]
[1]Eurac Research, Institute for Renewable Energy, Viale Druso 1, Bolzano, Italy
[2]Bequerel Institute, Via Kufstein 5, Trento, Italy

ABSTRACT: Building-integrated photovoltaics (BIPV) require technologies that balance energy performance, durability, and aesthetics. Shingled heterojunction (HJT) solar cells offer high efficiency, excellent low-light response, and design flexibility, making them a promising candidate for façade applications. This study investigates the performance and stability of shingled HJT modules fabricated with different material combinations and color configurations. Eight modules were subjected to accelerated aging through humidity-freeze (HF10) testing, and their behavior was evaluated using IV characterization, electroluminescence (EL) imaging, visual inspection, and colorimetry. Results indicate that color integration reduces electrical output by 4–11% compared with reference modules, a trade-off consistent with typical BIPV requirements. Aesthetic stability, assessed through colorimetry, remained largely unchanged after stress testing, with ΔE values below or close to perceptibility thresholds, confirming good visual durability. Performance losses after HF10 were primarily linked to technological issues such as delamination and string mismatch rather than intrinsic limitations of the shingled HJT concept. Overall, the findings demonstrate that shingled HJT modules are a strong candidate for next-generation BIPV, provided that material compatibility and lamination processes are further optimized to ensure long-term reliability in real-world building applications.
Keywords: Building-integrated photovoltaics, shingled HJT, accelerated aging, color stability, module reliability

1 INTRODUCTION

This research is set within the framework of shingled technology for BIPV applications, where shingled strings perform at high voltage and low current, minimizing resistive losses, enhancing energy conversion efficiency, and reducing inactive areas, resulting in photovoltaic modules with superior power density compared to conventional architectures [1], [2]. Unlike the PERC technology [3], [4], [5], which has established performance benchmarks in the literature, shingled HJT modules represent an innovative and emerging approach in BIPV research.

HJT cells offer superior efficiency compared to PERC (up to 25-26% mass production efficiency [6], [7], [8], [9]) and are gaining market traction [10], making them well-suited for BIPV applications. To the best of our knowledge, no BIPV laboratory prototypes have been developed using shingled HJT cells specifically for colored BIPV, nor has an in-depth study been conducted on their electrical performance and aesthetic integration.

This study addresses this gap by maximizing the visual appeal of the modules through variations in front glass coloring, encapsulant polymers, and backsheet materials. Beyond aesthetics, the study also focuses on performance characterization, compensating for the lack of data on shingled HJT BIPV modules. Flash tests were conducted to determine electrical characteristics, while EL analysis assessed structural integrity, identifying microcracks and validating the positive effects of optimized lamination. The research aims to extend to accelerated tests performance monitoring, bridging the gap between laboratory fabrication and real-world deployment. Humidity freezing tests were performed in a climatic chamber. This study provides a comprehensive methodology, from material selection and optimized lamination to controlled indoor testing. By systematically investigating both aesthetic and functional aspects, it offers critical insights into the adoption of shingled HJT technology in the rapidly evolving BIPV sector.

2 MATERIALS AND METHODS

The following section describes materials and methods involved in the realization of high-aesthetic shingled HJT modules.

2.1 Module Design and Bill of Materials

The selection of materials and interlayers was carried out in order to maximize the aesthetic properties and to evaluate the integration potential of shingled HJT in BIPV environment. The prototypes were designed to maximize the aesthetic appeal and visual appearance, utilizing different Bills of Materials (BoM) and module configurations. The lamination was performed on both Glass-Glass (GG) and Glass-Backsheet (GBS) configurations, with reference modules produced without colored encapsulants or colored front glass. Shingled HJT strings provided by Applied Materials Italy srl were used for the tests. Due to an extended storage time between string fabrication and lamination trials (several months), the mechanical quality of the cell interconnexion was markedly degraded, which materialized into a high string breakage during our preliminary handling tests. In order to reduce the breakage rate, a custom-made string flipper was built, which reduced the breakage rate to a minimum. The front glass options included transparent or terracotta, while the rear cover featured colored (orange or grey) or transparent glass, as well as a black backsheet. The color glasses were provided by GruppoSTG. Encapsulation materials included both transparent (EVA UV clear, EPE UV clear, TPO clear) and colored (POE black, TPO black) variants.

2.2 Soldering and lamination process

The module architecture was defined connecting in series all the strings within the module. The interconnection between strings was performed in our laboratory, using a standard soldering station in combination with flux pens to remove oxide layers and ensure proper soldering quality. To balance technical performance, aesthetic appeal, and energetic requirements, both uncolored metallic ribbons and black-coated ribbons were tested. In some cases, black tape was applied over

10.4229/EUPVSEC2025/4BO.17.5
020254-001

uncolored ribbon to enhance visual uniformity.

For each module, a specific lamination recipe was defined, depending on the materials and interlayers adopted. Laminator TECNO PANAMAC SL-DM121 was employed, with adjustable parameters for pressure, temperature, and cycle duration. Moreover, modules were visually inspected and classified according to their aesthetic quality. Only modules with "medium" or "high" aesthetic rating were selected for indoor and outdoor testing. Modules classified as "low" exhibited severe delamination, large air bubbles, or poor adhesion between materials. By contrast, "high" aesthetic quality referred to flawless integration of the cells into the stack, with no visible defects. All defects were recorded to be compared with post-stress results after aging in the climatic chamber.

2.3 Electrical characterization setup

EL imaging was conducted in the laboratory before and after each lamination to verify proper interconnection and electrical performance. The EL camera is a VIS-SWIR InGaAs camera with a quantum efficiency over 60% at 1-2 µm and sensor of 640 x 512 pixels. This camera enables the implementation of the test following IEC TS 60904-13:2018 [11] indications.

' I-V curves were measured indoor at standard test conditions (STC), using a Pasan solar simulator with Class A+A+A, in compliance with the IEC 60904-9 [12]. It measures the electrical performance of the PV modules. The tests were performed at STC according to the international standard IEC 61215:2021 [13].

2.4 Colorimetry measurements

Color coordinates were measured with a Spectrophotometer 3Color SV300 in the CIE Lab color space, both on cells and on non-cell areas. For the strings, measurements were taken at the center of each string to evaluate intra-string and string-to-string uniformity. For the periphery, an additional points was recorded along the module periphery to assess string-to-periphery variations.

The same measurement points were maintained before and after the ten humidity-freeze cycles (HF10) stress sequence, ensuring direct comparison of color stability under aging. The color difference (ΔE) was used as a criterion to assess uniformity, with ΔE=2 taken as threshold for perceptible variation to human eye [14].

2.5 Reliability testing

Reliability tests were then performed in an Angelantoni PV4500 climatic chamber, according to the to the international standard IEC 61215:2021 [13]. The modules underwent ten humidity-freeze cycles (HF10) to simulate environment stress. Humidity freeze was selected to accelerate delamination, if any.

After climatic exposure, EL imaging, I-V measurements, visual inspection, and colorimetry were repeated to assess the impact of accelerated aging on both aesthetic and electrical performance of the shingled HJT modules.

3 RESULTS

The following section reports the main results concerning lamination of the modules, indoor characterization and reliability assessment.

A total of 12 BIPV prototype modules were processed, using shingled HJT strings. The modules, each measuring 1x0.75 m², with 28 cells per string in a shingled

configuration. Out of the 12 prototypes, for further investigations 8 modules were selected: four glass–glass (GG) and four glass–backsheet (GBS), including one reference module for each configuration. The reference modules served as benchmarks for comparison of electrical performance with the other prototypes.

An overview of the 8 modules selected and their characteristics is reported in **Figure 1**, whereas **Figure 2** shows the final appearance (RGB photographs) of the modules along with their aesthetic evaluation.

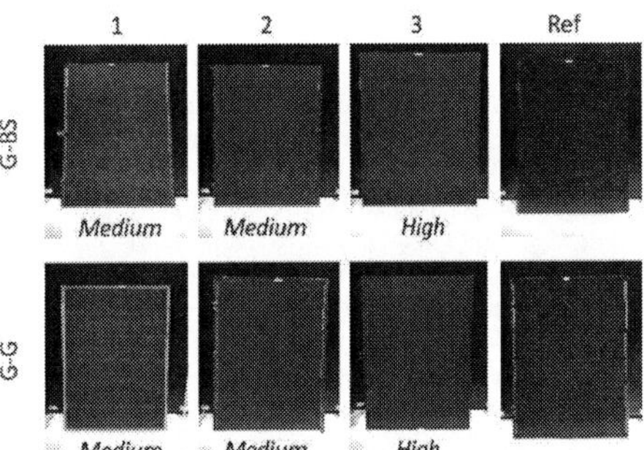

TYPOLOGY	FRONT COVER	FRONT ENCAPSULANT	BACK ENCAPSULANT	REAR COVER	AESTHETIC EVALUATION
G-BS 1	Colored Glass Orange	EPE UV clear	EPE UV Clear	Black Back-sheet	Medium
G-BS 2	Colored Glass Orange	EPE UV clear	EPE UV Clear	Black Back-sheet	Medium
G-BS 3	Colored Glass Orange	EPE UV clear	EPE UV Clear	Black Back-sheet	High
G-BS Reference	Glass Transparent	EPE UV clear	EPE UV Clear	Black Back-sheet	Reference
G-G 1	Colored Glass Orange	EPE UV clear	EPE UV Clear	Colored Glass Orange	Medium
G-G 2	Colored Glass Orange	TPO Clear	Black TPO	Colored Glass Orange	Medium
G-G 3	Colored Glass Orange	EVA Clear	Black TPO	Colored Glass Grey	High
G-G Reference	Glass Transparent	TPO Clear	Black TPO	Glass Transparent	Reference

Figure 1: Overview of the modules laminated in Eurac laboratory with shingled HJT technology and their characteristics. Configuration adopted were both Glass-Glass (G-G) and Glass-Backsheet (G-BS).

Figure 2: Final appearance of the modules selected for the study along with their aesthetic evaluation. Reference modules are also included.

3.1 Visual inspection

Before the HF10 stress test, most modules showed good lamination quality, with only minor defects observed in G-BS1 and G-BS2. In contrast, G-G1 presented poor aesthetics in the middle of some strings, where air bubbles were visible. After HF10, G-G1 was the most affected module, showing pronounced delamination, while the defects in G-BS1 and G-BS2 remained stable and did not extend. These observations confirm that degradation was mainly linked to specific material and use of old batch of strings rather than being systematic across all module types. A summary of the defects is reported in **Figure 3**.

Figure 3: Representative images of the main defects observed in the modules: (a) localized delamination at the corner of G-BS1 before HF10 stress test; (b–c) minor corner delamination in G-BS2 before the HF10 stress test; (d) extensive delamination in G-G1 after the HF10 stress test.

3.2 I-V characterization

The initial IV measurements (showed **Figure 4**) conducted prior to the HF10 stress sequence confirm a generally good technological integration of the shingled HJT strings. The G-BS series displayed maximum power outputs (Pmpp) between 105–113 W, corresponding to a reduction of approximately 5–11% relative to the uncolored reference module (119 W). This power loss is attributed to the effect of coloration, which partially hinders photon absorption in the cells.

In the G-G configuration, modules exhibited slightly smaller losses, with power outputs between 118–119 W, equivalent to a 4–5% reduction compared with the reference (124 W). However, G-G3 produced only 39 W, which was linked to a hotspot and disconnected strings as revealed by electroluminescence imaging, and the maximum power (Pmpp) is related to the central strings.

Overall, the results demonstrate that shingled HJT modules can achieve stable integration even in colored BIPV applications, with acceptable efficiency trade-offs. The primary performance concern arises not from the coloring itself but from isolated technological issues such as string disconnection and localized defects.

		P_{mpp} [W]	V_{oc} [V]	I_{sc} [A]
G-BS	1	113	122	1.2
	2	110	120	1.2
	3	105	120	1.2
	Ref	119	121	1.3
G-G	1	118	121	1.3
	2	119	121	1.3
	3	39	40	1.3
	Ref	124	121	1.3

Figure 4: Initial IV parameters (Pmpp, Voc, Isc) of G-BS and G-G modules before HF10 stress testing. Reference (uncolored) modules are reported for comparison.

After the HF10 stress sequence, the overall maximum power point (Pmpp) remained relatively stable across both G-BS and G-G module configurations (see **Figure 6**). However, specific modules exhibited significant performance losses. G-BS3 showed a reduction of approximately 8%, which can be attributed to strong cell mismatch within its strings, as showed in **Figure 5**.

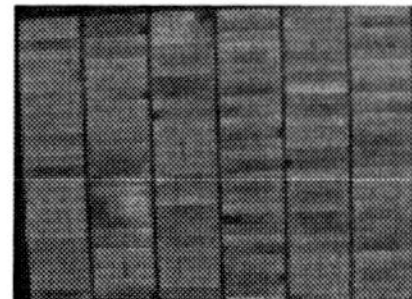

Figure 5: Electroluminescence (EL) image of shingled HJT G-BS 3 module, showing pronounced cell mismatch. This mismatch results in uneven electrical performance and contributes to overall module power losses.

Similarly, G-G1 experienced a power loss of up to 9%, primarily caused by delamination effects observed during visual inspection. These results indicate that the general performance of shingled HJT modules is preserved after stress testing, but localized technological issues or intrinsic material limitations are the dominant factors affecting reliability.

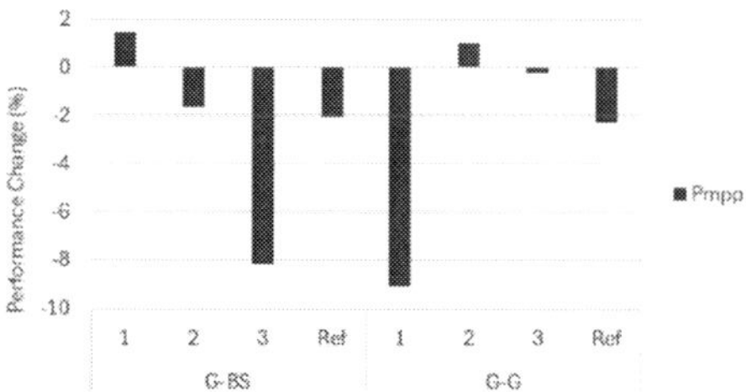

Figure 6: Relative change in maximum power point (Pmpp) of G-BS and G-G modules after HF10 stress testing. While most modules remained stable, G-BS3 and G-G1 exhibited significant power losses (≈8–9%) due to cell mismatch and delamination, respectively.

3.3 Electroluminescence imaging

Electroluminescence (EL) imaging was performed before and after the HF10 stress test at two current injection levels (100% Isc, 1.3 A, and 10% Isc, 0.13 A) in order to identify microcracks, interconnection faults, and other structural defects. An overview of the EL images is given in **Figure 7**. The analysis revealed that the main anomalies were associated with an old batch of strings, as also evidenced by the inhomogeneous patterns visible in the EL images. In the G-G3 module, a pronounced hot-spot and a missing string connection were observed, leading to severe non-emissive areas consistent with its low power output measured in IV characterization.

Across the other modules, the EL images demonstrated good visual stability, with only minor differences between the pre- and post-stress conditions. This stability is in agreement with the electrical performance results, which indicated that most modules maintained their output after HF10. The combined use of high and low injection levels proved valuable for distinguishing between fully disconnected areas and regions affected by higher series resistance or partial cracks. Overall, EL analysis confirmed that performance losses were primarily linked to localized interconnection defects, while the shingled HJT design itself remained robust under stress testing.

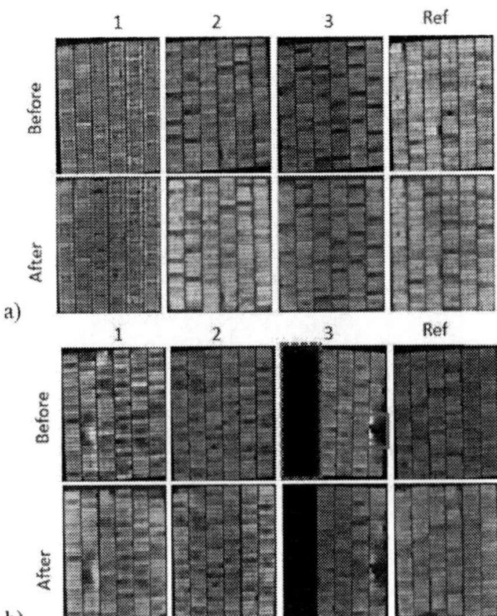

Figure 7: Electroluminescence (EL) images of a) G-BS and b) G-G modules acquired before and after HF10 stress testing at 100% and 10% Isc. The main defects are linked to the use of an old batch of strings, with G-G3 showing a hot-spot and a missing connection (highlighted with dotted red rectangle). Overall, visual stability was maintained, consistent with electrical performance results.

3.4 Colorimetry analysis

Colorimetric analysis was carried out before and after the HF10 stress test to evaluate both intra-module and overall visual uniformity. Measurement points were selected at the center of each string across the module, as well as at the periphery, in order to capture both string-level and periphery-related variations (Figure 8). Comparisons were performed by assessing string-to-string uniformity within the same module and string-to-periphery uniformity, using a randomly chosen color target as reference. After the stress test, the analysis focused on periphery-to-periphery comparison within the same module to detect periphery color variation, and on string-to-string evaluation to assess possible color changes between strings. This methodology allowed a consistent evaluation of both global and localized variations in aesthetic stability following accelerated aging.

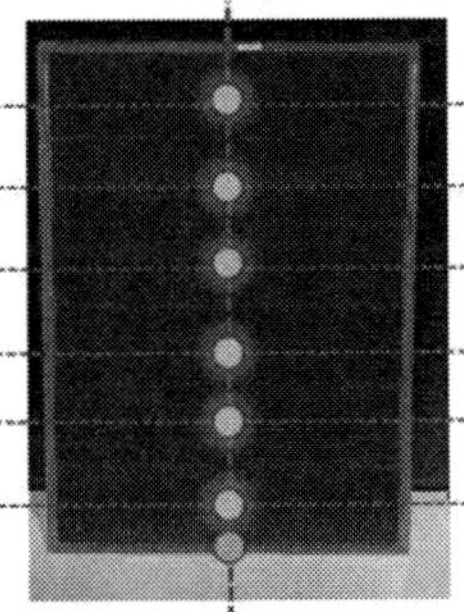

Figure 8: Colorimetric analysis of a shingled HJT module before and after HF10 stress testing.

Measurement points were consistently maintained in both cases: green markers indicate points located at the

center of each string, while orange markers correspond to points on the periphery. Comparisons were performed for string-to-string and string-to-periphery uniformity, using a randomly selected color target as reference. After stress testing, the same measurement points were re-evaluated to assess periphery-to-periphery and string-to-string degradation.

As shown in Figure 9, the initial colorimetric assessment was performed before the HF10 stress sequence to evaluate both intra-module (string-to-string) and overall module (string-to-periphery) uniformity. Most ΔE^*ab values were below or close to 2, the threshold at which color differences become perceptible to the human eye, confirming a generally good level of visual uniformity at the start of testing.

An exception was observed for module G-G1, which showed the highest ΔE^*ab values and large variability across measurement points. This behavior can be attributed to the absence of a black back layer in this configuration, which resulted in a greater difference between string and periphery colors. In contrast, modules with a black layer on the back exhibited much lower string-to-periphery differences, confirming that this design approach enhances visual integration and improves overall aesthetic performance.

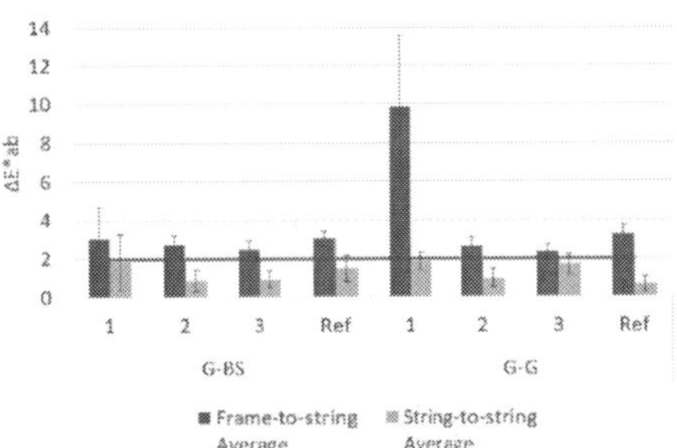

Figure 9: Colorimetric results of G-BS and G-G modules before HF10 stress testing. Most ΔE^*ab values remain below or close to 2, indicating good visual uniformity. G-G1 shows the highest variability due to the absence of a black back layer, which increased string-to-periphery differences compared to other modules. Error bars are larger for string-to-periphery measurements, while string-to-string uniformity remains consistent.

After the HF10 stress sequence, the colorimetric analysis confirmed that overall degradation remained within acceptable limits, with ΔE^*ab values generally ≤2, corresponding to differences that are not perceptible or perceptible only to an expert human eye (Figure 10). The results indicate that string-to-string uniformity was well preserved, while periphery-to-periphery comparisons showed slightly higher variability in some modules. In particular, G-G2 presented the largest color variation at the periphery, although still within acceptable thresholds. These findings demonstrate that the visual appearance of the shingled HJT modules remained stable after accelerated aging, confirming their suitability for BIPV applications where aesthetic durability is a critical requirement.

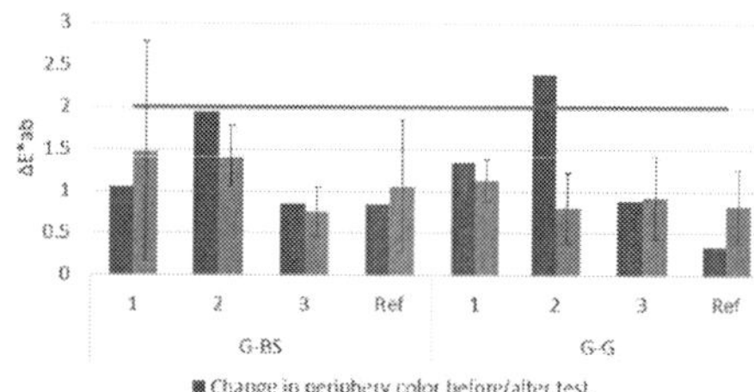

Figure 10: Colorimetric results of G-BS and G-G modules after HF10 stress testing. Color changes remain within acceptable limits ($\Delta E^*ab \leq 2$), with more uniformity observed at string level compared to the periphery. The largest variation was recorded in G-G2 at the module periphery, though still within perceptibility thresholds.

4 DISCUSSION

The results of this study demonstrate that shingled HJT modules maintain high visual stability after accelerated aging, with no significant aesthetic degradation observed in color coordinates after the HF10 stress sequence. While coloration introduced a modest reduction in electrical performance (–5 to –11% for G-BS and –4 to –5% for G-G compared with reference modules), this effect is consistent with typical BIPV trade-offs and remains within acceptable limits for façade integration. The strongest decreases in power output following the HF10 test were not associated with color but rather with technological issues such as delamination and increased cell mismatch/interconnection failure, highlighting the importance of material compatibility and process control in module fabrication. Importantly, no clear correlation was found between color degradation and electrical performance losses after testing, suggesting that optical stability and electrical reliability are indeed governed by different mechanisms. Taken together, these findings confirm that shingled HJT technology offers a promising solution for BIPV applications, provided that further optimization of lamination processes and interconnection quality is achieved to ensure long-term reliability.

However, despite the positive results, the HF10 stress test alone may not be fully representative for a comprehensive assessment; therefore, longer-term or alternative testing procedures are required to obtain a complete evaluation.

5 CONCLUSIONS

This work supports the view that shingled HJT modules have strong potential for building-integrated photovoltaic applications, as they successfully combine energy performance, technological feasibility, and aesthetic quality. The accelerated aging tests confirmed that the modules maintain stable visual appearance, with no significant color degradation after stress exposure. While coloration led to a modest decrease in electrical output, this trade-off is consistent with the requirements of BIPV integration and does not compromise the overall suitability of the technology. The most relevant performance issues were linked to lamination defects and string mismatch, pointing to the need for process/material optimization rather than fundamental design limitations.

The findings indicate that shingled HJT technology is a promising pathway toward aesthetically pleasing and reliable solar façades, and with further improvements in manufacturing quality, it can play an important role in advancing the integration of photovoltaics into the built environment.

6 AKNOWLEDGMENTS

This study was developed within the Project "Network 4 Energy Sustainable Transition—NEST", Project code PE0000021, promoted by the Ministero dell'Università e della Ricerca, funded by the European Union - NextGenerationEU - National Recovery and Resilience Plan (PNRR).
Funded by the European Union. Views and opinions expressed are however those of the author(s) only and do not necessarily reflect those of the European Union. Neither the European Union nor the granting authority can be held responsible for them.

This study is also a result of the research project "FotovOltaico efficiente in facciata per il fUturo pRossimo della rEte elettRica ' [FOURIER], funded by the Italian Ministry of the Environment and the Energy Security, through the Research Fund for the Italian Electrical System (type-B call, published on G.U.R.I. n. 312 on 17-12-2020).

The authors would like to express their gratitude to Applied Material Italia and GruppoSTG for their collaboration and support. Special thanks are extended to colleagues Lukas Koester, Juan Stivanello, and Alexander Astigarraga for their valuable contributions and assistance in the laboratory work.

7 REFERENCES

[1] D. Tonini, G. Cellere, M. Bertazzo, A. Fecchio, L. Cerasti, and M. Galiazzo, "Shingling Technology For Cell Interconnection: Technological Aspects And Process Integration," *Energy Procedia*, vol. 150, pp. 36–43, Sept. 2018, doi: 10.1016/j.egypro.2018.09.010.

[2] S. Harrison *et al.*, "Challenges for Efficient Integration of SHJ Based Solar Cells in Shingle Module Configuration," *37th European Photovoltaic Solar Energy Conference and Exhibition; 223-227,* p. 5 pages, 8165 kb, 2020, doi: 10.4229/EUPVSEC20202020-2BO.5.5.

[3] M.-J. Park, S. Youn, K. Jeon, S. H. Lee, and C. Jeong, "Optimization of Shingled-Type Lightweight Glass-Free Solar Modules for Building Integrated Photovoltaics," *Applied Sciences*, vol. 12, no. 10, p. 5011, May 2022, doi: 10.3390/app12105011.

[4] Eunbi Lee, Min-Joon Park, Minseob Kim, Jinho Shin, and Sungmin Youn, "Fabrication of High-power Shingled PV Modules Integrated with Bent Steel Plates for the Roof," *Current Photovoltaic Research, 11(2),* pp. 54–57, June 2023.

[5] Ji-Su Park, Won-Je Oh, Jang-Hun Joo, Jun-Sin Yi, Byung-You Hong, and Jae-Hyeong Lee, "Design of High-Power and High-Density Photovoltaic Modules Based on a Shingled Cell String," *Journal of Nanoscience and Nanotechnology, 20(11),* pp. 6996-7001(6), Nov. 2020, doi: https://doi.org/10.1166/jnn.2020.18837.

[6] B. Liang *et al.*, "Progress in crystalline silicon heterojunction solar cells," *J. Mater. Chem. A,* vol.

13, no. 4, pp. 2441–2477, 2025, doi: 10.1039/D4TA06224H.

[7] A. Lakhe, S. Upadhye, Y. Goshikwar, and T. Lakhe, "STUDY OF MODERN SOLAR TECHNOLOGIES: PERC and HJT," vol. 09, no. 07, 2022.

[8] "How efficient are heterojunction cells compared to traditional solar cells | NenPower." Accessed: Sept. 01, 2025. [Online]. Available: https://nenpower.com/blog/how-efficient-are-heterojunction-cells-compared-to-traditional-solar-cells/

[9] "Top Efficiency Of Each Cell Technology." Accessed: Sept. 01, 2025. [Online]. Available: https://taiyangnews.info/technology/top-efficiency-of-each-cell-technology-2

[10] D. M. Fischer, "ITRPV | ITRPV 2024 | Dr. Markus Fischer | PV CellTech, Frankfurt/Main, March 13 2024," 2023.

[11] "IEC TS 60904-13:2018 | IEC Webstore." Accessed: Sept. 03, 2025. [Online]. Available: https://webstore.iec.ch/en/publication/26703

[12] "IEC 60904-9:2020 | IEC Webstore." Accessed: Sept. 03, 2025. [Online]. Available: https://webstore.iec.ch/en/publication/28973

[13] "IEC 61215-1:2021 | IEC Webstore." Accessed: Sept. 03, 2025. [Online]. Available: https://webstore.iec.ch/en/publication/61345

[14] W. Mokrzycki and M. Tatol, "Color difference Delta E - A survey," *Machine Graphics and Vision*, vol. 20, pp. 383–411, Apr. 2011.

PV-PLANNING AND SIMULATION, DAYLIGHT SIMULATION AND ENERGY-CERTIFICATE CALCULATION BASED ON AN OPEN-BIM-BUILDING-MODEL

Astrid Schneider and Karin Stieldorf, TU Wien, Faculty of Architecture and Planning, Institute of Architecture and Design, Karlsplatz 13, 1040 Wien, Austria astrid@astrid-schneider.de, astrid.schneider@tuwien.ac.at, karin.stieldorf@tuwien.ac.at
Christian Schranz and Harald Urban, TU Wien, Research Unit Digital Building Process, christian.schranz@tuwien.ac.at;
Alfred Waschl, buildingSMART, alfred.waschl@buildingsmart.co.at;
Markus Feichtner, Sonnenkraft Energy GmbH, Markus.Feichtner@sonnenkraft.com;
Fedele Rende and Andreas Aiello ACCA Software, fedele.rende@almasoft.it;
Martin Hauer, Bartenbach GmbH, Martin.Hauer@bartenbach.com;
Kurt Battisti, Markus Dörn and Jacqueline Scherret, A-Null Development GmbH, kurt.battisti@archiphysik.com;
Martin und Christoph Treberspurg, Treberspurg und Partner Ziviltechniker, christoph.treberspurg@treberspurg.at

ABSTRACT: The TU Wien is leading the research project "BIM4BIPV – Future aspects of Building Integrated Photovoltaic (BIPV) in the cross system Building Information Modelling (BIM)". Goal of this project is to develop an open BIM-based planning and simulation workflow suitable for project specific Photovoltaic (PV) modules for Building Integration (BIPV) as well as for standard PV-modules to design, plan and simulate BIPV-modules with individual layers of encapsulants, front- and back sheets and different cell types, cell string layouts and cell distributions. At the EUPVSEC 2025 it could be the first time presented, that it is possible to equip the architect's BIM-model of an example building in the authoring software with custom-designed solar modules and their simulation values, to then export the BIM-model as an open BIM IFC-format into PV-simulation software and to perform the photovoltaic system simulation directly on this model. The PV-simulation software recognizes the PV-modules within the 3D-BIM-model and can read and use their electric values as well as their orientation and tilt.

Keywords: Building Integrated Photovoltaics (BIPV), Building Information Modelling (BIM), Industry Foundation classes (IFC), Simulation, Architecture

1   INTRODUCTION

The TU Wien is leading the research project "BIM4BIPV – Future aspects of Building Integrated Photovoltaic (BIPV) in the cross system Building Information Modelling (BIM)". Goal of this project is to develop an open BIM-based planning and simulation workflow suitable for project specific Photovoltaic (PV) modules for Building Integration (BIPV) as well as for standard PV-modules. Both shall be represented in the open BIM exchange format of the Industry Foundation Classes (IFC). The workflow can be used to design, plan and simulate BIPV-modules with individual layers of encapsulants, front- and back sheets and different cell types, cell string layouts and cell distributions. As a result, it shall be possible to execute a flexible, suit and integrated multidisciplinary workflow, in which PV-modules can be represented in an architect's or engineer's BIM-planning software such as Archicad, including classifications and property sets relevant for different planning disciplines. This includes – but is not restricted to - property sets for Photovoltaic and daylight planning and simulation, for energy certificate calculation and for environmental impact evaluation. At the EUPVSEC 2025 it could be the first time presented, that it is possible to equip the architect's BIM-model of an example building in the authoring software with custom-designed solar modules and their simulation values, to then export the BIM-model as an open BIM IFC-format and to perform the photovoltaic system simulation directly on this model. An existing building, planned and constructed in 1990 serves as an experimentation platform for the newly developed open BIM-process. Planning goal is to find the optimal balance between optimization of solar power generation, potential overheating in the summer, sufficient daylighting, passive solar gains in wintertime, energy efficiency and the preservation of the solar house aesthetic with excellent views to the sky and the garden, while at the same time embracing a glass house daylight level and feeling.

2   STATE OF THE ART AND INNOVATION

2.1 State of the Art
Today solar modules are represented by the producers mostly as PDF-datasheets. Furthermore the industry is feeding the solar module data into industrial proprietary data bases to be used in PV-planning and simulation programs such as Solarius-PV, PV-Syst or PV*Sol. Other innovative software such as BIMsolar by ENERbim is generating BIPV-modules within their own proprietary software, which is aiming to be compatible with the REVIT-BIM-planning software through a plugin.

2.2 Innovation
The research project BIM4BIPV is striving to innovate the representation of PV and BIPV-modules alike by offering an open source open BIM process, which is non-proprietary and allows a high compatibility with different software tools for planning, simulation, operation and documentation.

The workflow is currently under development, the first development stage has been concluded and first planning and simulation results are presented at the EUPVSEC 2025.

The PV- / BIPV-modules are designed in the authoring BIM-planning software and were sucessfully exported as an open BIM-format IFC-file. This format is the exchange format between different BIM-model authoring tools and specific planning and simulation software tools as a standard in architecture, urban and infrastructure planning.

This BIM-model was then imported including the electric values into the PV-simulation software.

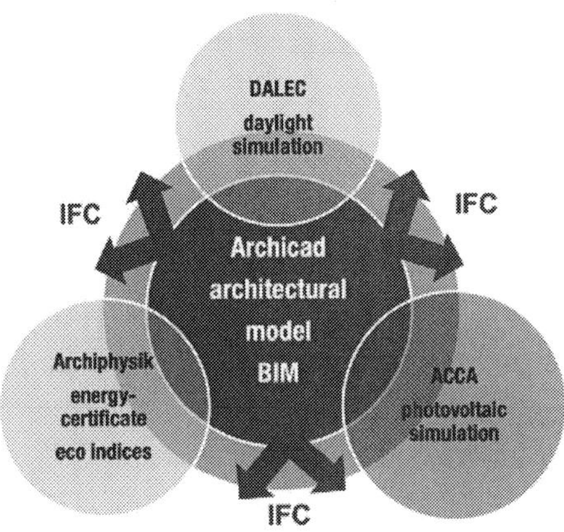

Figure 1: IFC-based multidisciplinary planning and simulation process on an open BIM model. Source: Astrid Schneider, TU Wien

3 HOUSE HAFNER IN VIENNA AS A MODEL CASE STUDY

2.1 House Hafner: a Passive Solar House from 1990

An existing building, "Haus Hafner" [0] planned and constructed in 1990 serves as an experimentation platform for the newly developed opem BIM-process. House Hafner was designed as an early example of solar architetcure – in that case as a passive solar building by the Austrian architects Treberspurg and Partner. The building opens to the south and features a fully glazed winter garden, which spans through the whole building from top to bottom.

Planned with the idea of optimization for passive solar gains and daylighting the building today suffers overheating due to climate change.

Figure 2: Fotos House Hafner. Source: Treberspurg and Partners ZT

At the same time active solar power generation is wished. The solar active design and planning with Building integrated PV now has to solve the balance between optimization of solar power generation, including the question of potential overheating in the summer, sufficient daylighting and passive solar gains in wintertime.

This multidisciplinary planning task was solved by using a 3D-BIM-model as a basis for planning and simulation. The model is drawn using the Archicad BIM-software as an authoring software.

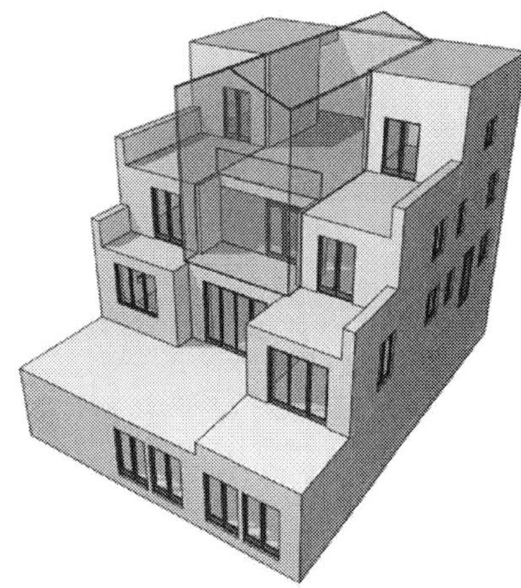

Figure 3: BIM-Model House Hafner without PV. Source: Treberspurg and Partners ZT

2.1 House Hafner: BIPV-Design as a Retrofit

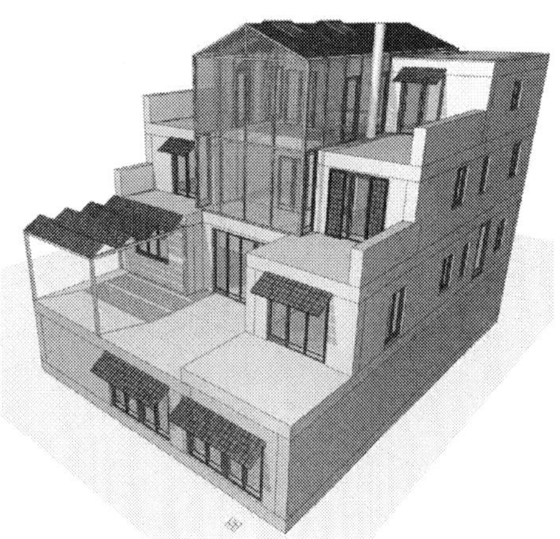

Figure 4: BIM-Model House Hafner with various BIPV-Systems drawn in Archicad BIM-Authoring Software. Source: Astrid Schneider, TU Wien and Treberspurg and Partners ZT

For the test set up the model of Hause Hafner was equipped with the following integrated BIPV-systems:

- integration of PV-panels into the atrium insulation glazing

- canopy roofs over windows
- solar window shutters
- pergola BIPV-roof over terrace

The BIPV-solar modules were drawn with the authoring BIM-software "Archicad", a well market introduced frequently used professional planning software in architecture in Europe. The module drawings do not have to follow any special requirements to be suitable to be attached with Photovoltaic module properties. The planning stage is "design planning".

However the real size of market available crystalline solar cells has been chosen for the design: 158 x 158 mm wide mono-crystalline Topcon solar cells. Th cell type to be chosen was agreed upon with the consortial partner Sonnenkraft, the largest PV-manufacturer of Austria as an available solar cell for BIPV-module manufacturing.

4. THE WORKFLOW FOR IFC-MODEL BASED PV- / BIPV-SIMULATION

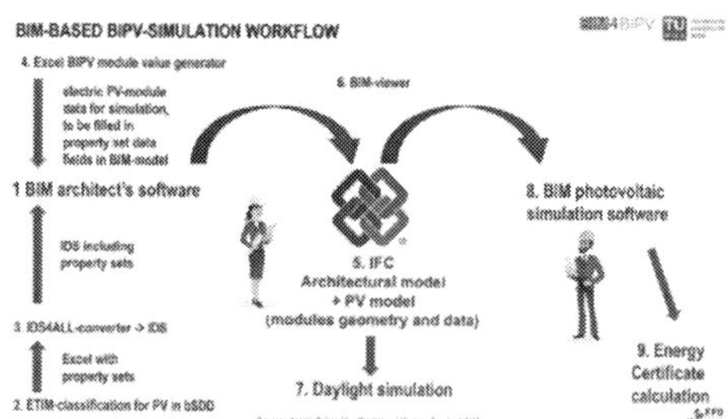

Figure 5: Workflow for BIM-based BIPV-Simulation
Source: Astrid Schneider, TU Wien and Fedele Rende, ACCA Software

Figure 5 shows the workflow steps and components for a multidisciplinary planning, calculation and PV-simulation. We will go through the steps according to the numbers in the figure 5.

4.1 Building Model Design by the Architect in a BIM-Planning Software including BIPV-Modules
    The architect will design the solar modules in accordance with design ideas, clients wishes and as agreed in the planning process.

Figure 6: BIM-Model of the Architect in Archicad
Source: Astrid Schneider, TU Wien and Treberspurg and Partners Architects

The size of solar cells and modules will already be discussed and adjusted with potential market offers or producers and technical consultants. Here a format of 158 x 158 mm solar cells war chosen. The solar cell layout in the panels, the density and aesthetics can already be determined according to the building design. The solar modules are drawn with precise geometry an measures.

4.2 ETIM Classification EC001746 "Photovoltaics module"
    As a preparatory step the ETIM [1] Classification EC001746 "Photovoltaics module" [2] was transferred in an Excel sheet. The sheet as well defines, for which entities in the BIM-model this classification can be used. This process has only to be done once in an architect's or planner's office to generate an Information Delivery Specification (IDS). The subsequent IDS can then forever been used in the office for different projects.

4.3 Generation of an Information Delivery Specification (IDS) for Photovoltaic Simulation Values
    To be able to generate the property fields for the electric properties of a PV-module in the architectural or engineering authoring software it is one option to do it automated via an IDS. The advantage is, that the fields "pop up" in the authoring software in this case in Archicad. The TU Wien in collaboration with buildingSMART Austria [3] generated and published an "IDS4ALL-converter" [4], which converts via up- and download the excel sheet into an IDS-file, which can be imported into the Archicad software.

4.4 Excel BIPV Module Value Generator
    The electric values of a PV-module are normally taken from the producers data sheet. In case the architect designs the BIPV-module herself to be produced custom sized to fit the specific project there are different options. One is, that the producer delivers the electric values of such a module to the architect or the planner himself calculates the values. Sonnenkraft the biggest Austrian Photovoltaic producer uses internally as well for the first a calculation via Excel, based on the cell used for the module and the module layout including the thickness of the glasses. These electric values are then feeded into the property sets popping up when the specific object is activated in the BIM software as shown in figure 7 below.

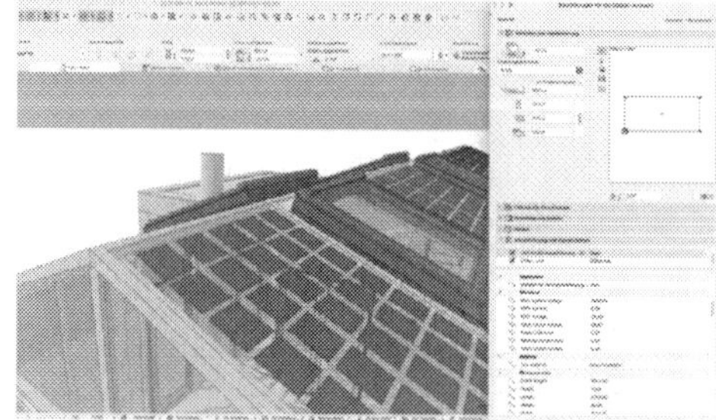

Figure 7: BIM-Model of the Architect in Archicad with opened property set field for PV-modules
Source: Astrid Schneider, TU Wien

4.5 Export as an IFC File

Once the BIPVmodules have been described the whole building model will be exported from the authoring software as an IFC-file, which will include all the properties specified earlier in the IDS and brought to the architect' BIM-model.

4.6 Value Control with the BIM-Viewer

As a very important step the values can now be controlled in a BIM-viewer as shown in figure 7.

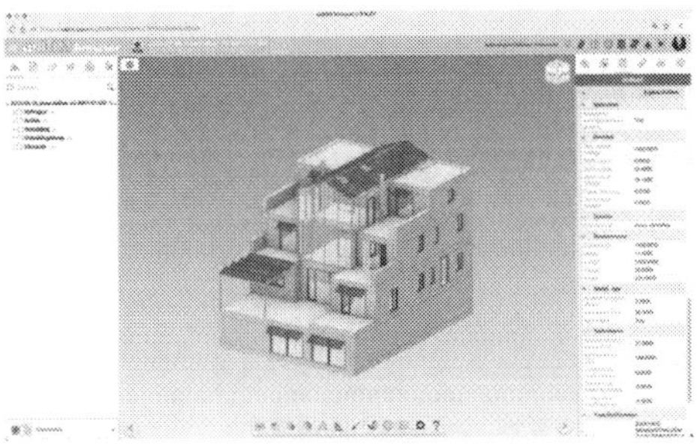

Figure 7: BIM-Model of the Architect in the BIM-Viewer. Source: Astrid Schneider, TU Wien

The BIM-viewer allows in a platform agnostic manner to check an uploaded IFC-model regarding the content and correctness of information, which is included in the model. By clicking the solar modules the electric and other values of the BIPV-element are popping up. The information stored can be regarding all disciplines, in this case we look at the electric values according to the ETIM-classification Photovoltaics Module. As a BIM-viewer the ACCA-usBIM [5] has been used. In the control view it can be seen, that the desired electric values of the solar modules have been exported successfully and are incorporated in the generated exportfile in the IFC-format.

4.7 Daylight Simulation

The project partner Bartenbach used "Climate Studio" Daylight simulations are performed using Climate Studio ClimateStudio is a plugin for the Rhinoceros (Rhino) 3d modeling software. The data path to use the BIM-model fort he daylight simulation and evaluation ist he following:

- The IFC-file was directly imported into Rhino, using ggIFC - an „Add-on application" in Rhino
- After manual modifcations on the imported geometry in Rhino, the model was able to be used by Climate Studio

General problem:

- Daylight simulation tools only consider geometry from IFC-files
- Daylight specific parameters (surface reflection values, visual transparancy values,…) have to be set manually

Several daylighting factors have been simulated and evaluated. As a result it can be clearly seen, that the House Hafner has a problem, in the actual variant without any BIPV.

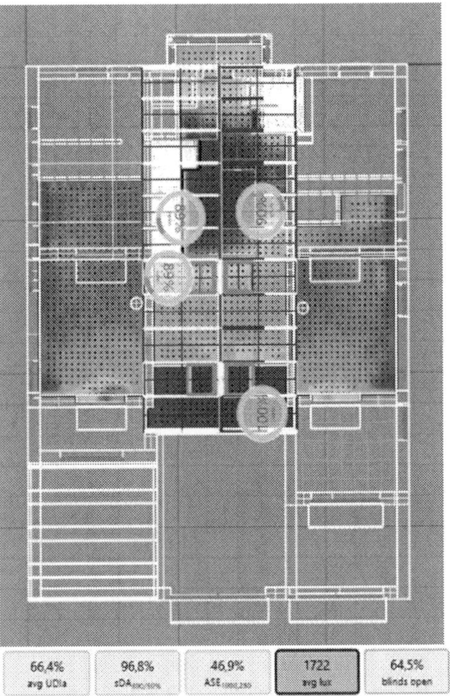

Figure 8: Evaluation of the Daylight-values UID and ASE without BIPV
Source: Martin Hauer, Bartenbach

Figure 8 shows the building without BIPV. The following factors were evaluated:

Useful Daylight Illuminance (UDI)

- is a modification of daylight autonomy
- This criterion divides the hourly data into three evaluation categories
  - 0-100lx (underlighting)
  - 100 - 2000lx (pleasant lighting conditions)
  - >2000lx (overlighting)
- In the range of 100-2000lx, daylight input is rated as useful

Annual Sunlight Exposure (ASE)

- refers to the percentage of space that receives too much direct sunlight (1000 Lux or more for at least 250 occupied hours per year), which can cause glare or increased cooling loads

As a result the observed overheating in the summer can be clearly seen in the simulation:

- Annual Sunlight exposure (ASE) is very high → glare and summer overheating
- Useful daylight illuminance (UDI) is reduced → too much exceeding illuminance lelvels

As an alternative the variant with BIPV-glazing was simulated.

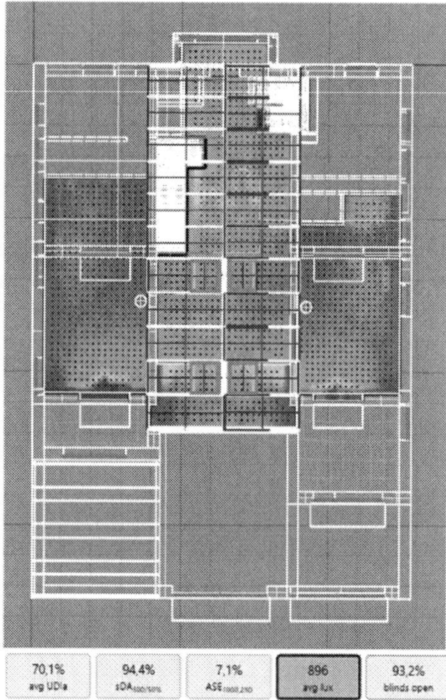

70,1%	94,4%	7,1%	896	93,2%
avg UDIa	sDA500/50%	ASE1000,250	avg lux	blinds open

Figure 9: Evaluation of the daylight-values UID and ASE with BIPV. Source: Martin Hauer, Bartenbach

In this variant the BIPV plays a crucial role to enhance the thermal and optical performance of the building. The BIPV-variant of figure 9 is:

- **PV on canopy (non transp.)**
- **PV on Roof + Side windows (semitransp.)**

As a result of this BIPV deployment it could be observed:

- Significant improvement by semitransparent PV on roof and side windows of the attic brings a siginficant improvement
  → Annual Sunlight exposure in an acceptable range (<10%)
- Highest levels on Useful Daylight illuminance UDI → 70%

A similar picture was observed regarding the daylight factor as shown in the presentation.

4.8 Photovoltaic System Planning and Simulation

As a very important step now the PV-system electric planning and simulation can be done directly based on the architectural model. To do so the IFC-file with the overall building model is imported into the Photovoltaic simulation program Solarius PV from the research partner ACCA.

As an advantage the BIM-model contains all the electric values specified in the IDS based on the ETIM property set for Photovoltaic modules. Those values are the input parameters for the PV-system planning and simulation.

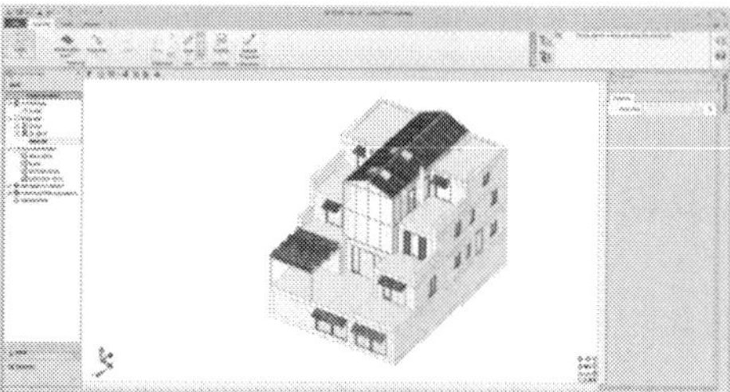

Figure 10: Import of the building model into the Solarius PV Photovoltaic simulation program
Source: Fedele Rende, ACCA.

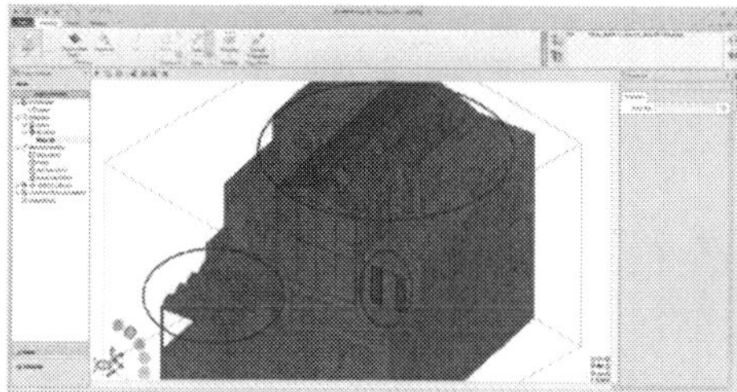

Figure 11: Automatic recognition of the PV-elements within the building open BIM IFC-model
Source: Fedele Rende, ACCA

The most important step to close the BIPV-simulation workflow was performed successfully: within the research project the Solarius PV-software was adopted to be able to detect BIM-elements with the ETIM classification EC001746 "Photovoltaics module" automatically.

Figure 12: Electric PV-module-data data read from the architectural model by Solarius PV
Source: Fedele Rende, ACCA

This step is crucial, as it is not necessary to place modules "on top" of existing BIPV-surfaces to "simulate" a BIPV-module. Instead elements which are just right at the place they should be can be activated as PV-modules and thus even in a digital model fulfil the double function to be a building element and an electric system element (PV-module) at the same time. With this data the normal PV-

system planning and simulation process can start.
As a result the PV-yield can be simulated as shown in figure 13:

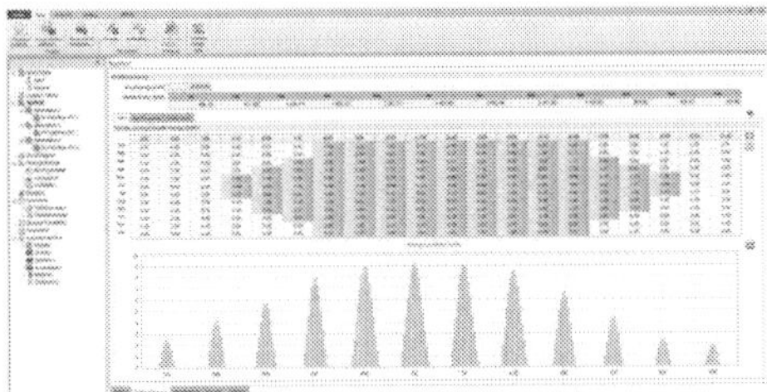

Figure 13: PV yield of House Hafner BIPV-plants calculated with the PV-simulation program
Source: Fedele Rende, ACCA

4.9 Calculation of the Energy Certificate
The same IFC-building model can be used to calculate the energy certificate of the building. The Energy Certificate evaluates, how the building is complying with the requirements set out in the European Union (EU) Energy Performance of Buildings (EPD) directive and in this case the national Austrian legislation and building standards requirements putting the EPD into force in Austria. This calculation is made by the project partner A0-Development with their own self developed software Archiphysik. For the Energy Certificate calculation the BIPV-elements – especially when integrated into shading devices, windows or glazed façade and roof elements are relevant regarding their thermal, visual and electric impact.

4.9.1Parameters of the PV-System taken into account for the Energy Certifcate Calculation:

The building physics program Archiphysik can read the BIM-model and evaluate the values and geometry:

Regarding the BIPV-glazing- and shading-elements the following inputs are taken from model for the thermal evaluation of the building envelope:

Thermal input parameters:
- shading geometry of PV-modules in front of the window or glazed area (share of opaque and transparent area)
- G-value of the glazing
- U-value of the glazing
    - calculation of solar radiation entering the space
        - thermal comfort fulfilment
        - heating and cooling demand calculation in kWh/m^2

Glazing and summer overheating
Large glazed areas may cause overheating under sunlight. In the summer only a limited reduction is possible through night ventilation.

BIPV-approach Haus Hafner: solar gains through glazing have to be reduced. PV shutters and BIPV glazing in the are used to reduce the solar input to cause less overheating.

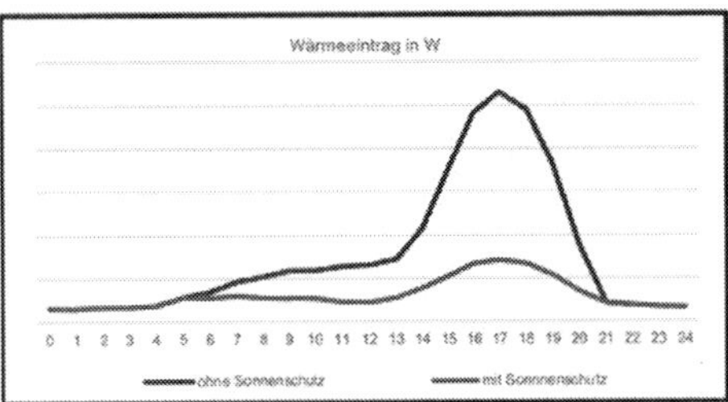

Figure 14: Heat Input through a glazed area with and without sun protection during 24 hours of a summer day.
Source: Markus Dörn A-Null Development GmbH

PV-module inputs taken from model:
- Wp – Power
- location, orientation
    - solar power produced
- reduction of primary fossil energy consumed
- fulfilment of required installation capacity by construction laws

4.9.2 Photovoltaic electricity in the energy balance
Electricity generated by PV can be included in the energy balance for the Energy Performance Certificate. Depending on the national legal framework of the EU-country , PV electricity can fully or partially replace other energy carriers. Some EU-countries allow to take simulated PV-power production into account, while others only allow an extremely simplified calculation based on system power and location plus orientation.
The amount of creditable PV electricity is legally defined and restricted to schematically defined times, when PV-power production and energy system consumption are expected to overlap.
Surplus PV electricity is shown in the EPC as PV export.

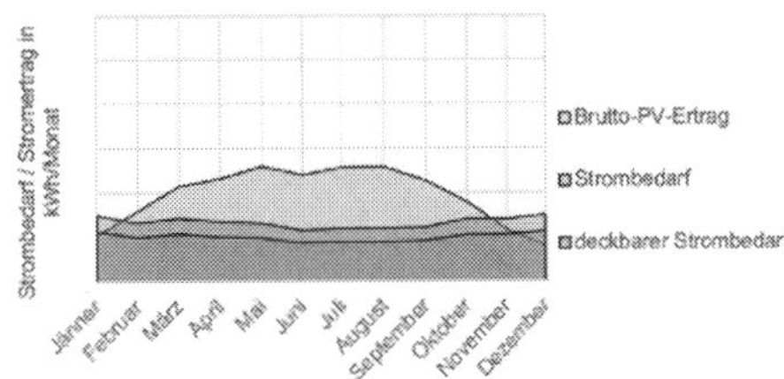

Figure 15: Solar power generated by the BIPV-system and it's consideration in the Energy Certificate calculation according to the Austrian rules
Source: Markus Dörn A-Null Development GmbH

5. DIFFICULTIES FACED IN THE PROCESS

The workflow was achieved the first time successfully in the project. However there are many hurdles on the way to be faced:
- compatibility problems of different software products and formats
- multiple model transfers causing faults
- missing data after model transfer
- correct transfer of location, direction and axis is

- a challenge and not yet fully achieved
- material transfer / display of materials
- the IFC standard is not yet fully adopted and implemented by all actors / software companies

Due to the above mentioned hurdles some data had to be corrected by hand.

4 OUTLOOK

4.1 PV and BIPV-simulation

It would be senseful to have a PV / BIPV-module generator, which would display a PV-module directly in IFC including active single cells as shown in figure 16.

Figure 16: PV-module with activated single cell
Source: BIM4BIPV

The main purpose is, to be able to determine the area and substring of a PV-module affected by especially near shade. To do so an analysis will be needed, which cell / cell string is affected by shade.

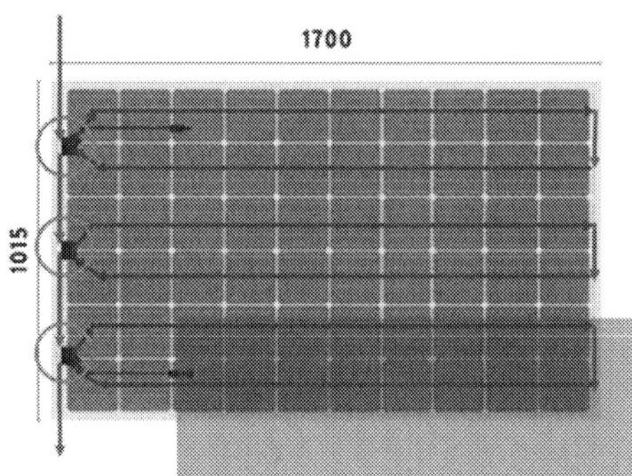

Figure 17: PV-module with shade falling on one module string
Source: Astrid Schneider, TU Wien

This kind of analysis is especially relevant in BIPV-applications as they face more shade problems. Due to the strong rise of bifacial modules the near shade aspect is as well more and more important regarding the module supporting structures.

4.2 IFC-Module Database

As soon as the workflow is established and gains traction in the market a worldwide database of PV and BIPV-modules could start arising, which would allow to drag and drop PV-modules into construction designs. This option is however strongly dependent on the compatibility of different software.

4.3 Software Compatibility

The construction planning and solar simulation software should be adopted and made compatible, so that PV and BIPV can be integrated easily into digital planning flows. The following aspects have to be taken into consideration:

- optimized near shade and bifaciality simulation
  - as well on cell, module and string level
- inclusion of multidisciplinary data of PV / BIPV into construction models
- ability for multidisciplinary simulation such as
  - daylighting
  - shade and heat effects
  - energy planning
  - green construction
- as well important for agri-PV, infrastructure, OEM of large solar parks ...

Especially a full compliance and adaptation of the IFC-standard by different software developers and providers would enable the swift flow of data and enable integrated multidisciplinary planning workflows based on IFC-project models.To achieve this, it is important to standardize the property and property set names to enable interoperability across PV / BIPV and construction / infrastructure industry. An ongoing international collaboration within in Task 15 of the IEA International Energy Agency Power systems Program PVPS is under way, to help unifying the needed property and classification data.

4.3 References

[0] **Article House Hafner:** "Geöffnet zu Sonne und Gärten", Fachjournal "Architektur Aktuell 143", Juni 1991

[1] **ETIM International:** As of 05.10.2024
https://www.etim-international.com/

[2] **ETIM classification EC001746 "Photovoltaics Module"**
As of 17.05.2025
https://identifier.buildingsmart.org/uri/etim/etim/9.0/class/EC001746

[3] **buildingSMART international:**
As of 02. September 2024:
https://www.buildingsmart.org/

[4] **IDS4ALL-Converter**
As of 12. September 2025:
https://openbim-knowledgebase.org/ids4all/

[5] **BIM-viewer the ACCA-usBIM**
As of 10. September 2025:
https://www.accasoftware.com/de/bim-management-system

[6] **Climate Studio** As of 10. September 2025:
https://climatestudiodocs.com/index.html

[7] **buildingSMART Data Dictionary (bSDD)**
As of 07. September 2024:
https://www.buildingsmart.org/users/services/buildingsmart-data-dictionary/

PV-PLANNING AND SIMULATION, DAYLIGHT SIMULATION AND ENERGY-CERTIFICATE CALCULATION BASED ON AN OPEN-BIM-BUILDING-MODEL

Session 4BO.17.6 - Planning of PV Systems - Digital PV

Presentation 4BO.17.6
September 23rd

EUPVSEC 2025 – Spain - Bilbao

Astrid Schneider
TU Wien

Research Project BIM4BIPV

- **TU Wien Institute for Architecture and Design + Digital Construction Process**
  Karin Stieldorf, Astrid Schneider, Christian Schranz, Harald Urban
- **buildingSMART**
  Alfred Waschl
- **Archiphysik - A-Null Development GmbH**
  Kurt Battisti, Markus Dörn, Jacqueline Scherret
- **Solarius PV - ACCA Software / ALMA**
  Fedele Rende, Andrea Aiello
- **Bartenbach GmbH**
  Martin Hauer
- **Sonnenkraft GmbH**
  Markus Feichtner
- **Treberspurg and Partner Architects ZT**
  Christoph Treberspurg, Martin Treberspurg

Project website: https://bim4bipv.project.tuwien.ac.at/

BIM4BIPV · TU WIEN · TECHNISCHE UNIVERSITÄT WIEN

BUILDING INFORMATION MODELLING (BIM)

What is „BIM"?

- **Modelling of element information (mostly) in the three dimensional space**
- **modern construction world plans in „BIM"**
- **Drawing-elements with complex informations attached**
  - geometry
  - materials
  - visual appearance
  - properties regarding different disciplines

BIM-3-D-model enables the „Digital Twin"

Source: BIM4BIPV – Haus Hafner

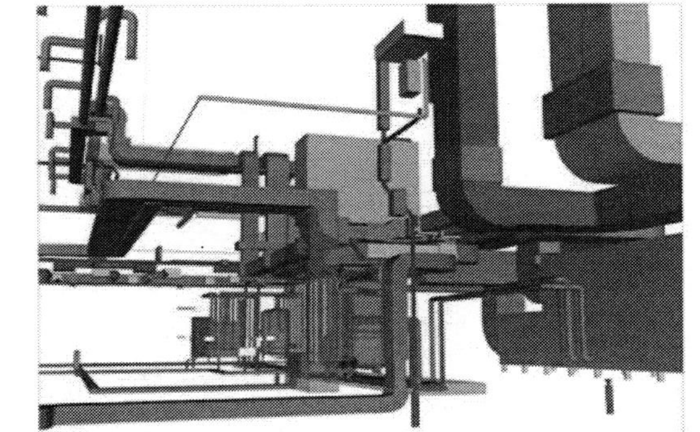

Source: „Bio-Institut der HBLFA Raumberg-Gumpenstein, TU Wien

FFG

BIM4BIPV TU WIEN TECHNISCHE UNIVERSITÄT WIEN

BIM REPRESENTATION OF A BIPV-MODULE

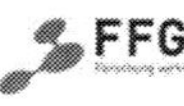

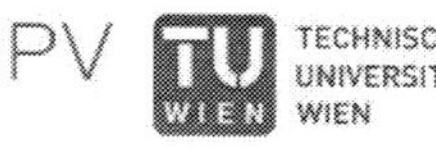

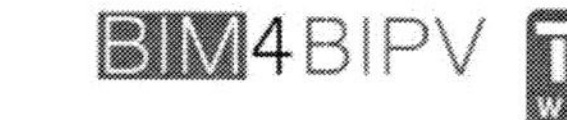

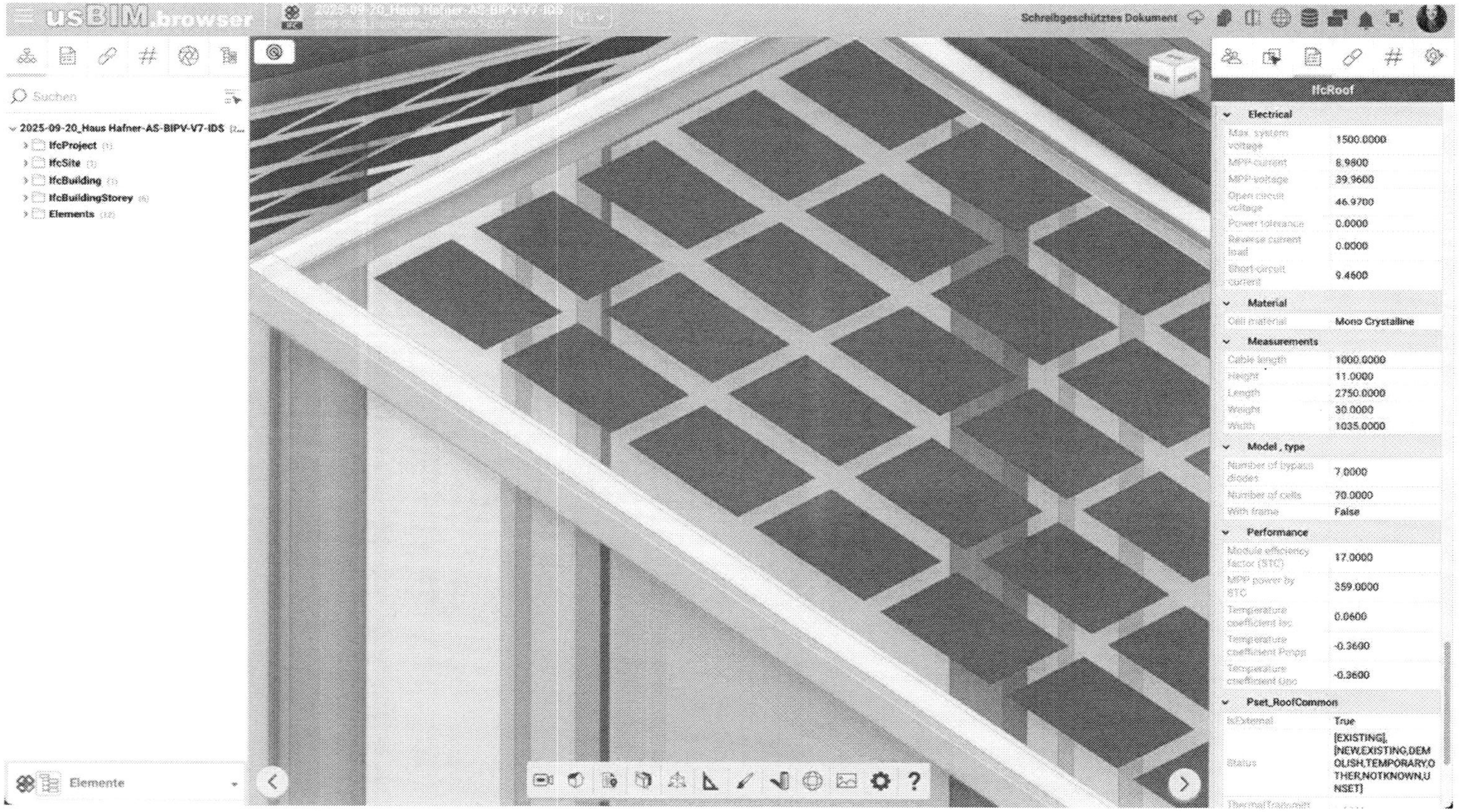

Source: Astrid Schneider TU wien

BIPV-Project seen in a BIM-viewer - source: BIM4BIPV - https://www.accasoftware.com/en/bim-management-system

FFG

OPEN BIM STANDARD IFC

.ifc

- Data exchange via open BIM „Industry Foundation Classes (IFC) Standard between different proprietary planning platforms (Revit / Archicad …) and planning and simulation tools of various disciplines
- The IFC-standard is developed by buildingSMART and published as ISO 16739-1 – Industry Foundation Classes (IFC)
- .ifc = open exchange format like „PDF" „JPG" …. of the 3D-model
- Information Delivery Specification (IDS) is a buildingSMART standard for defining information requirements in a computer interpretable form
- PV / BIPV belongs into the picture of construction + infrastructure planning processes

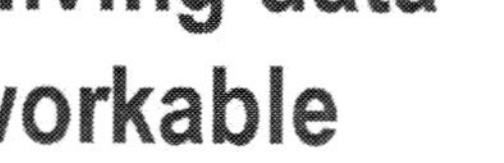

OUR GOAL: „LIVING" PV- / BIPV PRODUCT INFORMATION

Source: Sonnenkraft

PDF

**open
BIM-Data**

.ifc

Model , type	
Number of bypass diodes	7.0000
Number of cells	70.0000
With frame	False
Performance	
Module efficiency factor (STC)	17.0000
MPP power by STC	359.0000
Temperature coefficient Isc	0.0600
Temperature coefficient Pmpp	-0.3600
Temperature coefficient Uoc	-0.3600

„dead data"
informative

Source: Astrid Schneider TU Wien

„living data"
workable

BIM4BIPV · TU WIEN · TECHNISCHE UNIVERSITÄT WIEN

GOAL: DIGITAL PV-MODULES TO BE PRECISELY PLACED IN BIM-CAD-SOFTWARE

PV-Producer

is responsible to provide use case specific relevant product data

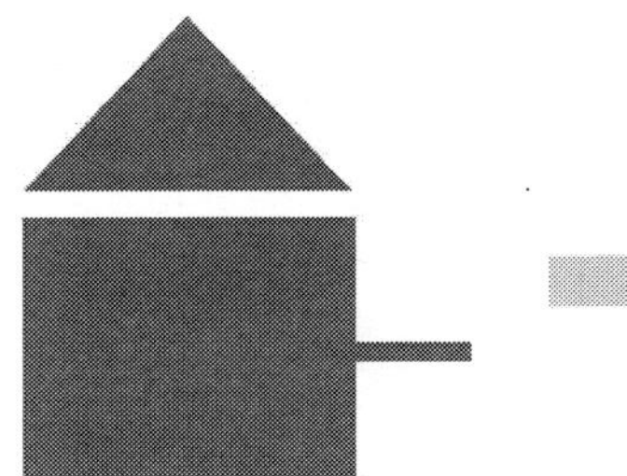

SONNENKRAFT

PV- BIPV-Product

Data-Scheme for PV / BIPV

PV- / BIPV-Data

in BIM / IFC-format

PV- Database in BIM / IFC – formate

optimally public

Architect

plans building / construction and puts PV- / BIPV-BIM-elements into CAD / BIM project design

(generic, product specific, custom sized)

BIM-project

design

- visual

Engineer

uses detailled PV- / BIPV- BIM project design to plan and simulate PV / BIPV-system

BIPV-system

- PV-system design and yield calculation
- daylighting
- energy
- structural
- environment

FFG

Source: Astrid Schneider TU Wien

SIMULATION OF HAUS HAFNER

HAUS HAFNER,
1190 Wien, Austria

- designed by Treberspurg and Partner Architects ZT, Vienna
- built 1991
- now suffering serious overheating in the atrium
- wish for BIPV-integration for shading and solar power

HAUS HAFNER – SOLAR HOUSE OF THE FIRST GENERATION 1991

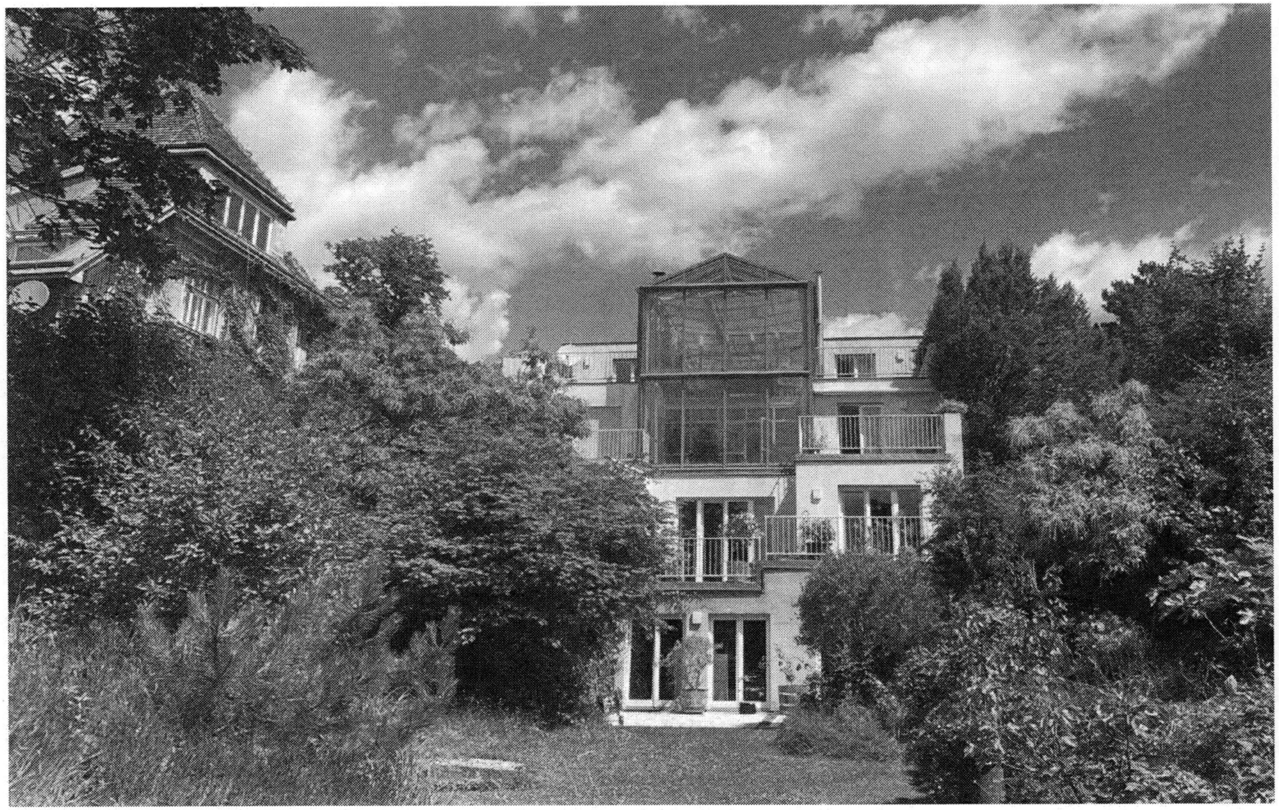

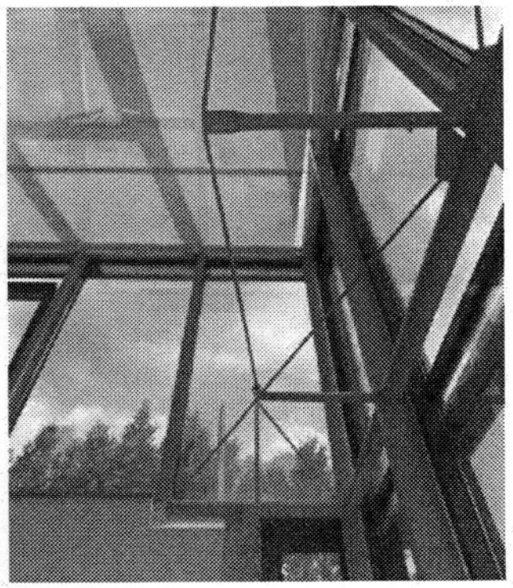

Fotos: Astrid Schneider TU Wien

Optimized design for passive solar gains: building opened towards the south with glass house

HAUS HAFNER – SOLAR HOUSE OF THE FIRST GENERATION 1991

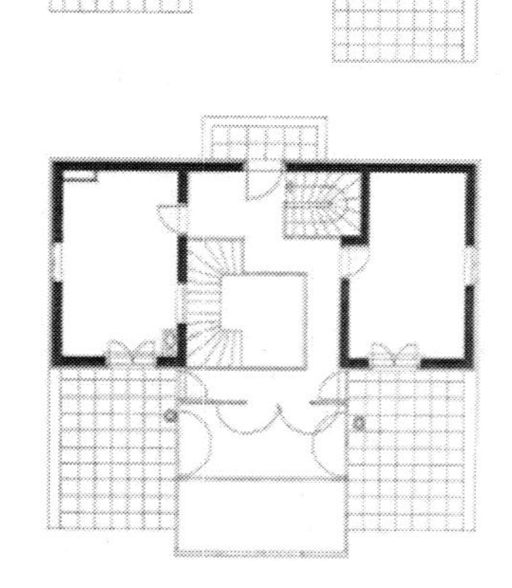

Glass house and inner atrium – today affected from summer overheating

HAUS HAFNER – BIM MODEL WITH BIPV AS DRAWING ELEMENTS

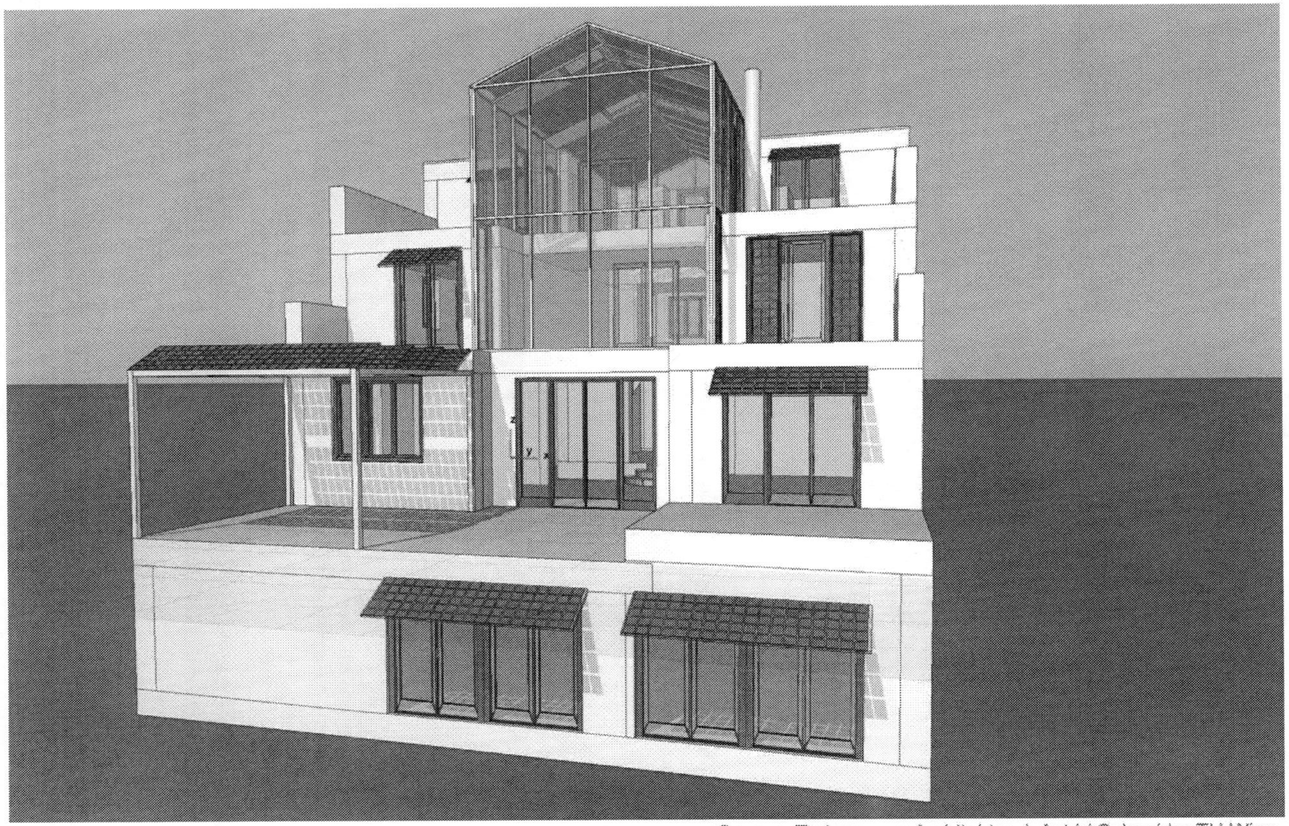

Source: Treberspurg Architekten / Astrid Schneider TU Wien

South view with different BIPV-systems in architect's BIM-planning program Archicad

HAUS HAFNER WITH BIPV AS DRAWING ELEMENTS

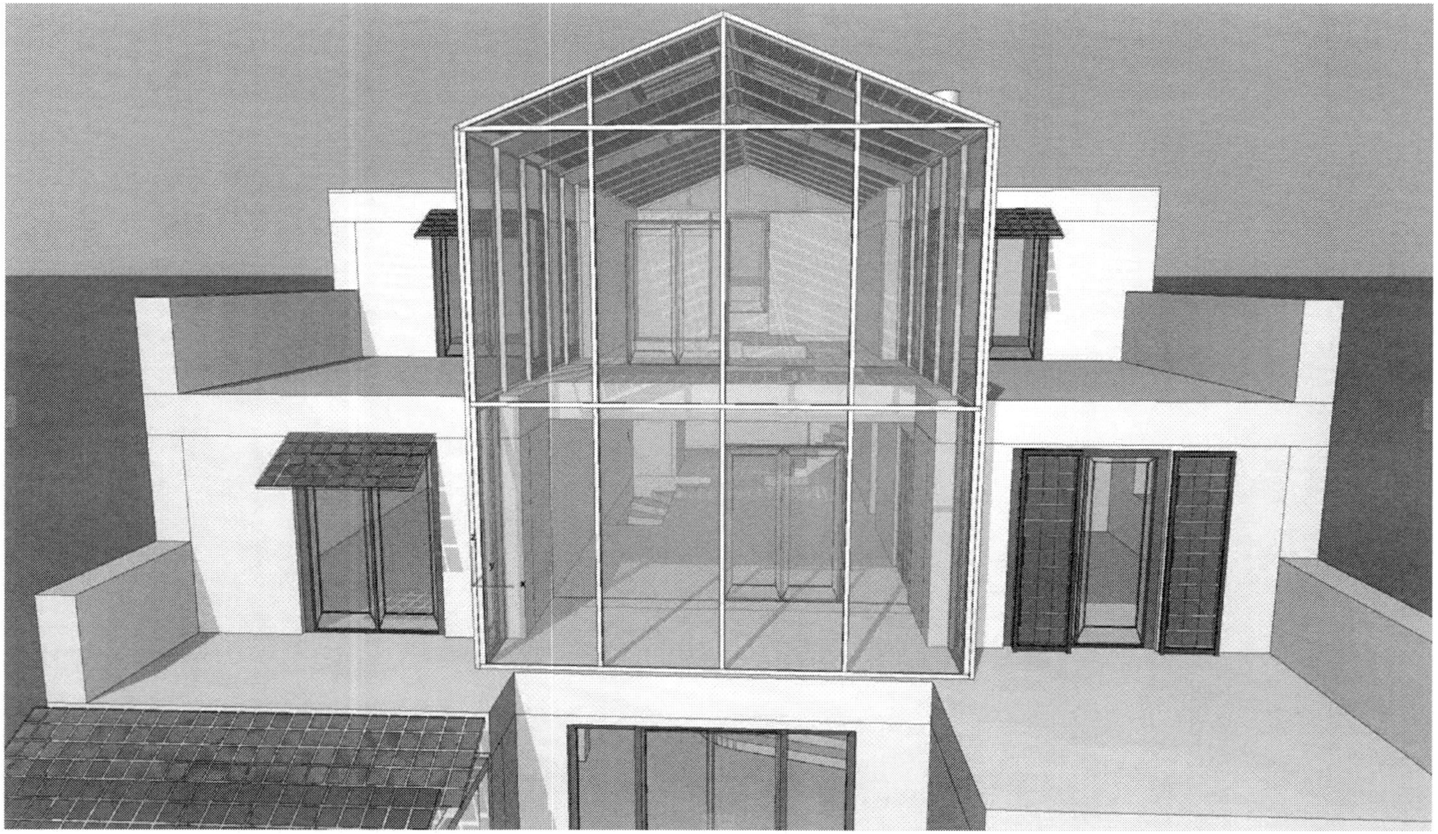

View to the atrium / different BIPV-systems

Source: Treberspurg Architekten / Astrid Schneider TU Wien

HAUS HAFNER WITH BIPV AS DRAWING ELEMENTS

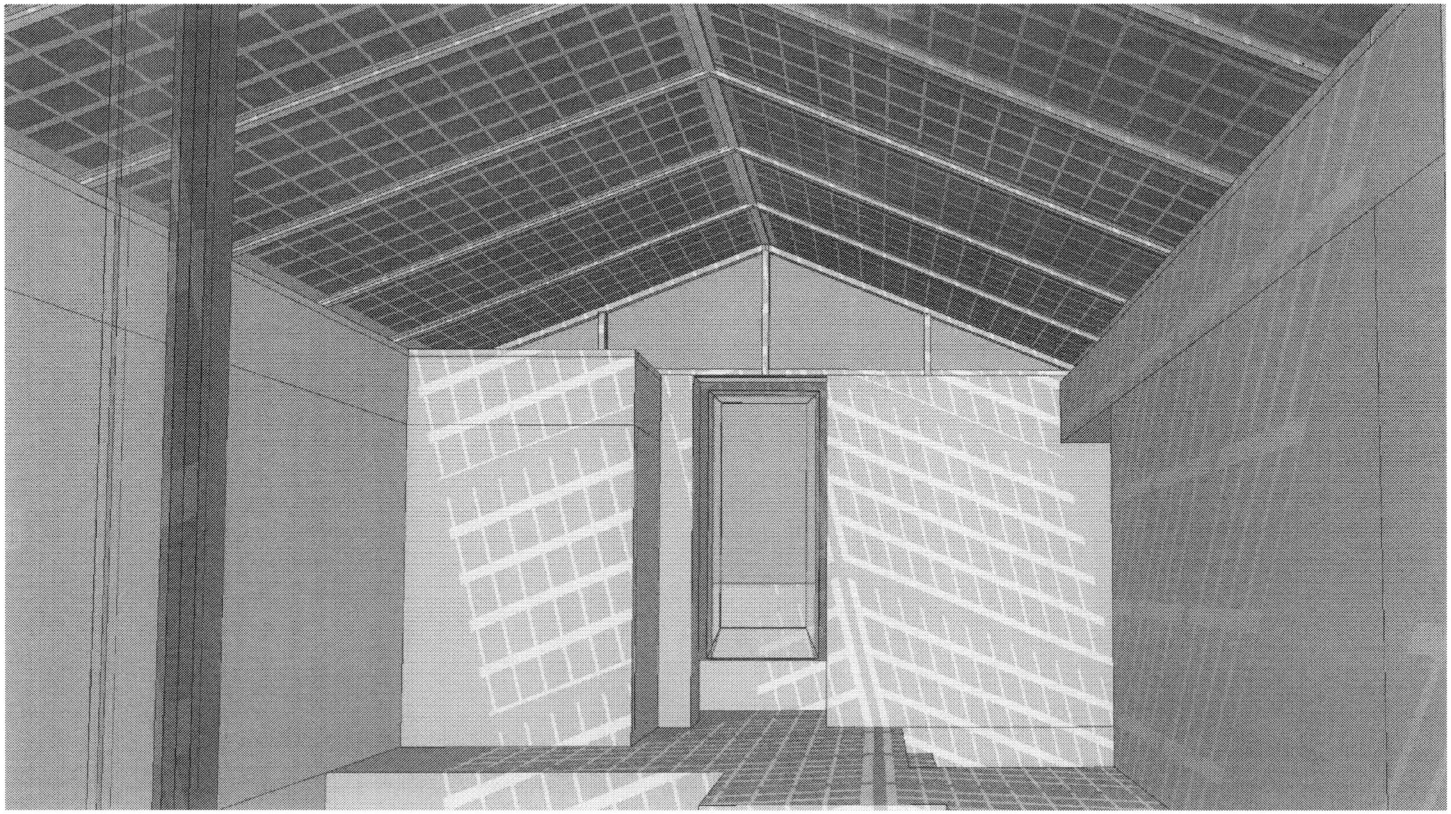

Interior view atrium

Source: Treberspurg Architekten / Astrid Schneider TU Wien

BIM4BIPV TU WIEN TECHNISCHE UNIVERSITÄT WIEN

HAUS HAFNER WITH BIPV AS DRAWING ELEMENTS

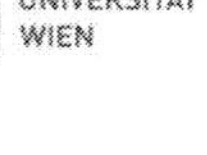

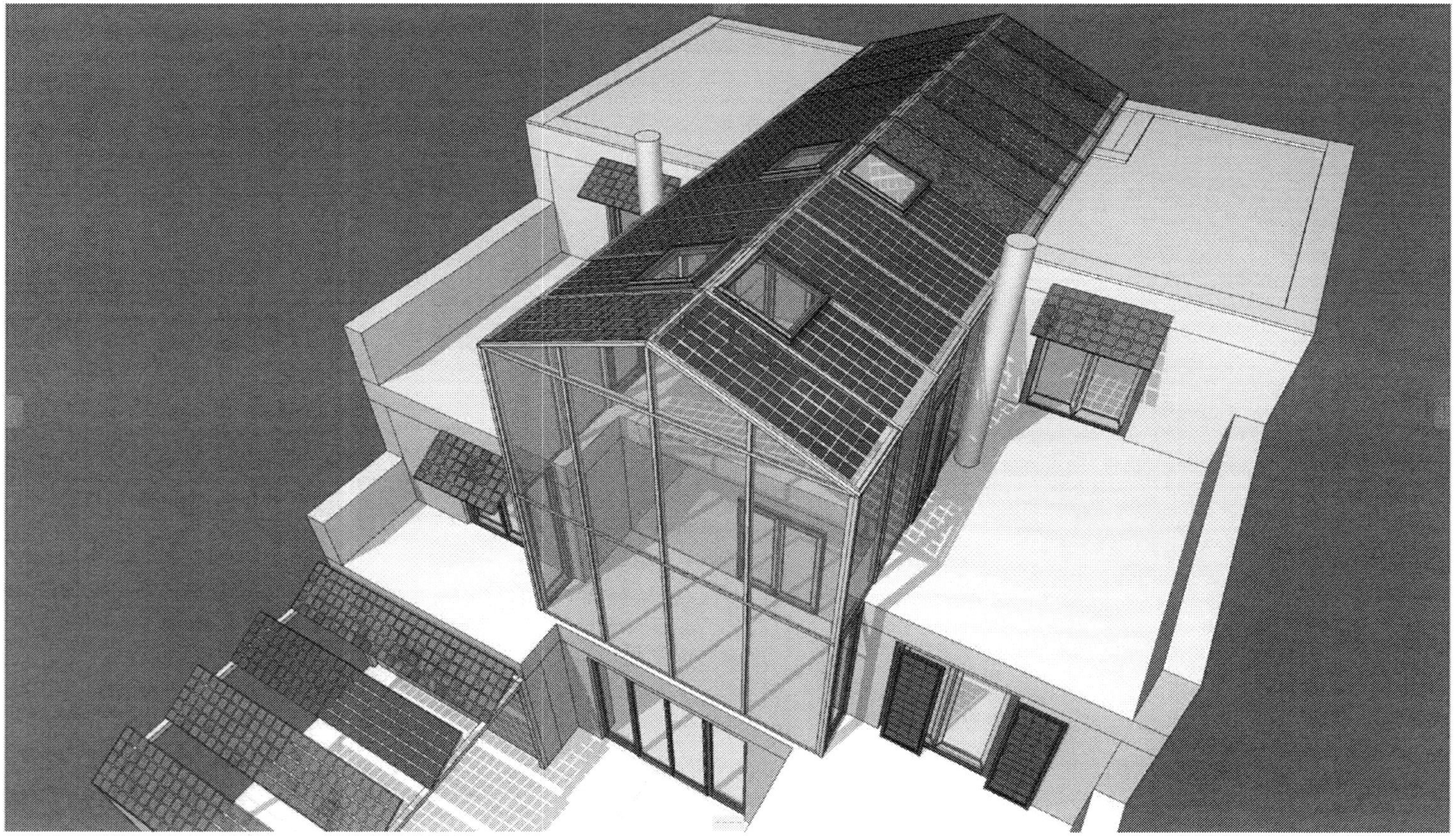

FFG

HAUS HAFNER – BIM MODELL WITH BIPV IN ARCHICAD

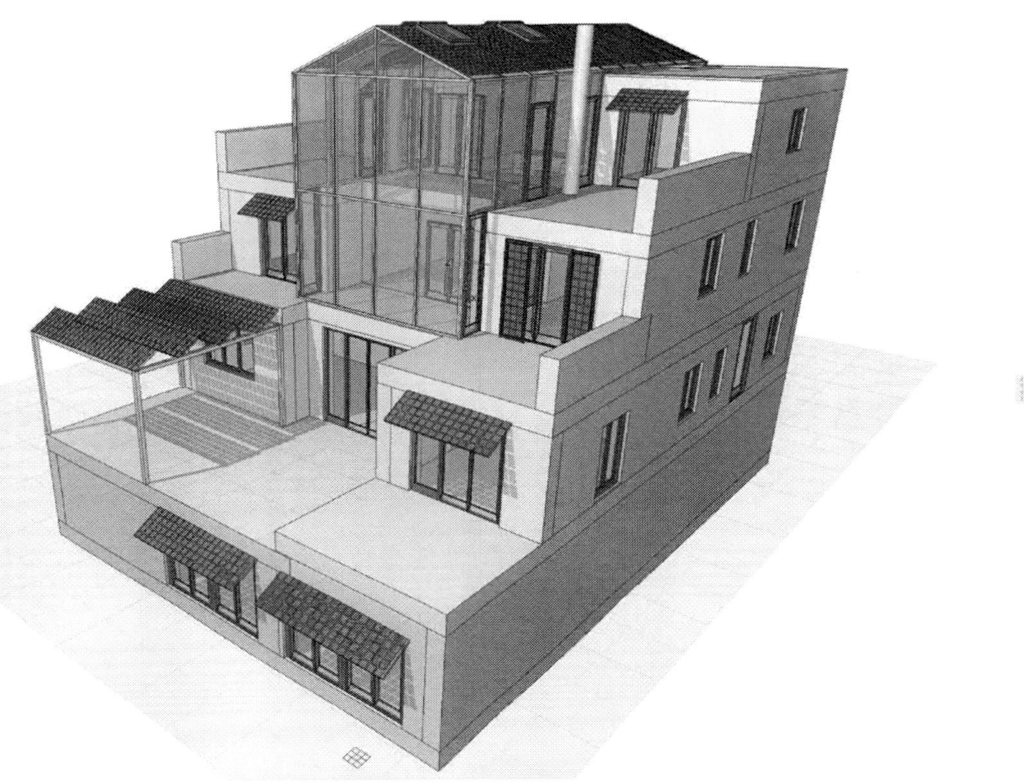

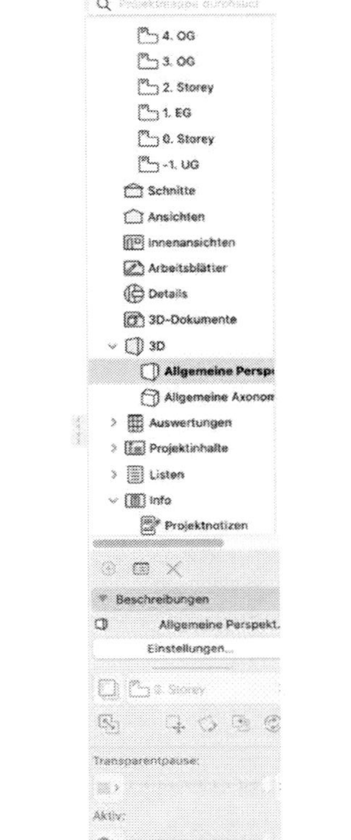

Source: Treberspurg Architekten / Astrid Schneider TU Wien

Perspective view in architect's BIM-planning program Archicad

020256-015

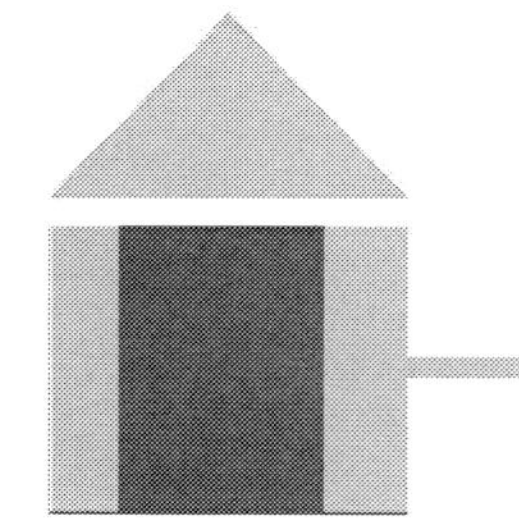

HOW CAN WE MAKE THE BIPV-PLANNING AND SIMULATION PROCESS WORK?

SONNENKRAFT

PV- BIPV-Product

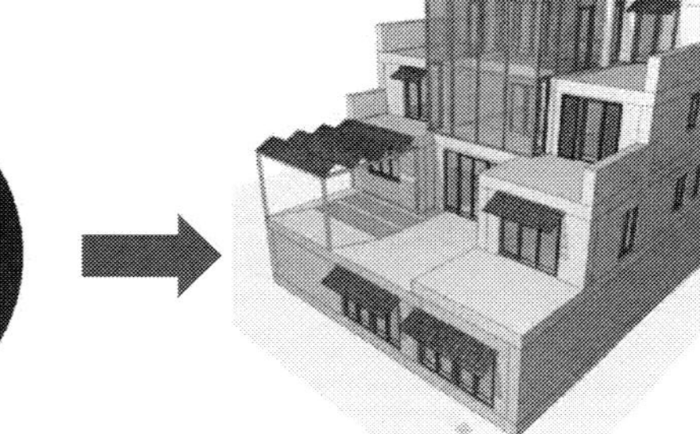

**PV- Database in BIM /
IFC – formate
optimally public**

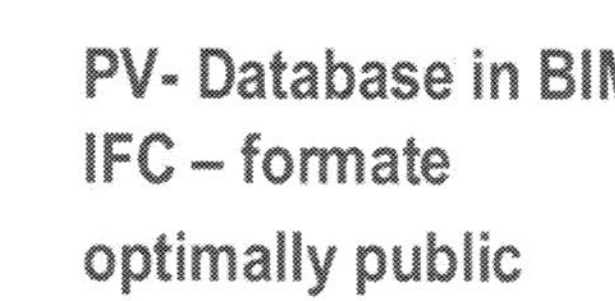

**BIM-project
design**

- visual

BIPV-system

- PV-system design and yield calculation
- daylighting
- energy
- structural
- environment

Source: Astrid Schneider, TU Wien

FFG
Forschung wirkt.

BIM4BIPV TU WIEN TECHNISCHE UNIVERSITÄT WIEN

BIM-BASED BIPV-SIMULATION

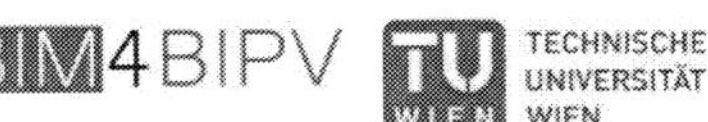

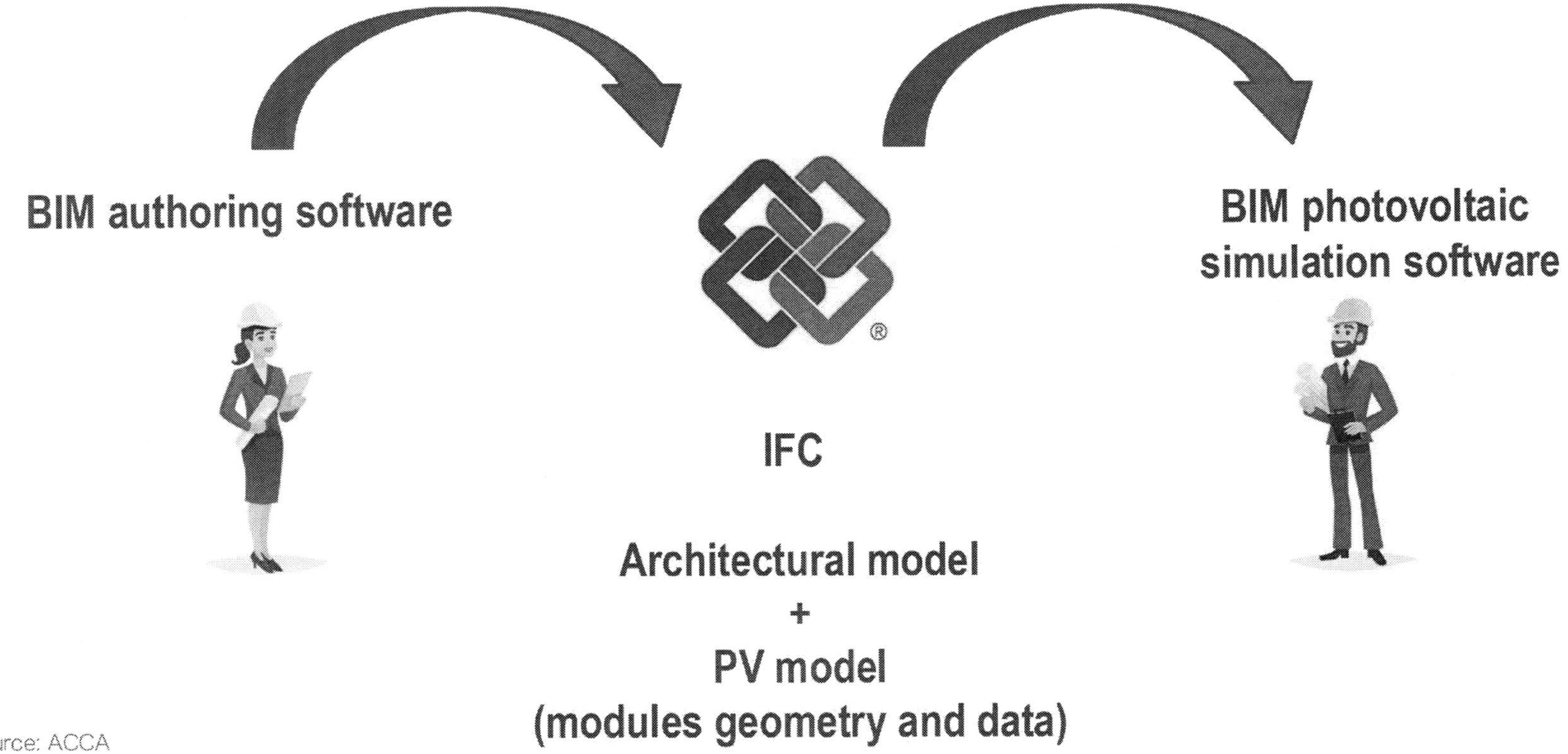

Source: ACCA

FFG

BIM4BIPV — TU WIEN — TECHNISCHE UNIVERSITÄT WIEN

BRINGING THE PV-MODULE INFORMATION INTO THE ARCHITECTURE MODEL

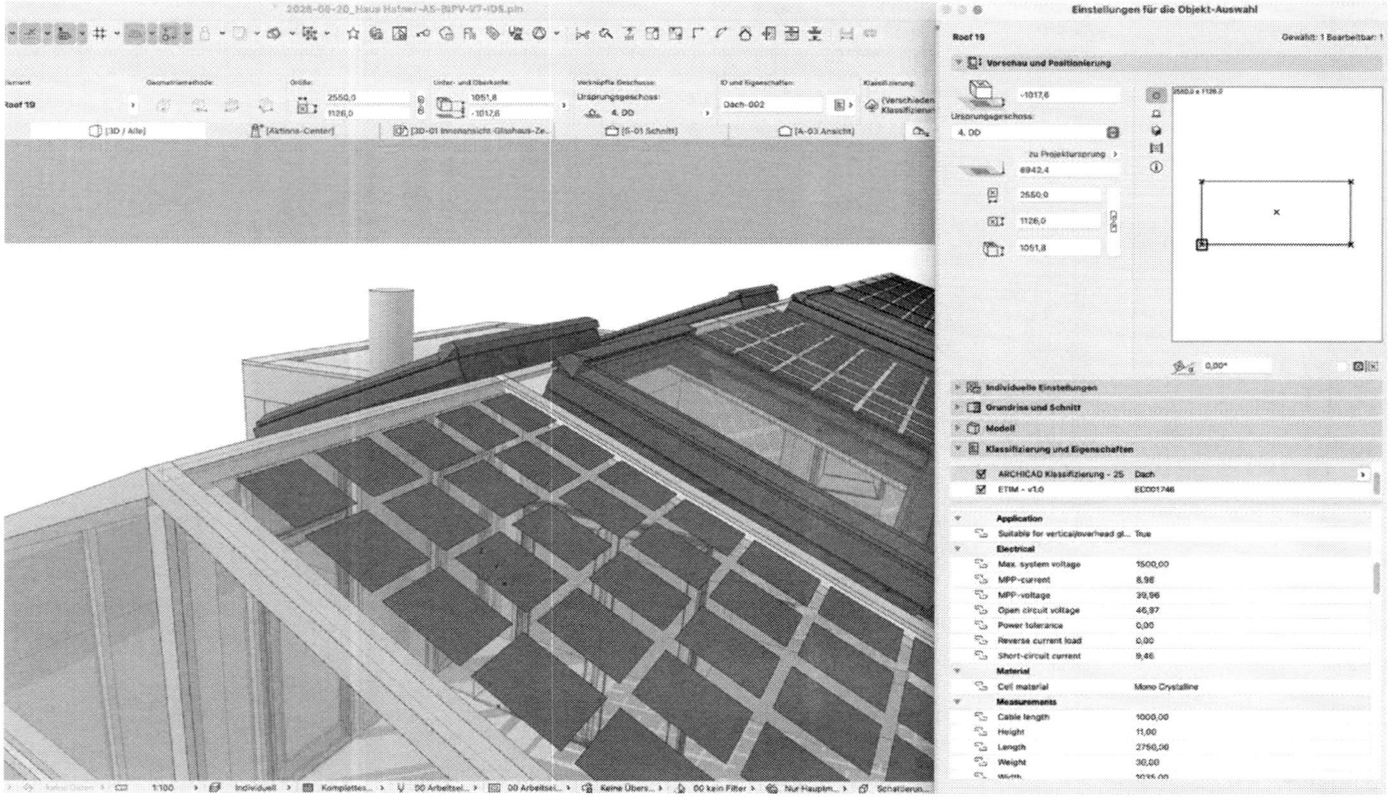

Source: Astrid Schneider, TU Wien

Archicad Haus Hafner Model with PV-property set filled in for the marked roof module

FFG

BIPV-PROPERTIES IN THE BIM-MODEL (ARCHICAD)

The „ETIM"-classification EC001746 „Photovoltaics module" was used.

Via an „IDS Information Delivery specification" the ETIM properties could be brought into the architects BIM authoring software Archicad.

The fields to be filled with the electric properties of the specific BIPV-modules were now pesent in the architectural BIM-software and filled with the relevant information for electric PV-simulation.

ETIM „Photovoltaics module"
https://identifier.buildingsmart.org/uri/etim/etim/9.0/class/EC001746

IDS4ALL converter
https://openbim-knowledgebase.org/en/ids4all-converter/

☑	ARCHICAD Klassifizierung - 25	Dach	⟩
☑	ETIM - v1.0	EC001746	
	Application		
	Suitable for vertical/overhead gl...	True	
	Electrical		
	Max. system voltage	1500,00	
	MPP-current	8,98	
	MPP-voltage	39,96	
	Open circuit voltage	46,97	
	Power tolerance	0,00	
	Reverse current load	0,00	
	Short-circuit current	9,46	
	Material		
	Cell material	Mono Crystalline	
	Measurements		
	Cable length	1000,00	
	Height	11,00	
	Length	2750,00	
	Weight	30,00	
	Width	1035,00	

Source: Astrid Schneider, TU Wien

Archicad BIM model with ETIM-classification and BIPV-element's electric property set (only partially shown, excerpt)

BIM VIEWER TO CONTROL THE EXPORTED VALUES IN THE MODEL

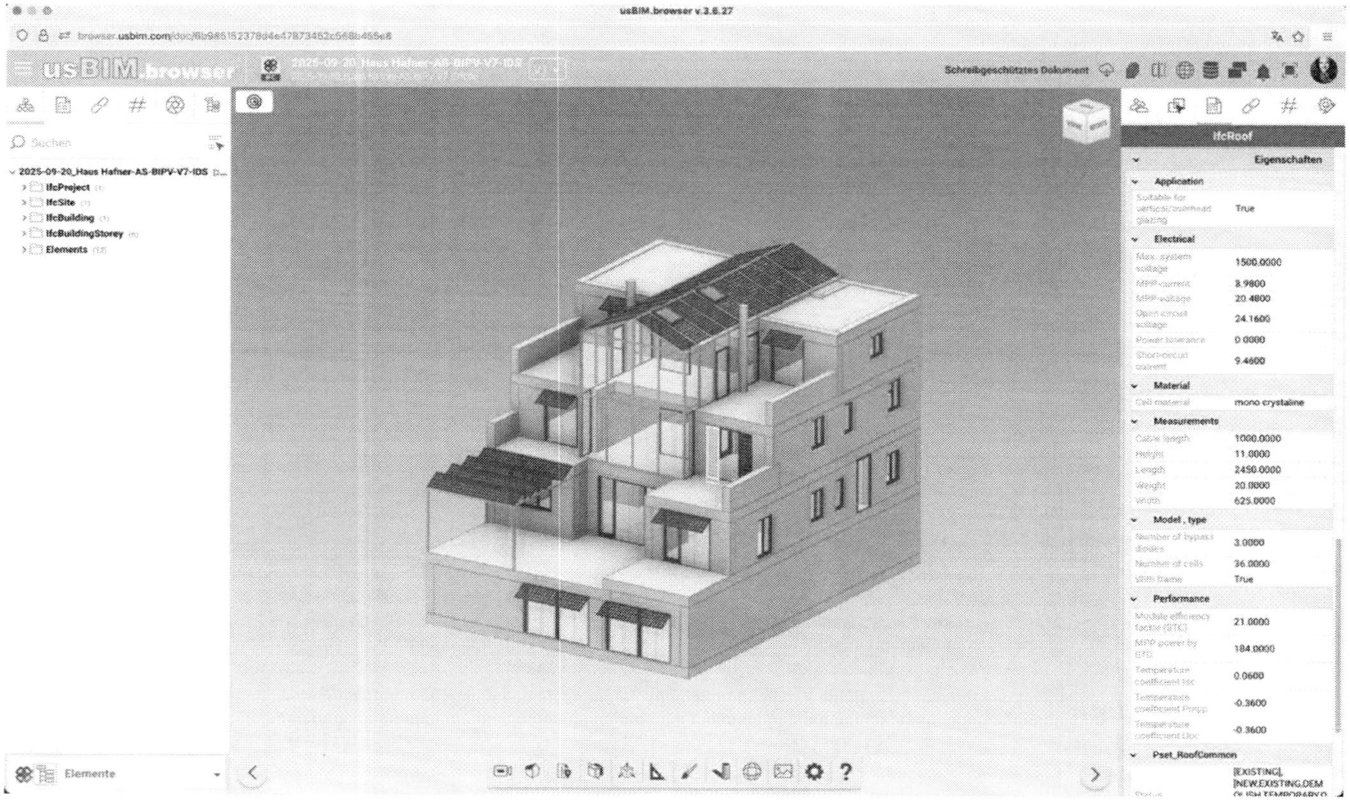

The Architectural BIM model is exported in the IFC-format. In the IFC-viewer by ACCA the BIPV data can be checked

https://www.accasoftware.com/de/bim-management-system

BIM VIEWER TO CONTROL THE EXPORTED VALUES IN THE MODEL

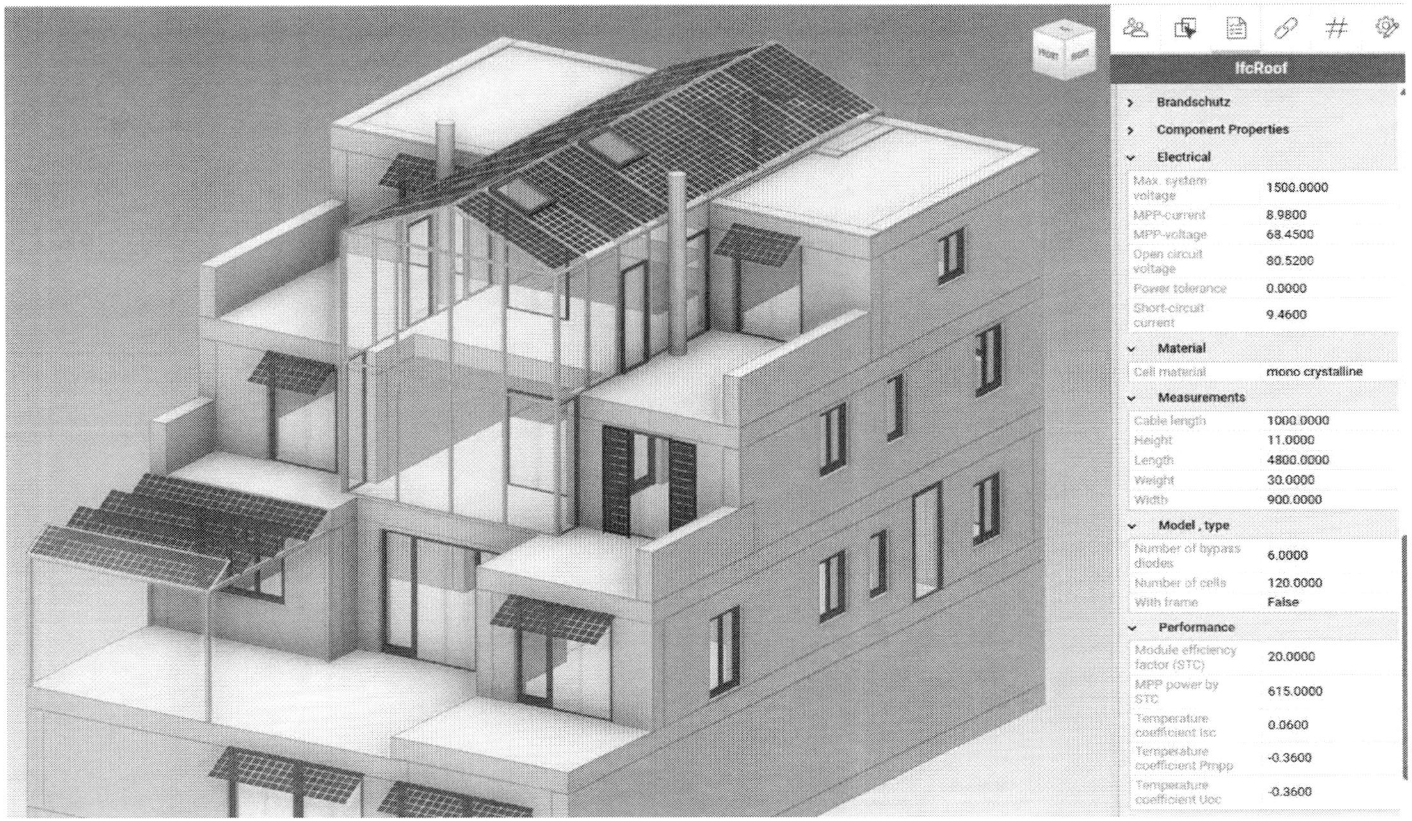

BIM4BIPV — TU WIEN — TECHNISCHE UNIVERSITÄT WIEN

The Architectural BIM model is exported in the IFC-format. In the IFC-viewer by ACCA the PV data can be displayed / seen

https://www.accasoftware.com/de/bim-management-system

FFG

TRANSFERE OF THE MODEL TO SOLARIUS PV SIMULATION SOFTWARE

BIM4BIPV

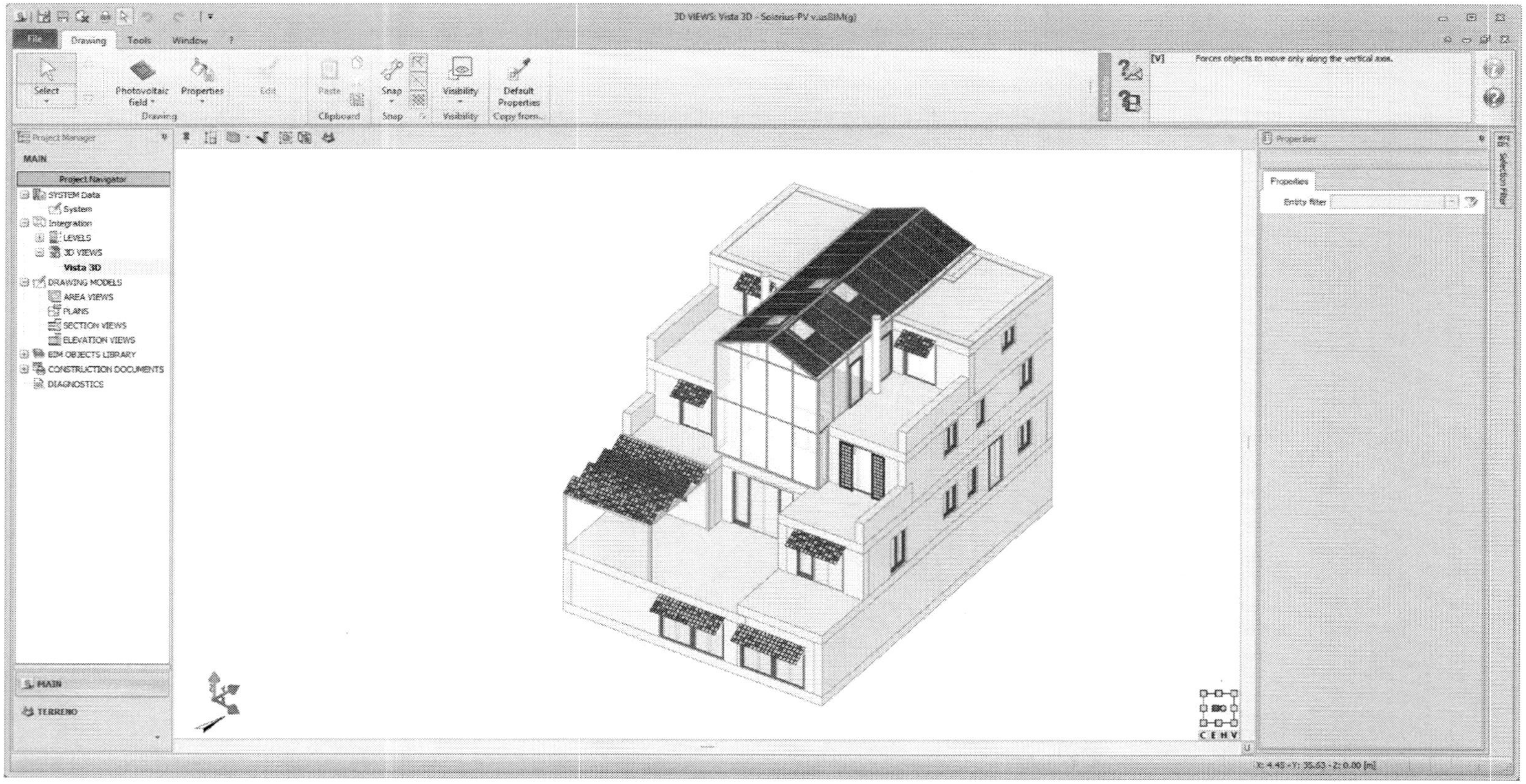

The IFC open BIM-model can be directly imported into the simulation software

Source: ACCA

TRANSFERE OF THE MODEL TO SOLARIUS PV SIMULATION SOFTWARE

BIM4BIPV

TU WIEN — TECHNISCHE UNIVERSITÄT WIEN

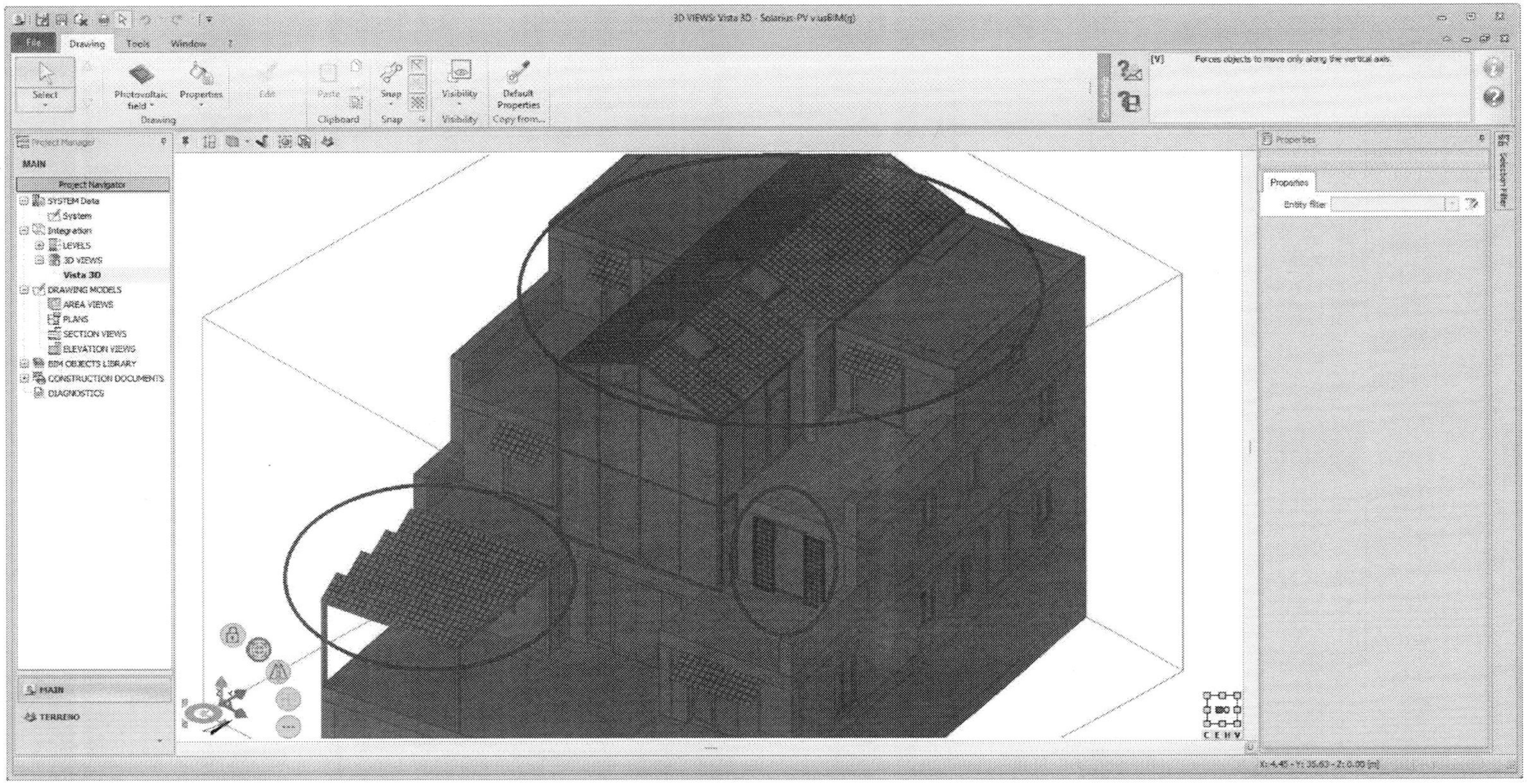

The PV-modules are recognized by the program

Source: ACCA

THE PV-MODULE VALUES CAN BE READ AND TAKEN OVER

BIM4BIPV · TU WIEN · TECHNISCHE UNIVERSITÄT WIEN

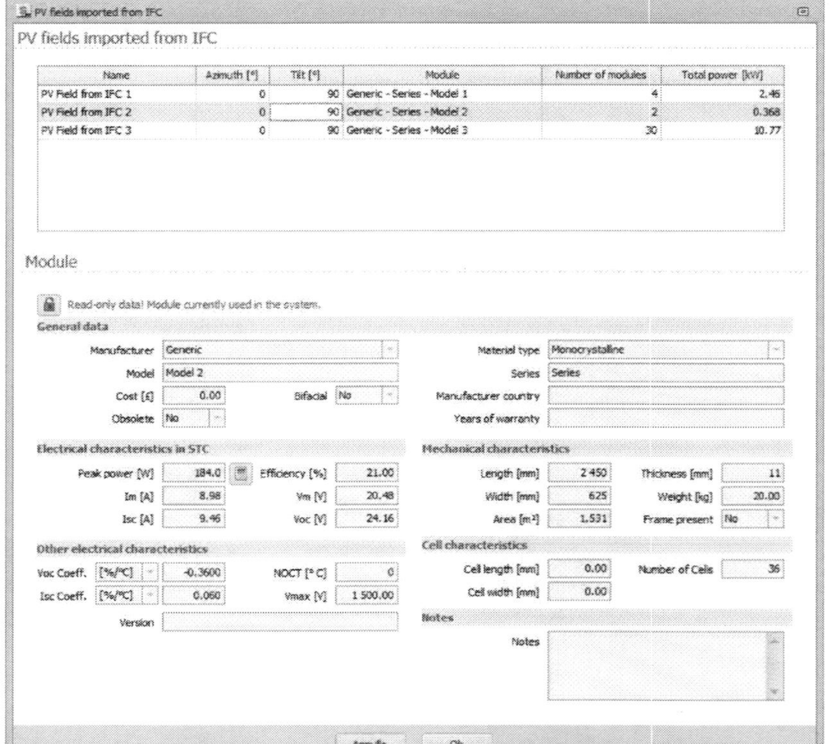

Name	Azimuth [°]	Tilt [°]	Module	Number of modules	Total power [kW]
PV Field from IFC 1	0	90	Generic - Series - Model 1	4	2.46
PV Field from IFC 2	0	90	Generic - Series - Model 2	2	0.368
PV Field from IFC 3	0	90	Generic - Series - Model 3	30	10.77

Module

Read-only data! Module currently used in the system.

General data

Manufacturer	Generic	Material type	Monocrystalline
Model	Model 1	Series	Series
Cost [£]	0.00	Bifacial No	Manufacturer country
Obsolete	No	Years of warranty	

Electrical characteristics in STC — **Mechanical characteristics**

Peak power [W]	615.0	Efficiency [%]	20.00	Length [mm]	4 800	Thickness [mm]	11
Im [A]	8.98	Vm [V]	68.45	Width [mm]	900	Weight [kg]	30.00
Isc [A]	9.46	Voc [V]	80.52	Area [m²]	4.320	Frame present	No

Other electrical characteristics — **Cell characteristics**

| Voc Coeff. [%/°C] | -0.3600 | NOCT [°C] | 0 | Cell length [mm] | 0.00 | Number of Cells | 120 |
| Isc Coeff. [%/°C] | 0.060 | Vmax [V] | 1 500.00 | Cell width [mm] | 0.00 | | |

Version — Notes

Annulla | Ok

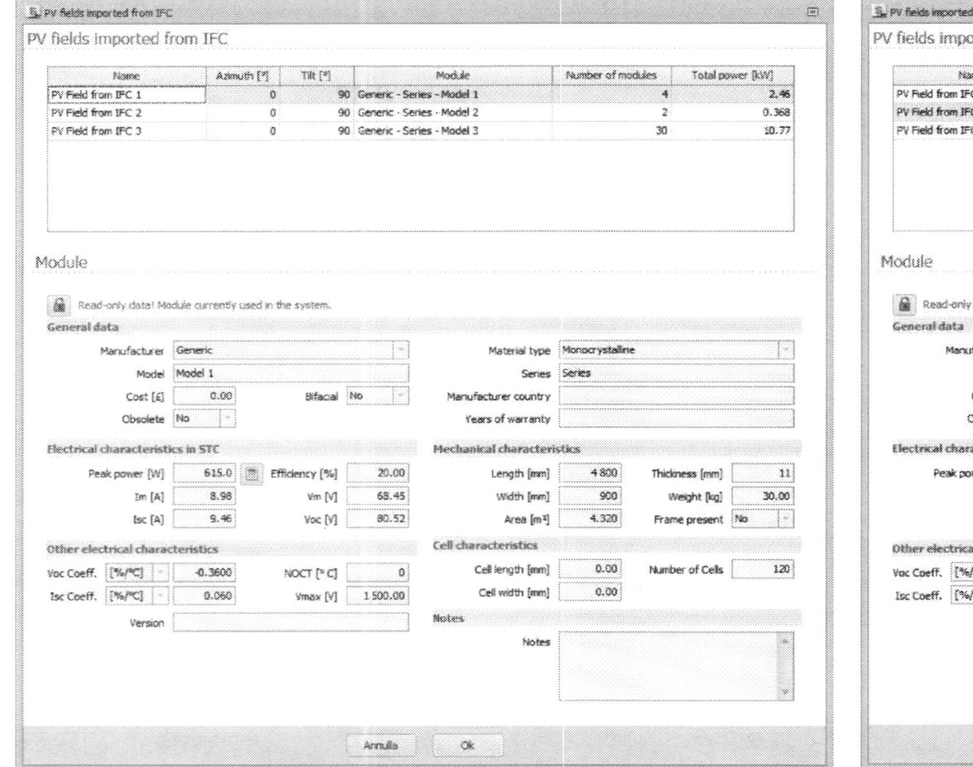

Name	Azimuth [°]	Tilt [°]	Module	Number of modules	Total power [kW]
PV Field from IFC 1	0	90	Generic - Series - Model 1	4	2.46
PV Field from IFC 2	0	90	Generic - Series - Model 2	2	0.368
PV Field from IFC 3	0	90	Generic - Series - Model 3	30	10.77

Module

Read-only data! Module currently used in the system.

General data

Manufacturer	Generic	Material type	Monocrystalline
Model	Model 2	Series	Series
Cost [£]	0.00	Bifacial No	Manufacturer country
Obsolete	No	Years of warranty	

Electrical characteristics in STC — **Mechanical characteristics**

Peak power [W]	184.0	Efficiency [%]	21.00	Length [mm]	2 450	Thickness [mm]	11
Im [A]	8.98	Vm [V]	20.48	Width [mm]	625	Weight [kg]	20.00
Isc [A]	9.46	Voc [V]	24.16	Area [m²]	1.531	Frame present	No

Other electrical characteristics — **Cell characteristics**

| Voc Coeff. [%/°C] | -0.3600 | NOCT [°C] | 0 | Cell length [mm] | 0.00 | Number of Cells | 36 |
| Isc Coeff. [%/°C] | 0.060 | Vmax [V] | 1 500.00 | Cell width [mm] | 0.00 | | |

Version — Notes

Annulla | Ok

The electric parameters / properties were successfully transported into the simulation program

Source: ACCA

FFG

THE PV SIMULATION PROGRAM CAN DO THE PV-SYSTEM SIMULATION

PV-Planning and simulation in "Solarius PV"

SOLAR YIELD CALCULATION

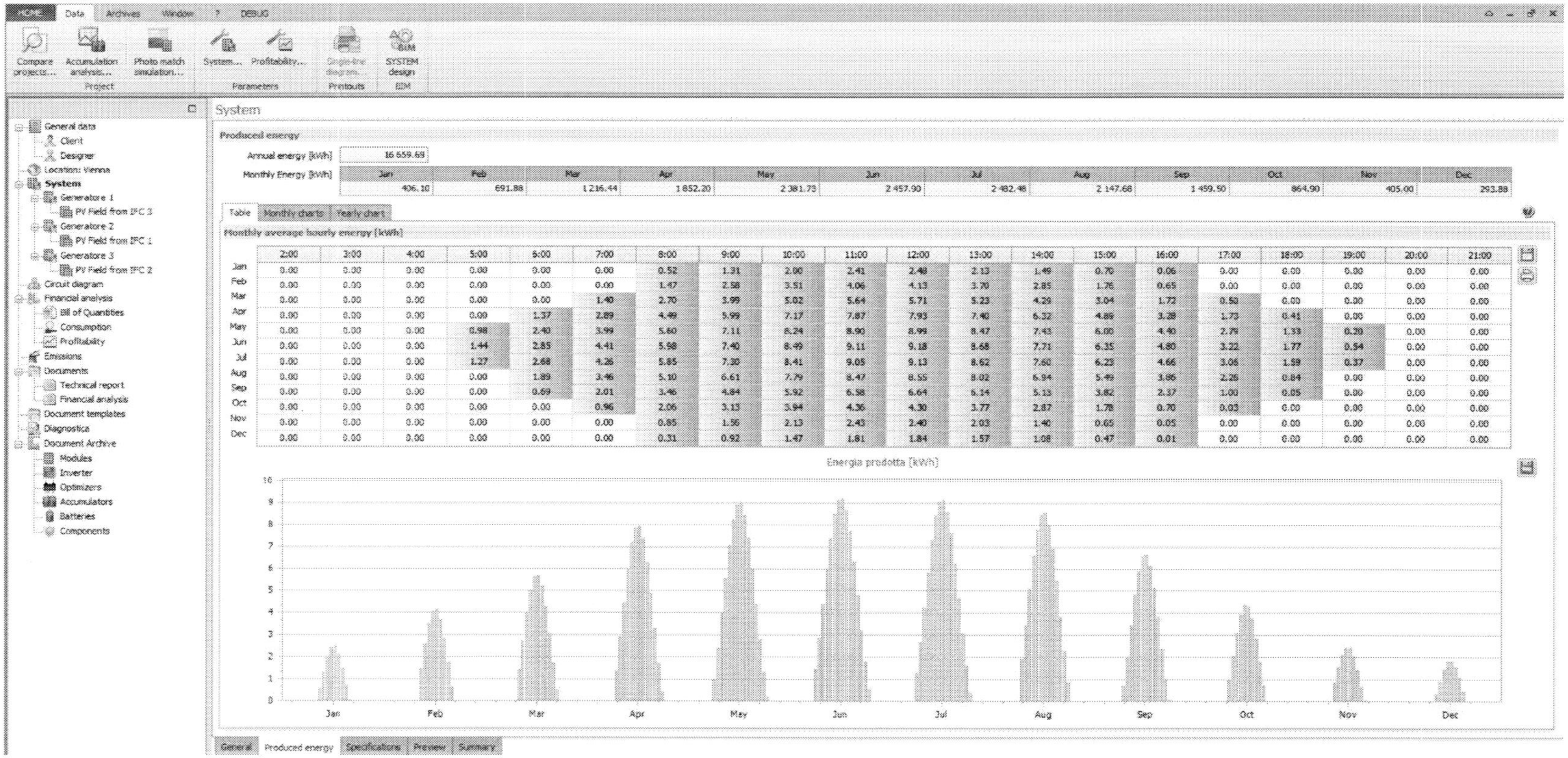

BIM4BIPV — TU WIEN — TECHNISCHE UNIVERSITÄT WIEN

Produced energy — Annual energy [kWh]: 16 659.69

Monthly Energy [kWh]:

Jan	Feb	Mar	Apr	May	Jun	Jul	Aug	Sep	Oct	Nov	Dec
406.10	691.88	1 216.44	1 852.20	2 381.73	2 457.90	2 482.48	2 147.68	1 459.50	864.90	405.00	293.88

Table | Monthly charts | Yearly chart

Monthly average hourly energy [kWh]

	2:00	3:00	4:00	5:00	6:00	7:00	8:00	9:00	10:00	11:00	12:00	13:00	14:00	15:00	16:00	17:00	18:00	19:00	20:00	21:00
Jan	0.00	0.00	0.00	0.00	0.00	0.00	0.52	1.31	2.00	2.41	2.48	2.13	1.49	0.70	0.06	0.00	0.00	0.00	0.00	0.00
Feb	0.00	0.00	0.00	0.00	0.00	0.00	1.47	2.58	3.51	4.06	4.13	3.70	2.85	1.76	0.65	0.00	0.00	0.00	0.00	0.00
Mar	0.00	0.00	0.00	0.00	0.00	1.40	2.70	3.99	5.02	5.64	5.71	5.23	4.29	3.04	1.72	0.58	0.00	0.00	0.00	0.00
Apr	0.00	0.00	0.00	0.00	1.37	2.89	4.49	5.99	7.17	7.87	7.93	7.40	6.32	4.89	3.28	1.73	0.41	0.00	0.00	0.00
May	0.00	0.00	0.00	0.98	2.40	3.99	5.60	7.11	8.24	8.90	8.99	8.47	7.43	6.00	4.40	2.79	1.33	0.20	0.00	0.00
Jun	0.00	0.00	0.00	1.44	2.85	4.41	5.98	7.40	8.49	9.11	9.18	8.68	7.71	6.35	4.80	3.22	1.77	0.54	0.00	0.00
Jul	0.00	0.00	0.00	1.27	2.68	4.26	5.85	7.30	8.41	9.05	9.13	8.62	7.60	6.23	4.66	3.06	1.59	0.37	0.00	0.00
Aug	0.00	0.00	0.00	0.00	1.89	3.46	5.10	6.61	7.79	8.47	8.55	8.02	6.94	5.49	3.86	2.25	0.84	0.00	0.00	0.00
Sep	0.00	0.00	0.00	0.00	0.69	2.01	3.46	4.84	5.92	6.58	6.64	6.14	5.13	3.82	2.37	1.00	0.05	0.00	0.00	0.00
Oct	0.00	0.00	0.00	0.00	0.00	0.96	2.06	3.13	3.94	4.36	4.30	3.77	2.87	1.78	0.70	0.03	0.00	0.00	0.00	0.00
Nov	0.00	0.00	0.00	0.00	0.00	0.00	0.85	1.56	2.13	2.43	2.40	2.03	1.40	0.65	0.05	0.00	0.00	0.00	0.00	0.00
Dec	0.00	0.00	0.00	0.00	0.00	0.00	0.31	0.92	1.47	1.81	1.84	1.57	1.08	0.47	0.01	0.00	0.00	0.00	0.00	0.00

The PV-simulation can be concluded

Source: simulation with Solarius PV by ACCA

BIM4BIPV
TU WIEN — TECHNISCHE UNIVERSITÄT WIEN

GOAL: DIGITAL PV-MODULES TO BE PRECISELY PLACED IN BIM-CAD-SOFTWARE

PV-Producer
is responsible to provide use case specific relevant product data

PV- / BIPV-Data
in BIM / IFC-format

Architect
plans building / construction and puts PV- / BIPV-BIM-elements into CAD / BIM project design
(generic, product specific, custom sized)

Engineer
uses detailled PV- / BIPV- BIM project design to plan and simulate PV / BIPV-system

for PV / BIPV
Data-Scheme

NEU
SONNENKRAFT

PV- BIPV-Product

Excel calculation
BIPV-module values

ETIM
+ IDS

PV- Database in BIM / IFC – formate optimally public

BIM-project design
visual

Integration of BIPV- values into architectural BIM-model

IFC- export

BIPV-system
PV-system design and yield calculation
daylighting
energy
structural
environment

FFG

020256-027

BIM-BASED BIPV-SIMULATION WORKFLOW

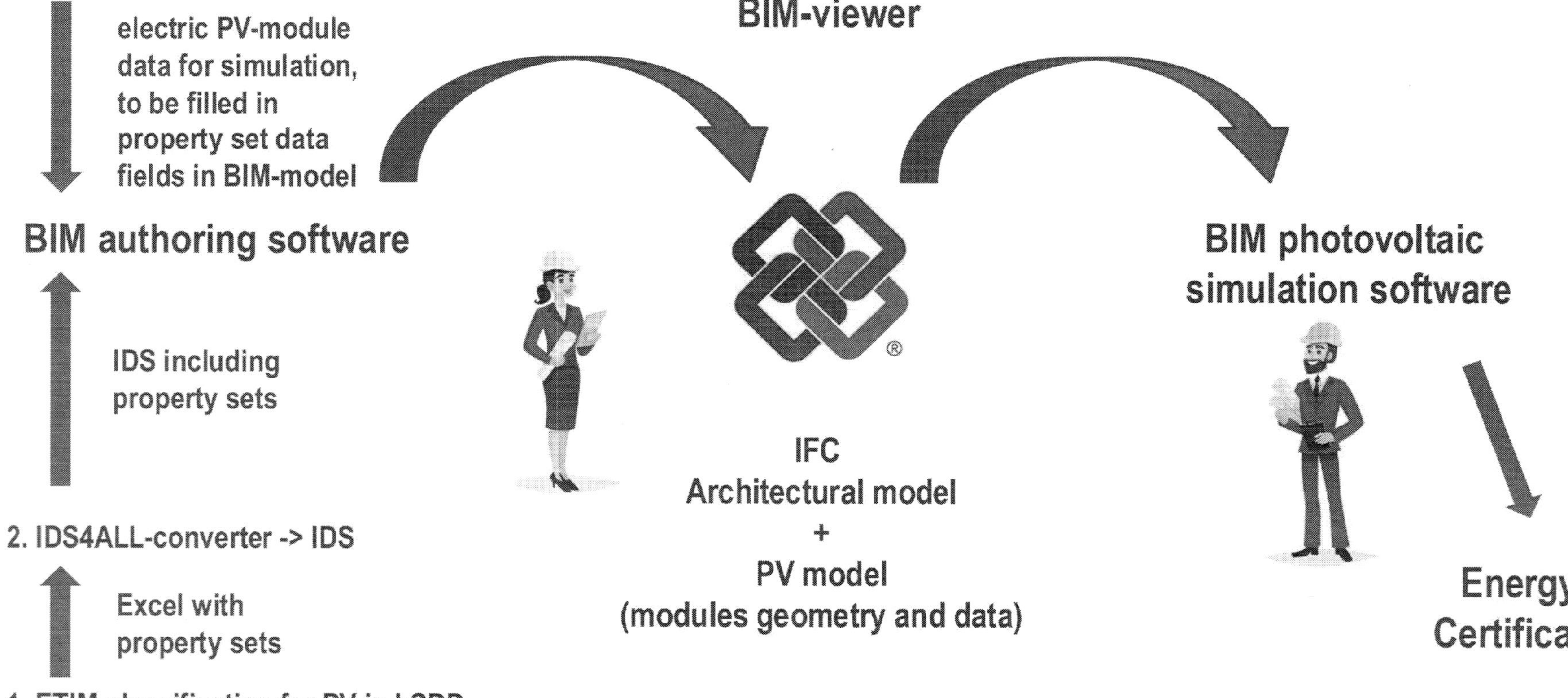

Source: ACCA – Astrid Schneider TU Wien

HAUS HAFNER ATRIUM AS A MULTI-DISCIPLINARY PLANNING TASK

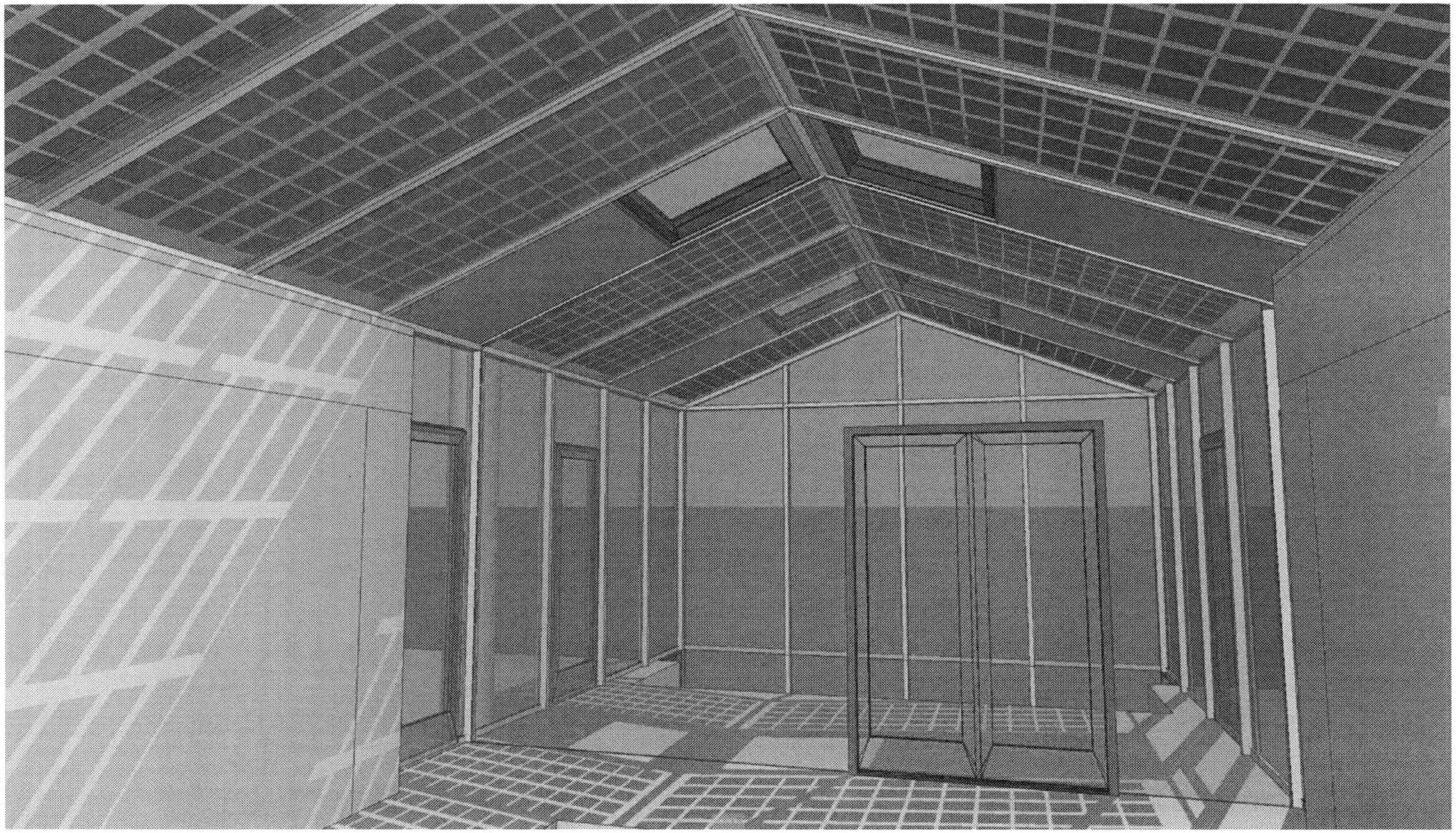

Source: Treberspurg Architekten / Astrid Schneider TU Wien

Interior view atrium

DAYLIGHT SIMULATION - DAYLIGHT FACTOR

- **Sky model CIE Overcast sky (no sun)**
  $L_{Zenith} : L_{Horizon} = 3{:}1$

$$TQ[\%] = \frac{E_{innen}}{E_{außen}} * 100$$

- **Average DF range offices:**
  - **min. 2% at work places (accord. to regulations)**
  - **not too high to avoid daylight glare**

- **Average DF range living area:**
  - **No specific noramative regulations**
  - **Less strict in terms of glare**
  - **Range of 2,5 – 8% is reasonable**
  - **Too high values >10% tend to overheating**

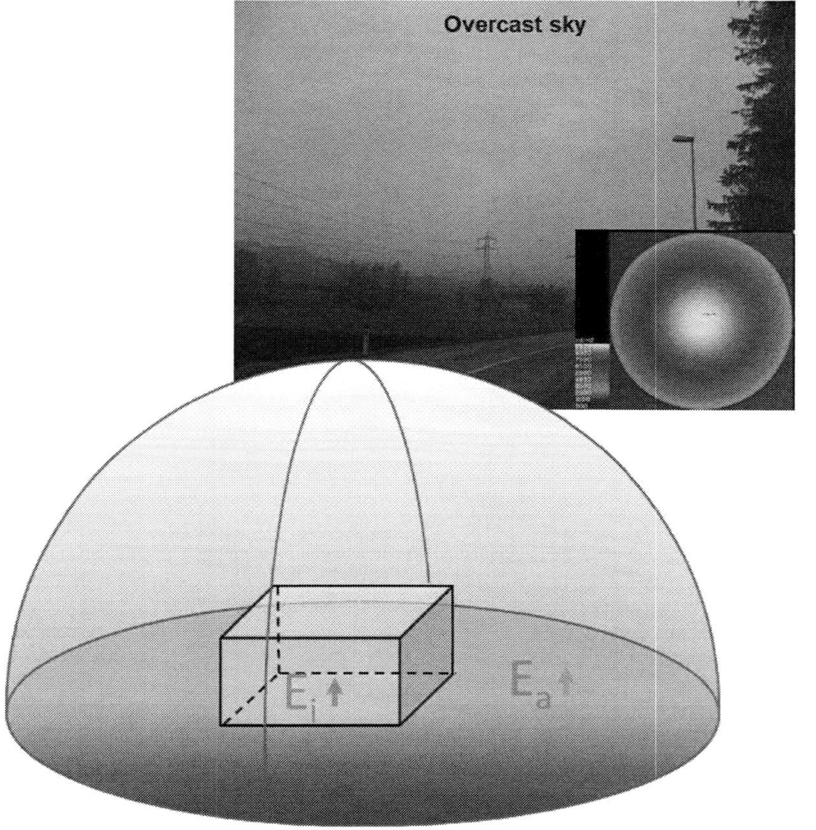

Source: Bartenbach

020256-030

DAYLIGHT SIMULATION OF HAUS HAFNER - DAYLIGHT FACTOR – FIRST FLOOR

VARIANTS

Only Glazing (no PV)

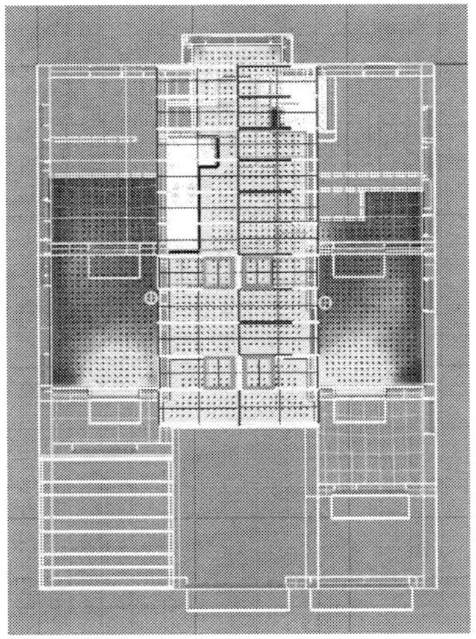

PV on canopy (non transp.)
PV on Roof (semitransp.)

PV on canopy (non transp.)
PV on Roof + Side windows
(semitransp.)

PV on canopy (non transp.)
PV Roof (full) + Side windows
(semitransp.)

DAYLIGHT DISTRIBUTION

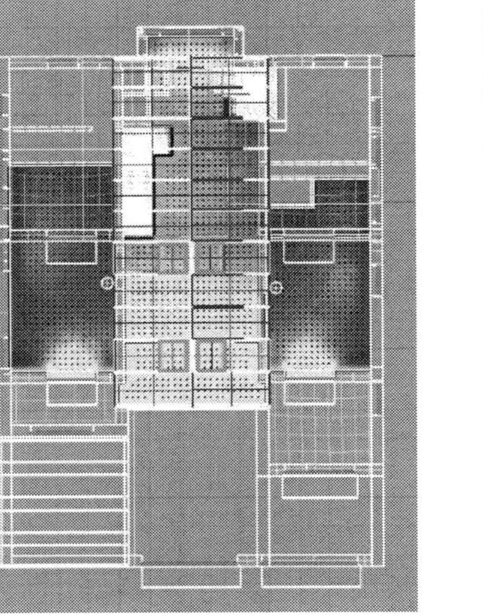

EVALUATION

Average Daylight Factor: 11.2 %

- Exceeding values in Daylight availability
- → proper shading, especially of the glazed central part is needed.

Source: Bartenbach

Average Daylight Factor: 6.2 %

- Daylight factor in acceptable range, but on the higher end
- Spatial exceedings only in the central front part (which might be acceptable at the terrace or as winter garden)

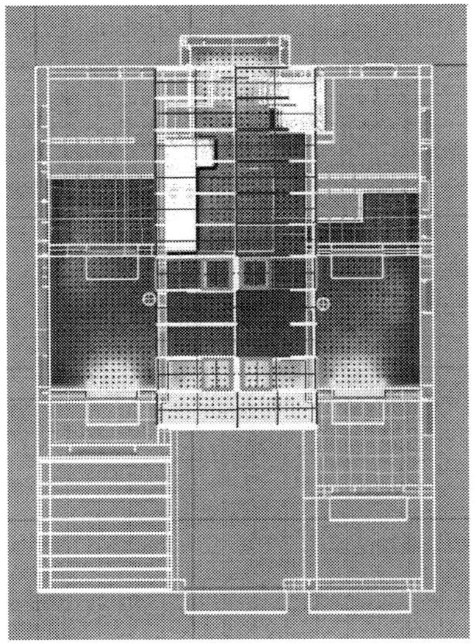

Average Daylight Factor: 2,6 %

- Daylight factor in in optimal range (between 2% and 5% for living areas)

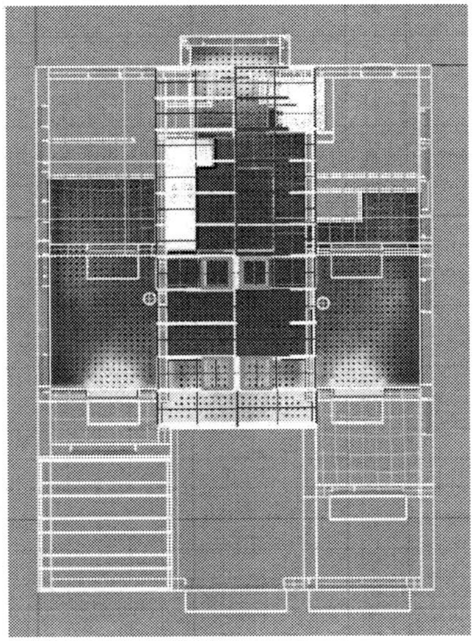

Average Daylight Factor: 2,2 %

- Daylight availability on the lower end – especially the central part tends to receive too less daylight

BIM4BIPV

020256-031

CLIMATE BASED DAYLIGHT CALCULATION

Useful Daylight Illuminance (UDI)

- is a modification of daylight autonomy
- This criterion divides the hourly data into three evaluation categories
  - 0-100lx (underlighting)
  - 100 - 2000lx (pleasant lighting conditions)
  - >2000lx (overlighting)
- In the range of 100-2000lx, daylight input is rated as useful

Annual Sunlight Exposure (ASE)

- refers to the percentage of space that receives too much direct sunlight (1000 Lux or more for at least 250 occupied hours per year), which can cause glare or increased cooling loads

Source: Bartenbach

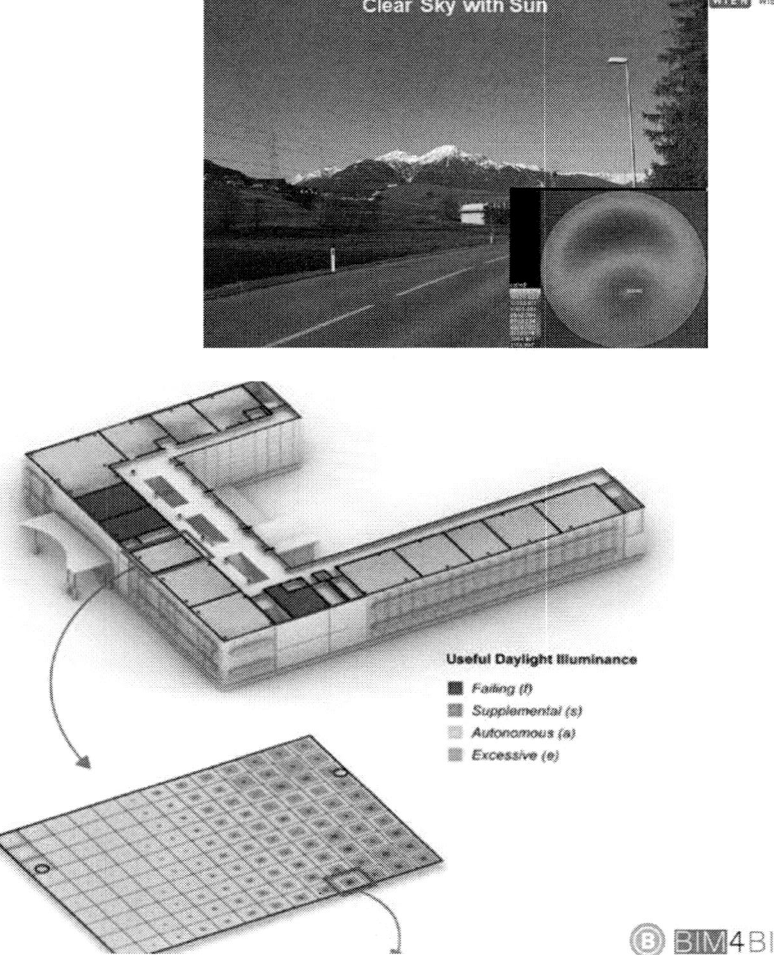

HAUS HAFNER CLIMATE BASED DAYLIGHT CALCULATION (ANNUAL) FIRST FLOOR

VARIANTS

| Only Glazing (no PV) | PV on canopy (non transp.)
PV on Roof (semitransp.) | PV on canopy (non transp.)
PV on Roof + Side windows
(semitransp.) | PV on canopy (non transp.)
PV Roof (full) + Side windows (semitransp.) |

DAYLIGHT DISTRIBUTION

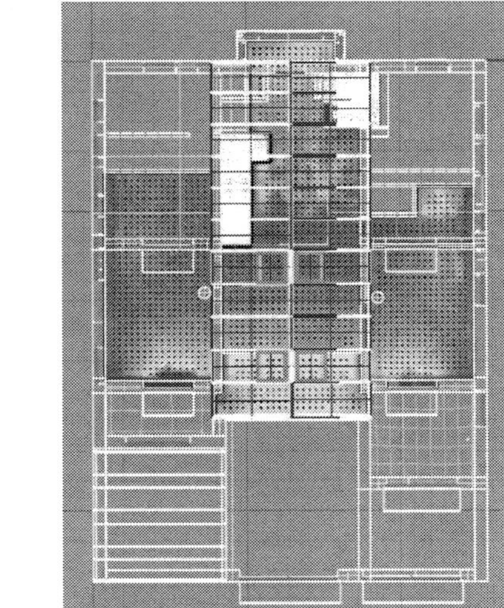

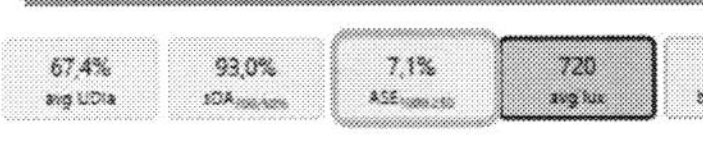

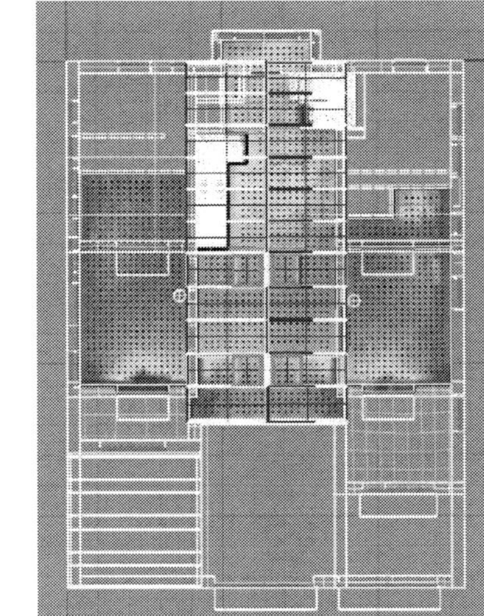

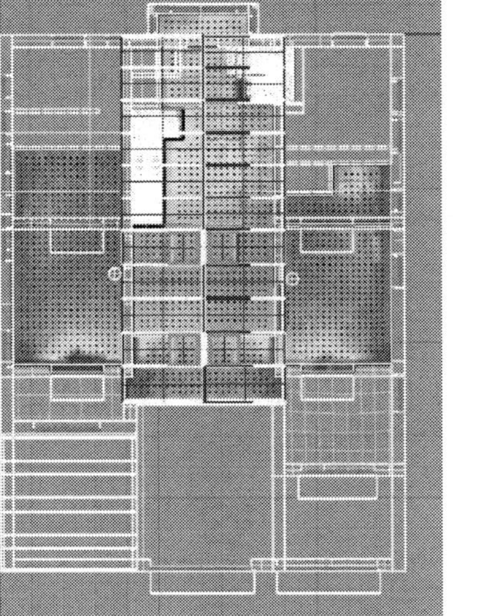

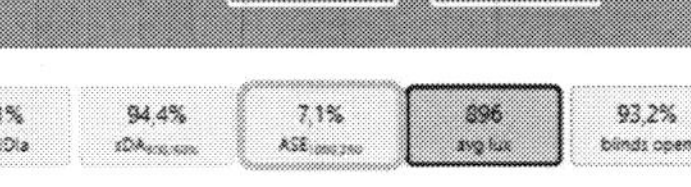

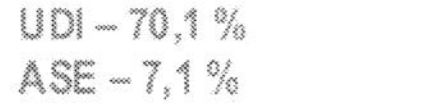

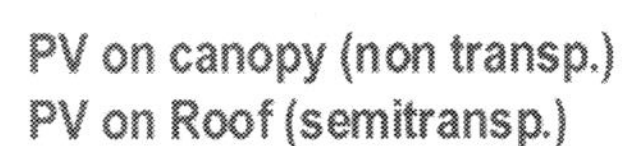

EVALUATION

UDI – 66,4 %
ASE – 46,9 %

Glare and overheating

Source: Bartenbach

UDI – 66,8 %
ASE – 32,2 %

improvements by semtransparent
BIPV roof

UDI – 70,1 %
ASE – 7,1 %

* Significant improvement by semitransparent PV on roof and side windows of the attic
* Highest levels on Useful Daylight illuminance UDI → 70%

UDI – 67,4 %
ASE – 7,1 %

**too much shading
less daylight**

BIM4BIPV

GEOMETRY IMPORT FOR DAYLIGHT SIMULATION

Daylight simulations are performed using Climate Studio (https://climatestudiodocs.com/index.html)

ClimateStudio is a plugin for the Rhinoceros (Rhino) 3d modeling software

Data Path:

- The IFC-file was directly imported into Rhino, using ggIFC - an „Add-on application" in Rhino
- After manual modifcations on the imported geometry in Rhino, the model was able to be used by Climate Studio

General problem:

- Daylight simulation tools only consider geometry from IFC-files

- Daylight specific parameters (surface reflection values, visual transparancy values,…) have to be set manually

Source: Bartenbach

BIM4BIPV

ENERGY CERTIFICATE CALCULATION OF BIPV-APPLICATIONS

Archiphysik can read in the BIM-model and evaluate the values and geometry:

BIPV-glazing-element inputs taken from model:

- shading geometry in front of the window or glazed area
- G-value
- U-value
  - ➢ calculation of solar radiation entering the space
- ➢ thermal comfort fulfillment
- ➢ heating and cooling demand calculation in kwh/m^2

PV-Module inputs taken from model:

- Wp – Power
- location, orientation
  - ➢ solar power produced
- ➢ reduction of primary fossil energy consumed
- ➢ fulfillment of required installation capacity by construction laws

Source: Astrid Schneider, TU Wien

BIM4BIPV

ArchiPHYSIK

PHOTOVOLTAICS AND ENERGY PERFORMANCE CERTIFICATE

- **Photovoltaic electricity in energy balance**
  - Electricity generated by PV can be included in the energy balance for the Energy Performance Certificate
  - Depending on legal framework, PV electricity can fully or partially replace other energy carriers
  - The amount of creditable PV electricity is legally defined
  - Surplus PV electricity is shown in the EPC as PV export

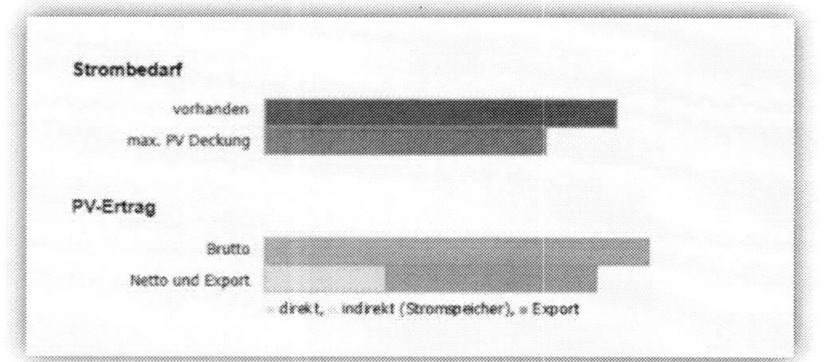

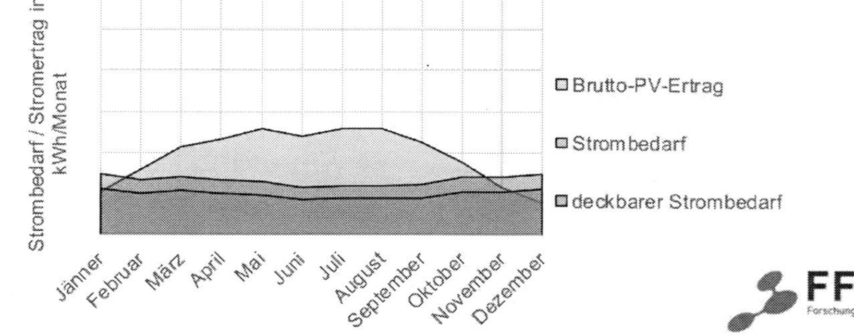

Source: A-NULL Development with Archiphysik

FFG Forschung wirkt.

020256-036

BIM4BIPV

≋ ArchiPHYSIK

OVERHEATING FROM GLAZING

- **Glazing and summer overheating**
  - Large glazed areas may cause overheating under sunlight.
  - Winter: Indoor temperatures can be lowered by controlled ventilation.
  - Summer: Only limited reduction possible through night ventilation.
  - Approach: Reduce solar gains through glazing.
  - Haus Hafner: PV shutters and BIPV glazing in the conservatory reduce solar input → less overheating

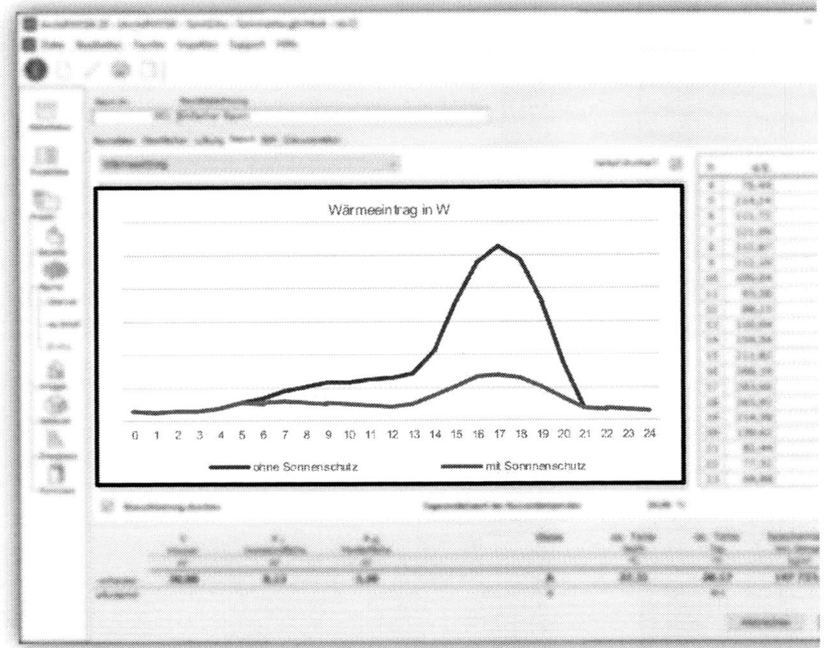

FFG
Forschung wirkt.

Source: A-NULL Development with Archiphysik

PROBLEMS TO BE SOLVED

- compatability problems
- multiple model transferes
- missing data after model transfer
- correct transfere of: location, direction, axis
- material transfere / display of materials

- the IFC standard is not yet fully adopted and implemented by all actors

GOALS TO BE ACHIEVED

- **PV and BIPV to be integrated in digital planning flows easily**
- **optimized near shade and bifaciality simulation**
  - **as well on module celle and string level**
- **inclusion of multidisciplinary data of PV / BIPV into construction models**
- **ability for multidsiciplinary simulation such as**
  - **daylighting**
  - **shade and heat effects**
  - **energy planning**
  - **green construction**
- **as well important for agri-PV, infrastructure, OEM of large solar parks …**

Source: TU Wien / A-NULL Development

BUILDING INFORMATION MODELLING (BIM)

IEA-Task 15 Photovoltaic Power systems Program C1:

- it is important to standardize the property and property set names to enable interoperability across PV / BIPV and construction / infrastructure industry
- International collaboration in Task 15

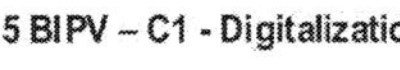

THANKS!

Astrid Schneider, TU Wien - astrid.schneider@tuwien.ac.at - astrid@astrid-schneider.de

Coauthors:

- Dr. Karin Stieldorf, TU Wien, Institute of Architecture and Design, Karlsplatz 13, 1040 Wien, Austria, karin.stieldorf@tuwien.ac.at
- Dr. Christian Schranz and Dr. Harald Urban, TU Wien, Research Unit for Digital Planning Process, christian.schranz@tuwien.ac.at;
- Alfred Waschl, buildingSMART, alfred.waschl@buildingsmart.co.at;
- Markus Feichtner, Sonnenkraft GmbH, Markus.Feichtner@sonnenkraft.com
- Fedele Rende and Andrea Aiello ACCA Software, fedele.rende@almasoft.it;
- Martin Hauer, Bartenbach GmbH, Martin.Hauer@bartenbach.com;
- Kurt Battisti, Markus Dörn and Jacqueline Scherret, A-Null Development GmbH, kurt.battisti@archiphysik.com;
- Martin und Christoph Treberspurg, Treberspurg und Partner Architekten, christoph.treberspurg@treberspurg.at

We thank FFG – Austrian funding agency for their support

Project partners BIM4BIPV:

Collaboration with Task 15 BIPV – C1 - Digitalization

 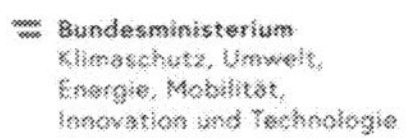   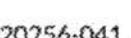

FABRICATION OF A NOVEL SEMI-TRANSLUCENT BIPV MODULE PROVIDING HIGH POWER DENSITY AND ACTIVE DAYLIGHT MANAGEMENT

Almudena Garcia-Sanchez[1], Guido Vallerotto[1], Jaime J. Hernández[2], Alejandro García-Cañas[2], Steve Askins[1], Ignacio Antón[1], Isabel Rodríguez[2] and César Domínguez[1]

[1] Instituto de Energía Solar, Universidad Politécnica de Madrid (UPM), Madrid (Spain)
[2] Madrid Institute for Advanced Studies in Nanoscience (IMDEA Nanoscience), Madrid (Spain)

ABSTRACT: Building-integrated photovoltaics (BIPV) provides a sustainable method for solar energy generation without requiring additional productive land. However, conventional semi-transparent modules often suffer from low efficiency and visual discomfort. This work presents a novel BIPV solution using micro-concentrator photovoltaics (micro-CPV) with integrated solar tracking to improve both energy output and daylight quality. The system features a glass front layer embedded with linear asymmetric Fresnel lenses and a transparent backplane with solar cell strips. It blocks direct sunlight, converting it into electricity, while allowing diffuse light to pass through, producing soft, glare-free interior lighting. A micro-tracking mechanism adjusts the solar cells to follow the sun's path, enhancing light capture throughout the day. Designed for translucent applications such as skylights or non-view façades, the module also reduces heat gain indoors. Lens arrays of 5 lenses of 2.25 × 10 cm fabricated by roll-to-plate UV imprinting on solar glass show a peak optical efficiency of 80%, remaining above 70% up to a 60° angle of incidence. Outdoor tests confirm improved visual comfort, with a reduction in an order of magnitude in the peak illuminance point, an average of 1500 lx, and a peak-to-average ratio lowered by 7 points, demonstrating the module's potential for both energy and daylighting management.

Keywords: Concentrator photovoltaics, Building-integrated photovoltaics, Micro-concentrator optics

1 INTRODUCTION

The cumulative PV capacity in Europe would need to reach 455–605 GW to meet the ambitious target of the European Green Deal target of a 55% net reduction in greenhouse gas emissions by 2030 [1]. Building-integrated photovoltaics (BIPV) is especially interesting because it does capture productive land and contributes to nearly zero-energy buildings (NZEBs) and decarbonization of cities. It is often designed to achieve additional architectural functions, such as thermal insulation or daylighting. However, conventional semi-transparent BIPV modules employ spaced solar cells that allow direct light to enter the building, thus reducing active area (and power density) and producing stark light-shadow contrasts that create visual discomfort: an obstacle to massive adoption [2].

2 AIM AND APPROACH

To solve the limitations of conventional building-integrated photovoltaics (BIPV), we propose a smart, translucent BIPV module capable of achieving high-efficiency electricity generation while simultaneously providing uniform indoor illuminance and minimizing glare. This system is based on micro-concentrator photovoltaics (micro-CPV) and incorporates a front glazing composed of a matrix of linear micro-concentrator optics. These optics focus direct sunlight onto a transparent backplane equipped with an array of narrow-strip crystalline silicon (c-Si) solar cells. In contrast, diffuse light is transmitted through the module into the interior of the building, contributing to comfortable and natural daylighting (see Figure 1).The module is designed to function as a semi-translucent architectural element

suitable for integration into skylights, curtain walls, canopies, or solar shading systems.

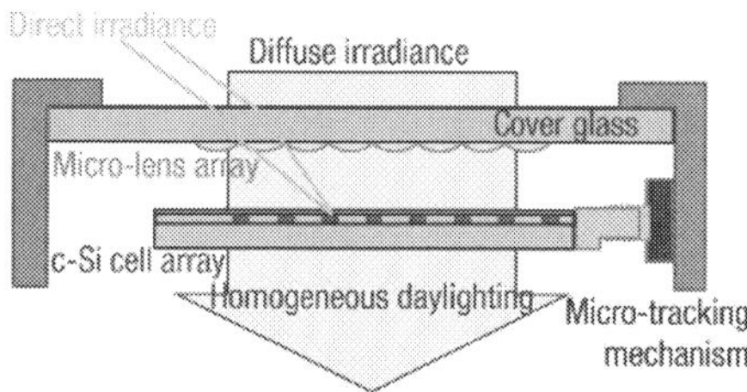

Figure 1: Schematic of the structure and working principle of the semi-transparent smart BIPV module. Direct light is concentrated to produce electricity, while diffused light is transmitted for daylighting. A planar micro-tracking mechanism shifts the backplane with the changing solar position.

3 OPTICAL DESIGN

In the initial phase of the project, the optical design of the module was defined. We implemented ultra-thin linear Fresnel lenses with a facet height of 40 microns, selected to ensure compatibility with low-cost roll-to-plate fabrication using UV-curable resin on glass substrates. The 2D asymmetric lens profile was developed using Fermat's principle, ensuring that rays with a nominal angle of incidence (AOI_T) converge at a common focal point at the lens edge as it is shown in Figure 2. A large draft angle was incorporated to maintain high optical efficiency and prevent self-shading.

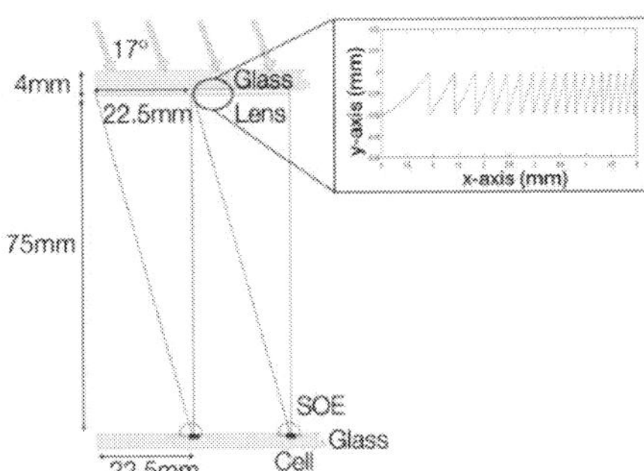

Figure 2: Schematic of the optical design at nominal AOI, together with a close-up of the asymmetric Fresnel lens profile.

The lens geometry was optimized for a non-normal angle of incidence, specifically $AOI_T = 17°$, which corresponds to the solar elevation at the summer solstice in Madrid. This optimization was chosen to maximize optical efficiency and enhance solar protection during periods of high solar heat gain. To maintain a compact form factor consistent with typical building components, the maximum focal length was set to 7.5 cm, resulting in an overall module thickness of approximately 10 cm.

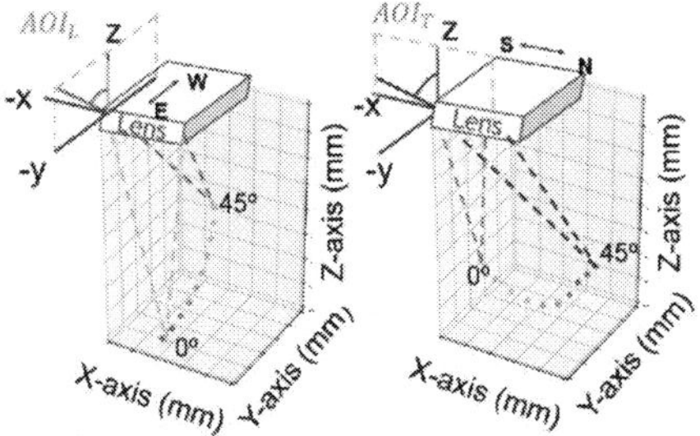

Figure 3: Focus position (Petzval curve) for longitudinal and transverse AOI.

Monte Carlo ray-tracing simulations, which incorporated realistic material properties and accounted for the Sun's angular aperture and spectral distribution, were used to model light trajectories and evaluate optical efficiency as a function of both AOI_L and AOI_T (see Figure. 3). Moreover, the module features an active light transmission control mechanism. In blind mode or low transmission mode, the planar micro-tracking mechanism shifts the backplane position with the changing solar angle of incidence, to maintain the direct focus light over the solar cells. On the other hand, in skylight mode or high-transmission mode, the solar cells are removed from the direct light focal point, which passes directly through the module, mimicking the behavior of a conventional transparent window. This functionality was verified through photorealistic ray-tracing simulations, demonstrating the module's capability to switch between power generation and daylighting modes effectively (see Figure 4). Previous works have used micro-Fresnel lenses for BIPV, but light management was passive (seasonal)[3].

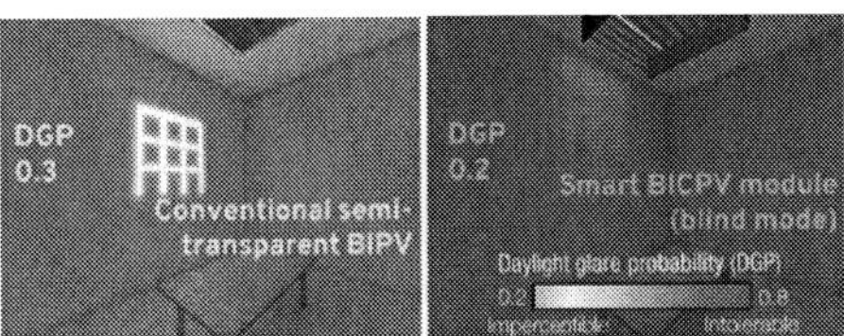

Figure 4: Daylighting properties of conventional semi-transparent BIPV (left) vs our novel concept (when solar cells are aligned to capture direct light, right) as a skylight component in a reference application.

4 FABRICATION METHODOLOGY

We fabricated the first prototypes of the proposed optical module using the roll-to-plate setup shown on Figure 5. The fabrication begins with the deposition of a UV-curable resin onto a glass substrate. The glass then passes under the precision-engraved drum, which continuously molds the resin into the desired optical pattern at a controlled speed of 40 cm/min. During the process, ultraviolet (UV) light cures the resin in situ, solidifying the optical structures. This process is continuous and inherently scalable, enabling the production of large-area Fresnel lens arrays directly onto glass sheets.

The molding drum serves as the master tool and is fabricated from steel with the lens profile precisely engraved via diamond machining. To ensure clean release and maintain optical quality, the drum is coated with a layer of optical-grade nickel-phosphide, providing both durability and anti-adhesive properties. The drum was custom-manufactured by Wielandts, based on the optical design developed in the earlier phase of the project.

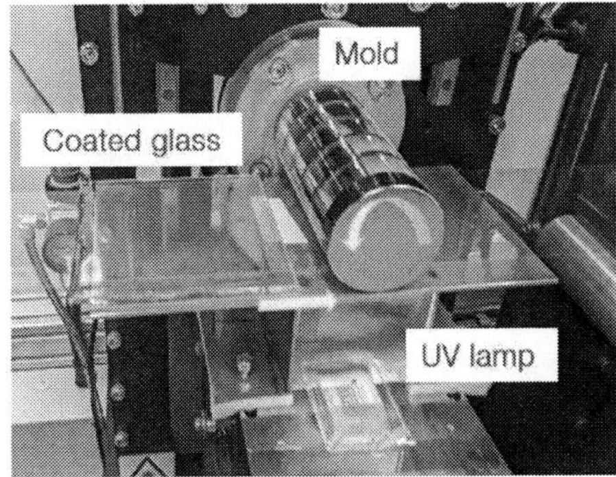

Figure 5: Roll-to-plate UV imprinting setup with continuous roller mold.

5 RESULTS AND DISCUSSION

Three prototype samples were fabricated with different resin base substrate thicknesses to assess the fidelity of lens formation and its impact on optical performance. As shown in the accompanying images (Figure 6), the first and second samples, with resin thicknesses exceeding 150 microns, successfully formed four complete lenses with low superficial roughness (<100 nm). However, the fifth lens, located closest to the drum axis, was only partially formed, likely due to limitations in the flow or pressure distribution of the resin during the molding process. In the third sample, which had a thinner resin layer, no lenses were fully formed, confirming a critical threshold for resin thickness required to achieve complete lens replication.

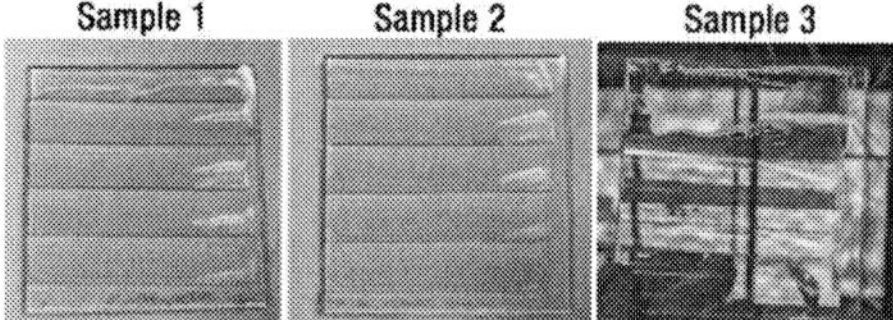

Figure 6: Comparison of the three resultant fabricated lens matrix samples with different resin base substrate thicknesses: sample 1 (380-280 μm), sample 2 (225-150 μm), sample 3 (150-30 μm).

The well-formed lenses closely matched the intended optical design, though minor deformations, such as tip and valley rounding, were observed. These are characteristic of the roll-to-plate process and are considered intrinsic to this type of manufacturing.

Following fabrication, the lenses were assembled with an array of narrow-strip solar cells for module-level characterization. Two types of tests were conducted:

- **Indoor testing** was performed using a collimated light solar simulator to simulate direct solar radiation, allowing for measurement of optical efficiency and concentration ratio.
- **Outdoor testing** was carried out under natural sunlight to evaluate the module's daylighting performance. This setup is composed of a 1:5 scale room with an opening in the ceiling where the lens sample is placed and a manual movable structure to place the lens array. In this way, we can test the sample under both direct and diffused light components, as shown in Figure 7.

Figure 7: Outdoor setup integrated by a 1:5 scale room with an opening in the ceiling where the lens sample is placed and a manual movable structure to place the lens array.

5.1 Indoor tests: Optical efficiency characterization

The optical efficiency of individual lenses was experimentally measured at various transverse angles of incidence. As shown in the results (see Figure 8), the measured optical efficiency is slightly lower than predicted by ray-tracing simulations. Nevertheless, the lenses demonstrate high optical efficiency across a broad angular range. A maximum optical efficiency of approximately 80% was achieved for incidence angles between 30° and 40°. Lenses 1 through 3 exhibit consistent performance, with minimal variation in efficiency and no observable deformation. The measured pitch distance remained uniform, indicating stable replication through the fabrication process. However, the fourth lens underperforms, failing to meet the target efficiency threshold. This discrepancy is currently under investigation and may be attributed to localized fabrication defects or alignment issues during the molding process.

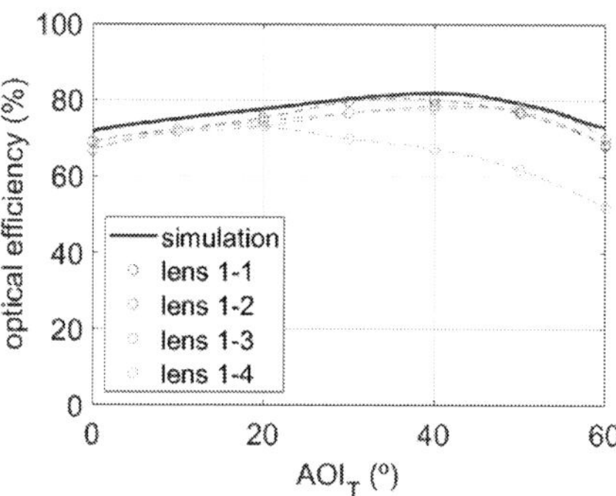

Figure 8: Comparisons of optical efficiency of the simulated lens (continuous line) and the manufactured lens (dashed line) of the sample 1 at 2.8x concentration.

5.2 Outdoor test: Illuminance characterization

Preliminary illuminance measurements were conducted to evaluate the modulation capacity of the module. At the point of maximum illuminance within the test room, results indicate a reduction in light intensity by approximately one order of magnitude when switching from skylight mode to blind mode, across varying angles of incidence. This confirms the system's ability to dynamically control indoor lighting levels based on solar position.

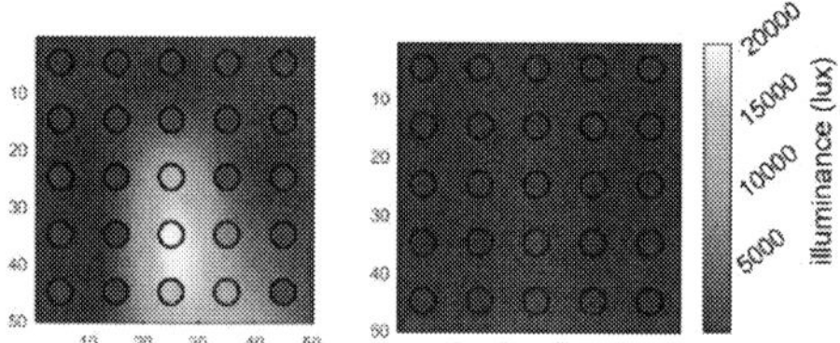

Figure 9: Comparison of the (left) skylight mode and (right) blind mode spatial illuminance matrix of the wall where the direct light falls, for an AOI$_T$ of 45°.

Additionally, we analyzed the spatial distribution of illuminance on the interior wall under a transverse angle of incidence of 45° (see Figure 9), comparing the experimental results with photorealistic ray-tracing simulations. As summarized in Table I, the measured average illuminance showed a reduction of approximately 1500 lux compared to skylight mode. Furthermore, a decrease in the peak-to-average illuminance ratio was observed across seven reference points, indicating a more uniform light distribution. However, both the average and peak illuminance values measured were higher than those predicted by simulation. This discrepancy is attributed to minor deformations in the molded lenses, which introduce optical losses and scattering not accounted for in the idealized simulation models.

Table I: Daylight illuminance parameters average illuminance and peak to average comparison for skylight mode and blind mode.

	skylight mode	blind mode
Average illuminance exp. (lx)	1885	319
Peak to average exp.	10.6	3.2
Peack to average sim.	5.7	2.9

6 CONCLUSIONS

This novel building-integrated concentrator photovoltaics module with daylighting functionality has been developed to simultaneously generate solar electricity and deliver comfortable, glare-free daylight. The system employs static linear Fresnel lenses to concentrate direct sunlight onto an array of c-Si solar cell strips mounted on a transparent, movable backplane. To follow the sun throughout the day, a planar micro-tracking system adjusts the position of the backplane, ensuring optimal alignment with the shifting focal lines. Meanwhile, diffuse light passes through the transparent areas of the module, providing uniform interior illumination with minimal glare.

Unlike conventional semi-transparent BIPV modules, where cells are spaced to allow some light transmission, this design captures nearly all direct irradiance, resulting in a significantly higher power density. The use of asymmetric Fresnel lenses with a wide draft angle minimizes self-shading and supports a compact, high-efficiency system. Arrays fabricated through scalable roll-to-plate UV imprinting achieved a peak optical efficiency of 80%, maintaining over 70% performance up to a 60° angle of incidence at ~3× concentration, closely aligning with simulation results. Outdoor testing further confirmed the system's visual benefits, including a tenfold reduction in peak illuminance, average indoor lighting levels around 1500 lux, and a 7-point drop in the peak-to-average illuminance ratio. These results highlight the dual function of the module as both a renewable energy generator and an effective daylighting and shading solution, supporting its integration into energy-efficient building design. This leads to improved visual comfort, reduced reliance on artificial lighting, and greater energy savings.

These combined benefits position this BIPV module as a compelling solution for accelerating the adoption of building-integrated photovoltaics in low-carbon urban design.

7 ACKNOWLEDGEMENTS

This work has been supported by project grants MICROBEAM ref. PID2021-127810OB-I00, funded by MCIN/AEI/10.13039/501100011033 "ERDF A way of making Europe", SMARTWIN TED2021-130920B-C21, funded by MCIN/AEI/10.13039/501100011033 and by the "European Union NextGenerationEU/PRTR" and 4EVERPV ref. "TEC-2024ECO-72", funded by Comunidad de Madrid.

8 REFERENCES

[1] A. Jäger-Waldau, I. Kougias, N. Taylor, and C. Thiel, "How photovoltaics can contribute to GHG emission reductions of 55% in the EU by 2030," Jul. 01, 2020, *Elsevier Ltd.* doi: 10.1016/j.rser.2020.109836.

[2] A. K. Shukla, K. Sudhakar, and P. Baredar, "A comprehensive review on design of building integrated photovoltaic system," Sep. 15, 2016, *Elsevier Ltd.* doi: 10.1016/j.enbuild.2016.06.077.

[3] D. Valencia-Caballero *et al.*, "Performance analysis of a novel building integrated low concentration photovoltaic skylight with seasonal solar control," *Journal of Building Engineering*, vol. 54, Aug. 2022, doi: 10.1016/j.jobe.2022.104687.

EU PVSEC 2025

Fabrication of a Novel Semi-Translucent BIPV Module Providing High Power Density and Active Daylight Management

Almudena Garcia-Sanchez[1], Guido Vallerotto[1], Jaime J. Hernández[2], Alejandro García-Cañas[2], Steve Askins[1], Ignacio Antón[1], Isabel Rodríguez[2] and César Domínguez[1]

[1] Instituto de Energía Solar, Universidad Politécnica de Madrid (UPM), Madrid (Spain)
[2] Madrid Institute for Advanced Studies in Nanoscience (IMDEA Nanoscience), Madrid (Spain)

020258-001

Outline

- State-of-practice in building-integrated photovoltaics

- Novel module concept

  - Optical design requirements

  - Energetical analysis

- Fabrication of optical arrays

- Prototype characterization

  - Efficiency

  - Illumination features

- Conclusion

020258-002

State-of-practice in building-integrated photovoltaics

INSTITUTO DE ENERGÍA SOLAR

The European Green Deal objectives:

- Need to reach 455-605 GW of PV

- Energy Performance of Buildings Directive (EPBD): new buildings to be nearly zero-energy (NZEB)

Increase util PV building area: glazing PV modules

Barriers to BIPV penetration

✖ Low efficiency compared to BAPV

✖ High cost/Wp

✖ No active management of daylighting/heat load

✖ Discomfort glare

✖ Poor color rendering index (CRI)

POLITÉCNICA

020258-003

Novel module concept

Building-Integrated Concentrator Photovoltaics + Daylighting management

- **Direct** light is converted into **electricity**
- **Diffuse** light is transmitted as **low-glare daylighting**

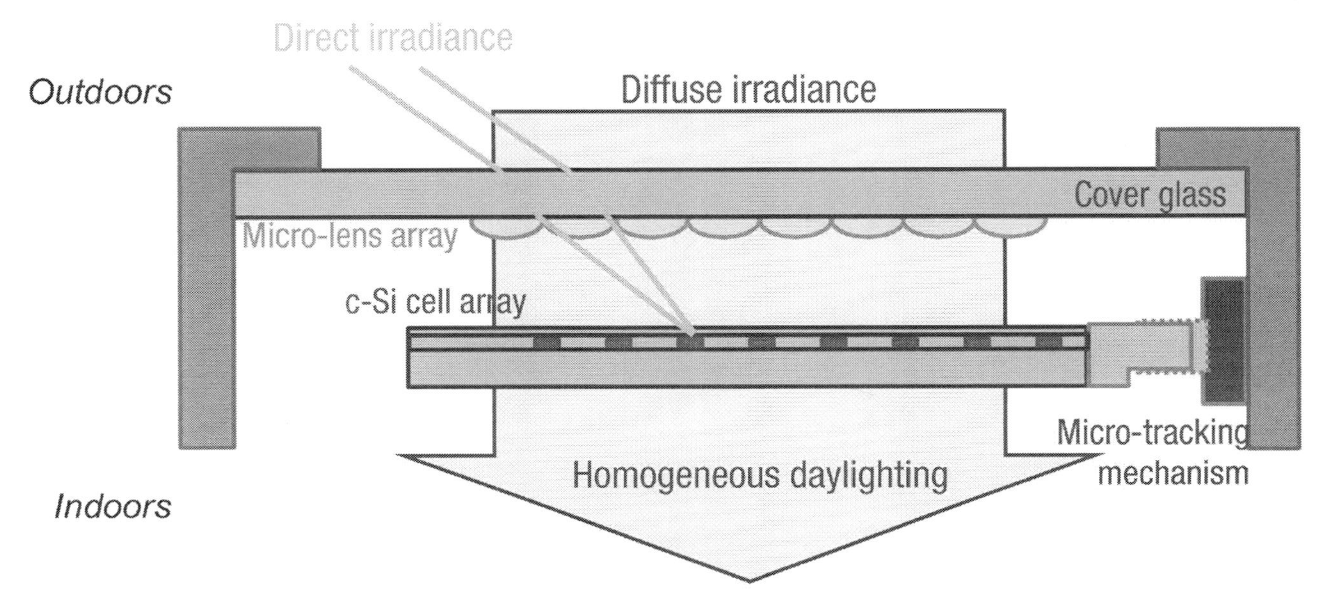

4

020258-004

Novel module concept

INSTITUTO DE ENERGíA SOLAR

Blind mode (low glare)

1:5 scale 2.8X configuration. AOI = 45°

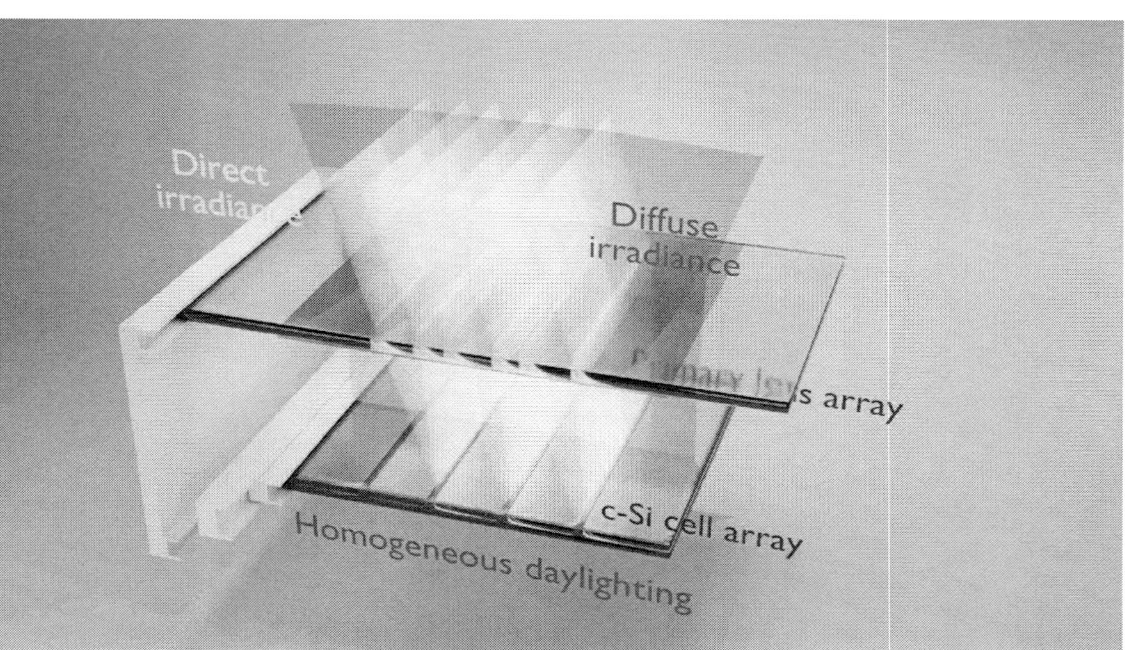

POLITÉCNICA

020258-005

INSTITUTO
DE ENERGÍA
SOLAR

Skylight mode (high transmission)

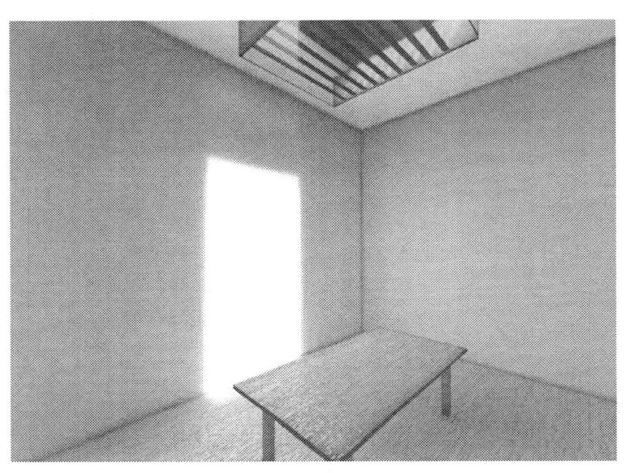

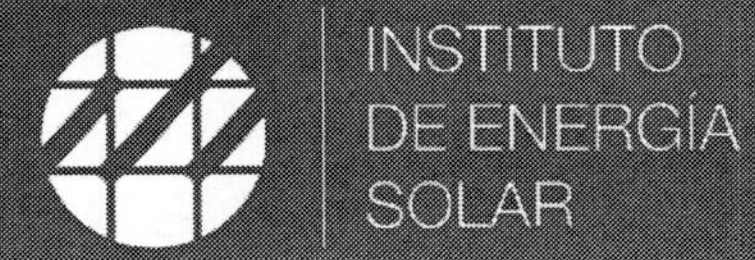

1:5 scale 2.8X configuration. AOI = 45°

POLITÉCNICA

020258-006

Optical design

INSTITUTO DE ENERGÍA SOLAR

- Ultra thin (40 µm) micro linear Fresnel lens
- Compatible with low-cost roll-to-plate process
- Asymmetric lens with large draft angle
- Optimized for 17° angle of incidence
- Max. focal distance 7.5 cm to ease integration in typical building components

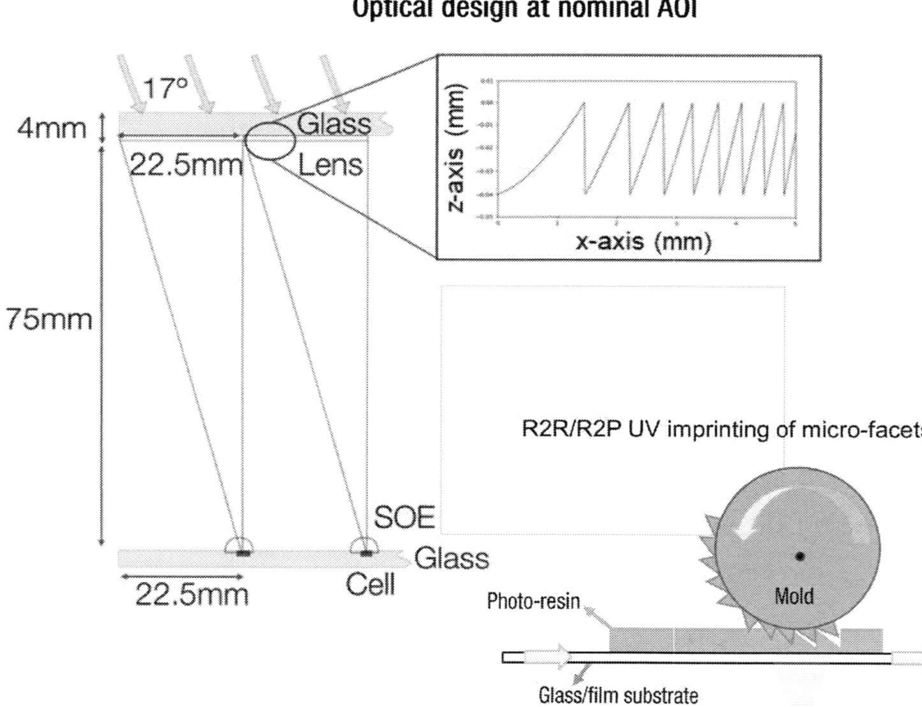

020258-007

Optical modeling methodology

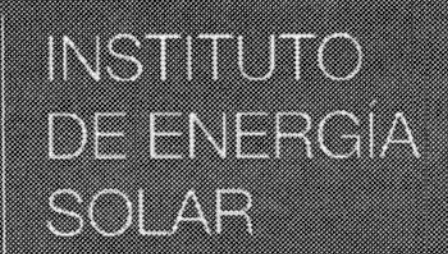

Definition and characterization

Ray-tracing software setup

Angle of incidence classification

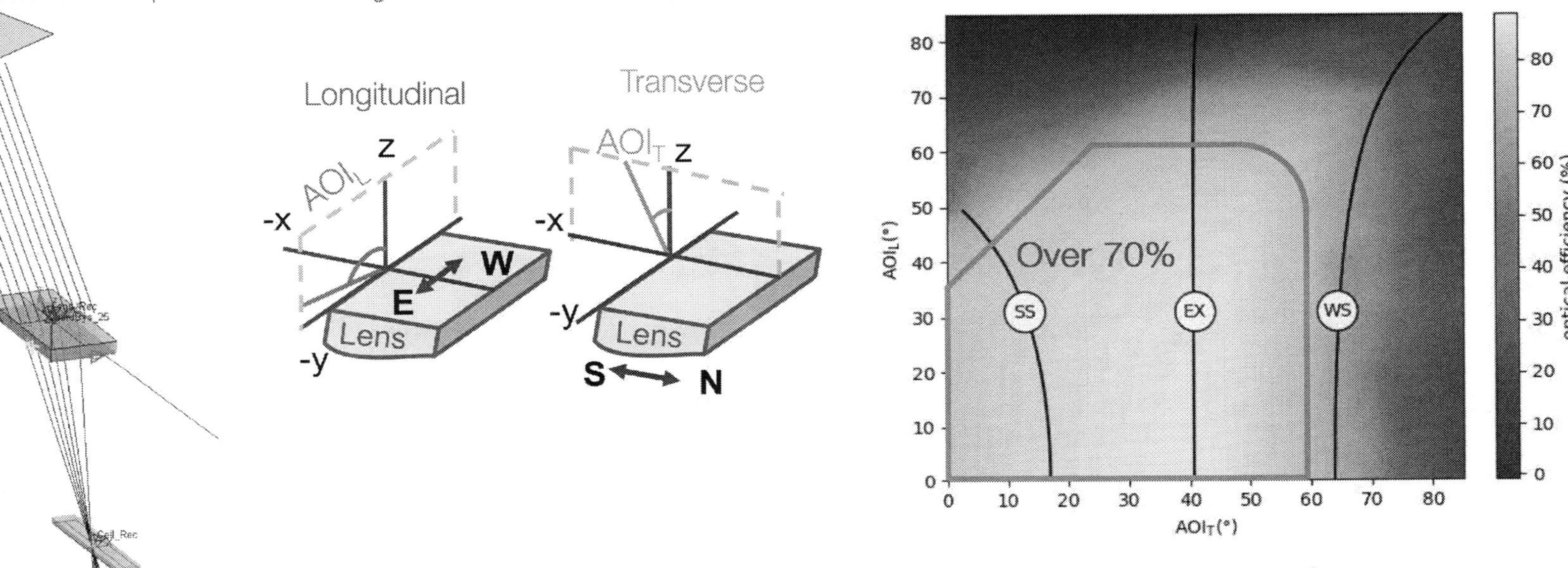

Optical efficiency vs AOI (2.8x)

$$\text{optical eff} = \frac{P_{rec}}{P_{lens}}$$

Energetical analysis

- Python Pvlib + PSPICE model
  - Location and orientation
  - Module size
  - Cell technology
  - Module interconnection

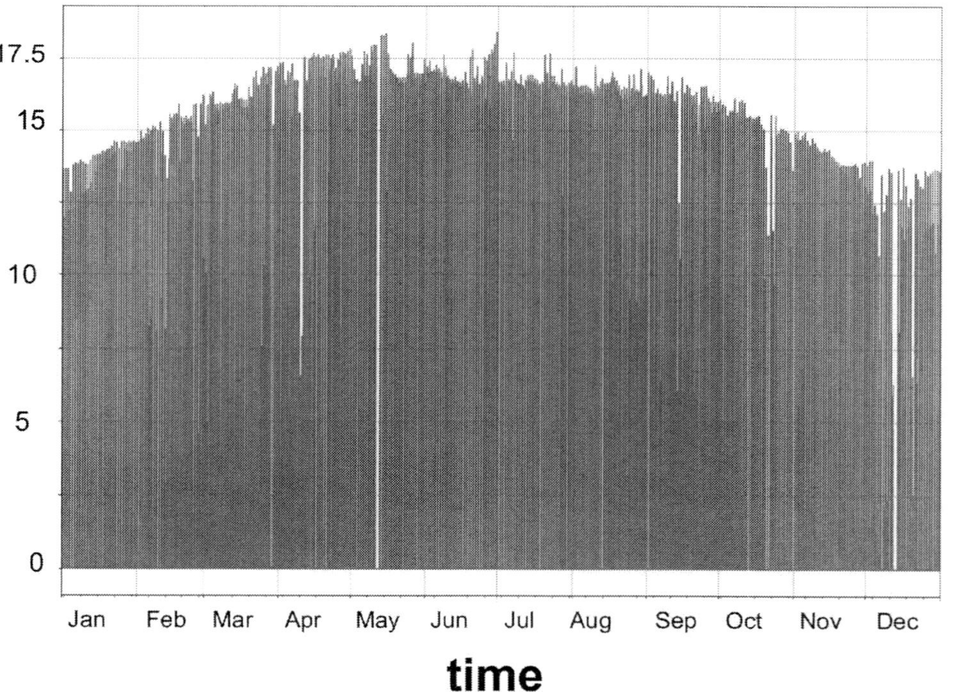

POLITÉCNICA

020258-009

9

Fabrication of optical arrays

- Scalable roll-to-plate fabrication on glass

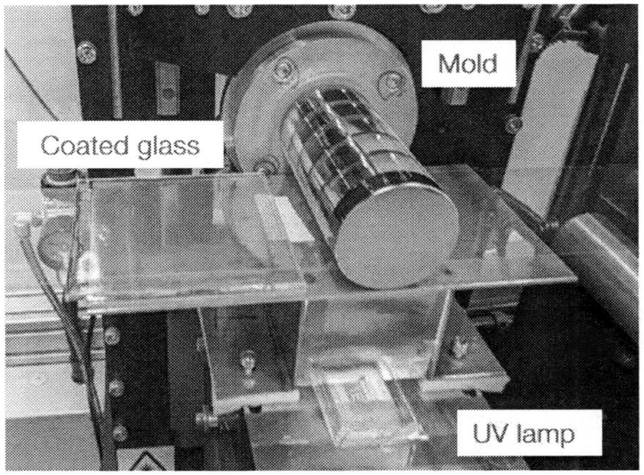

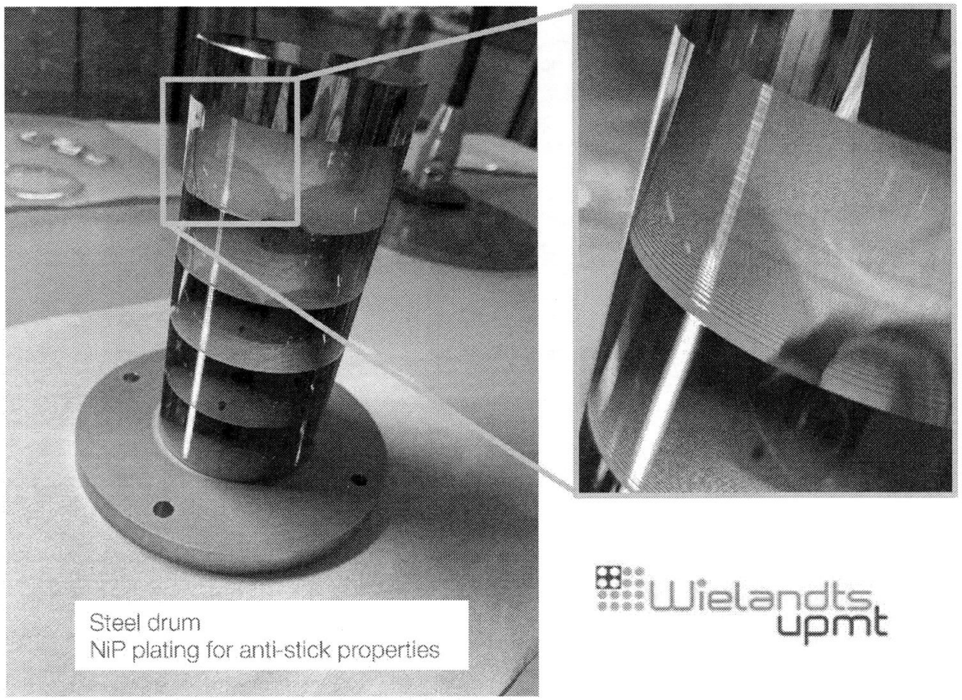

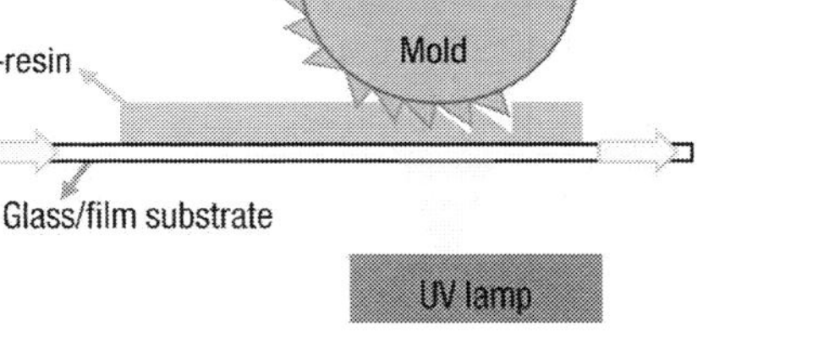

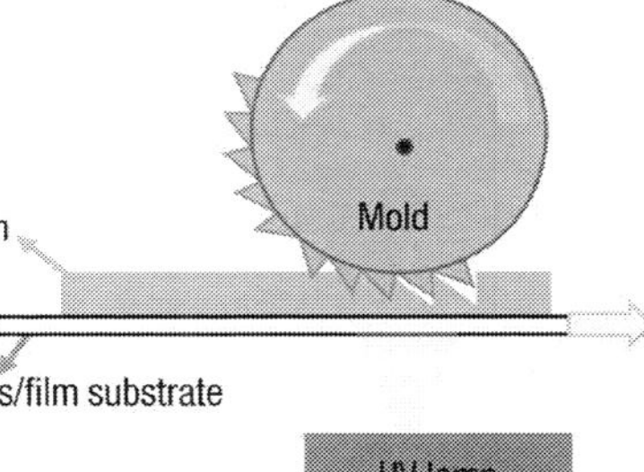

020258-010

Fabrication of optical arrays

- Scalable roll-to-plate fabrication on glass

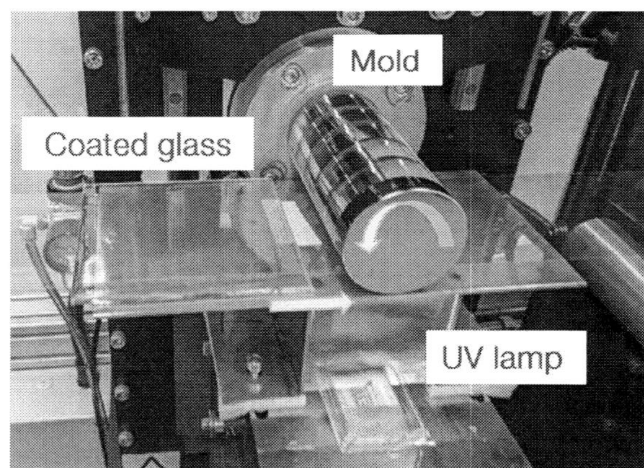

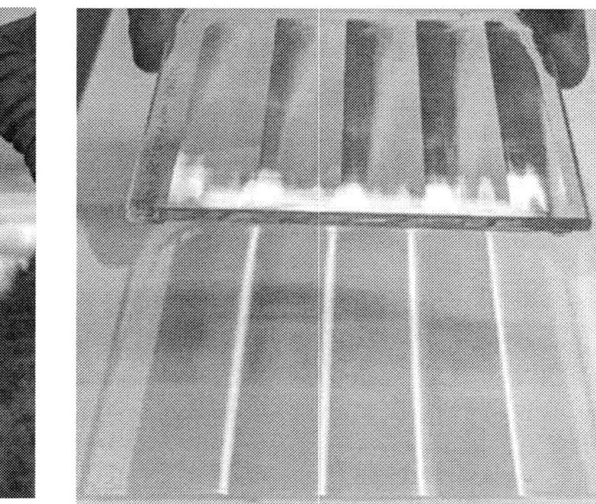
Natural daylighting

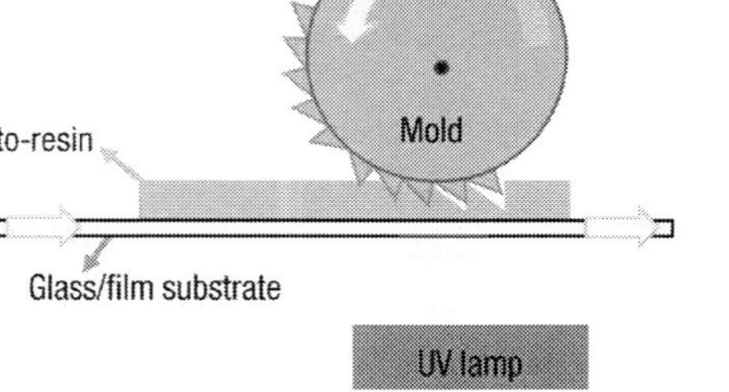
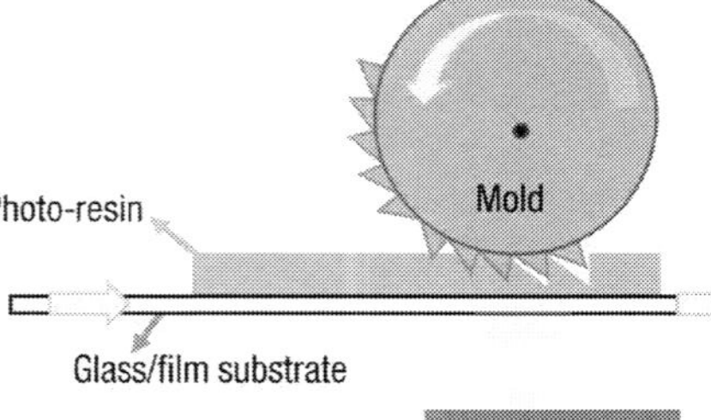
Direct light concentration

POLITÉCNICA

020258-011

Fabrication of optical arrays

INSTITUTO DE ENERGÍA SOLAR

- Scalable roll-to-plate fabrication on glass

imdea nanociencia

Sample 1 (thickness 380-280 µm)

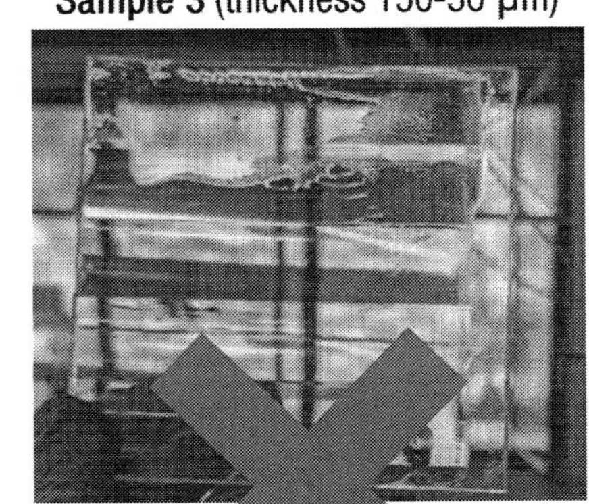

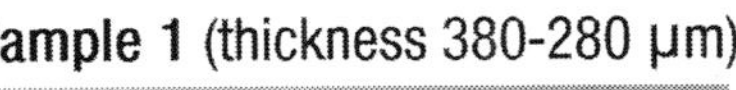

Sample 2 (thickness 225-150 µm)

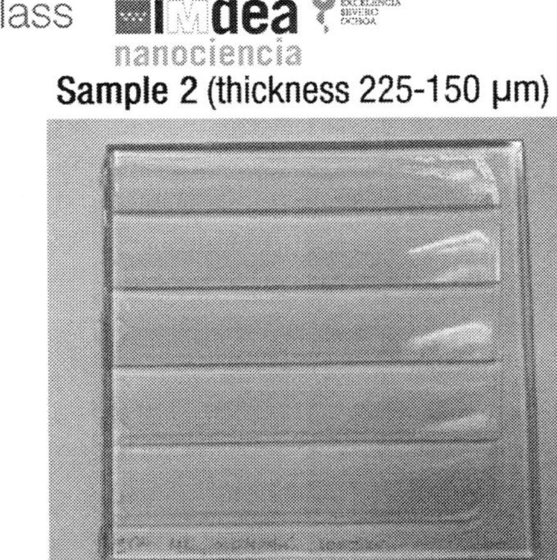

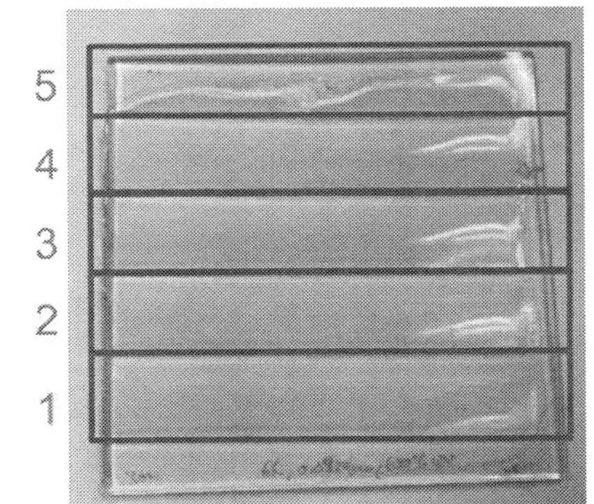

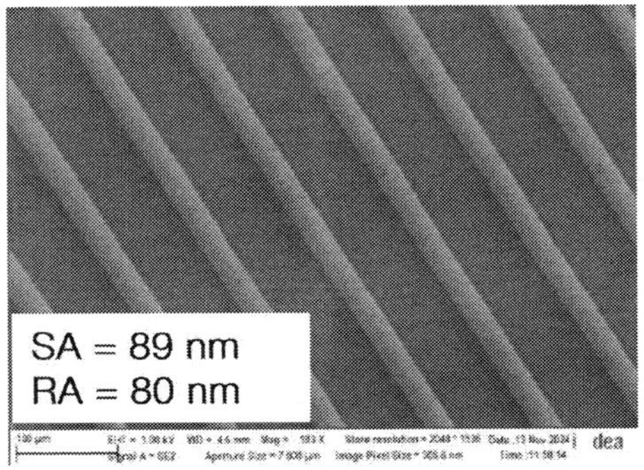

Sample 3 (thickness 150-30 µm)

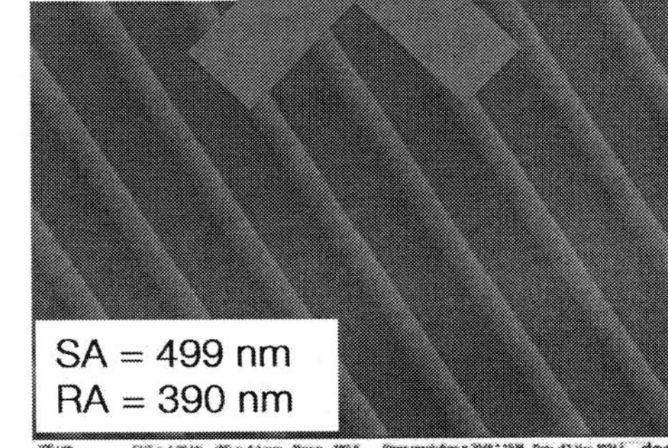

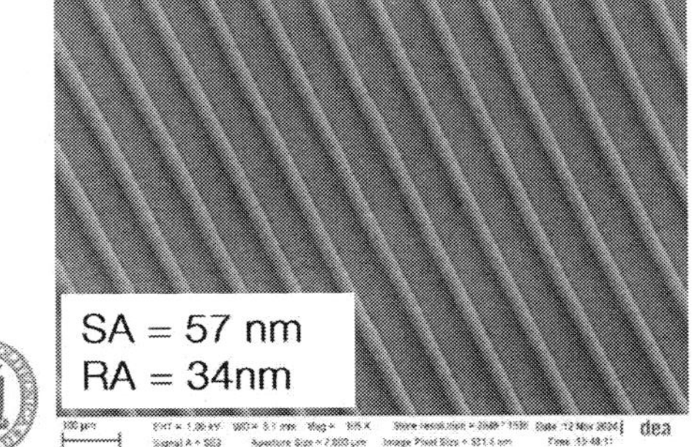

POLITÉCNICA

42nd EU PVSEC, Bilbao • 23/09/2025

Fabrication of optical arrays

- Scalable roll-to-plate fabrication on glass

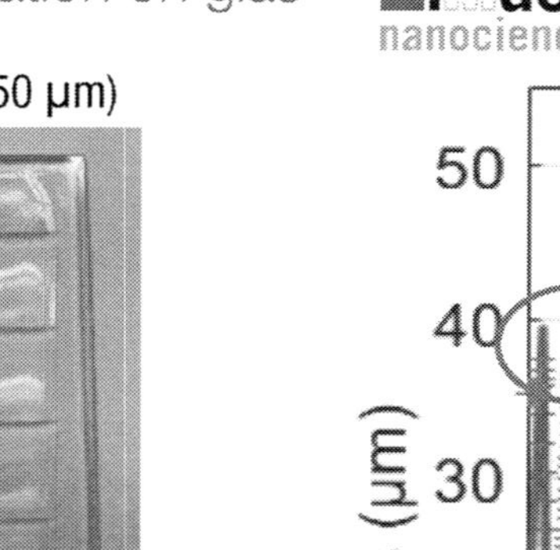

Sample 2 (thickness 225-150 µm)

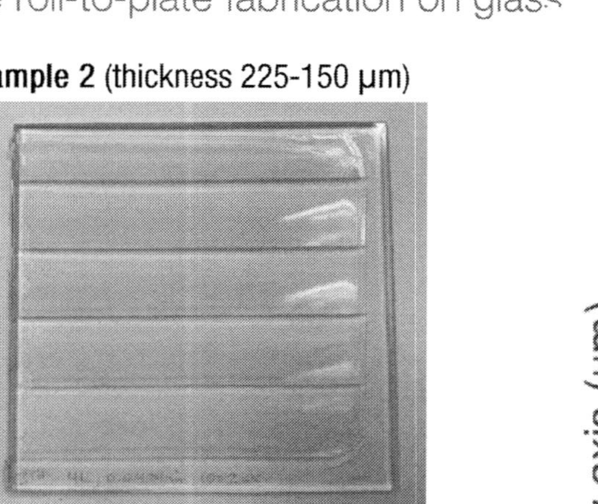

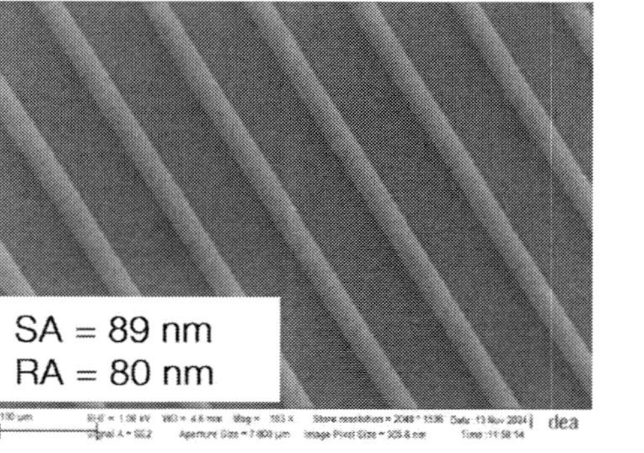

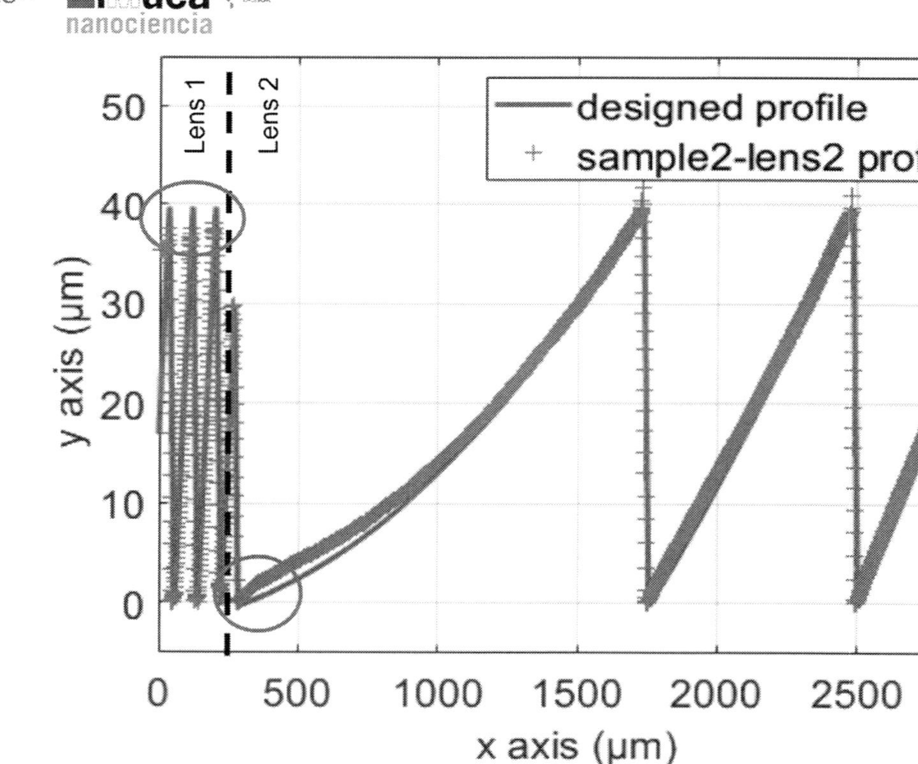

13

Prototype characterization:

INSTITUTO DE ENERGÍA SOLAR

Collimated solar simulator setup

Outdoor illuminance setup

POLITÉCNICA

020258-014

Prototype characterization: Indoor optical efficiency

- High optical efficiency for a wide range of angles of incidence

- Maximum optical efficiency measured 80%

- Consistent performance for lenses 1-3

$$\text{optical eff} = \frac{P_{rec}}{P_{lens}}$$

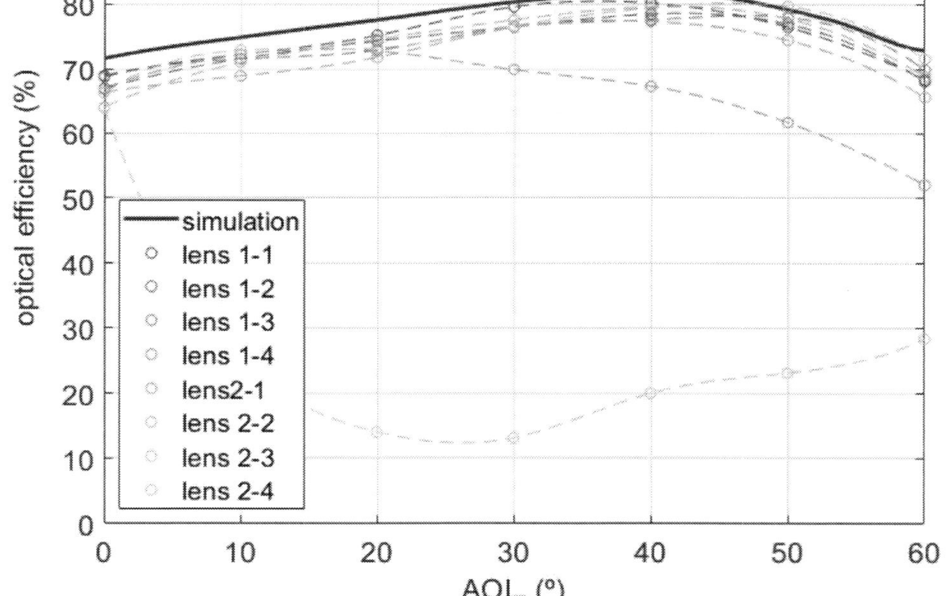

020258-015

Prototype characterization: Indoor optical efficiency

Profile shape for different AOI_T (1mm cell)

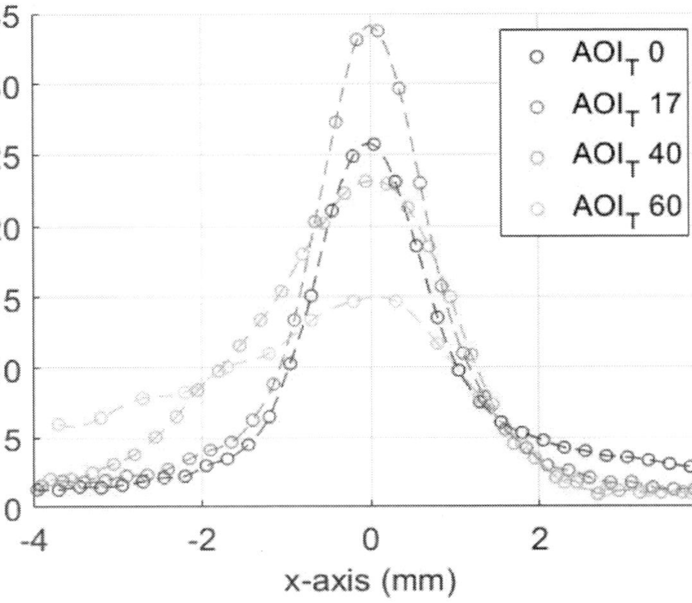

Relative encircled energy (%) for AOI_T 17°

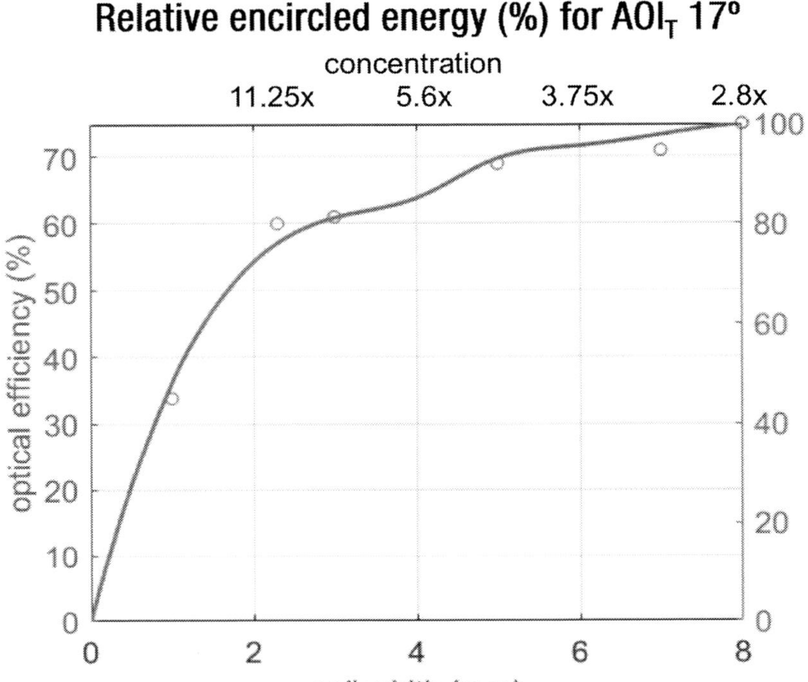

020258-016

Prototype characterization: Outdoor illuminance performance

INSTITUTO DE ENERGÍA SOLAR

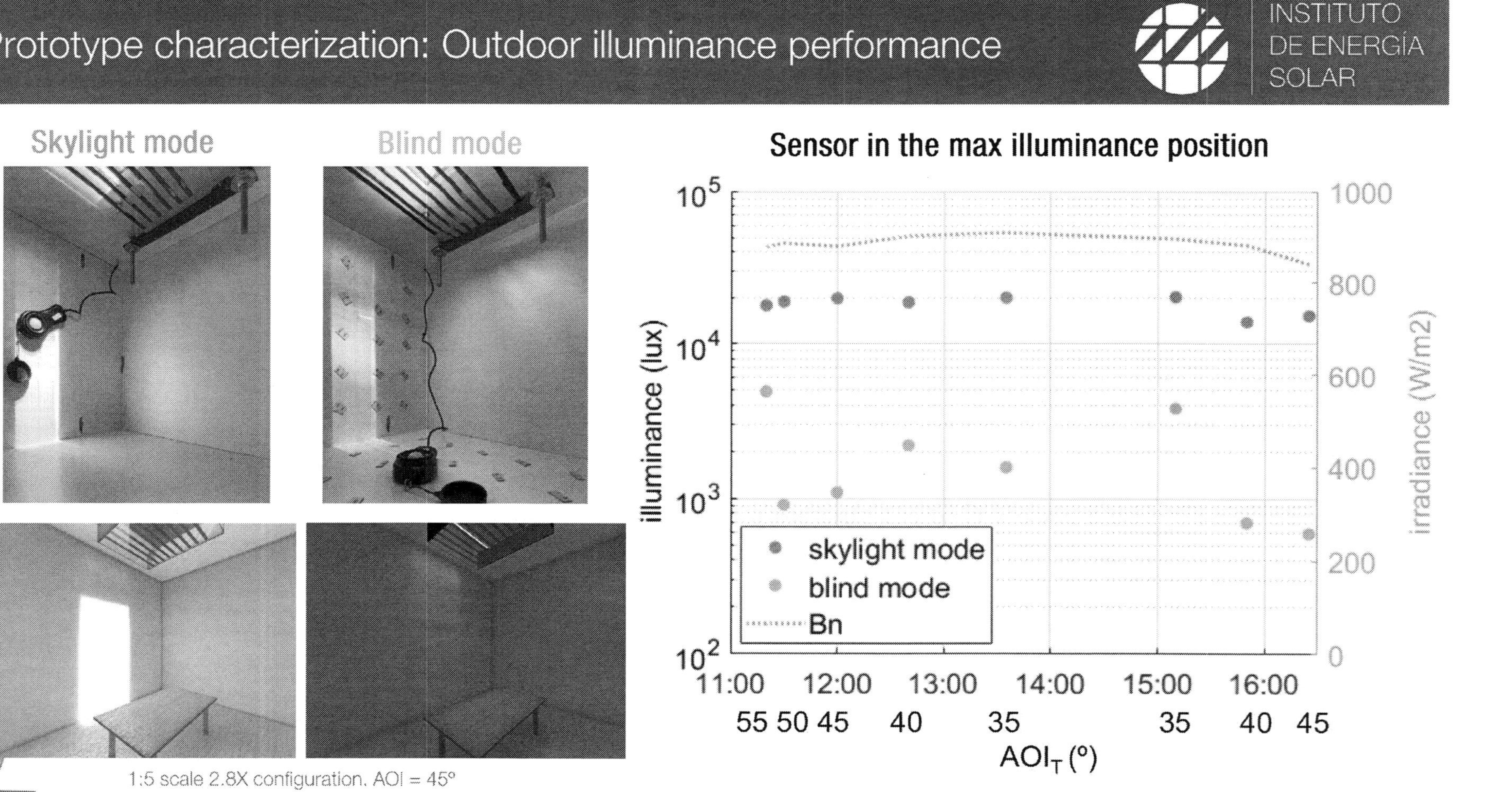

1:5 scale 2.8X configuration. AOI = 45°

POLITÉCNICA

Prototype characterization: Outdoor illuminance performance

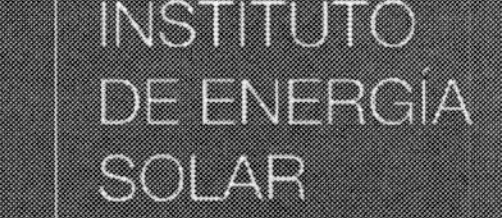

Skylight mode

Blind mode

Skylight mode

Blind mode

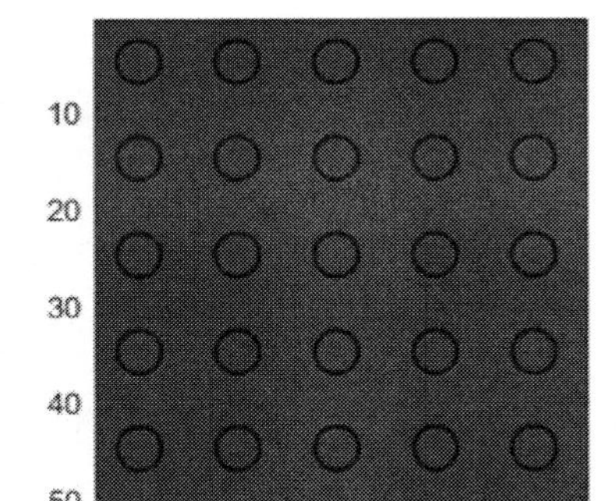
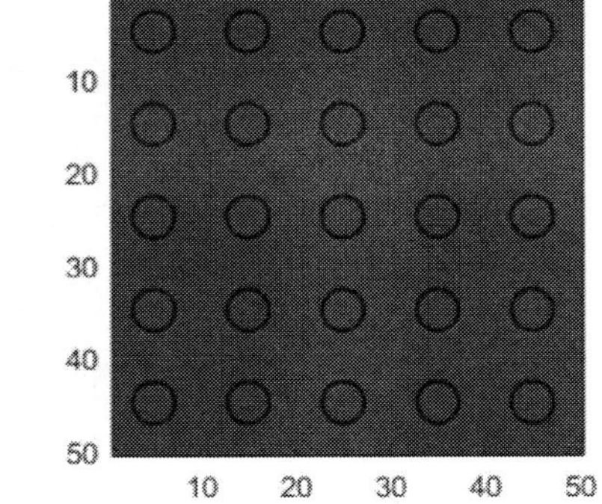
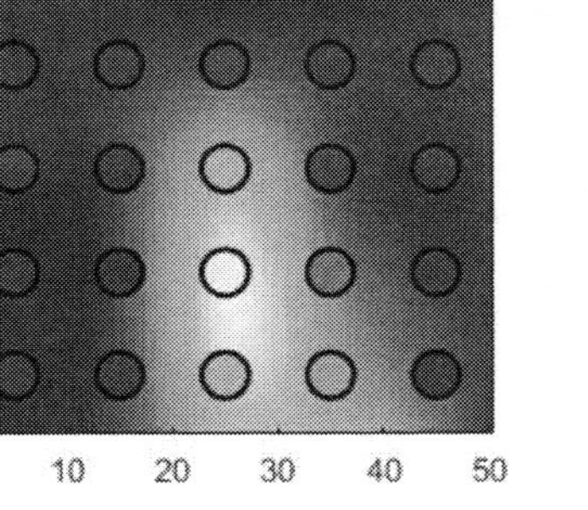
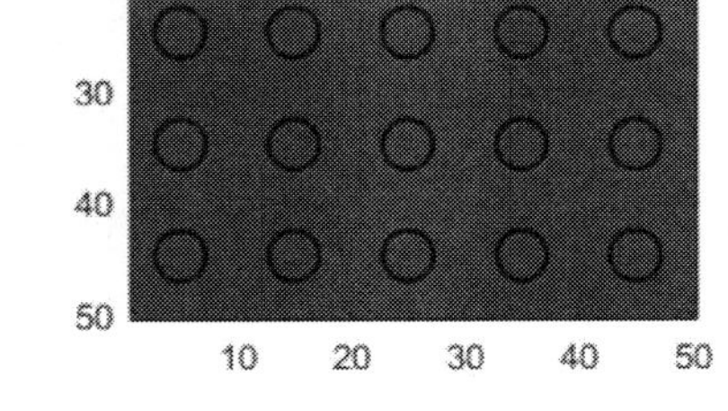

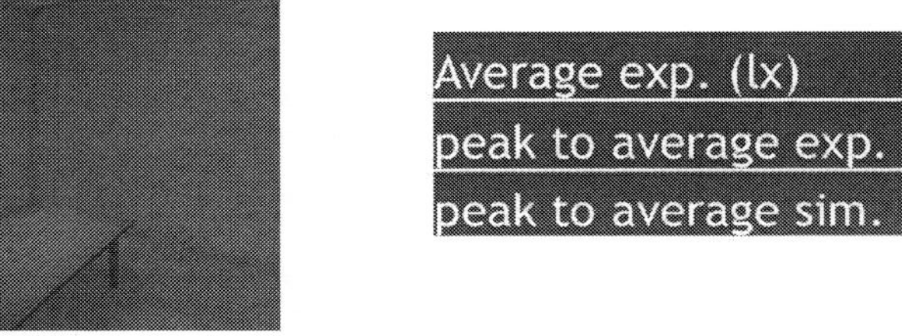

1:5 scale 2.8X configuration. AOI = 45°

	HT wall	LT wall
Average exp. (lx)	1885	319
peak to average exp.	10.6	3.2
peak to average sim.	5.7	2.9

020258-018

Conclusions

- Innovative BIPV approach to improve building energy balance and daylighting management

- Novel asymmetric linear Fresnel design compatible with scalable low-cost roll-to-plate manufacturing

- Prototype characterized by indoor and outdoor test demonstrates high optical efficiency and Glare-free daylighting capabilities

- Open to collaborations to take it to an industrial phase

020258-019

Thank you for your attention

INSTITUTO
DE ENERGÍA
SOLAR

Almudena Garcia-Sanchez

Almudena.garcia@upm.es

Happy to take your questions

We gratefully acknowledge the support of these institutions: This work has been supported by project grants MICROBEAM ref. PID2021-127810OB-I00, funded by MCIN/AEI/10.13039/501100011033 "ERDF A way of making Europe", SMARTWIN TED2021-130920B-C21, funded by MCIN/AEI/10.13039/501100011033 and by the "European Union NextGenerationEU/PRTR" and 4EVERPV ref. "TEC-2024ECO-72", funded by Comunidad de Madrid.

020258-020

INSTITUTO
DE ENERGÍA
SOLAR
Innovation in photovoltaics since 1979

A COMPARATIVE STUDY OF PHOTOVOLTAIC SHADING DEVICES FOR NET ZERO ENERGY BUILDINGS ACROSS FRENCH CLIMATES

Mohammad Nazififard, Erwin Franquet
Polytech'Lab, Université Côte d'Azur, Nice, France
Mohammad.NAZIFIFARD@univ-cotedazur.fr   Erwin.FRANQUET@univ-cotedazur.fr

ABSTRACT: By 2050, the European Union aims to achieve carbon neutrality and net-zero greenhouse gas emissions. Buildings account for a significant portion of the EU's energy consumption, making the integration of renewable technologies, such as photovoltaic (PV) modules in windows, roofs, façades, and above glazing, essential. Photovoltaic shading systems (PVSDs), which combine PV modules with awnings or louvres, generate electricity while reducing solar heat gain and lowering cooling energy demand. This study evaluates the impact of various PVSDs on the cooling, heating, and lighting demands of office buildings in four French cities with distinct climates: Brest, Clermont-Ferrand, Nice, and Strasbourg. Energy generation was calculated using PVSYST. The PVSD types modeled include horizontal canopies with single, double, and triple rows of PV modules, inclined canopies with single and double rows at a 30° tilt, and vertical panel canopies. Results show that the Nice inclined single canopy reduces annual energy use by up to 35.31% compared to the base model. In Clermont, the horizontal single-row canopy lowers energy use by 20.49%. In Strasbourg, the same canopy reduces consumption by 14.83%, while in Brest, it achieves a 13.31% reduction. These findings suggest that PVSDs are most effective in reducing cooling energy in Mediterranean climates. In colder regions like Strasbourg, designs should also optimize winter solar heat gain. This study establishes a quantitative framework for the design and evaluation of PVSDs in office buildings.

Keywords: Photovoltaic shading systems; Building energy efficiency; Renewable energy integration; Cooling load reduction; Climate-responsive design.

1 INTRODUCTION

The European Union has set an ambitious goal to achieve carbon neutrality by 2050, aiming to create a net-zero greenhouse gas emissions economy [1]. A critical component of this target is reducing carbon emissions from the heating and cooling sectors, which together account for approximately 42% of the European Union's final energy consumption. Currently, about 75% of this demand is still met by fossil fuels [2]. Improving the energy performance of buildings is widely recognized as a key strategy for achieving these goals, due to the substantial potential for energy savings and climate change mitigation within the European building stock [3]. The integration of renewable energy technologies to meet the energy demands of buildings further supports this objective [4] [5]. France, which has traditionally relied on nuclear power, has one of the lowest carbon-intensity electricity mixes in the world. In 2019, nuclear energy accounted for more than 70% of the country's domestic electricity production [6], [7]. However, most of France's nuclear reactors were commissioned between the late 1970s and early 1980s and are now approaching or exceeding their typical operational lifespan of 40 to 60 years, indicating the likelihood of imminent shutdowns [8]. As a result, France is actively transitioning toward renewable energy sources to reduce its reliance on both fossil fuels and nuclear power. Government policies prioritize the expansion of wind, solar, hydroelectric, and biomass energy sectors [9]. Compared to wind energy, which requires a substantial land area for installation, photovoltaic (PV) technology offers greater flexibility by allowing direct integration into building envelopes as building-integrated photovoltaic (BIPV) systems. In addition to on-site electricity generation, BIPV systems can significantly reduce building cooling loads [10]. Building facades play a critical role in regulating indoor thermal comfort and supporting occupant health. Integrating photovoltaic (PV) systems into building envelopes enhances energy efficiency by generating electricity while also affecting daylighting and thermal performance. Both experimental studies and simulation-based analyses have examined the daylighting characteristics, thermal behavior, and power generation potential of such facades. Additionally, PV panels can be incorporated into architectural elements such as eaves and canopies. Optimally designed solar awnings can generate significant amounts of electricity and reduce unwanted solar heat gain through windows, thereby lowering cooling energy demand during the summer months [11]. These systems have been widely implemented as PV shading solutions in both low-rise and multi-story buildings. Serving dual purposes, they not only generate electricity but also function as external shading devices that help reduce cooling loads [12]. Recent research has focused on optimizing the energy performance of solar shading systems, as discussed in the following sections.

2 LITERATUE REVIEW

Canopies play a critical role in sustainable architecture, particularly when integrated with PV systems. These hybrid solutions not only enhance energy generation but also optimize solar radiation control, improve natural lighting, and reduce thermal loads. In addition to maximizing solar energy efficiency, such systems significantly decrease cooling demand, increase daylight utilization, and improve occupant thermal comfort. Recent studies underscore the benefits of incorporating PV systems into building designs [13], [14], [15]. Hofer et al. [16] reported that in Zurich's climate, strategic orientation and spacing of PV panels increased energy efficiency by more than 50% compared to conventional configurations, with further improvements achieved using south-facing facades and horizontal shading elements. Nagy et al. [17] developed smart façade modules with precise adjustability, resulting in a 25% reduction in energy consumption while preserving architectural aesthetics. Jayathissa et al. [18] demonstrated that adaptive solar façades, responsive to both internal and external conditions, could reduce energy use by up to 80% in office buildings with high cooling loads.

Dynamic shading systems exhibit performance that varies with climate conditions. Gao et al. [19] analyzed PVwindows equipped with movable awnings in nine cities using a three-degree-of-freedom tracking system. Their study reported a 27.4% increase in energy production and a 19.17% improvement in module efficiency, while emphasizing the need for climate-specific adjustments to balance energy generation and glare control. Krarti and Karrech [20] demonstrated that hourly or monthly adjustmenets of movable awnings enabled net-zero energy consumption in Australian office buildings. Jiang et al. [21] compared three dynamic strategies: rotation, horizontal movement, and combined operation. They found energy savings between 32% and 50%, along with a 3.1% increase in useful daylight illuminance (UDI) for the combined strategy. Similarly, Krarti et al. [22] reported that hourly-adjusted dynamic awnings in Qatar reduced annual building energy use by 69.7%. These results highlight the importance of climate- and behavior-responsive design to optimize system efficiency.

Research on solar awnings confirms their energy-saving potential when designed with consideration for climate, solar position, and environmental radiation. Zhang et al. [10] demonstrated that, in Hong Kong, horizontal awnings on southwest-facing façades reduced lighting energy use by 45.7% (equivalent to 69.16 kWh/m² annually), with optimal performance achieved at a 30° tilt and a south-facing orientation. Li et al. [11], [23] emphasized that seasonally adjustable angles outperform fixed installations across five different climate zones in China, with south-facing awnings proving the most efficient. In Guangzhou, PV awnings offset 40% of a multi-story building's net electricity demand and outperformed roof-mounted systems in terms of cost-effectiveness [11]. Baghoolizadeh et al. [12] optimized window-integrated shading systems in five European cities using EnergyPlus-NSGA-II simulations, achieving electricity cost reductions of 17% to 34%. Skandalos and Karamanis [28] compared semi-transparent photovoltaic (PV) shading in Prague, Athens, and Dubai, reporting the highest savings of 73% in the Mediterranean climate of Athens. Qadourah [29] demonstrated that PV shading in Mediterranean residential complexes supplied 25.1% to 35.6% of electricity demand, outperforming standalone villas in terms of energy performance. These studies confirm that the effectiveness of solar awnings depends on climate-responsive design tailored to regional conditions, solar geometry, and building typology. Integrating solar awnings into building design requires a careful balance among energy production, daylight optimization, and visual comfort. Early research has identified inherent trade-offs among these factors.

Kim et al. [30] found that PV blinds with edge-angle control increased electricity generation by 32% but reduced lighting energy savings by 35%, highlighting conflicts between energy output and daylight quality. Qingsong et al. [31] reported that combining PV louver awnings with lighting controls in China saved 22.8% of energy but sometimes compromised indoor lighting, leading to increased artificial lighting use. Conversely, Li et al. [32] showed that bidirectional PV panels oriented east and west achieved up to 25.62% electrical efficiency with only modest indoor light reductions of 2.5% to 12%, depending on distance. This finding indicates that strategic orientation can balance energy generation and daylight goals. To address these challenges, recent research has focused on adaptive designs. Liu et al. [33] introduced a geometric, algorithmically optimized PV shading system for Guangzhou offices that reduced cooling and lighting demands by 48.7% while generating 1034.4 kWh/year of surplus energy. The system also improved useful daylight illuminance by 71.6%, demonstrating synergistic benefits. Li et al. [34] applied multi-objective optimization to double-sided awnings in warm climates, enhancing daylight by 39.44% and reducing ventilation energy consumption by 12.61%. Zheng et al. [35] advanced this approach in Shenzhen by using the SPEA2 algorithm to design rotating multilayer awnings that reduced glare by 53% and limited annual energy use to 100 kWh.

These findings illustrate that adaptive controls, multi-objective optimization, and climate-responsive geometries can mitigate trade-offs between energy efficiency and occupant comfort.

Jayathissa et al. [36] developed a comprehensive simulation framework for solar shading in Zurich, demonstrating that fixed configurations could reduce building energy use by 20% to 80%, with some cases achieving full energy self-sufficiency. Abdullah and Alibaba [37] reported that PV-integrated shading in a naturally ventilated office in Cyprus supplied 70% of the building's electricity needs while maintaining thermal comfort for 80% of the year. Comparative studies highlight the advantages of advanced shading systems over conventional designs. Peres et al. [40] simulated multi-layer canopy devices in Rio de Janeiro, reducing cooling loads by 14% to 19% and net energy demand by 32%. Jung et al. [41] confirmed that PV louver awnings in Michigan generated 47.9% more electricity than vertical facade installations.

The tilt angle of solar canopies is critical for both energy efficiency and architectural integration. Asfour [42] demonstrated that horizontal canopies tilted at 45° in Saudi Arabia received the highest annual solar radiation (104 kWh/m²) while providing 96% shading during the summer. Han et al. [43] recommended a 35° tilt for bifacial canopies in Hong Kong, noting that increasing canopy width raises total power output but reduces generation per unit area due to self-shading. Kim et al. [44] reported that monthly adjustments of blade angles in South Korea could not completely prevent self-shading at a 30° tilt, which reduced the output of the lower blades. Wang et al. [45] showed that real-time canopy angle control in Hong Kong reduced energy use by 36.5% and increased power generation by 11.4%. Their study also emphasized the importance of maintaining panel width-to-vertical distance ratios below 1:10 to minimize shading losses.

PV panel technology also affects canopy efficiency. Bahr [46] found that amorphous silicon panels perform best at latitude-equivalent tilt angles in Abu Dhabi, while crystalline silicon panels are more efficient in horizontal configurations. These findings highlight the importance of considering tilt angle, PV technology, and local climate in the design process.

Spacing and dimensions also significantly influence performance. Baghdadi and Abuhussain [47] demonstrated that horizontal louver blinds with a 40 cm depth reduced cooling loads in Riyadh from 101,000 kWh to 88,000 kWh, with a payback period of 8.6 to 10.2 years. Chen et al. [48] reported that reducing inter-panel spacing from 175 mm to 35 mm in a hot-summer/cold-winter climate increased power generation by a factor of five. These results underscore the critical impact of structural details on energy savings. Luo et al. [52] found that double-glazed façades with PV curtains reduced cooling demand by 12.16% to 25.57%. Evangelisti et al. [53] experimentally demonstrated a 38.7% reduction in summer thermal energy use in an Italian building employing active and passive solar shading. Akbari Paydar [54] reported that movable shading on south-facing windows in Tehran reduced heating loads by 12% to 20%, while generating electricity exceeding thermal demand by 70% to 290%. Ogbeba and Hoskara [55] simulated PV shading in Northern Cyprus, showing a 50% reduction in summer energy use along with 2800 W of electricity generation. Taveres-Cachat et al. [56] found that shading altered heating and cooling demands by 28% and 7%, respectively, in Norway.

Despite recent advancements, key challenges remain. Dynamic systems offer high energy savings but are often limited by mechanical complexity, cost, and maintenance issues. Many studies focus on energy, lighting, or comfort individually, with few adopting integrated, multi-objective approaches. Additionally, most research targets single climates and overlooks combined analyses of thermal performance, daylighting, and power generation.

This study introduces an integrated solar canopy model evaluated across four distinct French climates. The model aims to balance energy performance, thermal comfort, daylighting, and economic feasibility within a unified framework.

3 METHODOLOGY

3.1 Case study

This study examines the impact of PVSDs on cooling demand during warm seasons, heating requirements during cold seasons, and overall electricity consumption across four distinct climate zones in France. EnergyPlus, developed by the U.S. Department of Energy, is a free, reliable simulation engine widely used to evaluate building energy performance. It offers an efficient framework for processing both input and output data [57]. Detailed office building models were created using DesignBuilder for each climate zone. EnergyPlus was then used to assess the effects of solar shading systems on thermal loads and total energy consumption. Additionally, PVsyst calculated the solar energy generated by the shading systems. By comparing simulation results, the study identified the optimal solar shading configurations for maximizing energy efficiency in each climate.

To ensure generalizable results, a model office building with standardized characteristics was developed. The design reflects typical office architectural features and incorporates key factors influencing energy performance, such as geometry, materials, orientation, and natural lighting. The model represents a single-zone office space measuring 6 meters wide, 8 meters deep, and 3.9 meters high (Figure 1).

Material selection was based on previous research focused on passive building strategies [58], including energy-efficient materials and window configurations. The external walls and roof are highly insulated to minimize heat transfer and isolate the effects of shading devices. A large south-facing window measuring 2.0 meters by 1.84 meters was included to optimize solar gain, consistent with common energy-efficient design practices. High-performance double-glazed windows with low U-values were used to control heat and light transmission.

The building is equipped with a high-efficiency LED lighting system and a variable air volume HVAC system featuring an air-cooled chiller and reheat capabilities, suitable for maintaining thermal comfort in office environments. Operational parameters include occupancy from 8 a.m. to 5 p.m., Monday through Friday, an occupant density of 0.111 persons per square meter, and heating and cooling setpoints of 21°C and 26°C, respectively. Lighting controls were implemented in DesignBuilder to simulate realistic energy use, accounting for the impact of shading devices on daylight availability. Multiple solar shading configurations with varying heights and arrangements along the façade were simulated to evaluate their effects on energy performance. PVsyst software was used to simulate the performance and energy production of solar awning systems under various climatic conditions. Selecting an appropriate PV panel is essential, as it directly affects the system's efficiency and overall effectiveness. Based on a review of relevant studies and with the goal of maximizing performance, the solar panels listed in Table II were chosen for the simulations.

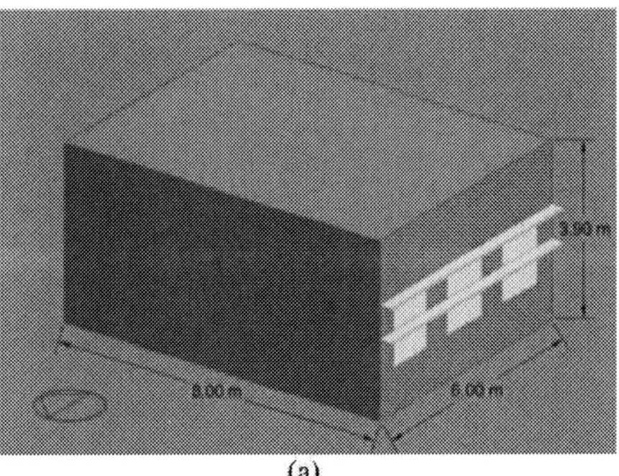

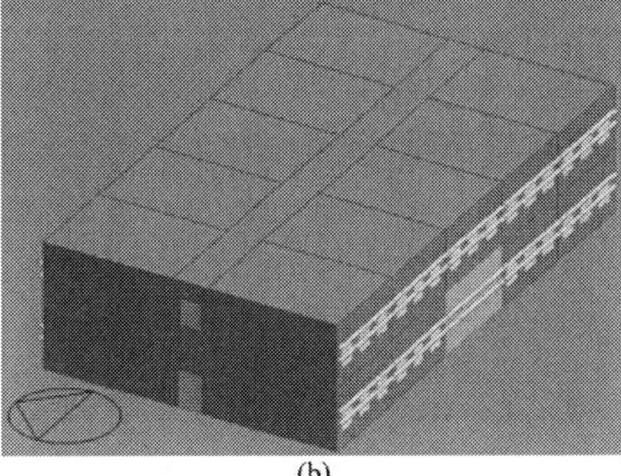

Figure 1: (a) Single-story buildings with PVSDs; (b) multi-story buildings with PVSDs.

High-performance double-glazed windows with a low U-value are used to regulate heat and light entering the building. An energy-efficient LED lighting system is modeled, along with a variable air volume (VAV) system equipped with an air cooler for climate control. This configuration is suitable for buildings requiring precise temperature regulation in different climate zones. The office building is occupied at a density of 0.12 persons per square meter and operates from 8:00 a.m. to 5:00 p.m., five days a week. The heating and cooling setpoints are 21°C and 26°C, respectively. Lighting management is also included in the simulation. Each PVSD is equipped with PV panels totaling 7.1 m² in surface area. To assess the effectiveness of PVSDs, their ability to reduce building energy consumption is first evaluated through passive shading performance. Subsequently, PV energy generation is estimated using PVsyst software. Simulation results for lighting, heating, cooling, and total energy use are compared with a baseline model across different climates to evaluate overall PVSD performance. These results demonstrate the contribution of PVSDs to reducing net energy consumption through both passive shading and active electricity generation.

Table I: Geometry and Simulation details in DESIGNBUILDER.

Model Name	Base Model	Horizontal Canopy Single
Model Type	No-shading	Single panel
Schematic		
Number of Rows	0	1
Distance PV panels (m)	0	0
Area of single PVSD (m²)	0	7.1
Total area of Panels (m²)	0	7.1
Model Name	Horizontal Canopy Double	Horizontal Canopy Triple
Model Type	Double panel	Triple panel
Schematic		
Number of Rows	2	3
Distance PV panels (m)	0.75	0.52
Area of single PVSD (m²)	3.55	2.36
Total area of Panels (m²)	7.1	7.1
Model Name	Canopy Inclined Single	Canopy Inclined Double
Model Type	Single panel 30°	Double panel 30°
Schematic		
Number of Rows	1	2
Distance PV panels (m)	0	0.75
Area of single PVSD (m²)	7.1	3.55
Total area of Panels (m²)	7.1	7.1
Model Name	Canopy Inclined Triple	Canopy Vertical Panel
Model Type	Triple panel 30°	Vertical Panel
Schematic		
Number of Rows	3	1
Distance PV panels (m)	0.52	0
Area of single PVSD (m²)	2.36	7.1
Total area of Panels (m²)	7.1	7.1

Table II. Specifications of the PV module used in the simulations.

Parameter	Value
Name	Xunlight Corporation
Power	150 W
Cell type	Monocrystalline
Dimensions (mm)	5480*454*1.5
Weight (kg)	6
Max. Power voltage (V)	30.0
Max. Current power (A)	5.00
Open circuit voltage (V)	40.5
Current short circuit I_{sc} (A)	6.35
Maximum system voltage	600 V

5 SCIENTIFIC INNOVATION AND RELEVANCE

Sun-shading techniques play an important role in reducing building energy consumption across various countries. The combined influence of PVSDs, through both shading and electricity generation, has been the focus of several studies. The significance of these systems in lowering overall energy use has been widely discussed in the literature.

However, only a limited number of investigations have explored specific factors such as the number and tilt angle of PVSDs and their effect on energy efficiency, particularly for heating, cooling, and lighting demands. This study provides a detailed analysis of PVSD performance under different climatic conditions. It also examines the combined effect of passive shading in reducing cooling demand and active energy production from PV panels integrated into various PVSD configurations.

4.1 Different climates in France

France's extensive geography and varied topography create multiple distinct climate zones that directly affect building energy consumption and the performance of solar energy systems. This section focuses on four principal French climates: oceanic, Mediterranean, mountainous, and continental. Each climate zone is defined by specific temperature ranges, solar radiation levels, humidity, and wind patterns, all of which influence the effectiveness of solar shading systems.

Oceanic climates, represented by Brest, exhibit moderate temperatures, high humidity, moderate to high precipitation, moderate solar radiation, and moderate wind speeds. Mediterranean climates, such as Nice, are characterized by hot, dry summers, mild and wet winters, high solar radiation, and strong winds. Mountainous climates, exemplified by Clermont, experience cold, snowy winters, cool summers, elevated solar radiation, low humidity, and significant temperature fluctuations. Continental climates, like Strasbourg, feature cold winters, warm and humid summers, moderate to high solar radiation, and moderate rainfall.

Figure 2 summarizes the geographical and meteorological data of these four representative cities. Their latitudes range from 43.71°N to 48.57°N. Among them, Nice, located in the Mediterranean zone, has the highest annual global horizontal irradiance (GHI) at 1562.2 kWh/m², while Brest, in the oceanic zone, records the lowest GHI at 1105.4 kWh/m². Diffuse horizontal irradiance (DHI) values are relatively consistent across these locations, ranging from 595.8 kWh/m² in Strasbourg to 617.3 kWh/m² in Nice. Temperature variations are also notable, with average maximum temperatures ranging from 17.1 °C in Brest to 25.4 °C in Nice, and average minimum temperatures from 2.3 °C in Strasbourg to 7.3 °C in Brest. These variations in solar radiation and temperature play a critical role in determining the energy performance of buildings and the effectiveness of solar shading systems.

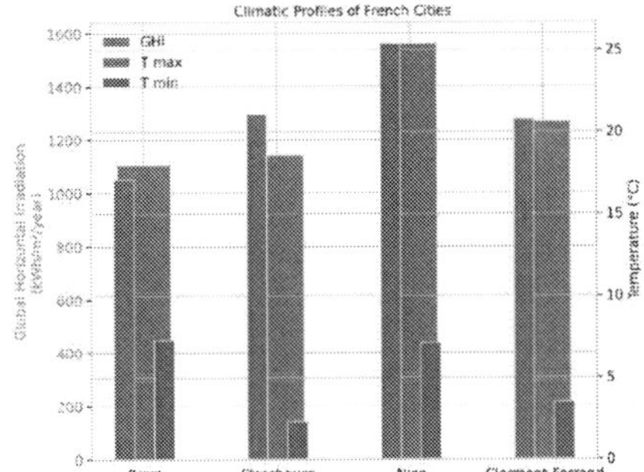

Figure 2: The weather condition in four cities in France.

6 RESULTS AND CONCLUSIONS

Figures 3 through 6 illustrate the office building's energy consumption and the PV electricity generation of various PVSD configurations. The simulation results indicate that the building in Brest has the lowest total energy consumption, at 48.11 kWh/m². In contrast, Strasbourg and Nice show the highest values, with 76.29 kWh/m² and 75.75 kWh/m², respectively. Clermont-Ferrand falls between these extremes, with an energy consumption of 65.09 kWh/m². Regarding PV electricity production, the Inclined Single Canopy model demonstrates the highest output in Nice, generating 15.08 kWh/m² (Figure 5). The same model also performs well in Clermont-Ferrand, producing 12.10 kWh/m² (Figure 4). Brest and Strasbourg show moderate results, with values of 10.5 kWh/m² and 10.71 kWh/m², respectively (Figures 3 and 6). Figure 7 presents the energy savings associated with different PVSD configurations for cooling, lighting, and heating. In Nice, the Inclined Single Canopy model achieved the highest reduction in total energy consumption, with savings of up to 35.31% compared to the base case. In Clermont, the Horizontal Single Canopy model reduced total energy use by 20.49%. In Brest and Strasbourg, this same model lowered energy consumption by 13.31% and 14.83%, respectively.   Regarding lighting energy use, results show that the Vertical Canopy Panel model increased overall consumption in all cities. The highest increase was observed in Brest, where lighting energy demand rose by 5.60%. This outcome may be explained by a substantial reduction in natural daylight reaching interior spaces, which likely increased reliance on artificial lighting. In contrast, the Horizontal Single Canopy model had the smallest negative effect on lighting energy consumption. Among all PVSDs studied, it caused the least increase in electric lighting demand. Even in the worst case, observed in Brest, this model led to only a 0.17% rise in lighting-related energy use. These findings highlight the significant influence of PVSDs on natural daylight availability and, consequently, on energy consumption related to lighting. The energy generated by PVSD systems can be used locally to supply power directly to building systems or to support nearby energy infrastructure.

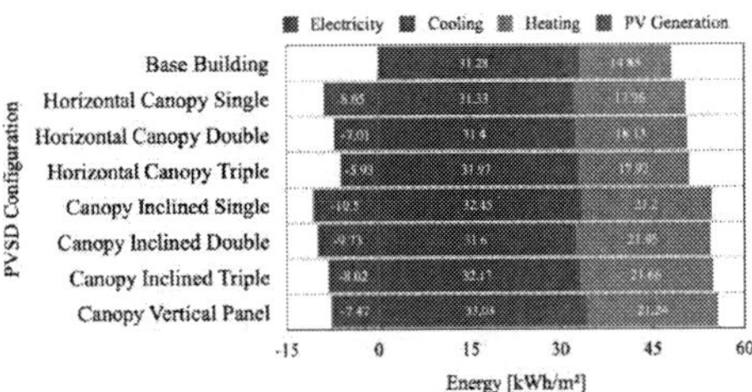

Figure 3: Energy consumption and PV electricity generation with different PVSDs in Brest.

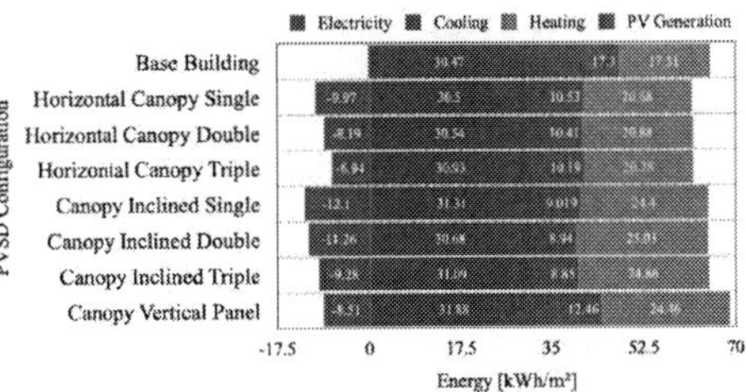

Figure 4: Energy consumption and PV electricity generation with different PVSDs in Clermont.

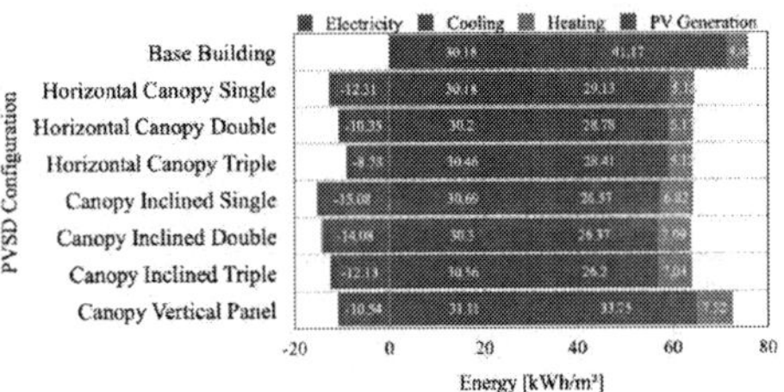

Figure 5: Energy consumption and PV electricity generation with different PVSDs in Nice.

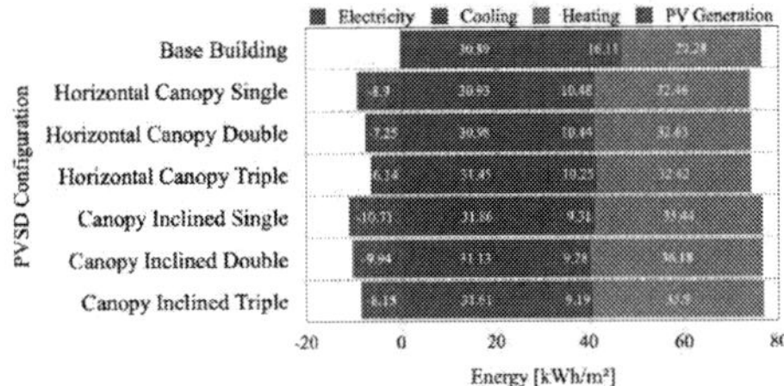

Figure 6: Energy consumption and PV electricity generation with different PVSDs in Strasbourg.

Depending on the configuration, this energy may be integrated into a local microgrid [59], enhancing the building's overall energy flexibility [14]. Surplus energy can also be routed to a smart energy hub [60], enabling efficient energy management, storage, and distribution. However, the accumulation of dust [61] [62] and other particulates on PV panels can reduce energy output over time, highlighting the importance of regular maintenance or self-cleaning surface technologies. These integration strategies not only promote energy self-sufficiency but also support demand-side management and contribute to grid stability, particularly in buildings equipped with advanced control systems and energy storage solutions.

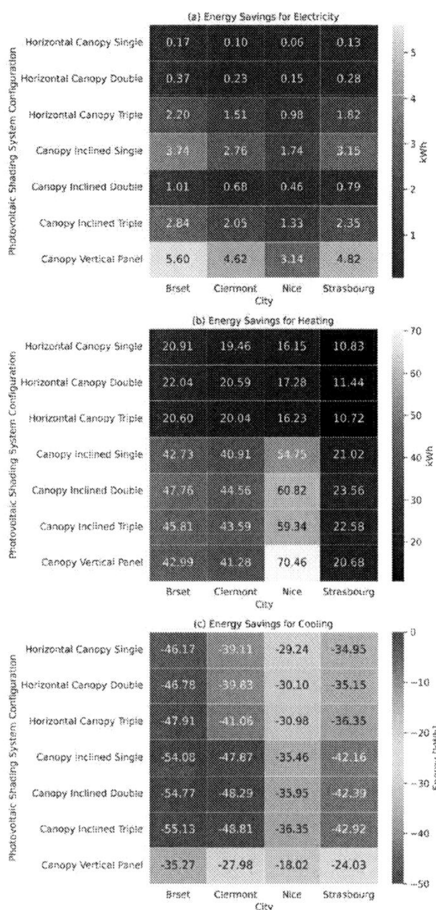

Figure 7: Energy savings analysis for (a) electricity, (b) heating, and (c) cooling consumption.

Figure 8 compares the energy-saving potential of different PVSD configurations. Among the models evaluated, the Inclined Single Canopy shows the highest annual energy savings. These findings contribute to ongoing research on climate-responsive PVSD design by providing performance-based insights across varying configurations.

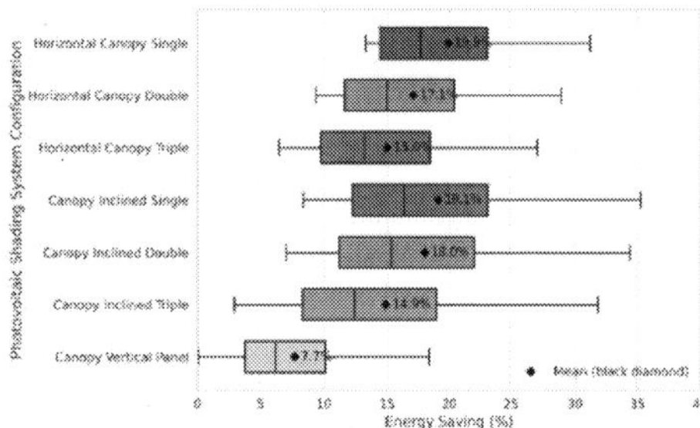

Figure 8: Comprehensive comparison of energy-saving potential by PVSDs in this study.

7 CONCLUSIONS

The simulation results demonstrate significant variations in the overall energy consumption of the office building across different French cities, emphasizing the impact of local climate. The lowest energy consumption was recorded in Brest at 48.11 kWh/m², while the highest values occurred in Strasbourg (76.29 kWh/m²) and Nice (75.75 kWh/m²). These differences highlight the climate-dependent nature of building energy performance, consistent with the findings of Shi et al. [24] and Long et al. [25], who emphasized the sensitivity of solar canopy performance to regional climate conditions. Regarding solar energy production, the Inclined Single Canopy model achieved the highest output in Nice, generating 15.08 kWh/m². This result reflects the favorable solar potential of the Mediterranean climate and aligns with the observations of Skandalos and Karamanis [28], who reported optimal performance of similar systems under comparable conditions. In terms of overall energy savings, the Inclined Single Canopy model in Nice achieved the greatest reduction in total building energy consumption, with a savings rate of 35.31%. This superior performance supports the findings of Hofer et al. [16] and Jayathissa et al. [18], who emphasized the importance of careful orientation and system design in enhancing the energy performance of solar shading solutions. The results also corroborate those of Gao et al. [19], who demonstrated that variations in panel angle and placement can significantly affect system efficiency. However, the Vertical Canopy Panel model was associated with increased lighting energy consumption across all cities, particularly in Brest (5.60%). This outcome is consistent with the findings of Kim et al. [30], who noted that while solar canopies can improve electrical performance, they may also reduce daylight availability and increase reliance on artificial lighting. In contrast, the Horizontal Single Canopy model showed the least adverse impact on lighting, with a maximum increase of only 0.17%. This favorable result, which has received limited attention in prior research, suggests the model's potential for applications requiring minimal disruption to daylight access. Overall, the findings indicate that PVSDs can significantly improve building energy efficiency when adapted to specific climatic contexts. These conclusions agree with those of Settino et al. [27] and Corti et al. [51], who stressed the importance of climate-responsive design, including considerations for solar orientation and daylighting needs.

Declaration of AI-assisted technologies in the writing process
The authors used AI-assisted English editing tools to improve readability and language, and they reviewed and revised the manuscript, taking full responsibility for the final version.

REFERENCES

[1] G. Erbach, "European climate law," *Regulation (EU)*, vol. 1119, 2021.

[2] K. Kavvadias, N. J. P. JIMENEZ, and G. THOMASSEN, *Decarbonising the EU heating sector: Integration of the power and heating sector*. 2019.

[3] M. Pacesila, S. G. Burcea, and S. E. Colesca, "Analysis of renewable energies in European

Union," *Renewable and Sustainable Energy Reviews*, vol. 56, pp. 156–170, 2016.

[4] M. Nazififard and S. Zeynali, "Analysis of Photovoltaic Panel Integration for Achieving Net-Zero Energy in French Residential Retrofits in a Mediterranean Climate," *E3S Web of Conferences*, vol. 545, p. 02006, Jul. 2024, doi: 10.1051/E3SCONF/202454502006.

[5] I. E. Agency, "Renewables 2021," 2021.

[6] A. Millot, A. Krook-Riekkola, and N. Maïzi, "Guiding the future energy transition to net-zero emissions: Lessons from exploring the differences between France and Sweden," *Energy Policy*, vol. 139, p. 111358, 2020.

[7] D. S. Pereira and A. C. Marques, "Could electricity demand contribute to diversifying the mix and mitigating CO2 emissions? A fresh daily analysis of the French electricity system," *Energy Policy*, vol. 142, p. 111475, 2020.

[8] C. E. Velasquez, F. B. G. L. e Estanislau, A. L. Costa, and C. Pereira, "Assessment of the French nuclear energy system–A case study," *Energy Strategy Reviews*, vol. 30, p. 100513, 2020.

[9] C. Sebi and A.-L. Vernay, "Community renewable energy in France: The state of development and the way forward," *Energy Policy*, vol. 147, p. 111874, 2020.

[10] W. Zhang, L. Lu, and J. Peng, "Evaluation of potential benefits of solar photovoltaic shadings in Hong Kong," *Energy*, vol. 137, pp. 1152–1158, Oct. 2017, doi: 10.1016/J.ENERGY.2017.04.166.

[11] X. Li *et al.*, "Optimal design of photovoltaic shading systems for multi-story buildings," *J Clean Prod*, vol. 220, pp. 1024–1038, May 2019, doi: 10.1016/J.JCLEPRO.2019.01.246.

[12] M. Baghoolizadeh, A. A. Nadooshan, A. Raisi, and E. H. Malekshah, "The effect of photovoltaic shading with ideal tilt angle on the energy cost optimization of a building model in European cities," *Energy for Sustainable Development*, vol. 71, pp. 505–516, Dec. 2022, doi: 10.1016/J.ESD.2022.10.016.

[13] S. Zeynali, M. Nazififard, and J. Divandari, "A Comparative Analysis of High-Rise Building Shapes and Orientations on the Performance and Energy Generation of Building Integrated Photovoltaic Systems in Tehran," *2024 9th International Conference on Technology and Energy Management, ICTEM 2024*, 2024, doi: 10.1109/ICTEM60690.2024.10631937.

[14] S. Zeynali and M. Nazififard, "Integrating Photovoltaic Systems into Urban Infrastructure: A Case Study of Tehran International Tower," *2024 11th Iranian Conference on Renewable Energy and Distribution Generation, ICREDG 2024*, 2024, doi: 10.1109/ICREDG61679.2024.10607829.

[15] M. Nazififard and E. Franquet, "Systematic analysis of roof-mounted photovoltaic systems for achieving net-zero energy in urban historic buildings in hot and arid climates: Potential and challenges," *Energy Build*, vol. 348, p. 116394, Dec. 2025, doi: 10.1016/J.ENBUILD.2025.116394.

[16] J. Hofer, A. Groenewolt, P. Jayathissa, Z. Nagy, and A. Schlueter, "Parametric analysis and systems design of dynamic photovoltaic shading modules," *Energy Sci Eng*, vol. 4, no. 2, pp. 134–152, 2016.

[17] Z. Nagy *et al.*, "The Adaptive Solar Facade: From concept to prototypes," *Frontiers of Architectural Research*, vol. 5, no. 2, pp. 143–156, 2016, doi: https://doi.org/10.1016/j.foar.2016.03.002.

[18] P. Jayathissa, J. Zarb, M. Luzzatto, J. Hofer, and A. Schlueter, "Sensitivity of Building Properties and Use Types for the Application of Adaptive Photovoltaic Shading Systems," *Energy Procedia*, vol. 122, pp. 139–144, 2017, doi: https://doi.org/10.1016/j.egypro.2017.07.319.

[19] Y. Gao *et al.*, "A photovoltaic window with sun-tracking shading elements towards maximum power generation and non-glare daylighting," *Appl Energy*, vol. 228, pp. 1454–1472, 2018, doi: https://doi.org/10.1016/j.apenergy.2018.07.015.

[20] M. Krarti and A. Karrech, "Evaluation of static and dynamic PV-Integrated shading systems for office spaces in Australia," *Solar Energy*, vol. 277, p. 112736, 2024, doi: https://doi.org/10.1016/j.solener.2024.112736.

[21] Y. Jiang, Z. Qi, S. Ran, and Q. Ma, "A Study on the Effect of Dynamic Photovoltaic Shading Devices on Energy Consumption and Daylighting of an Office Building," *Buildings*, vol. 14, no. 3, 2024, doi: 10.3390/buildings14030596.

[22] M. Krarti, M. A. Ayari, F. Touati, and M. R. Paurobally, "Energy Benefits of PV-Integrated Dynamic Overhangs for Residential Buildings in Qatar," *Energies (Basel)*, vol. 18, no. 5, 2025, doi: 10.3390/en18051156.

[23] X. Li, J. Peng, N. Li, M. Wang, and C. Wang, "Study on Optimum Tilt Angles of Photovoltaic Shading Systems in Different Climatic Regions of China," *Procedia Eng*, vol. 205, pp. 1157–1164, 2017, doi: https://doi.org/10.1016/j.proeng.2017.10.185.

[24] S. Shi, J. Sun, M. Liu, X. Chen, W. Gao, and Y. Song, "Energy-Saving Potential Comparison of Different Photovoltaic Integrated Shading Devices (PVSDs) for Single-Story and Multi-Story Buildings," *Energies (Basel)*, vol. 15, no. 23, 2022, doi: 10.3390/en15239196.

[25] W. Long, X. Chen, Q. Ma, X. Wei, and Q. Xi, "An Evaluation of the PV Integrated Dynamic Overhangs Based on Parametric Performance Design Method: A Case Study of a Student Apartment in China," *Sustainability*, vol. 14, no. 13, 2022, doi: 10.3390/su14137808.

[26] A. Mesloub, A. Ghosh, M. Touahmia, G. A. Albaqawy, E. Noaime, and B. M. Alsolami, "Performance Analysis of Photovoltaic Integrated Shading Devices (PVSDs) and Semi-Transparent Photovoltaic (STPV) Devices Retrofitted to a Prototype Office Building in a Hot Desert Climate," *Sustainability*, vol. 12, no. 23, 2020, doi: 10.3390/su122310145.

[27] J. Settino, C. Carpino, S. Perrella, and N. Arcuri, "Multi-Objective Analysis of a Fixed Solar Shading System in Different Climatic Areas," *Energies (Basel)*, vol. 13, p. 3249, Jun. 2020, doi: 10.3390/en13123249.

[28] N. Skandalos and D. Karamanis, "An optimization approach to photovoltaic building

integration towards low energy buildings in different climate zones," *Appl Energy*, vol. 295, p. 117017, Aug. 2021, doi: 10.1016/J.APENERGY.2021.117017.

[29] J. Abu Qadourah, "Evaluating solar-active shading solutions: a study of energy performance in Mediterranean residential architecture," *Architectural Engineering and Design Management*, vol. 20, pp. 1–16, Oct. 2023, doi: 10.1080/17452007.2023.2267570.

[30] S.-H. Kim, I.-T. Kim, A.-S. Choi, and M. Sung, "Evaluation of optimized PV power generation and electrical lighting energy savings from the PV blind-integrated daylight responsive dimming system using LED lighting," *Solar Energy*, vol. 107, pp. 746–757, 2014, doi: https://doi.org/10.1016/j.solener.2014.06.022.

[31] M. Qingsong, S. Ran, X. Chen, L. Li, W. Gao, and X. Wei, "Study on the effect of photovoltaic louver shading and lighting control system on building energy consumption and daylighting," *Energy Sources, Part A: Recovery, Utilization, and Environmental Effects*, vol. 45, pp. 10873–10889, Sep. 2023, doi: 10.1080/15567036.2023.2251439.

[32] C. Li, W. Zhang, J. Wu, Y. Lyu, and H. Tang, "Experimental study of a vertically mounted bifacial photovoltaic sunshade," *Renew Energy*, vol. 219, p. 119518, 2023, doi: https://doi.org/10.1016/j.renene.2023.119518.

[33] J. Liu, G. Bi, G. Gao, and L. Zhao, "Optimal design method for photovoltaic shading devices (PVSDs) by combining geometric optimization and adaptive control model," *Journal of Building Engineering*, vol. 69, p. 106101, 2023, doi: https://doi.org/10.1016/j.jobe.2023.106101.

[34] C. Li, W. Zhang, F. Liu, X. Li, J. Wang, and C. Li, "Multi-Objective Optimization of Bifacial Photovoltaic Sunshade: Towards Better Optical, Electrical and Economical Performance," *Sustainability*, vol. 16, no. 14, 2024, doi: 10.3390/su16145977.

[35] Y. Zheng *et al.*, "A novel sun-shading design for indoor visual comfort and energy saving in typical office space in Shenzhen," *Energy Build*, vol. 328, p. 115083, 2025, doi: https://doi.org/10.1016/j.enbuild.2024.115083.

[36] P. Jayathissa, M. Luzzatto, J. Schmidli, J. Hofer, Z. Nagy, and A. Schlueter, "Optimising building net energy demand with dynamic BIPV shading," *Appl Energy*, vol. 202, pp. 726–735, Sep. 2017, doi: 10.1016/J.APENERGY.2017.05.083.

[37] H. K. Abdullah and H. Z. Alibaba, "Towards Nearly Zero-Energy Buildings: The Potential of Photovoltaic-Integrated Shading Devices to Achieve Autonomous Solar Electricity and Acceptable Thermal Comfort in Naturally ventilated Office Spaces," in *Proceedings of the 16th International Conference on Clean Energy, Famagusta, North Cyprus*, 2018, pp. 9–11.

[38] U. Haider, E. Trepci, and E. Rodriguez-Ubinas, "Assessment of Photovoltaics Shading Devices (PVSD) Impact on the Energy Generation, Cooling Load, and Daylighting in an Office Building in Dubai," in *2023 Middle East and North Africa Solar Conference (MENA-SC)*,

2023, pp. 1–5. doi: 10.1109/MENA-SC54044.2023.10374491.

[39] Z. Cai, W. Zhang, J. Chen, and P. Su, "Photovoltaic Integrated Shading Devices in the Retrofitting of Existing Buildings on Chinese Campuses Within a Regional Context," *Buildings*, vol. 14, no. 11, 2024, doi: 10.3390/buildings14113577.

[40] A. C. Peres, R. Calili, and D. Louzada, "Impacts of photovoltaic shading devices on energy generation and cooling demand," in *2020 47th IEEE Photovoltaic Specialists Conference (PVSC)*, IEEE, 2020, pp. 1186–1191.

[41] S. K. Jung, Y. Kim, and J. W. Moon, "Performance Evaluation of Control Methods for PV-Integrated Shading Devices," *Energies (Basel)*, vol. 13, no. 12, 2020, doi: 10.3390/en13123171.

[42] O. Asfour, "Solar and Shading Potential of Different Configurations of Building Integrated Photovoltaics Used as Shading Devices Considering Hot Climatic Conditions," *Sustainability*, vol. 10, p. 4373, Nov. 2018, doi: 10.3390/su10124373.

[43] M. Han, L. Lu, and B. Sun, "Overall energy performance of building-integrated bifacial photovoltaic sunshades with different installation and building parameters in hot and humid regions," *Solar Energy*, vol. 275, p. 112619, 2024, doi: https://doi.org/10.1016/j.solener.2024.112619.

[44] J. Kim, H. Lee, M. Choi, D. Kim, and J. Yoon, "Power performance assessment of PV blinds system considering self-shading effects," *Solar Energy*, vol. 262, p. 111834, 2023, doi: https://doi.org/10.1016/j.solener.2023.111834.

[45] M. Wang, Z. Jia, L. Tao, W. Wang, and C. Xiang, "Optimizing the tilt angle of kinetic photovoltaic shading devices considering energy consumption and power Generation— Hong Kong case," *Energy Build*, vol. 326, p. 115072, 2025, doi: https://doi.org/10.1016/j.enbuild.2024.115072.

[46] W. Bahr, "A comprehensive assessment methodology of the building integrated photovoltaic blind system," *Energy Build*, vol. 82, pp. 703–708, 2014, doi: https://doi.org/10.1016/j.enbuild.2014.07.065.

[47] A. Baghdadi and M. Abuhussain, "In-Depth Analysis of Photovoltaic-Integrated Shading Systems' Performance in Residential Buildings: A Prospective of Numerical Techniques Toward Net-Zero Energy Buildings," *Buildings*, vol. 15, no. 2, 2025, doi: 10.3390/buildings15020222.

[48] H. Chen, B. Cai, H. Yang, Y. Wang, and J. Yang, "Study on natural lighting and electrical performance of louvered photovoltaic windows in hot summer and cold winter areas," *Energy Build*, vol. 271, p. 112313, 2022, doi: https://doi.org/10.1016/j.enbuild.2022.112313.

[49] Y. Ibraheem, E. R. P. Farr, and P. A. E. Piroozfar, "Embedding Passive Intelligence into Building Envelopes: A Review of the State-of-the-art in Integrated Photovoltaic Shading Devices," *Energy Procedia*, vol. 111, pp. 964–973, 2017, doi: https://doi.org/10.1016/j.egypro.2017.03.259.

[50] A. Kirimtat, M. F. Tasgetiren, P. Brida, and O. Krejcar, "Control of PV integrated shading devices in buildings: A review," *Build Environ*, vol. 214, p. 108961, Apr. 2022, doi: 10.1016/J.BUILDENV.2022.108961.

[51] P. Corti, P. Bonomo, and F. Frontini, "Paper Review of External Integrated Systems as Photovoltaic Shading Devices," *Energies (Basel)*, vol. 16, no. 14, 2023, doi: 10.3390/en16145542.

[52] Y. Luo *et al.*, "A comparative study on thermal performance evaluation of a new double skin façade system integrated with photovoltaic blinds," *Appl Energy*, vol. 199, pp. 281–293, 2017, doi: https://doi.org/10.1016/j.apenergy.2017.05.026.

[53] L. Evangelisti, C. Guattari, F. Asdrubali, and R. de Lieto Vollaro, "An experimental investigation of the thermal performance of a building solar shading device," *Journal of Building Engineering*, vol. 28, p. 101089, Mar. 2020, doi: 10.1016/J.JOBE.2019.101089.

[54] M. Akbari Paydar, "Optimum design of building integrated PV module as a movable shading device," *Sustain Cities Soc*, vol. 62, p. 102368, Nov. 2020, doi: 10.1016/J.SCS.2020.102368.

[55] J. E. Ogbeba and E. Hoskara, "The Evaluation of Single-Family Detached Housing Units in terms of Integrated Photovoltaic Shading Devices: The Case of Northern Cyprus," *Sustainability*, vol. 11, no. 3, 2019, doi: 10.3390/su11030593.

[56] E. Taveres-Cachat, K. Bøe, G. Lobaccaro, F. Goia, and S. Grynning, "Balancing competing parameters in search of optimal configurations for a fix louvre blade system with integrated PV," *Energy Procedia*, vol. 122, pp. 607–612, Sep. 2017, doi: 10.1016/J.EGYPRO.2017.07.357.

[57] T. Mendis, Z. Huang, S. Xu, and W. Zhang, "Economic potential analysis of photovoltaic integrated shading strategies on commercial building facades in urban blocks: A case study of Colombo, Sri Lanka," *Energy*, vol. 194, p. 116908, 2020, doi: https://j.energy.2020.116908.

[58] M. Nazififard and S. Zeynali, "Analysis of Photovoltaic Panel Integration for Achieving Net-Zero Energy in French Residential Retrofits in a Mediterranean Climate," in *E3S Web of Conferences*, EDP Sciences, 2024, p. 02006.

[59] A. Imanloozadeh, M. Nazififard, and H. Hashemi-Dezaki, "Optimal technoeconomic reliability-oriented design of islanded multicarrier microgrids with electrical and hydrogen energy storage systems considering emission concerns," *Energy Sci Eng*, vol. 12, no. 6, pp. 2702–2745, Jun. 2024, doi: 10.1002/ESE3.1774.

[60] A. Imanloozadeh, M. Nazififard, and S. A. Sadat, "A new stochastic optimal smart residential energy hub management system for desert environment," *Int J Energy Res*, vol. 45, no. 13, pp. 18957–18980, Oct. 2021, doi: 10.1002/er.6991.

[61] M. Nazififard and N. Torabi, "Experimental Analysis of Dust Accumulation on the Panels of a Microgrid-Connected Photovlitaic System in an Arid Climate," *2023 13th Smart Grid Conference, SGC 2023*, 2023, doi: 10.1109/SGC61621.2023.10459274.

[62] S. Ali Sadat, J. Faraji, M. Nazififard, and A. Ketabi, "The experimental analysis of dust deposition effect on solar photovoltaic panels in Iran's desert environment," *Sustainable Energy Technologies and Assessments*, vol. 47, Oct. 2021, doi: 10.1016/j.seta.2021.101542.

MODULE LAYOUT FOR RELIABLE ALUMINUM-BASED BUILDING-INTEGRATED PHOTOVOLTAICS

Wiebke Wirtz[1], Kevin Meyer[1], Rolf Brendel[1,2], Henning Schulte-Huxel[1]
[1]Institute for Solar Energy Research Hamelin (ISFH), Am Ohrberg 1, 31860 Emmerthal, Germany
[2]Institute of Solid State Physics, Leibniz University Hannover, Appelstraße 2, 30167 Hannover, Germany

ABSTRACT: When manufacturing photovoltaic (PV) modules with aluminum rear covers, for instance for building integration purposes, one has to consider the large thermal expansion of the aluminum compared to silicon and glass. This holds for the manufacturing process as well as for the reliability of the resulting building-integrated PV (BIPV) modules. Concerning module reliability, the mismatch in thermal expansion coefficients of silicon solar cells and aluminum rear cover leads to mechanical stress in the solar cell strings under temperature changes. After several temperature shifts during operation, the copper wires interconnecting the silicon solar cells might suffer from fatigue breakage and thereby the module power output could be drastically reduced. This work investigates the influence of module layout in terms of solar cell width and solar cell string length on the electrical degradation of crystalline silicon PV modules with aluminum sheets as rear covers in thermal cycling tests. As a result, we find that aluminum-based modules with wide cells degrade faster and fail earlier in the thermal cycling test than modules with narrow cells. This can be explained by an increased cell gap change during thermal cycling for solar cell strings with wider cells. Furthermore, thermal cycling of modules with aluminum rear covers in lengths from 20 cm to 240 cm and accordingly long cell strings resulted in earlier degradation and failure of longer strings. In conclusion, from a thermomechanical point of view, a module layout with short strings of narrow cells is recommended.
Keywords: BIPV, reliability, thermal stress

1 INTRODUCTION

The installation of building-integrated photovoltaics (BIPV) enables generation of renewable energy without additional land use [1]. It also offers the advantage of generating electricity directly where it is consumed, as buildings contribute 20% to 40% of the total final energy consumption [2]. Vertical mounting and orientation in various cardinal directions help to align generation with demand over the course of day and year [3]. All these reasons make BIPV a valuable contribution to energy efficiency of buildings [4] and climate change mitigation by transition to renewable energy production [5]. However, BIPV will only gain widespread adoption if it is both aesthetically pleasing and financially viable.

Since BIPV combines two different sectors, photovoltaics (PV) and buildings, it is a straight-forward approach to combine commonly used materials from these areas, allowing BIPV modules to function as both energy generators and building envelopes. In this study, we investigate the combination of PV modules with aluminum sheets as module rear covers. Aluminum is a common façade material in the construction industry due to its light weight and its durability [6]. Thus, it is an interesting material for adopting it in building-integrated PV applications. Using aluminum offers the chance of an easy market entry because the resulting PV-activated façade elements are similar to handle for planners and installers as common aluminum façade elements. However, a significant challenge lies in the combination of materials such as glass front covers, polymer sheets for encapsulation, silicon solar cells, copper wires and aluminum rear cover, which have differing thermal expansion coefficients. This mismatch induces mechanical stress under variation in temperature, leading to accelerated degradation of such BIPV modules with aluminum rear covers [7], which contradicts the typically long lifespan of building skins of up to 50 years [8].

In this work, we investigate the influence of module layout on the reliability of lightweight BIPV modules with aluminum rear covers and polymeric frontsheets in thermal cycling tests. Other publications show an influence of module layout, especially in terms of cell size, on thermal stress in glass-backsheet and glass-glass PV modules [9, 10]. We expect the effect stemming from mismatches in thermal expansion coefficients of silicon ($\alpha_{Si} = 2.614 \times 10^{-6}$ K^{-1} [11]) and glass ($\alpha_{glass} = 9 \times 10^{-6}$ K^{-1} [12]) to be even more pronounced in PV modules with aluminum rear covers ($\alpha_{Al} = 23.5 \times 10^{-6}$ K^{-1} [13]). Therefore, we extend our investigation on varying cell widths [7] by experiments varying the string length in order to find module layout recommendations for optimal robustness of BIPV modules with aluminum rear covers against thermal stress.

2 EXPERIMENTAL

2.1 Method

We fabricate two sets of test samples of PV modules with aluminum rear covers, one with varying cell width in strings of approximately the same length (see also [7]) and one with varying string length using one cell format. Instead of manufacturing several test modules of few configurations for statistics, we fabricate one test module of many configurations to derive trends in the degradation behavior. The test modules are characterized by measuring the current-voltage (*IV*) characteristics at standard test conditions in a flash tester and by taking electroluminescence (EL) images in regular intervals between thermal cycling tests according to the standard IEC 61215 [14]. The resulting degradation behaviors and dependences are interpreted with the help of simplified (analytical) models of the material compound.

2.2 Samples

For investigating the effect of cell width on module power degradation, we fabricate four test modules with varying cell width according to the material stack depicted in Fig. 1. The 1 mm thick aluminum rear covers are coated with a thin layer of polyethylene (PE) on the front side for coloring and are 130 cm long and 25 cm wide. The rest of the module stack is 120 cm long and positioned in the center of the aluminum sheet. The test modules contain one string of industrial PERC+ solar cells from the same tier 1 manufacturer each, encapsulated with polyolefin

(PO) encapsulant. We place one 500 μm thick layer of PO encapsulant each between the aluminum sheet and the 50 μm PVF insulation layer, between the insulation layer and the cell string and between the cell string and the 400 μm PET-based frontsheet. Table I lists the different string configurations with varying cell widths.

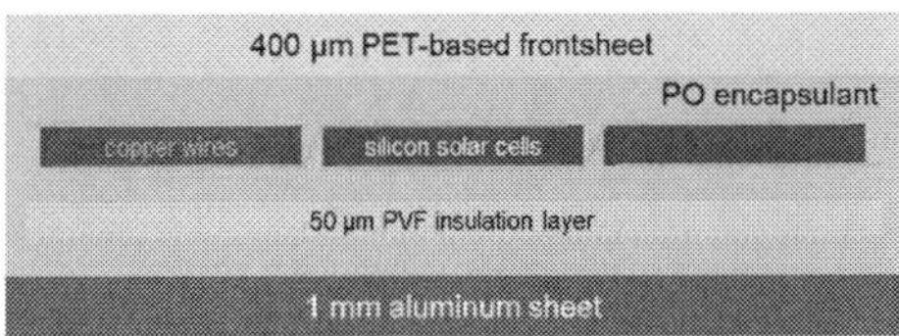

Figure 1: Schematic cross-section (not to scale) of the material stack of lightweight BIPV modules with aluminum rear cover as they are manufactured for this work (adopted from [7]).

Table I: Solar cell string configurations of aluminum test modules with varying cell width.

Module name	Cell Width (mm)	Number of cells	Cell gap (mm)	String length (mm)
M6 quarter	41.5	26	2	1129
M6 half	83	13	2	1103
M12 half	105	10	2	1068
M12 full	210	5	2	1058

For investigating the effect of string length on module power degradation, we fabricate ten test modules with varying string and module length from 20 cm to 240 cm according to the material stack depicted in Fig. 1. The 1 mm thick and 25 cm wide aluminum rear covers are uncoated in this set of samples and the aluminum sheets are completely covered with encapsulant and frontsheet. The test modules contain one string of industrial half-cut M6 PERC+ solar cells each. Table II lists the different string configurations and module lengths. The module with a string of six cells in the center of a 120 cm long aluminum sheet is fabricated for investigating the effect of uncovered parts of the aluminum sheets next to the cell strings.

Table II: Solar cell string configurations of aluminum test modules with varying string length and module length given by the length of the aluminum rear cover.

Module name	Number of cells	Cell gap (mm)	Aluminum length (cm)
2 cells	2	2	20
3 cells	3	2	30
4 cells	4	2	40
6 cells	6	2	60
6 cells on 120 cm	6	2	120
9 cells	9	2	80
10 cells	10	2	90
11 cells	11	2	100
13 cells	13	2	120
27 cells	27	2	240

3 RESULTS

3.1 Varying cell width

Figure 2 shows the results of thermal cycling of the four aluminum-based BIPV modules with different cell widths. This is the extension of the results published in [7]. The test module with the widest cells "M12 full" fails first, followed by the modules with the second biggest cell width "M12 half" and the third biggest cell width "M6 half". The module with the smallest cells "M6 quarter" is the most stable one after an initial drop resulting from the non-optimized metallization design for quarter-cutting. It still delivers 75.4% of its initial power after 1200 thermal cycles before it drops to 0. Small cell widths are thus advantageous for the reliability of BIPV modules with aluminum rear covers and PET frontsheet. However, it has to be mentioned that all tested 120 cm long modules with cell widths smaller than M12 full cells pass the criterion of less than 5% power loss after 200 thermal cycles from IEC 61215 [14].

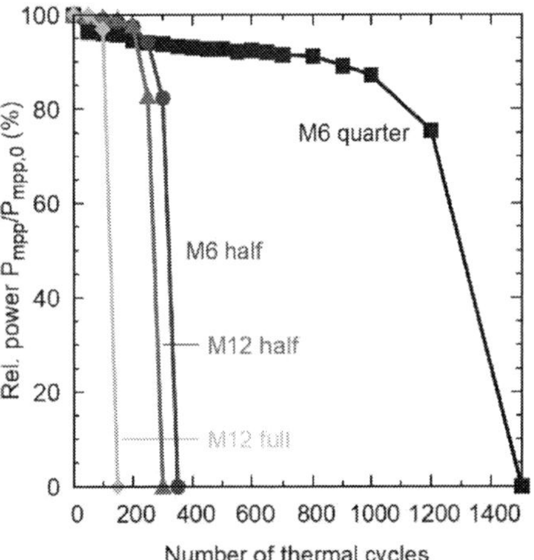

Figure 2: Measured maximum powers of BIPV modules with aluminum rear covers and varying cell width during thermal cycling relative to the initial measurements. The modules fail in the order of decreasing cell width.

As explained in [7], the difference in thermal expansion coefficients of silicon and aluminum leads to a change in cell gap width in BIPV modules with aluminum rear covers during thermal cycling. For a rough quantitative estimation of this cell gap change resulting in mechanical stress in the solar cell interconnectors, we assume linear thermal expansion of the aluminum sheet and the silicon solar cells with temperature-independent expansion coefficients, which dominates the effect of cell gap change. We neglect the influence of all other materials in the module for sake of simplicity and concentrate on the stiff components in the stack. Together with the assumption that the positions of the solar cell centers are all fixed relative to the aluminum sheet, one can roughly estimate the cell gap change per Kelvin

$$\Delta g/\Delta T = (\alpha_{Al} - \alpha_{Si})\, w + \alpha_{Al}\, g \qquad (1)$$

as a function of the cell width w and the cell gap g [7]. We only consider the dependence of cell gap change $\Delta g/\Delta T$ on cell width w. Experimentally varying the cell gap g in a range of a few millimeters would only have minor influence on $\Delta g/\Delta T$. The solid line in Fig. 3 shows the cell gap change of silicon solar cells with a cell gap of 2 mm in an aluminum module for cell widths from 10 mm to 220 mm as calculated by Eq. 1. The theoretical cell gap changes of the examined test modules are indicated as well. They range from 0.91 μm/K for M6 quarter cells to 4.43 μm/K for M12 full cells, i.e. the interconnectors in modules with wider cells are stressed more than in modules with smaller cells. This correlates with our observation of BIPV modules with aluminum rear covers and varying cell width failing in the order of decreasing cell width, i.e. decreasing stress on the interconnectors by less change of cell gap width during thermal cycling.

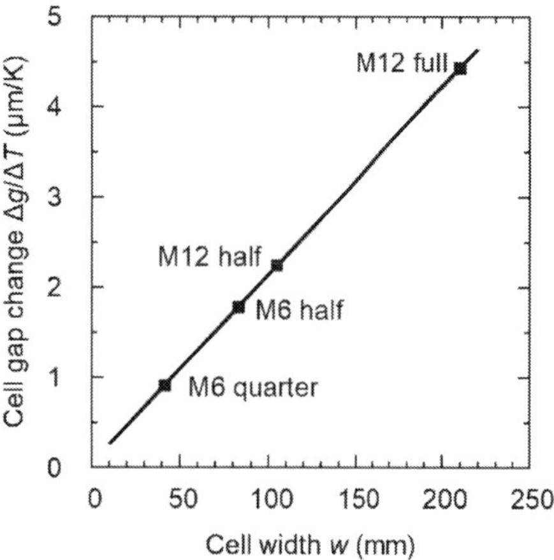

Figure 3: Theoretical cell gap change $\Delta g/\Delta T$ in PV modules with aluminum rear covers according to Eq. 1 (solid line). The markers indicate the theoretical cell gap changes of the test modules with varying cell width in this work.

3.2 Varying string length

In addition to the intuitive linear effect of cell width on cell gap change and module reliability, we also observe an effect of string length on module power degradation in thermal cycling tests. Figure 4 shows the measured relative powers of the first nine test modules from Table II during thermal cycling. It is evident that long strings degrade and fail earlier in the test sequence than short strings. The module with a length of 27 half-cut M6 cells on 240 cm falls below 75% of its initial power after 200 thermal cycles. A remaining power of 75%, however, could be expected for some commercial glass-glass modules after 50 years of operation, if their power warranty is extrapolated to 50 years [15]. After 250 thermal cycle no current can be extracted anymore because all interconnection wires of one cell gap are broken. The module with a length of 3 half-cut M6 cells on a 30 cm long aluminum sheet reaches the 75% threshold after 450 thermal cycles and still delivers over 40% of its initial power after 600 thermal cycles. As the dominant degradation mechanism of these modules is fatigue of the solar cell interconnectors, the observation of long modules degrading and failing earlier can be explained by strain adding up from the string ends resulting in more strain in the interconnectors of longer strings and therefore earlier fatigue. The reason for that is the fact that the silicon solar cells are not rigidly fixed to the aluminum rear cover, as assumed in the simplified consideration in the previous

section. The encapsulant linking the two materials allows a certain amount of elasticity and therefore an inhomogeneous distribution of strain and stress in the solar cell interconnectors increasing towards the center of the solar cell string. This also aligns with our observation of most severe degradation and earliest interconnector fatigue in the center of BIPV modules with aluminum rear covers in thermal cycling tests, as can be seen in the EL image in Fig. 5.

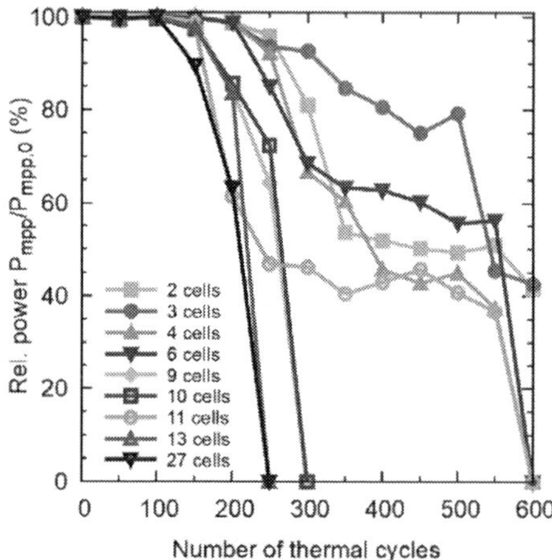

Figure 4: Measured maximum powers of BIPV modules with aluminum rear cover and varying string length during thermal cycling relative to the initial measurements. Modules with long strings degrade and fail earlier in the test than modules with short strings.

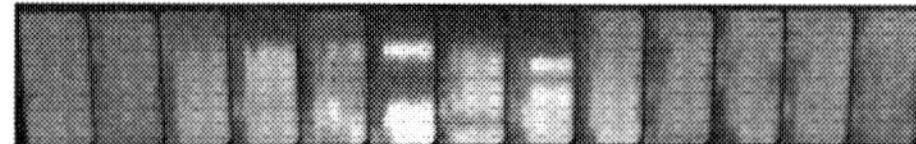

Figure 5: EL image of the test module with 13 half-cut M6 cells on a 120 cm aluminum sheet after 150 thermal cycles. Interconnection wires start to break in the center of the solar cell string, as the dark regions around whole busbars indicate.

In the considered set of test modules with varying string length, the uncovered parts of the aluminum sheets next to the cell strings are differently long. In order to clarify if the module length, i.e. the aluminum substrate length, is a critical parameter for the module power degradation, we fabricate a test module with a string of 6 half-cut M6 cells positioned in the center of a 120 cm aluminum sheet. Figure 6 shows the power degradation of this module in comparison to a test module with a string of 6 half-cut M6 cells on a 60 cm aluminum sheet and a test module with 13 half-cut M6 cells on a 120 cm aluminum sheet. The power output of the string of 6 cells not fully covering the 120 cm aluminum sheet degrades analogously to the string of 6 cells fully covering the 60 cm aluminum sheet. The string of 13 cells degrades and fails much earlier in the thermal cycling test. From these results we conclude that the surrounding aluminum sheet does not affect the degradation of aluminum-based BIPV modules in thermal cycling tests.

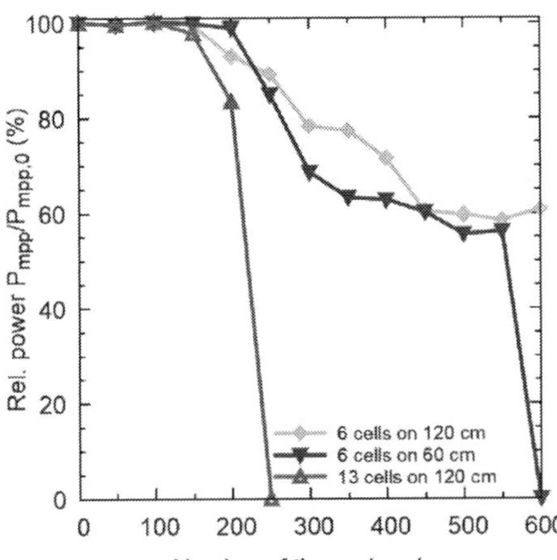

Figure 6: Measured maximum powers of BIPV modules with aluminum rear cover and varying string and module length during thermal cycling relative to the initial measurements. Six cells positioned in the center of a 120 cm aluminum sheet degrade analogously to 6 cells on a 60 cm aluminum sheet.

4 CONCLUSIONS

In conclusion, our experiments with aluminum-based BIPV modules show that both cell width and string length have a strong influence on module reliability. However, varying the cell width is more critical than varying the string length. The effect of the cell width can simply be explained by the difference in thermal expansion coefficients of the silicon solar cells and the aluminum module rear cover resulting in higher cell gap changes for wider cells during thermal cycling. The string length has an influence on module reliability because the silicon solar cells are not rigidly fixed to the aluminum rear cover but the two materials are linked in a viscoelastic way [16], leading to stress adding up from the string ends to the center. Therefore, there is more stress adding up in longer strings resulting in earlier interconnector fatigue during thermal cycling.

In summary, we recommend preferably short strings of narrow cells. This can, for instance, be realized by placing the strings along the short side of rectangular modules. This is also advantageous for the robustness against mechanical load and solar cell breakage [17, 18], as well as against partial shading [19]. Furthermore, we can conclude from our experimental results that aluminum-based BIPV modules with relevant lengths of at least 1 m on the short side of rectangular modules and PET frontsheets are able to pass the thermal cycling test from IEC 61215. For passing stricter criteria like less than 5% power loss after 600 thermal cycles, to be on the safe side, such modules have to be adapted in other ways than just the module layout. One approach is for example adapting the interconnection of the silicon solar cells and introduce a strain relief in the shape of a horizontal crimp in order to make the interconnectors more robust against expanding and shrinking cell gaps [7].

5 ACKNOWLEDGMENTS

The authors thank I. Kunze and K. Moliya for performing EL and *IV* measurements and the company MN Metall GmbH for providing the aluminum sheets. The authors appreciate the funding of this work by the German Federal Ministry of Economic Affairs and Climate Action (Project "AluPV", contract no. 03EN1069A) and the German State of Lower Saxony.

6 REFERENCES

[1] D. van de Vehn et al., "The potential land requirements and related land use change emissions of solar energy", Scientific Reports, Vol. 11, 2907, 2021

[2] L. Pérez-Lombard et al., "A review on buildings energy consumption information", Energy and Buildings, Vol. 40, p.394-398, 2008

[3] S. Freitas and M.C. Brito, "Non-cumulative only solar photovoltaics for electricity load-matching", Renewable and Sustainable Energy Reviews, 2018

[4] Directive (EU) 2018/844 of the European Parliament and of the council of 30 May 2018 amending Directive 2010/31/EU on the energy performance of buildings and Directive 2012/27/EU on energy efficiency

[5] Parties to the United Nations Framework Convention on Climate Change, "Paris Agreement", 2015

[6] D. Skejic et al., "Aluminium as a Material for Modern Structures", Gradevinar 67 (2015) 11, 2015

[7] W. Wirtz et al., "Improved robustness against thermal stress for building-integrated PV modules built on aluminum façade elements", Progress in Photovoltaics: Research and Applications, Vol. 33, No. 6, pp. 717-725, 2025

[8] C.Y. Cheong et al., "Life cycle assessment of curtain wall facades: A screening study on end-of-life scenarios", Journal of Building Engineering, Vol. 84, 2024

[9] A.J. Beinert et al., "The Effect of Cell and Module Dimensions on Thermomechanical Stress in PV Modules", IEEE Journal of Photovoltaics, Vol. 10, No. 1, 2020

[10] H. Hanifi et al., "Loss analysis and optimization of PV module components and design to achieve higher energy yield and longer service life in desert regions", Applied Energy, Vol. 280, 116028, 2020

[11] R.B. Roberts, "Thermal expansion reference data: silicon 300-850 K", Journal of Physics D: Applied Physics, Vol. 14, No. 10, 1981

[12] J. Wurm, "Glass Structures: Design and Construction of Self-Supporting Skins", Birkhäuser, Basel, 2007

[13] P. Hidnert and H.S. Krider, "Thermal Expansion of Aluminum and Some Aluminum Alloys", Journal of Research of the National Bureau of Standards, Vol. 48, No. 3, 1952

[14] "Terrestrial photovoltaic (PV) modules - Design qualification and type approval - Part 2: Test procedures", IEC 61215-2:2022-02

[15] Trina Solar, "Global limited warranty for Trina Solar brand crystalline solar photovoltaic modules", https://static.trinasolar.com/sites/default/files/PS-M-0135WarrantyMarch2022.pdf, 2022, accessed

August 15th, 2025
[16] U. Eitner, "Thermomechanics of photovoltaic modules", dissertation, Martin-Luther-Universität Halle-Wittenberg, 2011
[17] N. Bosco, "Turn Your Half-Cut Cells for a Stronger Module", IEEE Journal of Photovoltaics, Vol. 12, No. 5, pp. 1149-1153, 2022
[18] A.J. Beinert et al., "Thermomechanical design rules for photovoltaic modules", Progress in Photovoltaics: Research and Applications, Vol. 31, No. 12, 2022
[19] R. Witteck et al., "Three Bypass Diodes Architecture at the Limit", IEEE Journal of Photovoltaics, Vol. 10, No. 6, 2020

eurac
research

Cost-Benefit Analysis of Luminescence Techniques vs. Infrared Thermography in Utility-Scale PV Inspections

Lukas Koester, Sandra Gallmetzer, Mousa Sondoqah,
Giampaolo Manzolini, David Moser, Atse Louwen, Luis Fialho

EUPVSEC 2025 – 23.09.2025

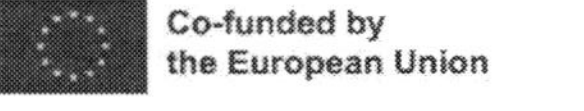

020261-001

Motivation

Infrared thermography (IRT) is standard in best practice guidelines (SPE2025) and in practice.

Electroluminescence (EL) is suggested to do for better understanding of problems.

Question: if luminescence techniques (EL or daylight photoluminescence (DPL)) offer more insights than IRT, which are the (economical) constrains prioritizing them?

	Imaging speed (MW/h)	References
IRT	1 – 4	IEA-PVPS T13 2021, Bakir2023
EL	0.4 - 0.8 (~2.5)	AEPVI, (QE2025)
DPL	0.3 (1.2 estimated)	Doll2023, (Koester2024)

Matrix references: cf. L. Koester, "Review of photovoltaic module degradation, field inspection techniques and techno-economic assessment", RSER 2022

Performance reducing observations	CPL/DR Commonly described	I-V Affected parameters (from [1])	Inspection Method — Inspection methods with a possibility of detecting one respective observation, degradation mode or failure in the corresponding categories. Images are example appearances.
Fractured Solar Cell	CPL up to 1-15 % [2]		VI, IRT, EL, dPL, UV-F — Snail Trail; Type-C crack [1]; Type-A, -B and -C cracks; Visible type-A and -C cracks; Crack type not clear [3]
PID	CPL: up to 100 % [1]; DR: 1-4 %/a [4] up to 20 % in first year [5]		IRT, EL, dPL, - — [1]; [1]; [6]
Glass Breakage	Module failure (exchange necessary)	Depending on severity	VI, IRT, EL, dPL, UV-F — Breakage of glass and module parts; Glass breakage caused hot spots [7]; Similar pattern as in dPL; Fragmented glass; Zero signal due to photo bleaching
Quick Connector Failure	CPL: up to 100 %		VI, IRT, (EL), (dPL), - — Burned quick connector [8]; Module in open circuit [1]; No signal due to missing connection; No signal due to missing connection
Delamination	CPL: 0-4 % [1]		VI — Front cell delamination [2]; Backsheet delamination [8]
Internal Circuitry Discoloration	DR: 1 %/a [9]		VI, EL — Corrosion string interconnect [5]; Humidity corrosion [1]
Encapsulation Discoloration	CPL: up to 45 % [10]; DR: 0.5-1 %/a [5]		VI, IRT, -, UV-F — EVA browning [1]; Hot spot as possible root; Increased fluorescence signal [9]
Junction Box / Bypass diode	CPL: up to 100 %		(VI), IRT, EL, dPL, - — Junction box missing lid [5]; Short circuit bypass diode [1]; Short circuit bypass diode [1]; Short circuit bypass diode [1] ©JohnWiley & Sons. Inc.
LID / LeTID	CPL: up to 6 % (LID [61]) or 16 % (LeTID [64])		EL, dPL, - — Chess pattern due to LeTID [66]; Chess pattern due to LeTID

Inspection cost – baseline technical minimum

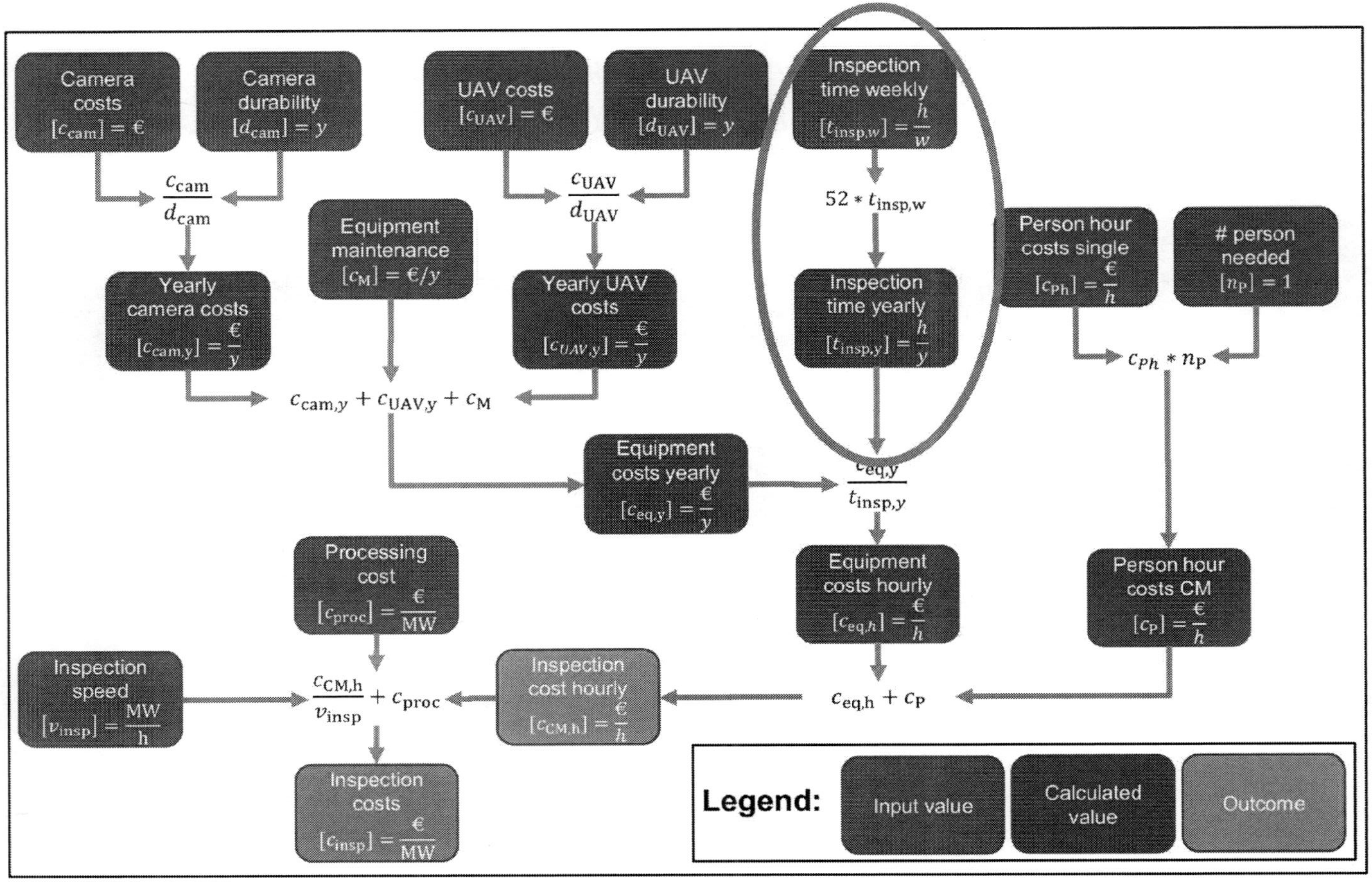

Info	units	IR	EL (night)	DPL
Camera cost	€	3000	20000	20000
Camera durability	y	5	5	5
UAV cost	€	10000	15000	15000
UAV durability	y	4	4	4
Maintenance cost	€/y	500	500	500
Person hour cost	€	35	45	35
Person needed		2	2	2

Values are best estimations from several references, experience, discussions with involved partners / experts

SUPERNOVA

Inspection requirements

Analysis of the available time in a year (Inspection Time yearly) to perform an inspection, based on the required specifications.

Aerial inspection

- Low wind speed < 5.5 m/s
- No precipitation

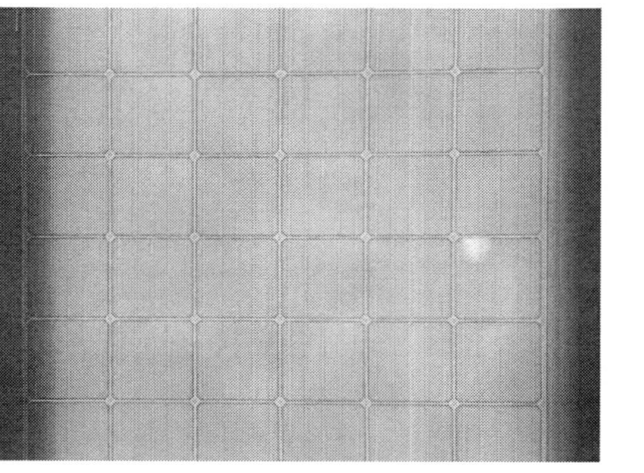

Credits: Eurac Research

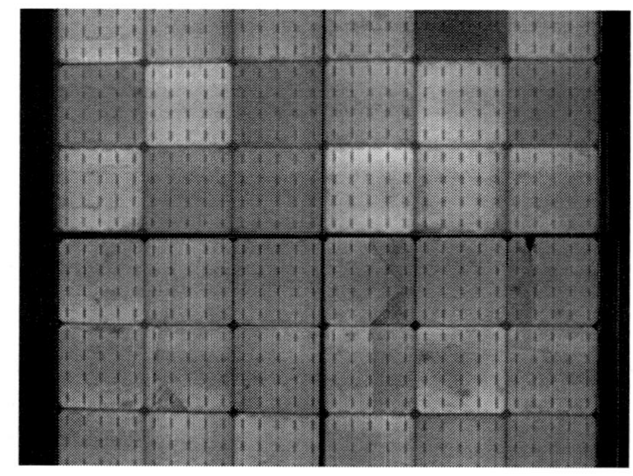

Credits: Eurac Research

Credits: Eurac Research

Infrared Thermography

- High irradiance > 600 W/m2
- Very low to none cloud cover
- Temperature < 40°C

Electroluminescence

- Low irradiance < 100 W/m2
- Temperature < 30°C

Daylight Photoluminescence

- Irradiance > 200 W/m2
- Low cloud cover
- Temperature < 30°C

SUPERNOVA

Inspection time yearly

Köppen-Geiger-Photovoltaic climate classification

For each zone, calculated for 3 locations and 5 years (2014-2019), results averaged per zone.

Filtering of all hours fulfilling requirements.

Temperature-Precipitation (TP):
A – Tropical
B – Desert
C – Steppe
D – Temperate
E – Cold
F – Polar

Irradiation (I):
K – Very High
H – High
M – Medium
L – Low

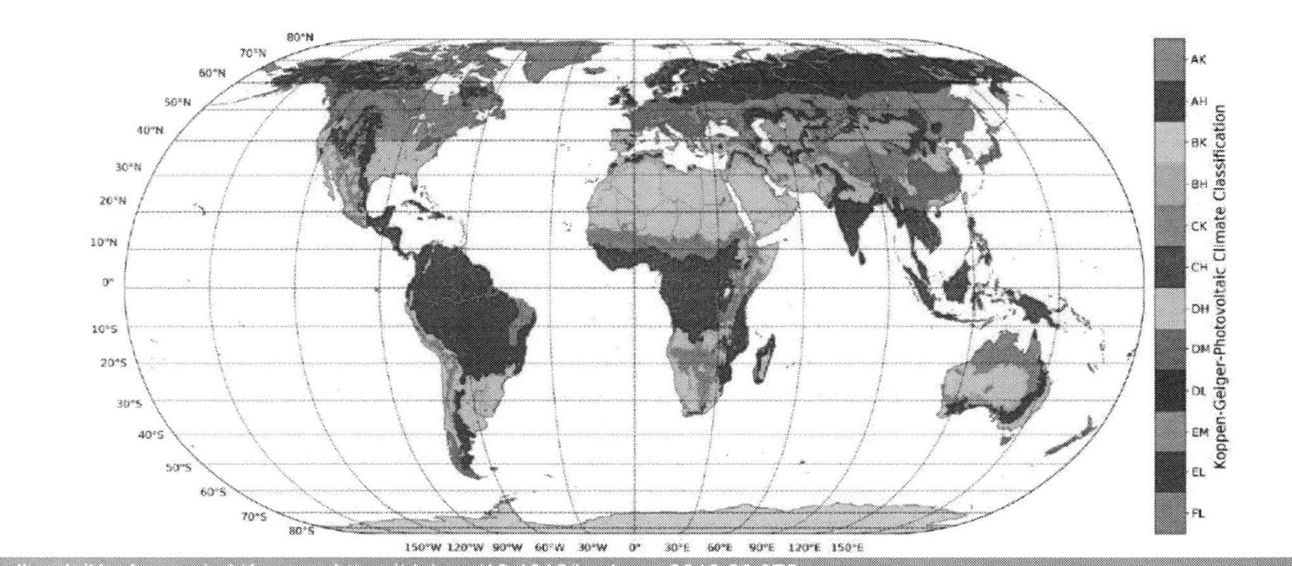

Yearly inspection time per KGPV climate zone

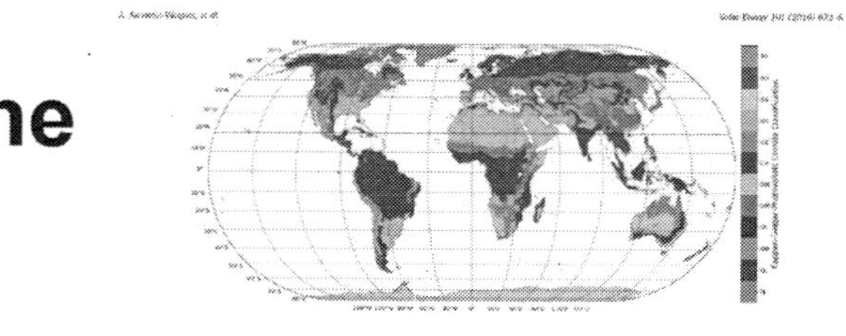

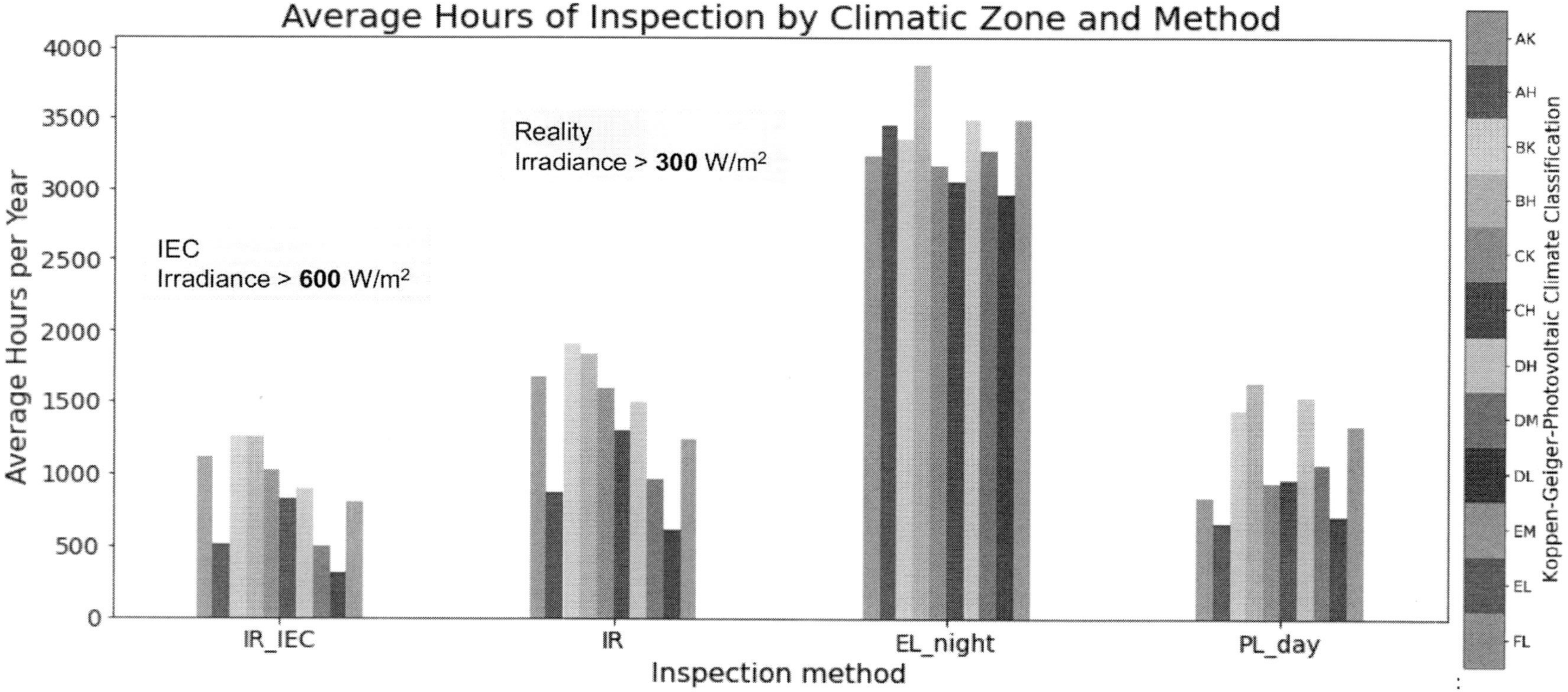

Inspection cost – baseline technical minimum

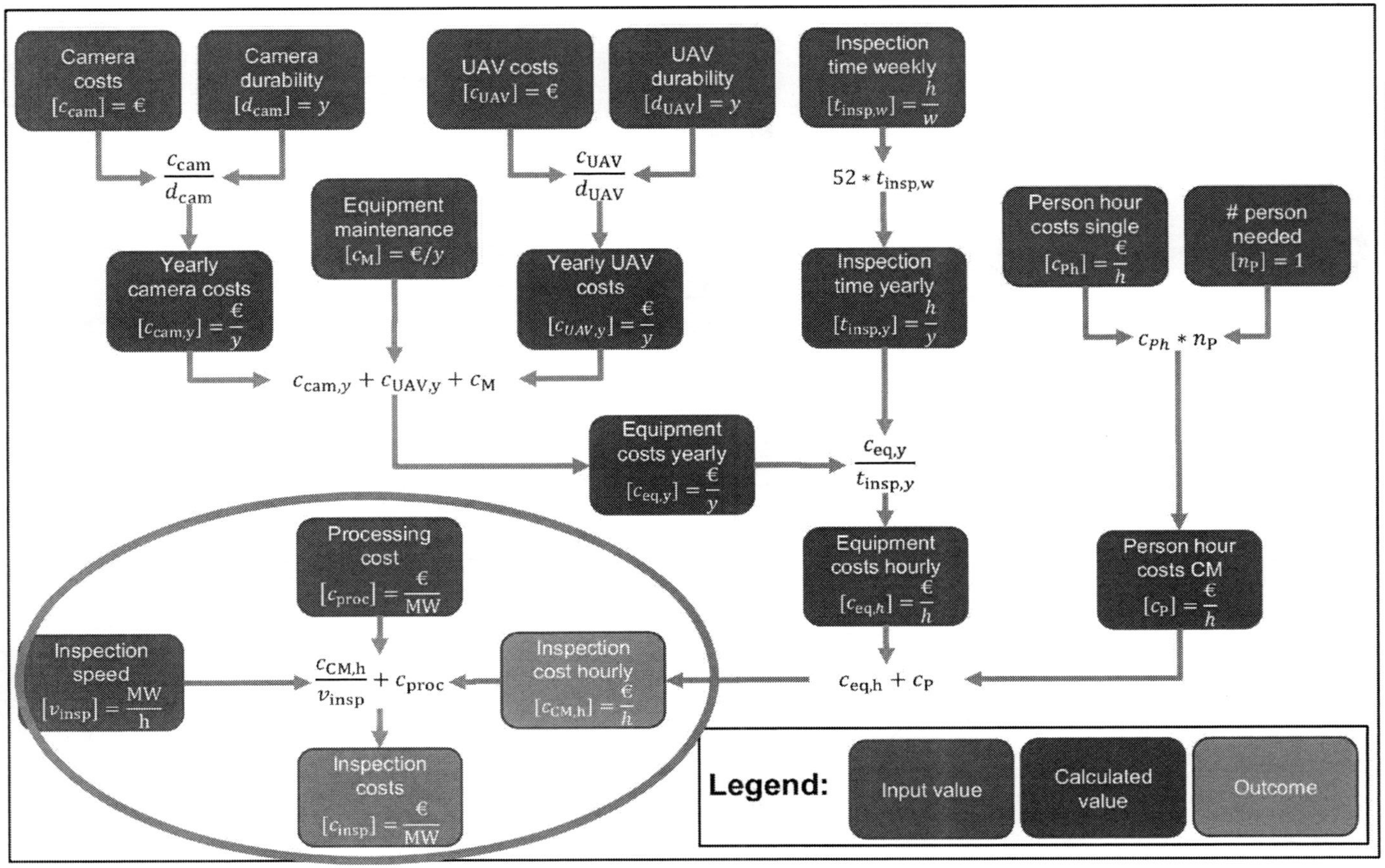

Info	units	IR	EL (night)	DPL
Camera cost	€	3000	20000	20000
Camera durability	y	5	5	5
UAV cost	€	10000	15000	15000
UAV durability	y	4	4	4
Maintenance cost	€/y	500	500	500
Person hour cost	€	35	45	35
Person needed		2	2	2

Values are best estimations from several references, experience, discussions with involved partners / experts

020261-007

Hourly Inspection Costs

Info	units	IR	EL (night)	DPL
Camera cost	€	3000	20000	20000
Camera durability	y	5	5	5
UAV cost	€	10000	15000	15000
UAV durability	y	4	4	4
Maintenance cost	€/y	500	500	500
Person hour cost	€	35	45	35
Person needed		2	2	2

Values are best estimations from several references, experience, discussions with involved partners / experts

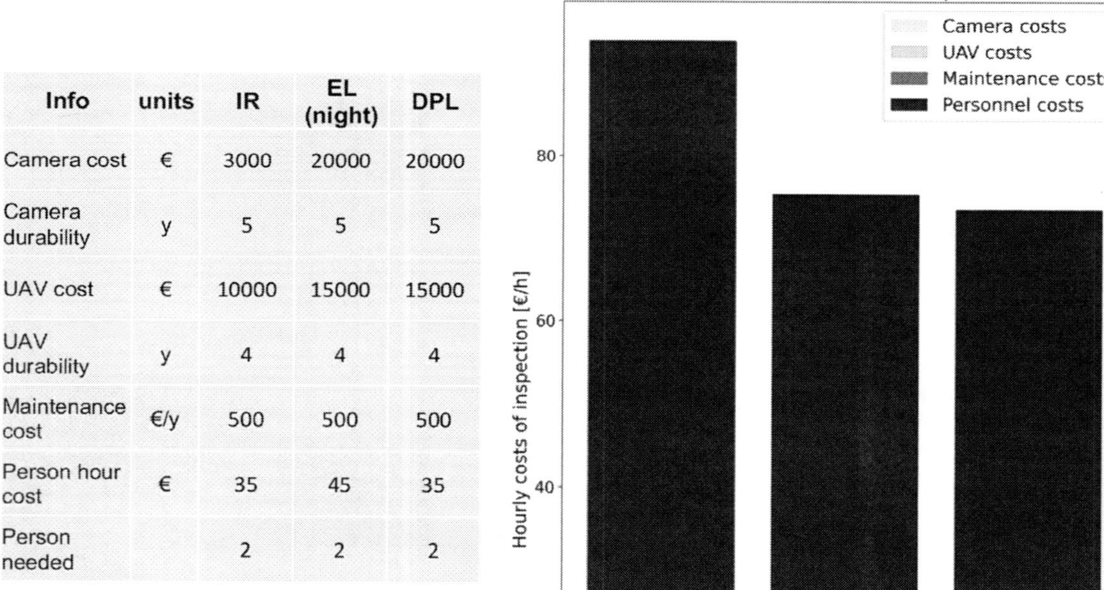

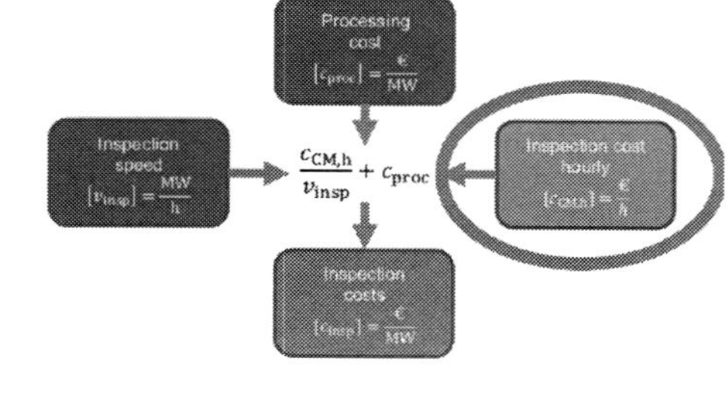

→ Purchase of IR equipment lowest, but due to possible inspection time, relative equipment cost decreases for DPL and even more for EL.

→ Personnel costs are main driver of inspection costs (EL at night more expensive)

→ Inspection speeds dominate the difference of inspection costs.

Processing Costs

General assumptions:

- Fully automated analysis (no personnel costs)
- Processing time per module: IRT=2s, EL=5s, DPL=10s
- 500 Wp module capacity

$$c_{insp}\left[\frac{€}{MW}\right] = \frac{c_{eq}}{v_{insp}} + \frac{c_P}{v_{insp}} + c_{proc}$$

Two approaches to calculate processing cost per hour:

1. Owned server/GPU:
   - Purchase cost: 3000-5000 €; reliability: 20,000 h; consumption: 0.5-1 kW/h with 0.3-0.6 €/kWh
   - → Processing cost: 0.25-0.80 €/h

2. Cloud based processing (rental):

GPU Type	Vast.ai (P25)	AWS	CoreWeave	Lambda
RTX 5090	$0.36/hr	--	--	--
H200	$2.35/hr	$10.60/hr	$6.31/hr	--
H100	$1.65/hr	$12.30/hr	$6.16/hr	$3.29/hr
RTX 4090	$0.31/hr	--	--	--
RTX 3090	$0.13/hr	--	--	--

Reference: vast.ai

Resulting processing cost per inspection method:

	kWp per hour	€/kWp min	€/kWp max
IRT	900	0.00029	0.00088
EL	360	0.00073	0.00220
DPL	180	0.00147	0.00439

IRT: < 0.1 €cent / kWp
EL: < 0.2 €cent / kWp
DPL: < 0.5 €cent / kWp

SUPERNOVA

Inspection Speed

Analysis based on geometrical parameters and boundary conditions:

Parameters influencing the imaging speed (MW/h):
- Ground sampling distance (GSD) in m/pixel,
  - given by drone height, camera resolution, focal length, orientation between camera and PV module.
  - GSD is a threshold value to get proper images (**2 cm/pixel for IR, 0.5 cm/pixel for EL/DPL**)

Considering close-up images for detailed inspection.

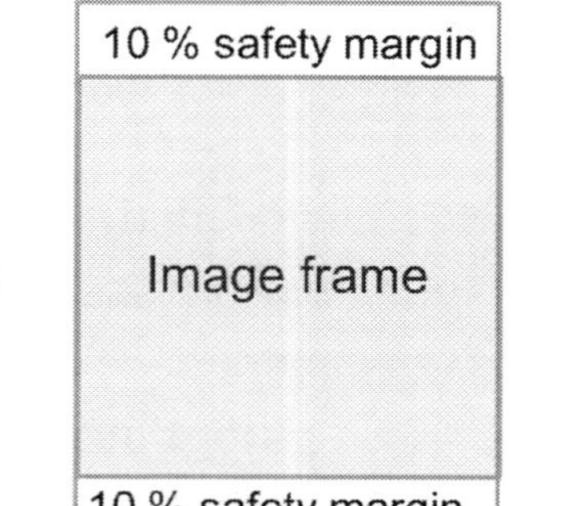

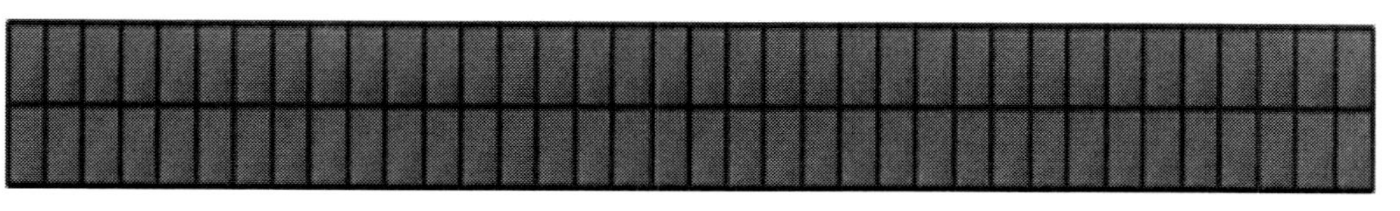

640 pixel → 12.8 m
(for GSD=2cm/pixel)

10 % safety margin

Image frame

10 % safety margin

512 pixel → 10,24 m
(for GSD=2cm/pixel)

$$c_{insp} \left[\frac{€}{MW} \right] = \frac{c_{eq}}{v_{insp}} + \frac{c_P}{v_{insp}} + c_{proc}$$

Inspection Speed

Ground imaging ratio (GIR): MWp/m
→ a value describing how many MWp are covered in 1m of the image
→ simple calculation of imaging speed by using drone speed in m/s

$$GIR = \frac{PV\ modules\ in\ image\ frame\ width * \#PV\ modules\ covered\ in\ 1m\ (travel\ direction) * PV\ module\ nominal\ power}{}$$

$$v_{insp}\left[\frac{MW}{h}\right] = GIR\left[\frac{MWp}{m}\right] * v_{drone}\left[\frac{m}{s}\right] * 3600\left[\frac{s}{h}\right] * C_{path} * C_{battery}$$

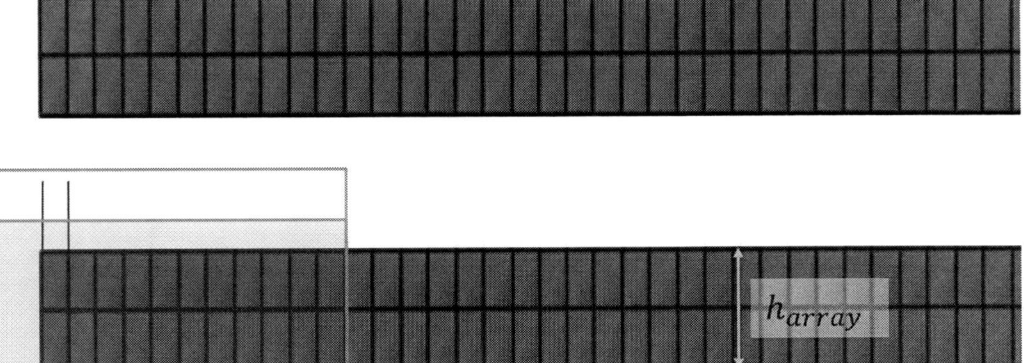

→ 4 PV modules * 400 Wp
→ $GIR = 1.6\,\frac{kWp}{m} = 0.0016\,\frac{MWp}{m}$

Inspection Speed

Inspection speed for example PV plant (100 MWp, double

Module row, 500Wp per module).

Current values (GSD, drone speed, plant layout) for model verification.

Current developments for potential speed.

Imaging method	Imaging speed current (MW/h)	Imaging speed potential (MW/h)
IRT	3.0	10
DPL	1.5	4
EL	2.0	5

Impact of PV plant size on inspection speed

(from 1 MWp to 1 GWp):

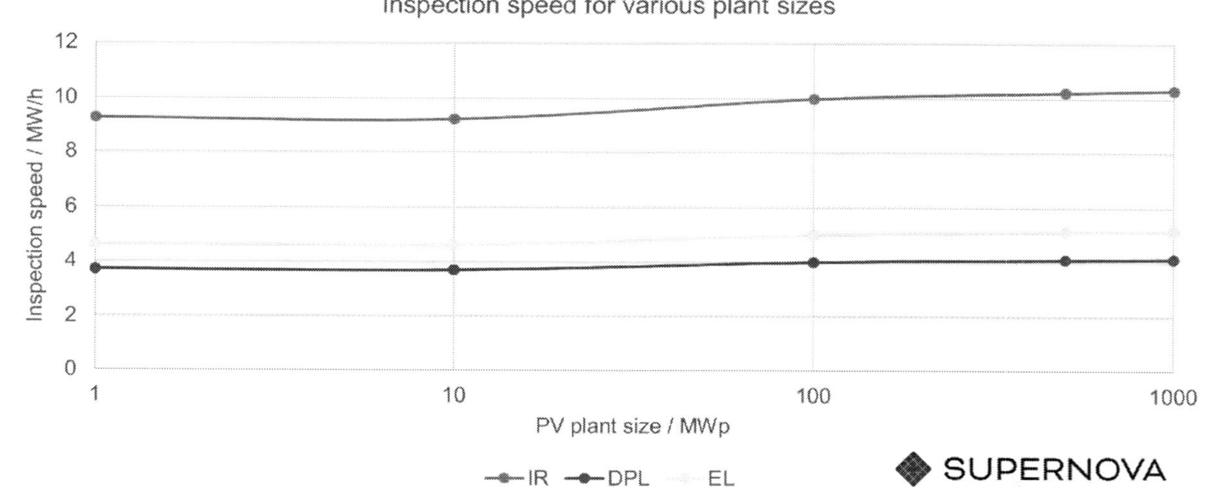

020261-012

Inspection cost

$$c_{insp}\left[\frac{€}{MW}\right] = \frac{c_{eq}\left[\frac{€}{h}\right] + c_P\left[\frac{€}{h}\right]}{v_{insp}\left[\frac{MW}{h}\right]} + c_{proc}\left[\frac{€}{MW}\right]$$

Baseline of technical minimum costs.

Missing to calculate actual costs:
- planning & mobilization
- Company overhead (insurance, admin, margin)
- Minimum project fees

Imaging method	Imaging speed potential (MW/h)	Inspection cost (€/MWp)
IRT	10	7.2
DPL	4	18.5
EL	5	18.6

Model can be used to measure technical improvements (better camera resolution, effect of drone speed on inspection speed, battery charging time, robotic solutions, …)

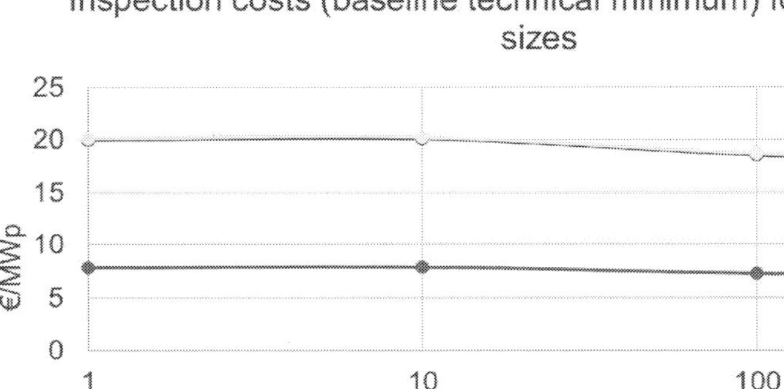
Inspection costs (baseline technical minimum) for various plant sizes

020261-013

Ground-based vs. aerial (autonomous) inspection

Aerial inspection faster, thus cheaper.

Battery charging for autonomous inspection important (no exchange of batteries – longer idle time.
Battery capacity (operational time) becomes more crucial.

Vehicle type	Assumed moving speed (m/s)	Imaging speed potential (MW/h)	Inspection cost (€/MWp)
Aerial	3	3	24
Ground-based	0.5	0.5	148

As overheads are main share of inspection, days spent (in person) at PV site of importance.

6-7 days on site vs. 2-3 days on site (installation and pick up) plus 2 months of autonomous operation.

Advantages of ground-based robots:
- Rear-module images
- Inclusion of several sensors – all at once

	Moving speed (m/s)	Exchange time of battery (minutes)	Operational time (minutes)	Total imaging time for 100 MWp PV plant (h)
Ground-based autonomous	0.5	120	120	400
Aerial in-person inspection	3	5	40	37

Conclusions

On the pure technical side, we calculated inspection costs of only 7–9 €/MWp. However, real-world service prices are much higher, because fixed project costs dominate. This means that incremental technical improvements (e.g., faster drones) do not drastically reduce €/MWp prices — unless the whole workflow is restructured (autonomous inspection, hybridization of robotic solutions).

Take aways

Model gives an estimate for **baseline costs for the technical minimum** of inspection methods.

Modification of different **parameters** to calculate their **impact on imaging speed** and costs.

Main **reason for difference** in potential inspection speed is **required detail** (GSD): Even with new SWIR cameras, difficult to cover two rows at the same time with EL/DPL. IRT can cover 2-3 rows

Automization has potential to **reduce costs** but only in very **large PV plants** (significantly less on-site days). Seamless communication needed → Universal API mapper – open source in SUPERNOVA.

Ground-based robotics significantly slower, but potential for additional detail (**rear side**) and several sensors at once (**IRT+DPL**). → **hybridization** of robotic solutions in SUPERNOVA.

The Project:

The Universal Mapper:

SUPERNOVA

Thank you

Contact: lukas.koester@eurac.edu

Co-funded by
the European Union

References

SPE2025: Solar Power Europe, Operation & Maintenance Best Practice Guidelines v6.0, 2025

Bakir2023: Hale Bakır. Detection of Faults in Photovoltaic Modules of SPPS in Turkey; Infrared Thermographic Diagnosis and Recommendations. *Journal of Electrical Engineering & Technology*, 18(3):1945–1957, May 2023.

IEA-PVPS T13 2021: Werner Herrmann et al. IEA-PVPS task 13: Performance, operation and reliability of photovoltaic systems - qualification of photovoltaic (PV) power plants using mobile
test equipment. Report, International Energy Agency, 2021.

AEPVI: AEPVI. Aerial PV Inspection GmbH - Website, February 2024

QE2025: QELabs. Quantified Energy Labs - Website, September 2025 (https://quantified-energy.com/increasing-contactless-drone-el-throughput-to-5000-pv-modules-per-hour-using-direct-injection-from-ingeteam-inverters/)

Doll2023: Bernd Doll et al. Aerial Photoluminescence Imaging of Photovoltaic Modules. physica status solidi (RRL) – Rapid Research Letters, 17(12):2300059, December 2023.

Koester2024: Lukas Koester, Multispectral Imaging And Correlation Of Image Signatures Of Pv Failures With Electrical Signatures, PhD thesis, July 2024

Importance of detailed knowledge beyond direct financial impact

1. PV plant status before/after commissioning or acquisition
2. Extreme weather events, e.g. hailstorm
3. Knowledge about PV plant health status

- Insurance policies based on visual analysis
- No knowledge about internal damage
- Performance loss and (future) safety issues not considered
- Suggestion: detailed analysis after hail event and adaption of insurance policies

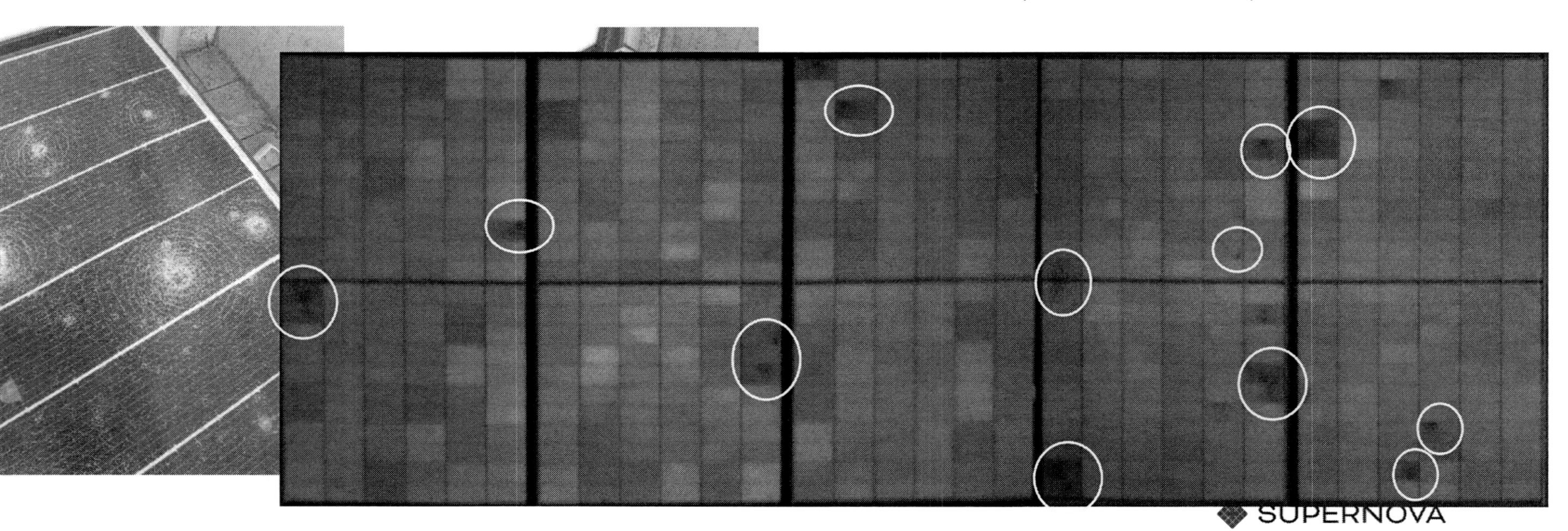

Application of DPL

Roof-top PV after hail
Several defects visible in "healthy" PV modules
2 DPL images for 5 PV modules

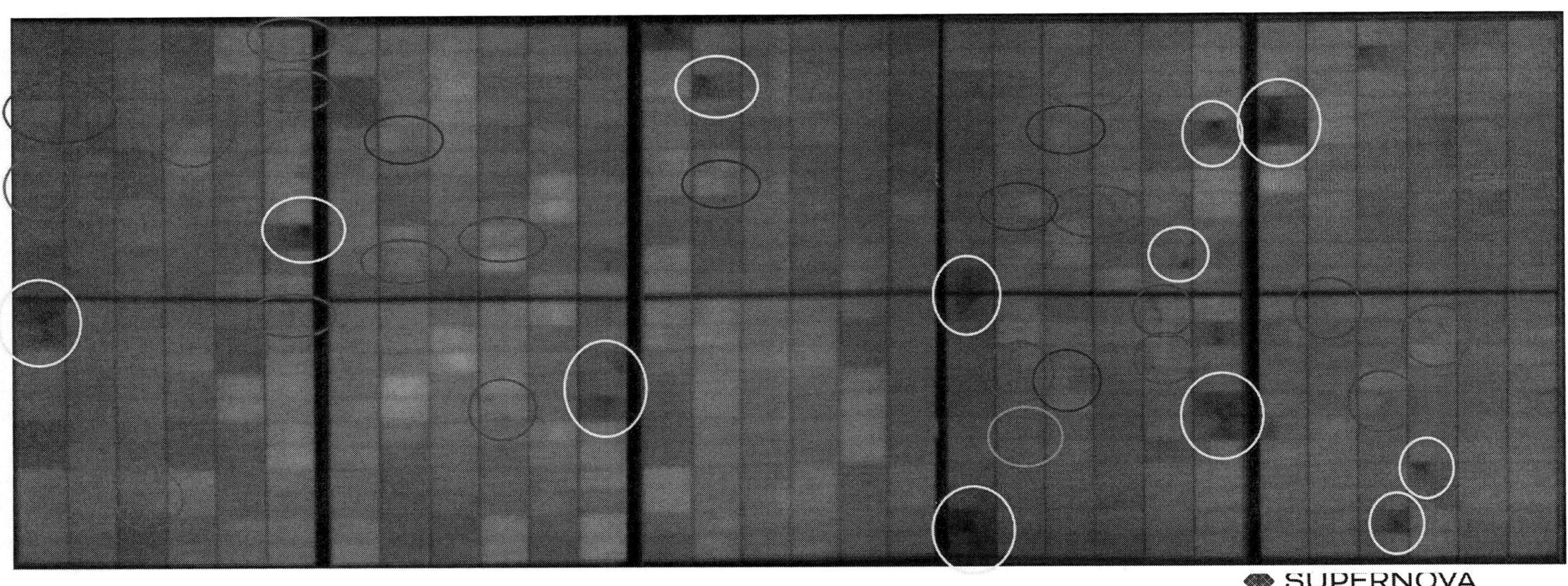

This presentation was selected by the Sc. Committee of the EU PVSEC 2025 for submission of a full paper to one of the EU PVSEC's collaborating peer-reviewed journals.

LIDAR MEETS MODELLING:
COLLABORATIVE INSIGHTS FROM A ROUND-ROBIN OF VERTICAL BIFACIAL PV SIMULATIONS

Ioannis (John) A. Tsanakas[1]*, Stéphane Mollier[1], Hervé Colin[1], Ismaël Lokhat[2], Branislav Schnierer[3], Daniel Chrkavy[3], Martin Opatovsky[3], S. Prithivi Rajan[4], Jesús Robledo[4], Jonathan Leloux[4]

[1] CEA, Liten, Univ. Grenoble Alpes, Campus INES, 73375 Le Bourget du Lac, France
[2] Cythelia Energy, 73290 La Motte-Servolex, France
[3] Solargis s.r.o., 81109 Bratislava, Slovakia
[4] LuciSun, 1495 Villers-la-Ville, Belgium

*corresponding author: ioannis.tsanakas@cea.fr

ABSTRACT: Vertical bifacial photovoltaic (PV) systems have emerged as a promising solution for maximizing land use efficiency while achieving high energy yields. This study investigates the modeling and simulation of a vertical bifacial PV plant located in southeastern France, utilizing advanced drone-based LiDAR (Light Detection And Ranging) data for detailed environmental characterization. In a collaborative effort, in the context of H2020 SERENDI-PV project, four partners – CEA, Cythelia, Lucisun, and Solargis – applied their unique PV modeling tools to assess the plant's energy yield, shading losses, and diffuse irradiance contributions. The study focused on comparing methodologies in a round-robin framework, analyzing results from an common PV monitoring dataset. Key findings highlight the critical impact of accurate terrain and shading modeling on simulation reliability. This paper presents selected results, including shading loss analysis, module-level energy yield comparisons, and key performance indicators (KPIs), emphasizing the significance of LiDAR-enhanced modeling.

Keywords: Vertical bifacial PV; LiDAR; energy yield simulations; shading analysis; round-robin study; PV modeling.

1 INTRODUCTION: CONTEXT and AIM

Validating the economic viability and bankability of bifacial PV projects depends on accurate energy yield prediction, a task complicated by complex light-harvesting mechanisms [1,2]. Unlike monofacial modules, bifacial systems generate energy from both sides, with rear-side gains highly sensitive to the installation environment (albedo, mounting height, array geometry, shading) [1,2]. The industry's inability to precisely model these gains is a primary source of uncertainty, causing significant discrepancies between simulation tools [3,4].

This challenge is greater in complex settings like built environments or agrivoltaics [5,6]. Bifacial vertical PV (BVPV) – used in fencing, noise barriers, and east-west agrivoltaic systems – is a particularly demanding use case [7,8]. Their performance is dictated by diffuse and reflected light, with a strong dependence on anisotropic sky conditions and ground properties, pushing existing modelling paradigms to their limits [9,10].

Modelling approaches represent a trade-off between speed and fidelity [11]:

- *Transposition Models:* Calculate plane-of-array irradiance but assume uniform ground illumination and isotropic reflectivity [7,12]. They are simple and fast but can have high errors (~15%) for non-optimal orientations and are limited for bifacial rear-side simulation [10-12].
- *View Factor (VF) Models:* Offer a better approach by using geometric view factors to calculate ground-reflected irradiance. Errors of 5-16% have been reported [13,14], but they assume isotropic reflection and struggle with 3D obstruction shading, often requiring user-defined loss factors.
- *Ray Tracing (RT) Models:* Are the gold standard for accuracy. Tools like NREL's bifacial_radiance trace

light paths in a 3D scene for high fidelity [15-18]. However, this accuracy comes with immense computational cost [19].

Accurate rear-side modelling is complicated by interlinked parameters [20,21]:

1. **Mounting Height:** Increases rear-side irradiance but accentuates edge effects, which VF models underestimate [15,18].
2. **Albedo:** Higher albedo augments rear-side irradiance [14], but VF models fail with time-dependent or anisotropic surfaces [9,10].
3. **Mounting Structure:** Causes shading that reduces performance, a factor not intrinsically accounted for in VF models [14,22].

BVPV intensifies these challenges. Its radically different view factors and dominance of diffuse/reflected light push the simplifying assumptions of transposition and VF models to their limits. High-fidelity ray tracing is likely essential but computationally burdensome [19,23].

Current RT models also lack two key features: the capacity for spectrally-resolved simulations (critical for tandem cell technologies) [24-26] and the efficient simulation of time-varying albedo (e.g., from snow), which is vital for forecasting accuracy [27,28].

This collaborative study, in the framework of the H2020 SERENDI-PV project, attempts to shed light into (and address) the modelling challenges of simulation the energy yield and losses of complex PV installations by employing drone-based LiDAR data to create precise 3D representations. The particular case of a vertical bifacial PV plant's (Fig. 1) environment has been thoroughly modelled and studied. The PV plant analyzed in this study is located in southeastern France, 60km south of the city of Lyon, along a canal of the Rhône river. The specific site, being in the Rhône valley, is characterized by uneven terrain and is surrounded by high vegetation (mostly trees) in close proximity, as also seen in Fig. 1. The PV system features a linear (length of 350m in total) vertical bifacial configuration with six sections of PV modules aligned approximately along a north-south axis. Each section contains a combination of 24 or 48 bifacial frameless PV modules, type Trina Solar's TSM-DEG14C.07 (II), stacked in two rows, throughout the installation, which totals a capacity of 104 kW$_p$. The system's unique vertical design and complex surroundings make it an ideal candidate for advanced modeling studies that incorporate shading, albedo, and terrain effects, using precise LiDAR-enhanced data to improve simulation accuracy.

Figure 1: The (linear) vertical bifacial PV system investigated in the collaborative round-robin study of PV simulations by Solargis, Lucisun, Cythelia and CEA.

Through this work, we aimed to leverage these insights to improve simulation accuracy across diverse modeling tools while comparing results in a collaborative round-robin framework. The presented study involves contributions from four SERENDI-PV partners, with their corresponding proprietary (commercial or research) tools for advanced PV modelling:

- **CEA** with its *Trifactors v2* tool,
- **Cythelia** employing *archelios PRO*,
- **Lucisun** using its *LuSim* tool,
- **Solargis** with *Evaluate*, its advanced simulation platform.

Each partner utilized LiDAR-derived 3D meshes to model terrain effects, shading patterns, and energy yields, fostering a deeper understanding of the strengths and limitations of each modelling approach

2 METHODOLOGY - APPROACH

2.1 LiDAR Data Acquisition and Processing

The LiDAR dataset was acquired using drone flights over the aforementioned PV plant, generating a dense 3D point cloud with over 80 million points. This data was processed into a simplified 3D mesh containing 6,000 triangular elements, retaining critical details like canopy height and terrain slopes. The mesh was distributed to all partners in COLLADA (.dae) format for integration into their respective modeling tools. Figure 2 illustrates the processed LiDAR-based 3D terrain model used for simulations.

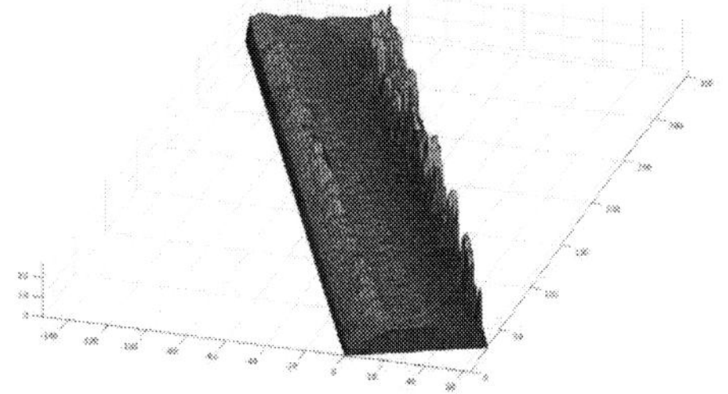

Figure 2: Reconstructed 3D mesh of the studied vertical bifacial PV system, from LiDAR data.

2.2 Modeling Tools and Innovations

CEA's Trifactors v2 tool utilized the LiDAR mesh to model irradiance and shading effects. It allowed the decomposition of irradiance into direct, diffuse, and reflected components for shading-loss quantification. Cythelia employed the archelios PRO API, integrating bifacial modeling advancements from previous projects. The tool emphasized electrical sizing and shading analysis. Lucisun's LuSim adopted GPU-accelerated methods to simulate shading profiles and Global Tilted Irradiance (GTI) at high temporal and spatial resolutions, enabling accurate module-level assessments. Through Evaluate, Solargis implemented its ray-tracing simulator to evaluate bifacial performance using harmonized datasets and advanced shading calculations.

2.3 Collaborative Round-Robin Framework

Each partner applied their tool to the same exactly dataset (which underwent comprehensive data quality control prior to the main modelling work), focusing on four representative days in 2023: March 24 (cloudy/overcast conditions), June 25 (sunny/clear-sky conditions), September 9 (sunny/clear-sky conditions), and December 3 (partial sunny conditions). Simulations were compared at PV module-level resolution, emphasizing consistency and reproducibility rather than competitive benchmarking.

3 RESULTS and DISCUSSION

3.1 Shading Analysis

The LiDAR-enhanced 3D mesh enabled accurate characterization of shading effects from terrain and vegetation. Indicatively, CEA's simulations highlighted seasonal shading losses, which varied from 3.15% in summer to 10.92% in winter, with PV modules at the bottom row of the vertical PV arrays, experiencing greater shading than those at the top row (Fig. 3). The findings underscore the significant impact of seasonal and positional variations on shading losses, emphasizing the importance of detailed environmental modeling for accurate yield predictions.

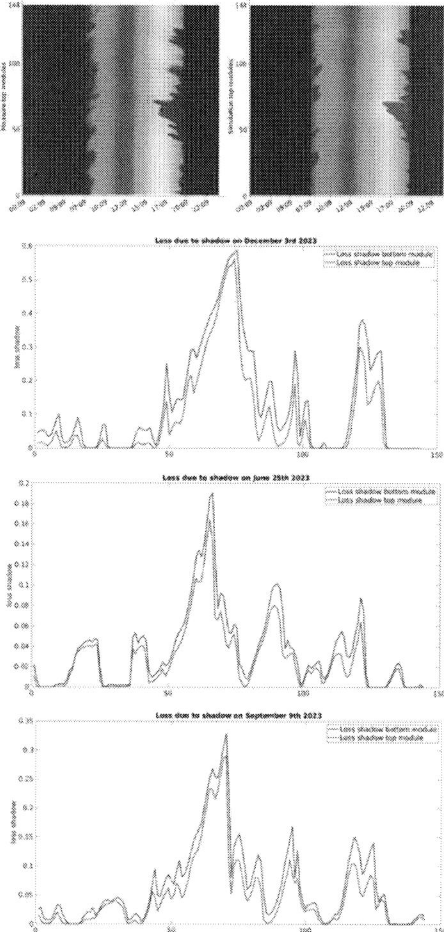

Figure 3: Spatio-temporal representation of the system's DC power output over the day of the September 9th 2023 (upper figure) and shading losses for top and bottom modules across selected days.

3.2 Module-level Energy Yield Comparison

Simulations revealed the characteristic double-peak profile of vertical bifacial systems. Figure 4 compares DC power outputs for two selected modules (48th and 68th positions) simulated by the partners for June 25 and September 9, showing good agreement despite variations in shading modeling. While good agreement was observed across the partners' tools, slight variations in DC power outputs highlight differences in shading and irradiance modeling approaches, as well as how each tool handles complex terrain and diffuse light conditions.

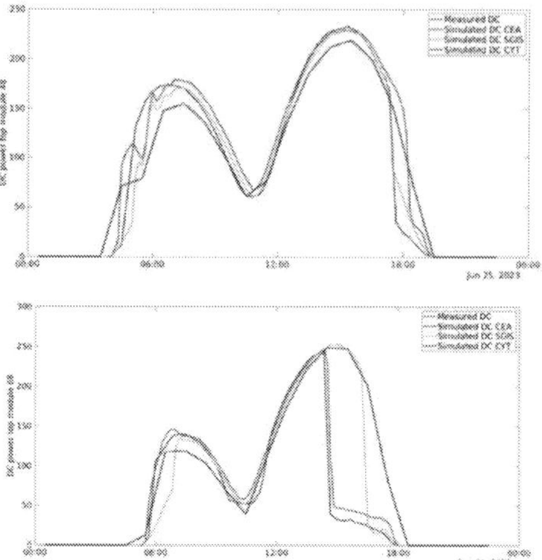

Figure 4: DC power comparison for modules 48 and 68 on representative days.

3.3 Model Accuracy and Key Performance Indicators (KPIs)

Lucisun's LuSim demonstrated the lowest Mean Absolute Error (MAE) for shading predictions, showcasing the benefits of GPU-accelerated methods and high temporal resolution in capturing dynamic shading patterns. Solargis' results highlighted the advantages of harmonized input datasets for accurate bifacial performance predictions. Table 1 summarizes the KPIs for all partners, revealing complementary strengths and areas for refinement in each modeling tool.

Table 1. Summary of KPIs for module-level simulations.

Date	PV Mod ule #	MAE (Wh) Trifactors v2	MAE (Wh) Evaluate	MAE (Wh) archelios PRO	MAE (Wh) LuSim
25/06/ 2023	28	6.98	10.90	9.00	1.36
	48	11.40	6.63	15.10	4.46
	68	9.93	7.37	12.75	3.61
	120	6.75	7.83	8.01	9.08
09/09/ 2023	28	6.41	5.42	10.54	2.70
	48	11.55	6.40	9.37	1.93
	68	6.04	21.99	28.77	4.28
	120	8.44	10.70	13.88	3.84
03/12/ 2023	28	6.98	10.90	9.00	8.14
	48	11.40	6.63	15.10	2.00
	68	9.93	7.37	12.75	2.08
	120	6.75	7.83	8.01	6.77

3.4 Diffuse and Direct Irradiance Insights

Diffuse irradiance was found to be a significant contributor to energy yield during cloudy conditions, with notable impacts on modules with greater exposure to terrain shading. Heatmaps generated by Lucisun (Fig. 5) illustrated diffuse and direct irradiance distributions, validating the influence of terrain features on light capture. These results demonstrate the importance of accurately modeling diffuse irradiance to optimize bifacial PV performance, particularly in locations with variable weather conditions.

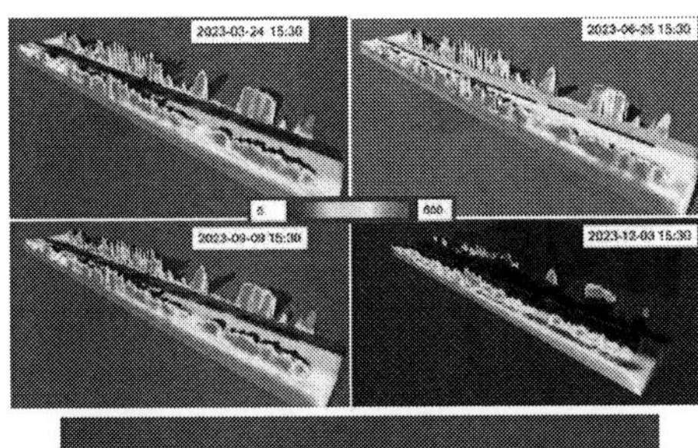

Figure 5: Heatmaps of direct (upper 4 figures) and diffuse irradiance (middle and bottom figure) for selected days.

4 FURTHER DISCUSSION – KEY TAKEAWAYS

The round-robin exercise successfully consolidated results from multiple modeling chains, moving beyond competition to reveal a consistent picture of vertical bifacial system performance. This provides a shared foundation for methodological improvements.

All partners accurately captured the system's distinctive double-peak daily pattern. Disagreements were primarily confined to the steep shading transitions at sunrise and sunset, which serve as critical stress tests for shading algorithms and highlight key areas for improvement. The analyses clearly identified predictable patterns: increased shading losses occurred in winter and for lower rows of the array, where nearby obstacles and low sun angles worsen horizon shading. These scenarios rigorously test 3D scene and terrain modeling.

At a monthly scale, random variations diminished, revealing a low, stable bias. This confirms that upstream harmonization steps—like resource preprocessing and albedo alignment—effectively reduced systematic errors. Benchmarking also showed that module-level (e.g., MAE) and plant-level indicators (e.g., EPI, AC output) are complementary, together providing a coherent and self-consistent view of system performance.

A primary source of variation was uncertainty at the LiDAR-to-simulation interface. Manual placement of the 3D mesh and its acquisition in a non-representative season contributed to differences. Refining this process will further narrow the already small model spread. Finally, the exercise validated the benefit of separating the physical (irradiance, shading) and electrical domains, which brings clarity and helps pinpoint the source of discrepancies.

Collectively, these findings boost confidence in the modeling framework. The remaining spread between models is now well-characterized, traceable to known causes, and largely correctable. This effort not only validates current bifacial modeling but also creates a shared roadmap for its refinement.

5 CONCLUSIONS - OUTLOOK

Vertical bifacial (BVPV) systems are gaining traction for their land-use efficiency and applications in agrivoltaics and built environments. However, their performance is highly sensitive to factors like terrain, vegetation, albedo, and diffuse light, making yield prediction difficult. Discrepancies between existing modeling tools have historically undermined confidence in project bankability.

This collaborative study of the Sablons plant demonstrates that integrating high-resolution LiDAR data with advanced modeling significantly improves prediction accuracy.

The key conclusions are:

1. **High-resolution site characterization is essential.** Drone-based LiDAR created a precise "digital twin" of the terrain and vegetation. This was critical for accurately simulating the complex shading and light effects that impact rear-side energy gains.
2. **Tools consistently captured key performance signatures.** All models successfully reproduced the distinctive double-peak output profile of vertical bifacial modules. Remaining discrepancies occurred at sunrise/sunset, highlighting the need for better modeling of horizon obstructions and diffuse light.
3. **Shading is the dominant variable.** Seasonal and positional shading caused the highest energy losses, particularly for lower rows in winter. Site-specific topography created asymmetric shading, necessitating bifacial-aware, high-resolution modeling.
4. **Benchmarking revealed complementary tools.** Module-level (MAE) and plant-level (EPI) metrics provided a complete picture. GPU-accelerated tools excelled at capturing complex shading, while harmonized datasets ensured robust long-term predictions. Remaining variations were traceable to specific, correctable factors like LiDAR processing.
5. **A trade-off exists between accuracy and speed.** Ray-tracing is the most physically accurate but computationally expensive. Hybrid approaches offer a practical balance for large-scale use.

On the basis of the presented results, successful outcomes and identified challenges/gaps, future research directions include:

- Incorporating dynamic albedo (snow, crops) and spectral light data.
- Automating LiDAR processing to minimize manual errors.
- Integrating thermal and electrical models for fuller system understanding.
- Expanding benchmarking to diverse sites and climates.
- Standardizing these methods to achieve bankable predictions with 2-4% accuracy.

In summary, this study provides a robust foundation for bifacial PV modeling. It shows that current uncertainties are identifiable and manageable, charting a clear pathway to reliable design and assessment for vertical bifacial projects.

ACKNOWLEDGEMENTS

This work has been carried out in the framework of the H2020 SERENDI-PV project. SERENDI-PV project has received funding from the European Union's Horizon 2020 research and innovation programme under grant agreement No. 953016. For CEA team, part of this work was also supported by the French National Program "Programme d'Investissements d'Avenir - INES.2S" under Grant Agreement ANR ANR-10-IEED-0014 0014-01.

The authors extend their sincere appreciation and gratefully acknowledge the valuable contribution – through interviews, provision of data and information, and permission to use certain photos – of Mr Kévin Garcia and Mrs Chloé Monet, on behalf of the R&D and technical team of CNR (Compagnie Nationale du Rhône), SERENDI-PV partner and owner/operator of the studied PV plant.

REFERENCES

1. U. A. Yusufoglu, T. M. Pletzer, L. J. Koduvelikulathu, C. Comparotto, R. Kopecek and H. Kurz, "Analysis of the Annual Performance of Bifacial Modules and Optimization Methods," in IEEE Journal of Photovoltaics, vol. 5, no. 1, pp. 320-328, Jan. 2015, doi: 10.1109/JPHOTOV.2014.2364406.

2. J.S. Stein et al., "Bifacial Photovoltaic Modules and Systems: Experience and Results from International Research and Pilot Applications," Report IEA-PVPS T13-14:2021.

3. J. Libal and R. Kopecek, Bifacial Photovoltaics: Technology, applications and economics. London, U.K.: Institution of Engineering and Technology, 2018. doi: 10.1049/pbpo107e.

4. D. Riley *et al.*, "A Performance Model for Bifacial PV Modules," *2017 IEEE 44th Photovoltaic Specialist Conference (PVSC)*, Washington, DC, USA, 2017, pp. 3348-3353, doi: 10.1109/PVSC.2017.8366045.

5. M.Trommsdorff et al. (2025), "Dual Land Use for Agriculture and Solar Power Production: Overview and Performance of Agrivoltaic Systems", Report IEA-PVPS T13-29:2025

6. Bonomo, P., Frontini, F., Loonen, R., & Reinders, A. H. M. E. (2024). Comprehensive review and state of play in the use of photovoltaics in buildings. Energy and Buildings, 323, 114737. https://doi.org/10.1016/j.enbuild.2024.114737.

7. Badran, G., Dhimish, M. Comprehensive study on the efficiency of vertical bifacial photovoltaic systems: a UK case study. Sci Rep 14, 18380 (2024). https://doi.org/10.1038/s41598-024-68018-1.

8. Szabo, L., Moner- Girona, M., Jäger-Waldau, A. et al. Impacts of large-scale deployment of vertical bifacial photovoltaics on European electricity market dynamics. Nat Commun 15, 6681 (2024). https://doi.org/10.1038/s41467-024-50762-7.

9. E. Tonita, S. Ovaitt, H. Toal, K. Hinzer, C. Pike and C. Deline, "Vertical Bifacial Photovoltaic System Model Validation: Study With Field Data, Various Orientations, and Latitudes," in IEEE Journal of Photovoltaics, vol. 15, no. 4, pp. 600-609, July 2025, doi: 10.1109/JPHOTOV.2025.3561395.

10. Øgaard, M. B., Nysted, V. S., Rønneberg, S., Otnes, G., Foss, S. E., Mongstad, T., & Riise, H. N. (2024). Vertical bifacial PV systems: irradiance modeling and performance analysis of a lightweight system for flat roofs. EPJ Photovoltaics, 15(13). https://doi.org/10.1051/epjpv/2024012.

11. Kang, J., Jang, J., Reise, C., & Lee, K. (2019, September 9-13). Practical comparison between view factor method and ray-tracing method for bifacial PV system yield prediction [Conference presentation]. 36th European PV Solar Energy Conference and Exhibition, Marseille, France.

12. Xie, Y., & Sengupta, M. (2016, June 20-24). Performance analysis of transposition models simulating solar radiation on inclined surfaces [Conference presentation]. European PV Solar Conference and Exhibition (EU PVSEC), Munich, Germany.

13. Ayala Peláez, S., Deline, C., Marion, B., Sekulic, B., & Stein, J. (2019, December 18). *Understanding bifacial PV modeling: Raytracing and view factor models* [Webinar]. PV Magazine Webinar. National Renewable Energy Laboratory.

14. Berrian D, Libal J. A comparison of ray tracing and view factor simulations of locally resolved rear irradiance with the experimental values. Prog Photovolt Res Appl. 2020; 28: 609–620. https://doi.org/10.1002/pip.3261

15. Schinke, C., Vogt, M.R. and Bothe, K. (2018). Optical Modeling of Photovoltaic Modules with Ray Tracing Simulations. In Photovoltaic Modeling Handbook, M.F. Müller (Ed.). https://doi.org/10.1002/9781119364214.ch3

16. Kosmopoulos, P., Dhake, H., Kartoudi, D., Tsavalos, A., Koutsantoni, P., Katranitsas, A., Lavdakis, N., Mengou, E., & Kashyap, Y. (2024). Ray-Tracing modeling for urban photovoltaic energy planning and management. Applied Energy, 369, 123516. https://doi.org/10.1016/j.apenergy.2024.123516

17. S. Ayala Pelaez and C. Deline, Bifacial_radiance: a python package for modeling bifacial solar photovoltaic systems, J. Open Source Software, 5 (NREL/JA-5K00-75222), 2020.

18. Honningdalsnes, E. H., Marstein, E. S., Nygård, M. M., Wiig, M. S., & Riise, H. N. (2025). Benchmarking irradiation models for photovoltaic applications: A comparative analysis of radiance-based tools. *Solar Energy, 296*,113566. https://doi.org/10.1016/j.solener.2025.113566

19. Andres C, Ruben C, David G, et al. Time-varying, ray tracing irradiance simulation

approach for photovoltaic systems in complex scenarios with decoupled geometry, optical properties and illumination conditions. *Prog Photovolt Res Appl*. 2023; 31(2): 134-148. doi:10.1002/pip.3614

20. Parenti, M., Memme, S., & Fossa, M. (2025). Sky radiance distribution based model for rear and front insolation estimation on PV bifacial modules. Solar Energy Materials and Solar Cells, 289, 113677. https://doi.org/10.1016/j.solmat.2025.113677

21. Mollier, S. and Tsanakas, J. A. (2023). Assessing uncertainties from reflected irradiance in bifacial PV simulations through a 3D view factor model and rear sensor measurements. In Proceedings of the 40th EU PVSEC 2023 (pp. 020230-001–020230-004). WIP.https://doi.org/10.4229/EUPVSEC2023/3AV.3.33

22. Merodio, P., Martínez-Moreno, F., & Lorenzo, E. (2025). Experimental determination of the structure shading factor and mismatch losses for bifacial photovoltaic modules on variable-geometry, single-axis trackers. Solar Energy, 291, 113400. https://doi.org/10.1016/j.solener.2025.113400

23. Jouttijärvi, S., Thorning, J., Manni, M., Huerta, H., Ranta, S., Di Sabatino, M., Lobaccaro, G., & Miettunen, K. (2023). A comprehensive methodological workflow to maximize solar energy in low-voltage grids: A case study of vertical bifacial panels in Nordic conditions. *Solar Energy, 262*, 111819. https://doi.org/10.1016/j.solener.2023.111819

24. Riedel-Lyngskær, N., Ribaconka, M., Pó, M., Thorseth, A., Thorsteinsson, S., Dam-Hansen, C., & Jakobsen, M. L. (2022). The effect of spectral albedo in bifacial photovoltaic performance. Solar Energy, 231, 921–935. https://doi.org/10.1016/j.solener.2021.12.023

25. Tonita EM, Valdivia CE, Russell ACJ, Martinez-Szewczyk M, Bertoni MI, Hinzer K. Quantifying spectral albedo effects on bifacial photovoltaic module measurements and system model predictions. Prog Photovolt Res Appl. 2024; 32(7): 468-480. doi:10.1002/pip.3789

26. Onno, A., Rodkey, N., Asgharzadeh, A., Manzoor, S., Yu, Z. J., Toor, F., Holman, Z. C. (2020). Predicted power output of silicon-based bifacial tandem photovoltaic systems. Joule, 4(3), 580–596. 10.1016/j.joule.2019.12.017.

27. Ghafiri, S., Darnon, M., Davigny, A., Trovão, J. P. F., & Abbes, D. (2024). A comprehensive performance evaluation of bifacial photovoltaic modules: Insights from a year-long experimental study conducted in the Canadian climate. EPJ Photovoltaics, *15*, Article 28. https://doi.org/10.1051/epjpv/2024025

28. Su, X., Luo, C., Chen, X. et al. Numerical modeling of all-day albedo variation for bifacial PV systems on rooftops and annual yield prediction in Beijing. Build. Simul. 17, 955–964 (2024). https://doi.org/10.1007/s12273-024-1120-y

This presentation was selected by the Sc. Committee of the EU PVSEC 2025 for submission of a full paper to one of the EU PVSEC's collaborating peer-reviewed journals.

DETAILED ANALYSIS OF DEGRADATION RATES OF OPERATING PV ASSETS IN TROPICAL CLIMATE CONDITIONS

Xiaoqi Xu[a], André M. Nobre[b], Han Cao[a], Yu Xu[a], Ian Marius Peters[c], Thomas Reindl[a]
a. Solar Energy Research Institute of Singapore, National University of Singapore, 117574, Singapore
b. PV Doctor Pte Ltd, 18 Cross Street, #02-101, 18 Cross, 048423, Singapore
c. Forschungszentrum Jülich GmbH, Institut für Energietechnologien, IET-2, Erlangen, 91058, Germany

ABSTRACT: This study presents an evaluation of photovoltaic system performance loss rates in tropical climates. We analysed a dataset of 35 sites totalling 22.3 MWp installations across seven countries, spanning residential, commercial, and industrial applications. Data collection periods ranged from two to 11.7 years. Meteorological and power data were recorded at one-minute to 15 minutes intervals, enabling both sensor-based performance calculations and modelled clearsky irradiation analysis. The study includes different c-Si wafer types (multi-crystalline, mono-crystalline), different silicon solar cell technologies (p-type multi-crystalline silicon, mono-crystalline silicon, PERCand n-type mono-crystalline silicon), as well as thin-film types (largely CdTe). The database was further classified by climate zones (within the tropical classification), module types (mono-facial vs. bi-facial), installation types (rooftop vs. ground-mounted), and module configurations (full cell vs. half cell).. The analysis identified mean and median performance change across systems of -1.41 %/year and -1.10 %/year, respectively, with degradation accelerating over time. This is higher than typically assumed in PV system design and financial modelling (often using 0.7-1.0%/year for the tropics). The analysis shows that there is a trend towards accelerating performance losses with system age, indicating that studies of newer systems may underestimate long-term degradation. This work serves as a solid foundation for further studies into the root causes of the higher PLRs in tropical climates, which then would enable the development of suitable strategies for optimizing the long-term performance and reliability of PV systems in the challenging environmental conditions of the tropics.

1 INTRODUCTION

The global solar industry is experiencing unprecedented growth, with the annual installations in 2024 exceeding 600 GWp and total capacity having reached 2 TWp by the end of 2024 [1]. The tropical sunbelt regions contribute >100 GWp of installed capacity in 2024 [2], representing >5% of global installations, with a huge growth potential due to the large population living there [3]. Accurately assessing the historic and current performance of PV installations in the harsher conditions of the tropics (constant high temperatures and high humidity levels) is critical for correctly projecting durability, reliability and yield over the systems' lifetime - which ultimately leads to lower levelized cost of electricity (LCOE) of the operating assets [4].

While South- and Southeast Asian countries are blessed with abundant solar energy potential, there has been reports about the accelerated decline in solar PV performance in hot and humid environments [5]. Environmental interactions can significantly influence and accelerate degradation mechanisms, leading to reduced material lifetimes of different PV technologies.

This study analyses a diverse dataset to investigate performance loss rates across tropical Asian regions using methodologies that enables direct comparison with existing studies.

2 EXPERIMENTAL DETAILS

2.1 DATABASE DESCRIPTION

The study analyses PV systems in 35 sites across India and Southeast Asia (Fig. 1), covering broad range of system sizes and module technologies.

All locations fall within a Köppen-Geiger climate classifications of Af (tropical rainforest) or As/Aw (tropical savanna/monsoon). The database comprises 35 sites with a total capacity of 22.3 MWp and a median system size of 422 kWp, providing comprehensive insights into PV performance in tropical climate conditions.

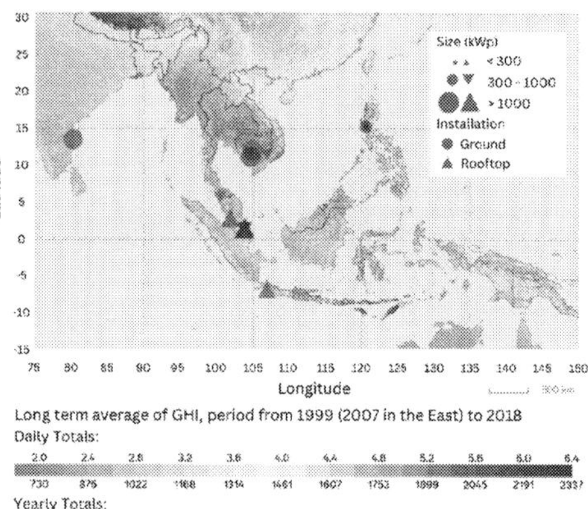

Figure 1: Graphical distribution of PV systems under study against the backdrop of the Solargis irradiance map [6]

2.2 ANALYSIS METHOD

Data collected at intervals between one to 15 minutes in this work enables detailed performance analysis across the region. The analysis utilizes DC-side inverter data when available, defaulting to AC-side measurements otherwise. Environmental parameters are recorded at all sites, with irradiance measured as either global horizontal irradiance (GHI), plane-of-array (POA) irradiance, or both simultaneously. Ambient temperature is recorded at every site, while module temperature and wind speed data are available for select locations.

Site analyses were performed using two datasets: measured local irradiance and temperature values (called "Sensor" dataset) and modelled irradiance and temperature under clear-sky conditions (called "Clearsky" dataset). Operational data were normalized using PVWatt [7] as expected power ($P_{expected}$) and described by

$$P_{expected} = \frac{G_{POA}}{1000 \cdot P_{stc}}\left(1 + \gamma_T(T_{mod} - 25\ {}^\circ C)\right) \quad (1)$$

Here, G_{POA} is in-plane irradiance measured or transposed from GHI using the Perez model [8], P_{stc} is the nameplate power at STC conditions, γ_T is the temperature coefficient of the respective PV module technology and T_{mod} is the module temperature. The normalized data were then filtered using the following criteria: normalized values greater than 0.01, irradiance range of 200–1,200 W/m², and ambient temperature range of -50°C to 110°C.

Data were aggregated to daily values for year-on-year (YOY) statistical analysis.

3 RESULTS AND DISCUSSIONS

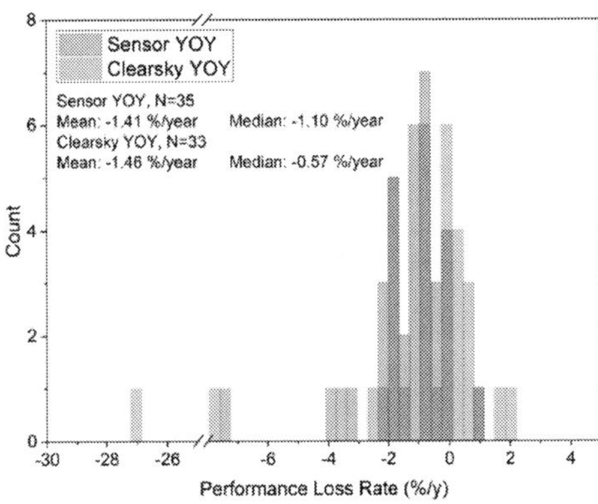

Figure 2: Performance loss rate (PLR) distribution of PV systems in this study, with sensor-based normalization ("Sensor YOY") in blue and modelled irradiance clearsky-based normalization ("Clearsky YOY") in orange. Negative values signify system performance degradation, while positive values may arise from data quality issues or methodological uncertainties.

Fig. 2 presents the PLR (Performance Loss Rate) distribution for the 35 tropical PV sites, comparing two analytical approaches: Sensor-based YOY and Clearsky YOY. The methods result in mean PLR rates of -1.41%/year for Sensor and -1.46%/year for Clearsky (YOY) and respective medians of -1.10%/year and -0.57%/year. The p-values was found at 0.33 (>0.05) suggesting that the observed difference could easily occur by random chance and there is no statistically significant difference between the two means. Due to the high variance and some extreme outliers in the Clearsky YOY, the results and discussion presented below uses only data from the Sensor YOY.

Comparing these tropical PLR values against other climate regions reveals notable differences. A study of a 7.2 GW PV fleet across the United State revealed a median of -0.75%/year [9]. The analysis of 8400 residential systems in Europe showed the mean and median PLR's of -0.86%/year and -0.67% in Sensor YOY method Sensor YOY method using satellite irradiance [10]. The higher

median PLR (-1.09%/year) observed in the tropical portfolio analysed here aligns with expected accelerated degradation in tropical versus temperate climates, despite a variance of 2.28%/year.

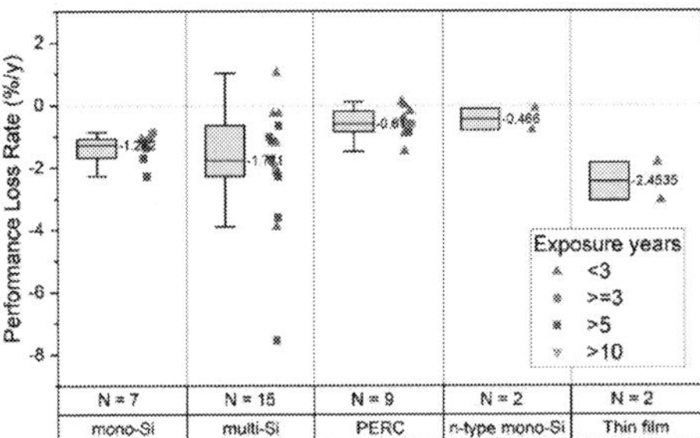

Figure 3: The PLRs of tropical solar systems by different cell technologies. [The subset sample sizes are only preliminary and will be much higher in the EPJ Photovoltaics]

Fig. 3 summarizes the PLRs across different PV cell technologies. Multi-Si and Mono-Si modules exhibited median PLRs of -1.77%/year and -1.27%/year, respectively. The observed exceptions likely stem from PLR analysis variance, highlighting the need for larger sample sizes to draw definitive conclusions. A broader study in temperate climates [11] similarly confirmed higher PLRs in Multi-Si modules.

It is also evident that technologies such as PERC, n-type mono-Si, and thin-film (largely CdTe modules) lack data points for exposure years greater than 5 years – which is exactly when degradation variance appears highest as can also be seen from the Fig. 3. These newer technologies' datasets have limited observations, averaging 2.7 years with maximum exposure of 5.9 years. In contrast, Multi-Si and Mono-Si datasets span 2.3-8.5 years and 2.0-11.7 years respectively. Thus, despite apparent PLR differences across cell technologies, the data at this stage are only indicative regarding degradation of newer cell technologies.

Fig. 4 presents PLR distributions across four other categorizations.

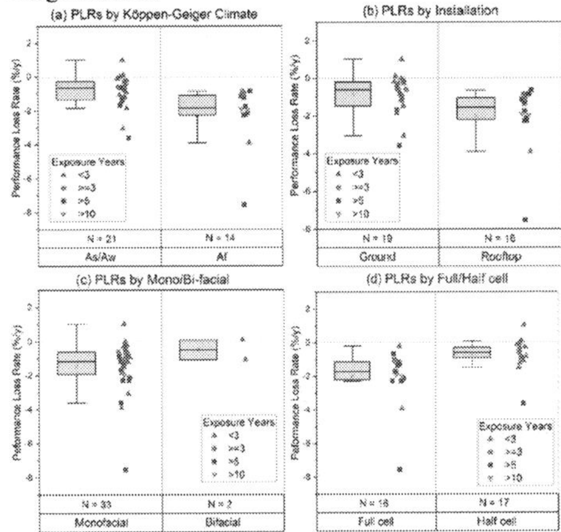

Figure 4: The PLRs by categories (a) by Köppen-Geiger climate classification; (b) by installation types; (c) by

mono-facial or bi-facial modules; (d) by full cell or half-cell configuration.

In the current sample size of 35 sites, PV systems located in As/Aw climate zones are mostly ground-mounted installations, while those in Af zones are predominantly rooftop systems. This will likely be harmonised in the full sample size later on. Furthermore, As/Aw or ground mount systems datasets lack longer exposures, introducing temporal bias similar to that discussed in the technology comparison. This interrelation necessitates further investigation to determine whether PLR differences stem from climatic conditions, installation methods, or temporal bias in the dataset.

Preliminary comparison between mono-facial and bi-facial systems suggests potential similarities in performance, though the limited bifacial sample size prevents definitive conclusions. While t-test results for full-cell versus half-cell systems indicate statistical significance (t-value = -1.38, p = 0.40), this finding requires cautious interpretation as most samples represent systems under 3 years of operation. Thus, current data cannot substantiate claims of superior reliability of half-cell technology.

4 CONCLUSIONS

The analysis of PV system degradation in tropical regions presented here (using a current dataset of 35 sites totalling 22.3 MWp), reveals mean and median PLRs of -1.41%/year and -1.10%/year respectively, higher than typically assumed in PV system design and financial modelling. While Sensor YOY methodology demonstrates robust PLR estimates, the study uncovers a critical temporal bias in systems operating beyond 5 years, highlighting the necessity for extended operational data.

The manuscript submitted to EPJ PV will expand this analysis to encompass more sites with a larger portfolio, also incorporating larger solar farms. This expanded study will complement YOY analysis with traditional linear regression approaches, enabling direct comparison with existing literature. Furthermore, the influence of environmental factors on degradation rates will be examined in greater detail to identify the key drivers of performance loss across different categorizations.

REFERENCES

[1] Global Solar Council, "Global Solar Council announces 2 terawatt milestone achieved for solar," Global Solar Council.

[2] IRENA (2025), Renewable Capacity Statistics 2025. Abu Dhabi: International Renewable Energy Agency, 2025. [Online]. Available: www.irena.org.

[3] World Population Review (2025), Countries in the Tropics 2025. https://worldpopulationreview.com

[4] I. M. Peters, J. Hauch, C. Brabec, and P. Sinha, "The value of stability in photovoltaics," Joule, vol. 5, no. 12, pp. 3137–3153, Dec. 2021, doi: 10.1016/j.joule.2021.10.019.

[5] D. C. Jordan, S. R. Kurtz, K. VanSant, and J. Newmiller, "Compendium of photovoltaic degradation rates," Progress in Photovoltaics: Research and Applications, vol. 24, no. 7, pp. 978–989, Jul. 2016, doi: 10.1002/pip.2744.

[6] Solargis, "Solar resource maps of Asia, Global Horizontal Irradiation," Solar resource map © 2021 Solargis.

[7] National Renewable Energy Laboratory, "PVWatts version 5 manual," 2014, NREL: 5.

[8] F. Almonacid, P. J. Pérez-Higueras, E. F. Fernández, and L. Hontoria, "A methodology based on dynamic artificial neural network for short-term forecasting of the power output of a PV generator," Energy Convers Manag, vol. 85, pp. 389–398, 2014, doi: 10.1016/j.enconman.2014.05.090.

[9] D. C. Jordan et al., "Photovoltaic fleet degradation insights," Progress in Photovoltaics: Research and Applications, vol. 30, no. 10, pp. 1166–1175, Oct. 2022, doi: 10.1002/pip.3566.

[10] S. Lindig, J. Ascencio-Vasquez, J. Leloux, D. Moser, and A. Reinders, "Performance Analysis and Degradation of a Large Fleet of PV Systems," IEEE J Photovolt, vol. 11, no. 5, pp. 1312–1318, Sep. 2021, doi: 10.1109/JPHOTOV.2021.3093049.

[11] D. C. Jordan, C. Deline, S. R. Kurtz, G. M. Kimball, and M. Anderson, "Robust PV Degradation Methodology and Application," IEEE J Photovolt, vol. 8, no. 2, pp. 525–531, Mar. 2018, doi: 10.1109/JPHOTOV.2017.2779779.

Detailed Analysis of Degradation Rates of Operating PV Assets in Tropical Climate Conditions

Xiaoqi XU, André M. NOBRE*, Han CAO, Yu XU, Ian Marius PETERS, Thomas REINDL

EU PVSEC, Bilbao, 23rd Sep 2025

* PV DOCTOR Pte. Ltd.

NATIONAL RESEARCH FOUNDATION
PRIME MINISTER'S OFFICE
SINGAPORE

ENERGY MARKET AUTHORITY
Our Clean Energy Future

EDB:
SINGAPORE

SERIS is a research institute at the National University of Singapore (NUS). SERIS is supported by NUS, the National Research Foundation Singapore (NRF), the Energy Market Authority of Singapore (EMA) and the Singapore Economic Development Board (EDB).

020264-001

SERIS

Solar Energy Research Institute of Singapore

- National Lab founded at NUS in 2008; supported by NUS, NRF, EMA & EDB
- Focuses on applied solar energy research (solar cells, PV modules, PV systems)
- > 120 staff & PhD students; state-of-the-art labs, ISO certified (9001, 17025)
- Close collaborations with companies & government agencies

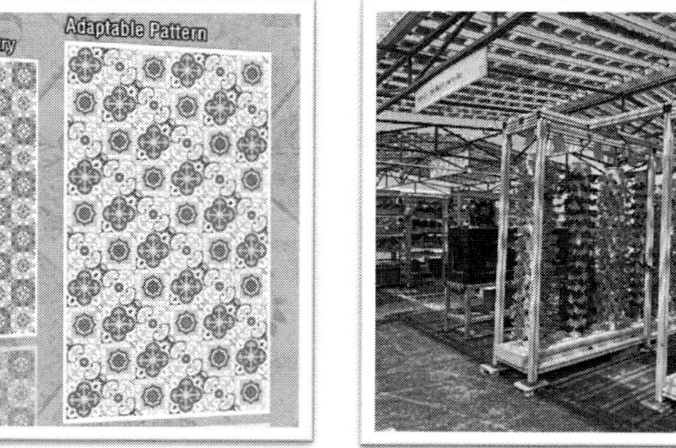

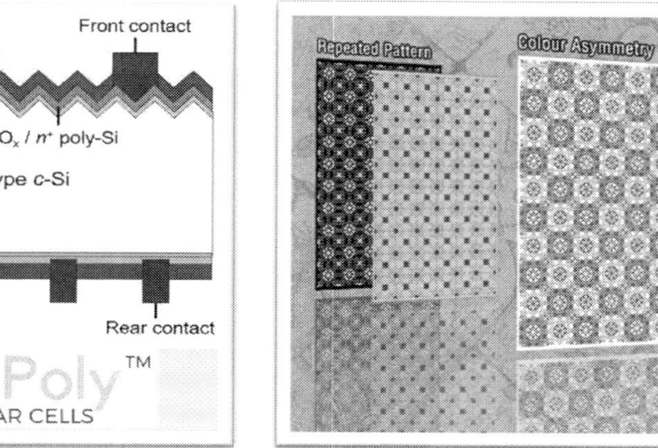

020264-002

The Motivation

- Years of operation and degradation rate rank as the two most sensitive **operational** factors for IRR, stressing the economic importance of performance reliability — and the two are linked.
- The tropical sunbelt regions contribute approximately 97 GW [1] of installed capacity, representing ~7% of global installations as of 2023 [2].

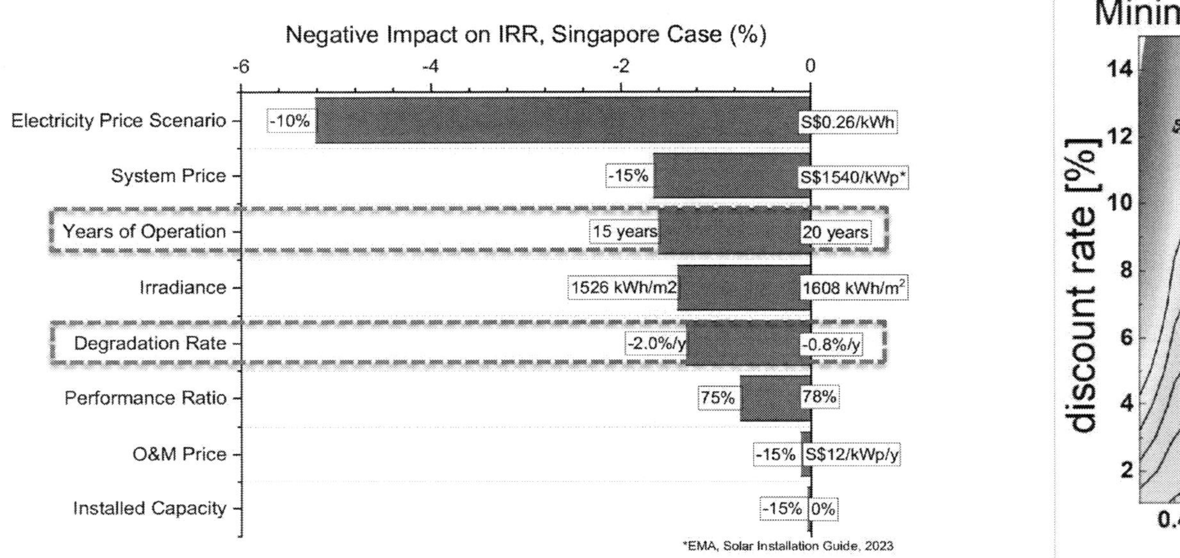

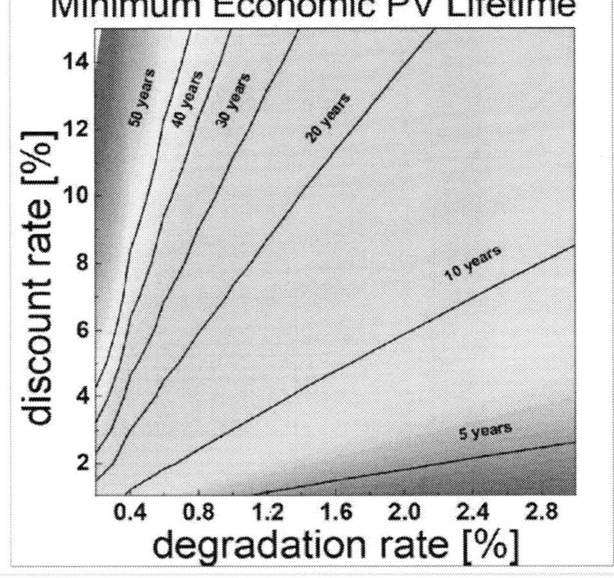

[1] IRENA, Renewable Capacity Statistics 2024, 2024
[2] IEA PVPS, Snapshot of Global PV Markets, 2020–2025
[3] Peters, I.M., et al., Joule 5, 3137–3153, 2021

020264-003

Degradation Study in Tropical Climates

❑ We analysed a dataset of 40 sites totalling 90.6 MWp installations across 7 countries, spanning residential, commercial, and industrial applications.
❑ Through collaboration with PV Doctor, this study draws on one of the most comprehensive tropical PV degradation datasets to date, which will expand >10x data in upcoming work through SERIS / PV Doctor.

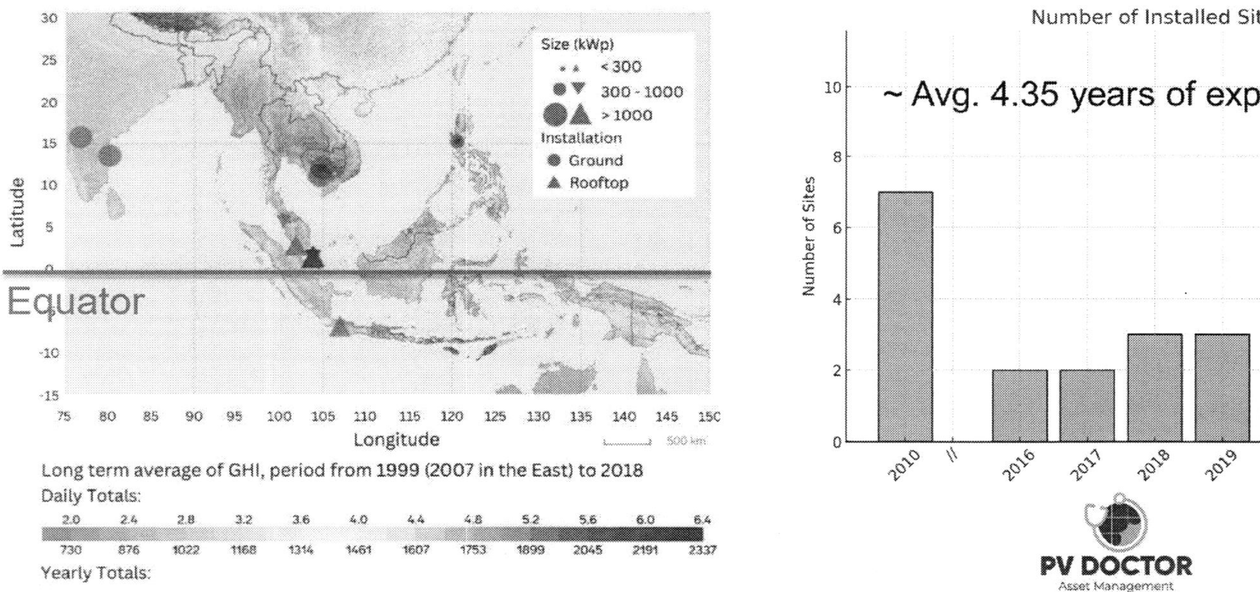

Backdrop Graph: Solar resource map © 2021 Solargis
https://solargis.com/resources/free-maps-and-gis-data?locality=asia

Data Source: PV Doctor, Singapore (http://pv.doctor/en)
(In preparation for publication) X.XU | EU PVSEC 2025| 23/09/2025

Methodologies and Results

- ❏ Three different analytical methods [1] implemented to obtain **system-level** Performance Loss Rates (PLRs)
- ❏ **"Sensor YOY" provides robust method, identifying mean and median of -1.4%/y and -1.2%/y**

Our Research Findings:

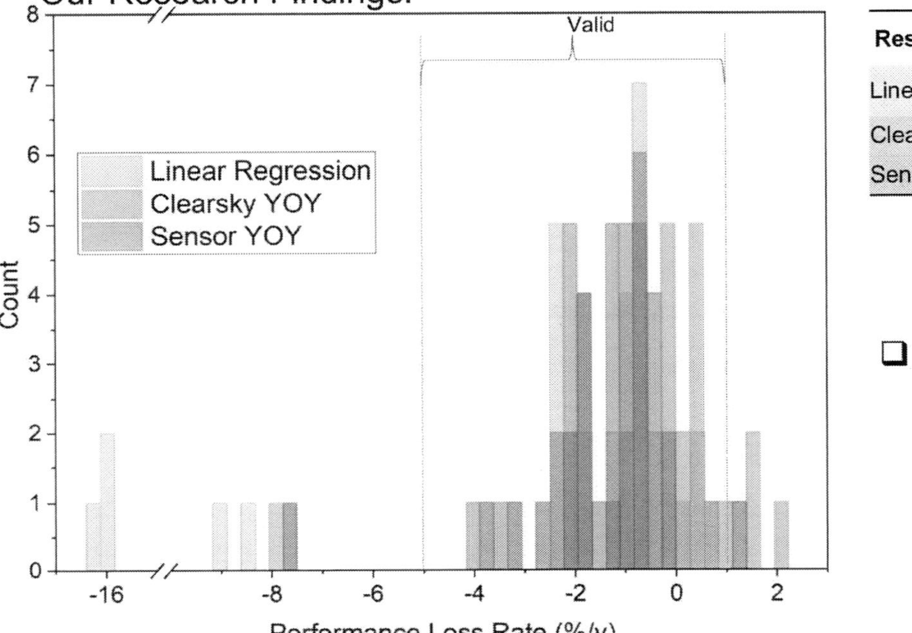

Results Summary	N total (Valid/Data)	Mean (%/y)	Median (%/y)	Std.Dev (%/y)
Linear Regression	31/39	-1.30	-1.05	1.09
Clearsky YOY	29/35	-0.58	-0.57	0.97
Sensor YOY	38/40	-1.44	-1.21	0.96

- ❏ This is in stark contrast to the PV module manufacturers' warranties, which are in some cases even as low as: -0.5%/y

[1] D.C. Jordan et al., IEEE J. Photovolt., 8(2), pp. 525–531, 2018

(In preparation for publication) X.XU | EU PVSEC 2025| 23/09/2025

020264-005

PLRs in the Tropics

- Past literature on tropical degradation studies are compiled, which largely agree with this study
- **Module-level**: mean degradation of -1.3%/y with lower variability ($\sigma \approx 0.7$%/y) reported;
  System-level: studies show a higher mean of -1.5%/y with greater variability ($\sigma \approx 1.5$%/y)

Tropical Literature	N total	Mean (%/y)	Median (%/y)	Std.Dev (%/y)
Literature, Module level	127	-1.28	-1.33	0.75
Literature, String/System level	35	-1.45	-1.13	1.53
This study, System level	38	-1.44	-1.21	0.96

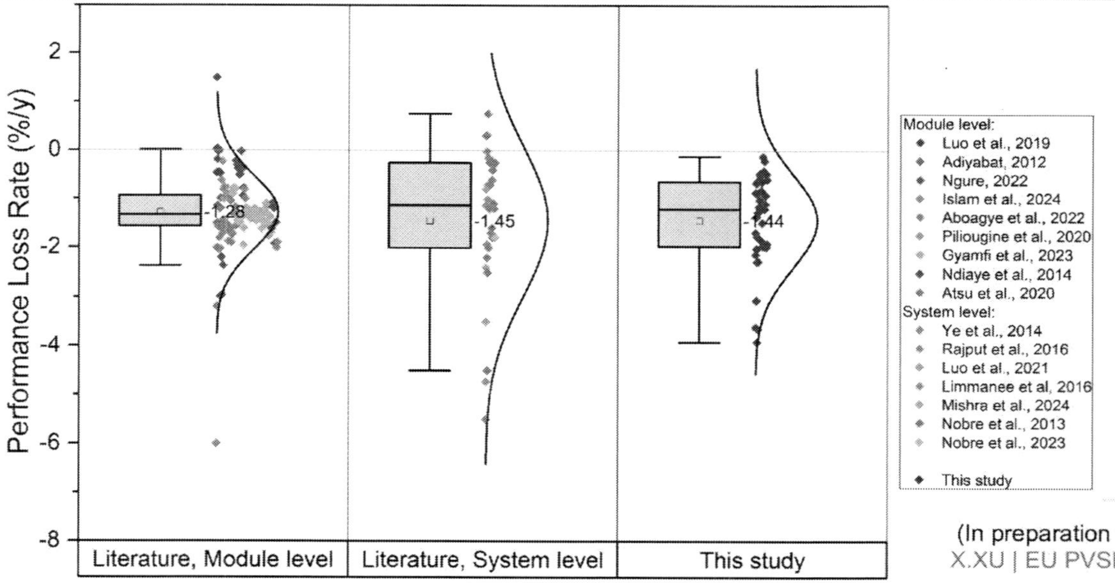

(In preparation for publication)
X.XU | EU PVSEC 2025| 23/09/2025

020264-006

PLRs by Regions

❑ The observed PLR are at faster decline in tropical climates, than those reported in temperate regions
❑ **By Regions**: Europe (Residentials), USA fleet and this study — the results of Levene's test (variances), Welch's ANOVA (means), and the Kruskal-Wallis test (non-parametric) all indicated <u>statistically differences</u>

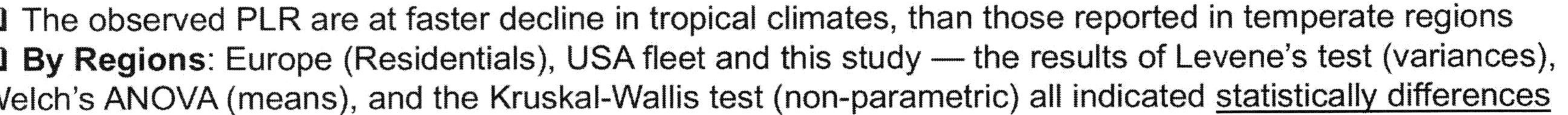

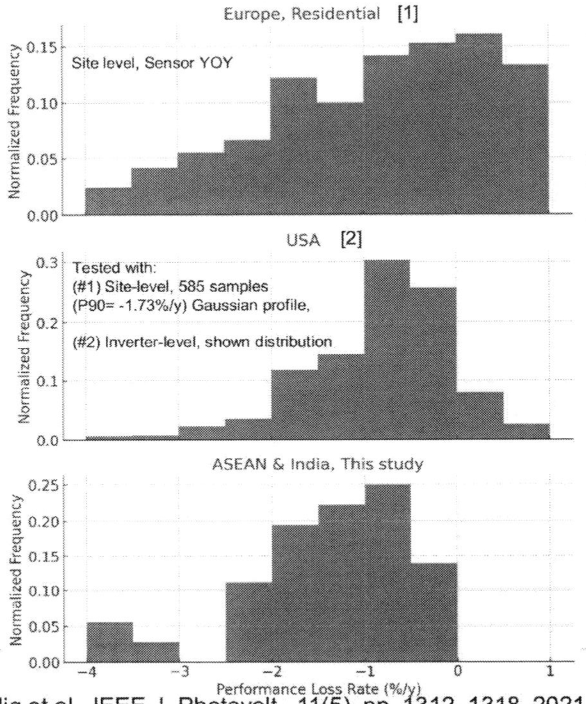

Tropical Literature	N total	Mean (%/y)	Median (%/y)	Std.Dev (%/y)
#1. Europe, Residential [1]	361	-0.86	-0.67	1.40 (est.)
#2. USA [2], Inverter-level	4915	-0.88	-0.75	0.60 (est.)
#3. USA [2], System-level	585	-0.86	-0.68	0.68 (est.)
#4. ASEAN & India, this study	38*	-1.44	-1.21	0.96

* Based on current dataset, will be tackled more in future works

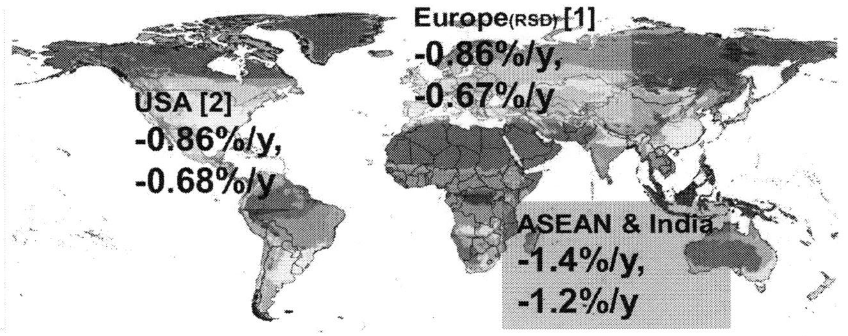

(In preparation for publication) X.XU | EU PVSEC 2025| 23/09/2025

[1] S. Lindig et al., IEEE J. Photovolt., 11(5), pp. 1312–1318, 2021
[2] D.C. Jordan et al., Progress in Photovoltaics, 2022
[3] H.E. Beck et al., Sci. Data, 5:180214, 2018

PLRs by Cell Technologies and Age

❑ **By Cell Technology**: Mean PLRs vary (mono-Si ~-1.3%, multi-Si ~-2.0%, PERC ~-0.6%, n-mono ~-0.7%, thin-film ~-2.5%), but "Analysis of Variance" (ANOVA) shows no statistically significant difference
❑ **By Exposure Years**: PLRs range from about -0.8% to -2.1% depending on field age group, yet differences are not statistically significant

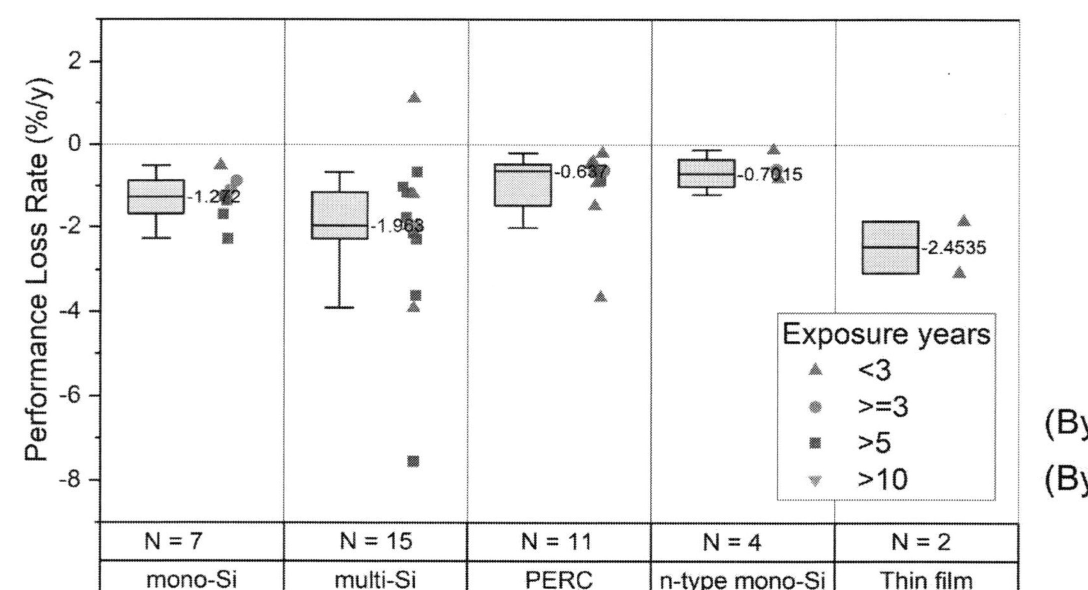

(In preparation for publication) X.XU | EU PVSEC 2025| 23/09/2025

020264-008

PLRs by Other Categories

- **Climate & Installation**: Current dataset shows Af zones mainly rooftop, As/Aw zones mainly ground-mount, with fewer long-term exposures → possible temporal bias. Further work needed to separate climate, installation type, and age effects on PLR.
- **Mono/Bi-Facial & Full/Half cell**: Preliminary data suggest monofacial ≈ bifacial PLRs; half-cell vs. full-cell shows no reliable difference

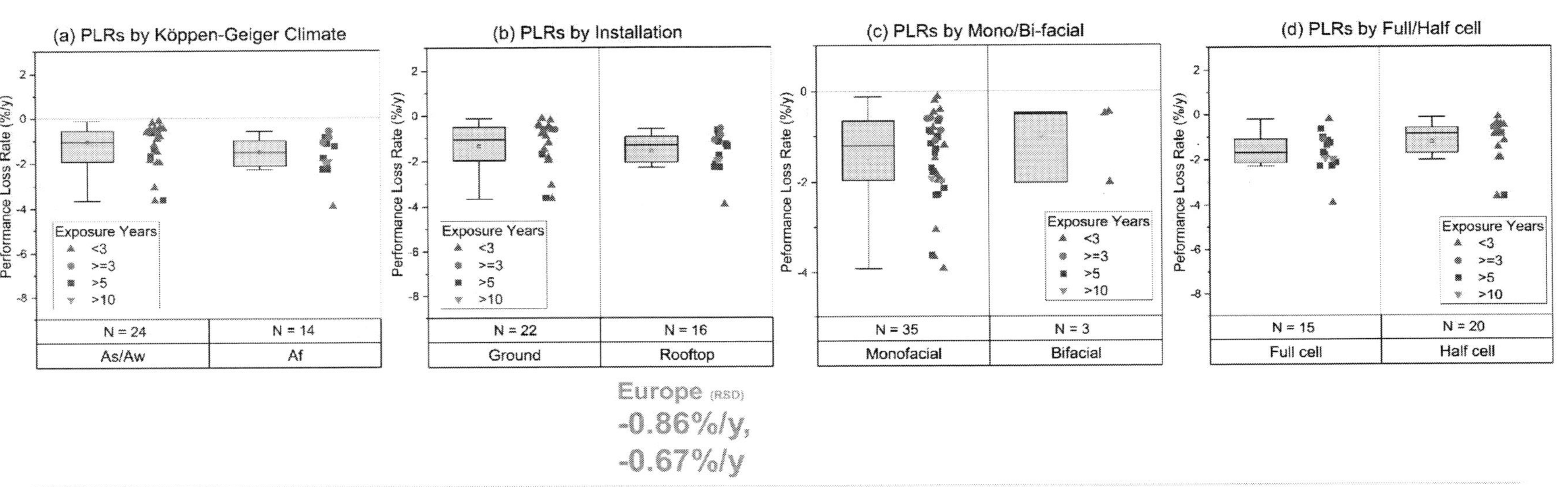

Koeppen-Geiger Climate classification: **Af** = Tropical rainforest; **As** = Tropical Savanna (dry summer); **Aw** = Tropical Savanna (dry winter)[9]

(In preparation for publication) X.XU | EU PVSEC 2025| 23/09/2025

Climate Difference in Tamb and Irradiance

❑ Environmental stressors such as ambient temperature, irradiance, and cumulative UV exposure were examined to explore potential factors that may influence PLR.

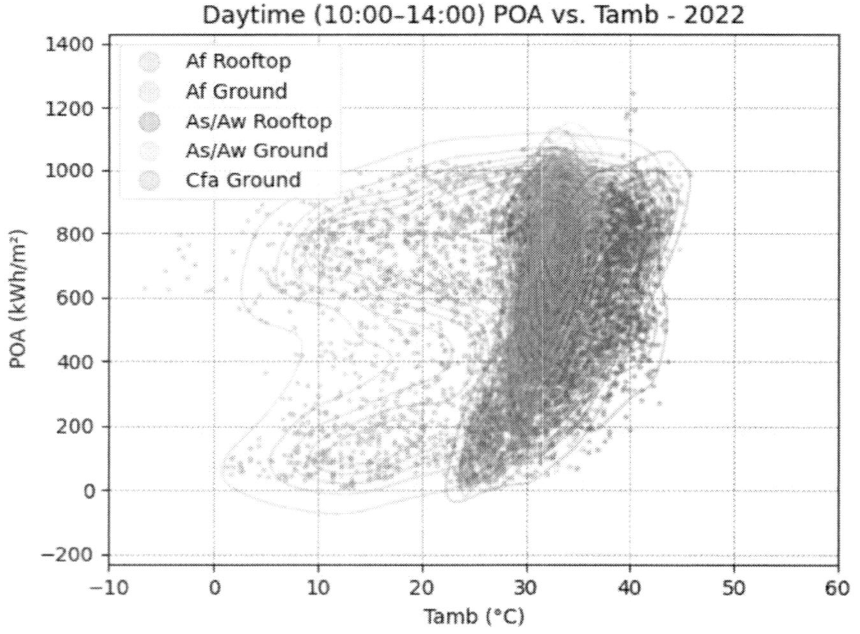

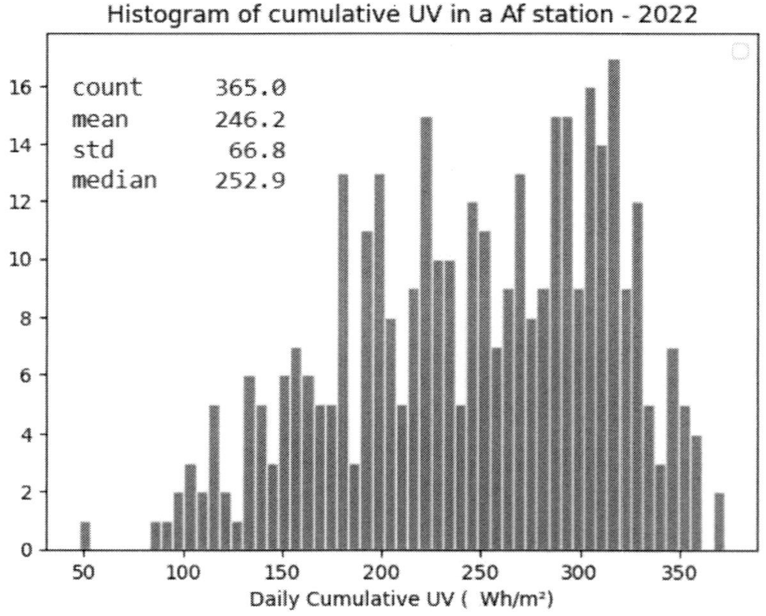

Cfa data: NREL. (2021). Photovoltaic Data Acquisition (PVDAQ) Public Datasets [Station ID:3D33]

(In preparation for publication)

Climate Difference in Tmod

- Median: +8.9 °C (As/Aw ground) and +11.1 °C (Af rooftop) vs. Cfa ground.
- 25% quantile: Cfa ground shows much lower values (longer left tail).
- Spread: Cfa ground has the widest variability (σ = 13.5 °C).

Module Temperature		Mean (°C)	Median (°C)	25% (°C)	75% (°C)	90% (°C)	Std (°C)
Ground	As/Aw	46.7	48.1	42.7	51.9	54.9	7.3
	Cfa	37.8	39.0	28.4	48.1	54.4	13.5
Rooftop	Af	48.9	50.0	41.0	57.9	62.4	11.2

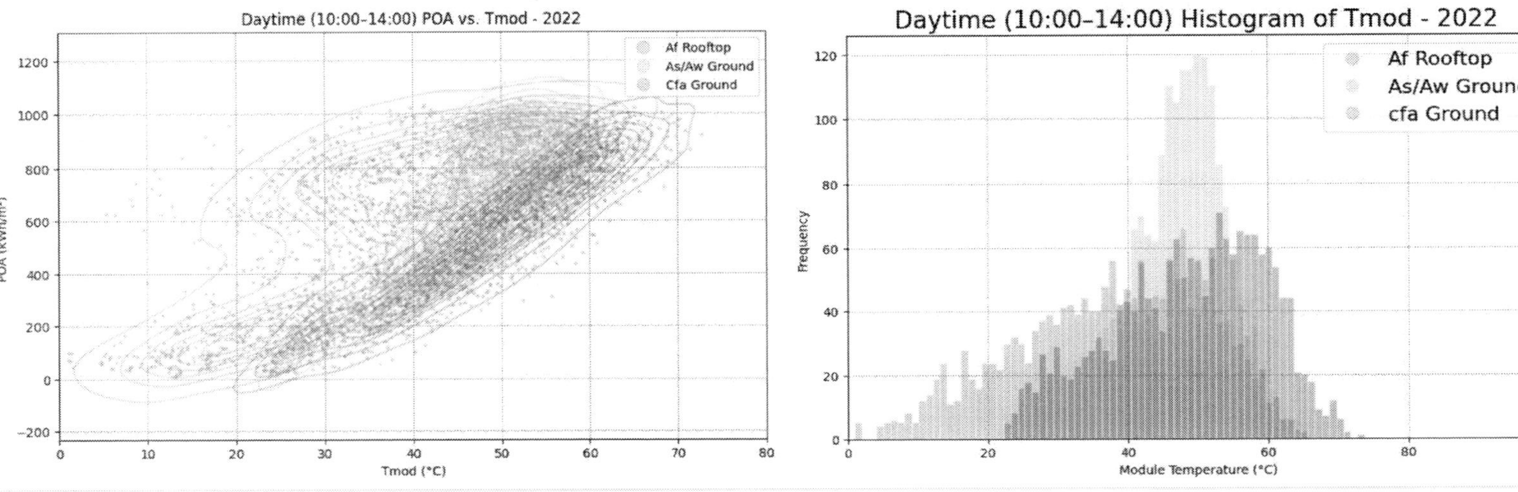

Cfa data: NREL. (2021). Photovoltaic Data Acquisition (PVDAQ) Public Datasets [Station ID:3D33]

(In preparation for publication)

Conclusions

- Years of operation and degradation rate rank as the two most sensitive operational factors for IRR, stressing the economic importance of performance reliability — and the two are linked.

- Tropical regions PV now account for ~97 GW (~7% of global PV as of 2023), highlighting their rising importance in the global fleet.

- **PLRs in the tropics identified mean and median of -1.4%/y and -1.2%/y, respectively, based on current dataset.**

- Our findings are consistent with past datasets in tropical regions and further demonstrate that PV degradation progresses significantly faster in the tropics compared to Europe and the USA.

- There is no clear statistical difference across cell technologies, system ages, installation types, or mono vs. bifacial and half-cell vs. full-cell designs, highlighting the need for a larger dataset.

- The characterisation of Tamb, irradiance, UV, and Tmod across Af and As/Aw applications were provided, forming a basis for future research to better interpret their role in degradation outcomes.

- Tropical climate degradation remains under-studied — advancing knowledge requires broader datasets, open data sharing, and stronger collaboration across stakeholders.

020264-012

Thank you for your attention!
Contact: Lucia XU
lucia.xu@nus.edu.sg

More information at www.seris.sg

We are also on:

020264-013

This presentation was selected by the Sc. Committee of the EU PVSEC 2025 for submission of a full paper to one of the EU PVSEC's collaborating peer-reviewed journals.

MODELING THE ELECTRICAL MISMATCH CAUSED BY POTENTIAL INDUCED DEGRADATION IN CRYSTALLINE SILICON PHOTOVOLTAIC MODULES AND STRINGS

Aysha Mahmood, Gisele Alves dos Reis Benatto, Sune Thorsteinsson, Peter B. Poulsen and Sergiu V. Spataru
Department of Electrical and Photonics Engineering, Technical University of Denmark
Frederiksborgvej 399, 4000, Roskilde, Denmark.

ABSTRACT: Potential induced degradation (PID) is known to cause, depending on its mechanism, degradation in the current and/or voltage of a solar cell and affect photovoltaic (PV) modules within a PV string non-uniformly. The purpose of this work is to model and estimate the additional power loss that occurs due to current and/or voltage mismatch in the system, caused by polarization and shunting type of PID. The impact of PID on the current-voltage (I-V) characteristics is modeled for a PV array consisting of eight parallelly connected strings with 22 serially connected 60-cell PV modules using PySpice where each solar cell in the PV array is represented by a two-diode equivalent circuit model. The degradation is introduced by adjusting the input parameters of the model to values that are reported in literature. To generate realistic I-V curves, the model considers variability in solar cell performance within a module and string due to non-uniform degradation. The power mismatch loss is calculated for twelve different degradation scenarios to assess the long-term performance of the degraded PV arrays. The P_{LOSS} of the PV array affected with PID-p is ~5.25 % and the ML is 0.72 %. The PV array with PID-s has a P_{LOSS} of ~ 10 % and a ML of 2.35 % at the most degraded stage.
Keywords: Modeling, Electrical mismatch, Potential-induced degradation, Crystalline silicon, Photovoltaic system.

1 INTRODUCTION

Photovoltaic (PV) modules deployed in utility scale PV systems can be affected by different faults and/or degradation modes due to exposure to several operational and environmental stress factors. These external stress factors may, depending on the susceptibility of the deployed PV technology or a PV module composite to a certain fault and/or degradation mode, non-uniformly impact the interconnected modules and cause mismatch in their electrical current-voltage (I-V) characteristics [1,2]. This may not only affect the output power of the modules but may limit the power production of the entire PV system as modules in serial and parallel connections are limited by the current and voltage of the lowest rated module, respectively [1,2]. This represents a power loss in addition to the actual module degradation and can increase over time. This may in the long term also have an impact on the annual energy production of the PV system.

Potential induced degradation (PID) is one such degradation mode that, depending on the mechanism, can affect both the current and voltage output of a PV system that is operating at a high system voltage [3,4]. In the case of shunting type of PID (PID-s) both the current and the voltage at maximum power point (MPP) are limited due to 1) increase in second diode dark saturation current (J_{o2}) and ideality-factor (n_2) and 2) decrease in shunt resistance (R_{SH}), fill factor (FF) and open circuit voltage (V_{OC}) [3]. A PV module affected by polarization type of PID (PID-p) is mainly limited by the current at MPP due to 1) increase in first diode dark saturation current (J_{o1}) and ideality factor (n_1) and 2) decrease in short circuit current (I_{SC}) and V_{OC} [4].

The impact of PID is mostly characterized on either cell or module level. To what extent do the different PID types impact the electrical performance of a PV plant and how does this translate into the long-term performance of a PV plant is not clarified as it is not easily identified and/or isolated from other faults and/or degradation modes that cause similar deviation on the I-V characteristics.

The aim of this work is to model and investigate the impact of PID-s and PID-p on PV array I-V characteristics, and to quantify the additional mismatch loss caused by PID at array level, considering 1) the underlying PID mechanisms 2) variability in solar cell performance in a module due to non-uniform potential on the module's surface and 3) variability in module performance in/of a string due to different level of voltage stress depending on the location of the modules in the PV string.

2 MODELING

2.1 Modeling of solar cells affected by PID

The modeling of a PV system is done in Python using the PySpice library. Each solar cell is represented by a two-diode equivalent circuit model with the following input parameters: light generated photocurrent (I_{PH}), series resistance (R_S), shunt resistance (R_{SH}), dark saturation currents (I_{o1} and I_{o2}) and ideality factors ($n1$ and $n2$) of the two diodes (referred to as cell level model). The electrical circuit model of the solar cell simulates a light I-V characteristic curve at a given irradiance and temperature level by doing a voltage sweep from 0 V to V_{DC} and measure the current running through a resistor (R_{LOAD}) that is generated from light source I_{LIGHT} (Fig. 1).

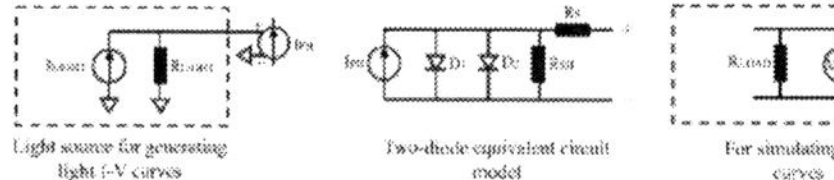

Figure 1: The two-diode equivalent circuit model implemented with PySpice library.

Table I shows the input parameters of the two-diode equivalent circuit model that is used for simulating a healthy solar cell. For introducing PID, the most affected two diode model parameters are adjusted to what is experimentally observed and reported in the literature. The modeling of PID-p is based on mechanism that is observed on the front side of a p-type crystalline silicon (c-Si) PV module stressed with high positive voltage potential. A 5 % decrease in the I_{PH} and increase of I_{o1} from 1.0e-10 A to 5.0e-10 A is applied for the most degraded solar cell in the simulation, corresponding to a P_{LOSS} of 10 % on the cell level [5]. However, to consider non-uniform PID-p degradation, a range of I_{SC} and I_{o1} between the given

10.4229/EUPVSEC2025/4BO.7.4

values are applied to the solar cells. Similarly, for PID-s, observed on the front side of a p-type c-Si PV module operating under high negative voltage potential, the degradation in solar cells are introduced by reducing the R_{SH} of the solar cells from 1000 Ω to ~0.1 Ω and increasing the I_{02} and n_2 from 1.0e-19 A and 2 to 1.0e-1 A and 9, respectively [6,7]. This corresponds to a P_{LOSS} > 30 % on the cell level [6].

Table I: Input parameters of the two-diode equivalent circuit model for a healthy, PID-p and PID-s solar cell.

Model input parameters	Healthy	PID-p	PID-s
I_{PH} [A]	9.85	9.3575	9.85
R_S [Ω]	0.005	0.005	0.005
R_{SH} [Ω]	1000	1000	0.1
I_{01} [A]	1.0e-10	5.0e-10	1.0e-10
n_1	1	1	1
I_{02} [A]	1.0e-19	1.0e-19	1.0e-1
n_2	2	2	9

2.2 Modeling of PV modules affected by PID

Solar cells are serially connected into a module as three 20-cell substrings, each connected parallelly to a bypass diode. Identical solar cells are grouped into a single two-diode equivalent circuit model with input parameters: I_{PH}, $R_S \cdot N_X$, $R_{SH} \cdot N_X$, I_{01}, I_{02}, $n_1 \cdot N_X$ and $n_2 \cdot N_X$ (number of solar cells within a group, N_X).

2.3 Modeling of PV strings affected by PID

To scale the voltage of the PV system and consider string level PID characteristics, 22 modules are serially connected into a string. Total eight modules closest to the positive end of a string are modeled with PID-p. It is assumed that the voltage stress is greatest at the positive end and therefore, the PID is more severe at the ends. Similarly, Total five modules closest to the negative end of a string are modeled with PID-s. The remaining healthy PV modules are grouped together and connected serially to the degraded modules.

2.4 Modeling of PV array affected by PID

The final model is an array with eight strings connected parallelly together. One string diode is connected serially to each PV string to block reverse current flow.

2.5 PV array degradation scenarios

The severity of PID in the array is increased by reducing the I_{PH} and R_{SH} values of solar cells affected with PID-p and PID-s by 0.5 % and 50 % from their previous values, respectively. In total twelve different degradation scenarios are created for a PV array affected by PID-p and PID-s, and each scenario is set to represent a point in time (i.e. degradation stages represent degradation after each month in a year).

2.6 Mismatch losses

The mismatch loss (ML) is calculated by taking the difference between the array level P_{LOSS} and the average P_{LOSS} calculated from each PV module in the PV system, at STC (Eq. 1). The P_{LOSS} is calculated as the relative change between module/array P_{MAX} and P_{MAX} of a healthy (reference) module/array (Eq. 2).

$$ML\ [\%] = P_{LOSS,array} - \frac{\sum_{i=1}^{176} P_{LOSS,Module\ i}}{176} \qquad (1)$$

$$P_{LOSS}\ [\%] = abs\left(\frac{P_{MAX}-P_{MAX,reference}}{P_{MAX,reference}} \cdot 100\ \%\right) \qquad (2)$$

3 RESULTS AND DISCUSSION

3.1 Mismatch losses caused by PID-p in the PV array

Figure 2 shows I-V curves of twelve different degradation scenarios representing different PID stages (t=0 to t=365). The non-uniformity in the electrical performance of the PV modules in the PV strings, that is caused by PID-p, is translated into a drop in the current output of the system due to activation of the bypass diodes of the degraded module cell-substrings and re-direction of the current (i.e. current mismatch within a PV module and in the PV strings) (Fig 2). The I_{SC} of the system is not affected. The I_{MPP} of the system, on the contrary, is highly impacted. The I_{MPP}/I_{SC} ratio reduces from 0.9483 (healthy state, t=0 d) to 0.9383 (degraded state, t=31 d) when PID-p is introduced in the PV modules with ~0.5 % degradation in the I_{PH} on the cell level at STC and it reduces further to 0.917 (degraded state, t=365 d) with cell level I_{PH} degradation of ~5 %. This effect is prominent on the I-V curves due to formation of a step near the MPP that is tilted due to the non-uniformity in the current output of the degraded cell-substrings (Fig. 2). As degradation in the cell-substrings reaches the PID-p saturation point (- 5 % degradation in I_{PH}), the step levels out.

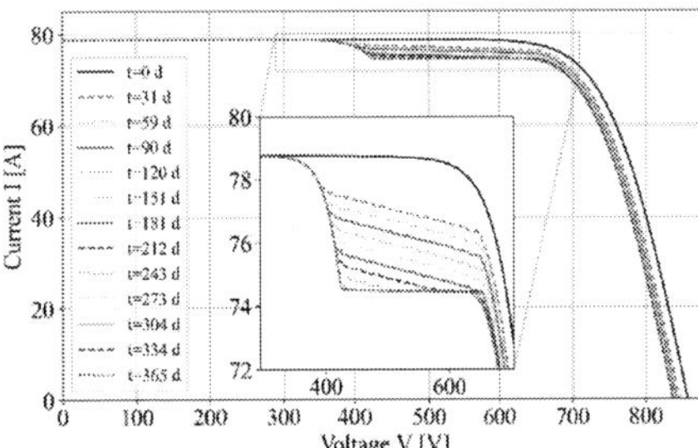

Figure 2: Simulated I-V curves of a PV array affected by PID-p at different degradation stages, and at STC.

The fraction of the absolute change in the system I_{MPP} at t=31 d and t=365 d is ~1 % and ~3.2 %, respectively (Fig. 3). The V_{OC} and V_{MPP} degrade from 1.4 % (t=31 d) to 2.4 % and 2 % (t=365 d), respectively. The resulting P_{LOSS} of the system is ~ 5.25 % and the corresponding FF reduces with ~ 3 % (t=365 d) at STC. The ML increases from 0.13 % to 0.72 % (Fig. 3).

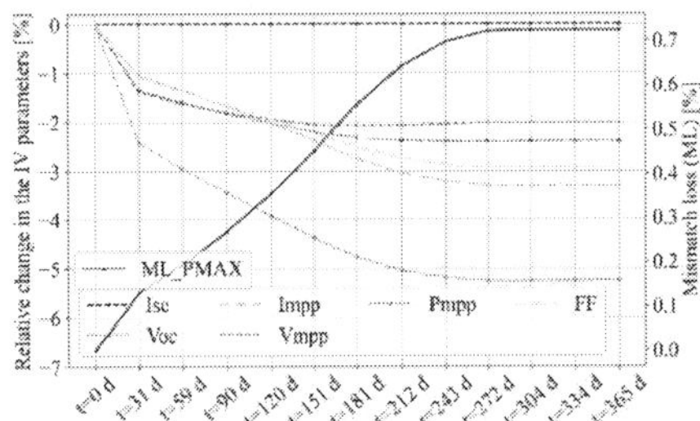

Figure 3: The relative change in the I-V parameters extracted from simulated I-V curves of the PV array

(dashed lines) and the mismatch losses (solid line) at different PID-p degradation stages, and at STC.

3.2 Mismatch losses caused by PID-s in the PV array

The array affected with PID-s is relatively more impacted, considering that the degradation is introduced in fewer PV modules (t=365 d, Fig 4). However, the R_{SH} has to reduce more than 90 % before degradation is observed on the I-V (t=181 d, $R_{SH} < 14\ \Omega$, Fig. 4). Nevertheless, a slope appears near the MPP due to the reduction in the R_{SH} and causes drop in the current and voltage output of the system.

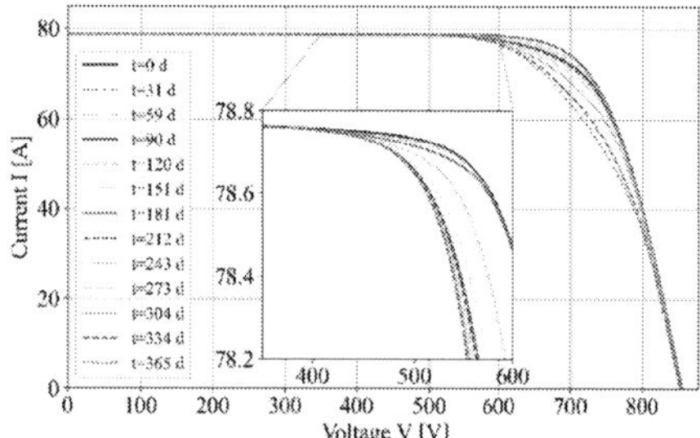

Figure 4: Simulated I-V curves of a PV array affected by PID-s at different degradation stages, and at STC.

The I_{MPP} reduces by 4.47 % is the main contributor to the P_{LOSS} and reduction in the FF at the first few degradation stages (t=120 d to t=272 d). As the MPP changes its position due to change in the shape of the I-V curves, the I_{MPP} recovers with 2.53 % while the V_{MPP} starts to drop (reduces by 8 % at t=365 d) and causes mismatch in the string output voltage. The P_{LOSS} increases to 9.87 % (reduces from 51920 W at t=0 d to 46796 W at t=365 d) and the FF drops by 9.54 % (t=365 d, $R_{SH} < 2\ \Omega$, Fig. 5).

Similar to, in the case of PID-p, the I_{SC} remains unaffected. The drop in V_{OC} is insignificant (reduced by 0.36 %), different from what is typically observed on the module level. This may suggest that the degradation in I_{o2} introduced in the solar cells is less severe (1.0e-1 A) and there is a greater contribution from the healthy solar cells in each PV string as a larger voltage drop in the string would otherwise limit the voltage of the array (to the voltage of most degraded string) and cause a reduction in the V_{OC} of the system. Figure 5 shows the ML which increases to 2.96 % (t=304 d) but reduces to 2.35 % (t=365 d) due to increased PID severity in all three cell-substrings of the degraded PV modules.

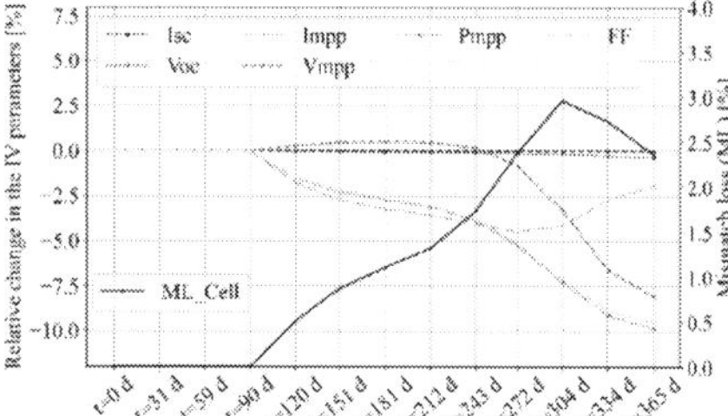

Figure 5: The relative change in the I-V parameters extracted from simulated I-V curves of the PV array (dashed lines) and the mismatch losses (solid line) at different PID-s degradation stages, and at STC.

4 CONCLUSIONS

The impact of PID-p and PID-s on the I-V characteristics of a PV array is modeled and quantified using cell level PID characteristics reported in the literature. A healthy PV array is composed of eight parallelly connected PV strings, each with 22 serially connected 60-cell PV modules. PID-p is introduced in total eight PV modules in each PV string of a PV array by reducing the I_{PH} and I_{o1} of the solar cells. The P_{LOSS} of the system at the most degraded state is ~5.25 % from which 0.72 % is due to the mismatch loss that is caused by non-uniform degradation and progression of PID in the PV strings. PID-s is modeled with reduction in the R_{SH}, I_{o2} and n_2 of the solar cells in five PV modules in each PV string. The P_{LOSS} is ~10 % and the mismatch loss is 2.35 % at the most degraded state. The power and mismatch losses are relatively high considering that fewer PV modules are degraded with PID-s compared to PID-p.

5 ACKNOWLEDGDEMENT

This research is carried out in the DTEC project: High voltage stress testing for potential induced degradation and recovery modeling of utility scale PV.

6 REFERENCES

[1] S. Pingel et al., "Potential Induced Degradation of solar cells and panels," 2010 35th IEEE Photovoltaic Specialists Conference, Honolulu, HI, USA, 2010, pp. 002817-002822, doi: 10.1109/PVSC.2010.5616823.

[2] Dhass, A. D. et al., A Review on Factors Influencing the Mismatch Losses in Solar Photovoltaic System, International Journal of Photoenergy, 2022, 2986004, 27 pages, 2022. https://doi.org/10.1155/2022/2986004.

[3] Luo, W., et al., "Potential-Induced Degradation in Photovoltaic Modules: A Critical Review." Energy & Environmental Science 10, no. 1 (2017): 43–68.

[4] Molto, C et. al., (2023), Review of Potential-Induced Degradation in Bifacial Photovoltaic Modules. Energy Technol., 11: 2200943. https://doi.org/10.1002/ente.202200943.

[5] Seira Yamaguchi et al., Polarization-Type Potential-Induced Degradation in Front-Emitter p-Type and n-Type Crystalline Silicon Solar Cells, ACS Omega 2022 7 (41), 36277-36285, DOI: 10.1021/acsomega.2c03866.

[6] Mahmood, A., Del Prado Santamaria, R., Kari, T., Poulsen, P. B., Spataru, S. V., Diagnosing Potential Induced Degradation in Crystalline Silicon Photovoltaic Modules, 2024, Proceedings of EU PVSEC, DOI 10.4229/EUPVSEC2024/3AV.2.22.

[7] D. Lausch et al., "Potential-Induced Degradation (PID): Introduction of a Novel Test Approach and Explanation of Increased Depletion Region Recombination," in IEEE Journal of Photovoltaics, vol. 4, no. 3, pp. 834-840, May 2014, doi: 10.1109/JPHOTOV.2014.2300238.

020266-001

Modeling the Electrical Mismatch Caused by Potential Induced Degradation in Crystalline Silicon Photovoltaic Modules and Strings

Aysha Mahmood, Gisele Alves dos Reis Benatto, Sune Thorsteinsson, Peter Behrensdorff Poulsen and Sergiu Viorel Spataru

DTU Electro, Technical University of Denmark, Roskilde, Denmark

4BO.7.4 – Field Insights, Performance and Modelling of PV systems
42nd European Photovoltaic Solar Energy Conference – Bilbao, Spain, 2025

020266-002

Introduction and Motivation

- **Utility scale PV systems**
  - Exposed to several operational and environmental stress factors
  - Gets affected by different faults and degradation modes
  - **Non-uniform degradation cause additional mismatch loss in a PV system**

DTU

Introduction and Motivation

- **Utility scale PV systems**
  - **Non-uniform degradation cause additional mismatch loss in a PV system**

- **Mismatch loss**
  - Definition: losses due to differences in electrical performance of solar cells/PV modules in a PV system
    - Serial connection: limited by lowest current value

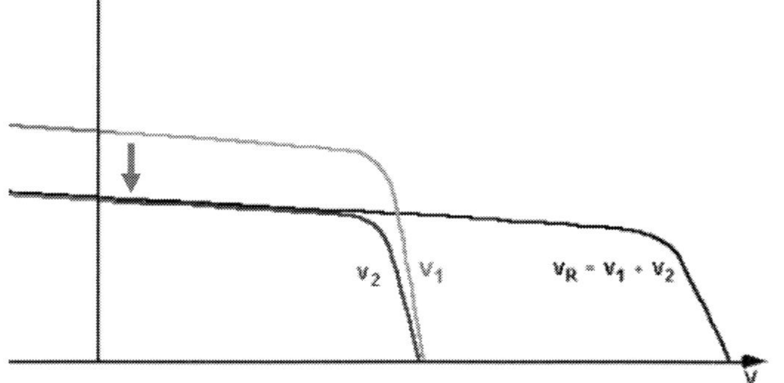

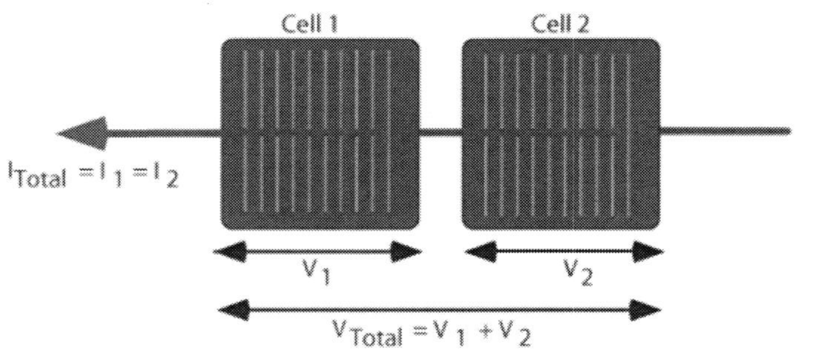

Mismatch Effects | PVEducation

020266-004

DTU

Introduction and Motivation

- **Utility scale PV systems**
  - **Non-uniform degradation cause additional mismatch loss in a PV system**

- **Mismatch loss**
  - Definition: losses due to differences in electrical performance of solar cells/PV modules in a PV system
    - Parallel connection: limited by lowest voltage value

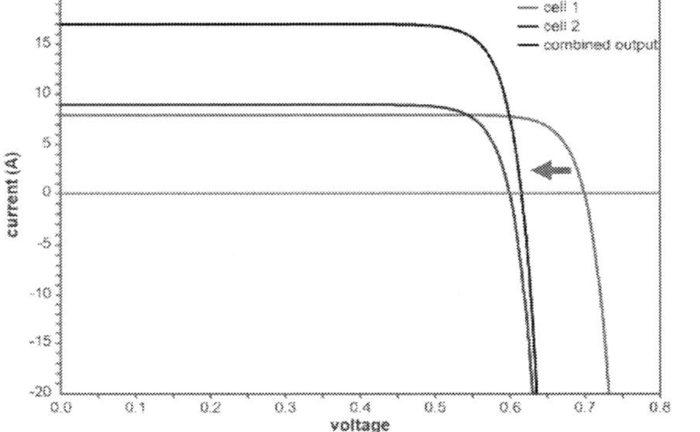

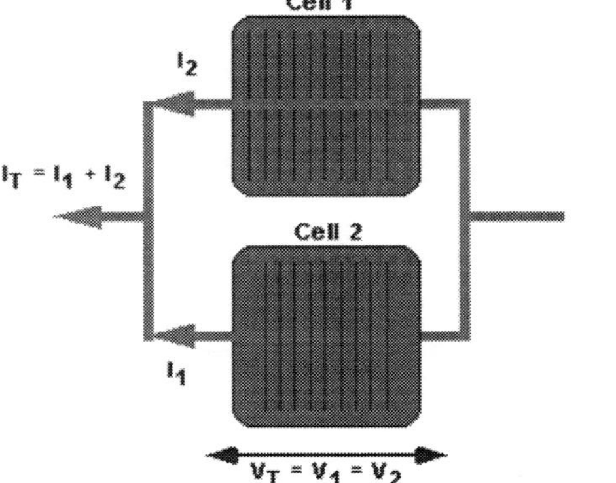

Mismatch Effects | PVEducation

020266-005

Introduction and Motivation

- **Potential induced degradation (PID)**
  - High voltage difference between operating cells and grounded module frame and/or surface
  - **Cause degradation in output current and/or voltage of a PV module**
  - **Cause mismatch loss in PV systems**

- PID types
  - Underlying mechanism
  - PV technology
  - Operating conditions

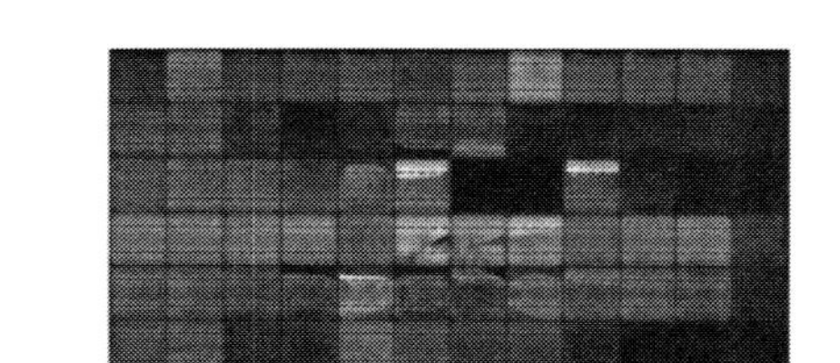

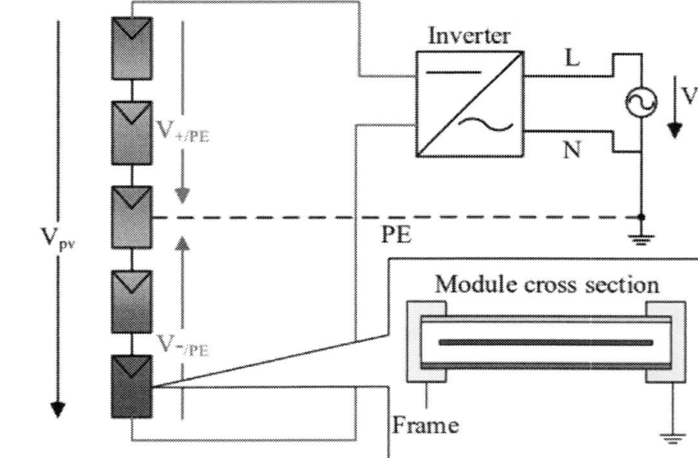

AG, S S T, SMA: Technical Information on PID. Undated, SMA Solar Technology AG: Niestetal, Germany. p. 1-4. Report PID-TI-UEN113410.

S. Pingel et al., "Potential Induced Degradation of solar cells and panels," 2010 35th IEEE Photovoltaic Specialists Conference, Honolulu, HI, USA, 2010, pp. 002817-002822, doi: 10.1109/PVSC.2010.5616823.

020266-006

Introduction and Motivation

- Potential induced degradation (PID)
  - Characterized on cell and module level

  - **To what extent do PID impact the electrical performance of a PV plant?**

  - **What is the additional mismatch loss in a PV plant affected by PID?**

- Model PID on the I-V characteristics of a PV array
  - Considering PID characteristics reported on
    - Cell, module and string level

- Quantify the additional mismatch loss caused by PID

020266-007

How to model a solar cell affected by PID?

- Modeling in Python using PySpice
  - Each solar cell is represented by a **two-diode equivalent circuit model**

- Degradation in specific electrical and/or physical parameters
  - **Polarization type of PID**
    - Mechanism: change in front passivation layer
    - PV technology: mono facial p-type PERC
    - Operating condition: + voltage potential

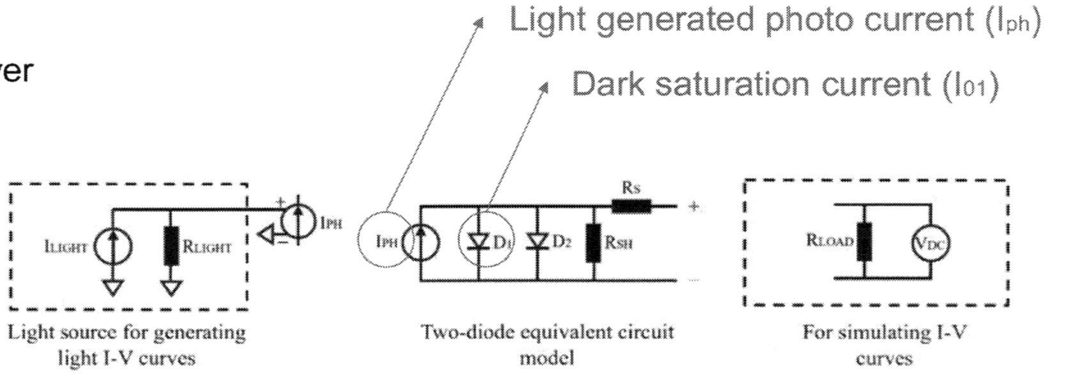

020266-008

How to model a solar cell affected by PID?

- Modeling in Python using PySpice
  - Each solar cell is represented by a **two-diode equivalent circuit model**

- Degradation in specific electrical and/or physical parameters
  - **Polarization type of PID**
    - Mechanism: change in front passivation layer
    - PV technology: mono facial p-type PERC
    - Operating condition: + voltage potential
  - **Shunting type of PID**
    - Mechanism: Na+ penetration
    - PV technology: mono facial p-type PERC
    - Operating condition: - voltage potential

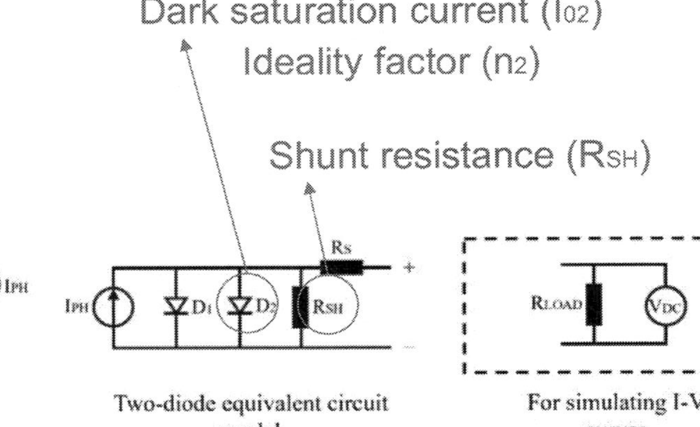

020266-009

How to model a PV module affected by PID?

- 60-cell PV module
  - 20 cell per cell-substring connected serially together
    - Each connected parallelly to a bypass diode
  - Model input parameters are defined for each solar cell
    - Identical solar cells are grouped together within a cell-substring

- **Variability in solar cell performance within a PV module**
  - Non-uniform voltage stress on module surface
  - High voltage stress near the grounded module frame

- Degradation pattern on module level:
  - **Polarization type of PID (PID-p):**
    - Homogenous degradation
  - **Shunting type of PID (PID-s):**
    - Chessboard pattern
    - Close to module frame and negative end

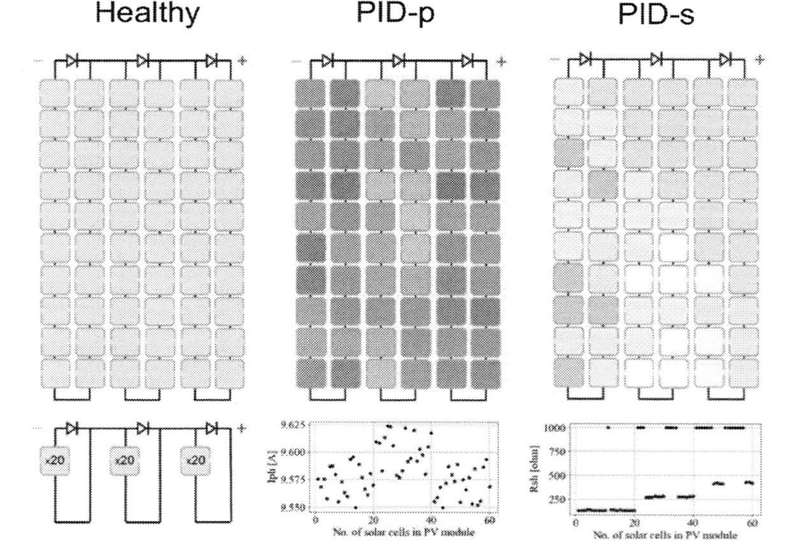

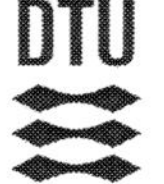

How to model a PV string affected by PID?

- PV string with 22 PV modules serially connected

- Floating grounding configuration
  - 11 modules under negative polarity
  - 11 modules under positive polarity
  - **High voltage stress at the string ends**

- Degradation pattern on string level:
  - High voltage stress near the string ends
  - **Polarization type of PID:**
    - Eight modules degraded close to positive end
  - **Shunting type of PID:**
    - Five modules degraded close to negative end

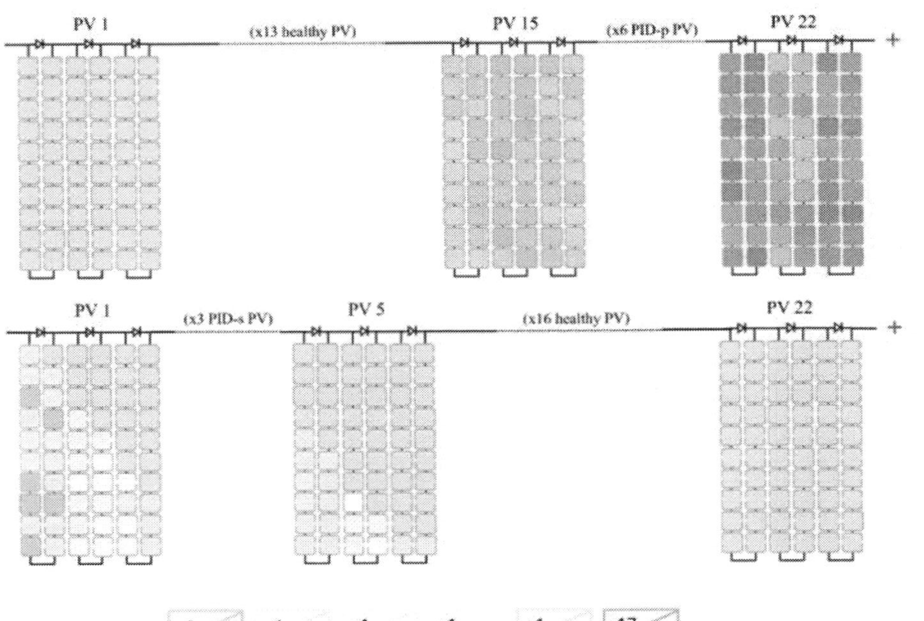

DTU

Modeling of PV array affected by PID

- PV array with 8 PV strings connected parallelly
  - Each connected to a string diode

- PV strings are not completely identical
  - PV modules are degraded with different levels

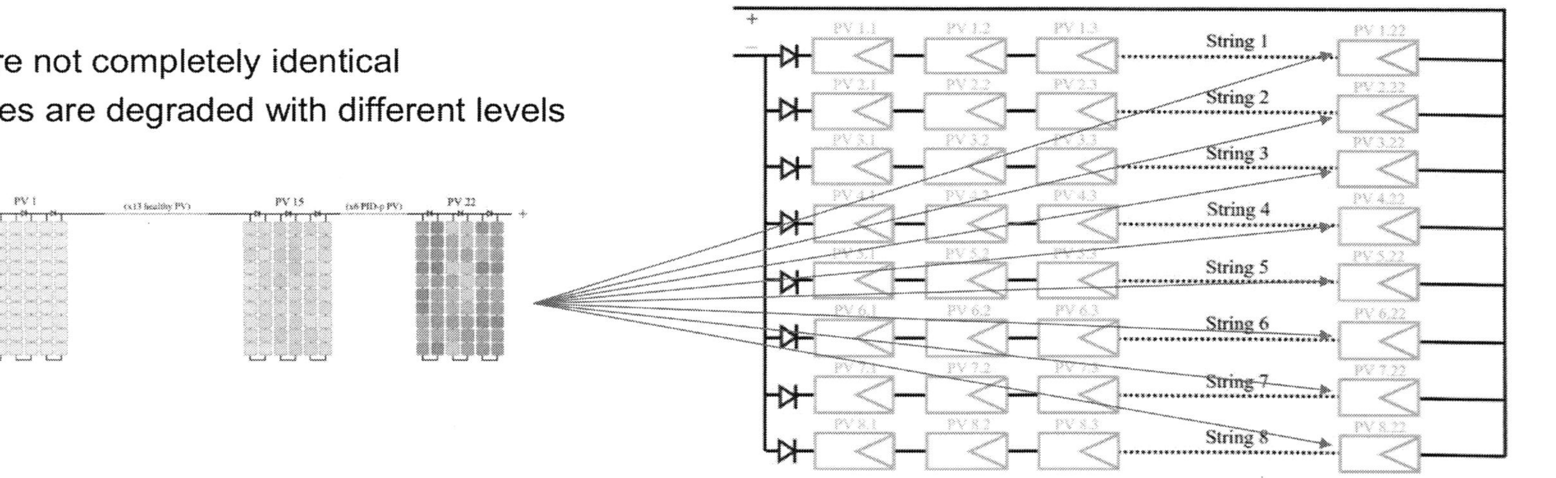

DTU

Modeling of PV array affected by PID

- PV array with 8 PV strings connected parallelly
  - Each connected to a string diode

- PV strings are not completely identical
  - PV modules are degraded with different levels

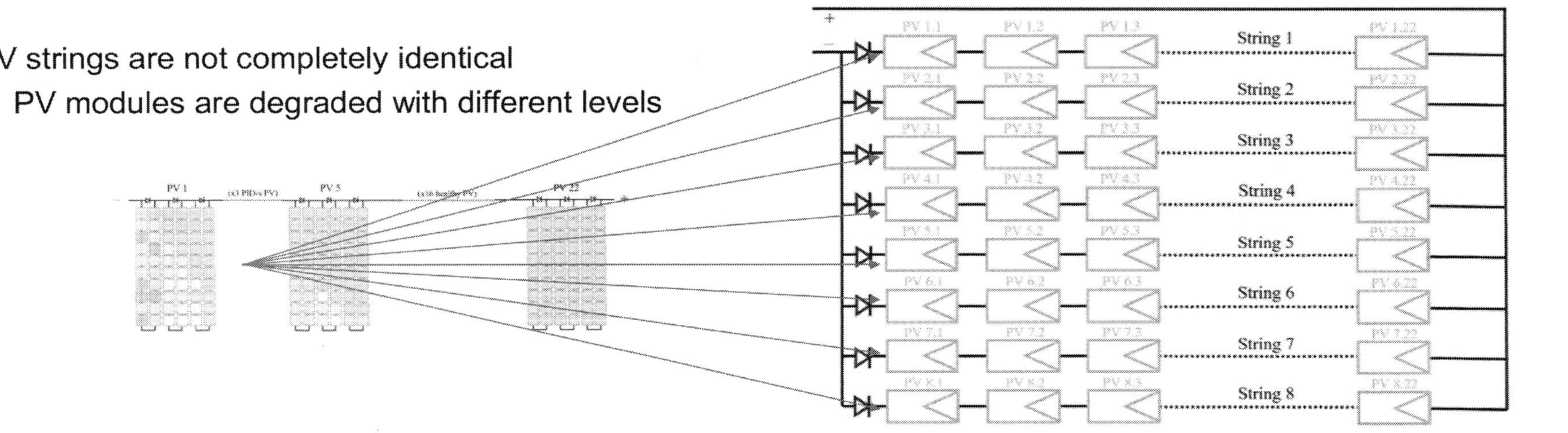

020266-013

DTU

Quantifying the mismatch losses at STC

- A PV system with one healthy and one PID degraded module
  - Degraded: 7.92 % Ploss
  - Average Ploss of the two modules: 3.96 %
  - String Ploss: 4.16 %

$$ML\ [\%] = P_{Loss,Array} - \frac{\sum_{i=1}^{2} P_{Loss,Module,i}}{2}$$

$$P_{Loss}\ [\%] = abs\left(\frac{P_{MAX} - P_{MAX,reference}}{P_{MAX,reference}} \cdot 100\ \%\right)$$

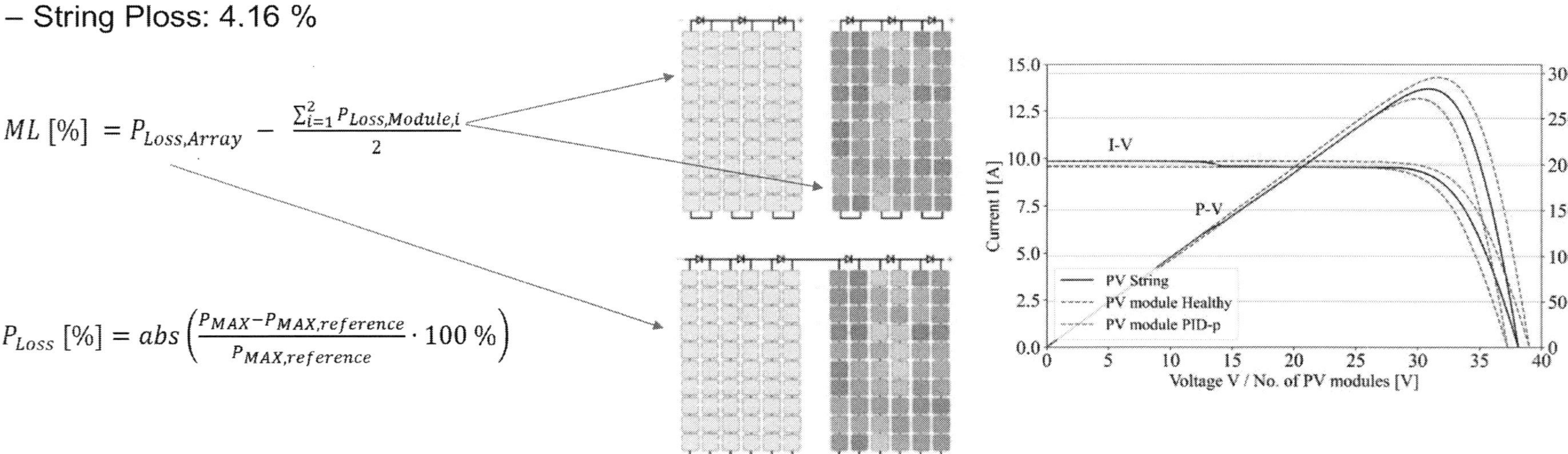

020266-014

How to quantify long-term impact of PID?

- **The impact of PID as it progresses**
  - Increases the severity of PID in solar cells
  - Apply linear degradation rate
  - **Create twelve different degradation scenarios/stages**

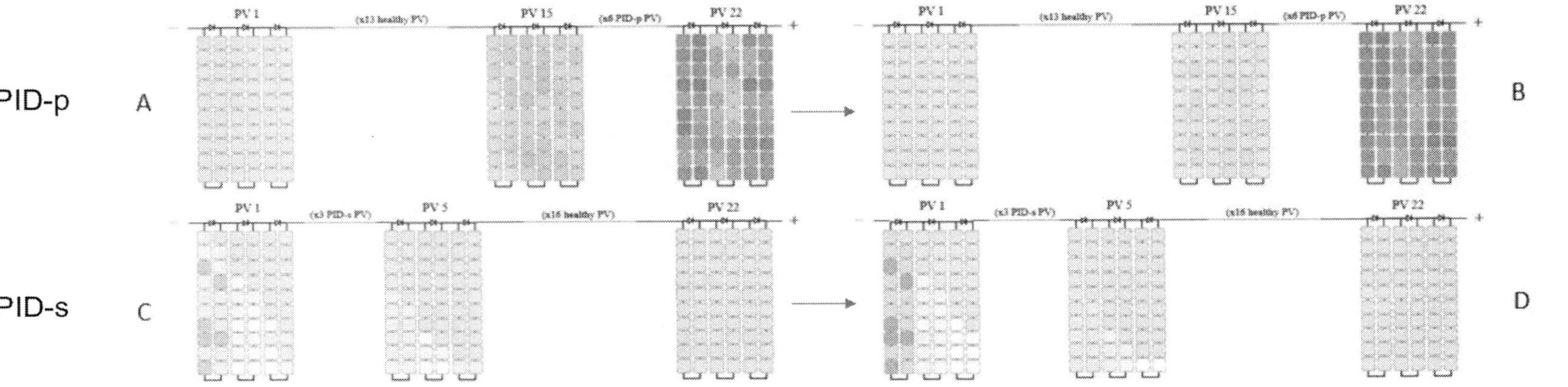

020266-015

DTU

How to quantify long-term impact of PID?

- Add temporal dimension to the analysis
  - Long term impact of PID
  - **One year simulation**
    - G_{POA} and T_{CELL}
      - Location: 55.696 latitude and 12.105 longitude
      - Roskilde, Denmark
      - Fixed tilt of 25°

$$E_{Annual}\ [kWh] = \sum_{i=0}^{3959} P_{MAX,hourly}\ [kW]$$

- >10,000 solar cells in the PV system
  - 3840 solar cells with PID and different model input parameters

- **Reducing the granularity of the model**
  - Defining model input parameters on module level
    - Grouping solar cells to one group/cell-substring
    - Using in-module worst performing solar cell

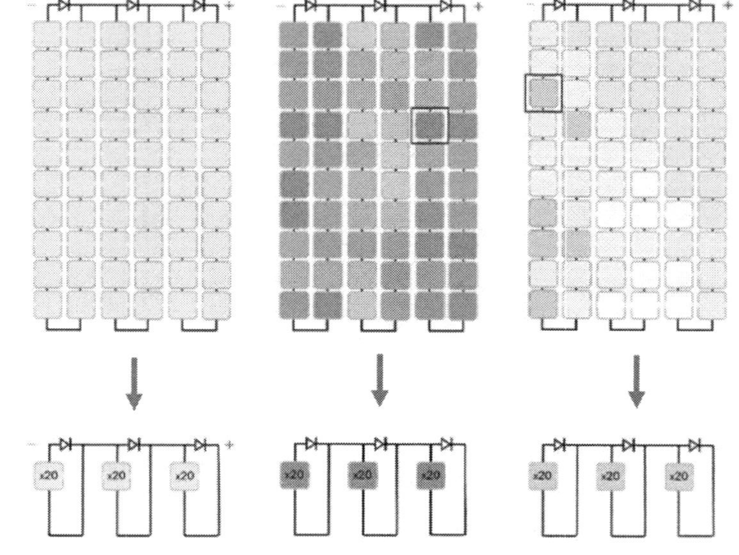

020266-016

DTU

Simulation time for generating an I-V curve

- Single simulation of an array using cell level model
  - 6720 healthy solar cell
    - Grouped into one group per cell-substrings
  - 3840 PID affected solar cells with different model input parameters
  - **1 minutes and 20 seconds at STC**

- Module level model (reduced model granularity)
  - 112 healthy PV modules
  - 64 PID affected PV modules with different model input parameters
  - **< 1 second at STC**

  - **One year simulation: ~ 5 hours**
    - Voltage sweep from 0 to 880 V with 0.1 steps
    - G_{POA} and T_{CELL}

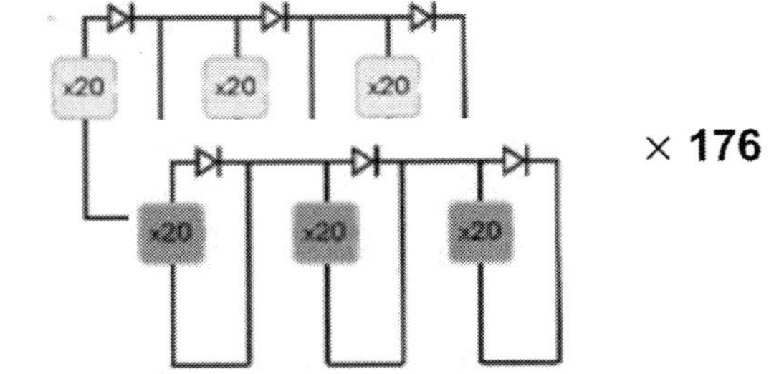

020266-017

DTU

Results of simulations of different degradation stages at STC

- PV array affected by PID-p
  - Twelve different degradation scenarios/stages

Pmpp_deg ≈ 5 %

Voc_deg and Vmpp_deg ≈ 2 %

Impp_deg ≈ 3 %

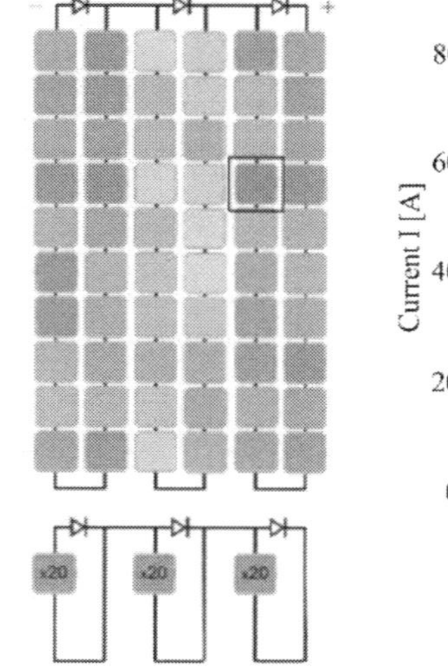

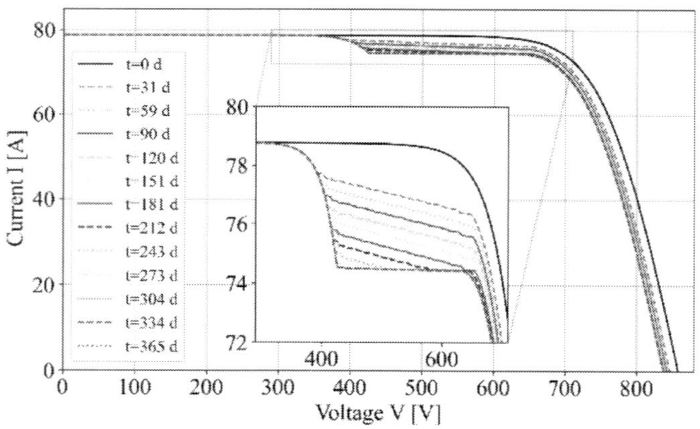

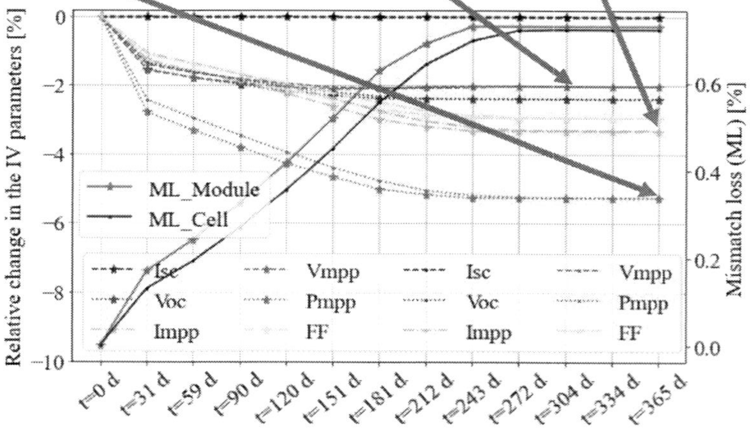

DTU

Results of simulations of different degradation stages at STC

- PV array affected by PID-p
  - Twelve different degradation scenarios/stages

Mismatch loss range: 0.15 to 0.72 %

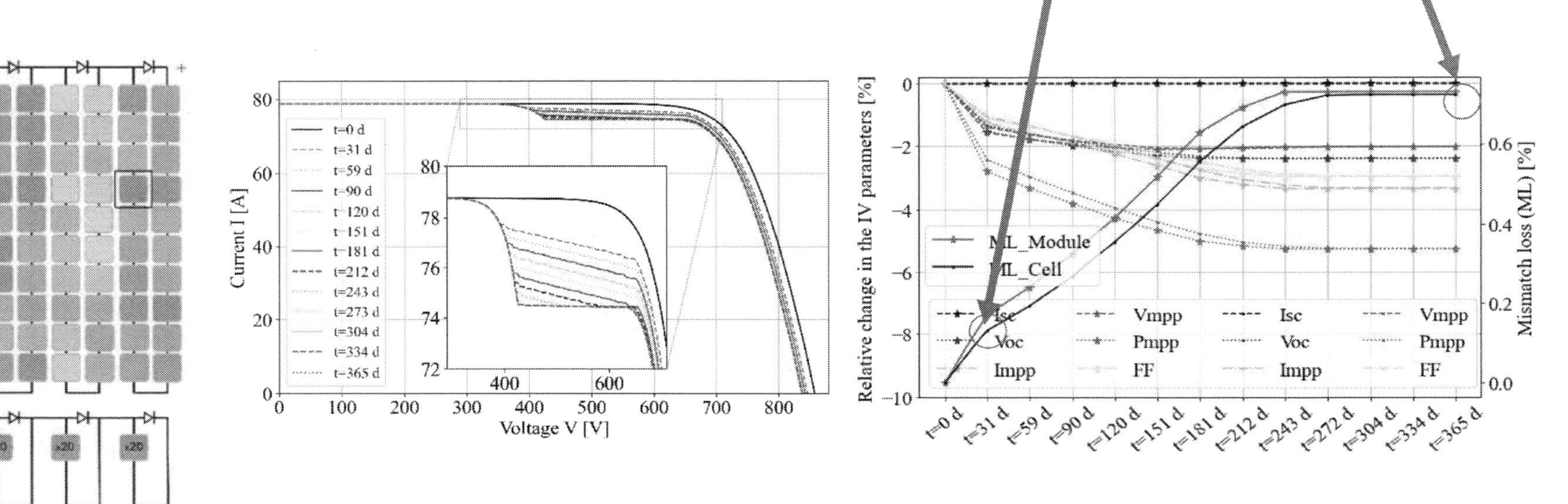

020266-019

DTU

Results of simulations of different degradation stages at STC

- PV array affected by PID-s
  - Twelve different degradation scenarios/stages

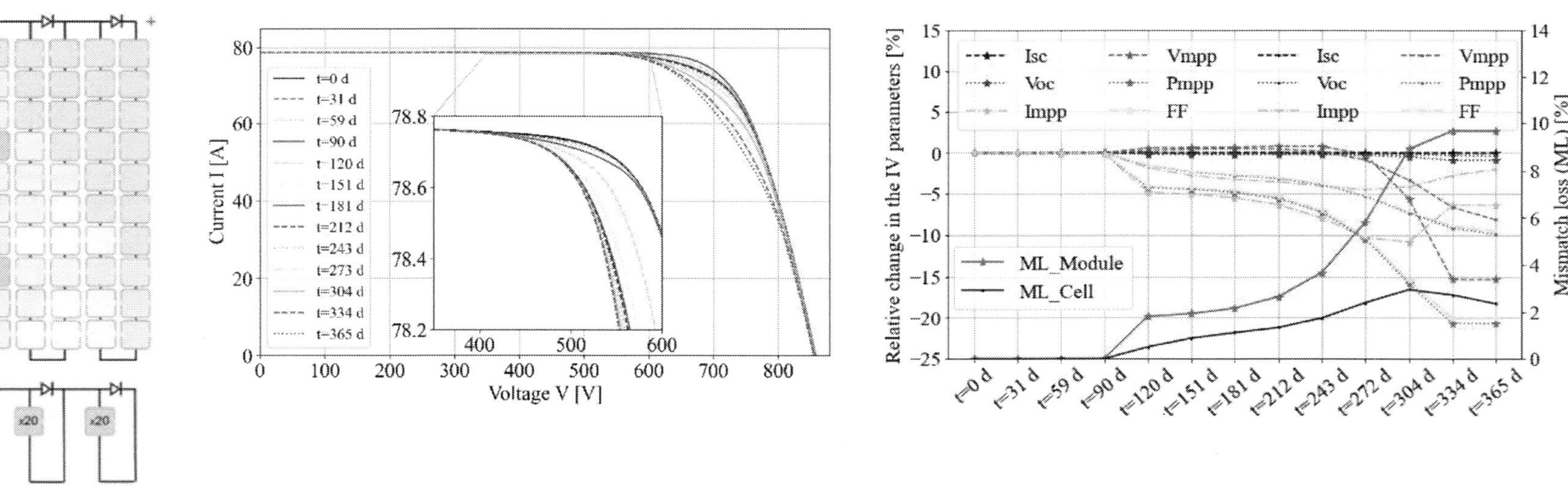

020266-020

Results of simulations of different degradation stages at STC

- PV array affected by PID-s
  - Twelve different degradation scenarios/stages

Pmpp_deg ≈ 10 %

Vmpp_deg ≈ 7 %

Impp_deg_max ≈ 5 %

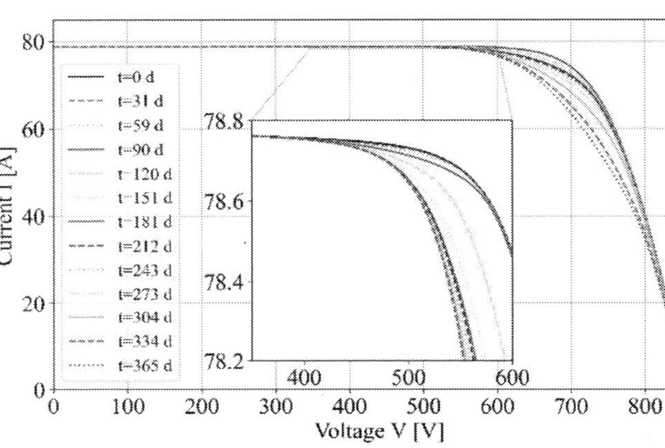

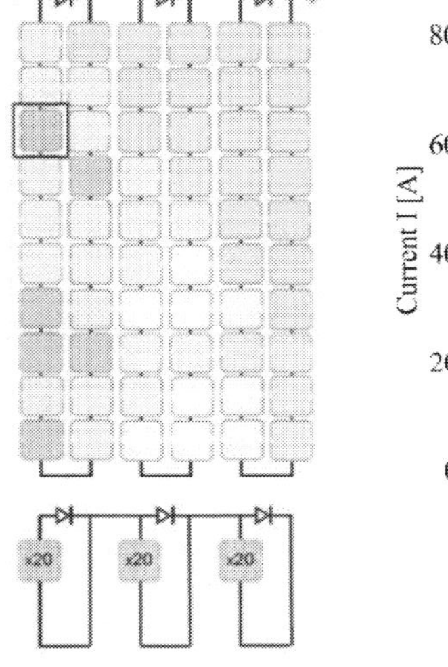

020266-021

DTU

Results of simulations of different degradation stages at STC

- PV array affected by PID-s
  - Twelve different degradation scenarios/stages

Mismatch loss range: 0 to 2.96 %

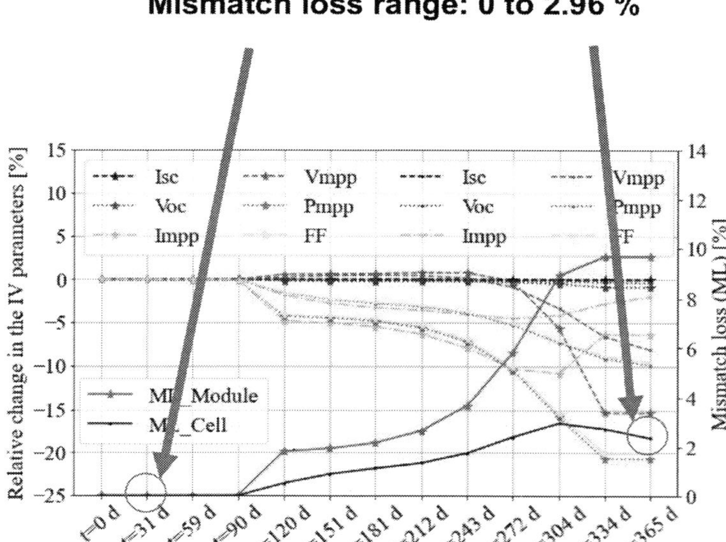
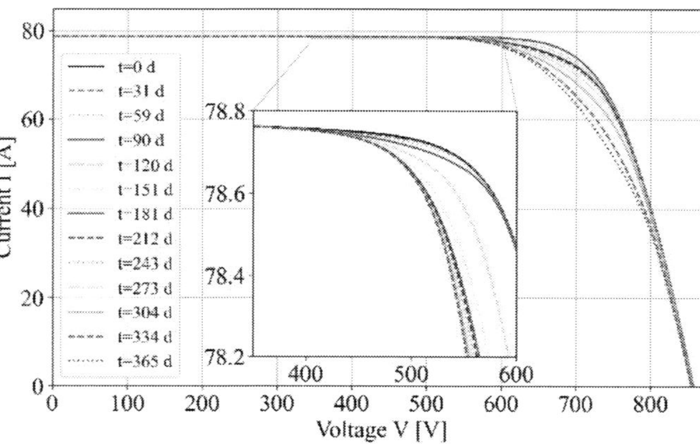
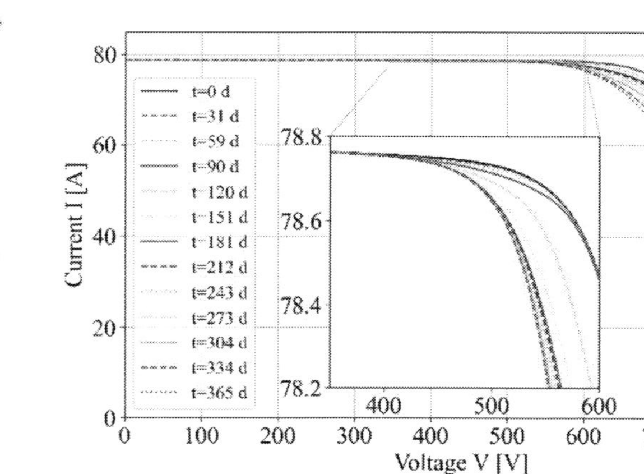
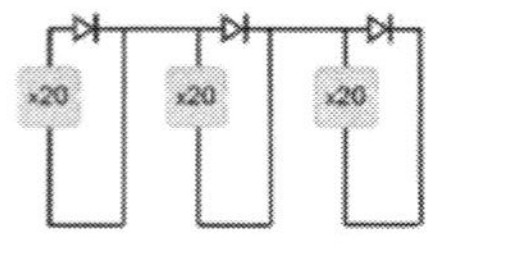

Conclusions

PySpice Model

- Possible to implement cell, module and string level PID characteristics on array level
  - Estimate the impact of two or more failure and/or degradation modes

- Asses long-term impact of a failure and/or degradation mode
  - Quantify power and mismatch losses as degradation progresses

- Identify diagnostic parameters from array or string I-V
  - Develop/optimize fault detection algorithms
  - Training fata for fault detection methods

- Generate realistic I-V curves
  - Apply non-linear degradation
  - Develop code script for newer PV technologies

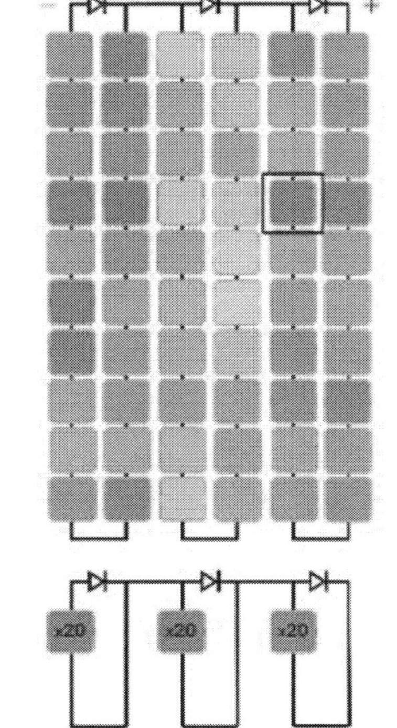

020266-023

Acknowledgement and contact information

DTEC project: High voltage stress testing for potential induced degradation and recovery modeling of utility scale PV.

Collaboration between TotalEnergies and Technical University of Denmark.

Thank you for you attention!

DTEC

TotalEnergies

Contact information:

Aysha Mahmood aysma@dtu.dk

Sergiu Viorel Spataru sersp@dtu.dk

Solar Photovoltaic Systems Group (SPVS)

DTU Electro, Risø Campus, Roskilde, Denmark

020266-024

EVALUATING THE ACCURACY OF SINGLE-CAMERA IRRADIANCE FORECASTING

Jacob K. Thorning[1]*, Adam A. Jensen[2], Sergiu V. Spataru[1], Peter B. Poulsen[1]
*Corresponding author: jkrtho@dtu.dk
[1]Technical University of Denmark (DTU), Department of Electrical and Photonics Engineering, Frederiksborgvej 399, 4000 Roskilde, Denmark
[2]Technical University of Denmark (DTU), Department of Civil and Mechanical Engineering, Koppels Allé, 2800 Kgs. Lyngby, Denmark

ABSTRACT: We present results from a newly established all-sky imager (ASI) testbed at DTU Risø Campus. Three calibrated ASIs capture hemispheric sky images every 30 seconds and provide input for cloud detection and irradiance mapping. Each camera was calibrated using the Scaramuzza fisheye model, yielding lookup matrices that map pixels to azimuth and zenith angles. Based on these, equidistant projections were created, and cloud transmittance maps were derived using a normalized color index. Ground-level irradiance was then estimated by projecting cloud transmittance onto the terrain using solar geometry. The estimated Global Horizontal Irradiance (GHI) was compared to pyranometer measurements at a meteorological station 1 km from one of the cameras. Results show good agreement in daily GHI dynamics and highlight challenges in accurately reproducing irradiance ramps near solar noon and under broken cloud conditions. This testbed provides a basis for systematic evaluation of ASI-based irradiance forecasting methods. Data collected in this testbed will be made available to the community to facilitate further research and development of ASI-based solar forecasting methods, and we aim to release a larger dataset in the future.
Keywords: all-sky imagers, solar irradiance forecasting, cloud detection, hemispheric cameras, photovoltaic systems, cloud base height estimation, image processing, solar nowcasting

1 Introduction

The integration of photovoltaic (PV) generation into modern power systems continues to accelerate worldwide [1], driven by climate goals and the falling costs of solar technology. At the same time, the variability of solar irradiance, particularly on short timescales of seconds to minutes, presents challenges for grid operators and PV plant owners [2]. Rapid fluctuations in PV output can cause voltage instability, complicate scheduling, and increase the need for balancing reserves. Accurate, high-resolution forecasts of solar irradiance are therefore increasingly important for both operational stability and efficient market participation [3].

Clouds are the dominant driver of intra-hour solar variability [4]. Their spatial extent, optical thickness, and movement across the solar disk determine when and how strongly irradiance ramps occur at the surface. Satellite imagery provides valuable information on cloud fields and is widely used for solar forecasting at hourly and longer horizons [5–7]. However, the temporal and spatial resolution of geostationary satellite images is insufficient for intra-hour predictions at higher resolutions than 1 km and 5 minutes.

Ground-based All-Sky Imager (ASI) fill this gap by capturing hemispheric views of the sky dome with sub-minute cadence. By detecting clouds in succes-

sive images, estimating their motion, and projecting their shadows onto the ground, ASIs enable nowcasting of solar irradiance at horizons up to 30 minutes, depending on cloud height and speed. In addition, ASIs can be deployed close to PV plants, making them particularly suitable for site-specific forecasting.

This work establishes an ASI testbed at the DTU Risø Campus in Denmark, where three imagers have been installed roughly 1 km apart. Each camera has been geometrically calibrated using a fisheye lens model using SuMo, enabling per-pixel mapping of raw images to solar azimuth and zenith angles. Based on these calibrations, equidistant projections of the sky are generated, from which cloud transmittance maps are derived using a simple color index method. These transmittance maps are then projected onto the ground using the solar position at the time of capture, yielding spatial irradiance maps.

We present the first usable results obtained with the DTU Risø All-Sky Imager Testbed dataset [8], which provides raw sky images, calibration matrices, and validation GHI from a meteorological station. The purpose of this work is to validate our ASI-based irradiance estimation method and to publish the dataset openly so that other researchers can test and develop their own methods using this testbed.

The purpose of this paper is to establish and validate the foundational components of an ASI-based solar forecasting system. We evaluate the ability of the calibrated ASIs to reproduce ground-measured Global Horizontal Irradiance (GHI) at the location of a solar meteorological station, representing the critical first step in developing accurate short-term irradiance predictions. An example day (September 4, 2025) is analyzed in detail, showing the complete processing chain from raw images to transmittance maps, ground projections, and final GHI comparisons. The results demonstrate that the ASI system can capture the overall diurnal evolution of irradiance and reproduce major cloud-induced ramps, establishing the viability of the approach while also identifying key areas for improvement such as binary cloud classification and uncertainties in cloud base height that must be addressed for operational forecasting applications. By building and validating this end-to-end pipeline, we aim to provide a foundation for future work on ASI-based solar forecasting. Next steps will include multi-day evaluation, refinement of cloud optical thickness estimates, and the integration of cloud motion vectors for true short-term forecasts.

2 Methodology

2.1 Testbed setup

Three ASIs were deployed at DTU Risø Campus during spring 2025, located 800-1200 meters apart. The sites are referred to as Farm, Wind, and Pier based on their campus locations. In parallel, a solar meteorological station equipped with an EKO MS80 class A pyranometer records GHI for validation. A map of the campus with camera and station locations is shown in Figure 1. The distances between the different locations are summarized in Table I.

Table I: Distances (meters) between ASI locations and solar meteorological station at DTU Risø Campus.

Location	Solar met	Pier	Wind
Farm	270	1540	790
Wind	570	1200	
Pier	1280		

The ASIs and sensors at the solar meteorological station are cleaned weekly. Each camera system is a Wematics Pyranovision camera (Figure 2), equipped with a 180° fisheye lens, a pyranometer, and configured to capture 4K resolution hemispheric images every 30 seconds.

Figure 2: All-Sky Imager at the DTU Risø PV farm.

2.2 Camera calibrations

Each camera was calibrated using the Scaramuzza SuMo [9] which implements the Scaramuzza fisheye lens model [10] and external orientation of the image sensor. The calibration provides two lookup matrices per camera: 1. an azimuth matrix, giving the solar azimuth angle corresponding to each pixel and 2. a zenith matrix, giving the solar zenith angle corresponding to each pixel, shown in for the Pier camera in Figure 3a and Figure 3b respectively. These matrices allow direct mapping from pixel coordinates to angular coordinates on the sky dome.

2.3 Cloud detection and transmission mapping

Cloud pixels are identified using a normalized color index *nbrbr*:

$$T(u,v) = \frac{B(u,v) - R(u,v)}{B(u,v) + R(u,v)} > 0, \qquad (1)$$

where B and R are the blue and red channel intensities of pixel (u,v). A fixed threshold of 0 on T classifies pixels as clear sky (1) or cloud (0).

2.4 Cloud base height estimation

Cloud base height is estimated using a modified lifting condensation level (LCL) approach based on ambient temperature and relative humidity measurements. The method employs a three-step parametric model [11] optimized for local conditions at DTU Risø campus. The dew point temperature T_{dew} is calculated using a modified Magnus formula shown in Equation 2 and Equation 3.

$$\gamma = \ln\left(\frac{RH}{100}\right) + \frac{a \cdot T}{b + T} \qquad (2)$$

$$T_{\text{dew}} = \frac{b \cdot \gamma}{a - \gamma} \qquad (3)$$

where T is the ambient temperature in °C, RH is the relative humidity in %, and a and b are fitted parameters. The cloud base height is then calculated as the lifting condensation level shown in Equation 4.

$$\text{CBH} = k \cdot (T - T_{\text{dew}}) \qquad (4)$$

where k is a scaling factor and CBH is expressed in meters. The parameters were optimized against

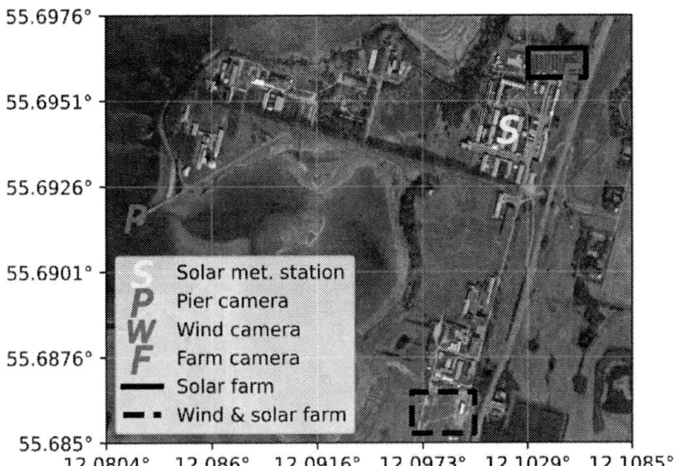

Figure 1: Map with locations of All-Sky Imagers, solar meteorological station and PV plants at DTU Risø campus.

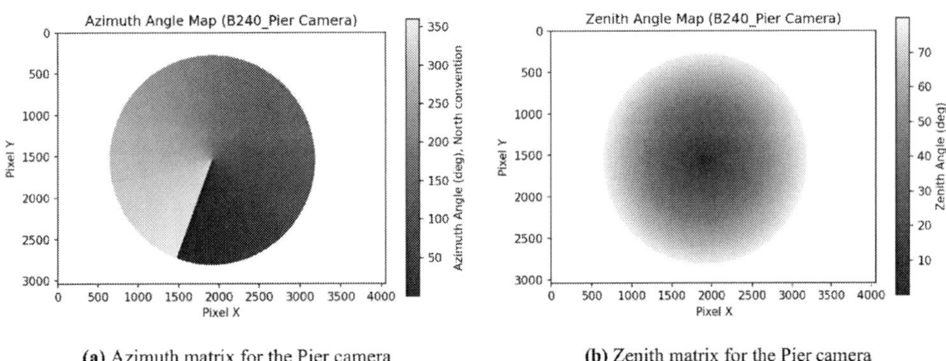

(a) Azimuth matrix for the Pier camera

(b) Zenith matrix for the Pier camera

Figure 3: Azimuth and zenith matrices for the Pier camera, generated using SuMo.

a one-year dataset of cloud base height from ERA5 hourly data on single levels from 1940 to present [12] at DTU Risø campus shown in Equation 5.

$$a = 0.3644 \tag{5}$$

$$b = 49.0 \tag{6}$$

$$k = 26.7283 \tag{7}$$

2.5 Ground projection of cloud shadows

The binary transmission map is projected onto ground coordinates using the solar position (azimuth and elevation) at the image timestamp according to Equations 8, 9 and 10.

$$d = \tan(\theta_z) \cdot CBH, \tag{8}$$

$$dx = \cos(90 - \gamma_s) \cdot d, \tag{9}$$

$$dy = \sin(90 - \gamma_s) \cdot d \tag{10}$$

This projection estimates the regions on the ground affected by cloud shadows and clear-sky conditions. A satellite map of the DTU Risø area with an example projection is shown in Figure 6.

2.6 Validation against ground measurements

For each ground location, GHI is estimated by combining the transmission map with Direct Normal Irradiance (DNI) and Diffuse Horizontal Irradiance (DHI) from the Simplified Solis [13] clear-sky model as shown in Equation 11.

$$GHI(x, y) = T(x, y) \cdot DNI \cdot \cos(\theta_z) + DHI, \tag{11}$$

where θ_z is the solar zenith angle. This yields a 2D irradiance map covering the campus region at each

30-second timestep. The projected GHI at the location of the solar meteorological station is extracted from the irradiance maps and compared to pyranometer measurements. Visual validation is performed for a day with scattered clouds (September 4, 2025, from 05:30 to 18:45, local time).

3 Results

The results are based on, and validated using, the DTU Risø All-Sky Imager Testbed dataset [8]. This dataset provides one week of sky images and calibration data from the DTU Risø Campus, Denmark, captured from September 1st to 7th, 2025, to support research in solar forecasting, cloud detection, and image-based irradiance modeling. The dataset includes images from three calibrated all-sky cameras: the Farm camera (15-second cadence, missing September 5th-7th), Wind camera (30-second cadence), and Pier camera (30-second cadence), along with comprehensive meteorological measurements including global horizontal irradiance, diffuse horizontal irradiance, direct normal irradiance, relative humidity, air pressure, and wind data. Each image contains measured GHI in the EXIF metadata field "ApogeeIrradiance", enabling direct validation of image-based irradiance estimates.

3.1 Example image processing pipeline

To illustrate the processing steps, Figure 4 shows a raw hemispheric image from the Pier ASI at 12:10 local time on September 4, 2025 (at solar noon).

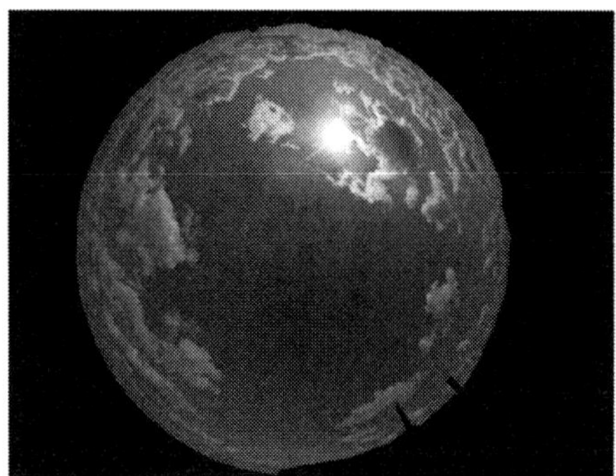

Figure 4: Original image from the Pier ASI at 12:10 local time on September 4, 2025 (at solar noon).

This raw image is converted into an equidistant projection, producing the equidistant sampled representation of the sky dome, shown at approx. 6 by 6 meters resolution in Figure 5a.

From the equidistant image, a binary transmittance map is generated using the normalized color index $(B-R)/(B+R)$ as shown in Equation 12. Clear-sky pixels were classified as transmissive ($T = 1$), while cloudy pixels were set to $T = 0$ (Figure 5b).

$$T = \frac{B - R}{B + R} > 0 \qquad (12)$$

The ground projection of the binary transmittance map around the DTU Risø campus is shown in Figure 6 at 50 by 50 meters resolution. This reduced resolution is due to the high resolution of the original image and the need to reduce the computational cost of the projection. A full resolution projection would have the same resolution as the projected image in Figure 5a, which is approx. 6 by 6 meters.

Figure 6: Ground shadow map of the DTU Risø campus at 50 by 50 meters resolution.

Together, these figures demonstrate the complete processing pipeline: raw sky image → calibration-based projection → cloud classification → ground irradiance mapping.

3.2 Time series validation

A full-day comparison between projected and measured GHI is shown in Figure 7. The dataset spans from 05:30 to 18:45 local time at 30-second resolution for the projection 1-second resolution for measured GHI. The left axis shows GHI from both the ASI-based projection (blue) and the pyranometer measurements (orange), while the right axis shows the cloud base height estimated from the lifting condensation level (gray, right y-axis).

4 Discussion

The first results from the DTU Risø ASI testbed highlight both the potential and current limitations of image-based irradiance mapping.

A key strength of the system is the calibration framework [9]. The fisheye model provides stable azimuth and zenith angle mappings across all three cameras, which is essential for reproducible projections. The consistency observed between calibration

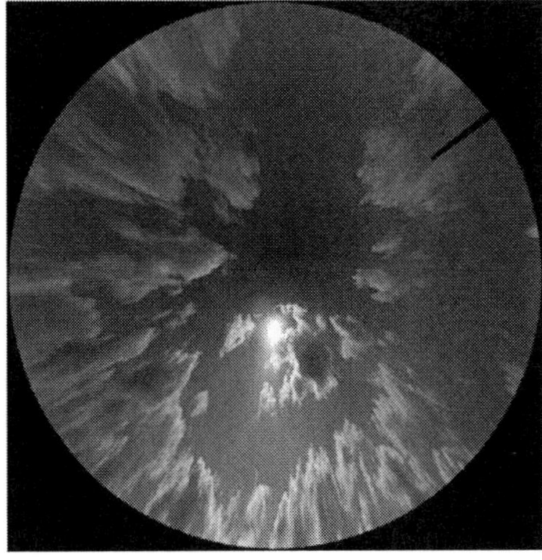

(a) Equidistant projection

(b) Binary transmission map

Figure 5: Image processing pipeline: (a) equidistant projection of the sky dome and (b) binary transmission map derived from normalized color index.

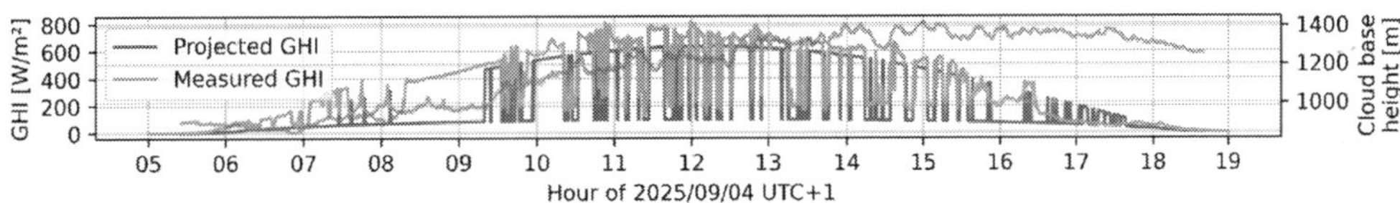

Figure 7: Projected and measured global horizontal irradiance comparison and cloud base height timeseries.

outputs and solar position suggests that geometric uncertainties are not the dominant source of error in the irradiance maps. This is further validated in Figure 7 where the projected and measured GHI show extremely good agreement in variation during the main part of the day (though not in absolute values), indicating that cloud shadows are projected correctly.

The projected and measured GHI align remarkably well during the main part of the day, demonstrating that our system correctly projects cloud shadows. This accuracy depends critically on Cloud Base Height (CBH) estimation, where our simple, locally adapted physical model performs surprisingly well. The model successfully tracks the CBH increase from approximately 1100 meters at 09:30 to 1400 meters at 14:00 and beyond, shown by the correct alignment of the projected and measured GHI throughout this period with changing CBH. Here we want to particularly highlight the period 10:15 to 10:50 with approx. 1200 meters CBH, and 14:40 to 15:30 with CBH ranging from 1350 to 1450 meters.

The use of the Simplified Solis [13] clear-sky model for DNI and DHI estimation is simple and easy to implement, however it is clear that the model underestimates the irradiance throughout the entire day. Figure 7 shows a series of cloud-enhancement events between 10:30 and 13:00, where the clear-sky model is not expected to produce the observed irradiance levels, but at no time does the model estimate correct irradiance levels. This observation is supported by the validation of the clear-sky model by Ineichen [14], where even the best performing models are found to systematically underestimate DNI, and estimations of GHI deviate in the order $\pm 3\%$.

A serious deviation between projected and measured GHI is observed around 08:15 to 09:20 where the projected GHI shows only diffuse light (cloud-shaded conditions), while the measured GHI clearly indicates clear-sky conditions. This discrepancy is likely due to limitations in the transmittance calculation method when the projection direction aligns with the sun direction, which occurs during this particular period (east-northeast relative to the pier camera's location). The images from this period clearly show atmospheric whitening below the sun's elevation, which is then misclassified as cloudy even when no clouds are present.

5 Conclusion

This work presented first results from the DTU Risø ASI testbed, where three calibrated hemispheric cameras were deployed and evaluated for irradiance mapping. The DTU Risø dataset [8] enables validation of ASI-based irradiance mapping, and our results demonstrate that even with binary transmittance, strong agreement with ground truth can be achieved using this comprehensive dataset.

The SuMo calibration tool [9] provides reliable azimuth and zenith lookup tables, enabling equidistant projections and consistent geometric correction across all three cameras.

Binary cloud transmittance maps derived from the normalized color index $(B - R)/(B + R)$ successfully capture major irradiance variations and reproduce the diurnal GHI evolution with good temporal alignment.

Spatial projection of cloud shadows demonstrates excellent agreement with ground-based pyranometer measurements, even during periods with changing CBH.

The lifting condensation level approach for CBH estimation performs surprisingly well, correctly tracking height variations from 1100 to 1400 meters throughout the day. However, significant discrepancies occur during low solar elevation periods (08:15–09:20) due to atmospheric whitening misclassification, and systematic underestimation of irradiance levels indicates limitations in the used clear-sky model.

6 Further work

The testbed establishes a robust platform for advancing ASI-based solar forecasting. Future work will address current limitations through several key developments.

Improving the cloud transmittance model will move beyond binary classification to implement algorithms based on local adaptive thresholds that can better represent thin and semi-transparent clouds, even cloud-enhancement events.

Improved CBH estimation will involve training enhanced models on higher-quality observational data by leveraging the multi-camera setup to derive stereoscopic CBH estimates, reducing reliance on reanalysis data.

Advanced clear-sky irradiance modeling will implement more sophisticated clear-sky models and explore decomposition approaches that utilize the camera system's own GHI measurements rather than relying solely on theoretical clear-sky estimates.

Short-term forecasting capabilities will use cloud motion tracking algorithms based on temporal analysis of equidistant projections to predict future cloud positions and enable true solar forecasting at 15–30 minute horizons.

Comprehensive validation will extend evaluation to multi-day and seasonal datasets to quantify quantitative performance across varying meteorological conditions and solar geometries.

Through these developments, the DTU Risø ASI testbed will contribute to the broader effort of integrating high-resolution solar forecasting into renewable energy systems and grid management applications.

References

[1] International Energy Agency. *World Energy Outlook 2024*. Licence: CC BY 4.0 (report); CC BY NC SA 4.0 (Annex A). Paris: IEA, 2024. URL: https://www.iea.org/reports/world-energy-outlook-2024.

[2] Brian Tarroja, Fabian Mueller, and Scott Samuelsen. "Solar power variability and spatial diversification: implications from an electric grid load balancing perspective". In: *International Journal of Energy Research* 37.9 (2013), pp. 1002–1016.

[3] Amanpreet Kaur et al. "Benefits of solar forecasting for energy imbalance markets". In: *Renewable energy* 86 (2016), pp. 819–830.

[4] Lucien Wald. *Fundamentals of solar radiation*. CRC Press, 2021.

[5] Guanghui Huang et al. "Estimating surface solar irradiance from satellites: Past, present, and future perspectives". In: *Remote Sensing of Environment* 233 (2019), p. 111371.

[6] Yang Cui et al. "Solar radiation nowcasting based on geostationary satellite images and deep learning models". In: *Solar Energy* 282 (2024), p. 112866.

[7] Nils Straub, Wiebke Herzberg, and Elke Lorenz. "HelioNet-IR: Combining Infrared and Visible Satellite Images for Solar Irradiance Forecasting in the Early-Morning Hours". In: *Solar RRL* 9.16 (2025), p. 2500365.

[8] Jacob K. Thorning et al. *DTU Risø All-Sky Imager Testbed: One-Week Sky Image and Calibration Dataset*. 2025. DOI: 10.11583/DTU.30164002. URL: https://doi.org/10.11583/DTU.30164002.

[9] Niklas Blum et al. "Geometric calibration of all-sky cameras using sun and moon positions: A comprehensive analysis". In: *Solar Energy* 295 (2025), p. 113476.

[10] Davide Scaramuzza, Agostino Martinelli, and Roland Siegwart. "A toolbox for easily calibrating omnidirectional cameras". In: *2006 IEEE/RSJ International Conference on Intelligent Robots and Systems*. IEEE. 2006, pp. 5695–5701.

[11] Jun Yin et al. "Land and atmospheric controls on initiation and intensity of moist convection: CAPE dynamics and LCL crossings". In: *Water Resources Research* 51.10 (2015), pp. 8476–8493.

[12] H. Hersbach et al. *ERA5 hourly data on single levels from 1940 to present*. Accessed on 10-08-2025. 2023. DOI: 10.24381/cds.adbb2d47.

[13] Pierre Ineichen. "A broadband simplified version of the Solis clear sky model". In: *Solar Energy* 82.8 (2008), pp. 758–762.

[14] Pierre Ineichen. "Validation of models that estimate the clear sky global and beam solar irradiance". In: *Solar Energy* 132 (2016), pp. 332–344.

Evaluating the Accuracy of Single-Camera Irradiance Forecasting

Jacob K. Thorning*, Sergiu V. Spataru, Adam R. Jensen, Peter B. Poulsen
Solar Photovoltaic Systems, DTU Electro, Technical University of Denmark (DTU), *email: jkrtho@dtu.dk

Introduction

- Variable PV production causes balancing challenges in grids and energy traders incur imbalance fees
- Clouds are the dominant driver of intra-hour irradiance variability
- All-Sky Imagers (ASIs) provide hemispheric sky images that can be transformed into irradiance maps and forecasts
- This testbed at **DTU Risø Campus** explores how well calibrated ASIs can reproduce ground-measured Global Horizontal Irradiance (GHI)
- Research and data published from testbed

Methodology

Wematics Pyranovision

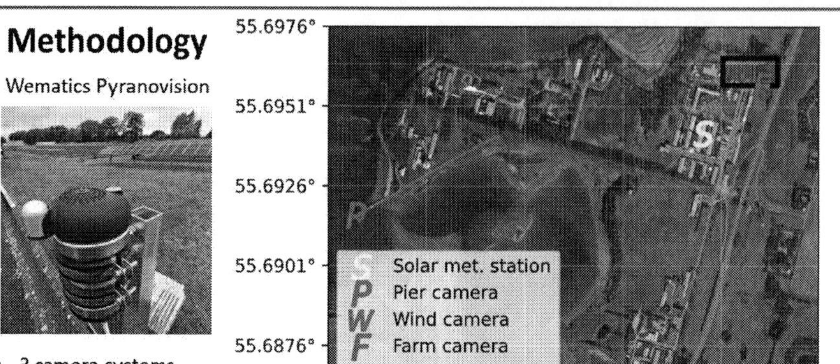

- 3 camera systems approx. 1000 meters apart
- Calibration with SuMo[1]
- Cloud based height from lifting condensation level as a function of temperature and relative humidity
- Equidistant projections generated based on raw image, calibration result and 3d cartesian coordinates
- Binary cloud transmittance map $T = \frac{blue-red}{blue+red} > 0$
- Ground horizontal irradiance $GHI = T \cdot DNI \cdot \cos(\theta_z) + DHI$

[1] Blum, Niklas, et al. Solar Energy
DOI:j.solener.2025.113476

Results

Raw 4k image 2025/09/04 12:10 (solar noon)

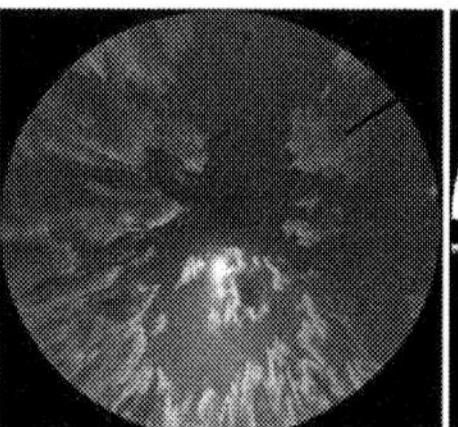

Corresponding equidistant projection

Transmittance map T

Distance $d = \tan(zenith) * altitude$ [m]
Distance east $dx = \cos(90 - azimuth) * d$ [m]
Distance north $dy = \sin(90 - azimuth) * d$ [m]

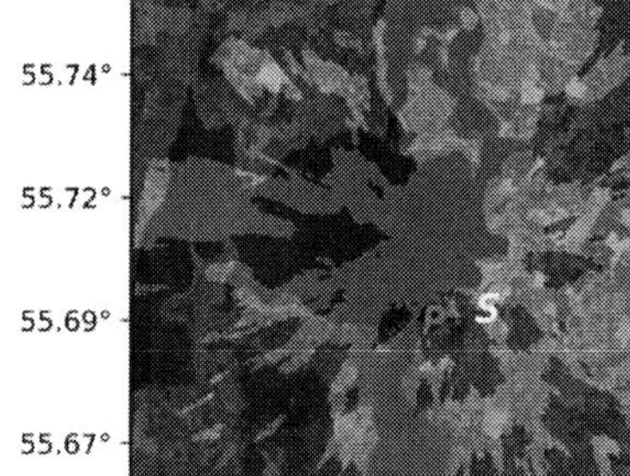

Dataset QR

Calibration output: Azimuth and zenith matrices

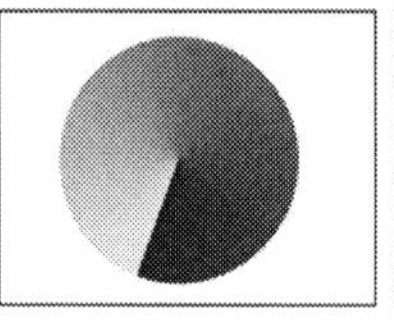

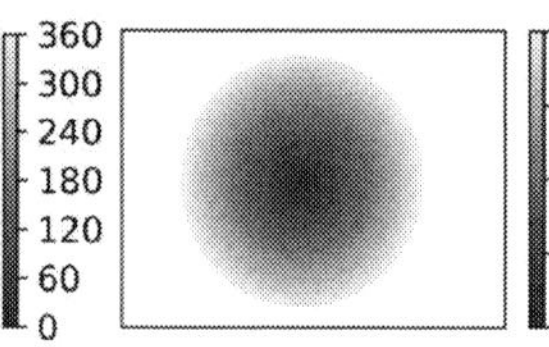

Conclusions and Outlook

- Calibration successful with nRMSD (sun pixel distances) of $\approx 1.5\%$
- Cloud transmittance works poorly in the solar area and area below the sun
- 1 week period dataset with images
- Variations in projected GHI vs measured GHI matches except when sun and projection direction are the same

LinkedIn

This project has received funding from the Energy Technology Development and Demonstration Program (EUDP) under grant agreement no. 134243-534203. The project "IEA Task 16" is coordinated by DTU Electro and aims to advance international collaboration on photovoltaic system integration.

This project has received funding from the European Union under grant agreement no. 101146377. The SOLARIS project – *Solar Operational Lifecycle and Asset Reliability Intelligence System.*

020268-001

New Empirical Model for Backside Irradiance

Kristijan Brecl, Marko Topič
University of Ljubljana, Faculty of Electrical Engineering, Ljubljana, Slovenia

Emilio Muñoz Cerón, Juan de la Casa Higueras
IDEA Research Group, Centre for Advanced Studies in Earth Science, Energy and Environment,
University of Jaén, Spain

FE | UNIVERSITY OF LJUBLJANA
Faculty of Electrical Engineering

Universidad de Jaén

Abstract

The widespread of bifacial PV modules raises the question of whether current performance assessment models are still good enough or whether they need to be adapted. The main challenge in simulating the performance of bifacial PV modules is the correct definition of the backside irradiance. Currently, analytical or very complex ray tracing models are used to estimate the backside irradiance. These models are usually computationally intensive and require a detailed information of the PV system and surrounding. Here we are presenting a new empirical model for backside irradiance. The model is developed on measured data at a very sunny location in southern Spain and afterwards validated in a central European climate. The measured backside irradiance data is evaluated with regard to the diffuse light, solar azimuth angle, and seasonal changes over the whole year. A Gaussian correlation between observed parameters is used in the new model. Additionally, the seasonal changes are considered as variations in the parameters of the Gaussian model.

Backside irradiance

Test site at UJA, Spain

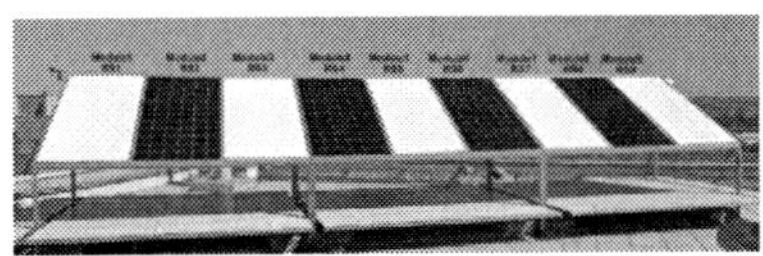

Test bifacial PV system at the University of Jaén, Spain. Five of the nine PV modules were covered from the front to only absorb light from the back.

G_{back} over a day

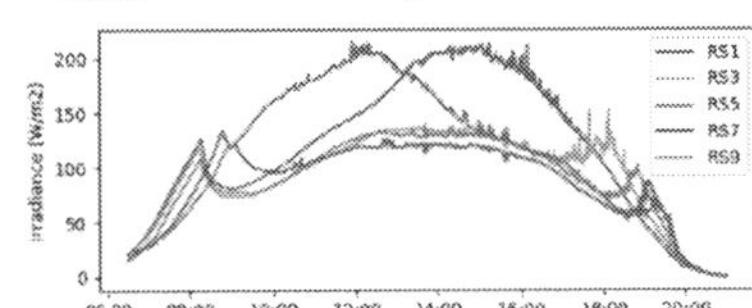

Backside irradaince on the observed modules over the course of a clearsky day in July. The modules at the beginning and at the end of the row (RS1, RS9) receive more light from the back. In the early morning and late afternoon the modules receive some direct light.

G_{back} vs. solar azimuth

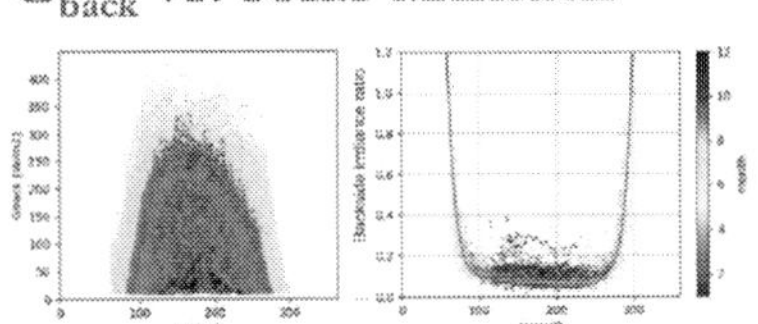

Backside irradiance versus solar azimuth angle (left) and backside irradiance ratio (right). Backside irradiance ratio is defined as backside irradiance devided by front plane-of-array irradiance.

Empirical model

Gaussian equation

$$G_{back\_ratio} = y0 + a \cdot e^{-0.5 \cdot \left(\frac{|az - az_0|}{b} \right)^c}$$

coefficient	value	comment
a	-800	tail slope
b	130-170	width
c	15	width and "sharpness"
az_0	184	azimuth shift (183-184 for Jaén)
y_0	800.14	$|a|$ + effective albedo

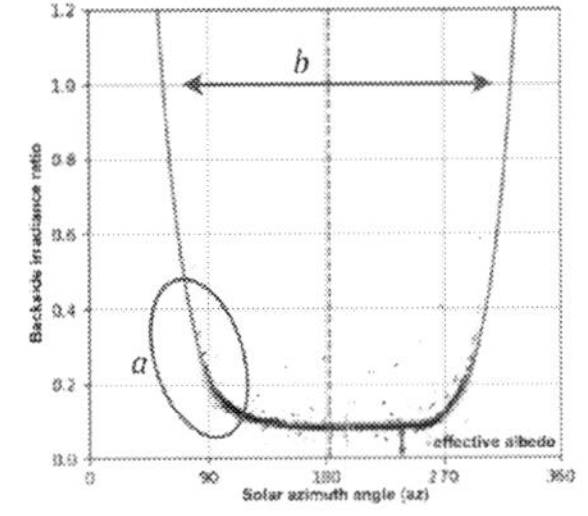

Presentation of Gaussian parameters on the clearsky backside irradiance ratio chart.

Results

Simulated backside irradiance in Jaén and Ljubljana

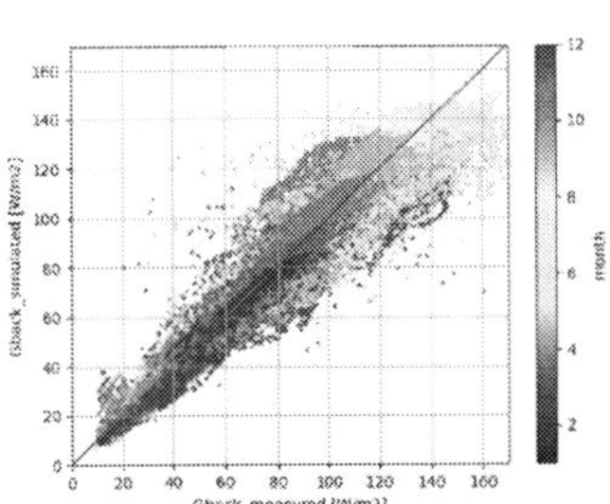

Validation of backside irradiance in Jaén.

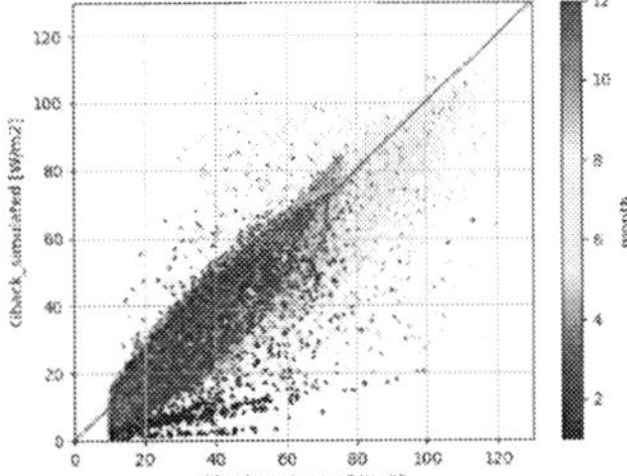

Validation of backside irradiance in Ljubljana.

Conclusion

The most appropriate way to simulate the backside irradiance is by determining its ratio relative to the front G_{poa}. The share of the back irradiance in the total irradiance received by a bifacial module is generally consistent throughout the day, with deviations in the morning and evening hours in summer when the sun shines from behind. Our new empirical model simulates the backside irradiance ratio as a ratio of the back to front irradiance with respect to the solar azimuth. The ratio is modelled by a Gaussian equation with the parameters derived from the measured data in the training period.

More information:

K. Brecl et al., "Is an exact backside irradiance modelling essential for bifacial PV systems?",
Renewable Energy 256 (2026) 123942
https://doi.org/10.1016/j.renene.2025.123942

Acknowledgments

- Slovenian Research and Innovation Agency (Research Programme P2-0415).

- This work has been possible also thanks to the project "Demo_BI-FV: Development of Advanced Models for the characterization of bifacial photovoltaic systems (PID2021-124161OB-I00)" funded by the Spanish Ministry of Science and the State Innovation Agency within the European Regional Development Fund (MCIN/AEI/ 10.13039/501100011033/FEDER, UE).

DEEP LEARNING-BASED SOLAR IRRADIANCE DECOMPOSITION MODELS FOR NORDIC REGIONS

Alfredo Sanchez Garcia and Berhane Darsene Dimd
SINTEF AS
alfredo.sanchez@sintef.no, berhane.dimd@sintef.no

This work presents a comparative evaluation of machine learning (ML) and deep learning (DL) models for solar irradiance decomposition in Nordic regions, where traditional empirical models often struggle. Using data from the Alpha Centauri outdoor test facility in Trondheim, Norway, the present work benchmarks the performance of Histogram-based Gradient Boosting (HGB), Artificial Neural Networks (ANN), and Long Short-Term Memory (LSTM) networks against the Erbs model. Results indicate that HGB performs best on the initial evaluation set, achieving strong R^2 scores for both DNI and DHI, while requiring minimal computational resources. However, in a zero-shot prediction scenario using independent data, HGB's performance drops significantly, suggesting overfitting to seasonal patterns. ANN maintains the highest accuracy for DNI decomposition, capturing nonlinear dependencies more effectively, whereas LSTM shows mixed results, particularly underperforming in DNI estimation.

1 INTRODUCTION

Accurate modeling of solar irradiance components—global horizontal irradiance (GHI), direct normal irradiance (DNI), and diffuse horizontal irradiance (DHI)—is essential for optimizing photovoltaic (PV) system performance. Traditional physical decomposition models, such as DISC, DIRINT, and Erbs, have been extensively applied to estimate these components from measured GHI [1]. These models rely on empirical relationships and atmospheric parametrization, which have been validated primarily in low and mid-latitude regions, where they provide consistent and reliable results. However, in Nordic regions, these models often struggle due to unique atmospheric conditions, including low solar elevation angles, which influence the optical path length and scattering effects [2]; frequent cloud cover and diffuse-dominated radiation, leading to increased uncertainty in DNI estimation [3]; seasonal variations, with long periods of low irradiance and rapid transitions in daylight duration [2]; and snow and albedo effects, which alter surface reflectance and impact model accuracy [4]. These challenges introduce significant discrepancies in the decomposition process, ultimately affecting PV performance predictions, energy yield assessments, and system design optimizations.

In recent years, machine learning (ML) and deep learning (DL) have gained popularity for predictive modeling by enabling data-driven approaches to complex, nonlinear problems [5]. Unlike traditional physical models that rely on empirical relationships and explicit parameterization, ML and DL methods can extract patterns from large datasets, making them particularly suitable for dynamic and highly variable environments such as Nordic climates. Early applications focused on enhancing empirical models with ML techniques. For example, gradient boosting algorithms have been shown to significantly improve DNI and DHI estimation from GHI and meteorological inputs, with relative DNI errors as low as 7.45%, although DHI predictions remained less accurate [6]. DL methods have been investigated to overcome these limitations at finer timescales. Recurrent architectures such as long short-term memory (LSTM) models have achieved improvements exceeding 7% in relative RMSE for DNI at sub-hourly intervals compared to classical models [7]. These findings indicate that ML and DL approaches can outperform empirical models under variable atmospheric conditions.

Motivated by these findings, this work aims to evaluate whether ML and DL methods can provide accurate estimates of DNI and DHI in the challenging Nordic regions. This goal is further reinforced by recent findings showing that having access to a complete set of irradiance components enhances the accuracy of PV power predictions [8]. To this end, three representative learning models —Histogram-based Gradient Boosting (HGB), a feed-forward artificial neural network (ANN), and a recurrent LSTM network— are trained to predict DNI and DHI from measured GHI and solar position features using high-resolution (1-min) data collected at the Alpha Centauri outdoor test facility in Trondheim, Norway. Training spans August 2022–May 2023, and generalization is assessed in a zero-shot setting on April–May 2024 data to probe seasonal transfer. Furthermore, the ML models are evaluated against the empirical Erb's model to determine whether data-driven decomposition methods are better suited for Nordic regions.

2 BACKGROUND

Accurate decomposition of solar irradiance into its direct and diffuse components has traditionally relied on empirical models, while recent developments in ML and DL have introduced data-driven alternatives. This section reviews the conventional empirical approach used as a benchmark in this study and describes the ML/DL methods evaluated.

2.1 Empirical decomposition models

Empirical models estimate the diffuse and direct components of solar irradiance from measured GHI using correlations with the clearness index and solar geometry. Among these, the Erbs model [1] is one of the most widely used due to its simplicity and low computational cost. The Erbs model estimates the diffuse fraction (DF) as a piecewise function of the ratio of global to extraterrestrial irradiance on a horizontal plane, commonly expressed through the clearness index. Then, DHI and DNI follow

$$DHI = DF \times GHI, \qquad (1)$$

$$DNI = \frac{GHI - DHI}{\cos\theta_z}, \qquad (2)$$

where θ_z is the zenith angle.

2.2 Machine and deep learning methods

Machine learning and deep learning approaches offer

flexible, data-driven alternatives to empirical models by learning complex nonlinear relationships directly from data [5]. Three representative algorithms were selected to cover different modeling paradigms:

Histogram-based Gradient Boosting (HGB) is an ensemble method that constructs additive decision trees using gradient boosting with histogram-based binning for efficient split finding. It is well-suited for tabular data and can capture nonlinear feature interactions without requiring feature scaling. HGB is computationally efficient and robust to heterogeneous feature distributions, making it a strong baseline among ML methods.

Artificial Neural Networks (ANN) consist of layers of interconnected nodes that apply linear transformations followed by nonlinear activation functions. ANNs are universal function approximators, meaning they can model highly complex relationships between inputs and outputs when provided with sufficient data and appropriate architecture. They are widely used in regression, classification, and forecasting tasks across many domains but require careful tuning of architecture and regularization to avoid overfitting.

Long Short-Term Memory (LSTM) networks are a specialized type of recurrent neural network (RNN) designed to handle sequential data and capture long-range dependencies. Unlike standard RNNs, LSTMs incorporate gating mechanisms—input, output, and forget gates—that regulate the flow of information and mitigate issues such as vanishing or exploding gradients. This makes them particularly effective for time-series modeling and other applications where temporal context is critical.

3 METHODS

The aim of the present work is to compare the performance of ML and DL algorithms for solar irradiance decomposition. Specifically, the goal is to assess these models' ability to predict DNI and DHI from measured GHI. The models will be benchmarked against the empirical Erbs model.

3.1 Data and Preprocessing

The analysis uses data from the Alpha Centauri outdoor test facility in Trondheim, Norway [9]. The site includes eight bifacial PV modules mounted on four dual-axis trackers and a meteorological station equipped with two pyranometers and one pyrheliometer. Measurements of GHI, DNI, and DHI were recorded at a 1-minute resolution for a period spanning from August 2022 to May 2023. Solar zenith and azimuth angles were computed from timestamp and location coordinates using the Python library pvlib [10].

Standard preprocessing techniques were applied to construct the dataset. These involved the removal of missing values, discarding rows with zero irradiance across and normalization to ensure stable training. Zenith and azimuth angles were added to the dataset. For the LSTM model, sequences were generated using a sliding window so that the model captures temporal dependencies.

3.2 Model Setup and Training

Three models were evaluated: HGB, ANN and LSTM. For all models, inputs consisted of GHI and solar geometry, while targets were the corresponding DNI and DHI values. This is illustrated in Figure 1, using an ANN

as an example.

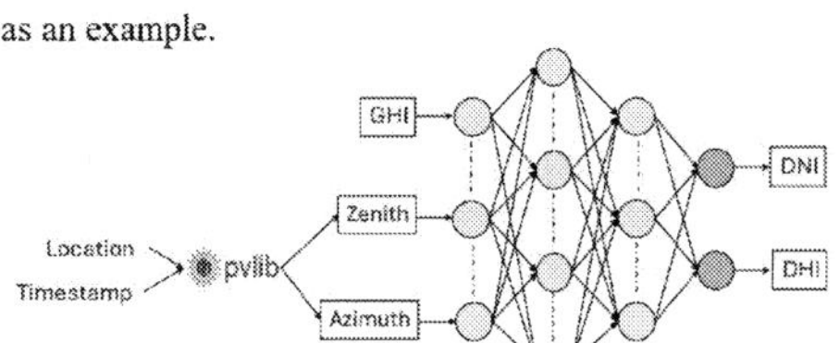

Figure 1: Proposed methodology exampled with an ANN.

The HGB model was trained using default hyperparameters, due to its low sensitivity to tuning. In contrast, the ANN and LSTM models underwent extensive hyperparameter tuning and employed advanced training strategies such as learning rate scheduling and early stopping to improve convergence and prevent overfitting. For the DL methods, the root mean squared error (RMSE) was employed as loss function. Let y_{pred} and y_{true} denote the model predicted and true values, respectively. The RMSE is then given by

$$RMSE = \sqrt{\frac{1}{N}\sum_{i=1}^{N}\left(y_{true,i} - y_{pred,i}\right)^2}. \qquad (3)$$

3.3 Evaluation Protocol

The dataset from August 2022 to May 2023 was split into 80% for training and 20% for validation. To assess generalization, an independent dataset from April–May 2024 was reserved for zero-shot evaluation, representing unseen seasonal conditions. Model performance was quantified using the coefficient of determination (R^2), which measures the proportion of variance in the target explained by the model. If $\bar{y}$ is the mean of the true values and $e_i = y_{true,i} - y_{pred,i}$ is the residual, then R^2 is given by

$$R^2 = 1 - \frac{\sum_i^N e_i^2}{\sum_i^N \left(y_{true,i} - \bar{y}\right)^2} = 1 - \frac{SSR}{SST}, \qquad (4)$$

where SSR is the sum of squared residuals and SST of the total sum of squares.

3 RESULTS

Figure 2 shows the learning curves for the ANN and LSTM models over 20,000 training steps. In Figure 2, RMSE (blue and red curves) rapidly decreases in the early training phase before stabilizing, indicating convergence of both ANN and LSTM models. The R^2 values for DNI and DHI (black, orange, purple, and green curves) increase as training progresses, showing that both models improve their predictive capabilities. Figure 2 shows that the R^2 scores for the ANN model improve steadily and reach a stable maximum at approximately 5,000 training steps, after which little additional gain is observed. In contrast, the LSTM model exhibits unstable behavior in R^2 during the initial training phase, particularly over the first few thousand steps. It begins to stabilize around 7,500 steps and continues to improve gradually, especially for the DHI prediction. This behavior motivated extending the training to 20,000 steps, despite the ANN model showing limited improvement beyond the early plateau. The ANN model reaches a higher final R^2 for DNI compared to LSTM, while LSTM achieves a better R^2 for DHI. This suggests that ANN is better suited for predicting DNI, whereas LSTM performs better in estimating DHI. The final model performance on the evaluation set (20% of the training/testing split) is summarized in Table 1, which presents the R^2 scores for DNI and DHI across all tested models. The results indicate that HGB outperforms both deep learning models, achieving the highest R^2 scores for both DNI and DHI. Among the DL methods, ANN performs better than LSTM in predicting DNI, while LSTM outperforms ANN for DHI estimation. Compared to the HGB method, it is worth mentioning that the DL methods required significantly more computational time and specialized training strategies, such as learning rate scheduling and hyperparameter tuning, to achieve acceptable performance. It is also worth mentioning that HGB is the model that required the least training time, and no hyperparameter tuning to achieve high performance. These results suggest that tree-based ensemble methods, like HGB, may be well-suited for this type of structured tabular data, particularly when irradiance decomposition patterns are well-represented in the training set. However, the model's high performance without tuning may also reflect overfitting to specific seasonal or geometric patterns.

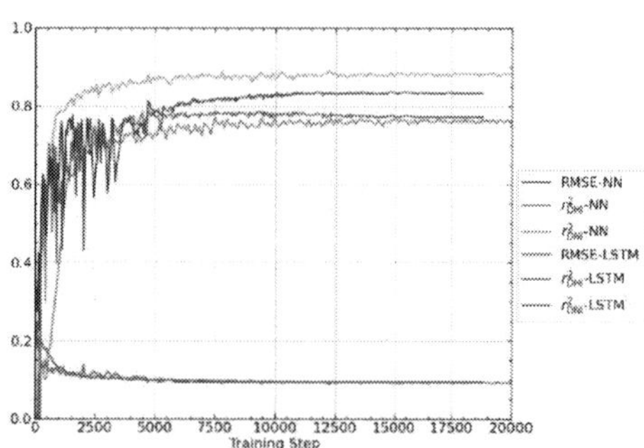

Figure 2. Learning curves for the ANN and LSTM models. RMSE (blue and red) is used as the loss function. R^2 for DNI and DHI (black, orange, purple, and green) is used as the performance metric.

Table I: R^2 scores for DNI and DHI on the evaluation set. The results compare HGB, ANN and LSTM.

Model	DNI	DHI
HGB	0.90	0.90
ANN	0.88	0.76
LSTM	0.78	0.83

To assess the models' ability to generalize beyond the training conditions, an additional evaluation was carried out using an independent dataset collected during April–May 2024. This period, not included during training, was chosen to reflect a different seasonal regime, thereby testing the robustness of the models under unseen atmospheric conditions. Figure 3 compares the predictions of the tested ML/DL models (HGB, ANN, and LSTM) with those of the Erbs model, using measured DHI and DNI as reference values. Table 2 summarizes the R^2 scores for DNI and DHI predictions across the models. Compared to the accuracies for the evaluation dataset

presented in Table 1, all models show an expected decrease in accuracy.

Figure 3a presents the DHI predictions during the April–May 2024 period. Unlike in the evaluation set, the HGB model now underperforms, achieving the lowest R^2 among the machine learning models (0.19). The ANN model provides the most accurate and consistent predictions of DHI (0.43), followed by LSTM (0.27). This performance shift suggests that HGB's earlier success may have been tied to its ability to capture structured seasonal patterns present in the training data—patterns that do not generalize well to the independent evaluation period. In contrast, the ANN and LSTM models appear more capable of capturing the diffuse and less structured nature of DHI, which is more sensitive to short-term variability in cloud cover. The empirical Erbs model achieves an R^2 of 0.36, second best after the ANN model.

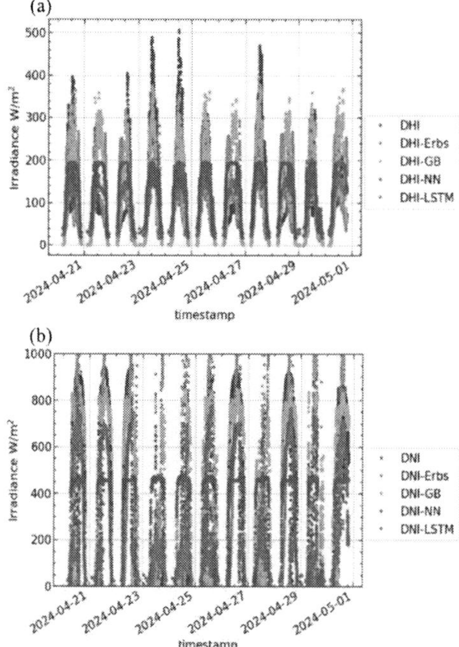

Figure 3. Comparison of model predictions with measured values for (a) DHI and (b) DNI during the April–May 2024 evaluation period.

Table II: R^2 scores for DNI and DHI predictions across tested models.

Model	DNI	DHI
HGB	0.62	0.19
ANN	0.77	0.43
LSTM	0.22	0.27
Erbs	-0.83	0.36

Figure 3b shows the model performance for DNI prediction. The HGB model, which had achieved the highest accuracy during evaluation, experiences a substantial drop in generalization, with an R^2 of 0.62 on the independent test set. Despite this decline, it still outperforms LSTM, which yields the lowest R^2 (0.22) among all the ML/DL models. The ANN model maintains the best performance, achieving an R^2 of 0.77, and demonstrates a stronger ability to generalize across seasonal and atmospheric changes. These results support the notion that HGB may be overfitting to structured patterns in the training data, particularly those related to solar geometry or seasonality, and is less adaptable to changes in irradiance conditions. In contrast, the ANN model appears more effective at capturing nonlinear dependencies between GHI and DNI that remain valid outside the training distribution. The weak performance of LSTM for DNI further suggests that time-sequential modeling contributes little to decomposition tasks focused on instantaneous irradiance components.

The Erbs decomposition model was also included in the April–May evaluation to benchmark the ML and DL models. Results in Table 2 and Figure 3 show that while Erbs provided moderate performance for DHI, it yielded negative R^2 values for DNI. This is indicative of systematic overestimation. This is noticeable in Figure 3b, where Erbs models DNI estimations (green dots) are highly overestimated even during midday hours when zenith angles were lowest. This suggests that the model's limitations may stem not only from geometric sensitivity but also from its inability to capture rapid irradiance variability and diffuse-dominated conditions, which are common in Nordic regions. Similar findings have been reported in previous studies on the shortcomings of empirical decomposition models under variable sky conditions and in northern climates [11, 12]. These results reinforce the need for more adaptive, data-driven methods, such as those evaluated in this work.

4   CONCLUSIONS AND OUTLOOK

This work has compared empirical, machine learning, and deep learning approaches for solar irradiance decomposition in the context of Nordic conditions.

Results show that while Histogram-based Gradient Boosting achieved the highest accuracy on the evaluation set, its performance degraded significantly in zero-shot scenarios, indicating sensitivity to seasonal patterns. In contrast, the Artificial Neural Network demonstrated better generalization, particularly for DNI estimation. The LSTM model offered limited benefits, suggesting that temporal dependencies play a minor role compared to the interactions of nonlinear features.

The Erbs model provided moderate performance in predicting DHI but systematically overestimated DNI values, likely due to its inability to adapt to rapid irradiance variability. Importantly, all ML and DL models outperformed the Erbs model in predicting DNI, confirming the advantage of data-driven approaches for high-latitude environments.

The results presented in this work suggest that ANN-based models may be the most robust choice for operational forecasting in Nordic climates, while tree-based methods like HGB can deliver strong performance when seasonal patterns are well represented in the training data.

Future work will focus on enhancing the deep learning models, particularly for DHI decomposition, by integrating physics-informed neural networks (PINNs). These models will combine empirical solar physics with data-driven learning, improving generalization and robustness for irradiance decomposition in the Nordic regions.

ACKNOWLEDGEMENTS

This work was partially performed within the Norwegian Research Center for Solar Energy (FME SOLAR) and is also part of the INTEREST project, funded by the European Union under Grant Agreement No. 101160594. The center is co-sponsored by the Research Council of Norway and their research and industry partners. The views and opinions expressed are those of the author(s) only and do not necessarily reflect the views of the European Union. Neither the European Union nor the granting authority (The European Climate, Infrastructure and Environment Executive Agency [CINEA]) can be held responsible for them.

REFERENCES

[1] Erbs, D. G., et al. (1982). Estimation of the diffuse radiation fraction for hourly, daily and monthly-average global radiation. Solar energy, 28(4), 293-302.

[2] Boxwell, M. (2010). Solar electricity handbook: A simple, practical guide to solar energy-designing and installing photovoltaic solar electric systems. Greenstream publishing.

[3] Mol, W. B., van Stratum, B. J., Knap, W. H., & van Heerwaarden, C. C. (2023). Reconciling observations of solar irradiance variability with cloud size distributions. Journal of Geophysical Research: Atmospheres, 128(5), e2022JD037894.

[4] Øgaard, M. B., et al. (2021). Identifying snow in photovoltaic monitoring data for improved snow loss modeling and snow detection. Solar Energy, 223, 238-247.

[5] Goodfellow, I. (2016). Deep learning (Vol. 196). MIT press.

[6] Rajagukguk, R. A., & Lee, H. (2025). Application of explainable machine learning for estimating direct and diffuse components of solar irradiance. Scientific Reports. https://doi.org/10.1038/s41598-025-91158-x

[7] Ri, A., & Arifin, R. (2023). Enhancing the performance of solar radiation decomposition models using deep learning. Journal of the Korean Solar Energy Society, 43(3), 73–86. https://doi.org/10.7836/kses.2023.43.3.073

[8] Garcia, A. S. and Dimd, B. D. (2025). Enhanced bifacial photovoltaic power prediction through procedural training and comprehensive irradiance data [Manuscript submitted for publication].

[9] SINTEF. Alpha Centauri – Field Laboratory for Testing of Solar Modules. Available at: https://www.sintef.no/en/all-laboratories/alpha-centauri-field-laboratory-for-testing-of-solar-modules/

[10] Holmgren, W., et al. "pvlib python: a python package for modeling solar energy systems." Journal of Open Source Software, 3(29), 884, (2018). DOI: 10.21105/joss.00884.

[11] Tschopp, D., et al. (2021). Measurement and modeling of diffuse irradiance masking and terrain shading for complex PV installations. Solar Energy, 221, 416–427. https://doi.org/10.1016/j.solener.2021.04.026

[12] Manni, M., et al. (2024). Performance variability of solar irradiance model chains with high-resolution input data at high latitudes. Solar Energy, 272, 112065. https://doi.org/10.1016/j.solener.2024.112065

Deep Learning-Based Solar Irradiance Decomposition Models for Nordic Regions

Alfredo Sanchez Garcia and Berhane Darsene Dimd
Sustainable Energy Technology, SINTEF Industry, Trondheim

Introduction

Accurate modeling of solar irradiance components (GHI into DNI and DHI) is important for optimizing PV system performance. Physical decomposition models such as DISC, DIRINT, and ERBS have been widely used for this purpose. These models typically perform well in low and mid-latitude regions, providing consistent and reliable results. However, in high-latitude regions, their performance can be inadequate due to the unique and complex atmospheric conditions. Recently, deep learning-based models have emerged as a promising alternative for solar irradiance decomposition. This study presents a comprehensive comparative analysis of deep learning-based solar irradiance decomposition models and established physical models for an outdoor test facility (Alpha Centauri) located in Trondheim, Norway.

Experimental setup

Alpha Centauri

* Field laboratory for testing of solar modules in Trondheim.
* 8 bifacial PV modules on 4 dual-axis trackers.
* Meteorological station on site. Two **pyranometer and a Pyrheliometer.**

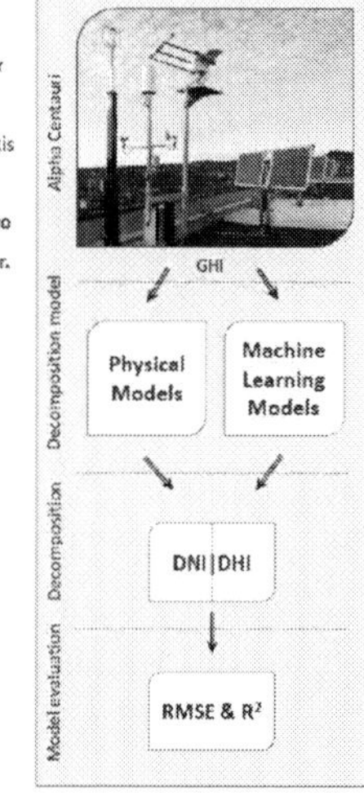

Data Collection

* Frequency: 60 s.
* GHI, DHI and DNI.
* August 2022 – May 2023

Evaluation

* GHI, DHI and DNI
* April 2024 – May 2024
* Metrics: R^2, RMSE
* Tested against Erbs Model

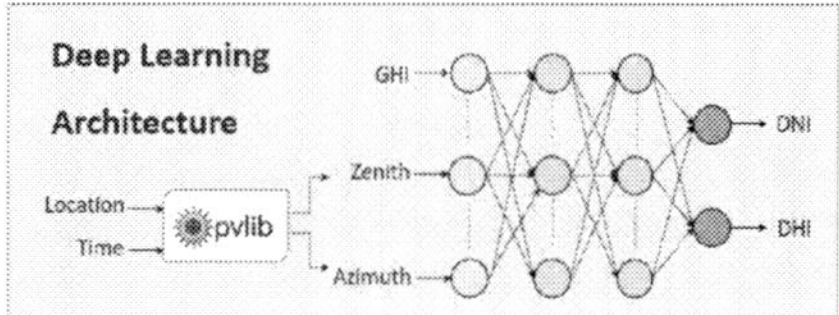

Machine Learning

Traditional machine learning (ML) techniques and one deep learning (DL) method were applied in this study. For all methods, the training-validation split was of 80/20.

Classical Machine Learning

* **Histogram-based Gradient Boosting (HGB)** Iterative algorithm that improves its predictions over time by minimizing the mean squared error function. Can handle a wide variety of data types and is resistant to overfitting.

Deep Learning Techniques

* **Artificial Neural Networks (ANN)** ANNs are powerful tools for modeling complex relationships between inputs and outputs, inspired by biological neural networks.
* **Long Short-Term Memory (LSTM)** Type of Recurrent Neural Network (RNN) that are particularly adept at handling time-series data due to their ability to remember past information.

Acknowledgement

This work was partially performed within the Norwegian Research Center for Solar Energy (FME SOLAR) and is also part of the INTEREST project, funded by the European Union under Grant Agreement No. 101160594. The center is co-sponsored by the Research Council of Norway and their research and industry partners. The views and opinions expressed are those of the author(s) only and do not necessarily reflect the views of the European Union. Neither the European Union nor the granting authority (The European Climate, Infrastructure and Environment Executive Agency [CINEA]) can be held responsible for them.

Results

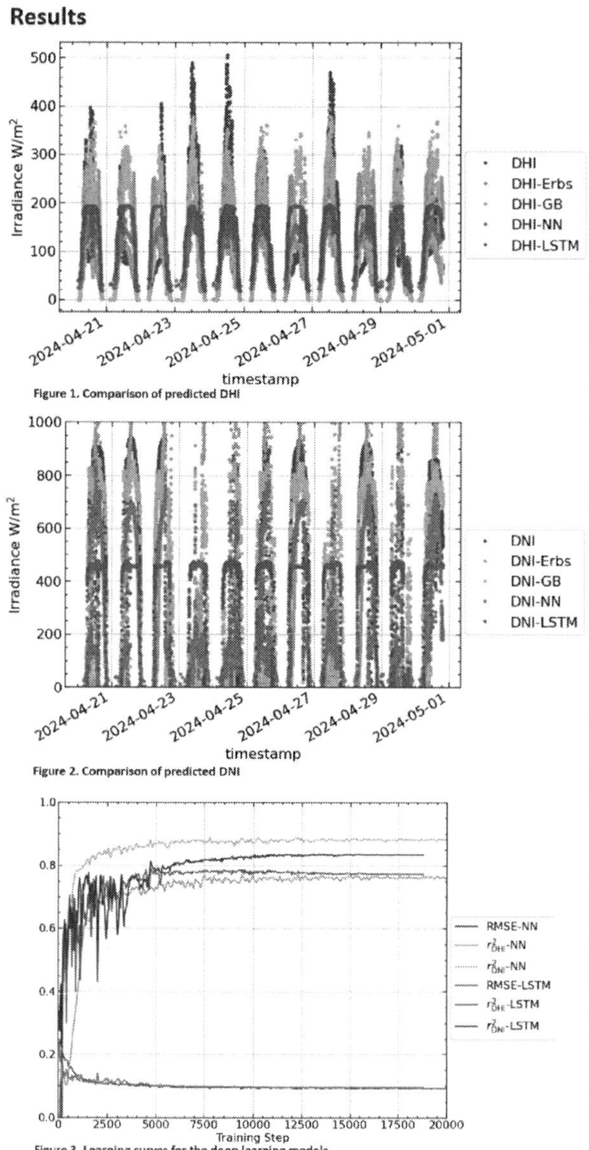

Figure 1. Comparison of predicted DHI

Figure 2. Comparison of predicted DNI

Figure 3. Learning curves for the deep learning models

High Performance and fast execution: HGB is the most accurate and fastest of the tested models.

Superiority of Physical Model: Erbs model outperforms DL models in prediction of DHI. DL models outperform Erbs in prediction of DNI.

Comparative Performance in DL methods: ANN better at predicting DNI than LSTM. LSTM better at predicting DHI than ANN.

Resource Intensive Optimization: DL methods require more time and special training strategies (learning rate scheduling, hyperparameter tuning) for OK performance.

Coefficients of Determination

Model	DNI	DHI
HGB	0.90	0.90
ANN	0.88	0.76
LSTM	0.78	0.83

Conclusions and Further Work

* HGB was the fastest and most accurate of the tested models with $R^2 = 0.9$.
* Investigate the use of more advanced deep learning methods, such as Transformers.
* Physics Informed Neural Network: Incorporate physical models in training loss.

Technology for a better society

ADVANCING VERY SHORT-TERM SOLAR IRRADIANCE FORECASTING IN AFRICA: A LOW-COST SKY IMAGING AND MACHINE LEARNING-BASED APPROACH

Martin Ansong[1,2], Gan Huang[1], Thomas N. Nyang'onda[2], Robinson J. Musembi[2], Bryce S. Richards[1]
[1]Institute of Microstructure Technology, Karlsruhe Institute of Technology, Germany
[2]Department of Physics, University of Nairobi

ABSTRACT: Africa holds immense potential for solar energy, thanks to its high year-round solar irradiation. Advances in photovoltaic (PV) technology and declining costs have made solar energy viable across the continent. However, fluctuating solar irradiance (SI), caused by factors like humidity, temperature and cloud cover, poses challenges for PV systems, causing power quality issues. This could be mitigated by utilising accurate SI forecasting, for optimal integration and operation of PV systems. Very short-term SI forecasts can play a crucial role in minimising energy storage requirements, enhancing power scheduling, and stabilising energy supply in real-time. In Africa, where weak grids usually coincide with abundant solar resources, such forecasts are especially valuable for improving load matching and grid reliability. Despite this, SI forecasting remains limited due to scarce historical SI data and high equipment prices. To address these challenges, the Karlsruhe low-cost sky imager (KALiSI) has been developed for approximately €500, for very short-term SI forecasting. Five KALiSI systems have been deployed in Africa, with data from one system installed in German being used in the present work to train a deep learning model, based on convolutional neural network – long short-term memory (CNN-LSTM) to predict SI. The model consistently delivered lower error rates across different forecast horizons compared to persistence, achieving average normalised root mean square error of 35% at 30 min horizon compared to persistence (50%). Future efforts will adapt this model to the African sites, utilising localised data to refine SI and subsequently PV power predictions, enhancing robustness and accuracy under diverse climatic conditions.

Keywords: Very short-term solar forecasting, Deep learning, Africa, low-cost sky imager,

1 INTRODUCTION

Solar energy presents a huge opportunity for Africa. The continent receives some of the highest year-round solar irradiation levels in the world with solar energy potential is of about 7900 GW, indicating vast potential for the generation of solar power [1]. The innovations in solar photovoltaic (PV) technology, coupled with the decreasing costs have made solar energy a very viable option for many African countries. However, the development and integration of PV in power systems is highly dependent on climatic conditions such as humidity, temperature and cloud cover, which can change rapidly over a short duration, causing fluctuations in solar irradiance (SI). This inherent fluctuations in SI can pose significant challenges in PV systems. SI fluctuations can negatively impact PV power quality, resulting in voltage fluctuations, voltage dips and flickers and frequency oscillations [2]. Therefore, accurate SI forecasts are required for the optimal operation of grid-connected PV power systems. SI forecasting can help to significantly reduce energy storage capacity required for energy balancing, as well as aiding power scheduling and dispatch decision. In addition, SI forecasting can help minimize the need for power curtailment and reduce the cost of electricity generation, thereby increasing revenues from electricity trading [3].

SI is typically forecasted for different forecast horizons including very short-term, short-term and long term, depending on the specific application. Very short-term forecasting focuses on predicting SI values for time frames that generally span a few seconds up 30 mins into the future. Techniques that work well for very short forecasting intervals might not be equally suitable for longer time scales [4]. A variety of methods can be applied to forecast SI, including persistence models, physical models, satellite models, statistical and machine learning - based approaches, ground-based sky imaging techniques.

1.1 Motivation

Most SI forecasting approaches rely heavily on the availability of historical data and typically provide long-term forecasts, ranging from a few hours to several days ahead. However, in many developing countries, especially in Africa, such historical data is often unavailable, significantly hindering solar energy development. Ground-based sky imaging techniques are therefore favoured. These techniques perform well within very short time horizons, may not require extensive historical data, and are increasingly being explored for solar resource assessment and forecasting as well as cloud monitoring [5]. Very short-term SI forecasting is particularly valuable for managing fluctuations in energy supply caused by rapidly changing weather conditions, thereby supporting real-time decision-making. Accurate and timely SI predictions on a very short-term basis enable solar power systems to adjust their operations, maintaining stable power output and ensuring consistent supply to the grid. Furthermore, such forecasts impact the financial performance of PV power plants. In developing regions like Africa, where weak power grids often coincide with abundant solar resources, accurate very short-term SI predictions can add more value by facilitating better load matching – aligning electricity demand with supply – and creating more robust electricity grids [5].

Despite the advantages of very short-term SI forecasting, particularly for solar energy exploitation, its application in Africa remains limited. Challenges to this include insufficient research, inadequate historical SI data, high cost and complexity of solar radiation measuring stations, which hinder the collection of reliable quality data. Another significant challenge is the lack of open-source imagery data from multiple locations across Africa with consistent imaging system setups. This data gap limits the ability to advance image-based SI forecasting and conduct related studies effectively.

Figure 1: Map showing locations where the KALiSI have been installed across Africa.

To address these challenges, the Karlsruhe low-cost sky imager (KALiSI) which is suitable for SI forecasting and can be assembled for approximately US$ 600 has been developed [6]. Five of these systems have been deployed in various geographic locations across Africa including Ghana, Kenya, Tanzania and Namibia to collect data for SI forecasting, as depicted in the map in Fig.1. The KALiSI was first deployed at the Karlsruhe Institute of Technology (KIT) in southwest Germany, where it has demonstrated full functionality comparable to more expensive commercial sky imagers, after several rounds of testing and modifications [6].

This low-cost system holds significant potential not only for grid integration of PV systems, but also for microgrid and small-scale PV systems, where very short-term forecasting is often necessary [7]. Additionally, the system facilitates data collection for subsequent analysis. The KALiSI is constructed around the Raspberry Pi Model 4B single-board computer and 8 MP camera module with a fisheye lens which provides high computational capability, resulting in faster processing, improved multitasking, and enhanced overall performance compared to other low-cost imagers in its class. The design is simple, allowing the components to be assembled quickly and easily, typically within two days

2 MATERIALS AND METHODS

2.1 Data collection and processing

It should be noted from the foregoing that while the present study uses data collected from Karlsruhe, in Germany, this will ultimately be replaced with data collected from the different sites in Africa where the KALiSI systems are currently installed, in order to establish localised models for very short-term SI and PV-power prediction for these areas.

The sky images captured by the KALiSI installed in KIT solar park (49°05'56.2"N 8°26'14.5"E) at every minute from sunrise to sunset were collected from February to July 2024 to train a convolutional neural network – long short-term memory (CNN-LSTM) model to forecast SI for the locations. The corresponding global horizontal (GHI) values are measured and logged directly on the KALiSI by a SI sensor (IMT Technology GmbH, Si-V-1.5TC-T, Germany) connected to it. Data processing involved masking out unwanted areas, downsizing and normalization of images to make them suitable for training the model. A hybrid cloud detection algorithm was applied

to obtain the cloud cover from the pre-processed images.

To obtain the cloud cover images are categorized into cloudy, partly cloudy, and clear based on average pixel intensity, excluding the sun's region. The cloud cover of clear images is set to zero without further processing. For cloudy and partly cloudy images, if the sun is not detected, a fixed threshold is used to segment cloud pixels from sky pixels. Otherwise, the Otsu adaptive threshold is applied before calculating cloud cover as the ratio of cloud pixels to total pixels within the fisheye circle in the image. The segmentation is based on the red-to-blue pixel ratio to enhance contrast between cloud and sky pixels [6]. Figure 3 shows a pre-processed image from the KALiSI with its corresponding binarized images used in cloud cover calculation shows an overview of the forecasting model design.

The cloud cover as well as their corresponding images downsized to 64 x 64 pixels were then stacked in sequence according to the forecast horizon, to capture the cloud dynamics, and used as input to the CNN-LSTM model to forecast the SI.

Figure 2: Pre-processed image (right) from the KALiSI with corresponding binary image (left) used in cloud cover determination.

2.2 Model architecture

The proposed model integrates handcrafted and learned features from ground-based sky images to predict GHI. Initially, pre-processed sky images are processed using a red–blue ratio algorithm to enhance cloud detection, after which a cloud fraction estimation algorithm quantifies the proportion of the sky covered by clouds [6]. These cloud fraction values are subsequently incorporated as auxiliary inputs to the model. In parallel, the pre-processed sky images are down-sampled and passed through two sequential convolutional blocks, each consisting of a 3×3 convolutional layer, batch normalization, and max pooling to extract progressively higher-level spatial representations of cloud structures and brightness patterns. The resulting feature maps are then flattened to form a compact representation. Next, the handcrafted cloud fraction features and the convolutional feature representations are concatenated to create a unified feature vector, which is reshaped into a temporal sequence and processed by the LSTM layer to model temporal dependencies between successive images. The LSTM output is further refined through a stack of dense and dropout layers that provide nonlinear regression capability and regularization, finishing in a final dense layer that produces the predicted GHI values.

2.3 Model Training and Evaluation

Each sample given to the network is composed of a sequence of images equal to the forecast horizon as well as corresponding sequence of cloud cover values. Samples collected from sunrise to sunset over the six months period were randomly allocated to the validation and the training sets.

The model was trained and tested on 3 days of different weather conditions, clear, partly cloudy and very cloudy days. The training objective involved decreasing the mean square error by utilising the Adam optimiser. K-fold cross-validation was employed, such that the training set was divided into 10 folds and each of the 10 folds was used as the validation set in turn. The final prediction is taken as the ensemble mean of the different sub-models.

Hyperparameters of the model such as the batch size, LSTM cells and learning rate were tuned to achieve the best forecasting performance on the 10-min ahead forecast. The same network architecture has been used to train models for the 5-min to 30-min ahead forecasts.

The performance of the model is evaluated using the root mean squared error (RMSE) and mean absolute error (MAE), defined in Eq. (1) and (2), respectively. The RMSE and MAE are widely used in the evaluation SI prediction accuracies. Smaller values of RMSE and MAE indicate lower deviation of the predicted values from the observed values and hence better predictive performance. The RMSE and MAE are normalised to the mean of the measured data using Eq. (3) and Eq. (4) [8] to provide a more standardised way of measuring errors and enable a fair comparison across different models or datasets with varying scales [9]. The persistence model, a commonly used reference model in SI forecasting, which always forecasts the last measured value irrespective of the time horizon is added as a reference model over the test set to also assess the performance of the model in forecasting. In SI forecasting, the persistence model assumes that the SI value at time $t+1$, is the same as the SI value at time t [10]:

$$\text{RMSE} = \sqrt{\tfrac{1}{N}\sum_{i=1}^{N}\left(\text{GHI}_{p,i} - \text{GHI}_{m,i}\right)^2} \qquad (1)$$

$$\text{MAE} = \tfrac{1}{N}\sum_{i=1}^{N}\left|\text{GHI}_{p,i} - \text{GHI}_{m,i}\right| \qquad (2)$$

$$\text{nRMSE} = \frac{\sqrt{N}}{\sum_{i}^{N}\text{GHI}_{m,i}}\sqrt{\tfrac{1}{N}\sum_{i=1}^{N}\left(\text{GHI}_{p,i} - \text{GHI}_{m,i}\right)^2} \qquad (3)$$

$$\text{nMAE} = \left(\frac{1}{\sum_{i}^{N}\text{GHI}_{m,i}}\right)\sum_{i=1}^{N}\left|\text{GHI}_{p,i} - \text{GHI}_{m,i}\right| \qquad (4)$$

where $GHI_{p,i}$ and $GHI_{m,i}$ are the respective predicted and measured GHI values in W/m^2, and N is the total number of times predictions are performed.

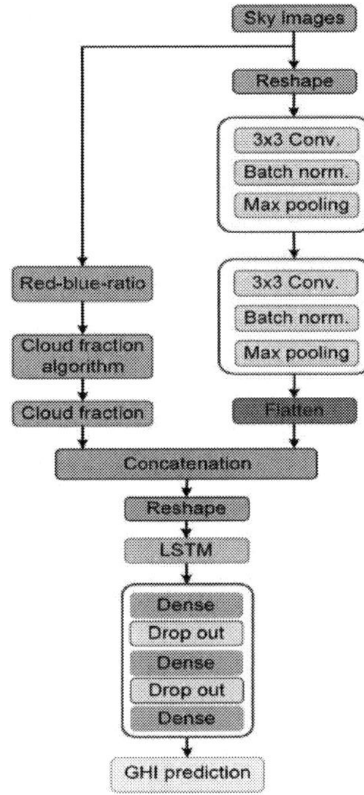

Figure 3: Overview of the forecasting model architecture

3 RESULTS AND DISCUSSIONS

The results were assessed by comparing with persistence model in terms of RMSE and MAE over the selected days. The results obtained for 10-min ahead GHI prediction for each of the 3 selected days is presented in Figure 4 and summarised in Table I. The model outperforms the persistence under all weather conditions achieving the best performance under clear sky with a RMSE and MAE of 18 and 13 W/m^2 respectively.

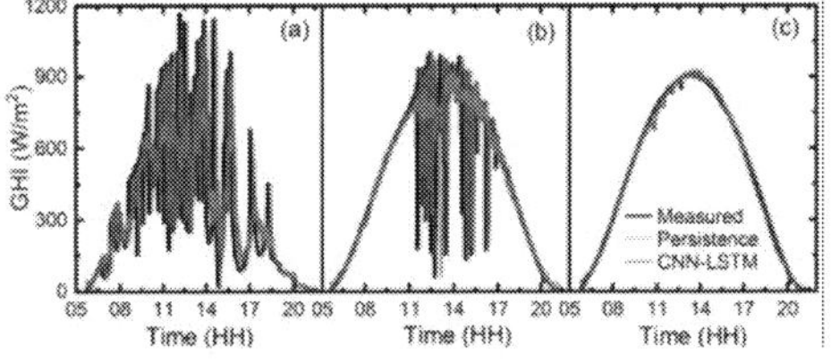

Figure 4: Performance of the CNN-LSTM model compared to persistence at 10 min ahead forecast (a) very cloudy (b) partly cloudy (c) sunny (Data taken from [6])

Table I: Performance of the model for the selected days in terms of RMSE (W/m^2) and MAE (W/m^2)

	Cloudy		Partly cloudy		Clear		All	
	RMSE	MAE	RMSE	MAE	RMSE	MAE	RMSE	MAE
Persistence	246	146	246	146	22	20	158	86
CNN-LSTM	**187**	**127**	**186**	**126**	**18**	**13**	**116**	**67**

Figure 5 also shows the average nRMSE and nMAE of the 3 selected for the CNN-LSTM model compared to the persistence over different forecast horizons. The proposed model achieved lower average nRMSE and nMAE than the persistence for all forecast horizons. For nRMSE (Figure 4a), CNN-LSTM starts at 30% at 5 mins and increases to 35% at 30 mins, while persistence rises sharply, to 50%. Similarly, for nMAE (Figure 4b), CNN-LSTM increases from 17% to 23%, compared to persistence's sharp rise from 17% to 35%.

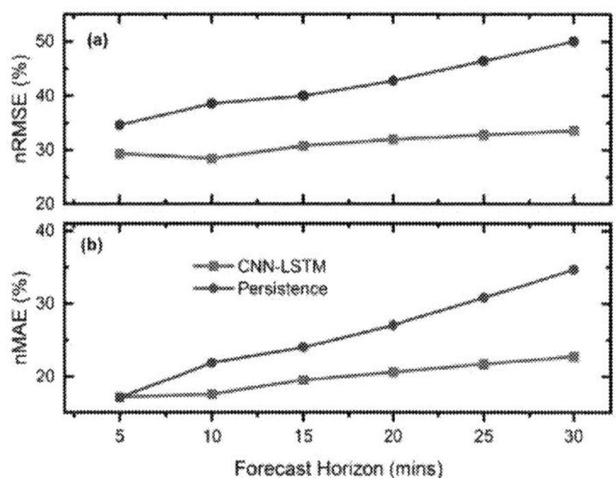

Figure 5: Performance of the CNN-LSTM model compared with persistence at different forecast horizons (a) nRMSE and (b) nMAE (Data taken from [6])

4 CONCLUSIONS

In summary, the images captured by the low-cost sky imaging (KALiSI) system in Karlsruhe, southwest, Germany have been used to train a hybrid model that combines CNN with LSTM. The model outperformed the persistence on forecast horizon of 5- 30 min. The KALiSI have been installed in five sites in Africa with different climatic and weather conditions, therefore future work will involve using the data collected in the sites in Africa and the model employed in the present study to establish localised forecast models for very short-term SI and PV power prediction for these location as well as optimising the models to improve it robustness and accuracy.

5 REFERENCES

[1] International Renewable Energy Agency (IRENA) and African Development Bank (AfDB), "Renewable Energy Market Analysis: Africa and Its Regions," Abu Dhabi and Abidjan, 2022.

[2] I. Ranaweera, O.-M. Midtgård, and G. H. Yordanov, "Short-term intermittency of solar irradiance in southern norway," in *29th European Photovoltaic Solar Energy Conference and Exhibition (EUPVSEC)*, 2014, pp. 2635-2638,

[3] N. Krishnan, K. R. Kumar, and C. S. Inda, "How solar radiation forecasting impacts the utilization of solar energy: A critical review," *Journal of Cleaner Production*, vol. 388, p. 135860, 2023.

[4] R. Samu *et al.*, "Applications for solar irradiance nowcasting in the control of microgrids: A review," *Renewable and Sustainable Energy Reviews*, vol. 147, p. 111187, 2021.

[5] M. Ansong, T. N. Nyang'onda, R. J. Musembi, and B. S. Richards, "Very Short-term Solar Irradiance Forecasting for Photovoltaic Power Integration with the Grid: Potentials and Challenges for Africa," presented at the 2024 IEEE PES/IAS PowerAfrica Conference, 2024.

[6] M. Ansong, G. Huang, T. N. Nyang'onda, R. J. Musembi, and B. S. Richards, "Very short-term solar irradiance forecasting based on open-source low-cost sky imager and hybrid deep-learning techniques," *Solar Energy*, vol. 294, p. 113516, 2025.

[7] M. Ansong, E. O. Ogunniyi, B. P. Jiménez, and B. S. Richards, "Renewable energy powered membrane technology: Integration of solar irradiance forecasting for predictive control of photovoltaic-powered brackish water desalination system," *Applied Energy*, vol. 401, p. 126651, 2025.

[8] T. E. Hoff, R. Perez, J. Kleissl, D. Renne, and J. Stein, "Reporting of irradiance modeling relative prediction errors," *Progress in Photovoltaics: Research and Applications*, vol. 21, no. 7, pp. 1514-1519, 2013.

[9] M. Paulescu and E. Paulescu, "Short-term forecasting of solar irradiance," *Renewable Energy*, vol. 143, pp. 985-994, 2019.

[10] M. Diagne, M. David, P. Lauret, J. Boland, and N. Schmutz, "Review of solar irradiance forecasting methods and a proposition for small-scale insular grids," *Renewable and Sustainable Energy Reviews*, vol. 27, pp. 65-76, 2013.

Advancing very short-term solar irradiance forecasting in Africa: A low-cost sky imaging and deep learning approach

<u>Martin Ansong</u>[1,2], Gan Huang[1], Thomas N. Nyang'onda[2], Robinson J. Musembi[2], Bryce S. Richards[1]

[1]*Institute of Microstructure Technology, Karlsruhe Institute of Technology;* [2]*Department of Physics, University of Nairobi*

Introduction

- Advances in photovoltaic (PV) with declining costs and high solar potential have made solar energy viable across Africa.

- However, fluctuations in solar irradiance (SI) caused by factors like humidity, temperature and cloud cover, poses challenges for photovoltaic (PV) systems, causing power quality issues[1].

- This can be mitigated by very short-term SI forecasting (VSTSIF), for optimal operation of PV systems and managing supply in real-time[1,2]

Motivation

- In Africa, where weak grids coincide with high solar resources, VSTSIF can be valuable for improving load matching and reliability

- VSTSIF remains limited due to scarce data & high equipment and maintenance cost[1].

- To address the challenges, Karlsruhe low-cost sky imager (KALiSI) open-source system[3] has been developed for ~€500, for VSTSIF of 5-30 min[4]

Materials and Methods

- KALiSI is constructed around RaspberryPi with camera module, fisheye lens and integrated with SI sensor. Custom program captures an image every min and record the corresponding, global horizontal irradiance (GHI).

- VSTSIF model based on convolutional neural network – long short-term memory (CNN-LSTM) with data from KALiSI installed Karlsruhe

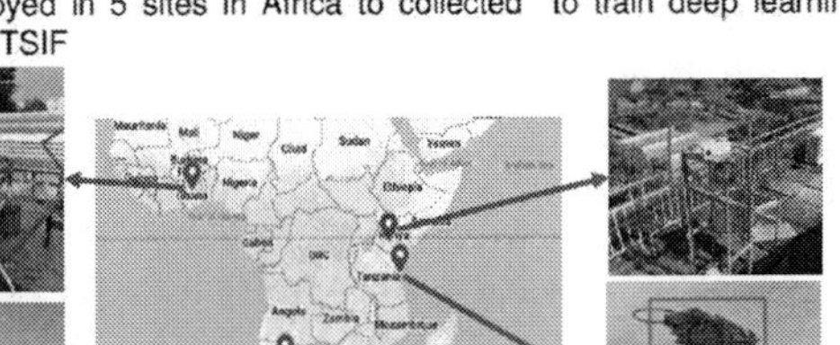

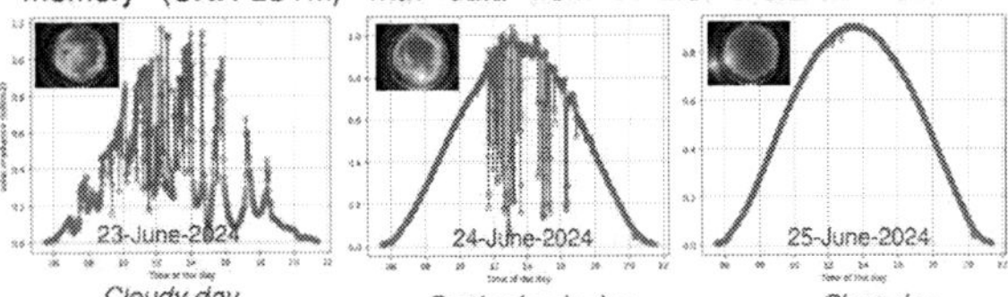

Cloudy day   *Partly cloudy day*   *Clear day*

- KALiSI deployed in 5 sites in Africa to collected to train deep learning model for VSTSIF

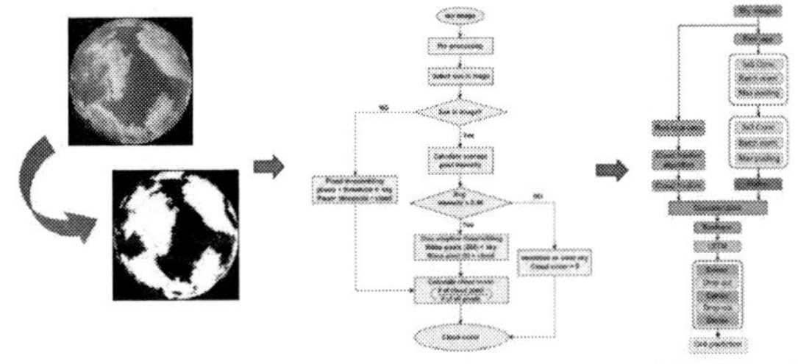

Image preprocessing   *Cloud fraction determination*   *CNN-LSTM model*

Results

	Cloudy		Partly cloudy		Clear		overall	
	RMSE	MAE	RMSE	MAE	RMSE	MAE	RMSE	MAE
Persistence	246	146	246	146	22	20	158	86
CNN-LSTM	187	127	186	126	18	13	116	67

Performance of the CNN-LSTM model for the selected days assessed by root mean error (RMSE) and mean absolute error (MAE) in W/m² for 10 min ahead forecast

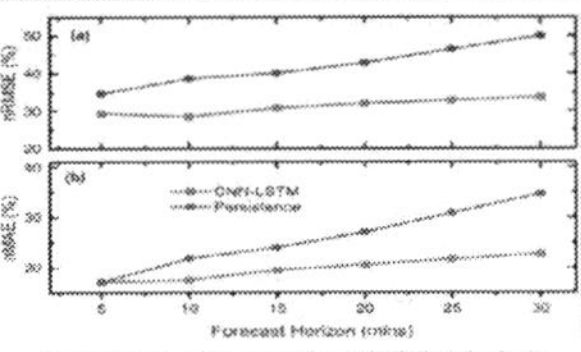

CNN-LSTM model compared to persistence at 10 min ahead forecast (a) very cloudy (b) partly cloudy (c) sunny

Performance of the model over different horizon compared to persistence assessed by (a) normalised RMSE (nRMSE) and (b) normalised MAE (nMAE)

Conclusions

- Data from KALiSI in Germany used to train the CNN-LSTM model, which outperforms persistence at all horizon from 5 to 30 min.

- Average nRME of 35% at 30 min horizon compared to persistence (50%).

- Future work will involve using data collected in Africa to establish localised models for VSTFSI and PV power prediction, and optimising models to improve performance and robustness.

References

[1] Ansong et al. In IEEE PES/IAS PowerAfrica Conference (2024)

[2] Ansong et al., Applied Energy (2025)

[3] https://github.com/KALiSI4SIFS/KALiSI/tree/main

[4] Ansong et al., Solar Energy (2025)

Contacts

Prof. Dr. Bryce S. Richards
E-Mail:bryce richards@kit edu

Martin Ansong
E-Mail:ansong.martin@gmail.com

Funding :

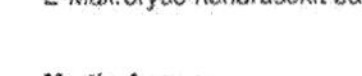

Lessons Learned in Automating Quality Control:
Challenges in Real World Ground Measurements

Camara A., Blstak Catlosova K., Cebecauer T., Jakubik M., Hulik Jansova M., Osvald O. | **Solargis, Bratislava, Slovakia**

Abstract

Acquiring **reliable** solar irradiance **data** under the real-world conditions poses numerous **challenges**. When left unaddressed, these issues will **affect further analyses and KPIs** used in photovoltaic (PV) project development and operation —including site adaptation of satellite models, data bankability, performance monitoring and evaluation and forecasting. We **quantified the impact** of compromised data on two key metrics, namely relative bias and relative root mean square deviation (rRMSD) between reference measurements with or without quality control and Solargis solar model.

To **automatically identify data degraded by issues**, it is crucial to understand common measurements issues and their typical manifestation in the data. To obtain precise references, and to ensure accurate metadata, as advanced automatic quality control methods heavily depend on these factors. We showcased examples from our developed quality control toolkit, demonstrating methods for **metadata verification and correction**.

Typical issues and their effect

The present work mainly targeted validating Global Horizontal Irradiance (GHI) of Solargis satellite solar resource model time series with ground measurements from 53 locations provided the validation reference in these analyses. Our aim is to analyse effect of different level of quality control on validation model. Table 1 details the most frequent problems found in GHI datasets, their prevalence and their effect on relative bias and rRMSD.

As demonstrated in Table 1 the occurrence and impact and presence of the individual issues is varying. Biggest impact on median and 90th percentile is caused by issue that medially affects the most data points, Shading. Some of these issues can substantially influence data integrity, even with sparse occurrences (e.g. Dirt/Soiling). These effects are more pronounced for Direct Normal Irradiance (subset of 41 validation datasets). A median of 16.34% data points were affected, mostly due to tracker issues. At the 90th percentile, all issues contributed to a 10.12% change in relative bias and 24.26% change in rRMSD. Soiling and shading impacts increased despite stable occurrence compare to GHI: shading caused 4.43% change in bias and 6.25% change in rRMSD; soiling, 2.20% change in bias and 5.91% change in rRMSD.

Table 1: Most common issues identified in compromised datasets of Global Horizontal Irradiance (53 validation datasets) by non-advanced automatic test (unless otherwise stated), proportion of affected datasets and data-points and corresponding impact of these issues on relative bias and relative root mean square error (rRMSD) with ground measurements used as reference for Solargis resource model.

Issue Type	Proportion of Affected Datasets (%)	Median Proportion of Affected Data Points (%)	Percentile of Absolute Effect on Relative Bias (%)			Percentile of Absolute Effect on rRMSD(%)		
			50th	90th	100[a]	50[a]	90[b]	100[a]
Below physical minimum	95.65	0.94	0.05	0.22	0.38	0.03	0.17	0.35
Postfiltering*	93.48	0.19	0.03	0.26	0.98	0.06	0.63	1.69
Shading*	91.30	6.80	1.03	2.23	2.86	1.10	2.55	2.87
Consistency	73.91	0.65	0.07	0.51	0.96	0.27	1.88	3.38
Maintenance*	65.22	0.31	0.03	0.50	0.70	0.07	0.86	1.13
Not-specified**	56.52	0.06	0.01	0.15	18.22	0.00	0.25	24.09
2-component test	41.30	0.00	0.00	0.02	0.06	0.00	0.10	0.44
Consecutive static values	39.13	0.02	0.00	0.07	0.49	0.00	0.05	0.55
Dirt/Soiling*	34.78	0.30	0.04	0.58	1.30	0.05	0.69	2.80
Dew/Frost*	32.61	0.09	0.05	0.11	0.32	0.04	0.11	0.33
All issues	100.00	11.38	1.15	3.12	15.92	2.19	5.53	29.22

* Issues that are identified either with advanced automatic test or by manual flagging.
** Issues that are flagged manually and are of atypical cause.

Time Reference Correction

Ground measurements frequently exhibit time reference issues stemming not only from site-specific timezones. These inconsistencies, varying from minor (5 minutes) to significant sub hourly, or daylight saving changes, create mismatches when validating the model data. These time shifts interfere with automatic quality control by distorting other data quality problems. This leads to incorrect identification of issues in ground measurement data. To ensure accurate data fitting with the Solargis model data and to avoid misinterpretation in automatic quality control, precise identification and correction of time reference issues are imperative. As shown on the **Figure 4**, all time shifts introduced changes to relative bias, time shift of 60 minutes can easily introduce change in relative bias of 2.24% and in more extreme cases 9.86% , caused just by incorrect flagging. However, using Solargis method to automatically detect and shift data to match with the used reference, effects of incorrectly identified issues on relative bias were minimised.

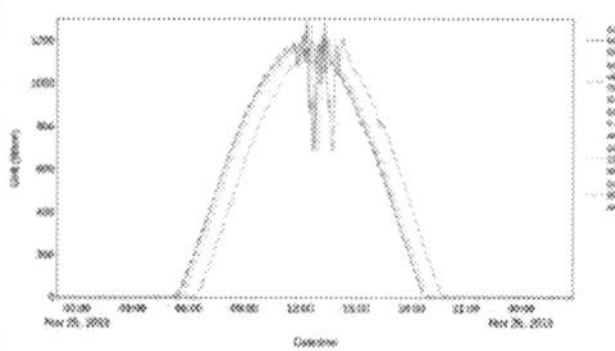

Figure 1: Time Series showcasing 3 different time reference misalignments for a single dataset on selected day.

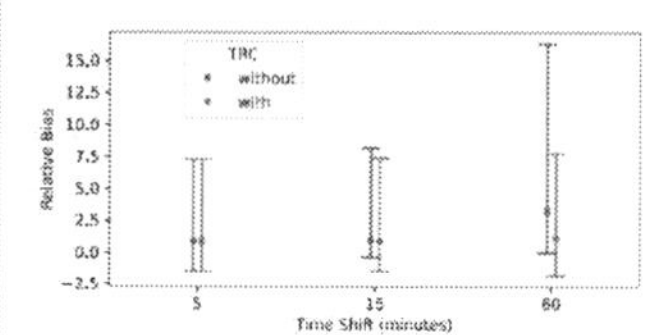

Figure 2: Showcasing the change in the in relative Bias when different timeshifts were introduced to 10 datasets and the effect of Time Reference Correction (TRC). Error bars represent 2.5th and 97.5th percentile.

Statistical Reference of Ground Measurements for Cloudless intervals identification

For quality control tests such as the identification of the type of measured irradiation (GHI, DNI, DIF, GTI, RHI), estimation of GTI mounting configuration (mounting type, tilt and azimuth), analysis of misalignment and other potential issues presented above, the statistical representation of cloudless situations (cloudless profile) is required. To identify the cloudless days we employed a statistical reference that used only ground measurements data as model data may suffer from inaccuracies in inputs not representing accurately local conditions (aerosols, water vapor) or the configuration of the mounting is not known upfront (e.g. GTI). To create the reference an uneven grid, inversely correlated to sun speed depicted on Figure 1 was used. A representative percentile was selected from each grid cell and the data was smoothed to provide a robust reference. This method enhanced cloudless day identification accuracy compared to a statistical reference based on regular grid (Figure 2). It has then direct impact on the quality of following QC tests.

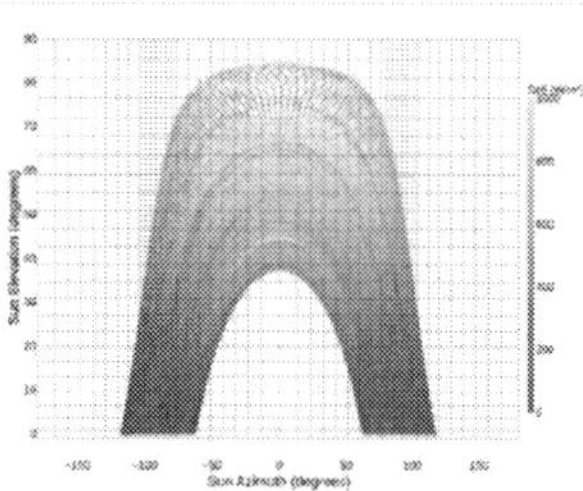

Figure 3: Unequidistant grid in sun azimuth and sun elevation space, used for creation of statistical reference that limits artifacts in higher elevations.

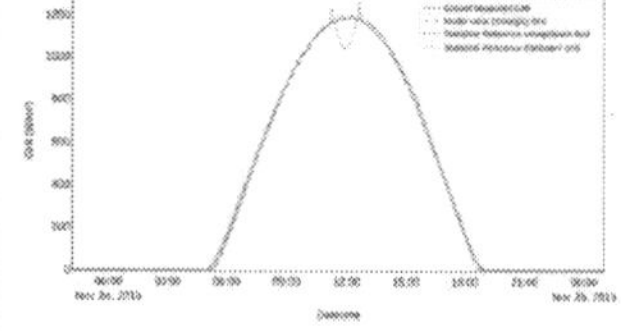

Figure 4: Comparison of ground measurements data, Solargis model data, statistical reference using unequidistant grid and statistical reference using regular grid. Regular grid reference has strong artifacts at the highest sun elevation due to the lower number of data points.

Conclusion

The analysis of ground measurements data from various sites revealed numerous common issues, and their impact on key metrics was quantified. We have showed the importance of quality control and how drastically it can influence model validation metrics. In addition to the measurement operations issues summarized in the Table1, the data from the PV projects can often suffer from the missing or incorrect metadata, such as GTI tilt and/or azimuth, instances of incorrect type of irradiation (e.g. incorrect column name), and inaccuracies in longitude and latitude and similar. Our diverse experience with datasets has highlighted the wide range of potential discrepancies. Missing or incomplete quality control can have strong impact on the utilization of measured data for tasks such as model site-adaptation or PV project performance evaluation. Such measurements issues can be in extreme cases off by tenths of percent. The developed automatic quality control methods can identify and significantly mitigate impact of incorrect measurements or meteostation metadata. The reliable quality control tools are critical for automation of the PV power plants operation, monitoring and performance evaluation as well as enhanced PV production forecasting.

© 2025 Solargis

AUTOMATED SOLAR DATA QUALITY REPORTING FRAMEWORK

Perez-Astudillo, Daniel, Bachour, Dunia A.
Qatar Environment & Energy Research Institute, HBKU
P.O. Box 34110, Doha, Qatar

ABSTRACT: Ensuring the collection and maintenance of high-quality solar data is essential for solar research and applications. The software provided with commercial data logging hardware, however, is generally limited to some basic data display and processing, usually just converting raw values to irradiance and doing simple averaging, and although this might suffice for a basic visualisation of data, it quickly proves inconvenient for advanced data analysis, such as assessing data quality, which requires calculations that may not be possible to incorporate in the provided software. This work presents a workflow that automates the periodic (daily, or configurable to other periods) assessment of the quality of solar irradiance measurements taken at 1-minute resolution; with a relatively simple set of scripts and freely available software, collected data are automatically analysed to produce a clear single-page report for each monitoring station, whether for one or several sites. All reports of one day are combined in one PDF file that is emailed to designated addresses.
Keywords: solar radiation, data quality, data pipeline, automation

1   INTRODUCTION

Managing the operation of a solar radiation monitoring station includes a number of activities aimed at maintaining the equipment in proper operating conditions and obtaining the highest-quality data from the equipment. Periodic preventive maintenance on the station (cleaning sensors, checking levelling, shading, etc.) and timely corrective adjustments or repairs are crucial for the hardware side of the system, and are usually carried out by designated technical personnel but, ultimately, the collected data must also be monitored frequently to confirm whether the equipment and maintenance are working as expected.

Generally, the data loggers used in solar radiation monitoring systems are provided with some way to display collected data in tabular or graphical form. However, these functionalities are quite limited; for example, in most cases no quality checks are or can even be implemented, other than perhaps simple limits such as a fixed maximum and/or minimum value.

While in some cases it may be possible to have a dedicated person or team to continuously monitor the data being collected, the task becomes increasingly difficult to manage as the number of data sources (stations) grows, not to mention the tediousness of the task, leading to higher chances of human error.

Given the above, a good solution is the automation of the data monitoring process. With a carefully planned solution, the amount and quality of provided information can be higher and optimised so that, for example, multiple indicators or stations can be seen in a compact form, saving large amounts of time in both the preparation and the ingest of the reported information. The process developed in this study is built upon a set of tests that evaluate the quality of the collected irradiance data, highlighting commonly found issues. The different steps of the process along with the tests and tools required for the implementation are described in more detail in the following section, so that other interested users can replicate the components shown here and adapt them as needed.

2   DESCRIPTION AND IMPLEMENTATION OF THE FRAMEWORK

The application package described here was developed to run on a server running Ubuntu Server 20.04, and the data from the stations is saved on a PostgreSQL database, so some components may differ in other systems (e.g. the scheduler to run the main script).

2.1 Pre-requisites
A clean Ubuntu installation, as many if not most Linux distributions, already includes many useful tools to automate and do some batch command line processing needed for the system described here; for example, 'sed' and 'cut' can be used to preprocess the input data files, although this is done here directly within Python to reduce dependencies and system command calls. Additional tools required: Python 3 (with a few additional packages), ROOT (https://root.cern/), unoconv, LibreOffice, systemd (with systemctl).
- Python 3: Apart from the default Python 3 installation, the following extra packages are needed: psycopg2 (to interact with the PostgreSQL database) and python-docx (to create DOCX files).
- ROOT: CERN's ROOT data analysis framework. Used for doing all calculations and to create the histograms and graphs for the report; the code is saved in files called "ROOT macros".
- unoconv: To convert the DOCX files to PDF.
- LibreOffice: unoconv can do its above-described task without a full LibreOffice installation, but when having LibreOffice also installed unoconv produces better formatting. To generate the report files, alternative methods are possible; for example, PDF files can be created without the intermediate DOCX files by using the Python package PyLaTeX (https://jeltef.github.io/PyLaTeX/current/index.html), although this does not necessarily reduce the storage use by much, as it requires a LaTeX compiler.
- systemd: To create and run services; already comes with Ubuntu and many Linux distributions.

2.2 Components
A service is created and scheduled to run once a day at a given time. Using systemd, this consists of two files: one timer file that sets the schedule to run the service, and one service file that defines the environment and runs a Python script (run.py) that does the following:

10.4229/EUPVSEC2025/4BV.3.16
020275-001

1. Check whether all needed files and subfolders are present. Working files and folders are automatically created if missing, but the user must provide a "sites" file containing site names, coordinates, and time zones (see below).
2. Export the data of the previous calendar day from the (PostgreSQL) database to CSV files, one file per site. First, a SQL script file is generated, then a connection to the database is made and the SQL script is run. The output files are saved to a local temporary location.
3. 'Clean' (preprocess) the CSV files, which consists of filling empty fields (i.e., between consecutive commas, or after a comma at the end of a line) with "-999" to signal missing entries; the final, clean files use a single space as field separator, and all lines should have the same number of fields.
4. Read the clean data files, store the data in binary "ROOT files" and process the data. Processing steps: calculate solar positions for every minute of the day to analyse, run quality checks, flag and filter data, and calculate hourly and daily averages. The flags, filtered data and averages are saved in ROOT files.
5. Run daily checks to report on the outputs of step 4, producing info graphs and log files. Separate ROOT macros are called in sequence.
6. Create a report. For each site, the outputs of step 5 are put into a one-page DOCX file and converted to PDF; then all PDF files are joined into one final PDF report, with 1 page per site.
7. Email the report and logs. The log files are compressed to a ZIP file; then, two final files, namely a PDF and a ZIP, are sent by email.
8. Clean-up: delete all files created in steps 2-7 except the ZIP and final PDF, which are moved to a local subfolder as backup.

Figure 1 shows a schematic graph and description of the code components, inputs, and outputs. The components with "()" appended to their names are the functions contained in the run.py script. This script also calls several ROOT macros (.C files) as described. As mentioned above, the user must create a file named sites.csv containing one line per each station that will be included in the report. Each line is given in the following format, with comma as field separator:

Code,Name,Lat,Lon,TZ

where:

- Code = 3-char short identifier for the station.
- Name = station name.
- Lat = station's latitude in degrees.
- Lon = station's longitude in degrees.
- TZ = station's time zone.

A total of 10 ROOT macros (.C files) are used. Separate, specialised macros were preferred during the development of this implementation, but these can be easily written as functions inside one single .C file if desired. Note also that, as the file extension implies, these ROOT macros were written in C++, but the default ROOT installation allows to write macros in either C++ or Python (called 'PyROOT') with the same functionalities, only importing ROOT and using the appropriate language syntax, so these macros could also be included in the Python script if desired.

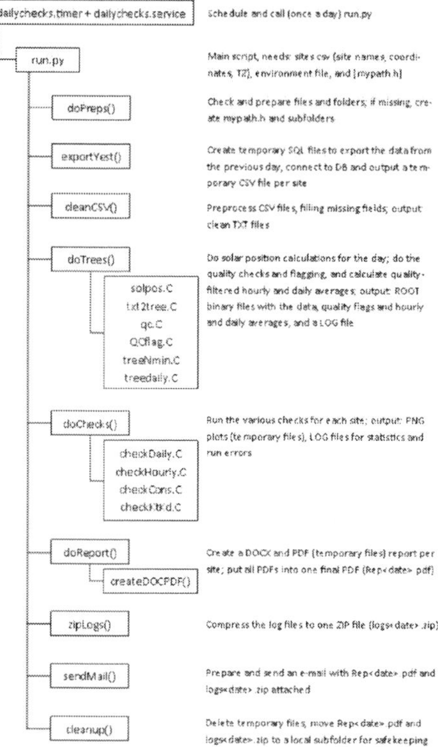

Figure 1: Structure and code components of the automated quality assessment reporting workflow.

2.3 Contents of the report

To provide a good amount of useful information in a clear and succinct way, a one-page-per-station report was designed, containing numerical and visual information that can be interpreted in one quick view.

Figure 2 shows an example page of one site's report. At the top of the page, the station and date are included; note that this date corresponds to the analysed data –when run automatically, the report of a day is done on the next day, but the main script can be run manually too and a specific date can be requested. Then, the page is divided into four sections: from the top, the first two sections give a view on the number and quality of collected measurements (with one-minute data, a day should contain 1440 entries for each irradiance), and the other two sections provide insights on the most common reasons for data quality failures. More details on each section are given in the following paragraphs.

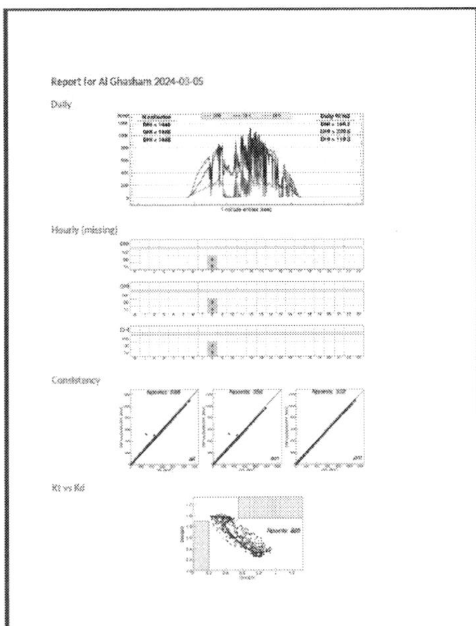

Figure 2: Sample report page for one station. The date corresponds to the analysed data.

"Daily"

The minute-by-minute profiles of each irradiance are plotted through the day, before any quality filtering; missing entries (i.e. not collected up to the time of reporting) are plotted with a value of -99, so they can be clearly identified (the bottom of the graph is below zero for this reason). In addition, the total number of minutes collected per irradiance (maximum of 1440) is shown, as well as the daily irradiance averages. The daily averages are calculated after removing daytime entries that fail the quality checks, which are applied to the one-minute records and based on the BSRN recommendations [1] and on the "Kt vs Kd" check (see section further below), so any missing daily averages (marked with value -99 and highlighted in red for easier identification) can indicate an insufficient number of collected entries and/or of good-quality entries. In the implementation shown here, if 15% or more of the daytime entries (from sunrise to sunset) fail the quality checks, the daily average is set to missing.

Figure 3 shows an example in which some entries were not collected (18 minutes, obtained by subtracting the collected entries, 1422, from 1440); although enough daytime entries were collected, the daily averages of DNI and DHI in this example are reported as missing (due to bad data quality, which can be seen from other parts of the report; in the daily graph one can see that DNI was zero and DHI was equal to GHI for a large part of the morning).

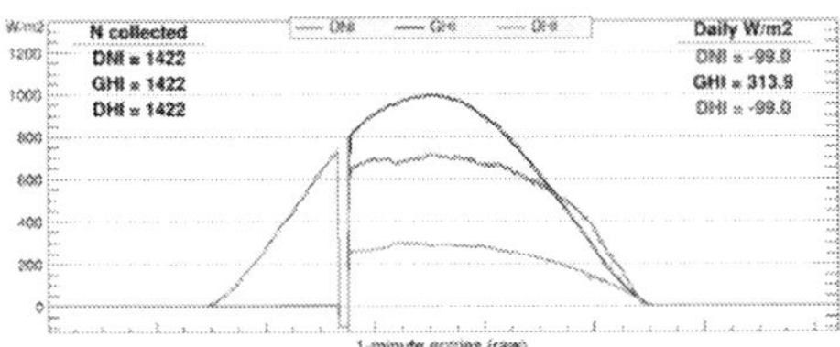

Figure 3: Example of daily section with some non-collected entries and missing daily averages.

"Hourly (missing)"

For each irradiance, the hourly averages are calculated after quality filtering of the 1-minute entries. If more than 50% of the entries in any given hour are missing (either not collected or quality-rejected), the average of that hour is set to missing (red-coloured box). The plots in this section show the following, for each irradiance and per hour (each box is one hour; the hours are given at the bottom of the graphs):
- In the top row, the hours in which the hourly average is missing are highlighted in red.
- "N/C" row: number of (one-minute) entries that were not collected.
- "QC" row: number of entries that failed the quality checks.
- "Tot": the sum of N/C and QC.

Hours with missing entries, i.e., Tot>0, are highlighted in light red, and a darker red when the hourly average is missing (Tot>30). Figure 4 shows an example, for the same site and day of Figure 3; this figure clarifies that the 18 uncollected minutes were: six at 8 am and twelve at 9 am (from Figures 3 and 4 one can conclude that these minutes are consecutive from 8:55 to 9:12). In addition, the DNI and DHI minutes before those (and starting from sunrise), although collected, failed the quality checks.

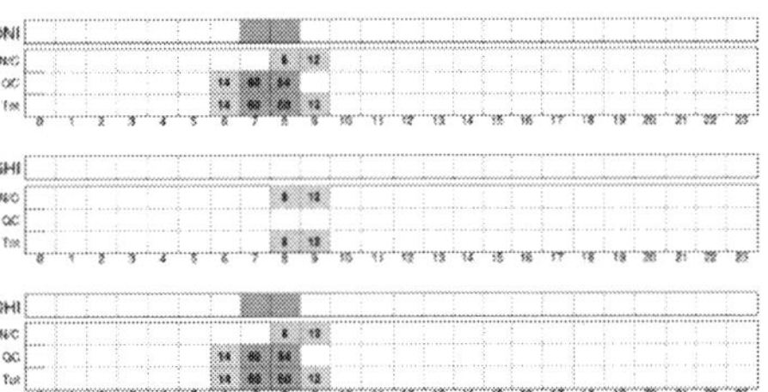

Figure 4: Hourly section with some missing entries and hourly averages.

"Consistency"

To help understand quality-rejected data, this section shows graphs of measured GHI vs calculated GHI = DHI + DNI*cos(SunZenithAngle) during daytime. Ideally, all points should be close to the red 1-to-1 line, and large deviations are flagged as bad quality. The graph on the left side (labelled "all") contains all daytime entries, while the other two ("am" and "pm") contain only the data before / after noon (defined in this graph as 12:00 pm, not solar noon). The example in Figure 5, for the same data as Figures 3 and 4, does not appear to show important issues (but the gap in the morning is visible) in this case.

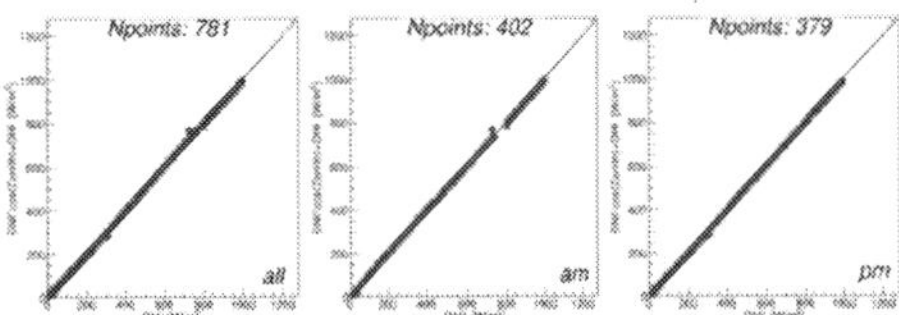

Figure 5: Consistency between measured and calculated GHI. "all" contains all daytime minutes; "am" and "pm" show the minutes before and after 12:00 pm, respectively.

"Kt vs Kd"

Plot of the relation between the clearness index Kt = GHI/ETh (where ETh is the top-of-the-atmosphere global horizontal irradiance) and the diffuse fraction $Kd = DHI/GHI$ for one-minute data. Here, one can define regions where few or no data points should be seen under normal conditions; these exclusion areas are highlighted in red, and any points inside the high-Kt-high-Kd zone are marked as bad quality (since they represent sun tracker issues, see [2]) and thus excluded from the hourly and daily average calculations. Figure 6 shows an example, for the same data as Figures 3-5, showing the reason for the rejected entries that caused the missing hourly and daily averages.

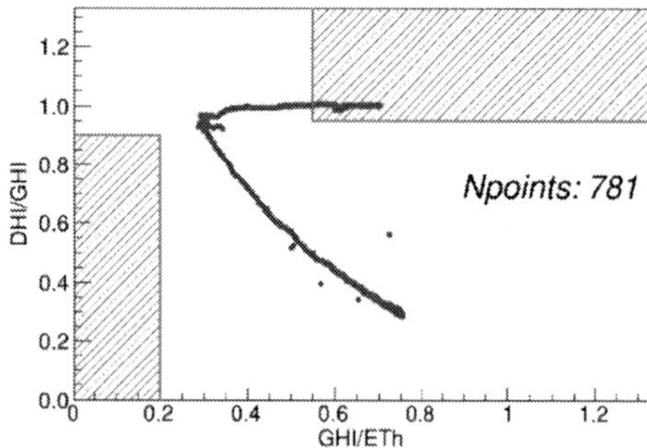

Figure 6: Kt (GHI/ETh) vs Kd (DHI/GHI) test. The red zones mark areas where few (or none) points should be normally seen; all points inside the top-right area are flagged as bad quality.

2.4 Emailing

Using the smtplib and email Python packages, an email is prepared containing, as attachments, the two files described in step 7 of Section 2.2. The email's body is simple text with the date of the report, and the same date is also specified in the email's subject. This automation requires an SMTP email server that supports such scripted use, and the specifics depend on the server; with Gmail, for example, simply providing valid credentials for an existing Gmail account used to be enough, but since the year 2023 the use of "App Passwords" has been mandatory, with additional configuration needed on the email account.

3 CONCLUSIONS

In this work, an automated data processing and reporting pipeline was developed to assess the collection and quality of solar radiation measurements. The output of the system is a (daily in the implementation presented here) report that provides a quick understanding of the collected measurements by identifying errors related to the collection, acquisition, or even some of the most commonly seen instrument and operation defects. From the first section of the report, i.e. the daily profile of the time series of the irradiances, one can visually review the data and inspect them in an easy way to identify the most evident problems quickly, including data not collected and anomalous profiles. In the next sections, more details about the found problems can be determined, such as the times of missing data due to communication issue or due to bad quality of the data, as well as their effect on aggregated averages, and some common issues can be identified on specific components (tracking, misalignment, etc.), to aid in planning and taking the

necessary corrective actions. Although the implementation shown here was developed for a specific use-case, the components can be adapted to other scenarios with different components and even data other than solar radiation.

4 ACKNOWLEDGMENT

Research reported in this work was supported by the Qatar Research Development and Innovation Council (Grant: ARG01-0523-230304). The content is solely the responsibility of the authors and does not necessarily represent the official views of Qatar Research Development and Innovation Council.

5 REFERENCES

[1] Long, C.N., Dutton, E.G., 2002. BSRN Global Network recommended QC tests, V2.0. Available online at http://epic.awi.de/30083/1/BSRN_recommended_QC_tes ts_V2.pdf, last access 2025-09-11

[2] Perez-Astudillo, D., Bachour, D., Martin-Pomares, L. Improved Quality Control Protocols on Solar Radiation Measurements. Solar Energy 169, 425–433 (2018). DOI:10.1016/j.solener.2018.05.028

HOW COMPLEX ARE SATELLITE-BASED IRRADIATION DATA?
FROM GLOBAL AVERAGES TO LOCATION-SPECIFIC ACCURACY

Philippe Malcorps
3E
Quai à la Chaux, 6 - 1000 Bruxelles - Belgium
pma@3e.eu
+32 485 72 99 34

Anastasia Dagla
3E
ada@3e.eu

Gofran Chowdhury
3E
gch@3e.eu

ABSTRACT: **3E irradiation data** is a service that **provides satellite-based solar resource data**. These data are derived from meteorological geostationary satellites using the Cloud Physical Properties (CPP) algorithm developed by the Royal Dutch Meteorological Institute. While it is demonstrated that the **accuracy of such data varies strongly depending on the location, global average numbers are still often applied** in long-term yield assessments and solar plant performance analyses. We aim to change that by systematically **studying the factors that impact this accuracy**. Using a dedicated validation framework, we benchmark our satellite-based data against more than 900 ground measurement sites worldwide. We then combine these results with statistical models to identify **which complexity factors matter most** and to predict the **expected accuracy at any given location**. The outcome is a set of global maps of accuracy, providing transparency on how reliable satellite-based irradiance data are, wherever you are on Earth.
Keywords: solar, resource, irradiance, accuracy

1   AIM AND APPROACH

3E irradiation data support long-term PV yield assessments and operational performance analysis. Although accuracy is known to vary locally, industry practice often relies on global averages. We aim to quantify accuracy as a function of location-specific complexity factors.

Since 2016, 3E has produced **near-real-time satellite-based irradiation data** using the CPP algorithm, which converts retrieved cloud properties into surface irradiance through a physics-based radiative transfer model. Data from four geostationary satellite series are processed every 10–15 minutes, covering most of the globe.

To **validate these data**, we built a dedicated framework that standardizes, parses, and quality-controls ground-based irradiation measurements. More than 900 sites are included, of which 426 passed quality and overlap filters (Figure 1). Validation metrics include the Normalized Mean Bias Error (NMBE) and the Normalized Root Mean Square Error (NRMSE) at multiple temporal resolutions.

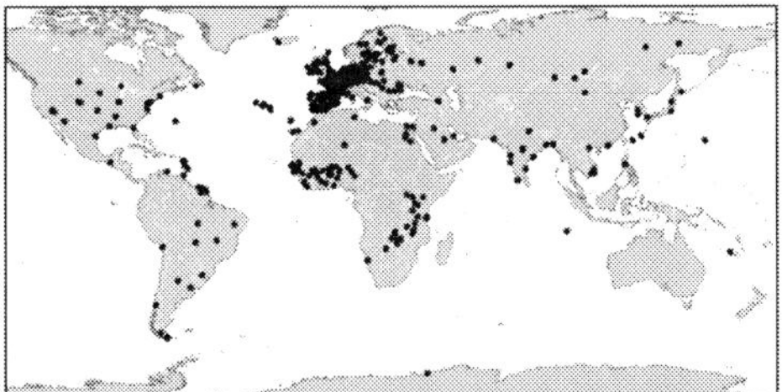

Figure 1: Validation sites used in the analysis (426)

Beyond benchmarking, we extracted **complexity factors** (climate type, terrain class, elevation, cloudiness, etc.) for each site and applied **machine learning models** (Random Forest, XGBoost, Linear Regression, etc.). These models were trained (80%) and tested (20%) to identify the most influential factors and **to predict expected accuracy depending on location**. The best-performing models were then applied to a global $1° \times 1°$ grid, where complexity factors were extracted and interpolated into global accuracy maps.

2   SCIENTIFIC INNOVATION AND RELEVANCE

This study innovates in several aspects:
- **Scale**: A unique validation framework combining >900 ground stations worldwide.
- **Methodology**: Moving beyond visual inspection, we statistically quantify how complexity factors influence accuracy.
- **Predictive modeling**: Machine learning models provide site-specific expected accuracy for NMBE, NRMSE daily, and NRMSE hourly.
- **Transparency**: For the first time, global maps of accuracy are produced, enabling users to anticipate how reliable satellite-based irradiance data will be at any given location.

Ultimately, this approach improves the robustness of long-term PV yield assessments, reduces uncertainty in financing and risk analysis, and supports operational decision-making with location-specific confidence levels.

3 RESULTS

From the 426 validated sites, overall results are consistent with other satellite-based irradiation providers (Table I). However, standard deviations across sites confirm that accuracy varies significantly with local conditions.

Table I: Overall validation results

Validation metric [%]	# of sites	Median	Mean	Standard Deviation
NMBE	426	1.22	1.9	3.69
NRMSE hourly	189	17.12	18.12	6.32
NRMSE daily	426	8.32	9.71	4
NRMSE monthly	426	4	5.06	3.35
NRMSE yearly	426	2.54	3.55	3.25

Using machine learning models, we identified the most influential complexity factors for three key metrics (NMBE, NRMSE daily, NRMSE hourly). XGBoost and Random Forest consistently performed best, achieving higher predictive skill (R^2, RMSE, CV RMSE) than linear models (e.g., Table II).

Table II: Model performance comparison (NRMSE daily)

Model	R^2 Score	RMSE	CV RMSE
Random Forest	0.719	3.784	3.604
XGBoost	0.714	3.822	3.560
Gradient Boosting	0.693	3.955	3.557
Ridge	0.534	4.876	4.442
Linear Regression	0.532	4.888	4.449
Lasso	0.528	4.909	4.496
ElasticNet	0.525	4.923	4.513

Feature importance analysis revealed that cloudiness, distance to satellite nadir, elevation, and terrain indices are among the strongest drivers of accuracy (e.g., Figure 2).

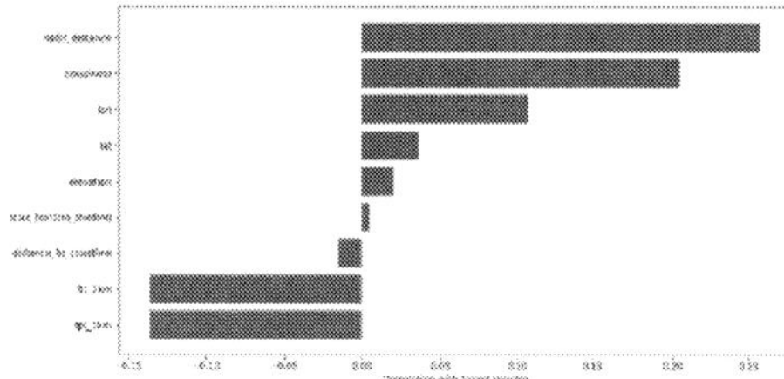

Figure 2: Feature importance analysis (NRMSE daily)

Applying the best-performing models to a global $1° \times 1°$ grid allowed us to calculate expected accuracy values worldwide. Interpolation of these results produced global maps that reveal how accuracy changes regionally and globally (Figure 3).

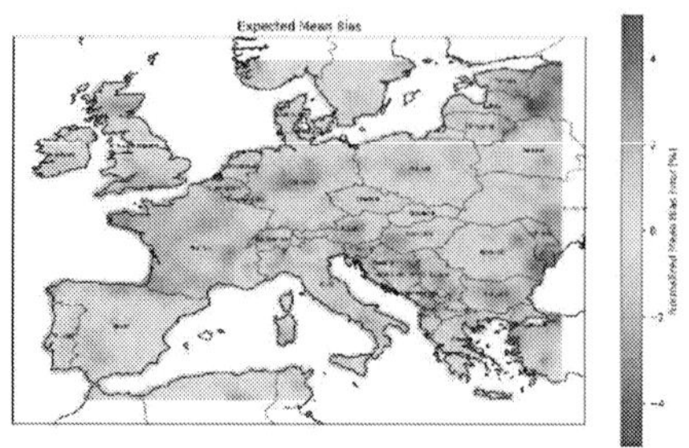

Figure 3: Expected mean bias in Europe (NMBE)

4 CONCLUSIONS

Rather than relying on global averages, **we now provide location-specific expected accuracy**. This represents a step-change for PV project developers, investors, and operators, who can now assess solar resource uncertainty with unprecedented transparency.

How Complex Are Satellite-Based Irradiation Data?
From Global Averages to Location-Specific Accuracy

Philippe Malcorps (3E)
pma@3e.eu
+32 485 72 99 34

Gofran Chowdhury (3E)
gch@3e.eu
+32 466 11 42 60

The Problem

- Satellite-based irradiation data = key for PV yield assessments
- But... accuracy varies a lot from place to place
- Current practice: use global averages → hides local errors

NMBE (%)

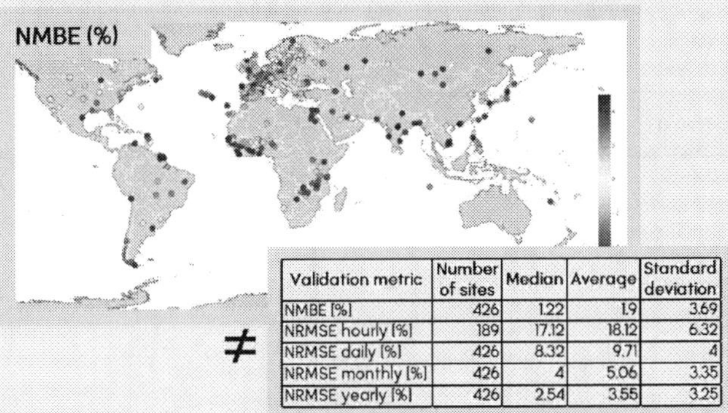

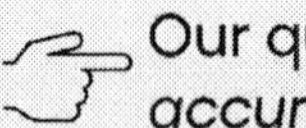

Validation metric	Number of sites	Median	Average	Standard deviation
NMBE [%]	426	1.22	1.9	3.69
NRMSE hourly [%]	189	17.12	18.12	6.32
NRMSE daily [%]	426	8.32	9.71	4
NRMSE monthly [%]	426	4	5.06	3.35
NRMSE yearly [%]	426	2.54	3.55	3.25

Our question: *Can we predict accuracy at any location?*

The Data

- 900+ ground stations worldwide
- Quality-controlled & standardized measurements
- Validation metrics: NMBE (bias), NRMSE daily, and NRMSE hourly
- Result: Large variability → driven by local factors (climate, terrain, elevation, cloudiness...)

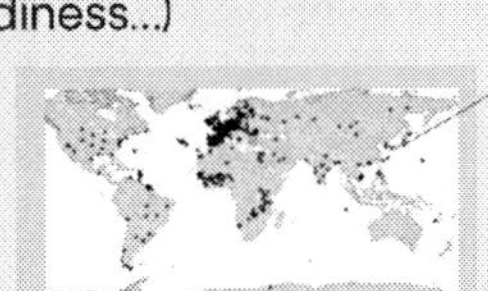
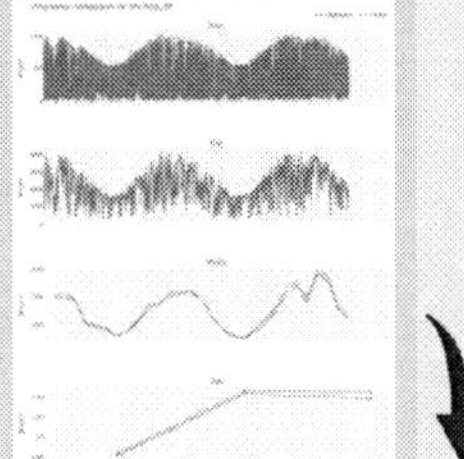
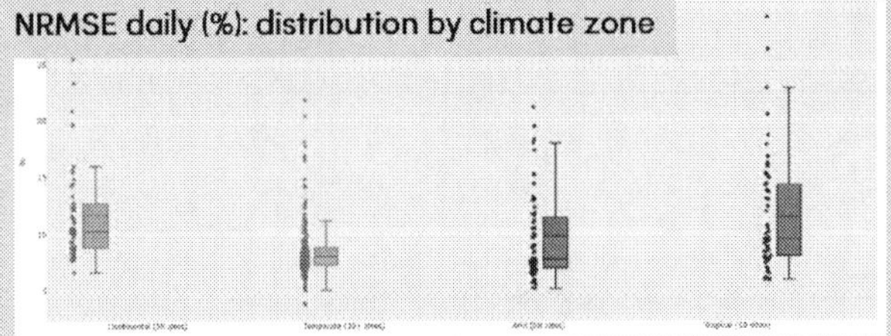

NRMSE daily (%): distribution by climate zone

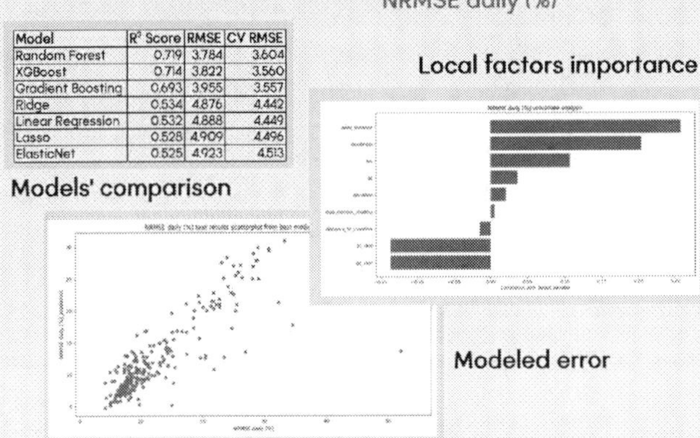
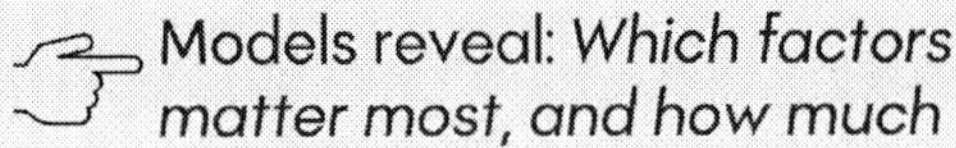

The Approach

We built models to predict accuracy:
- Machine Learning & Statistical Models (RF, XGBoost, Linear Regression...)
- 80% training / 20% testing
- For each metric, best model is selected by R^2, RMSE, CV RMSE

NRMSE daily (%)

Model	R^2 Score	RMSE	CV RMSE
Random Forest	0.719	3.784	3.604
XGBoost	0.714	3.822	3.560
Gradient Boosting	0.693	3.955	3.557
Ridge	0.534	4.876	4.442
Linear Regression	0.532	4.888	4.449
Lasso	0.528	4.909	4.496
ElasticNet	0.525	4.923	4.513

Local factors importance

Models' comparison

Modeled error

Models reveal: *Which factors matter most, and how much*

The Results

- Key complexity factors identified
- Best models applied on a 1° global grid
- Extracted factors at each point → predicted accuracy
- Interpolated into global maps of expected accuracy

Modeled mean bias based on local factors

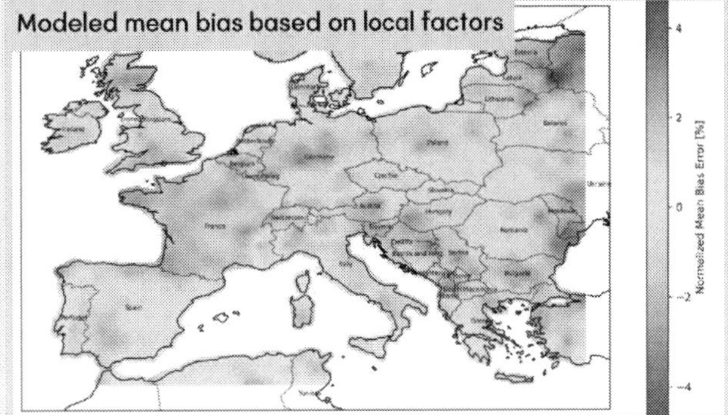
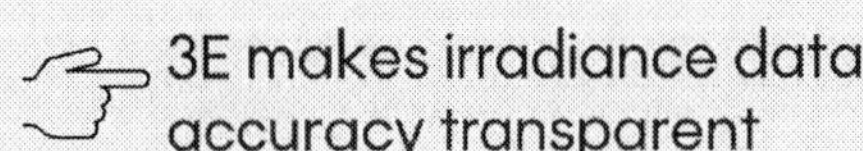

"Not just how accurate – but where accurate."

Why It Matters

- Location-specific accuracy = better PV yield assessments
- More confidence in bankability & risk analysis
- Improved performance monitoring worldwide

3E makes irradiance data accuracy transparent

EVALUATION OF MCCLEAR CLEAR SKY MODEL UNDER DUSTY CONDITIONS

Dunia A. Bachour[a], Daniel Perez-Astudillo[a], Abdulwahab Ziaullah[a]
[a] Qatar Environment & Energy Research Institute, P.O.Box 34110, Doha, Qatar.
dbachour@hbku.edu.qa, dastudillo@hbku.edu.qa, awahab@hbku.edu.qa

ABSTRACT: Clear-sky models play a crucial role in simulating solar radiation at the Earth's surface under cloudless conditions, with applications in several areas. For instance, clear-sky models help determine the maximum potential output of solar energy systems and calculate atmospheric indices which measure the atmospheric clarity and turbidity. In addition, these models are crucial for estimating the solar radiation from satellite images, providing the upper limits for irradiance under clear-sky conditions, before considering the cloud modelling. Clear-sky models also support quality control of solar data and can be used as reference to validate other models, such as transposition and decomposition models under clear-sky scenarios. A wide range of clear-sky models are described in scientific literature. This work examines commonly used clear-sky models for solar resource assessment, focusing on their performance in a region characterized by high aerosol concentrations. Specifically, the McClear model is compared to the Simple Model for the Atmospheric Radiative Transfer of Sunshine (SMARTS-2), and the European Solar Radiation Atlas (ESRA) model. The evaluation is conducted using days with varied aerosol content, including instances of significant atmospheric dust. Sun photometer aerosol-derived data and ground-based solar radiation measurements are used as inputs and to assess the performance of the models, respectively.
Keywords: Clear-sky, McClear, SMARTS2, DNI, AOD

1 INTRODUCTION

Modelling clear-sky irradiance is essential in solar energy analysis, as it establishes the theoretical maximum solar irradiance that can reach the Earth's surface in the absence of clouds. Clear-sky models play several vital roles in the field of solar energy analysis. They serve as a reference point for the design and simulation of solar energy systems, enabling precise estimation of the energy output potential under optimal atmospheric conditions. Furthermore, clear-sky irradiance is fundamental for atmospheric characterisation, as it allows for the calculation of indices such as clarity and turbidity, which assess the transparency and aerosol content present in the atmosphere. In terms of data integrity, these models act as a benchmark in solar resource assessment by aiding in the identification of measurement errors and outliers, achieved by comparing observed readings with expected values during cloudless periods. Additionally, clear-sky models are indispensable for verifying and validating the accuracy of solar irradiance models. Lastly, most satellite-based solar radiation models, first establish clear-sky irradiance estimates before adjusting for cloud effects using satellite observations.

A wide range of clear-sky models are described in scientific literature, and they are typically categorized by their approach. Empirical and parametric models estimate clear-sky solar irradiance using simplified statistical approaches based on key atmospheric inputs such as aerosol turbidity, ozone, water vapor, and solar geometry. In contrast physical models provide robust but computationally demanding calculations, by solving the radiative transfer equation to provide spectrally resolved irradiance that accounts for molecular absorption, scattering, aerosols, ozone, and water vapor. Hybrid parametric–physical models achieve a practical balance between accuracy and efficiency by combining radiative transfer simulations with parameterizations or look-up tables, making them suitable for operational and near real-time solar radiation modelling with acceptable accuracy but at significantly lower computational cost.

The clear-sky models evaluated in this work are selected from these three categories. The ESRA model [1] is an empirical clear-sky model based on the Linke turbidity factor, widely used in Europe and in known PV tools due to its simplicity and low input requirements, though its accuracy depends strongly on turbidity climatology. McClear [2] is a hybrid parametric–physical model derived from libRadtran simulations, using multiple inputs from the Copernicus Atmosphere Monitoring Service (CAMS) database to accurately model the effect of different aerosol types, and atmospheric constituents. It offers global applicability and near real-time data, making it central to operational services. In contrast, SMARTS2 [3] is a full radiative transfer model, capable of high spectral resolution and accuracy for irradiance under clear skies, often used as a reference tool for solar energy studies and applications, but computationally more demanding than ESRA or McClear.

2 METHODOLOGY

2.1 Data Used

The study is conducted in Doha, Qatar (25.32° N, 51,425° E). Minute-resolution data for direct normal irradiance (DNI, hereafter denoted as G_b), global horizontal irradiance (GHI), and diffuse horizontal irradiance (DHI) are collected with a solar radiation monitoring station equipped with thermopile sensors. Ground-based aerosol optical depth (AOD) measurements are obtained using a sun photometer, focusing on the 500 nm channel to ensure consistency with satellite-derived data and to accurately capture atmospheric scattering properties.

2.2 Model Inputs and Sources

To estimate clear-sky irradiance G_{bn} using the ESRA model, Equation 1 is applied, where G_0 represents the extraterrestrial irradiance on a plane perpendicular to the sun, TL is the Linke Turbidity factor, m is the relative optical air mass, and δ_R is the Rayleigh optical thickness for a standard atmosphere. A Linke turbidity value of 1 is used to determine the maximum direct irradiance component, representing an ideal clear atmosphere without aerosols or water vapor. This value is then adjusted using the AOD values obtained from sun photometer measurements to calculate the ESRA clear-sky irradiance, $G_{bn(ESRA)}$.

$$G_{bn} = G_0 \times \exp(-0.8662 \times TL \times m \times \delta_R \times AOD) \quad (Eq.1)$$

The SMARTS-2 clear-sky model is used in this study with fixed input parameters for atmospheric pressure (1013.25 mb), ozone abundance (0.34), altitude (20 m), precipitable water content (1.42 cm), CO_2 concentration (370 ppmv), and desert aerosol types representative of conditions in Doha. However, local AOD values at 500 nm were utilized to reflect site-specific aerosol conditions, with AOD data extracted from both the sun photometer and from the Copernicus CAMS database. These local AOD values are incorporated to generate broadband (280 to 4000 nm) irradiance outputs. The solar position values, including sun-earth distance correction, solar zenith, and solar azimuth angles, are updated for each simulation run.

For McClear, site-specific clear-sky irradiances Gb McClear were retrieved from the CAMS Radiation Service v4.6, which provides all-sky irradiation estimates.

2.3 Case Study

Two representative periods from the year 2022 were selected for analysis: November, which typically exhibits clearer skies, and May, characterized by higher turbidity. These periods allow for an effective comparison of model performance under distinct atmospheric conditions.

2.4 Validation and Comparison

To assess model accuracy and establish ground truth, measured and estimated irradiance values under clear-sky conditions were compared across different levels of AOD.

3 RESULTS

Figure 1 presents the daily mean AOD for the months under study (blue points), with error bars showing the standard deviation (σ) for each day (red vertical lines). Based on Figure 1, selected days spanning a range of AOD values were chosen for clear-sky models evaluation.

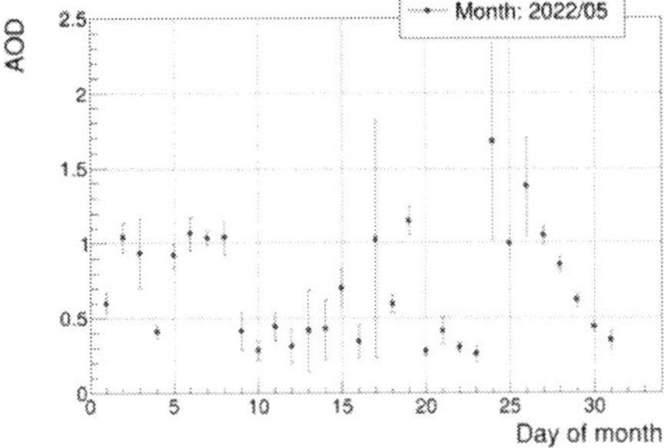

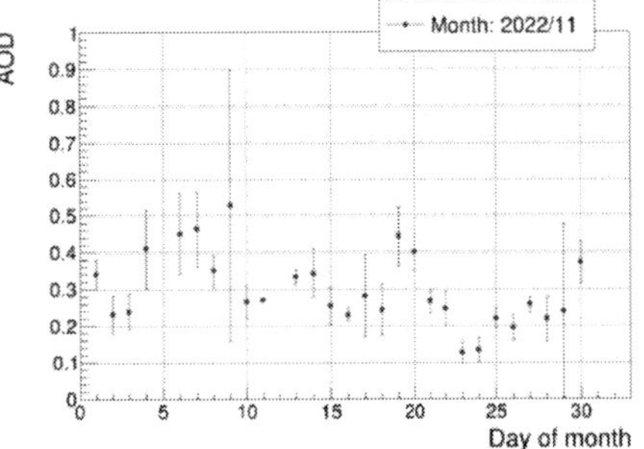

Figure. 1: Daily mean AOD with intra-day variability for 2022/05 (top) and 2022/11 (bottom)

Figures 2 and 3 compare the models with measurements for May and November, respectively, on days with distinct AOD conditions: 4 May (0.41 ± 0.04), 23 May (0.26 ± 0.05), 24 May (1.67 ± 0.65), 17 Nov (0.28 ± 0.11), 19 Nov (0.44 ± 0.08), and 23 Nov (0.13 ± 0.03).

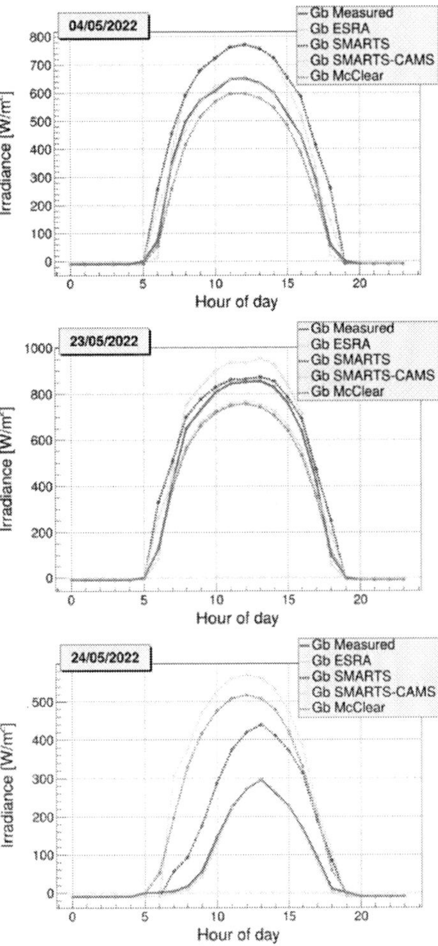

Figure. 2: Daily Gb profiles for different clear-sky models versus measured values on various days in May 2022.

On May 4th the SMARTS2 model, using CAMS-derived AOD data, most closely matches the measured clear-sky irradiance, followed by the McClear model. The mean AOD for this day is moderate (0.41) with limited variability, providing relatively stable atmospheric conditions. In contrast, the SMARTS2 and ESRA models using ground-based AOD at 500 nm overestimate the irradiance compared to measurements. This overestimation is likely because a single-wavelength AOD does not account for other atmospheric constituents—such as dust layers or fog—that also attenuate solar radiation and are common in May. These additional effects are not captured by ground-based AOD at 500 nm but are better assimilated by the CAMS data, which incorporates multiple wavelengths and atmospheric parameters. On May 23, AOD value is low and stable, the SMARTS2 physical model utilizing ground-based AOD closely matches the measured data. In contrast, both McClear and SMARTS2 using CAMS AOD data underestimate DNI, likely due to an underestimation of AOD in the input data. May 24, characterised by a high AOD (1.67) value and significant fluctuation (0.65). Under these conditions, the ESRA model scaled the irradiance using the provided hourly ground AOD. Since ESRA does not require detailed assumptions regarding aerosol type, spectrum, or vertical profile, it is less affected by potential errors in aerosol optical properties compared to SMARTS2. The SMARTS2 model overestimated the irradiance, likely due to its reliance on spectrally resolved AOD (not limited to 500 nm) and more comprehensive information about aerosol models, such as single scattering albedo, asymmetry parameter, and size distribution. This information becomes particularly important when there is high variability, contrary to the input provided in this instance with only 500 nm AOD and a default aerosol type. As a result, SMARTS2 extrapolated extinction across the spectrum based on assumed Ångström exponents and standard optical properties, which may have led to errors at this high AOD level. This is why SMARTS2 generally followed the measured curve but consistently overestimated values throughout the day. CAMS-based models (McClear, SMARTS2+CAMS) did not perform as well, as CAMS did not capture the magnitude or variability of the high-AOD event, and the input data used may have been smoothed to accurately reflect local conditions.

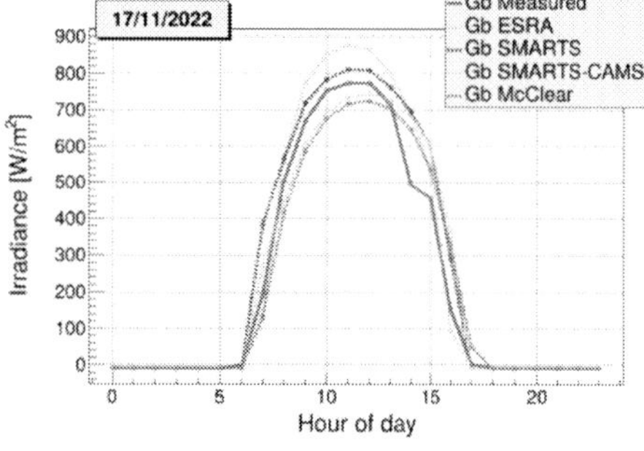

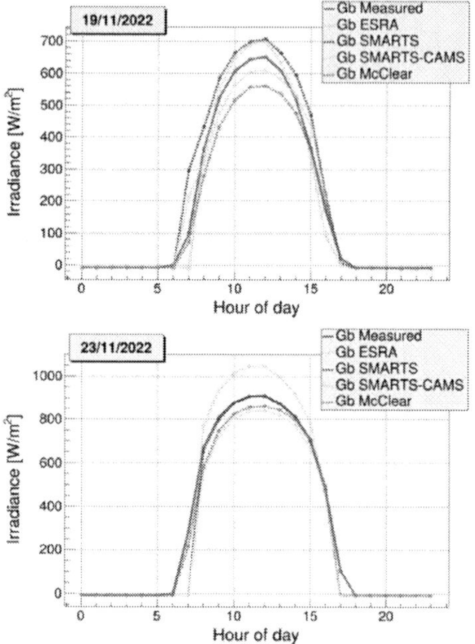

Figure. 3: Daily Gb profiles for different clear-sky models versus measured values on various days in Nov 2022.

For the selected November days, CAMS-based models, McClear and SMARTS2+AOD-CAMS, consistently underestimate the irradiance. On November 17, with low AOD and relatively moderate fluctuations, none of the models performed ideally, though SMARTS2 with ground-based AOD yielded the closest match. This can be attributed to SMARTS2's use of actual ground AOD, which proves most valuable under moderate variability, even if only single-wavelength data are available. In contrast, the ESRA model's broadband parameterization performed poorly with fluctuating aerosol. On November 19, with moderately high but stable AOD, both ESRA and SMARTS2 models overestimated irradiance at high irradiance levels, with somewhat different behavior at lower irradiance. This is due to the limited input information (500 nm AOD), which leads both models to underperform. Finally, on November 23, characterized by very low and stable AOD, ESRA overestimated irradiance as it does not consider molecular extinction. By contrast, SMARTS2 performed better, explicitly resolving Rayleigh scattering and gaseous absorption.

4   CONCLUSIONS

Clear-sky irradiance modelling is essential for accurate assessment, validation, and analysis of solar energy resource data, supporting both ground-based and satellite-based analyses. The comparative analysis presented in this work demonstrates that the accuracy of clear-sky irradiance models is strongly dependent on the prevailing aerosol regime. ESRA benefits from its simplicity under turbid and highly variable conditions, where direct scaling with ground-based AOD allows it to follow DNI reductions more effectively, but it systematically overestimates irradiance under clear skies because it does not explicitly represent molecular absorption (ozone, water vapor, mixed gases), for which the effect becomes relatively more important when aerosol levels are low. SMARTS2, in contrast, performs best specially when the input data are correct. Under low-AOD conditions, where SMARTS2 explicitly treats Rayleigh scattering and gaseous absorption yield good agreement with measurements. However, when AOD is higher, the underperformance of SMARTS2 in the studied case is attributed to incomplete input information, particularly the limited availability of aerosol spectral and microphysical data. CAMS-based models for the days studied here consistently underestimate irradiance, reflecting biases in CAMS AOD and in capturing short-term local variability. The results presented here demonstrate that clear-sky model suitability in high aerosol loads conditions depends on atmospheric conditions and highlight the importance of combining approaches according to the dominant aerosol regime. Using single-wavelength AOD data presents limitations, as it may neglect other atmospheric effects, such as larger particles or water droplets in fog, that also contribute to solar radiation attenuation. Furthermore, rapid fluctuations in AOD or missing parameters, like water vapor content and Ångström exponent, can diminish model accuracy on specific days, particularly during events involving dust or fog that are common in the study region. The analysis highlights the added value of multisource data. Models that incorporate comprehensive datasets, such as CAMS, benefit from assimilating information across multiple wavelengths and sources, allowing for a more complete representation of the atmospheric profile, leading to improved irradiance modelling in some complex and variable conditions.

5   REFERENCES

[1] C. Rigollier, O. Bauer, L. Wald, (2000). On the clear sky model of the ESRA – European Solar Radiation Atlas – with respect to the Heliosat method. Solar Energy, 68(1), 33-48. https://doi.org/10.1016/S0038-092X(99)00055-9

[2] M. Lefèvre, A. Oumbe, P. Blanc, B. Espinar, B. Gschwind, Z. Qu, L. Wald, M. Schroedter-Homscheidt, C, Hoyer-Klick, A, Arola, A. Benedetti, J.W. Kaiser, J.J. Morcrette, (2013). McClear: A new model estimating downwelling solar radiation at ground level in clear-sky conditions. Solar Energy, 94, 360–374. https://doi.org/10.1016/j.solener.2013.05.008

[3] C.A. Gueymard (2001). Parameterized transmittance model for direct beam and circumsolar spectral irradiance. Solar Energy, 71(5), 325–346. https://doi.org/10.1016/S0038-092X(01)00054-8

Weather and Air Quality Effects on Photovoltaic System Efficiency: A Modeling Approach

Carrillo Mejía, Luis
Universidad Distrital Francisco José de Caldas
lcarrillom@udistrital.edu.co

PhD Gaona García, Elvis Eduardo
Universidad Distrital Francisco José de Caldas
egaona@udistrital.edu.co

PhD Hernández Mora, Johann Alexander
Universidad Distrital Francisco José de Caldas
jahernandezm@udistrital.edu.co

Abstract — **This paper aims to evaluate the performance of different machine learning algorithms for predicting the instantaneous efficiency of photovoltaic systems. The study utilized a dataset collected over seven months from seven distinct geographical locations characterized by diverse climatological conditions representative of the Colombian territory. The dataset included solar irradiance, climatological variables, air quality variables, and measured active power. Instantaneous efficiency was calculated from these data and defined as the study's target variable. An initial descriptive statistical analysis was performed to characterize the dataset. Subsequently, various prediction algorithms were executed and evaluated using standard error metrics. The evaluation demonstrated that incorporating air quality variables improved the predictive accuracy across all evaluated models. A key finding from the correlation analysis and feature importance assessment is the negative association between higher levels of environmental pollution and instantaneous efficiency.**

Key Words — *Photovoltaic system, efficiency forecast, machine learning model, weather variables, pollution variables.*

I. INTRODUCTION

According to [1], as the use of traditional fossil fuels becomes more widespread, the issues of resource depletion and environmental pollution are becoming increasingly severe. Consequently, photovoltaic (PV) energy has gained global popularity due to its advantages: it is clean, non-polluting, and facilitates easy distribution. As [2] mentions, this has made photovoltaic power plants more competitive compared to fossil fuel plants in recent years. However, the fluctuating nature of solar irradiance and varying climatic and geographical conditions makes energy generation unpredictable, thereby affecting the performance of solar plants and the electrical grid.

Consequently, photovoltaic power prediction is a vital tool for solar plant operators and managers. It helps them avoid penalties for discrepancies between actual and desired photovoltaic power generation and allows for the evaluation of a location's suitability for solar plant installation during the planning stage, as noted in [3]. A large number of prediction models based on neural networks exist, which use climatic data (temperature, wind speed, relative humidity, and air pressure), irradiance, and panel soiling from various global locations. For example, [4] details a power generation prediction model using wavelet decomposition for Salento, Italy. Similarly, [5] proposes a model that uses a Feedforward Neural Network (FFNN) to predict the efficiency of a solar plant based on climatic variables and irradiance in Igdir, Turkey. Furthermore, [6] demonstrated that the efficiency of different types of solar panels in northern Nigeria is significantly impacted by the amount of dust on their surface. However, wind speed and rainfall had a cleaning effect on the soiling, indicating that panel cleaning schemes are necessary to prevent performance degradation. In the Sahara Desert of Algeria, [7] analyzed the performance and the soiling caused by dust on panels, finding a linear relationship between power loss and dirt accumulation.

The study's methodology comprised several stages. Initially, a seven-month dataset was consolidated from different geolocated sites. This dataset included irradiance variables (GHI, DNI, DHI), climatological variables (temperature, humidity, pressure, cloud cover, wind direction, and speed), and air quality variables (NH3, NO, NO2, CO, SO2, PM10, PM2.5). Instantaneous efficiency, calculated from the measured active power and other parameters, was defined as the target variable. A descriptive statistical analysis was conducted to explore the data properties. Subsequently, different machine learning algorithms were applied and evaluated for the prediction of instantaneous efficiency. Finally, a feature analysis was performed to determine which predictor variables had the greatest influence on predictive performance.

10.4229/EUPVSEC2025/4BV.3.20
020279-001

II.   METODOLOGY

A.   Data Collection

For data collection, a microservice was implemented to download data from various sources based on a time range and a geographical location. Accordingly, variables related to irradiance—GHI (Global Horizontal Irradiance), DHI (Diffuse Horizontal Irradiance), and DNI (Direct Normal Irradiance)—were downloaded from a NASA API [8]. As of the date of this writing, this API provided global data up to July 30, 2024, with a spatial resolution of $1°$ latitude x $1°$ longitude (approximately 12.3 km^2 near the equator and 8.7 km^2 at latitudes near $45°$). Data acquisition for this source is based on the processing of satellite imagery and atmospheric models.

Climatological and air quality variables were obtained via APIs from OpenWeather [9] y [10] respectively. These APIs provide data filters based on time range and geographical location, with data sourced from various origins including terrestrial weather stations, radar data, satellite observations, and proprietary models for air quality and climatic conditions. Finally, power generation data was extracted from PvOutput [11], a web platform where owners of photovoltaic systems share real-time and historical performance data. This platform exposes an API for the extraction of raw generated power data from various users.

Table 1, displays all the variables and their corresponding units of measurement.

Table 1. Dataset variables

Variable	Unit of measurement	Description of the variable
Datetime	Hour	
Latitude	Degrees	
Longitude	Degrees	
Temperature	Celsious degrees	
Wind_speed	meter/seg	
Wind_direction	Meteorological degrees	
Humedity	Percentage	
Pressure	Percentage	
Clouds	Percentage	
co	$\mu g/m^3$	Carbon monoxide
no	$\mu g/m^3$	Nitric oxide
no2	$\mu g/m^3$	Carbon dioxide
o3	$\mu g/m^3$	Ozone
so2	$\mu g/m^3$	Sulfur dioxide
nh3	$\mu g/m^3$	Ammonia
pm2.5	$\mu g/m^3$	Particulate matter 2.5
pm10	$\mu g/m^3$	Particulate matter 10
ghi	w/m^2	Global Horizontal Irradiance
dni	w/m^2	Direct Normal Irradiance
dhi	w/m^2	Diffuse Horizontal Irradiance
power	Watios	
ins_efficiency	Percentage	Instantaneous efficiency

From PvOutput, 12 photovoltaic systems were selected for the study. The selection criteria mandated that the systems have available manufacturer data, the number of installed panels, and tilt angle. Additionally, the selected sites needed to have a similar temperature profile to Colombia or be located within ±10 degrees of the equator. The purpose of this meticulous selection was to secure sufficient data for the calculation of panel efficiency and to apply a machine learning algorithm to the Colombian case study. Of the initial 12 systems, only seven were ultimately included in the study due to various data limitations with the remaining five.

Table 2, presents the geographical coordinates of the selected sites and the number of samples used in the study. The dates varied slightly for some locations but generally spanned from January 1, 2024, to July 31, 2024. The data resolution is hourly, resulting in a dataset with 22,475 samples.

Table 2. Samples per photovoltaic system selected

Location of the photovoltaic system	City	Samples
-38.380163,142.519164	Victoria, Australia	4211
-27.620304,153.127580	Brisbane, Australia	4277
-26.677141,-49.182458	Pomerode - Testo Salto, Brasil	4226
-17.878102,-41.507783	Teófilo Otoni, Brasil	2246
5.525135,72.842531	Maduvvari, Islas Malvinas	3968
34.170946,-118.366460	Los Angeles, EEUU	1278
40.884561,23.920283	Rodolivos, Grecia	2269

B.   Preprocessing

Initially, the instantaneous efficiency is calculated by applying Equation (1), as mentioned in [12] and [5]

$$\eta_{ins} = \frac{P_{ins}}{G_{in}*A_t} \tag{1}$$

Where P_{ins} corresponds to the measured instantaneous active power from PvOutput, G_{in}, is the instantaneous incident solar irradiance, and A_t is the total area of the photovoltaic installation. Additionally, if the global horizontal irradiance is less than 120 w/m^2, if the measurement is below the solar illumination threshold, the efficiency is set to zero. On the other hand, an efficiency exceeding 30% indicates an anomaly in the sample, and these samples are therefore removed from the dataset. Using this criterion, 1367 samples were eliminated. It is important to note that this preprocessing was conducted during the initial data ingestion phase, so the sample size remains as previously described.

The following columns are removed from the dataset: 'datetime', as a time-series analysis will not be performed. This is because a time-series approach would tie the selected algorithm to a specific time window and, more importantly, a particular location. It is proposed as future work to forecast each regressor based on a specific location and then use the model proposed herein. Consequently, 'latitude' and 'longitude' are also removed from the dataset. Finally, 'power' is also removed since this variable was used to calculate efficiency, and it would not be available in a planning case study.

C. Statistical Analysis

Fig 1 displays the distribution density of instantaneous efficiency. It is important to note that data points with zero instantaneous efficiency were removed, as they create a density spike that obscures other relevant peaks. The objective here is to validate these other peaks, revealing that when the system produces energy, it does so most frequently within a specific efficiency range. The primary peak is observed in the [5,12] interval, and the distribution does not follow a perfectly symmetric bell curve, which is characteristic of this variable.

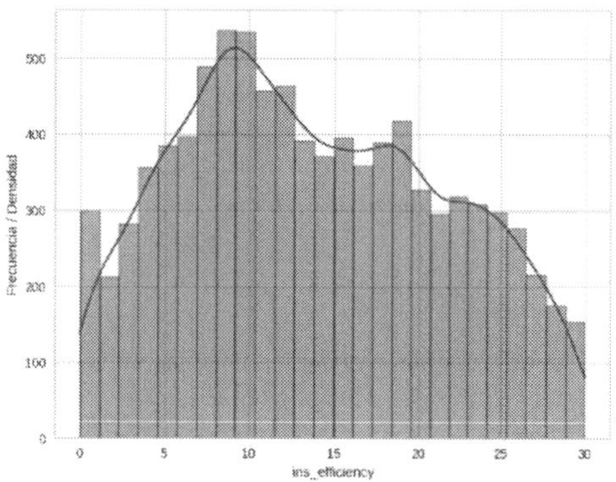

Fig 1. Distribution Density of Instantaneous Efficiency

The same analysis was conducted for each variable, revealing distributions that are not perfectly symmetrical. Fig 2 shows some of the distribution densities.

Heatmaps were generated to visualize the Pearson, Spearman, and Kendall correlations for the entire dataset, as shown in Fig 3. Additionally, these heatmaps were created for two specific locations, Rodolivos and Los Angeles, as shown in Fig 4, because the concentration of pollutants was highest at these sites.

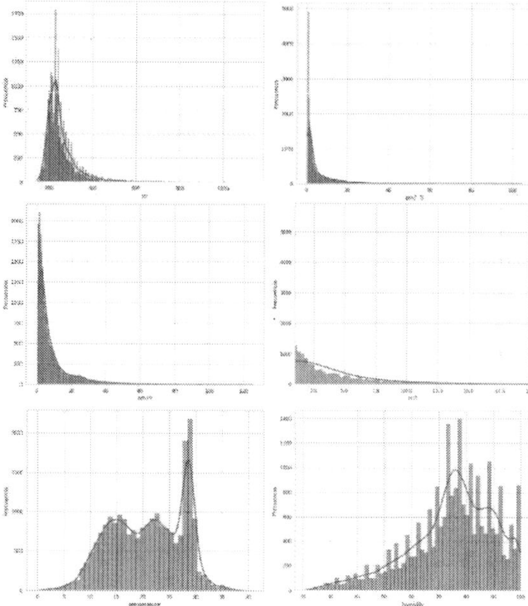

Fig 2. Distribution density for some of the variables under observation

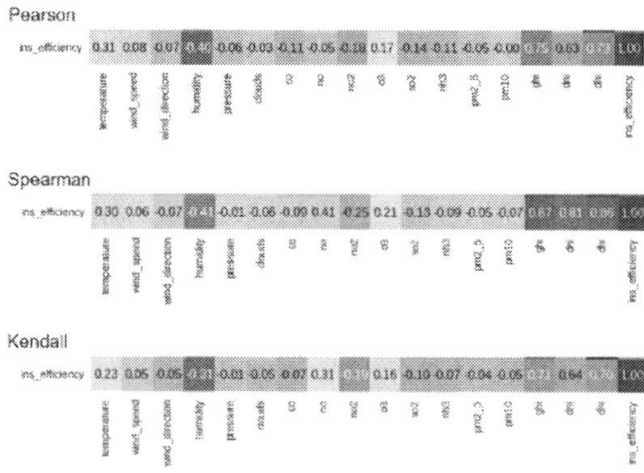

Fig 3. Heatmap of Correlations for the Entire Dataset

In these heatmaps, it can be seen that the air quality variables have a low and negative impact on instantaneous efficiency, with the exception of ammonia, whose impact is negligible. For the climatological variables, temperature and humidity have a positive and negative impact, respectively, on the variable under study. In the case of temperature, the results suggest that the studied photovoltaic systems have cooling systems, as a negative impact was expected, as mentioned in [13].

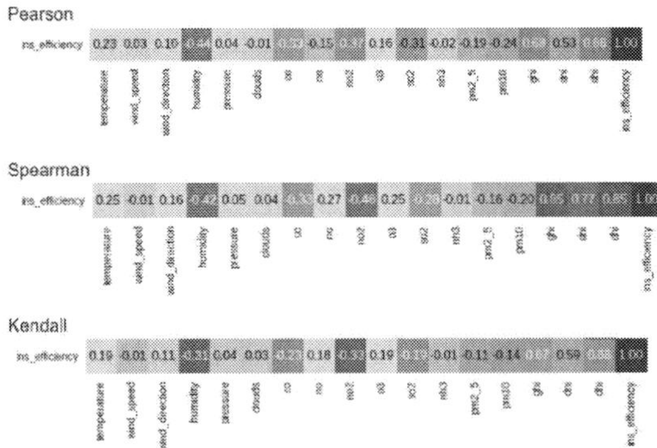

Fig 4. Heatmap of Correlations for Locations with the Highest Pollutant Concentration

D. Model selection

According to [14], [15] y [16] it is noted that Recurrent Neural Networks (RNNs), specifically Long Short-Term Memory (LSTM) networks, yield strong results for power prediction because they are better at learning temporal dependencies. This also means they better solve the vanishing gradient problem, as noted in [17]. However, the ultimate goal of the proposed algorithm is to have the regressors already projected into the future for application. Therefore, only a Multilayer Perceptron (MLP) neural network was included, in addition to 19 other algorithms.

To demonstrate the impact of air quality variables on efficiency, models were trained in several configurations: without these variables, with each variable individually, and finally with the variables that showed the greatest impact on prediction. The resulting models were then tabulated, and the top five were selected based on traditional error metrics: Root Mean Square Error (RMSE), Mean Absolute Error (MAE), Mean Absolute Percentage Error (MAPE), and R-squared (R2).

III. RESULTS

Table 3, Table 4 and Table 5, show the tabulated models and standard error metrics evaluated for training with all variables, without air quality variables, and with selected predictor variables, respectively.

Table 3. Training Metrics for all Dataset Variables

Model	RMSE	MAE	MAPE	R2
Random Forest	3.310	1.592	1.067	0.845
Extra Trees	3.358	1.636	1.147	0.841
Extreme Gradient	3.364	1.662	1.146	0.84
MLP	3.335	2.038	1.104	0.83
Gradient Boosting	3.507	1.796	1.124	0.823

Table 4. Training Metrics without Air Quality Variables

Model	RMSE	MAE	MAPE	R2
Random Forest	3.699	1.839	1.728	0.807
Gradient Boosting	3.735	1.893	1.701	0.803
Extra Trees	3.744	1.885	1.771	0.802
MLP	3.644	2.17	2.0	0.799
Extreme Gradient	3.88	2.011	1.565	0.788

Table 5. Training Metrics with Selected Predictor Variables

Model	RMSE	MAE	MAPE	R2
Random Forest	3.388	1.637	1.138	0.838
Extra Trees	3.431	1675	1.249	0.834
Extreme Gradient	3.448	1.714	1.207	0.832
MLP	3.437	2.061	2.22	0.821
Gradient Boosting	3.606	1.845	1.166	0.816

The results of this research, summarized in the training metrics tables, provide a clear picture of the impact of air quality variables. Table 4, which presents the training metrics without including these variables, shows that the Random Forest algorithm achieved the best performance with an $R^2 = 0.807$. The inclusion of pollutants in the model, as shown in Table 5, had a positive effect on the predictive capability of all algorithms, consistently improving their metrics. In this scenario, the Random Forest model maintained its lead with an $R^2 = 0.838$.

IV. CONCLUSIONS

Diverse machine learning algorithms were evaluated to predict the instantaneous efficiency of photovoltaic systems across seven geographical locations with varying climatological characteristics, representative of Colombian diversity.

The models were assessed using standard error metrics (MAE, MSE, RMSE, R^2), and the best-performing ones were selected. The main conclusions are presented below:

- Upon comparing the standard evaluation metrics of models trained with and without environmental pollution variables, a positive impact on predictive performance was evident. Specifically, the inclusion of these variables resulted in an improvement across all metrics for the evaluated algorithms.
- The feature importance analysis of the selected model (Random Forest) revealed that the predictor variables with the greatest influence on the prediction of instantaneous efficiency were:
  - Irradiance variables: GHI, DHI, and DNI.
  - Climatological variables: Temperature, humidity, and wind direction and speed.
  - Air quality variables: CO, NO2, O3, PM2.5, and PM10.
- The correlation analysis and the models' feature importance suggest that under conditions of higher environmental pollution, there is a negative association with instantaneous efficiency. The pollutants that showed the greatest influence on this negative relationship were NO2, followed by CO, SO2, PM10, and PM2.5.
- Unlike other pollutants, O3 showed a positive association with instantaneous efficiency, regardless of the overall pollution level of the location.

These findings have significant practical implications for the planning and operation of photovoltaic systems. The inclusion of air quality variables, alongside irradiance and climatological variables, improves the predictive accuracy of the algorithms. A more precise prediction of instantaneous efficiency allows for better estimation of system performance and optimizes operation and maintenance strategies, contributing to a more effective utilization of solar potential.

V.   REFERENCES

[1] Q. Hassan *et al.*, "A comprehensive review of international renewable energy growth," *Energy and Built Environment*, Jan. 2024, doi: 10.1016/J.ENBENV.2023.12.002.

[2] S. S. Chandel, A. Gupta, R. Chandel, and S. Tajjour, "Review of deep learning techniques for power generation prediction of industrial solar photovoltaic plants," *Solar Compass*, vol. 8, p. 100061, Dec. 2023, doi: 10.1016/J.SOLCOM.2023.100061.

[3] R. Sudirman, K. Ashenayi, and M. Golbaba, "Comparison of Methods Used for Forecasting Solar Radiation," in *2012 IEEE Green Technologies Conference*, 2012, pp. 1–3. doi: 10.1109/GREEN.2012.6200996.

[4] M. Malvoni, M. G. De Giorgi, and P. M. Congedo, "Forecasting of PV Power Generation using weather input data-preprocessing techniques," in *Energy Procedia*, Elsevier Ltd, Sep. 2017, pp. 651–658. doi: 10.1016/j.egypro.2017.08.293.

[5] G. Sahin, G. Isik, and W. G. J. H. M. van Sark, "Predictive modeling of PV solar power plant efficiency considering weather conditions: A comparative analysis of artificial neural networks and multiple linear regression," *Energy Reports*, vol. 10, pp. 2837–2849, 2023, doi: https://doi.org/10.1016/j.egyr.2023.09.097.

[6] Y. N. Chanchangi, A. Ghosh, H. Baig, S. Sundaram, and T. K. Mallick, "Soiling on PV performance influenced by weather parameters in Northern Nigeria," *Renew Energy*, vol. 180, pp. 874–892, Dec. 2021, doi: 10.1016/j.renene.2021.08.090.

[7] M. Memiche, C. Bouzian, A. Benzahia, and A. Moussi, "Effects of dust, soiling, aging, and weather conditions on photovoltaic system performances in a Saharan environment—Case study in Algeria," *Global Energy Interconnection*, vol. 3, no. 1, pp. 60–67, Feb. 2020, doi: 10.1016/J.GLOEI.2020.03.004.

[8] "NASA POWER | API Pages." Accessed: May 03, 2025. [Online]. Available: https://power.larc.nasa.gov/api/pages/

[9] "Historical weather API - OpenWeatherMap." Accessed: May 03, 2025. [Online]. Available: https://openweathermap.org/history

[10] "Air Pollution - OpenWeatherMap." Accessed: May 03, 2025. [Online]. Available: https://openweathermap.org/api/air-pollution

[11] "PVOutput." Accessed: May 03, 2025. [Online]. Available: https://pvoutput.org/

[12] F. Dincer and M. E. Meral, "Critical Factors that Affecting Efficiency of Solar Cells," *Smart Grid and Renewable Energy*, vol. 01, no. 01, pp. 47–50, 2010, doi: 10.4236/SGRE.2010.11007.

[13] F. Bayrak, "Prediction of photovoltaic panel cell temperatures: Application of empirical and machine learning models," *Energy*, vol. 323, p. 135764, May 2025, doi: 10.1016/J.ENERGY.2025.135764.

[14] D. K. Dhaked, S. Dadhich, and D. Birla, "Power output forecasting of solar photovoltaic plant using LSTM," *Green Energy and Intelligent Transportation*, vol. 2, no. 5, p. 100113, 2023, doi: https://doi.org/10.1016/j.geits.2023.100113.

[15] D. K. Dhaked, S. Dadhich, and D. Birla, "Power output forecasting of solar photovoltaic plant using LSTM," *Green Energy and Intelligent Transportation*, vol. 2, no. 5, Oct. 2023, doi: 10.1016/j.geits.2023.100113.

[16] A. Ait Mansour, A. Tilioua, and M. Touzani, "Bi-LSTM, GRU and 1D-CNN models for short-term photovoltaic panel efficiency forecasting case amorphous silicon grid-connected PV system," *Results in Engineering*, vol. 21, p. 101886, 2024, doi: https://doi.org/10.1016/j.rineng.2024.101886.

[17] S. Hochreiter and J. Schmidhuber, "Long Short-term Memory," *Neural Comput*, vol. 9, pp. 1735–1780, Apr. 1997, doi: 10.1162/neco.1997.9.8.1735.

Weather and Air Quality Effects on Photovoltaic System Efficiency: A Modeling Approach

Luis Carrillo Mejía, Elvis Eduardo Gaona, and Johann Hernández Mora

LIFAE, Faculty of Engineering, Universidad Distrital Francisco José de Caldas, Bogotá, Colombia.

Abstract

This research aims to evaluate the performance of different machine learning algorithms for predicting the instantaneous efficiency of photovoltaic systems. The study utilized a dataset collected over seven months from seven distinct geographical locations characterized by diverse climatological conditions representative of the Colombian territory. The dataset included solar irradiance, climatological variables, air quality variables, and measured active power.

Instantaneous efficiency was calculated from these data and defined as the study's target variable. An initial descriptive statistical analysis was performed to characterize the dataset. Subsequently, various prediction algorithms were executed and evaluated using standard error metrics. The evaluation demonstrated that incorporating air quality variables improved the predictive accuracy across all evaluated models. A key finding from the correlation analysis and feature importance assessment is the negative association between higher levels of environmental pollution and instantaneous efficiency

Methodology

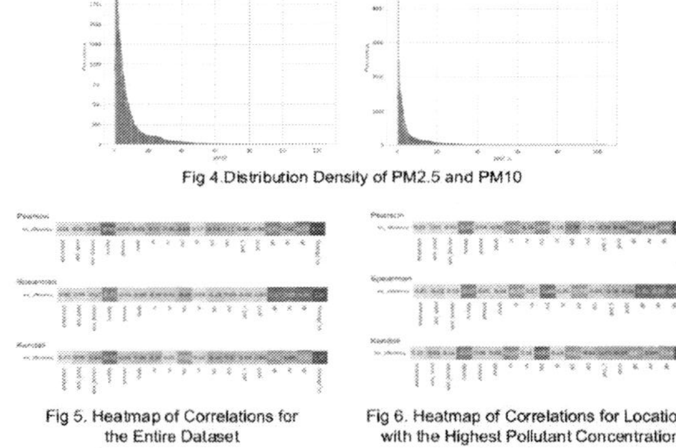

Fig 1. Components diagram of the microservice (PvIngestor).

Data Collection: A microservice was implemented to download data from various sources based on a time range and a geographical location.

- Irradiance: GHI, DHI and DNI were ingested from NASA API (free), and OpenWeather was implemented as well ($$$).
- Weather: Temperature, humidity, pressure, clouds, wind speed and direction were ingested from OpenWeather.
- Air quality: CO, NO, NO_2, O_3, SO_2, NH_3, PM2.5 and PM10, were ingested from OpenWeather
- Active Power: We used PvOutput which is a free service for sharing, comparing and monitoring live solar photovoltaic (PV) and energy consumption data.

To ensure the selected data was representative of a Colombian context, specific criteria were established for the PV systems chosen from PVOutput as it follows:

- The location's temperature had to be between 12° C and 35° C, or the site had to be situated within a ±10° latitude band around the equator.
- The installed panels had to be visually identifiable via satellite imagery of the geographical location.
- The manufacturer of the panels had to be a registered entity listed on either the Tier 1 A or B lists.
- The tilt angle and the total number of installed panels needed to be officially recorded in the dataset.

Fig 2. PvOutput and location of one of the training points selected

Preprocesing Data: We removed atypical data based on a solar illumination threshold of 120 W/m^2 , and the instantaneous efficiency was subsequently calculated by using next equation:

$$\eta_{ins} = \frac{P_{ins}}{G_{in} * A_t}$$

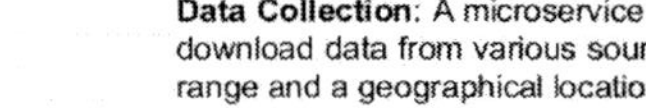

Fig 3.Distribution Density of Instantaneous Efficiency

Exploratory Data Analysis (EDA): The density distribution was plotted for each of the variables and, heatmaps were generated to visualize the Pearson, Spearman, and Kendall correlations for the entire dataset and for two specific locations; Rodolivos and Los Angeles, because the concentration of pollutants was highest at these sites.

Fig 4.Distribution Density of PM2.5 and PM10

Fig 5. Heatmap of Correlations for the Entire Dataset

Fig 6. Heatmap of Correlations for Locations with the Highest Pollutant Concentration

Model Selection: To demonstrate the impact of air quality variables on efficiency, models were trained in several configurations: without these variables, with each variable individually, and finally with the variables that showed the greatest impact on prediction. The resulting models were then tabulated, and the top five were selected based on traditional error metrics: R-squared (R2), Root Mean Square Error (RMSE), Mean Absolute Error (MAE) and Mean Absolute Percentage Error (MAPE).

Fig 7. Models trained

Results & Conclusions

- The results of this research, summarized in the training metrics tables, provide a clear picture of the impact of air quality variables. Fig 8.b, which presents the training metrics without including these variables, shows that the Random Forest algorithm achieved the best performance with an R² = 0.807. The inclusion of pollutants in the model, as shown in Table 8.c, had a positive effect on the predictive capability of all algorithms, consistently improving their metrics around 3%. In this scenario, the Random Forest model maintained its lead with an R² = 0.838.

Model	RMSE	MAE	MAPE	R2
Random Forest	3.310	1.992	1.067	0.845
Extra Trees	3.358	1.636	1.147	0.841
Extreme Gradient	3.364	1.682	1.146	0.84
MLP	3.435	2.038	1.104	0.83
Gradient Boosting	3.597	1.796	1.124	0.823

a) All dataset variables

Model	RMSE	MAE	MAPE	R2
Random Forest	3.699	1.839	1.728	0.807
Gradient Boosting	3.735	1.893	1.701	0.803
Extra Trees	3.543	1.885	1.773	0.802
MLP	3.644	2.17	2.0	0.799
Extreme Gradient	3.88	2.011	1.565	0.788

b) without Air Quality Variables

Model	RMSE	MAE	MAPE	R2
Random Forest	3.388	1.637	1.188	0.838
Extra Trees	3.431	1.625	1.249	0.854
Extreme Gradient	3.448	1.714	1.207	0.832
MLP	3.437	2.061	2.22	0.821
Gradient Boosting	3.606	1.845	1.166	0.816

c) with Selected Predictor Variables

Fig 8. Training metrics

- The correlation analysis and the models' feature importance suggest that under conditions of higher environmental pollution, there is a negative association with instantaneous efficiency. The pollutants that showed the greatest influence on this negative relationship were NO2, followed by CO, SO2, PM10, and PM2.5.
- Unlike other pollutants, O3 showed a positive association with instantaneous efficiency, regardless of the overall pollution level of the location.

020280-001

SPECIALIZED IRRADIATION MODELING FOR ALPINE REGIONS: CLEARSKY AND DIFFUSE FRACTION ESTIMATION

Bernhard Kubicek[1], Marcus Rennhofer[1], Philipp Weihs[2]

1: AIT Austrian Institute of technology GmbH, 2: Institute of Meteorology and Climatology, BOKU University, Vienna
Bernhard.kubicek@ait.ac.at

ABSTRACT: In the data driven performance evaluation of monitored PV systems, offsite irradiation sensors are of great help: either as the only irradiation data source in small residential systems, to estimate dust influence on local reference cells, or to check the calibration of the local irradiation sensors. Thereby, national meteorological measurement network (e.g. TAWES [1]) can be used, that features horizontal pyranometers in more than 250 sites in Austria. By geospatial interpolation, local estimations can be created based on this dense network.
For many of these PV evaluations, the hypothetical local clearsky irradiation is of great use, e.g. to filter data for dust evaluations, which is commonly estimated by the Ineichen [2] or King model. Using the historic data of the measurement network, a method is developed to obtain geolocalized correction factors to the Ineichen model. Deviations of more than 10% are observed at altitudes 3500m above sea level, that thereby can be corrected for.
As only the total horizontal irradiation is measured in the meteorological networks, an estimation of the diffuse horizontal irradiation is wanted, so that one can then use the Perez model to estimate module plane irradiations. A simplistic methodology is developed that estimates the diffuse irradiation purely based on local total horizontal irradiation, time, and geolocation within Austria. However, the methodology can be transferred any landmass worldwide, e.g. using the data within the GBON of the WMO [2].

1 GEOSPATIAL INTERPOLATION

The Austrian meteorological TAWES stations feature high quality historic irradiation time series at altitudes between 250m to 3400m above sea, and hence is a great test case for validation of irradiation modeling. For each of the more than 250 stations featuring irradiation sensors, the simulated clearsky horizontal irradiation (Ineichen/PVlib [5]) can be compared to actual measured irradiations. By creating a stable linear regression for the points that are considered cloud-free, localized calibrations to the Ineichen model can be obtained, see [4].

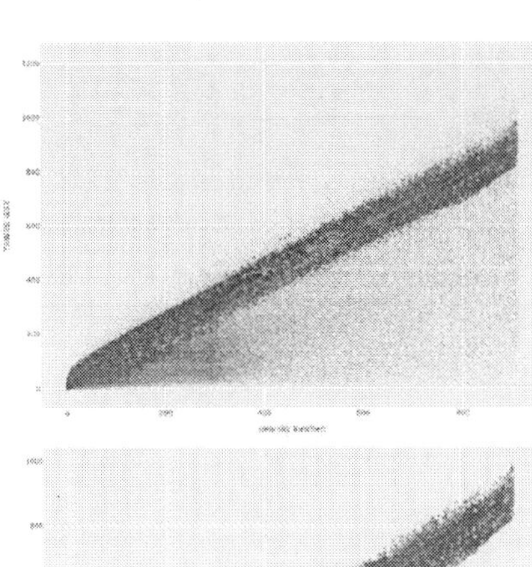

horizontal) to the measured total horizontal irradiation (vertical, [W/m2]) of one exemplary TAWES station. Above, all 10 min tuples of 9 years data are plotted, while below only clearsky states are shown. It can be seen that the blue linear regression line is non-diagonal, resulting in a linear calibration per station.

When comparing the linear calibrations to the Ineichen model, e.g. for a chosen reference clearsky irradiation, it can be found that the measured irradiation shows a strong sea height dependence, which is surprising, as the Ineichen model already contains the effect of decreasing airmass factors. By using a georeferenced scalar field of the Austrian elevation profile, the regional corrections can be put into georeferenced lookup tables, see Fig 2.

Figure 2: Georeferenced clearsky corrections for 1000W/m^2 Ineichen predictions. The Voronoi cells are effects of the weather stations individual corrections, while the height correction is supplemented [4].

Five of the TAWES sites in the measurement network are equipped with shadow bands. One now defines two quantities: the measured diffuse fraction as ratio of diffuse horizontal irradiation to total horizontal irradiation; And the "clearskyness", the ratio of measured total horizontal irradiation to the simulated clearsky irradiation, regarding corrections for the local deviations to the Ineichen model. By plotting these quantities, see fig 3, one can try to find linear functions to describe the correspondence.

Figure 1: Point cloud of the comparison „simulated clearsky horizontal irradiation [W/m2]" (PVlib/Ineichen,

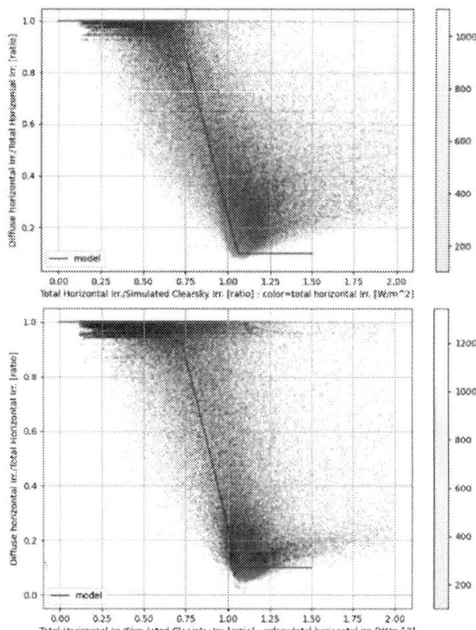

Figure 3: TAWES: The ratio of measured to clearsky irradiation, horizontally, versus the ratio of diffuse irradiation. Above, for Vienna, seaheight 320m, and below at the summit "Sonnblick", 3400m. An empiric stepwise function is fitted to the clouds, defining a simple diffuse fraction estimator.

2 ARAD REFINEMENT

The Austrian radiation monitoring network ARAD since 2011 records accurate direct and diffuse solar irradiation in 1 minute time averages [3] at five sites across Austria. Using this data, a refined approach can be derived. A plot similar to Fig 3 is shown in Fig 4. However, by creating a two dimensional binning of measured horizontal irradiation and calculated clearsky irradiation, the average diffuse fraction for each bin can be calculated, see Fig.5.

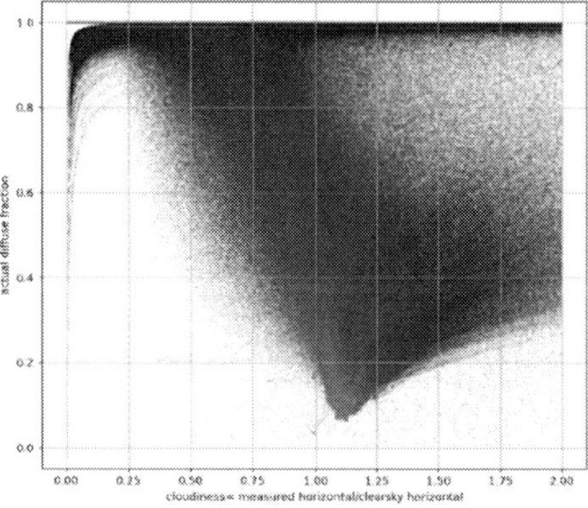

Figure 4: The ARAD based comparison for the station of Vienna, colorbar: Measured Horizontal irradiation [W/m^2]

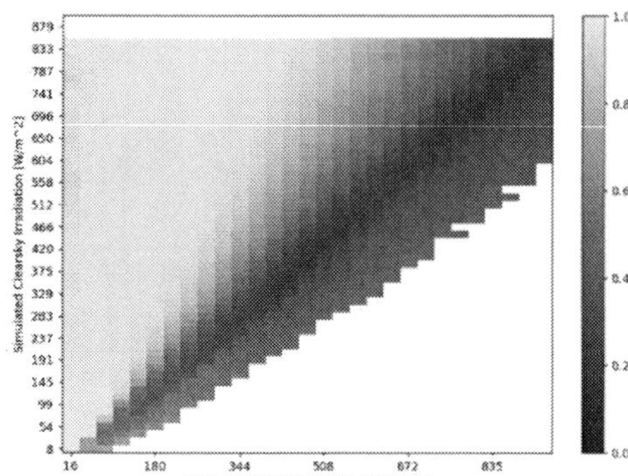

Figure 5: The ARAD based data plotted in 2d, while showing the average diffuse fraction of all data points in a bin as color, exhibits a much better structure than the previous figure. The centerpoint of the valley forms a slightly off-diagonal line, as the clearsky calibration is not yet performed on this dataset.

In figure 5, it can be seen that a coordinate transformation to the new parameter "over-irradiation" (measured horizontal irradiation − horizontal clearsky irradiation) is useful, as in this system the valley becomes mostly trivial, see figure 6. The curves there can be well approximated by piecewise linear functions, see figure 7.

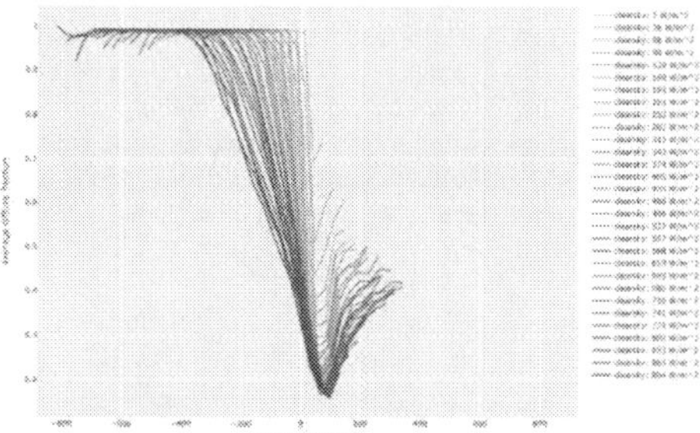

Figure 6: By plotting the ARAD data over a new quantity, the "over-irradiation", curves can be developed that can easily be approximated by piecewise linear functions on three intervals: the constant range from -1000 to a clearsky depending over-irradiation between [-400 and 0], followed by a decline to the actual clearsky diffuse fraction, followed by increase

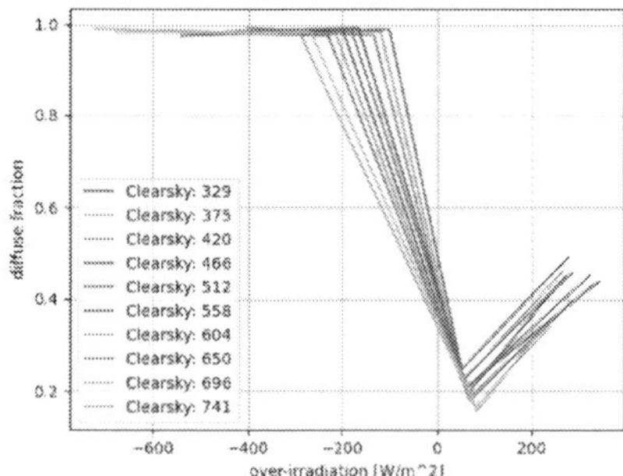

Figure 7: The curves of the previous plot can be approximate by three-interval piecewise linear functions.

The piecewise functions again have set of parameters, the initial plateau, that can be estimated constant, the position of the first decline, the depth of the decline, and the rise at times when the measured irradiation is larger than the clearsky irradiation. These parameters can be fitted by simple functions, see e.g. figure 8 and 9.

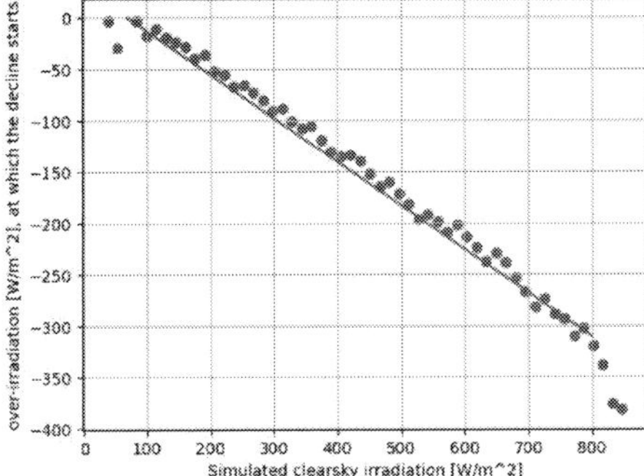

Figure 8: The over-irradiation, at which the decline occurs of the diffuse fraction occurs, can be well described by a linear function.

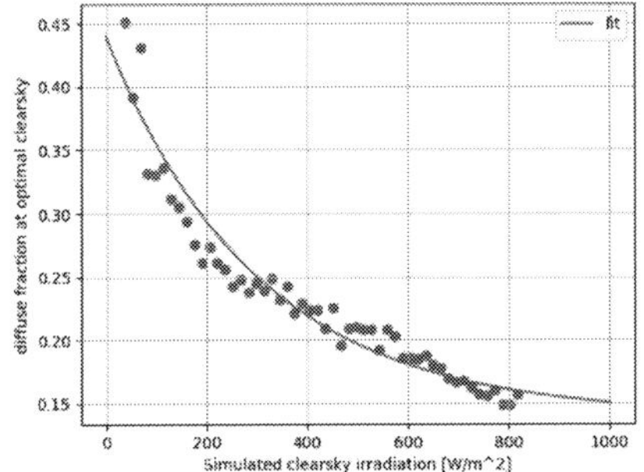

Figure 9: The minimum of the diffuse fraction can be described by a linear function plus an exponential decay.

2 CONCLUSIONS

By geospatial interpolation, one can obtain time series of the total horizontal irradiation in 10-minute intervals for all arbitrary sites in Austria. This requires a sea-height correction for both weather stations and the chosen sites. Using the approach presented, from the time and site-dependent calculated clearsky irradiation, and the interpolated horizontal irradiation, the time dependent diffuse fraction can now be estimated. This is useful, since to estimate the tilted plane irradiation for PV modules at the site, the diffuse irradiation needs to be known. Finally, by using this tilted plane irradiations, the performance ratio of PV systems that have no local irradiation measurement can be performed.

[1] Geosphere/ZAMG, "TAWES Messnetz", https://www.zamg.ac.at/cms/de/klima/messnetze/wetterst ationen

[2] P. Ineichen and R. Perez, "A New airmass independent formulation for the Linke turbidity coefficient", Solar Energy, vol 73, pp. 151-157, 2002.

[3] World Meteorological Organization, website: https://wmo.int/activities/global-basic-observing-network-gbon

[4] B. Kubicek, M. Rennhofer, "Georeferenced Correction Factors to the Ineichen Clearsky Model for the Alpine regions in Austria/Europe.", IEEE Photovoltaic Specialists conference 2025.

[5] Holmgren, W., Hansen, C., and Mikofski, M. "pvlib python: a python package for modeling solar energy systems." Journal of Open Source Software, 3(29), 884, (2018). DOI: 10.21105/joss.00884.

[6] Olefs, M., Baumgartner, D. J., Obleitner, F., Bichler, C., Foelsche, U., Pietsch, H., Rieder, H. E., Weihs, P., Geyer, F., Haiden, T., and Schöner, W.: The Austrian radiation monitoring network ARAD – best practice and added value, Atmos. Meas. Tech., 9, 1513–1531, https://doi.org/10.5194/amt-9-1513-2016, 2016.

Bernhard Kubicek[1], Marcus Rennhofer[1], Philipp Weihs[2]
1: AIT Austrian Institute of Technology GmbH, Center for Energy bernhard.kubicek@ait.ac.at
2: Institute of Meteorology and Climatology, BOKU University, Vienna

SPECIALIZED IRRADIATION MODELING FOR ALPINE REGIONS: CLEARSKY AND DIFFUSE FRACTION ESTIMATION.

Motivation

Most small PV systems lack in-plane irradiation sensors. To enable performance ratio estimations, interpolation of data from meteorological weather station networks can be used. They typically measure global horizontal irradiation, while for the module plane transformation, the diffuse fraction needs to be known. Longyear diffuse fraction measurement from the ARAD dataset is used to create such an estimator for the alpine areas of Austria.

Method

The ~230 stations of the Austrian meteorological measurement network 'TAWES' have been systematically equipped with pyranometers. This 10-minute data exists from 116m to 3400m above sea level. The frequently used Ineichen Clearsky radiation model [1] considers the time-dependent path of the sun and the altitude above sea level. In a previous work, the authors have developed a calibration method, that corrects the sea height effects using georeferenced lookup tables for Austria [2].

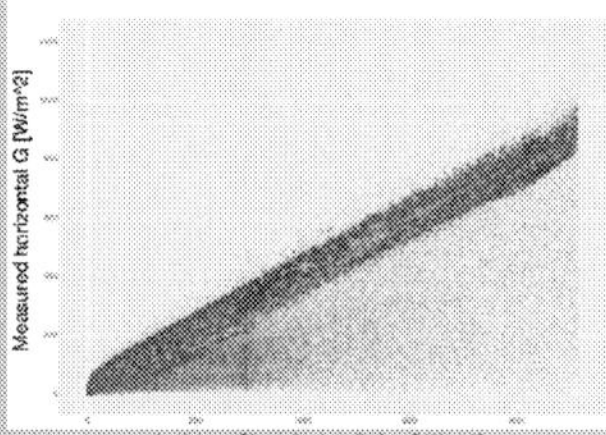
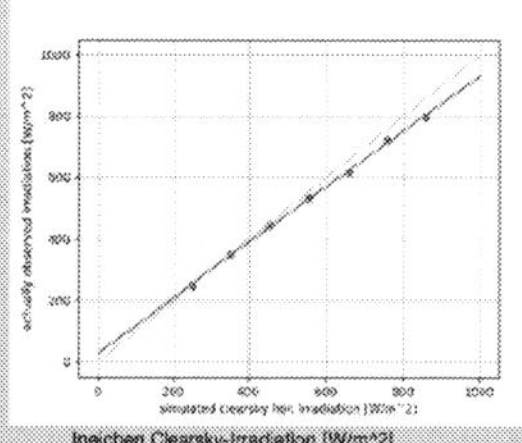

The fitted clearsky calibration for each TAWES station exhibits a bias and offset, that again depends on the sea height:

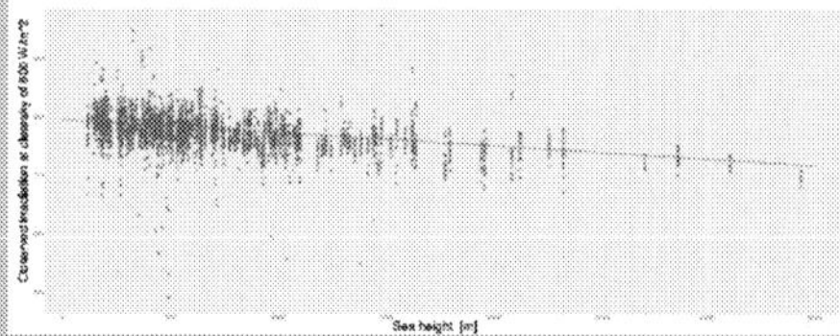

Spatial interpolation together with heightmaps can be used to apply the model, to obtain horizontal irradiation time series for arbitrary sites:

ARAD

The Austrian radiation monitoring network ARAD since 2011 records accurate direct and diffuse solar irradiation in 1 minute time averages [3]. One can define two quantities:

- the diffuse fraction: diffuse horizontal irradiation per total horizontal radiation
- The "clearskyness": total horizontal irradiation per simulated clearsky irradiation

This quantities can be plotted for each individual station, e.g. Vienna:

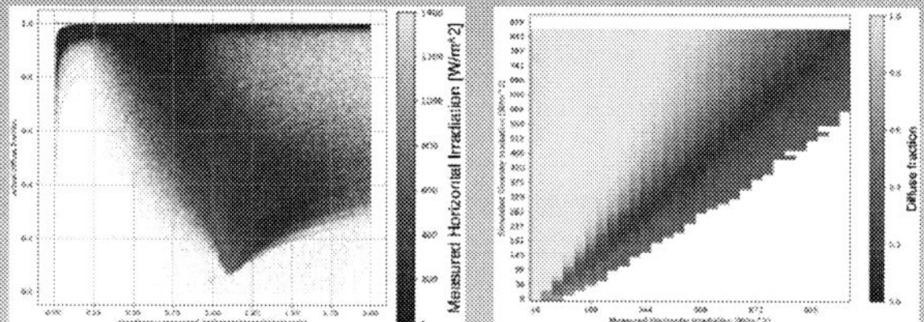

Thereby one can see (left), that diffuse fraction is not only a function of the cloudiness, but also of the measured irradiation. A 2d-plot (right) of the mean diffuse fraction occurring in the bins shows a clearer structure. The bias and slightly non-diagonality are the effects of the not yet performed clearsky calibration for the ARAD dataset. One can deduct, that the "over-irradiation" (measured horizontal – clearsky horizontal) is a good parameter:

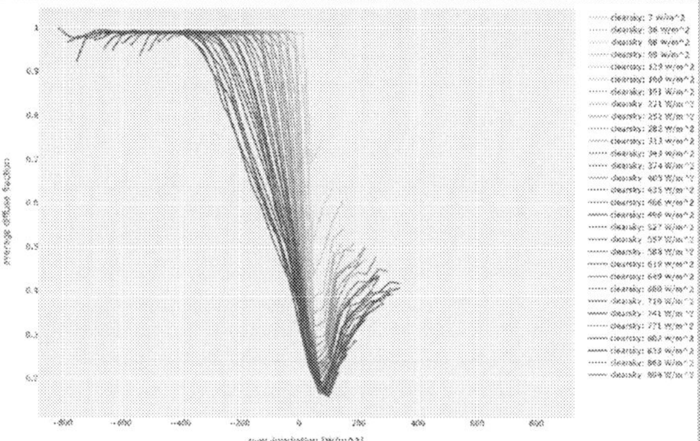

This can be well approximated by piecewise linear functions of three intervals, whose defining points can be functionally defined by the clearsky irradiation. E.g. one can describe the over-irradiation of the first decline by a linear function of the clearsky irradiation.

Conclusion

By a sea-height-aware interpolation, a historic time series of the local total horizontal irradiation can be generated for any point in Austria with 10-minute resolution. By comparison of the interpolated irradiation with the local clearsky irradiation, the diffuse fraction can be estimated. This enables to calculated arbitrary in-plane irradiations e.g. using the Perez model. Finally, this in-plane irradiation time series can be used to perform performance ratio estimations for non-sensored PV systems.

[1] P. Ineichen and R. Perez, "A New airmass independent formulation for the Linke turbidity coefficient", Solar Energy, vol 73, pp. 151-157, 2002.
[2] B.Kubicek, M. Rennhofer, "Georeferenced Correction Factors to the Ineichen Clearsky Model for the Alpine regions in Austria/Europe", PVSC, Montreal, 2025.
[3] Olefs, M., Baumgartner, D. J., Obleitner, F., Bichler, C., Foelsche, U., Pietsch, H., Rieder, H. E., Weihs, P., Geyer, F., Haiden, T., and Schöner, W.: The Austrian radiation monitoring network ARAD – best practice and added value, Atmos. Meas. Tech., 9, 1513–1531. https://doi.org/10.5194/amt-9-1513-2016, 2016.

This content was created within the „EASE" Austrian national project.

A NOVEL IMPLEMENTATION OF QUALITY CHECKS OF SPECTRAL DIRECT NORMAL IRRADIANCE MEASUREMENTS

Sergiu-Mihai Hategan[1,2]*, Jacob K. Thorning[3], Sergiu V. Spataru[3], Marius Paulescu[2]

[1]Institute for Advanced Environmental Research, West University of Timisoara, V. Pârvan 4, 300223, Timisoara, Romania
[2]Faculty of Physics, West University of Timisoara, V. Pârvan 4, 300223, Timisoara, Romania
[3]Technical University of Denmark, Department of Electrical Engineering, Frederiksborgvej 399, 4000 Roskilde, Denmark
*Corresponding author email: sergiu.hategan98@e-uvt.ro

ABSTRACT: This study develops a robust quality control (QC) method for spectral irradiance measurements to improve solar resource assessment accuracy. It combines QC techniques for spectral and broadband irradiance data to detect systematic and random errors. Using EKO MS-711 spectroradiometers at two research sites, the method applies logical checks for physically plausible values and compares measurements with SMARTS2 clear-sky simulations (using AERONET/MERRA2 atmospheric data). A Python interface simplifies data comparison, aiming to boost spectral modeling adoption in photovoltaic research. Preliminary results confirm the method's effectiveness and potential for future advancements.
Keywords: solar radiation, direct irradiance, spectral irradiance, quality control

1 INTRODUCTION

The precise measurement of ground-level spectral solar radiation is essential for fields ranging from atmospheric sciences, biology, medicine (UV radiation), and solar energy. Spectral direct normal irradiance (DNI) modeling and measurements are an important subset, with impacts on concentrating photovoltaic power as well as estimations of spectral irradiance on tilted surfaces. Although radiative transfer (i.e. MODTRAN [1]) and spectral transmittance models (SMARTS2 [2]) provide theoretical estimates, their accuracy depends on often-unavailable atmospheric inputs. Spectroradiometers offer direct measurements, but face trade-offs: monochromator-based systems deliver high accuracy at slow scan speeds, whereas fixed-grating array detectors multi-wavelength capture with lower resolution [3]. However, recent innovations have allowed for better resolution, around 0.4 nm [4].

A clear sky spectral irradiance quality control (QC) methodology was first proposed in [5], which compares measurements under clear sky conditions to simulated spectral irradiance. The simulations give a lower and an upper margin of possible spectral irradiance values under high turbidity or clear atmosphere, respectively. Another option involves the use of spectral indices such as average photon energy (APE) used for comparison between measured and simulated spectra for clear sky conditions [6]. A more recent QC framework was specifically tailored for spectral DNI measurements [7]. This method was successfully utilized on monochromator type spectroradiometer; however, due to the spectroradiometer measuring method, this framework can only be applied to clear sky conditions with low air mass values. Under these conditions, a good reference spectral is SMARTS2, with a long-tested good performance [8].

This model requires air mass values and some atmospheric parameter inputs, which can be obtained from measurements or reanalysis products.

Considering the need for QC verification of spectral measurements, we present an updated methodology that is based on logical checks, physically plausible value checks, and an extended comparison with broadband DNI measurements, based on SMARTS2 simulations. The proposed QC framework was tested at two locations with spectroradiometers installed, namely the West University of Timisoara (WUT) in Timisoara, Romania, and the Technical University of Denmark (DTU) Risø campus in Roskilde, Denmark. The implementation is enhanced by a publicly available Python-based interface.

2 METHODOLOGY AND DATA

Figure 1: The EKO MS-711N spectroradiometers at WUT (left) and DTU (right).

2.1 Instruments and Data Sources

Aerosol and other atmospheric parameter inputs, necessary for comparisons with spectral models, are obtained from two separate sources, depending on their availability. The first is AERONET [9], a federated network of ground-based solar photometers that measure aerosol optical depth (AOD) and other atmo-

10.4229/EUPVSEC2025/4BV.3.24
020283-001

spheric parameters such as ozone content, water vapor content and particle size distribution. AERONET serves as the reference standard for remote sensing aerosol datasets. MERRA-2 represents NASA's global atmospheric reanalysis system [10], which assimilates both ground-based (such as AERONET) and satellite measurements. MERRA-2 produces a high resolution, long-term, spatially continuous record of aerosols, clouds, meteorological, and atmospheric parameters, helping to bridge gaps in local measurements. A recent study has found good agreement between the AERONET and MERRA-2 inputs in the case of the SMARTS2 model [11].

The locations considered in this research are the Solar Platform at the Institute for Advanced Environmental Research in Timisoara, and the DTU Platform at DTU Risø (showcased in Fig. 1). The WUT Institute's Solar Platform, located in the center of Timisoara (latitude $45.76°N$, longitude $21.23°E$, altitude of 85 m a.s.l) consists of an EKO MS-711N DNI spectroradiometer installed on an EKO STR-32G Sun Tracker, an EKO ASI-16 camera coupled with a weather station, and an EKO MS-80 pyranometer measuring global horizontal irradiance. A functioning AERONET station is located nearby, at a distance of 1.5 km.

The DTU Platform is located at DTU Risø campus in Roskilde, Denmark (latitude $55.69°N$, longitude $12.08°E$, close to sea level). It consists of a similar EKO MS-711N DNI spectroradiometer, installed on an EKO STR-22G Dual type sun tracker, an EKO MS-80 GHI pyranometer, an EKO MS-56 pyrheliometer and an EKO MS802 DHI pyranometer. Atmospheric parameter data was obtained from MERRA-2 reanalysis.

The dataset for both locations comprises measurements recorded during the entire month of June 2024. DTU dataset contains both spectral data, broadband DNI and GHI measurements, as well as hourly values of the key atmospheric parameters, taken from MERRA-2. The DTU measures spectral data every 5 minutes, while WUT measures data every 10 minutes. The WUT dataset contains spectral data and AERONET level 1.5 atmospheric parameters, the missing values being filled with the hourly average value. The DTU dataset contains 6927 datapoints, while the WUT dataset contains 2316 datapoints.

We have marked as clear-sky the datapoints measured during days with completely clear-sky conditions or close to it, manually verifying the data.

2.2 Basic physical checks

Inspired by the already well-implemented broadband irradiance quality control procedures [12], we introduce three logical QC checks in our framework. The first check verifies if the measurement recording was correctly transmitted into the dataset (not a number - NaN check). The next two checks focus on physically plausible values for spectral irradiance measurements, namely they should be positive and the spectral irradiance integrated over the entire instrument's range (300-1100 nm) should be less than the irradiance over the same wavelength range at the top of the atmosphere (the AM0 check). This is an extension of the methodology presented in [5], valid for clear sky periods. However, the AM0 and positive value checks are applicable under all sky conditions.

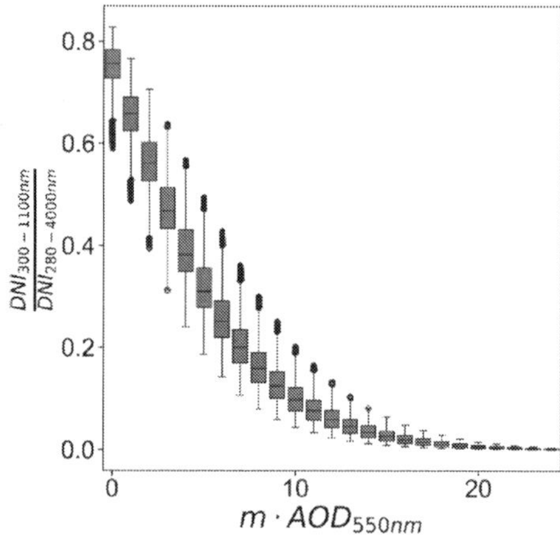

Figure 2: Boxplots showcasing the tolerance interval for each bin of simulated integrated fraction values.

2.3 Broadband DNI check

When a broadband irradiance measurement instrument is available, spectral measurements can be verified against that other measurement. The widely used SMARTS2 solar spectral irradiance model forms the basis of the broadband quality control check. As SMARTS2 is a clear-sky model, this check applies only to clear-sky periods. Broadband pyrheliometers operate in the optical spectral range of 280-4000 nm, while the EKO DNI spectroradiometers considered in this study operate in the 300-1100 nm range. Assuming the validity of the SMARTS2 model, we propose the following method to find measurement anomalies for spectroradiometers. First, we integrate the spectral irradiance measured by the spectral instrument in the 300-1100 nm range, and then divide it by the measured broadband irradiance, obtaining an integrated fraction f according to Equation 1. Afterwards, this integrated fraction is compared to typical values obtained by simulations employing the SMARTS2 model, both for the instrument's range (300-1100 nm) and for the broadband range (280-4000 nm).

$$f = \frac{\int_{300}^{1100} DNI(\lambda)d\lambda}{\int_{280}^{4000} DNI(\lambda)d\lambda} \qquad (1)$$

The SMARTS2 simulations were carried out in the following ranges of parameters: air mass between 1 and 10, with a step of 0.25, precipitable water vapor content between 0.1 and 5.2 g/cm^2 with a step of 0.3 g/cm^2, values of ozone column content $(0.25, 0.3, 0.35, 0.4\ cm \cdot atm)$, aerosol models spanning the four S&F models (rural, urban, tropospheric, maritime), and finally aerosol optical depth values (AOD) between 0 and 2.5, with a step of 0.5. The simulation was run twice, once for AOD at 500 nm (a variable provided by AERONET) and once for AOD at 550 nm (a variable provided by MERRA-2). Each simulated set of spectra contained 543456 datapoints, with values for the integrated fraction at each combination of input parameters. We have observed a clear correlation between the product $m \cdot AOD$, where m is air mass, and the integrated fraction. This correlation serves as the basis for the tolerance intervals of the integrated fraction, shown in Fig. 2.

The $m \cdot AOD$ values were grouped in 25 bins (between 0 and 25, with each bin width equal to 1), and the tolerance intervals were obtained using a boxplot for the integrated fraction values inside that bin. The tolerance interval was defined using a boxplot whisker length of 1.5 times the interquartile range, excluding outliers in the binned dataset.

Using these intervals for each bin of $m \cdot AOD$ values, we check whether the integrated fraction measured is within the tolerance interval; otherwise, it is flagged as anomalous. In addition to other studies, we have extended the air mass interval, allowing this quality control check to be performed throughout the day, provided that the sky is clear.

3 RESULTS AND DISCUSSION

Running all checks at both locations have shown the percentage of data flagged by each QC check in Fig. 3 (considering only data for air mass higher than 10). The logical NaN check and the physical AM0 check did not flag data during the period we considered. The newly devised Broadband check requires broadband DNI measurements, which were available only at DTU. For this location, 8.3% of the data was marked as being under clear sky conditions. Of that percentage, 13.7% were flagged as anomalous measurements, with our proposed integrated ratio check. This occurred at low solar elevation angles, corresponding to air masses greater than 3, where the presence of nearby buildings or other possible reflections could induce uncertainty in spectral measurements.

However, our QC implementation found negative measured values at both locations, in 0.2% of the WUT dataset and in 7.6% of all data at DTU. As can be seen in Fig. 4, negative values are found mainly in the 1000-1100 nm range, where the uncertainty of spectroradiometer measurement is highest due to the

detector band gap. Another possible situation for the occurrence of such anomalies is under severely overcast or cloudy conditions. Because the spectral DNI is severely reduced under such conditions, the inherent measuring uncertainty can lead to erroneous values, especially in the 1000-1100 nm range.

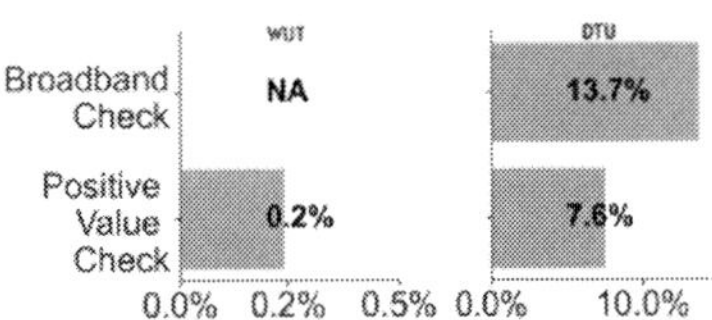

Figure 3: Amount of data flagged by the QC checks implemented. NaN and AM0 checks did not flag any datapoint.

In the case of the two unflagged data examples in Fig. 4, we observe a good agreement between the measurements and the SMARTS2 model. As expected, AERONET data inputs fit the measurements slightly better, with MERRA-2 inputs giving a slight overestimation of spectral irradiance. Future studies could be concerned with different atmospheric parameter inputs for locations without concurrent AERONET measurements, to select the proper reanalysis or satellite product. A possibility could be CAMS radiation products [13] or MODIS satellite measurements [14].

All checks have been implemented using a Python-based interface, available online [15].

4 CONCLUSIONS

In this research, we have introduced an extended methodology of QC checks for spectral DNI measurements [15]. Leveraging automated logical and physical plausibility verifications, the proposed methodology is applicable under all sky conditions. In addition, for clear sky data we have introduced a comparison with broadband DNI measurements, flagging anomalies based on SMARTS2 simulations. The SMARTS2 simulations have provided a tolerated range of values for spectral DNI depending on aerosol and air mass properties at the moment of measurement. The input consisted of measured atmospheric parameters (from AERONET) or reanalysis inputs (from MERRA-2), depending on availability.

The proposed methodology has been tested on a one month dataset (June 2024) in two locations: WUT and DTU. The main anomalies found were negative spectral DNI values in both locations and in clear sky conditions some measurements were considerably different to broadband measurements. Both types of flagged anomalous measurements were found at large air mass values, where measurement

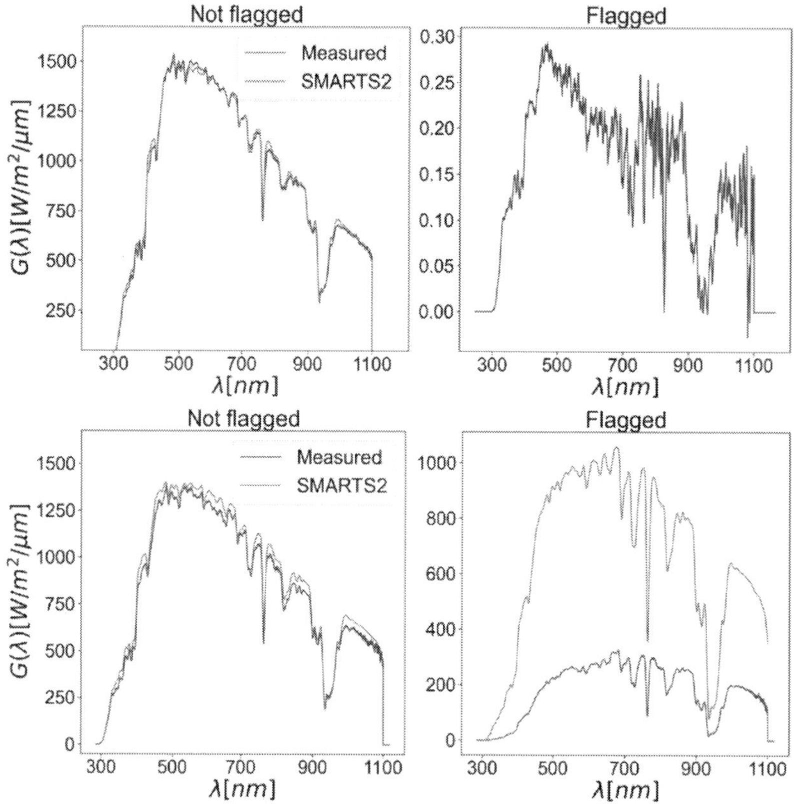

Figure 4: Examples of flagged and unflagged data measured at both locations (top - WUT, bottom - DTU). Unflagged data was compared to SMARTS2. At WUT, the datapoint was flagged by the Positive Value Check. At DTU the datapoint was flagged by the Broadband Check.

uncertainty is inherently higher than at low air mass. In the case of the flagged negative values, a possible source was the instrument's sensitivity in the 1000-1100 nm range. This led to anomalous measurements under cloudy or rainy conditions, when the overall DNI values are extremely low. Future work could focus on expanding upon the presented QC methods by adding other possible validation checks, or by adding methods for spectral global horizontal irradiance or diffuse irradiance.

References

[1] Gail P Anderson et al. "Reviewing atmospheric radiative transfer modeling: new developments in high-and moderate-resolution FASCODE/FASE and MODTRAN". In: *Optical spectroscopic techniques and instrumentation for atmospheric and space research II*. Vol. 2830. SPIE. 1996, pp. 82–93.

[2] Christian Gueymard et al. *SMARTS2: a simple model of the atmospheric radiative transfer of sunshine: algorithms and performance assessment.* Vol. 1. Florida Solar Energy Center Cocoa, FL, 1995.

[3] Aron Habte, Afshin Andreas, and Manajit Sengupta. "Spectral solar irradiance: calibration methods and measurement techniques". In: *Spectral Characteristics of Solar Radiation*. Elsevier, 2025, pp. 47–76.

[4] Rosa Delia García-Cabrera et al. "Aerosol retrievals from the EKO MS-711 spectral direct irradiance measurements and corrections of the circumsolar radiation". In: *Atmospheric Measurement Techniques* 13.5 (2020), pp. 2601–2621.

[5] Carsten Hoyer-Klick et al. "MESoR-Management and exploitation of solar resource knowledge". In: *SolarPACES 2009*. 2009.

[6] Gustavo Nofuentes et al. "Experimental evaluation of a spectral index to characterize temporal variations in the direct normal irradiance spectrum". In: *Applied Sciences* 11.3 (2021), p. 897.

[7] Aitor Marzo et al. "Field Quality Control of Spectral Solar Irradiance Measurements by Comparison with Broadband Measurements". In: *Sustainability* 13.19 (2021), p. 10585.

[8]   Christian A Gueymard. "The SMARTS spectral irradiance model after 25 years: New developments and validation of reference spectra". In: *Solar Energy* 187 (2019), pp. 233–253.

[9]   Brent N Holben et al. "AERONET—A federated instrument network and data archive for aerosol characterization". In: *Remote sensing of environment* 66.1 (1998), pp. 1–16.

[10]   CA Randles et al. "The MERRA-2 aerosol reanalysis, 1980 onward. Part I: System description and data assimilation evaluation". In: *Journal of climate* 30.17 (2017), pp. 6823–6850.

[11]   Sophie Pelland and Christian A Gueymard. "Validation of photovoltaic spectral effects derived from satellite-based solar irradiance products". In: *IEEE Journal of Photovoltaics* 12.6 (2022), pp. 1361–1368.

[12]   Anne Forstinger et al. "Expert quality control of solar radiation ground data sets". In: *ISES Solar World Congress*. 2021.

[13]   Christian A Gueymard and Dazhi Yang. "Worldwide validation of CAMS and MERRA-2 reanalysis aerosol optical depth products using 15 years of AERONET observations". In: *Atmospheric Environment* 225 (2020), p. 117216.

[14]   DA Chu et al. "Validation of MODIS aerosol optical depth retrieval over land". In: *Geophysical research letters* 29.12 (2002), MOD2–1.

[15]   *GitHub - Spectroradiometer-QC*. `https : / / github . com / Applied - PV - TEAM / Spectroradiometer-QC`.

Evaluating the Suitability of Köppen-Geiger Climate Classifications for Photovoltaic Systems: Micro-climate Analysis and Risk Assessment Maps

Pavan Kumar Panda[1], Hugo Sanchez[1], Leila Mortazavifar[1,2], and Ralph Gottschalg[1,2]
[1]Hochschule Anhalt University of Applied Sciences, Bernburger Str. 55, 06366, Köthen, Germany,
Email: Pavan.Panda@hs-anhalt.de
[2]Fraunhofer Center for Crystalline Silicon Photovoltaics CSP, Halle, Germany

ABSTRACT: The performance of photovoltaic (PV) systems are influenced by local climatic conditions. The widely used Köppen-Geiger (KG) classification system, focused mainly on agriculture, has limitations for PV applications due to its emphasis on general climate patterns rather than specific factors affecting PV material aging. This study evaluates the compatibility of KG classifications with relevant micro-climatic properties utilizing global meteorological data to create risk assessment maps for PV application. We used Principal component analysis (PCA) and clustering to simplify the micro-climate properties and found overlaps in KG classifications indicating challenges in capturing transitional micro-climate zones. These findings indicate that traditional clustering is inadequate for defining specific climate zones for PV use. Consequently, we developed a novel risk map tailored to degradation reaction rates in analyzed location, offering more detailed and valid climate classification for PV application. This study underscores the necessity for innovative mapping techniques that capture nuanced micro-climate variations relevant to PV system development.
Keywords: three to five keywords in order of importance

1 INTRODUCTION

Historically the KG climatic classification system has been mostly used for the broad categorization of global climates solely based on temperature and precipitation patterns [1], dividing the earth into 30 different zones. While KG is foundational in the ecological and botanical context [2], it has its limitations while meeting the specific needs of the PV systems. In response to these limitations, novel methodologies have emerged including the solar-specific metrics and adopting redefined climatic classifications models tailored to solar applications, such as Photovoltaic Climate Zones (PVCZ) [3] and Köppen-Geiger-Photovoltaic (KG-PV) [4].

These classifications made significant strides in correlating climatic classifications with PV system performance. Meanwhile, traditional KG classification omits addressing these critical micro-climatic stressors and their impact on different degradation drivers in PV systems.

Building on these foundations the present study seeks to bridge the gap between traditional climate classifications and the specific needs of PV-relevant classification through several key contributions. By employing detailed micro-climate modelling, this research calculated the immediate available environmental conditions surrounding the PV module, offering a precise understanding of climatic factors and their interdependencies. Additionally, through standardization, dimensional reduction, and PCA, the study simplifies climatic data into principal components, helping to reveal underlying patterns and identify the most significant variables.

The analysis uncovers substantial overlaps among these climatic groups, suggesting that traditional KG zones do not uniquely correspond to distinct PV micro-climate zones. This overlap indicates continuous and transitional zones and highlights the limitations of conventional classification. To address these insights non-reversible degradation rates are evaluated, by applying the peck's model proposed in [5] [6] specific to PV systems. The integration of degradation drivers into risk assessment plots provides a more accurate depiction of performance risk maps, ultimately advancing the efficacy and sustainability of PV developments.

2 METHODOLOGY

The proposed method involves several steps to achieve the microclimate data from meteorological data and later used in non-reversible degradation driver model is shown in figure 1.

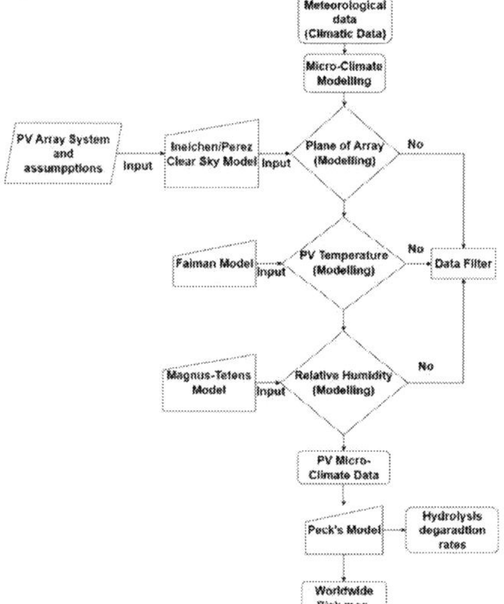

Figure 1: Process flowchart: conversion of meteorological data to PV micro climate data and degradation model development

2.1 Data Acquisition and Processing

The meteorological data used for this study was sourced from NASA's POWER project, specifically utilizing the CERES and MERRA-2 [7] datasets. The dataset spans from 2001 to 2020 years and the analysis corresponds to worldwide climate data of different climatic classifications.

2.2 Micro-climate modelling

Micro-climate data, specifically the plane of array (POA) irradiance on both front and back of a module is derived using Ineichen/Perez clear sky model [8] implemented by PVlib [9] and PVfactors [10] as expressed in by equation 1.

$$I_{POA} = [I_{beam,POA}] + [I_{diffuse,POA}] + [I_{reflected,POA}] \quad (1)$$

$$T_m = T_{amb} + \frac{E_{POA}}{U_0 + U_1 \cdot WS} \quad (2)$$

The module temperature is determined through Faiman's model and as outlined in equation 2. The relative humidity and saturation vapor pressure are calculated using the approach by Michael Koehl [11] as shown in equation 3.

$$RH_{mod} = RH * e^{\left(\frac{7.5 * T_{amb}}{T_{amb}+237.3}\right) - \left(\frac{7.5 * T_{mod}}{T_{mod}+237.3}\right)} \quad (3)$$

2.3 Standardization, Dimensionality Reduction, and Clustering

Derived micro-climate data is later standardized and PCA reduced the data to two-dimension PCA, enabling visual and computational insights into climatic variability. k-means clustering algorithm is applied to the data and stable clusters are obtained where centroids no longer change significantly [12]. Elbow method is used to identify optimal cluster number and later different cluster number are used to acquire perfect silhouette score [13].

2.3 Degradation Modeling and risk assessment maps

Reaction rates for hydrolysis were derived using Peck's model [14] [15], as represented in equation (4) for worldwide climate. Micro-climate-based degradation reaction rate risk maps were developed.

$$k_h = A_H * rh_{eff}^n * exp\left[\frac{-E_a}{k_B \cdot T_m}\right] \quad (4)$$

The data were then categorized into 20 zones from minimum to maximum value of that respective degradation rate.

3 RESULTS

3.1 Microclimate analysis

The global climate data obtained from NASA POWER dataset is input into various models to derive the micro climate data essential to understand the climate stressors on PV module performance.

Front side POA irradiance: During daylight hours, the POA irradiance on the front side consistently surpasses the global horizontal irradiance (GHI), as shown in figure 2 on a day (21.03.2018).

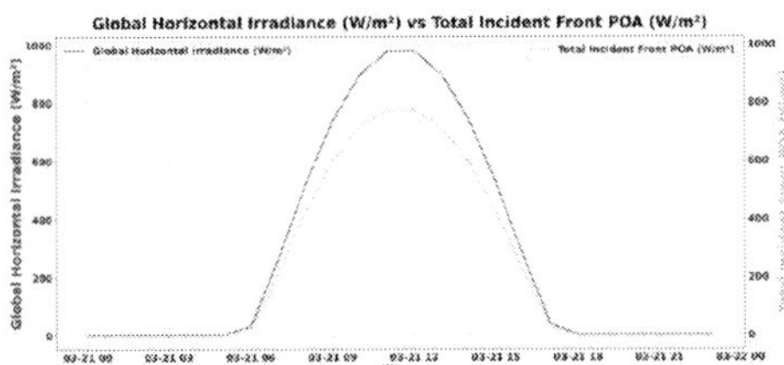

Figure 2: Daily variation of Irradiance: Comparison of GHI and POA front incident

In midday POA peaks, results from the panels tilt and orientation that optimize direct beam exposure and enhance the collection of diffuse irradiances

Rear side POA irradiance: The POA irradiance on the rear side is significantly lower than both GHI and POA front, as shown in figure 3 for a day. This lower level is only due the ground reflected irradiance, influenced by factors such as albedo, ground clearance ratios, PV row height and width.

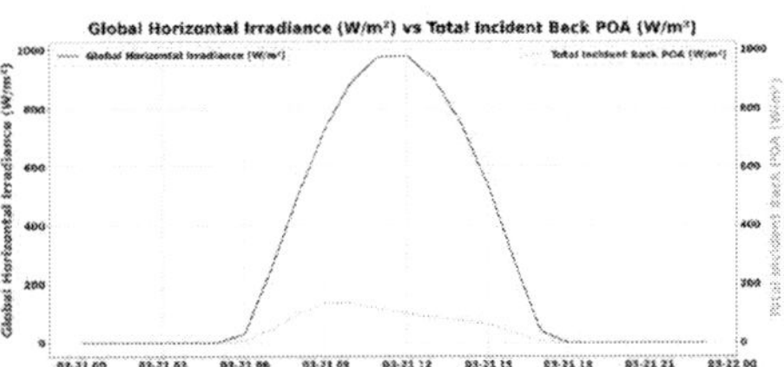

Figure 3: Daily variation of Irradiance: Comparison of GHI and POA back incident

Module temperature: The temperature of the PV module is higher than ambient air temperature, reaching notably high values at midday. Global PV module temperature distributed in 20 zones as shown in figure 4. The increase in temperature is driven due to the elevated POA on front and bank, partially offset from cooling due to wind speed are also observed.

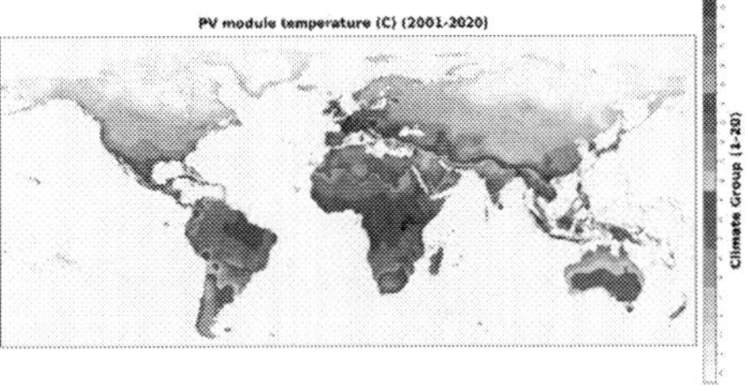

Figure 4: Global PV module temperature microclimate distribution in 20 zones

Module relative humidity: The relative humidity near the module drops considerably below the ambient relative humidity during peak solar hours. This decrease is caused by an increase in saturation vapor pressure, which lowers the local available humidity due to higher module temperature and POA irradiance, as shown in figure 5.

During the day, when temperature and POA at their peak, moisture egress the PV module. Conversely, in the evening and at night moisture starts ingress into the PV module.

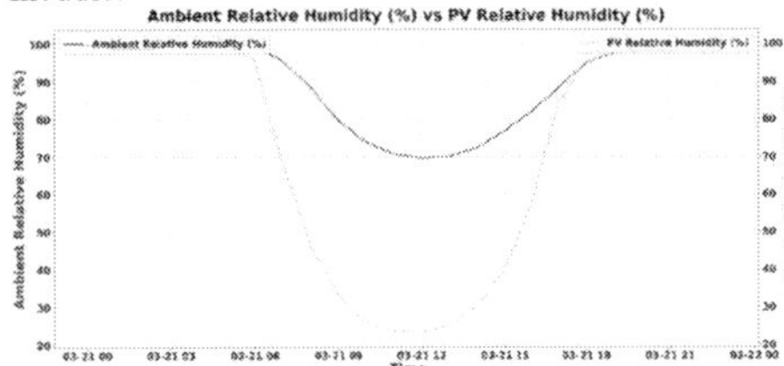

Figure 5: Daily variation of Relative humidity: Comparison of Ambient and PV Relative humidity

These results may vary on other days depending on variations of input parameters, emphasizing the dynamic nature of microclimate influence on PV performance.

3.2 Standardization, PCA, k-means cluster, and Silhouette score observations

To evaluate the efficacy of statistical clustering for PV climate zoning, we applied the principal component analysis (PCA) followed by k-means clustering to the derived PV microclimate properties such as module temperature, module relative humidity, saturation vapor pressure, POA on front, POA on back and precipitation.

The data were normalized and standardized, then the six selected variables reduced via PCA from 2 dimensions capturing 81.23% explain variance to 6 dimensions capturing 100% explained variance.

K-means clustering is performed with and the resulting cluster were assessed using the silhouette scores within cluster sum of squares (WCSS), visual inspection of cluster overlaps and comparisons with KG climate classifications. The elbow method is used to determine the optimal cluster number and the silhouette score is also calculated as an indicator that helps to understand the k-means [16] [17] cluster formed. The density k-means cluster of 2-dimensional PCA is shown in figure 6.

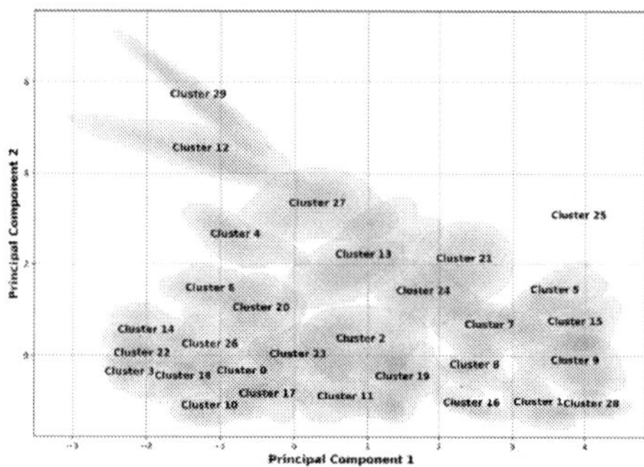

Figure 6: Global PV microclimate data with 30 cluster of two dimensional PCA

The generated cluster exhibited a low silhouette score of 0.36 with 15 clusters determined using the elbow method. Subsequently, the k-means analysis with 30 clusters also resulted in a low silhouette score of 0.37. Overall, low score across the cluster number 2 to 30 suggests poor clustering and potential overlaps among the microclimate data.

3.3 Risk assessment maps

The respective nonreversible degradation reaction rates were calculated and aggregated for 20 years for the world map. Figure 7 illustrates the global hydrolytic distribution of degradation rate.

It reveals, hydrolytic degradation (k_h) accounts for moisture driven degradation influenced by effective relative humidity (rh_{eff}^n) and module temperature (T_m). The risk maps suggest that the micro-climate for PV does not align strictly with KG's broader climate definitions.

(a) High degradation rates regions (Zones 15-19) are concentrated in humid equatorial regions. These climates, characterized by high moisture and temperature, exhibit accelerated chemical degradation breakdown of PV module materials, as humidity facilitates hydrolysis reactions.

(b) Moderate degradation rate regions (Zones 10-14) are observed in subtropical areas, where seasonal humidity contributes to intermediate degradation risks.

(c) Low degradation rates regions (Zones 0-9) are dominated by high latitude regions, reflecting limited moisture availability through year around.

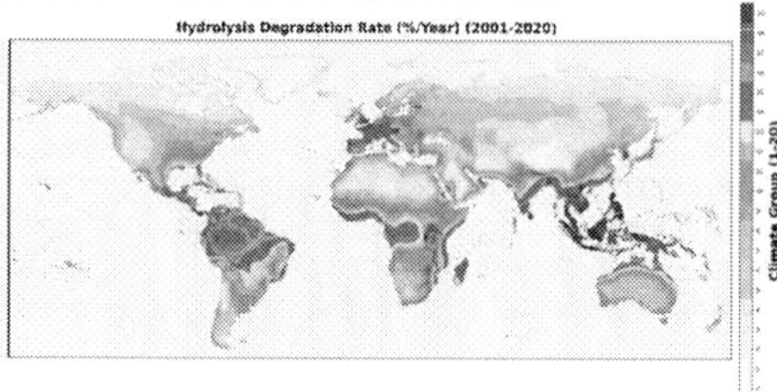

Figure 7: Global Maps of PV Hydrolytic Degradation Rate (k_h) in 20 zones

These risk maps are specific to degradation reaction rates for the analyzed locations. The resultant risk assessment maps in figure 7 significantly diverged from traditional KG classifications, offering enhanced granularity in providing the climatic classification specific to PV application. A summary of these findings is provided in Table 1.

Table 1: Overview of Degradation Mechanisms and High-Risk Regions for PV Systems

Primary Drivers	High-Risk Regions	Degradation mode
Effective relative humidity (RH_eff^h) and Module temperature (T_m)	Humid equatorial zones: Southeast Asia, Amazon Basin, Central Africa, Northern Australia	Corrosion Delamination Issues Discoloration effects Weaken solder bond

4 CONCLUSION

This study highlights that KG Classification is inadequate for precise PV system design. The analysis demonstrates that key micro-climate properties crucial for PV applications do not align with the broad climatic zones suggested by the KG. k-means clustering is unsittable for PV climate classification due to significant overlaps among climate groups. The continues and transitional nature of PV microclimate further complicates effective clustering, revealing a need for a more flexible approach.

Utilizing immediate micro-climate data alongside a degradation driven model can help us derive accurate risk assessment maps for the respective degradation type, ultimately improving the accuracy of PV reliability under varied climates. The insights from this study advocate for a shift towards leveraging detailed micro-climate analytics to enhance PV systems reliability and planning, providing a more adaptable and accurate framework than traditional KG classification. This progression highlights the transformative potential of integration advanced data analytics with environmental science to address the demand for sustainable energy sources.

4 ACKNOLEDGEMENT

The work generated from the members from Anhalt University of Applied Sciences is supported by the German Federal Ministry for Economic Affairs and

Climate Action (BMWK) under the funding program WIPANO – Knowledge and Technology Transfer through Patents and Standards under the project, "PolymAERA - Gebrauchstauglichkeitsprüfungen für Polymere als Rückseitenisolierung in Photovoltaikmodulen" (Project Number: 03TN0053C) and "Folie40 – Modellierung der foliendefinierten Moduldegradation" (Project Number: 03EE1173E)

5. REFERENCES

[1] Köppen, W. (1918). Classification of climates according to temperature, precipitation and seasonal cycle. Petermanns Geogr. Mitt, 64, 193–203.

[2] M. Kottek, J. Grieser, C. Beck, B. Rudolf, and F. Rubel, "World map of the Köppen-Geiger climate classification updated," Meteorologische Zeitschrift, vol. 15, no. 3, pp. 259–263, Jun. 2006, doi: 10.1127/0941-2948/2006/0130

[3] M. Kottek, J. Grieser, C. Beck, B. Rudolf, and F. Rubel, "World map of the Köppen-Geiger climate classification updated," Meteorologische Zeitschrift, vol. 15, no. 3, pp. 259–263, Jun. 2006, doi: 10.1127/0941-2948/2006/0130

[4] Karin, Todd & Jones, Christian & Jain, Anubhav. (2020). Photovoltaic climate zones: the global distribution of climate stressors affecting photovoltaic degradation. 10.4229/EUPVSEC20192019-4BO.13.1.

[5] Zhu J, Gottschalg R, Koehl M, Hoffmann S, Berger K, Zamini S, Bennett I, Gerritsen E, Malbranche P, Pugliatti P, Di Stefano A, Aleo F, Bertani D, Paletta F, Roca F, Graditi G, Pellegrino M, Zubillaga O, Cano P, Pozza A, Sample T. Changes of solar cell parameters during damp-heat exposure. (WCPEC-6); 2015. p. 1117-1118. JRC94887

[6] I. Kaaya, D. Mansour, P. Gebhardt, K. Weiß, D. Philipp, in 2021 IEEE 48th Photovoltaic Specialists Conf. (PVSC), Philadephia, USA 2021

[7] NASA Langley Research Center (LaRC) POWER Project. (2024). NASA Prediction of Worldwide Energy Resources (POWER) Project: CERES and MERRA-2 Data. Accessed on (2024). Retrieved from (https://power.larc.nasa.gov/)

[8] P. Ineichen and R. Perez, "A new airmass independent formulation for the Linke turbidity coefficient," Solar Energy, vol. 73, no. 3, pp. 151-157, Sep. 2002. doi: 10.1016/S0038-092X(02)00045-2.

[9] W. F. Holmgren, C. W. Hansen and M. A. Mikofski, "pvlib python: A python package for modeling solar energy systems", Journal of Open-Source Software, vol. 3, no. 29, pp. 884, 2018.

[10] M. Abou Anoma, D. Jacob, B. C. Bourne, J. A. Scholl, D. M. Riley, and C. W. Hansen, "View factor model and validation for bifacial pv and diffuse shade on single-axis trackers," in 2017 IEEE 44th Photovoltaic Specialist Conference (PVSC), pp. 1549–1554, IEEE, 2017.

[11] Köhl, Michael & Heck, Markus & Wiesmeier, Stefan. (2012). Modelling of conditions for accelerated lifetime testing of Humidity impact on PV-modules based on monitoring of climatic data. Solar Energy Materials and Solar Cells. 99. 282–291. 10.1016/j.solmat.2011.12.011.

[12] N. Zhang, K. Leatham, J. Xiong, and J. Zhong, "PCA-K-Means Based Clustering Algorithm for High Dimensional and Overlapping Spectra Signals," in 2018 Ninth International Conference on Intelligent Control and Information Processing (ICICIP), IEEE, Nov. 2018, pp. 349–354. doi: 10.1109/ICICIP.2018.8606667.

[12] N. Zhang, K. Leatham, J. Xiong, and J. Zhong, "PCA-K-Means Based Clustering Algorithm for High Dimensional and Overlapping Spectra Signals," in 2018 Ninth International Conference on Intelligent Control and Information Processing (ICICIP), IEEE, Nov. 2018, pp. 349–354. doi: 10.1109/ICICIP.2018.8606667.

[13] F. Wang, H. H. Franco-Penya, J. D. Kelleher, J. Pugh, and R. Ross, "An analysis of the application of simplified silhouette to the evaluation of k-means clustering validity," in Lecture Notes in Computer Science (including subseries Lecture Notes in Artificial Intelligence and Lecture Notes in Bioinformatics), Springer Verlag, 2017, pp. 291–305. doi: 10.1007/978-3-319-62416-7_21.

[14] Escobar, L. A. and W. Q. Meeker (2007, August). A Review of Accelerated Test Models. arXiv:0708.0369 [stat]. arXiv: 0708.0369. 11, 16, 24

[15] Jordan, D. and S. Kurtz (2010, June). Analytical improvements in PV degradation rate determination. In 2010 35th IEEE Photovoltaic Specialists Conference, pp. 002688– 002693. ISSN: 0160-8371, 0160-8371. 11

[16] Marutho, Dhendra & Handaka, Sunarna & Wijaya, Ekaprana & Muljono, Muljono. (2018). The Determination of Cluster Number at k-Mean Using Elbow Method and Purity Evaluation on Headline News. 533-538. 10.1109/ISEMANTIC.2018.85497

[17] Kladas, A., Lagast, K., Herteleer, B., & Cappelle, J. (Year). Climate clustering for photovoltaic interest. In Proceedings of the 41st European Photovoltaic Solar Energy Conference and Exhibition. KU Leuven Research Group ELECTA, Ghent, Belgium.

HOCHSCHULE ANHALT University of Applied Sciences

Evaluating the Suitability of Köppen-Geiger Climate Classifications for Photovoltaic Systems: Micro-climate Analysis and Risk Assessment Maps

Pavan Kumar Panda[1], Hugo Sanchez[1,2], Leila Mortazavifar[1,2], Ralph Gottschalg[1,2]

E-Mail: Pavan.Panda@hs-anhalt.de

[1] Hochschule Anhalt University of Applied Sciences, Bernburger Str. 55, 06366, Köthen, Germany

[2] Fraunhofer-Center for Silicon Photovoltaics CSP, Halle (Saale), Germany

Motivation

- Photovoltaic (PV) system performance and durability depend on local climate conditions. However, the widely used Köppen-Geiger (KG) climate classification, designed for ecology, is inadequate for PV climate classification
- KG's focus on temperature and precipitation overlooks critical micro climate factors that drive PV material degradation
- This gap leads to inaccurate climate zoning for PV, risking suboptimal system design and reduced reliability in diverse global environments
- Our research develops PV-Specific risk maps to address these limitations, enabling better and sustainability for the solar industry

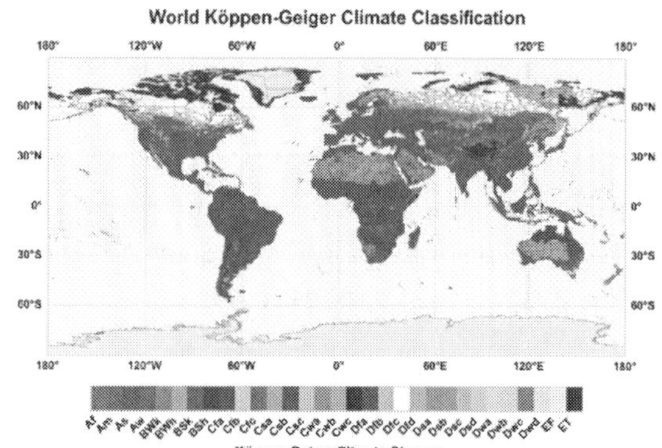

World Köppen-Geiger Climate Classification

Figure 1: World Map of the Köppen-Geiger climatic classification, generated using data

Methodology

- **Data Source:** Global data → NASA POWER (CERES/MERRA-2) → 2001-2020
- **Micro-climate model:**
  - Ineichen/Perez model - POA Irradiance back and front
  - Faiman's model - Module temperature
  - Magnus-Tetens approximation – Module saturation vapor pressure
  - Michael Koehl model - Module relative humdity
- **PV specific microclimate variables:** POA Irradiance front, POA Irradiance back, module relative humidity, module saturation vapour pressure, module temperature and wind speed
- **Analysis:** Standardize data; PCA (6 to 2 Dimension); k-means clustering (elbow method)
- **Degradation model:** Hydrolysis (Peck's) Model

PV module temperature (C) (2001-2020)

Figure 2: Global PV Module Temperature Distribution Across 20 Climate Zones

Results

PCA and Clustering Overlaps

- The available 6-dimensional micro-climate variables data is reduced into 2D PCA
- K-means clustering was assessed with silhouette scores, WCSS, and visual inspections.
- 2D PCA of micro-climate data (81.23% variance, silhouette score 0.37) shows massive overlaps in KG zones, indicating KG's inadequacy for PV-specific climates

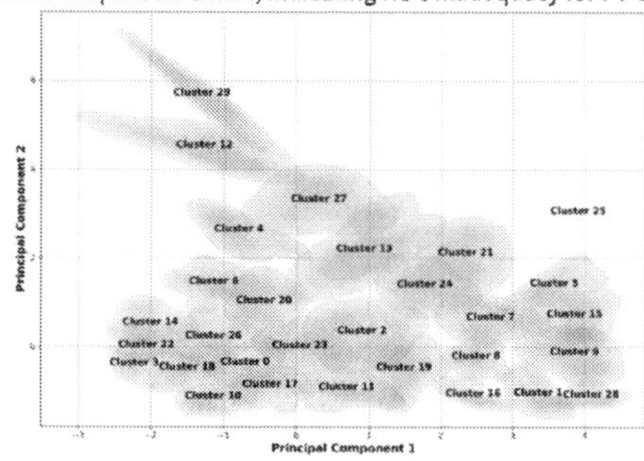

Figure 3: Global PV microclimate data with 30 cluster of two dimensional PCA

PV Hydrolysis Specific Degradation Map

- Using pecks model, non reversible hydrolysis degradation reaction rate were calculated and aggregated for 20 years for the world map
- High probability of corrosion, delamination, discoloration, and weakened solder joints degradation modes occur in top climate groups

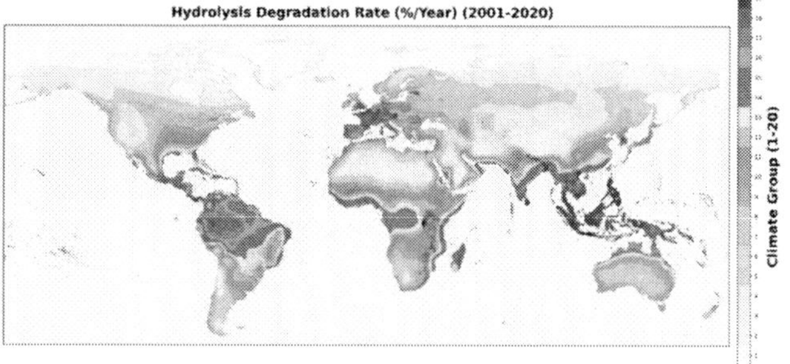

Hydrolysis Degradation Rate (%/Year) (2001-2020)

Figure 4: Global Maps of PV Hydrolytic Degradation Rate (K_h) in 20 zones

Conclusion

- KG does not map uniquely on hydrolydsis failure (nor on other failure modes)
- Current clustering shows significant overlaps and poor silhouette scores, indicating ineffective microclimate differentiation.
- Micro-climate along with degradation models enable precise PV risk assessment
- Derived 20 years aggregated risk maps diverge from KG, offering precise PV climate zoning
- Future Work: Expand degradation drives, integrate into design tools

References

[1] Köppen, W. (1918). Classification of climates according to temperature, precipitation and seasonal cycle. Petermanns Geogr. Mitt, 64, 193–203.

[2] Karin, Todd & Jones, Christian & Jain, Anubhav. (2020). Photovoltaic climate zones: the global distribution of climate stressors affecting photovoltaic degradation. 10.4229/EUPVSEC20192019-4BO.13.1.

[3] J. Ascencio-Vásquez, K. Brecl, and M. Topič, "Methodology of Köppen-Geiger-Photovoltaic climate classification and implications to worldwide mapping of PV system performance," Solar Energy, vol. 191, pp. 672-685, Oct. 2019. doi: 10.1016/j.solener.2019.08.072.

[4] NASA Langley Research Center (LaRC) POWER Project. (2024). NASA Prediction of Worldwide Energy Resources (POWER) Project: CERES and MERRA-2 Data. Accessed on (2024). Retrieved from (https://power.larc.nasa.gov/)

ACKNOWLEDGEMENT   This work is supported by the German Federal Ministry of Economics and Climate Protection (BMWK) under the project "PolymAERA", Funding code: 03TN0053C and project " Folie40" Funding code: 03EE1173E

020285-001

SATELLITE-DERIVED IRRADIANCE DATA FOR PV PERFORMANCE ASSESSMENT IN HIGH LATITUDES

Hugo Huerta[1], Juha Karhu[2], Shuo Wang[1], Sami Jouttijärvi[3], Samuli Ranta[1], Anders Lindfors[2], Kati Miettunen[3]
1. Turku University of Applied Sciences, Joukahaisenkatu 7, 20520 Turku, Finland
2. Finnish Meteorological Institute, Erik Palménin aukio 1, FI-00560 Helsinki, Finland
3. University of Turku, Vesilinnantie 5, 20500 Turku, Finland
Corresponding author: hugo.huerta@turkuamk.fi

ABSTRACT: The rapid adoption of photovoltaic (PV) systems in Nordic countries, has made accurate performance evaluation increasingly important. In Finland, microgenerators below 1 MW now collectively exceed 1 GW, and large-scale PV plants are being considered as part of the national energy strategy. Reliable performance assessments help verify energy yield, identify operational issues, and support planning for future installations. A key challenge is the limited availability of high-resolution meteorological data. Ground-based measurements are sparse and often located far from PV sites, reducing their usefulness for site-specific analysis. Satellite-derived solar radiation data offers a promising alternative, but its accuracy can be affected by latitude. Above 60° N, where many Finnish PV systems are located, geostationary satellite coverage becomes less precise, potentially introducing bias. This study evaluates the suitability of EUMETSAT's CMSAF SARAH-3 data for PV performance modelling in Finland. Multi-year PV production data from several sites is compared against simulations using both satellite-derived and ground-station datasets. Results indicate that SARAH-3 achieves good agreement with measured data with coefficient of determination above 0.9 for global horizontal irradiance, suggesting it can serve as a reliable alternative where ground data is unavailable, enabling improved PV performance monitoring and planning in high-latitude regions.
Keywords: Solar irradiance, satellite-derived, energy yield

1 INTRODUCTION

The rapid growth of photovoltaic (PV) systems in Nordic countries, particularly Finland, has created a need for robust methods to evaluate system performance and energy yield. In Finland, microgeneration installations with capacities below 1 MW have collectively surpassed 1 GW in only a few years, and the deployment of large-scale PV plants is increasingly being considered as part of the national energy strategy [1]. As PV adoption accelerates, performance assessment plays a crucial role in verifying expected yields, identifying operational challenges, and supporting planning decisions for future installations.

A major obstacle in conducting accurate performance evaluations lies in the availability and quality of meteorological data. High-resolution solar irradiance measurements are essential for determining site-specific energy production, yet ground-based meteorological stations are sparse in general and often located tens or even hundreds of kilometres from PV sites. This spatial limitation constraints performance analyses, especially in regions with highly variable weather patterns [2].

Satellite-derived solar radiation data offers a potential solution to this challenge. Such datasets provide continuous spatiotemporal coverage and can overcome the limitations of sparse ground measurements. However, their accuracy at high latitudes remains an open question. Above 60°N, where the PV systems under study are located, geostationary satellite coverage becomes less precise, leading to possible biases in irradiance estimates. As a result, it is critical to validate satellite-based data products against actual ground station measurements as well as their usage for simulating PV systems to determine their suitability for performance assessments in Nordic conditions.

This study addresses this gap by evaluating the reliability of irradiance data from EUMETSAT's Climate Monitoring Satellite Application Facility (CMSAF) SARAH-3 interim climate data record [3] for PV system performance modelling in Finland. Using historical data from PV systems with different configurations and distributed across different regions (**Figure 1**), we compare simulated energy yields, obtained using both satellite-derived and ground-station datasets, with measured production data over multiple years. Advanced PV system modelling, including 3D scene representations in PVsyst [4], is employed to ensure realistic simulations accounting for shading and site-specific effects.

By quantifying the deviations between simulated and measured energy yields, this work provides an assessment of the accuracy and applicability of satellite-derived irradiance data in high-latitude environments. The results offer practical guidance for PV operators, researchers, and energy planners on the use of satellite data for performance monitoring, resource assessment, and forecasting in northern climates.

2 METHODOLOGY

The methodology is organized into four stages: (i) data acquisition and processing, (ii) PV system modelling, (iii) simulation setup, and (iv) analysis and performance evaluation.

2.1 Data Acquisition and Processing

Historical PV production data was obtained from three grid-connected systems Helsinki, Kuopio, and Turku (Table I). Each system provided at least six consecutive years of production records at 1–5 minute resolution, enabling detailed time-series analysis and robust statistical comparison with simulated results. **Figure 2** illustrates the normalized daily energy production for one of the study sites, Kuopio, located near 63° N latitude. As shown, production drops to nearly zero during the winter months, reflecting the strong seasonal effect at high latitudes. This seasonal variability is a critical factor in performance assessment and underscores the importance of accurate data for simulation and yield estimation in Nordic climates.

10.4229/EUPVSEC2025/4BV.3.26

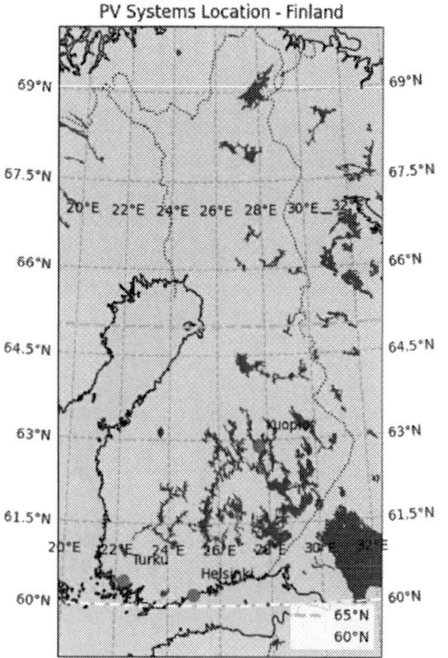

Figure 1: Geographic location of PV systems used for the study.

Table I: PV systems under study

Parameter	Location		
	Helsinki	**Kuopio**	**Turku**
Latitude (°)	60.204	62.892	60.447
Longitude (°)	24.961	27.634	22.297
Altitude (m)	30	85	29
Commission date	24/08/2015	19/08/2016	30/07/2017
PV module	SolarWorld	SolarWatt Blue	KingdomSolar
PV technology	Poly-Si	Poly-Si	Poly-Si
Nominal capacity of module (Wp)	250	260	250
Nominal capacity of system (kWp)	21	20.3	4.5

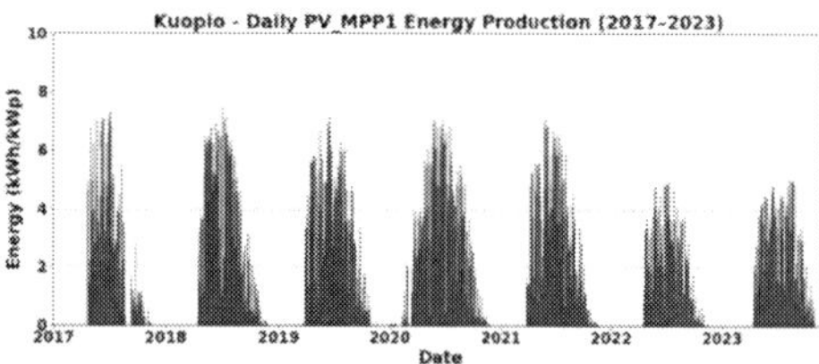

Figure 2: Normalized daily PV production for the Kuopio site (63° N).

Ground-based meteorological measurements, including global horizontal irradiance (GHI), direct normal irradiance (DNI), diffuse horizontal irradiance (DHI), and ambient temperature among some other weather variables, were also available at 1–10 minute intervals from the meteo stations available at the sites, and served as a validation benchmark. **Figure 3** illustrates the measured GHI at Kuopio's site.

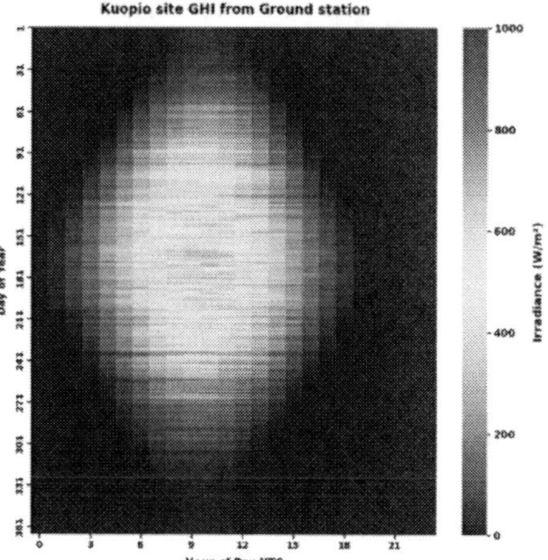

Figure 3: Measured GHI, agreggated to hourly values, for Kuopio site (63° N).

Satellite-derived irradiance data was obtained from the CMSAF SARAH-3 Interim Climate Data Record [3] at 30-minute temporal resolution. SARAH-3 is a satellite-based climate data record derived from Meteosat observations, providing solar surface irradiance (SIS) as well as direct horizontal (SID) and direct normal irradiance (DNI) on a $0.05° \times 0.05°$ grid. This data covers the region between $\pm 65°$ latitude and $\pm 65°$ longitude from January 1983 to the present, with operational updates available within about 5 days. For this study, DNI was calculated from SIS and SID.

Quality control checks on all datasets were performed to remove missing or anomalous data points before integration into the simulation environment. Figure 4 illustrates the SARAH-3 GHI at Kuopio's site.

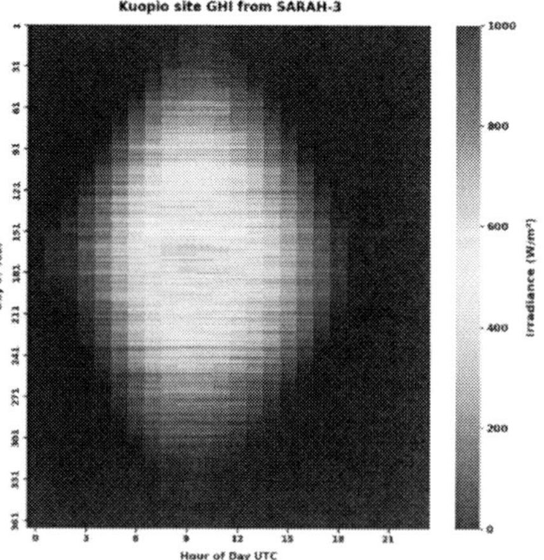

Figure 4: SARAH-3 GHI, agreggated to hourly values, for Kuopio site (63° N).

2.2 PV System Modelling

Each PV installation was modelled in PVsyst using detailed 3D representations of the site to capture geometric effects and near-shading losses from surrounding obstacles, **Figure 5**. System parameters, including module type, inverter configuration, tilt, azimuth, and system losses, were configured based on as-built data provided by the system owners. This level of detail ensured that simulated energy yields closely reflected actual system behaviour.

Figure 5: Accurate 3D model in PVsyst Software used in the simulations for Kuopio site (63° N).

2.3 Simulation Setup

Performance simulations were conducted in PVsyst using two input datasets:

1. **Ground-based dataset:** measured irradiance components and meteorological parameters from stations located few meters away from the PV systems.

2. **Satellite-derived dataset:** GHI, DNI and DHI (Estimated from GHI and DNI), and ambient temperature from closest station.

A comparison of both data sets for a summer day is shown in **Figure 6**. Simulations were performed over the entire multi-year historical period for which production data was available (minimum of six years per site), using its corresponding ground-based or satellite-derived meteorological dataset. This allowed for the evaluation of interannual variability and improved the robustness of the statistical analysis.

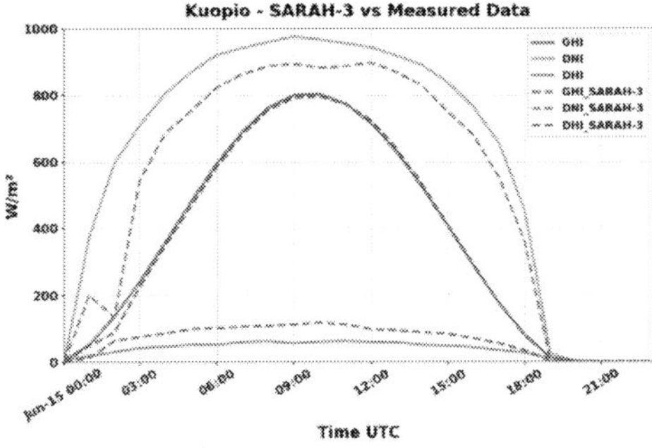

Figure 6: Irradiance components comparison from SARAH-3 and measured data for Kuopio site (63° N)

2.4. Analysis and Performance Evaluation

Metrics quantifying the deviation between SARAH-3 and measured irradiance components were computed, including mean bias error (MBE), root mean square error

(RMSE), and coefficient of determination (R^2). These metrics were selected as they provide complementary insights into data quality: MBE quantifies systematic bias between datasets, RMSE measures the magnitude of random and systematic deviations, and R^2 assesses the strength of correlation between measured and modelled values. Together, these metrics enable a comprehensive evaluation of both accuracy and precision. The same set of metrics was calculated for the simulated energy yields obtained using the two datasets, allowing a direct assessment of how input data discrepancies propagate to PV performance predictions

3 RESULTS AND DISCUSSION

In the following, results comparing satellite-derived irradiance data with ground-station measurements are presented, as well as hourly PV energy yield simulations.

Table 2 summarizes the metrics for the site closest to the spatial limits of SARAH-3 data coverage. Kuopio site is highlighted since, as described in Section 2.1, it lies near the northern boundary of reliable satellite retrievals, where larger deviations between measured and satellite-derived irradiance are expected.

Table II: Metrics for Irradiance components comparison

Kuopio site - Measured vs SARAH-3 data metrics				
	Year	MBE [W/m²]	RMSE [W/m²]	R^2
GHI	2018	-3.37	38.97	0.96
	2019	-5.23	39.92	0.95
	2020	-3.96	38.85	0.95
	2021	-1.00	41.04	0.95
	2022	-4.18	45.35	0.93
	2023	-2.86	42.5	0.95
DNI	2018	-25.34	111.63	0.84
	2019	-26.28	113.44	0.80
	2020	-26.20	104.83	0.83
	2021	-21.70	117.98	0.79
	2022	-26.69	124.72	0.77
	2023	-16.95	112.11	0.82
DHI	2018	4.54	32.6	0.76
	2019	4.00	32.73	0.81
	2020	5.63	31.47	0.81
	2021	5.22	30.64	0.81
	2022	4.27	33.37	0.80
	2023	1.73	32.26	0.80

Figure 7 summarizes the metrics for the three components of the irradiance for all the sites.

The results clearly indicate that the GHI irradiance component exhibits the highest accuracy across all sites. In contrast, DNI shows significantly larger deviations, which in turn propagate to the DHI component, leading to increased uncertainty in its metrics.

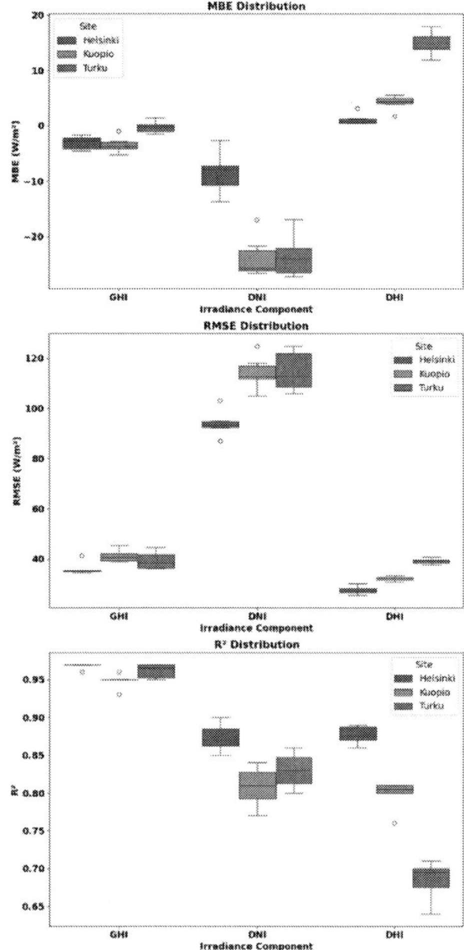

Figure 7: Irradiance components metrics for SARAH-3 and measured data, all sites.

Metrics from the simulation results, are summarized in **Table III**, once again, these metrics are for the site closest to the spatial limits of SARAH-3 data coverage.

Table III: Metrics for Irradiance components comparison

Kuopio site – Ground Station vs SARAH-3 Energy yield (Hourly) metrics			
Year	MBE [kWh]	RMSE [kWh/kWp]	R^2
2018	-0.10	0.05	0.92
2019	-0.04	0.04	0.96
2020	-0.10	0.04	0.95
2021	-0.07	0.04	0.95
2022	0.02	0.04	0.94
2023	-0.02	0.04	0.94

Results indicate that PV system simulations using satellite-derived irradiance data achieve acceptable accuracy when compared with reference ground-station simulations. Deviations in simulated energy yields are within approximately 0.04 kWh/kWp, with location-dependent variations. **Figure 8** provides a consolidated view of the deviations in energy yield estimates derived from hourly simulations for the three sites using satellite data.

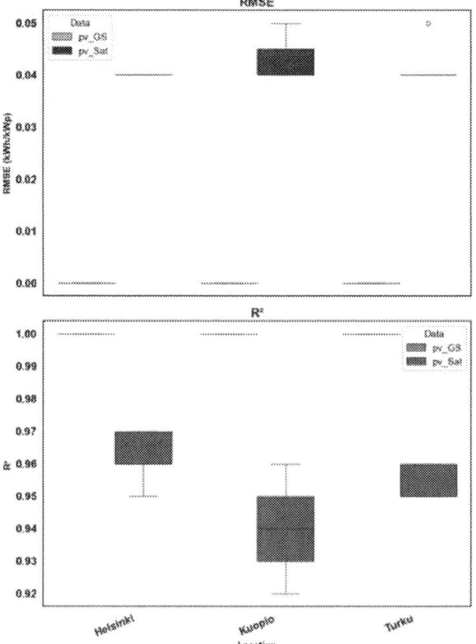

Figure 8: Enery yield metrics for SARAH-3 and ground station simulation, all sites.

Overall, the results are promising and demonstrate that satellite-derived datasets can serve as a reliable alternative for PV system performance assessment in regions where ground-station measurements are unavailable. This is particularly evident for the sites near 60° N latitude, such as Helsinki and Turku, which exhibited lower variability in errors and higher correlation (R^2) values compared to the northernmost site.

4 CONCLUSIONS

The analysis revealed that GHI is consistently the most accurate irradiance component across all sites, whereas DNI shows higher deviations, which propagate to the DHI component. This suggests that further improvement could be achieved by recalculating DNI using different models, taking GHI as the primary input and combining it with the clear sky model. Such an approach may reduce uncertainty in DNI- and DHI-based simulations and improve overall PV yield estimation accuracy.

This study is novel, as no prior research has systematically evaluated the performance of satellite-derived irradiance data for PV system assessment in Finland. While earlier studies have compared irradiance estimations from various geostationary and polar-orbiting satellites [5, 6] and addressed solar resource forecasting [7], this work specifically examines the influence of using satellite-based data on PV production estimates in high-latitude conditions.

5 AKNOWLEDGMENTS

The work is funded by the Strategic Research Council (SRC) established within the Research Council of Finland under the project RealSolar (project numbers 359141, 358542, 358543)

6 REFERENCES

1. Finnish Energy Authority, News, 2024. Solar power production capacity rose to 1,000 megawatts. https://energiavirasto.fi/en/-/solar-power-production-capacity-rose-to-1-000-megawatts, last access January 2025.
2. Herman Böök, Antti Poikonen, Antti Aarva, Tero Mielonen, Mikko R.A. Pitkänen, Anders V. Lindfors, Photovoltaic system modeling: A validation study at high latitudes with implementation of a novel DNI quality control method, Solar Energy, Volume 204, 2020, Pages 316-329, ISSN 0038-092X, https://doi.org/10.1016/j.solener.2020.04.068.
3. Pfeifroth, Uwe; Kothe, Steffen; Drücke, Jaqueline; Trentmann, Jörg; Schröder, Marc; Selbach, Nathalie; Hollmann, Rainer (2023): Surface Radiation Data Set - Heliosat (SARAH) - Edition 3, Satellite Application Facility on Climate Monitoring,DOI:10.5676/EUM_SAF_CM/SARAH/V 003, https://doi.org/10.5676/EUM_SAF_CM/SARAH/V00 3.
4. PVsyst Photovoltaic Software, Satigny, Switzerland. Version 8.0.13. https://www.pvsyst.com
5. Heine Nygard Riise, Magnus Moe Nygård, Bjørn Lupton Aarseth, Andreas Dobler, Erik Berge, Benchmark of estimated solar irradiance data at high latitude locations, Solar Energy, Volume 282, 2024, 112975, ISSN 0038-092X, https://doi.org/10.1016/j.solener.2024.112975.
6. Bilal Babar, Rune Graversen, Tobias Boström, Evaluating CM-SAF solar radiation CLARA-A1 and CLARA-A2 datasets in Scandinavia, Solar Energy, Volume 170, 2018, Pages 76-85, ISSN 0038-092X, https://doi.org/10.1016/j.solener.2018.05.009.
7. Viivi Kallio-Myers, Aku Riihelä, Panu Lahtinen, Anders Lindfors, Global horizontal irradiance forecast for Finland based on geostationary weather satellite data, Solar Energy, Volume 198, 2020, Pages 68-80, ISSN 0038-092X, https://doi.org/10.1016/j.solener.2020.01.008.

OPTIMIZED ALBEDOMETER HEIGHT: A SIMPLE MODEL FOR ACCURATE ALBEDO MEASUREMENT

Eneko Ortega[1,2], Eneko Cereceda[1], Nekane Azkona[1], Alona Otaegi[1], Vanesa Fano[1],
Jose Ruben Gutierrez[1] and Juan Carlos Jimeno[1]
[1] Technological Institute of Microelectronics, University of the Basque Country UPV/EHU, 48013, Bilbao, Spain
[2] Electricity and Electronics Department, University of the Basque Country UPV/EHU, 48940, Leioa, Spain
eneko.ortegam@ehu.eus

ABSTRACT: Albedo estimation is a key parameter to determine the performance of PV systems with bifacial technology. Effective albedo measurement relies on the measured irradiance by the rear side of the albedometer, which depends on the albedometer view factor, depending on the sensor placement height and sensor area. This study presents a simple mathematical model to determine the minimum albedometer height in function of the albedo sensor area and the admissible relative error during albedo measurement. The proposed model is freely available as an open-source code to determine minimum admissible height in function of specific albedometer area and admissible error for each specific application.
Keywords: photovoltaic systems, bifacial, irradiance measurement, albedo measurement, performance analysis

1 INTRODUCTION

Photovoltaic (PV) systems performance estimation is essential to determine PV systems production and to perform a correct monitoring of the PV system. This estimation relies on a series of parameters related to PV technology, the PV system design and layout and to the expected operating conditions, such as system location, climatic conditions or expected irradiation [1].

Among other parameters, surface albedo is a very relevant parameter for bifacial PV systems. Whereas for monofacial PV systems albedo has been traditionally considered constant [2] in function of the surface type of the PV system, for bifacial PV modules setting a constant albedo leads to errors ranging between 2 and 7% when estimating the PV system performance [3].

Surface albedo can be obtained from satellite measurements [2] or on-site measurements, which can provide with a higher spatial resolution [4] enhancing albedo value estimation, especially in non-uniform surfaces. The albedo value also exhibits variability associated with weather [5], humidity or seasonal effects [6], obtaining albedo variations within the same day of more than 60%. However, the uncertainty associated to the albedo measurement due to its variability is not completely aleatory and can be modeled and controlled [7], at least to determine which is the uncertainty of an on-site albedo measurement.

Several guidelines can be followed to minimize albedo measurement error, such as sensor selection and positioning [9]. Among them, the height at which the albedometer is placed plays an important role on the measurement of the actual albedo with no clear agreement of which height would be the most suitable one. While some manufacturers suggest that the placement height of the measuring systems should be around 1.5 meters, others advise placing the sensor closer to the ground [10].

Recent experimental studies indicate that lower sensor heights can significantly reduce the uncertainty in albedo measurements over heterogeneous surfaces, especially when the ground presents non-homogeneous textures or partial shading [11].

Conversely, higher albedometer placement may be advantageous when attempting to capture a more averaged or smoothed reflectance value over a larger area. Thus, the optimal height may depend on the spatial variability of the surface reflectance and the specific application of the albedo measurement.

This study implements and provides, in an open-source format, a simple model which allows for the estimation of the minimum albedometer placement height as a function of the albedometer sensor area and the admissible relative error. This model aims to ensure a correct measurement of the Ground Reflected Irradiance (GRI), which is directly linked to surface albedo.

The proposed model enables users to tailor the sensor setup to their specific environmental and technical constrains, balancing precision with practical deployment. Finally, the sensitivity of the proposed model is evaluated to assess how changes in height and sensor size influence the albedo measurement.

2 2D MATHEMATICAL MODEL

The albedo value is obtained as the ratio of the Ground Reflected Irradiance (GRI) and the Global Horizontal Irradiance (GHI). The GHI is measured by the front side of the albedometer and the GRI by the rear side. The amount of reflected irradiance is the amount of irradiation that reaches the ground surface ($G_{GROUND} = GHI$) and is reflected back (1). This value depends on the surface albedo (ρ).

$$G_{REAR} = \rho \cdot G_{GROUND} \qquad (1)$$

However, the GRI measured by the albedometer depends on the albedometer view factor, i.e., on the amount of ground surface seen by the sensor and, therefore, on the GRI the sensor receives. If we assume that the albedometer is placed horizontally and that the ground surface below is a homogeneous, uniformly illuminated with GHI, Lambertian reflector of infinite size, the albedometer view factor will depend on the height at which it is positioned and on the sensor area.

In addition, albedo measurement can be performed using pyranometers or solar cells as albedo sensors, which, in addition to having different spectral responses [11], have different sensor areas, which affect the albedo measurement.

To determine the albedometer rear irradiance (the amount of GRI that reaches the albedometer, G_{REAR}), the proposed model [12] can be divided into two steps. Firstly, if it is assumed that the albedometer is an infinitesimal flat

10.4229/EUPVSEC2025/4BV.3.27
020287-001

receptor (R), placed at a height h, it can be computed the contribution to this irradiance measured by the rear side of the albedometer of every ground segment within the field of view of the flat receptor.

For this flat receptor R, the contribution of the whole ground surface from $\phi_1 = -\frac{\pi}{2}$ to $\phi_1 = \frac{\pi}{2}$ would be equal to G_{REAR}. The contribution of a certain small segment $S_1 S_2$, as shown in Fig. 1, to the rear side irradiance of the albedo sensor can be obtained as the product of the radiance intensity, the emitted radiant flux per unit solid angle (c), and the 2D view factor of the sensor (2).

$$G_{REAR}^{S_{12}} = \int_{\phi_1}^{\phi_2} cx \cos \theta \, d\theta = cx(\sin \phi_2 - \sin \phi_1) \quad (2)$$

Where the radiance intensity is defined as:

$$c = \frac{\rho G_{GROUND}}{2} \quad (3)$$

and the angles ϕ_1 and ϕ_2 between the infinitesimal flat receptor $(0, h)$ and the edges of the segment $(S_1, 0)$ and $(S_2, 0)$ are computed as:

$$\phi_1 = \operatorname{atan}\left(\frac{S_1}{h}\right) \; and \; \phi_2 = \operatorname{atan}\left(\frac{S_2}{h}\right) \quad (4)$$

Finally, to obtain the rear irradiance due to the total ground surface, it can be obtained as the sum of the contributions of all the segments seen in Fig. 1, from $-90°$ to $90°$. Since the number of segments would be infinite with a 180 degrees view field, to compute this model the view field must be restricted (from $-89°$ to $89°$, for example), which generates a negligible error [13].

This model can be applied for an infinitesimal flat receptor R. For a real albedometer, having a receptor with a non-infinitesimal area, the same model, slightly modified, can be applied, computing the contribution of each surface segment for the whole sensor area, which will modify the view factor of the sensor. The flat receptor, instead of being at point $(0, h)$ will be placed from $(-\frac{x}{2}, h)$ to $(\frac{x}{2}, h)$, being x the sensor width.

3 OPTIMUM HEIGHT DETERMINATION

To validate the proposed model a set of sensor areas $(5, 10, 15 \; and \; 20 \; cm^2)$ were considered and for a theoretical case of $800 \, W/m^2$ GHI and an homogeneous surface albedo of 0.35 on an infinite reflector, the obtained albedo values as a function of the sensor positioning height were computed, as shown in Fig. 2.

As can be seen in Fig. 2, as the positioning height of the sensor increases, the view factor of the sensor increases also and, therefore, the irradiance reflected by the ground surface is measured more accurately which leads to smaller errors in the surface albedo estimation (the ratio between G_{REAR} and GHI).

This way, for heights above 4 meters, the error (due to the limited view factor of the ground surface at low heights source) between actual surface albedo ($\rho = 0.35$ in the proposed example) and the estimated ones (by G_{REAR} measurement) is below 1.5% for all the cases. For typical heights around 1.5 meters, the error ranges between 1.5% and 5% as a function of the sensor area between 5 to 20 cm^2.

For small sensor areas, however, even positioning the sensor at heights below 1 meter, the error between theoretical surface albedo and the estimated one remains below 3%. The evolution of the relative error between the theoretical surface albedo and the measured one, according to the proposed methodology, is shown in Fig. 3 for the same albedometer sensor areas.

The accuracy of the proposed model is also highly dependent on the sensor view factor. As previously stated, if the albedometer is placed horizontally and the ground surface is a homogeneous Lambertian reflector of infinite size the view factor depends only on the sensor area and placement height.

However, if the sensor view factor is reduced due to non-homogeneous surface or illumination, obstacles on the surrounding area or sensor geometry, among others, the sensor accuracy for determining the albedo value may be affected. Fig. 4 shows the measured albedo value with a view factor that goes between -10 and 10 meters. As can be seen in the figure, as the sensor height increases, the effect of the limited view factor reduces the accuracy of the sensor to determine albedo value.

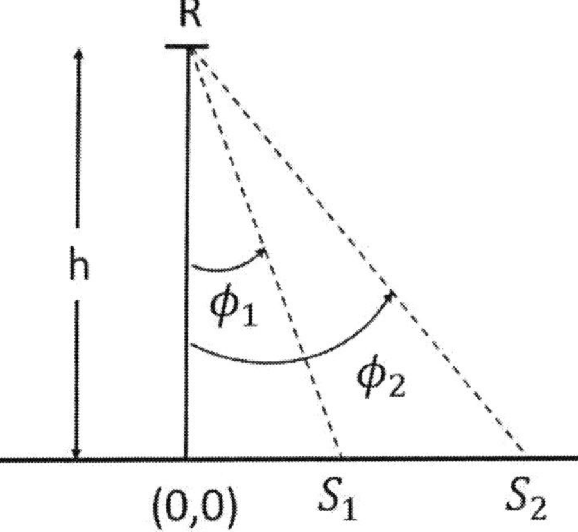

Figure 1: View factor corresponding to the S1-S2 segment for an infinitesimal flat receptor R placed at a vertical height h above the reference plane.

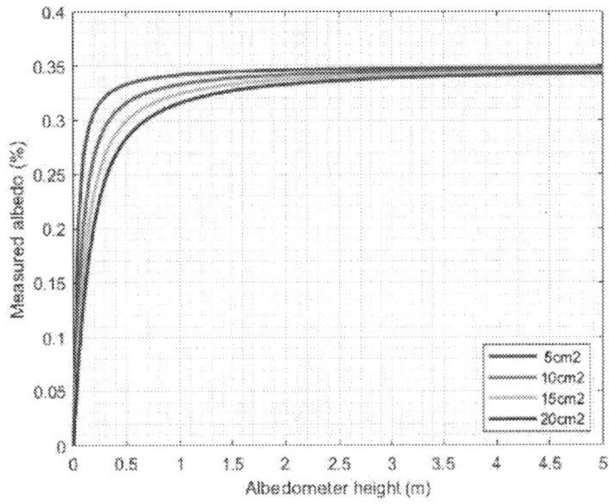

Figure 2: Estimated albedo, when considering a surface albedo of 0.35, in function of albedometer positioning height for $5, 10, 15 \; and \; 20 \; cm^2$ sensor areas.

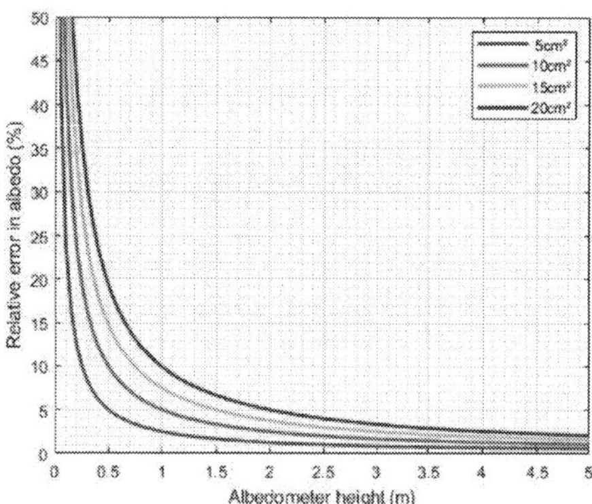

Figure 3: Relative error in albedo measurement, when considering a surface albedo of 0.35, in function of albedometer positioning height for $5, 10, 15$ and 20 cm^2 sensor areas.

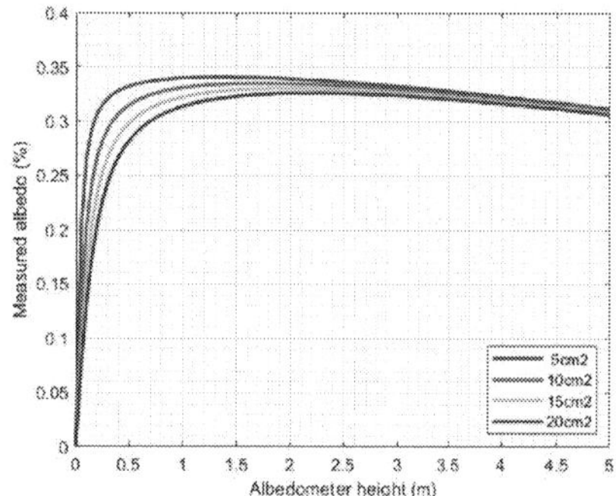

Figure 4: Measured albedo, when considering a surface albedo of 0.35, in function of albedometer positioning height for $5, 10, 15$ and 20 cm^2 sensor areas for a limited view factor between -10 and 10 meters.

4 USING THE MODEL

The proposed model has been encapsulated in a MATLAB function called *SensorHeight*. This function, for a given sensor area (given in cm^2) and a maximum admissible error (from 0 to 1), determines the minimum height at which the sensor should be placed.

The MATLAB project to determine the optimum sensor height for any specific application, in function of the admissible error, is available in a GitHub public repository:

https://github.com/EnekoOrtegaTiM/AlbedometerHeight.git

The GitHub repository contains the necessary explanations for integrating the project into MATLAB and testing the proposed function.

Fig. 5 shows an example of the use of the function to determine the minimum height at which the albedometer should be positioned when using a 15 cm^2 sensor and with a maximum permissible error of 3%.

```
>> Hmin = SensorHeight(15, 0.03); % Sensor of 10 cm2, error < 3%
>> disp(['Minimum required height: ', num2str(Hmin), ' m']);
Minimum required height: 0.9 m
>>
```

Figure 5: Example of the use of the function to determine the minimum height at which the albedometer should be positioned when using a 15 cm^2 sensor and with a maximum permissible error of 3%.

The function *SensorHeight* calculates the minimum height at which an albedometer should be positioned to ensure that the measured albedo stabilizes within a user-defined acceptable error margin. It simulates the irradiance received by a sensor of a given area located at varying heights above a reflective surface, assuming a constant ground irradiance and surface albedo. The ground is discretized into 1-meter segments, and the contribution of each segment to the sensor's measurement is integrated based on geometric considerations. The function then identifies the lowest height at which the relative difference between the measured albedo and its asymptotic value falls below the specified error threshold, thus ensuring a reliable and stable measurement.

5 CONCLUSIONS

The implemented model allows, by means of an open-source code, to determine the minimum height at which an albedometer should be positioned to achieve a maximum error requirement on the albedo estimation for several sensor areas. This could be of interest during on-site albedo measurement campaigns, since sensor positioning can become a difficult task in certain scenarios.

The model determines this height as the function of the albedometer area. Several factors have not been considered, such as surface non-homogeneity, albedometer inclination with respect to the ground surface or the sensor spectral response, among others. These new variables could be integrated on the model to boost the model accuracy to determine sensor positioning.

However, the implemented model facilitates, in a simple and fast way, to determine the minimum positioning height to ensure that at least one of the error sources during albedo measurement is under control. The developed model is available, on MATLAB, on a GitHub public repository.

Future work will be oriented to optimize the developed model to integrate the analysis of surface non-homogeneity in the albedo measurement, as well as the positioning and the inclination of the sensor. Also, the influence of the spectral response of the sensor, when measuring by a pyranometer or by reference cells based on different technologies, will be analyzed when estimating the albedo value.

6 ACKNOWLEDGEMENTS

The Spanish Agencia Estatal de Investigación MCIN/AEI/10.13039/ 501100011033 is acknowledged for financial support through the GREASE project (PID2020-113533RB-C32).

7 REFERENCES

[1] T. Georgitsioti, N. Pearsall, I. Forbes, G. Pillai, A combined model for PV system lifetime energy prediction and annual energy assessment, Sol. Energy 183 (2019). 738–744.

[2] B. Marion, Measured and satellite-derived albedo data for estimating bifacial photovoltaic system performance, Sol. Energy 215 (2021) 321–327.

[3] H. Sánchez-Ortiz, S. Dittmann, C. Meza, R. Gottschalg, The Impact of Real Albedo Values on Energy Estimation for Bifacial Modules, EU PVSEC 2021 (2021). 808 - 810.

[4] C.A. Gueymard, V. Lara-Fanego, M. Sengupta, A. Habte, Surface albedo spatial variability in North America: Gridded data vs. local measurements, Sol. Energy 227 (2021) 655–673.

[5] S. Suarez, et al. The long-term of the albedo stability under different weather conditions, EU PVSEC 2021.

[6] .N. Riedel-Lyngskær, M. Ribaconka, M. Pó, A. Thorseth, S. Thorsteinsson, C. Dam-Hansen, M.L. Jakobsen, The effect of spectral albedo in bifacial photovoltaic performance, Sol. Energy 231 (2022) 921–935.

[7] E. Ortega, et al. An statistical model for the short-term albedo estimation applied to PV bifacial modules. Renewable Energy, 2024, vol. 221, p. 119777.

[8] R. Urraca, C. Lanconelli, F. Cappucci, N. Gobron. Comparison of Long-Term Albedo Products against Spatially Representative Stations over Snow. Remote Sensing, 14(15) (2022), 3745.

[9] Gostein, Michael, et al. Measuring irradiance for bifacial PV systems. En 2021 IEEE 48th Photovoltaic Specialists Conference (PVSC). IEEE, 2021. p. 0896-0903.

[10] S. Suarez, et al., Towards optimising the albedo measurement. 37th EU PVSEC (2021).

[11] M. Rivera and R. Christian. Silicon sensors vs. Pyranometers–review of deviations and conversion of measured values. 37th European PV Solar Energy Conference and Exhibition. Vol. 7. 2020.

[12] J.R. Ledesma, R. H. Almeida, F. Martinez-Moreno, C. Rossa, J. Martín-Rueda, L. Narvarte, E. Lorenzo. A simulation model of the irradiation and energy yield of large bifacial photovoltaic plants. Solar Energy, 206 (2020), 522-538.

[13] N. Martin, J. Ruiz. Annual Angular Reflection Losses in PV Modules. Prog. Photovolt.: Res. Appl. 13, 9 (2005).

Optimized Albedometer height: A Simple Model for Accurate Albedo Measurement

Eneko Ortega[*,1,2], Eneko Cereceda[1], Nekane Azkona[1], Alona Otaegi[1],

Vanesa Fano[1], Jose Ruben Gutierrez[1] and Juan Carlos Jimeno[1]

*eneko.ortegam@ehu.eus

[1]Technological Institute of Microelectronics, UPV/EHU, 48013, Bilbao, Spain

[2]Electricity and Electronics Department, UPV/EHU, 48940, Leioa, Spain

INTRODUCTION

- The performance estimation of photovoltaic (PV) systems depends on parameters such as system design, PV technology, and operating conditions, including irradiation and albedo, specially for bifacial PV modules.
- Assuming a constant albedo in bifacial systems can lead to PV system performance estimation errors ranging from 2 to 7% [1].
- Albedo can be measured via satellite or on-site, showing high daily and seasonal variability that can be modeled to reduce uncertainty [2, 3].
- The placement height of the albedometer significantly affects measurement accuracy, with no clear consensus on the optimal height due to surface heterogeneity.

AIM

The objective of this study is to propose a simple, open-source model to estimate the minimum albedometer placement height based on sensor area and allowable relative error. This model aims to ensure a correct measurement of GRI and therefore surface albedo.

USING THE MODEL

Github repository:

```
https://github.com/EnekoOrtega
TiM/AlbedometerHeight.git
```

```
>> Hmin = SensorHeight(15, 0.03); % Sensor of 10 cm2, error < 3%
>> disp(['Minimum required height: ', num2str(Hmin), ' m']);
Minimum required height: 0.9 m
>> |
```

REFERENCES

[1] H. Sánchez-Ortiz, S. Dittmann, C. Meza, R. Gottschalg, The Impact of Real Albedo Values on Energy Estimation for Bifacial Modules, EU PVSEC 2021 (2021). 808 - 810.

[2] S. Suarez, et al. The long-term of the albedo stability under different weather conditions, EU PVSEC 2021.

[3] E. Ortega, et al. An statistical model for the short-term albedo estimation applied to PV bifacial modules. Renewable Energy, 2024, vol. 221, p. 119777.

ACKNOWLEDGEMENTS

The Spanish Agencia Estatal de Investigación MCIN/AEI/10.13039/501100011033 is acknowledged for financial support through the GREASE project (PID2020-113533RB-C32).

2D MATHEMATICAL MODEL

Albedo is obtained as the ratio between GRI and GHI:

$$G_{REAR} = \rho G_{GROUND} \quad (1)$$

- The GRI measured by the albedometer depends on the albedometer view factor.
- Albedometer placed horizontally and ground surface below is an homogeneous Lambertian reflector of infinite size. The albedometer view factor depends on:
  - The height at which it is positioned.
  - The sensor area.

For this flat receptor R, the contribution of the whole ground surface from $\phi_1 = -\frac{\pi}{2}$ to $\phi_1 = \frac{\pi}{2}$ would be equal to G_{REAR}. The contribution of a certain small segment $S_1 S_2$ to the rear side irradiance of the albedo sensor can be obtained as the product of the radiance intensity, the emitted radiant flux per unit solid angle (c), and the 2D view factor of the sensor:

$$G_{REAR}^{S12} = \int_{\phi_1}^{\phi_2} c\,x\,cos\theta\,d\theta = c\,x\,(sin\phi_2 - sin\phi_1) \quad (2)$$

and the angles ϕ_1 and ϕ_2 between the infinitesimal flat receptor $(0, h)$ and the edges of the segment $(S_1, 0)$ and $(S_2, 0)$ are computed as:

$$\phi_1 = atan(\frac{S_1}{h}) \quad and \quad \phi_2 = atan(\frac{S_2}{h}) \quad (3)$$

Finally, to obtain the rear irradiance due to the total ground surface, it can be obtained as the sum of the contributions of all the segments, from -90° to +90°.

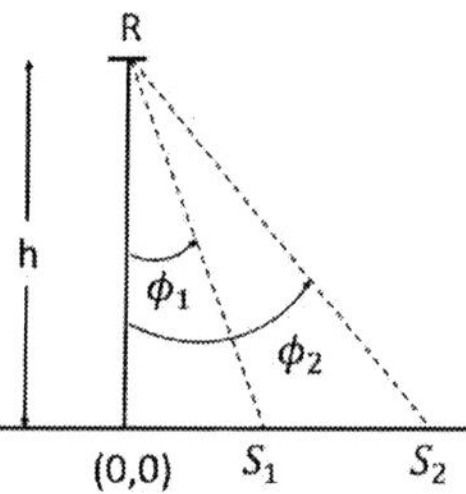

OPTIMUM HEIGHT DETERMINATION

Estimated albedo:

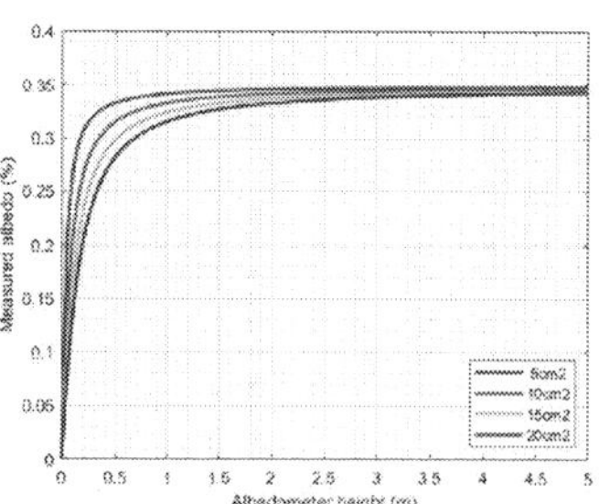

Relative error:

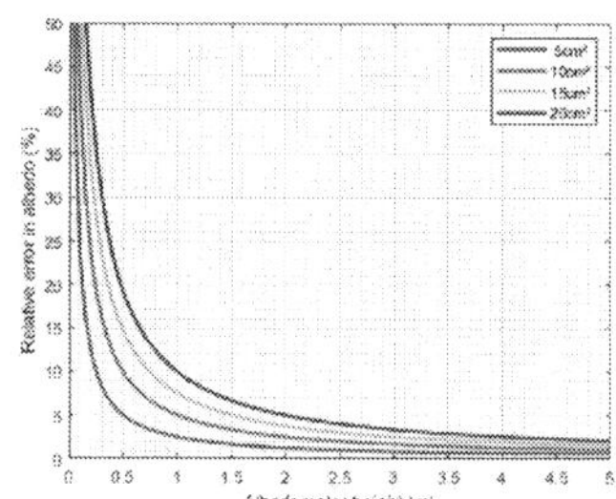

Estimated albedo, when considering a surface albedo of 0.35, in function of albedometer positioning height for 5, 10, 15 and 20 cm^2 sensor areas.

Relative error in albedo measurement, when considering a surface albedo of 0.35, in function of albedometer positioning height for 5, 10, 15 and 20 cm^2 sensor areas.

CONCLUSIONS

- The open-source model allows to determine the minimum height at which an albedometer should be positioned to achieve a maximum error requirement on the albedo estimation for several sensor areas.
- The developed model is available on a public repository.
- Future work will be oriented to optimize the model in order to integrate the analysis of surface non-homogeneity in the albedo measurement, spectral response of the sensor and positioning and inclination of the sensor.

OPEN SOURCE TOOL FOR WEATHER DATA ESTIMATION IN PHOTOVOLTAIC SYSTEMS MONITORING

Sonia Maria Rodriguez[1], Beatriz Chicote[2], Eneko Ortega[1,3], Gerardo Aranguren[3] and Juan Carlos Jimeno[3]
[1] Electricity and Electronics Department, University of the Basque Country UPV/EHU, 48940, Leioa, Spain
[2] Electronics and Computing Department, Mondragon University, 20500, Arrasate-Mondragon, Spain
[3] Technological Institute of Microelectronics, University of the Basque Country UPV/EHU, 48013, Bilbao, Spain
eneko.ortegam@ehu.eus

ABSTRACT: PV systems periodic monitoring is one of the tools with the greatest potential to maximize energy production, avoid failures and extend the life span of the different elements composing the PV system. PV modules energy production depends on weather conditions, mainly temperature and solar irradiation. Therefore, when the electrical parameters of the PV modules are monitored, thus, the I-V curve, it is also necessary to obtain the temperature and irradiance values at which the electrical measurement is performed. This will enable to determine whether the electrical measurements are consistent with the current operating conditions or are associated with anomalous behaviors, due to defects in the PV system. This work provides an open-source code that will enable to obtain the weather parameters, without the need of additional sensors, for a certain location and timestamp, to link this weather data to the measurements of the in-situ monitoring solution. Temperature, global, direct and diffuse irradiances, relative humidity, atmospheric pressure or wind speed are obtained, among others. The accuracy of the proposed solution is evaluated against surface weather measurements for different locations.
Keywords: photovoltaic systems, condition monitoring, performance ratio

1 INTRODUCTION

Solar photovoltaic (PV) electricity generation is increasing at an exponential rate, with an expected installed PV capacity growth of more than 500 GW per year [1]. In this context, maximizing the performance and reliability of PV systems becomes essential. The performance of PV systems is typically measured in terms of the performance ratio (PR) [2] which ranges between 85% and 95% for different PV systems in function of the module technology, system architecture, the PV system location climate or in function of the degradation of the PV system [3].

This means that power losses can be up to 15%, even for modern PV systems. Failures in PV modules, such as encapsulation failures, cell cracks, potential induced degradation or partial shadows, are behind a relevant part of PV systems power losses [4].

Periodic monitoring is the only way to detect these failures and to minimize power losses, boosting PV systems profitability. In this context, several monitoring techniques have been proposed [5]. Some monitoring methods are PV system-level oriented whereas others are string or module-level oriented. Module-level methods rely on visual inspection of the PV module, thermal images analysis, electroluminescence testing or electrical measurement. Monitoring methods based on electrical measurements, such as voltage, current or voltage-current (I-V) characteristic measurement, can be more easily automatized to be carried out in a regular and periodic way. In [6] and [7] the authors proposed a novel monitoring methodology, capable of performing partial measurements of individual PV modules I-V curve and reconstructing their characteristics, using a low-cost electronic circuit based on two capacitors controlled by six switches.

The I-V characteristic of the PV module depends, among other parameters, on the temperature and the solar irradiation. Therefore, this means that any monitoring system, in addition to the current and voltage measurements needs to know, at least, the solar irradiation and temperature values at which the PV module is operating. This way, the monitoring system would be able to determine if the values obtained during the monitoring correspond to a correct operation of the PV module or there is a defect in the module.

This requires the addition of temperature and solar irradiation sensors in the PV system location, which implies an additional cost, especially in small size PV systems. Other parameters, that could be relevant and have an impact on PV module performance [8,9], such as direct and diffuse irradiance, humidity or wind speed among others, are not typically measured. In addition, a correct measurement of meteorological parameters would allow to perform a better estimation of PV systems performance, especially in Bifacial PV systems, where Albedo estimation can be challenging [10].

In this context, this work provides an open-source code which will enable to estimate the weather parameters from an online weather application programming interface (API), for a certain location and timestamp, in order to link this information to the measurements carried out by the in-situ monitoring solution. In addition, from the data obtained from the API, several relevant parameters such as direct and diffuse irradiance or clearness index (K_T) will be computed. Finally, accuracy of the proposed model will be evaluated using for that weather data collected by the Durable Module Materials (DuraMAT) consortium [11] on several locations.

2 WHEATHER PARAMETERS COLLECTION

The developed code in Python takes advantage of the Timeline Weather API, provided by Visual Crossing [12], to obtain meteorological data relevant in the context of PV systems Operation & Maintenance (O&M). Its free payment plan allows to make 1000 calls to the API per day, and it includes a wide group of features, such as current weather conditions, 15-day forecasts and historical data collections from the past 50 years. Monthly or annual payment plans (professional or corporate oriented plans) include the possibility to make more (or unlimited) records per day, as well as some additional services.

The Timeline Weather API requires at least a free

account on Visual Crossing Weather and to create an API key in order to make requests to the API. The API uses a different form for each type of request in function of the desired information. The form for current weather conditions request, at a specific location defined by its coordinates, has the following structure:

https://weather.visualcrossing.com/ VisualCrossingWebServices/rest/services/ timeline/lat,lon?unitGroup=base&include= current&key=APIKEY&contentType=json

So the input parameters needed for the request are:

- *lat, lon*: a string with the latitude (lat) and longitude (lon) values corresponding to the measurement location.
- *key*: the API key related to the Visual Crossing account which is making the call.
- *contentType*: indicates the output format of the API. The available formats are JSON and CSV. By defect, the JSON option will be selected.

There are some other optional inputs, such as:

- *lang*: language of the translatable parts of the output. Can be chosen by using the ID of any available language. The default language is English (*en*).
- *unitGroup*: specifies the system of units used for the output data. Supported values are *us, uk, metric, base*. The default one is the US system of units. To facilitate the use of the proposed solution by the scientific community, the implemented code will report the data in scientific (base) units.

From the returned parameters by the API in a JSON format, the proposed model extracts and adapts the relevant ones, in the context of PV systems O&M, which are:
- *temp*: temperature, given in Kelvin degrees.
- *conditions*: a brief description of the weather conditions.
- *pressure*: the sea level atmospheric pressure, given in millibars (*mBar*).
- *humidity*: relative humidity, given in percentage (%).
- *windspeed*: the sustained wind speed measured as the average wind speed that occurs during the preceding one to two minutes to the requested timestamp, given in meters per second (*m/s*).
- *winddir*: direction from which the wind is blowing, given in degrees.
- *windgust*: instantaneous wind speed. It may be empty if it is not significantly higher than the value in *windspeed*, given in meters per second (*m/s*).
- *precip*: the amount of accumulated precipitation. The liquid-equivalent amount of any frozen precipitation such as snow or ice is included in the counting. Given in millimeters (*mm*).
- *cloudcover*: the percentage of sky that is covered with clouds.
- *solarradiation*: returns the Global Horizontal Irradiance (GHI) in the location, given in W/m^2.
- *datetimeEpoch*: number of seconds since 1st January 1970 in UTC time.
- *datetime*: ISO 8601 formatted time value (hh:mm:ss, where hh has a value between 00 and 24).
- *tzoffset*: time zone offset of the location in hours,

which is the difference between the time in the location and the UTC.
- *days*: date (the specific day) when the request has been made, by using the format YYYY-MM-DD.C.

If desired, it is possible to display the location address instead of coordinates. For that, a *geocoder* (a tool which links location addresses and its coordinates) is being used. The API which has been selected for that is provided by geocode.maps.co [13] and it does not require an API key to make a call. This is the format of the request:

https://geocode.maps.co/reverse? lat=latitude&lon=longitude

From GHI data obtained from Visual Crossing, and knowing the PV system location and timestamp of the measurement, several relevant parameters such as solar declination (δ), solar zenith angle (θ_{zs}), solar azimuth (ψ_s), K_T, Direct Normal Irradiance (DNI) or Diffuse Horizontal Irradiance (DHI) can be computed from the implementation of a well-known set of equations [14].

Firstly, the solar declination angle (δ) must be found. As the earth rotates around its central axis (the polar axis) once a day, the polar axis orbits around the sun with a constant angle of 23.45° with the elliptical plane. However, the angle between the equatorial plane and a straight line between the center of the earth and the center of the sun (δ) changes during the year. If we consider constant this angle during one day, the solar declination can be obtained from Eq. 1, where d_n is the day of the year.

$$\delta(°) = 23.45 \sin\left(\frac{2\pi}{365}(d_n + 284)\right) \quad (1)$$

The distance from the earth to the sun, the eccentricity (ε_0), also varies during the year due to the elliptic orbit of the earth around the sun and can be computed from Eq. 2.

$$\varepsilon_0 = 1 + 0.033 \cos\left(\frac{2\pi \cdot n_d}{365}\right) \quad (2)$$

In a particular location on the earth surface, where the PV system is located, the relative position of the sun to a horizontal surface is defined by θ_{zs} and ψ_s angles, which can be computed from Eq. 3.

$$\cos(\theta_{zs}) = \sin\delta_{rad} \cdot \sin\Phi_{rad} + \cos\delta_{rad} \cdot \cos\Phi_{rad} \cdot \cos h_{eg_{rad}} \quad (3)$$

From this data, the different components of the solar radiation that reach the PV system location can be estimated. The total radiation reaching a horizontal surface (GHI) is the sum of the direct (DNI), diffuse (DHI) and albedo radiation. Direct radiation is the radiation that reaches the surface in a straight line from the sun, and it is not reflected or scattered. Diffuse radiation is the radiation that comes from the whole sky except from the sun's disc. Diffuse radiation is the solar radiation that is reflected or scattered due to the interaction with different particles such as clouds, ozone, oxygen or water vapor when the radiation passes through the atmosphere. Finally, albedo radiation is the radiation reflected from the ground, which can be usually neglected, especially on monofacial PV systems.

The amount of GHI that reaches the horizontal surface during one hour is extremely variable. The extraterrestrial radiation also suffers from regular variations due to the relative position of the sun. The extraterrestrial radiation can be computed according to Eq. 4.

$$B_{oh} = B_0 \cdot \varepsilon_0 \cdot \cos\theta_{zs} \qquad (4)$$

where B_0, known as the solar constant, is the resultant power incident on a unit area perpendicular to the beam outside the earth's atmosphere.

$$B_o = 1367 \ W/m^2 \qquad (5)$$

The atmospheric transparency, or clearness index (K_T), can be estimated as the relation between the GHI and the B_{oh}.

$$K_T = \frac{GHI}{B_{oh}} \qquad (6)$$

From here, it is possible to estimate the correlation between the diffuse fraction of horizontal irradiation (DHI) and the K_T, named K_D. K_D expresses the proportion of GHI reaching the surface that corresponds to diffuse radiation. That is, the part of the radiation that has undergone scattering phenomena due to the atmosphere. Since diffuse radiation decreases as the brightness index increases, the correlation between K_T and K_D will be negative. Several empirical models have been proposed for K_D estimation [15] which vary according to the longitude and latitude and the duration of the dataset. For this study, the estimation shown in Eq. 7, 8 and 9 has been implemented. When $K_T < 0.2$:

$$K_D = 0.996 + 0.00424 \ K_T - 0.586 K_T^2 \qquad (7)$$

when $K_T > 0.2$ and $K_T < 0.7$:

$$K_D = 1.11 - 0.203 \ K_T - 2.52 K_T^2 + 0.617 K_T^3 + 1.603 K_T^3 \qquad (8)$$

and when $K_T > 0.7$:

$$K_D = -0.0169 - 0.99 \ K_T + 1.63 K_T^2 \qquad (9)$$

Finally, from K_D value the DHI and DNI estimation is immediate, as shown in Eq. 10 and 11.

$$DHI = GHI \cdot K_D \qquad (10)$$
$$DNI = GHI - DHI \qquad (11)$$

3 MEASUREMENT RELIABILITY

Reliability of the obtained values using Visual Crossing API will be evaluated using DuraMAT's "Albedo Data for Bifacial PV Systems" dataset. This dataset is composed of irradiance data and meteorological data from several locations across the United States during several years. From this dataset, GHI, DNI, DHI, temperature, relative humidity, wind speed or atmospheric pressure measurements, among others, will be available during several years.

Table 1 shows the dataset collected from DuraMAT's repository corresponding to 8 different locations across the United States with the above-mentioned variables that were selected to construct an equivalent dataset for each location. These were built using the *Hourly Historical*

Observations API from Visual Crossing Weather, which allowed for a comparative analysis.

Table I: DuraMAT's dataset location and time periods

PV system name	State	Period
Bondville	Illinois	2018-2019
Coyanosa	Texas	2018-2020
Davis	California	2018-2019
Desert Rock	Nevada	2018-2019
Fayette	Ohio	2019-2020
Goodwin Creek	Mississippi	2018-2019
Penn. State University	Pennsylvannia	2018-2019
Sabinal	Texas	2019-2020

The following filtering criteria were applied: Incorrect measurements (indicated by *flag* variables in DURAMAT datasets) or measurements where GHI was below $200 \ W/m^2$ where removed, since weather data during no irradiance conditions is not relevant regarding PV systems performance.

In order to compare the datasets in table 1 with the new equivalent Visual Crossing Weather datasets, two different calculations have been carried out:

- Relative Root Mean Squared Error (RRMSE):

$$RRMSE = \sqrt{\frac{\sum_{i=1}^{n} \left(\frac{x_i - y_i}{x_i}\right)^2}{n}} \qquad (12)$$

x_i are the reference values, which belong to DuraMAT's dataset and y_i are the values to check, corresponding to API responses. \$n\$ is the total number of mesasurements (lines) in the datasets. Typically, an RRMSE of 0 is associated with error-free estimation and for RRMSE less than 1 the model is considered adequate.

- Pearson correlation coefficient (r), which quantifies the linear relationship between two variables, ranging from -1 to 1. As r tends to $|1|$, datasets are more linearly related (directly, if r is positive or inversely, if r is negative).

$$r = \frac{Cov(X,Y)}{\sigma_X \cdot \sigma_Y} \qquad (13)$$

where X and Y are DuraMAT's reference and Visual Crossing Weather Historical datasets, for each weather parameter. *Cov* represents the covariance between X and Y and σ is the standard deviation of each of them.

The results of these calculations are shown in Table 2.

Table II: RRMSE and Pearson Correlation Coefficient calculation results, based on measurements from 8 different locations.

	GHI	Tdry	RH	Wspd	Wdir	Pres
RRMSE	0.50	0.36	0.14	1.21	49.13	0.07
Corr	0.66	0.99	0.97	0.76	0.56	0.99

Firstly, note that the locations of Sioux Falls and Boulder were excluded from the final computations in table 2 because the temperature error was excessive, surpassing 100%, making the data unreliable for analysis. Secondly, remark than in some locations where DuraMAT's measurements have been taken in 1-minute intervals temperature relative error remained low (below 10%). Excluding Sioux Falls and Boulder locations, temperature showed a correlation of 0.99 and a RRMSE of 0.36.

Regarding other meteorological variables, relative humidity and pressure showed coherent and low error margins (RRMSE of 0.142 and 0.069 respectively) and almost perfect correlation (0.97 and 0.99). Wind speed, however, presents higher RRMSE (1.21), although it maintains a good correlation (0.76), which could suggest that, although wind speed presents greater variability, the value obtained is reliable to represent the dynamics of wind speed. However, wind direction, with high RRMSE and low correlation (0.56) presents a behavior that seems that it cannot be estimated from Visual Crossing data.

As for Global Horizontal Irradiance (GHI) values, even if initially shows relatively low RRMSE and moderate correlation (0.658) it was detected that Visual Crossing tended to report a lower value than DuraMAT. Since Visual Crossing relies on satellite data to estimate the meteorological parameters, while the DuraMAT data are measured at the surface, the GHI value being obtained is not the same, consistently observing a lower GHI value in the Visual Crossing data than in the DuraMAT data. This effect was minimized by applying a polynomial regression to GHI data in function of Kt value and in the day of the year of the measurement.

The values for GHI were considerably improved, especially the correlation coefficient, which went from 0.658 to 0.941, showing high linearity and reducing the RRMSE error from 0.035 to 0.204, as shown in Table 3.

Table III: RRMSE and Pearson Correlation Coefficient Calculation results, based on measurements from 8 different locations, after applying corrections to the GHI.

	GHI	Tdry	RH	Wspd	Wdir	Pres
RRMSE	0.20	0.36	0.14	1.21	49.33	0.07
Corr	0.94	0.99	0.97	0.76	0.56	0.99

As a representative example, next figures show the most relevant data (Tdry and GHI) obtained from DuraMAT's dataset and from Visual Crossing for Sabinal (Texas) location. Fig. 1 shows the evolution of the temperature (Tdry) during eight months for DuraMAT (blue) and Visual Crossing (orange). Fig. 2 shows the Tdry evolution during a one month period on October-November 2019. As can be seen, the relative error between on-site Tdry measurements and estimations using the Visual Crossing API remains low (below 5% for Sabinal location) during the entire period. However, it can be seen how the Visual Crossing data present slightly lower Tdry values.

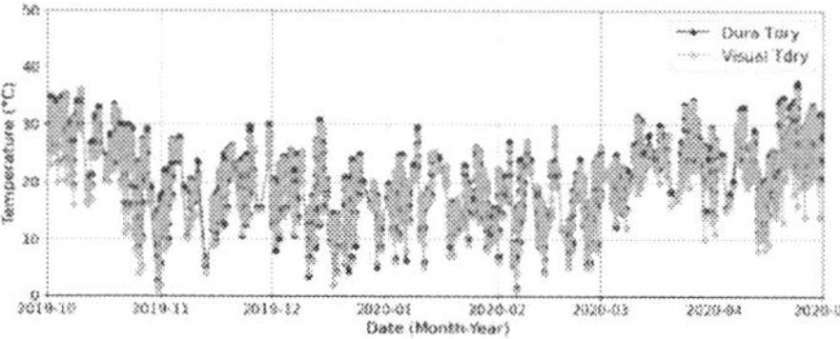

Figure 1: Evolution of Tdry temperature for Sabinal (Texas) using DuraMAT data (blue) and Visual Crossing data (orange) between October 2019 and May 2020.

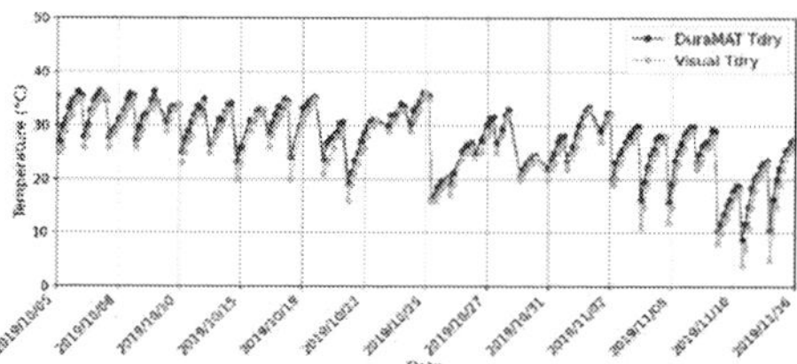

Figure 2: Evolution of Tdry temperature for Sabinal (Texas) using DuraMAT data (blue) and Visual Crossing data (orange) during a one month period in 2019.

Fig. 3 shows the GHI values during a 5-month period, both from DuraMAT and from Visual Crossing. Even after applying the polynomial regression GHI shows a relative error of 15.43% for Sabinal location data. However, as can be seen in Fig. 4, DuraMAT and Visual Crossing GHI values follow the same dynamic, with low error during most of the measurements.

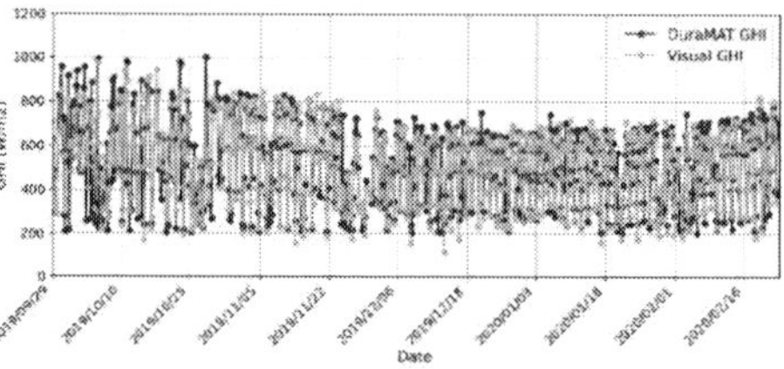

Figure 3: Evolution of GHI for Sabinal (Texas) using DuraMAT data (blue) and Visual Crossing data (orange) between October 2019 and February 2020.

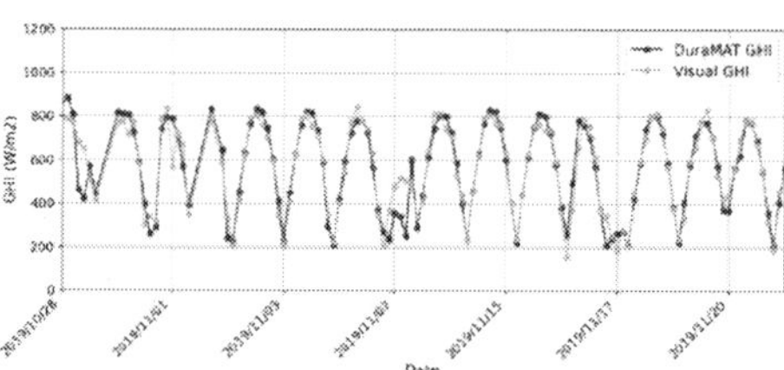

Figure 4: Evolution of GHI values for Sabinal Texas using DuraMAT data (blue) and Visual Crossing data (orange) during several days in October-November 2019.

4 USING THE MODEL

Once a personal API Key is generated, using this code any user will be able to obtain the weather parameters of an specific location and to link these data to its monitoring measurements. In the free version, the API only allows 1000 call each day. In function of their needs, users may need to switch to a paid API subscription.

The python function to obtain the weather conditions for any location, is available in a GitHub public repository (https://github.com/EnekoOrtegaTiM/WeatherParams-PVSystems.git). The GitHub repository contains the necessary explanations for integrating and testing the proposed model.

The script "weather_data_function.py" contains a function named "weather_data" that makes a request to the Visual Crossing Weather Current Conditions API and returns a pandas.DataFrame class object containing the collection of weather parameters that have been extracted from the response. This is the function call structure:

weather_data(lat, lon, UTC, api_key)

whose input arguments are:
- *lat:* latitude of the location, in degrees.
- *lon:* longitude of the location, in degrees.
- *UTC:* UTC offset of the location (difference from UTC time), in hours.
- *api_key:* Visual Crossing Weather user API key.

"weather_data" is made up of various class methods from the "call_class" and "radiation_class" scripts, which must be loaded along with the function script. These methods are responsible for handling API requests, managing response data, and properly formatting them. Additionally, these class methods provide users with different ways to view, use and store data. For instance:
- A single request can be displayed as text or saved in a .csv file (as in Fig.5).
- A database can be built to store multiple requests and can be updated whenever a new request is made.

In Fig.5, a call to the developed function is shown. The function returns the current weather conditions for the University of the Basque Country Campus, sited in Leioa (Spain) with 43.33 (latitude) and -2.97 (longitude) coordinates. It must be pointed that data availability is delayed by 30 minutes. This means that after an electrical measurement, the associated weather data is available 30 minutes afterwards.

```
Function call:
weather_data(lat, lon, UTC, api_key)

The weather data for 43.3314059°,-2.9706058° location at
2025-05-23 12:30:00 is:

- Location address: UPV/EHU Leioa-Erandio, Via Julia, Lertutza,
Leioa, Andraka, Biscay, Autonomous Community of the Basque
Country, 48620, Spain
- Temperature: 291.2K
- Weather conditions: Partially cloudy
- Pressure: 1023.0hPa
- Relative humidity: %62.0
- Wind speed: 3.7m/s
- Wind direction: 314.0°
- Wind gusts: 0.6m/s
- Precipitation: 0.0 mm
- Clouds: %50.0
- Global Horizontal Irradiance (GHI): 747.0W/m^2
- Direct Normal Irradiance (ONI): 356.8710487804023W/m^2
- Diffuse Horizontal Irradiance (DHI): 390.1289512195977W/m^2
- Solar time, in hours: -1.6233508086749708
- UTC timezone offset, in hours : 2
```

Figure 5: Data request for 43.33 (latitude) and -2.97 (longitude) coordinates, corresponding to the University of the Basque Country UPV/EHU Bizkaia campus, sited in Leioa (Spain).

5 CONCLUSIONS

The proposed solution will allow, using an open source code, to obtain for a given location and timestamp the solar irradiation and meteorological parameters at the same time instant in which the PV system is being monitored. Weather and solar irradiation data may be relevant in order to obtain more information on the operation of the PV system and to distinguish between normal operation and defects on the PV system or abnormal behaviors which can not be explained by weather conditions.

As it is shown in the Measurement Reliability section, the proposed model is able to obtain the weather parameters without the use of additional sensors. Specially for temperature, relative humidity and atmospheric pressure with low error. Even GHI values, although it initially presented high error, shows a correlation above 0.90 for all locations after applying a polynomial fitting of the measurement in function of the Kt value and the day of the year. New studies will be carried out to reduce estimated parameters error and improve the utility of the proposed model.

Every user, creating its own API Key, would be able to perform up to 1000 measurements every day using the code provided in the Github repository. For that, only API Key code, PV system location and timestamp are required. If desired, more daily calls to the API can be performed upgrading the subscription directly with the API owner.

The proposed model will be integrated into a smart PV modules monitoring solution that is being developed in the SUPERNOVA European Union Horizon project. In the context of this project, the UPV/EHU team is developing a microcontroller-based Internet of Things (IoT) system for the self-testing of individual PV modules by means of a junction box-embedded wireless monitoring solution. Since the IoT device will have internet connectivity, it will be possible to combine the electrical measurements performed by the IoT device with the temperature and irradiation parameters estimated by the proposed model, in order to determine the degradation of the PV modules.

6 ACKNOWLEDGEMENTS

The European Union's Horizon Europe programme is acknowledged for financial support through the SUPERNOVA project (Grant Agreement No 101146883).

7 REFERENCES

[1] A. Jager-Waldau, Snapshot of photovoltaics - February 2024. EPJ Photovoltaics, vol. 15, p. 21, 2024.

[2] G. Blaesser, PV system measurements and monitoring the European experience. Solar Energy Materials, vol. 47, pp. 167-176, 1997.

[3] A. Louwen, S. Lindig, G. Chowdhury and D. Moser, Climate-and Technology-Dependent Performance Loss Rates in a Large Commercial Photovoltaic Monitoring Dataset. Solar RRL, vol. 8, p. 2300653, 2024.

[4] H. Al Mahdi, P.G. Leahy, M. Alghoul and A.P. Morrison, A Review of Photovoltaic Module Failure and Degradation Mechanisms: Causes and Detection Techniques. Solar, vol. 4, pp. 43-82, 2024.

[5] E. Ortega, G. Aranguren, M.J. Saenz, R. Gutierrez and J.C. Jimeno, Study of Photovoltaic Systems Monitoring Methods, in 44th IEEE Photovoltaic Specialist Conference (IEEE PVSC), 2017.

[6] E. Ortega, G. Aranguren and J.C. Jimeno, New monitoring method to characterize individual modules in large photovoltaic systems. Solar Energy, vol. 193, pp. 906-914, 2019.

[7] E. Ortega, G. Aranguren and J.C. Jimeno, Photovoltaic modules transient response analysis and correction under a fast characterization system. Solar Energy, vol. 221, pp. 232-242, 2021.

[8] G.G. Kim, J.H. Choi, S.Y. Park, B.G. Bhang, W.J. Nam, H.L. Cha, N.S. Park and H.K. Ahn, Prediction model for PV performance with correlation analysis of environmental variables. IEEE Journal of Photovoltaics, vol. 9 (3), pp. 832-841, 2019.

[9] F. Shaik, S.S. Lingala and P. Veeraboina, Effect of various parameters on the performance of solar PV power plant: a review and the experimental study. Sustainable Energy Research, vol. 10 (1), p. 6, 2023.

[10] E. Ortega et al., An statistical model for the short-term albedo estimation applied to PV bifacial modules. Renewable Energy, vol. 221, pp. 119777, 2024.

[11] B. Marion, Albedo data set for bifacial PV systems, in 44th IEEE Photovoltaic Specialist Conference (IEEE PVSC), pp. 485-489, 2020.

[12] Visual Crossing Corporation. (2024). Timeline Weather API, Visual Crossing Weather. https://www.visualcrossing.com/

[13] Free Geocoding API, Geocode Addresses Coordinate, geocode.maps.co.https://geocode.maps.com

[14] E. Lorenzo. Energy collected and delivered by PV modules. Handbook of photovoltaic science and engineering, pp. 984-1042, 2011.

[15] S. Etxebarria et al., Empirical models for the estimation of solar sky-diffuse radiation. A review and experimental analysis. Energies, 13(3), 2020.

Open Source Tool for Weather Data Estimation in Photovoltaic Systems Monitoring

Sonia Maria Rodriguez[1], Beatriz Chicote[2], **Eneko Ortega**[*,1,3],

Gerardo Aranguren[3] and Juan Carlos Jimeno[3]

*eneko.ortegam@ehu.eus

[1] Electricity and Electronics Department, UPV/EHU, 48940, Leioa, Spain

[2] Electronics and Computing Department, Mondragon University, 20500, Arrasate, Spain

[3] Technological Institute of Microelectronics, UPV/EHU, 48013, Bilbao, Spain

INTRODUCTION

- PV systems power losses can be up to 15%. Failures in PV modules are behind a relevant part of power losses [1].
- Periodic monitoring of PV systems is useful for maximizing energy production, preventing failures, and extending PV systems lifespan.
- PV performance depends on weather conditions, mainly temperature and solar irradiation. Acquiring these values during I-V curve monitoring ensures consistency with operating conditions.

AIM

To provide an open-source code that estimates weather parameters from an online weather API for a certain location and timestamp, linking this data to in-situ monitoring electrical measurements [2, 3].

WEATHER PARAMETERS COLLECTION

Timeline Weather API (Visual Crossing) [4] allows making requests of weather data.

Input arguments:

- *lat,lon*: Latitude and longitude of the location (°).
- *key*: VC user account API key.
- *contentType*: format of the response.
- *lang*: output language (optional).
- *unitGroup*: metric, us (default), uk, or base unit system.

Output data:

- Temperature
- Sea level atmospheric pressure
- Relative humidity
- Wind speed and direction
- Accumulated precipitation
- Clouds covering the sky
- Global Horizontal Irradiance (GHI)

Solar declination (δ), zenith angle (θ_{zs}), azimuth (ψ_s), clearness index (K_T), direct and diffuse irradiance (DNI and DHI) are derived from Global Horizontal Irradiance (GHI) data and latitude and longitude using a well-known set of equations [5].

USING THE MODEL

Github repository:
```
https://github.com/EnekoOrtegaTiM/WeatherParams-PVSystems.git
```
Function call:
```
weather_data(lat, lon, UTC, api_key)
```

MEASUREMENT RELIABILITY

Model error estimation from 8 locations, by **DuraMAT**.

	GHI	Tdry	RH	Wspd	Wdir	Pres
RRMSE	0.503	0.362	0.142	1.207	49.129	0.069
Correlation (r)	0.658	0.991	0.968	0.763	0.561	0.997

Model reliability after applying polynomial fitting to the GHI.

	GHI	Tdry	RH	Wspd	Wdir	Pres
RRMSE	0.204	0.363	0.143	1.207	49.334	0.069
Correlation (r)	0.941	0.991	0.968	0.762	0.560	0.997

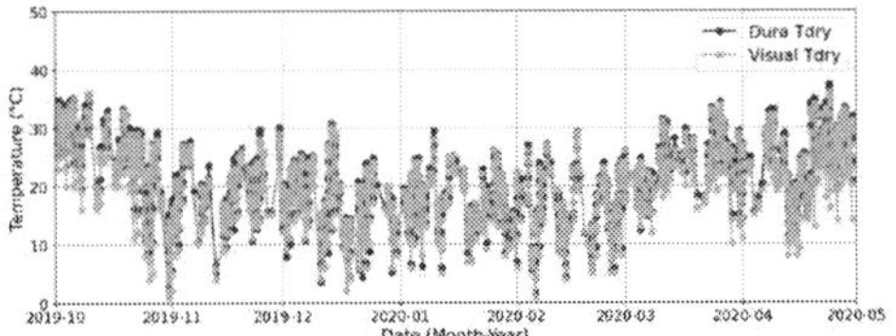

Temperature evolution in Sabinal (Texas), Oct. 2019 - May 2020

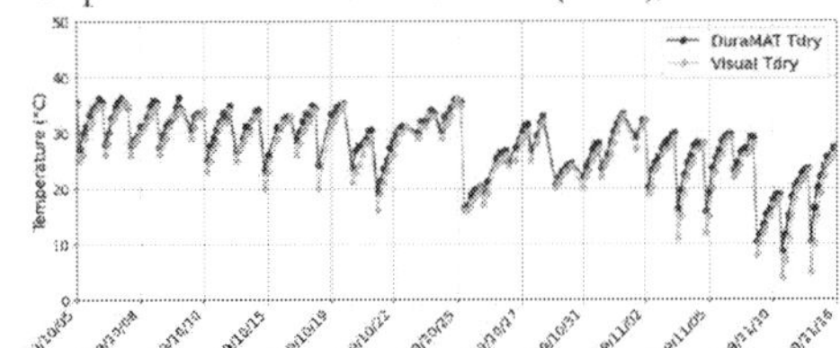

Temperature evolution in Sabinal (Texas), Oct.-Nov. 2019

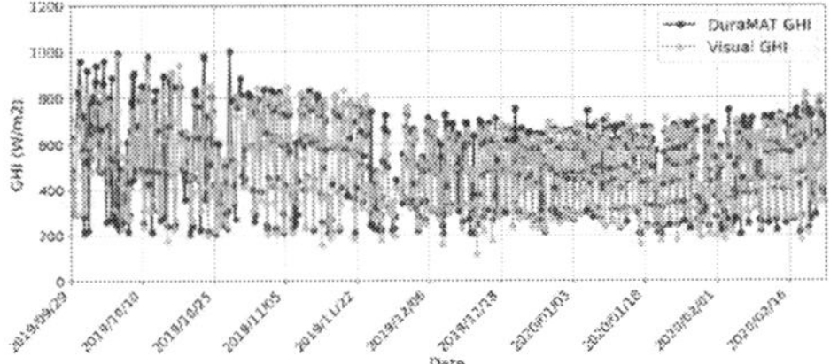

GHI evolution in Sabinal (Texas), Oct. 2019 - Feb. 2020

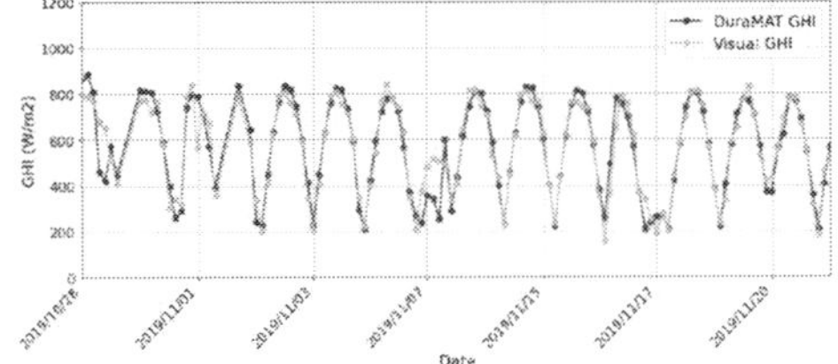

GHI evolution in Sabinal (Texas), Oct.-Nov. 2019

ACKNOWLEDGEMENTS

The European Union's Horizon Europe programme is acknowledged for financial support through the SUPERNOVA project (Grant Agreement No 101146883).

CONCLUSIONS

- The open-source solution retrieves solar and weather data for PV monitoring.
- The estimation of weather parameters achieves low error and correlation above 0.94 for temperature, humidity, pressure and GHI.
- The model will be integrated into the SUPERNOVA project's IoT-based smart PV monitoring system.

REFERENCES

[1] H. Al Mahdi et al., A Review of Photovoltaic Module Failure and Degradation Mechanisms: Causes and Detection Techniques. Solar, 2024.

[2] E. Ortega et al., New monitoring method to characterize individual modules in large photovoltaic systems. Solar Energy, 2019.

[3] E. Ortega et al., Photovoltaic modules transient response analysis and correction under a fast characterization system. Solar Energy, 2021.

[4] https://www.visualcrossing.com/

[5] E. Lorenzo. Energy collected and delivered by PV modules. 2011.

PERFORMANCE EVALUATION OF CAMS REANALYSIS FOR IMPROVED SOLAR RESOURCE ASSESSMENT AND FORECASTING IN QATAR'S DESERT CLIMATE

Abdul Wahab Ziaullah[1], Dunia Bachour[1*], Daniel Perez-Astudillo[1], Lionel Menard[2], and Philippe Blanc[2]

[1]Qatar Environment and Energy Research Institute, Hamad Bin Khalifa University, Doha, Qatar
[2]Centre Observation Impacts Energy (O.I.E.), MINES Paris, Université PSL, France
*Corresponding Author: dbachour@hbku.edu.qa

ABSTRACT: Solar resource assessment is essential for the planning and operation of solar energy projects, with ground-based measurements providing the most accurate data. In their absence, satellite-derived solar radiation products offer a valuable alternative due to their broad spatial and temporal coverage, though their accuracy must be carefully evaluated for reliable application. This study assesses the performance of the CAMS Radiation Service (CRS), a satellite-based solar radiation dataset from the European Union's Earth observation program, under the hot desert climate of Qatar. Historical CRS data—Global Horizontal Irradiance (GHI), Direct Normal Irradiance (DNI), and Diffuse Horizontal Irradiance (DHI)—were compared against ground-based measurements from QEERI's solar monitoring station in Doha, recorded at 1-minute resolution over a 38-month period. The evaluation employed statistical indicators including Pearson's correlation coefficient (Cf), relative root mean square error (rRMSE), and relative mean bias error (rMBE). Results show that CRS reproduces GHI with the highest accuracy, exhibiting the lowest rRMSE and rMBE, while DNI and DHI demonstrate significantly larger biases and errors. Furthermore, periodic monthly variations in rRMSE were observed across all components. These findings suggest that CRS-derived GHI can serve as a reliable substitute when ground measurements are unavailable, though greater caution is required when using DNI and DHI.

1 INTRODUCTION

Solar energy is increasingly recognized as a key component of sustainable energy systems worldwide, particularly in regions with abundant sunlight such as the Middle East. Accurate assessment of solar radiation resources is essential for the design, operation, and optimisation of solar energy projects, including photovoltaic (PV) and concentrated solar power (CSP) systems. Typically, the most reliable solar radiation data are obtained from ground-based measurement stations equipped with radiometers, which provide high-resolution, site-specific information. However, ground measurements are often limited in spatial coverage, expensive to maintain, and sometimes subject to data gaps or instrument errors.

To address these limitations, satellite-derived solar radiation datasets are an attractive alternative due to their extensive spatial and temporal coverage, enabling resource assessments over large and remote areas where ground measurements may be sparse or unavailable. Numerous satellite models provide estimates of solar radiation components such as Global Horizontal Irradiance (GHI), Direct Normal Irradiance (DNI), and Diffuse Horizontal Irradiance (DHI), which are crucial inputs for solar energy system design and performance analysis.

Despite their advantages, satellite-based products require validation against ground truth data to assess their accuracy and reliability, particularly when applied to specific climatic regions. Desert environments, such as Qatar's, present unique challenges due to high solar irradiance levels, frequent dust events, and atmospheric variability, all of which can affect the accuracy of satellite retrievals.

The Copernicus Atmosphere Monitoring Service (CAMS) Radiation Service (CRS), developed under the European Union's Earth Observation Programme, offers historical solar radiation data that can potentially supplement or replace ground measurements. This study aims to evaluate the applicability of CRS data in Qatar's desert climate by comparing 38-months of high-resolution CRS data with ground-based measurements from a solar monitoring station operated by the Qatar Environment and Energy Research Institute (QEERI) in Doha.

By analysing the performance of CRS data across overall, annual and monthly, resolutions using statistical parameters such as Pearson's correlation coefficient, relative root mean square error and relative mean bias error, this work contributes to understanding the strengths and limitations of satellite-derived solar radiation data in hot desert climates. The outcomes provide insights into the reliability of CRS data for hot desert environments and support improved methodologies for solar resource assessment in Qatar and similar regions.

2 BACKGROUND

Solar radiation is the primary energy input for solar power systems and thus plays a critical role in determining the feasibility and performance of solar energy projects. Accurate measurement of solar radiation components—Global Horizontal Irradiance (GHI), Direct Normal Irradiance (DNI), and Diffuse Horizontal Irradiance (DHI)—is essential for system design [6], performance prediction, and energy yield estimation [2].

Ground stations equipped with pyranometers and pyrheliometers provide high-quality solar radiation data. These instruments measure solar irradiance directly at specific locations, offering precise and high-resolution temporal data. However, the installation, maintenance, and calibration of such stations require significant resources. Moreover, data gaps frequently occur due to instrument failure or environmental factors, limiting the continuity and completeness of the dataset.

To overcome these limitations, satellite remote sensing offers an alternative by providing continuous solar radiation estimates over large geographical areas and often long time periods [7]. Satellite models use cloud cover, atmospheric parameters, and surface reflectance data to estimate the solar irradiance components. These datasets are especially valuable in regions where ground monitoring infrastructure is sparse or non-existent.

Several satellite-derived solar radiation products exist globally, each varying in spatial and temporal resolution, input data sources, and modelling approaches. The Copernicus Atmosphere Monitoring Service (CAMS) Radiation Service (CRS) is a prominent example, offering comprehensive radiation data derived from the European Earth Observation Programme. CRS provides historical data, since 2004 until 2 days before the present day, with global coverage, making it a useful tool for solar energy assessments.

Desert climates like Qatar's present specific challenges for satellite-based solar radiation estimates. High solar irradiance, intense dust storms, and atmospheric aerosols can alter the solar radiation reaching the surface and complicate satellite retrieval algorithms. These factors may reduce the accuracy of satellite-derived radiation data compared to ground-based measurements. Additionally, seasonal and diurnal variations in atmospheric conditions can introduce periodic errors in satellite estimates.

An initial study in Qatar was conducted using the HelioClim-3 v4 (HC3v4) database from SoDa [4]. HC3 utilizes the Heliosat-2 model, while CRS uses McClear for clear-sky conditions and Heliosat-4 for all-sky conditions, offering broader regional coverage. Moreover, CRS uses actual aerosol data, whereas HC3 relies on approximations. Given Qatar's high aerosol loading [11], CRS may be more suitable; however, a direct comparison is lacking, making such a study highly warranted. A new version of Helioclim, HC3v5, is also available, in which HC3v5 replaces the ESRA clear-sky model and static turbidity climatology of HC3v4 with the McClear clear-sky model. A study has been conducted in Morocco using five stations [8] and comparing HC3v4, HC3v5, and CRS. Another study assessed the real-time estimates of surface GHI produced by the improved SENSE2 operational system at high spatial resolution for various stations, including Athens, Cabauw, Camborne, Carpentras, and Cener. The study found that periods with changes in cloudiness contributed to higher variability in the satellite-derived GHI estimates [9]. Similarly, a study validated the performance of HelioClim-3 version 5 (HC3v5) against ground-based measurements at various stations in northeast Iraq [3].

A brief comparison of HC3v4, HC3v5, and CRS. is presented in Table 1.

This study builds on these concepts by assessing the performance of CAMS CRS data in Qatar, comparing it against a robust ground measurement dataset collected over 38-months by QEERI. Understanding the suitability and limitations of CRS data in Qatar's desert environment will support improved solar resource management and facilitate more accurate solar energy project planning.

3 METHODOLOGY

High-quality measurements of direct normal irradiance (DNI), global horizontal irradiance (GHI), and diffuse horizontal irradiance (DHI) were collected with QEERI's monitoring station in Doha (25.32° N, 51.42° E), covering 38-months period, from (Jan/2013 - Feb/2016). The data for GHI and DHI were collected using CMP11 pyranometers, while the data for DNI were collected using a CHP1 pyrheliometer. All irradiances were collected minute-by-minute in W/m^2 and quality checks were applied to the data to eliminate any erroneous values [10]. The corresponding CRA data was downloaded using CAMS API [5]. The relative root mean square error (rRMSE), relative mean bias error (rMBE), and Pearson's correlation coefficient (Cf) were calculated using formulas 1, 2 and 3, respectively.

$$rRMSE = \frac{\sqrt{\frac{1}{N}\sum_{i=1}^{N}(X_i - Y_i)^2}}{\overline{Y}} * 100\% \qquad (1)$$

$$rMBE = \frac{\frac{1}{N}\sum_{i=1}^{N}(X_i - Y_i)}{\overline{Y}} * 100\% \qquad (2)$$

$$Cf = \frac{\sum_{i=1}^{N}(X_i - \overline{X})(Y_i - \overline{Y})}{\sqrt{\sum_{i=1}^{N}(X_i - \overline{X})^2 \sum_{i=1}^{N}(Y_i - \overline{Y})^2}} \qquad (3)$$

where X and Y are the modelled and measured samples, respectively, overlines indicate the respective means, and N is the number of measurements in the sample.

4 RESULTS AND DISCUSSION

The overall performance of CAMS CRS solar radiation against ground measurements over the full period (Jan/2013 - Feb/2016) is summarized in Table 2. GHI exhibits the best agreement, with a relatively low rRMSE of 29.5%, a minor underestimation of −4.3%, and excellent correlation (0.97), indicating strong reliability for total horizontal irradiance. DHI shows moderate errors, with an rRMSE of 49.6% and a slight overestimation of +10.7%, while correlations remain high at 0.94. In contrast, DNI displays the weakest performance, with a very high rRMSE of 78.4% and a substantial underestimation of −40.7%, although correlations are moderate (0.87). These results highlight that CAMS CRS performs best for GHI, reasonably for DHI, and has limitations in accurately representing direct normal irradiance under the conditions studied.

The overall analysis is further broken down to yearly performance in Table 3, where both rRMSE and rMBE remain consistent with relatively low standard deviations, indicating limited year-to-year fluctuations. For DNI, CAMS shows the weakest agreement, with very high rRMSE values (75–80%) and a consistent underestimation of about −40%, though correlations are moderate (0.87–0.88). DHI performs better, with rRMSE values of 45–52% and a systematic overestimation of +8% to +14%, while correlations are high (0.94–0.95). The best performance is observed for GHI, with comparatively low errors (28–30%), only a

Feature	CAMS Radiation Service (CRS)	HelioClim-3 v4 (HC3v4)	HelioClim-3 v5 (HC3v5)
Cloud Data Source	Meteosat Second Generation (MSG) SEVIRI images	Meteosat Second Generation (MSG) SEVIRI images	Meteosat Second Generation (MSG) SEVIRI images
Algorithm	Heliosat-4 method	Heliosat-2 method	Heliosat-2 method (combined with McClear)
Clear Sky Model	McClear model	European Solar Radiation Atlas (ESRA) model with static turbidity climatology	McClear model
Atmospheric Input	Near real-time and forecast data for aerosols, water vapor, and ozone from CAMS/ECMWF	Static climatological data (Linke turbidity)	Combines the cloud and clear-sky models of HC3v4 with the more accurate atmospheric input from the McClear model
Temporal Resolution	1-minute, 15-minute, hourly, daily, and monthly	15-minute, hourly, daily, and monthly	1-minute, 15-minute, hourly, daily, and monthly
Coverage	Global (within satellite coverage)	Europe, Africa, Atlantic Ocean, and the Middle East	Europe, Africa, Atlantic Ocean, and the Middle East

Table 1: Comparison of CAMS Radiation Service, HelioClim-3 v4, and HelioClim-3 v5

Table 2: Overall Performance of CRS Solar Radiation vs Ground Measurements (Jan 2013- Feb 2016)

	rRMSE(%)	rMBE(%)	Cf
DNI	78.38	-40.70	0.87
DHI	49.57	10.70	0.94
GHI	29.48	-4.30	0.97

slight underestimation (around –4%), and excellent correlations (0.97–0.98).

Table 3: Yearly Performance Metrics for CRS vs. Ground Measurements

	DNI			DHI			GHI		
	rRMSE	rMBE	Cf	rRMSE	rMBE	Cf	rRMSE	rMBE	Cf
2013	77.91	-40.9	0.88	49.12	10.22	0.94	28.43	-4.27	0.98
2014	75.4	-40.45	0.88	52.18	14.22	0.94	28.52	-3.86	0.98
2015	79.84	-39.04	0.87	45.41	8.28	0.95	30.19	-4.44	0.97
Std	2.22	0.97	0.01	3.40	3.03	0.01	0.99	0.30	0.01

A monthly-level analysis of rRMSE, rMBE, and correlation coefficient (Cf) for the three solar radiation components was performed to identify potential climate-related variations in CRS data accuracy. The results are shown in Figures 1–4.

As seen in Fig. 1, GHI consistently exhibits the lowest rRMSE, while DNI shows the highest rRMSE across all months. A seasonal pattern is also apparent: errors are lowest during the mostly cloud-free months of May–June and highest in December–January, when cloudiness and occasional rainfall occur.

The monthly rMBE trends in Fig. 2 show that GHI fluctuates near zero, indicating minimal bias. DNI exhibits the largest negative bias, whereas DHI shows a moderate positive bias.

Correlation analysis (Fig. 3) indicates that CRS data are highly correlated with ground measurements (Cf > 0.8) for all components. GHI consistently shows the highest corre-

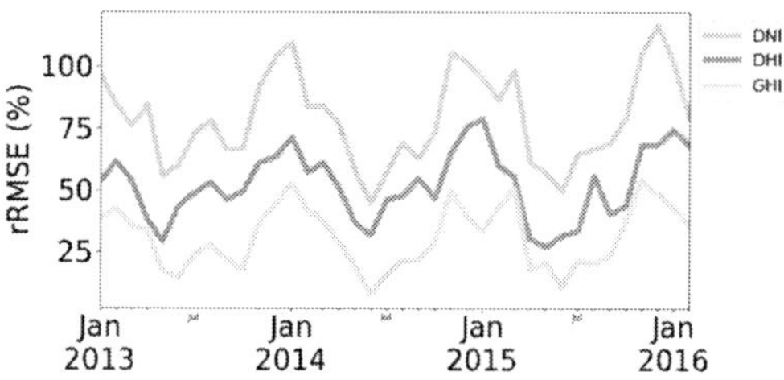

Figure 1: Monthly Trend of rRMSE on CRS Solar Radiation vs Ground Measurements

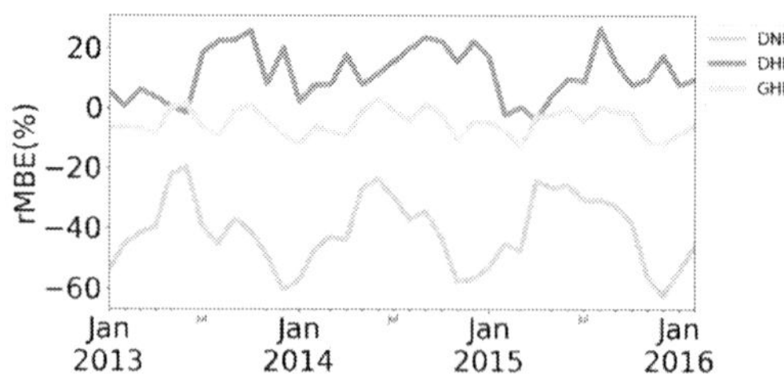

Figure 2: Monthly Trend of rMBE on CRS Solar Radiation vs Ground Measurements

lation, while DNI shows the lowest. Seasonal oscillations are visible but less pronounced than in rRMSE, reflecting the influence of atmospheric conditions on measurement accuracy. Among all three indicators, DNI exhibits the

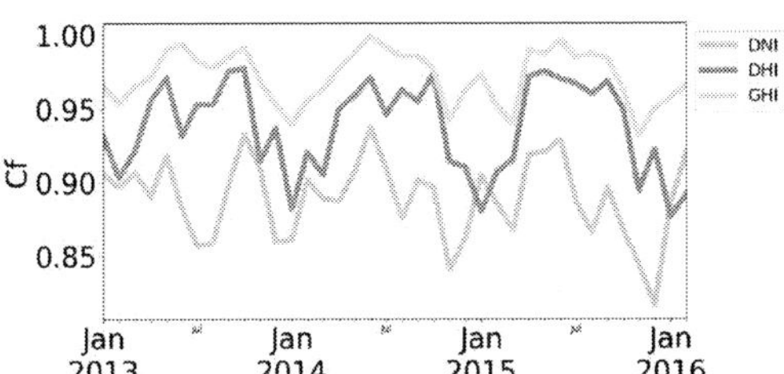

Figure 3: Monthly Trend of Cf on CRS Solar Radiation vs Ground Measurements

lowest performance. This may be attributed to the requirement for exact sensor alignment to capture the direct beam of sunlight, whereas satellites observe the scene from oblique angles.

To further examine the seasonal oscillation, cloud cover data were obtained from the Open-Meteo API [1] and are presented in Fig. 4. Cloud cover peaks in January and is minimal in July, which corresponds well with the rRMSE trends: higher errors coincide with higher cloudiness.

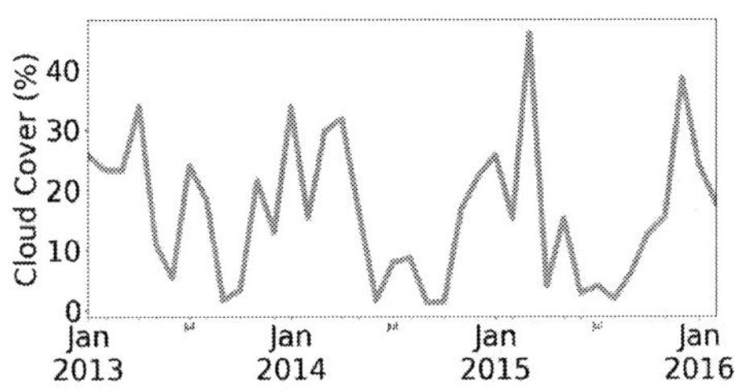

Figure 4: Monthly trend of Cloud Cover

Daily profiles were examined by randomly sampling days from January, May, June, and December, as shown in Figs. 5–8. On May 10, 2013, and June 15, 2015—typically cloud-free months—both CRS and ground measurements exhibit smooth profiles. GHI from CRS aligns closely with ground data, while DNI and DHI show greater sensitivity to atmospheric aerosols.

On January 5, 2014, CRS data capture cloud passages between approximately 09:00–12:00 and 14:00–16:00, reflected by decreased GHI and DNI and increased DHI, whereas ground measurements show smoother variations. December 4, 2015, represents a cloudy day with significant variability. The CRS DNI profile remains mostly flat, highlighting the challenge of accurately capturing direct normal irradiance under highly variable cloud conditions.

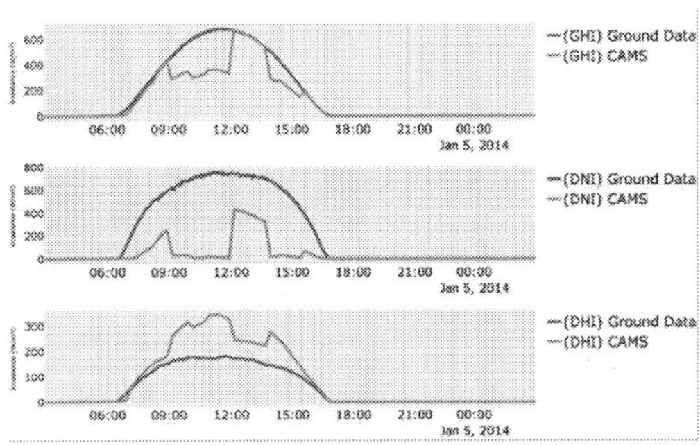

Figure 5: CRS and Ground Measurements on Jan 5, 2014

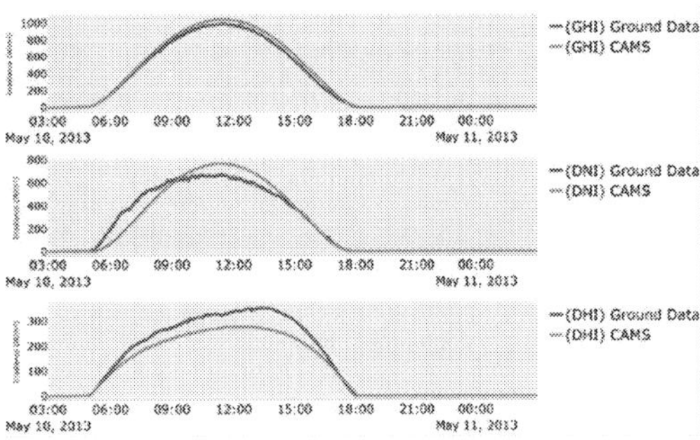

Figure 6: CRS and Ground Measurements on May 11, 2013

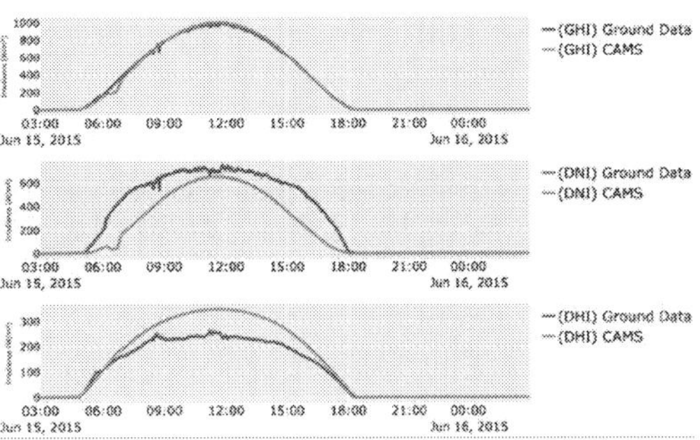

Figure 7: CRS and Ground Measurements on Jun 16, 2013

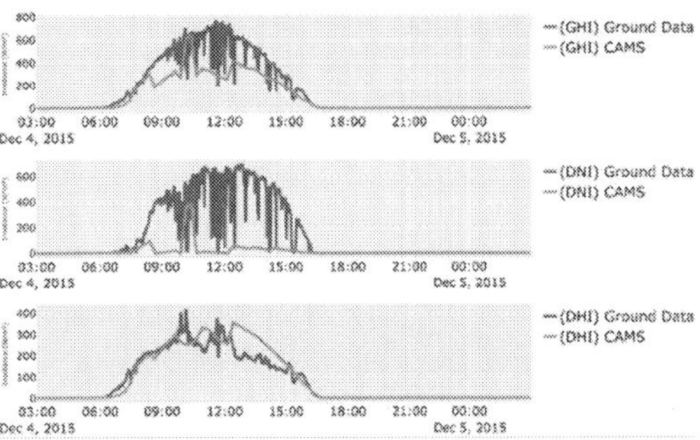

Figure 8: CRS and Ground Measurements on Dec 5, 2015

5 CONCLUSION

In this study, we assessed the performance of CAMS-CRS against high-resolution ground measurements collected in Doha over a 38-month period (Jan/2013 to Feb/2016). By comparing the three primary solar radiation components—GHI, DNI, and DHI—using statistical metrics such as rRMSE, rMBE, and the Pearson correlation coefficient, we observed that GHI data from CRS performed the best overall, exhibiting the lowest relative error and highest correlation with ground measurements.

The monthly trend analysis revealed a seasonal oscillation in CRS accuracy, with improved performance during the clearer summer months (May–June) and reduced accuracy during winter months (December–January), corresponding to observed variations in cloud cover. Among the components, DNI consistently showed the weakest agreement with ground measurements, primarily due to the difficulty of capturing direct beam radiation from spaceborne platforms without precise alignment, as well as its greater sensitivity to cloud detection and aerosol modeling. These observations are consistent with previous findings reported by Papachristopoulou et al. (2024) [9] and Ameen et al. (2018) [3], who also documented monthly fluctuations in satellite-derived solar radiation accuracy.

Daily profile analysis further confirmed that CRS data aligns more closely with ground observations on clear-sky days, whereas significant discrepancies, particularly in DNI, occur on cloudy days.

Overall, these findings underscore the utility of CRS data for solar energy applications in arid regions such as Doha, especially for GHI estimation. However, caution is advised when relying on CRS-derived DNI values, particularly under cloudy or high-aerosol conditions. Future work will focus on site adaptation models to enhance CRS reliability during periods of increased cloud cover and aerosol concentrations, with the goal of improving retrieval precision and validating results under Qatar's desert climate.

6 ACKNOWLEDGEMENT

Research reported in this work was supported by the Qatar Research Development and Innovation Council (Grant: ARG01-0523-230304). The content is solely the responsibility of the authors and does not necessarily represent the official views of Qatar Research Development and Innovation Council.

REFERENCES

[1] Free Open-Source Weather API | Open-Meteo.com — open-meteo.com. https://open-meteo.com. [Accessed 22-09-2024].

[2] J. AlFaraj, E. Popovici, and P. Leahy. Solar irradiance database comparison for pv system design: A case study. *Sustainability*, 16(15):6436, 2024.

[3] B. Ameen, H. Balzter, C. Jarvis, E. Wey, C. Thomas, and M. Marchand. Validation of hourly global horizontal irradiance for two satellite-derived datasets in northeast iraq. *Remote Sensing*, 10(10):1651, 2018.

[4] D. Bachour, D. Perez-Astudillo, H. Alhajri, and A. Sanfilippo. Validation of HelioClim-3-derived solar radiation products in arid desert conditions. In *AIP Conference Proceedings*, volume 2815. AIP Publishing, 2023.

[5] C. C. C. S. (C3S). Cams radiation service api. https://api.copernicus.eu/. Accessed: 2025-03-15.

[6] J. A. Duffie and W. A. Beckman. *Solar engineering of thermal processes*. John Wiley & Sons, 2013.

[7] G. Huang, Z. Li, X. Li, S. Liang, K. Yang, D. Wang, and Y. Zhang. Estimating surface solar irradiance from satellites: Past, present, and future perspectives. *Remote Sensing of Environment*, 233:111371, 2019.

[8] M. Marchand, A. Ghennioui, E. Wey, and L. Wald. Comparison of several satellite-derived databases of surface solar radiation against ground measurement in morocco. *Advances in Science and Research*, 15:21–29, 2018.

[9] K. Papachristopoulou, I. Fountoulakis, A. F. Bais, B. E. Psiloglou, N. Papadimitriou, I.-P. Raptis, A. Kazantzidis, C. Kontoes, M. Hatzaki, and S. Kazadzis. Effects of clouds and aerosols on downwelling surface solar irradiance nowcasting and sort-term forecasting. *Atmospheric Measurement Techniques Discussions*, 2023:1–31, 2023.

[10] D. Perez-Astudillo, D. Bachou r, and L. Martín-Pomares. Improved quality control protocols on solar radiation measurements. *Solar Energy*, 169:425–433, 2018.

[11] Qatar Environment and Energy Research Institute (QEERI). QEERI solar atlas: Qatar's first solar atlas to map renewable energy potential. Technical report, Hamad Bin Khalifa University, 2020. Accessed: 2025-05-21.

Performance Evaluation of CAMS Reanalysis for Improved Solar Resource Assessment and Forecasting in Qatar's Desert Climate

A. Ziaullah[1], D. Bachour[1], D. Perez-Astudillo[1], L. Menard[2], P. Blanc[2]

1. Qatar Environment & Energy Research Institute, Hamad Bin Khalifa University, Qatar
2. MINES Paris, Universite PSL, France

EUPVSEC 2025
22 – 26 September 2025

Overview

Solar resource assessment is fundamental for solar energy projects, with ground-based measurements offering the most accurate data. In the absence of such data, satellite-derived solar radiation products present a valuable alternative due to their broad spatial and temporal coverage. However, evaluating the accuracy of these satellite models is critical for their reliable application. This study evaluates the performance of the CAMS Radiation Service (CRS), a satellite-derived solar radiation dataset from the European Union's Earth observation program, in the hot desert climate of Qatar. The suitability of CAMS reanalysis is done by comparing historical CRS solar radiation data—Global Horizontal Irradiance (GHI), Direct Normal Irradiance (DNI), and Diffuse Horizontal Irradiance (DHI)—with ground measurements from a solar monitoring station in Doha. The objective is to determine the suitability of CAMS reanalysis for improved solar resource assessment and forecasting in Qatar's desert climate.

Methodology

Solar radiation components were recorded at 1-minute resolution over three years by QEERI's monitoring station. Statistical comparisons using correlation factor (Cf), relative mean bias error (rMBE), and relative root mean square error (rRMSE) were performed.

Ground Data

DNI ground measurements are obtained using a CHP1 pyrheliometer. GHI and DHI were collected using CMP11 pyranometers for the duration of 38 months (Jan 2013 – Feb 2016). All the data was collected on 1-minute resolution

CRS Data

CRS data was obtained from CAMS API with corresponding timestamps from (Jan 2013 – Feb 2016). All the data was collected on 1-minute resolution

Performance Indicators

3 performance indicators were used
Relative Root Mean Square Error (rRMSE)
Relative Mean Bias Error (rMBE)
Pearson's correlation coefficient (Cf)

Analysis and Results

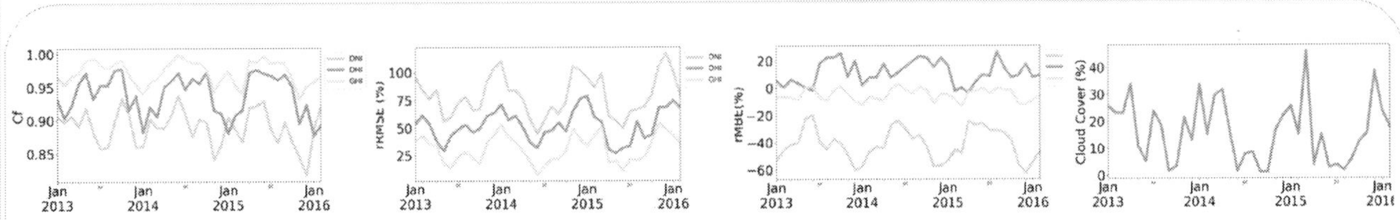

Monthly Variations of CRS vs Ground data left to right (Pearson's correlation coefficient, rRMSE , rMBE, Cloud cover)
Cloud cover data downloaded from https://open-meteo.com/

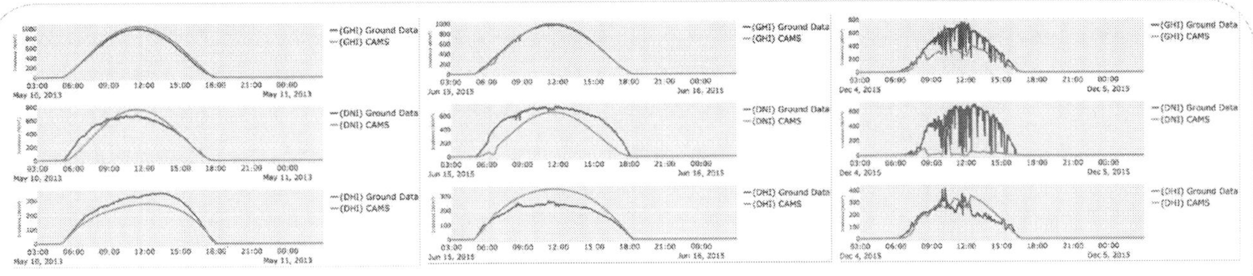

Daily Variations of CRS vs Ground data left to right (May 11, 2013 / June 16,2015 / Dec 5, 2015)

Discussions

By comparing the three primary solar radiation components—GHI, DNI, and DHI—using statistical metrics — rRMSE, rMBE, and the Pearson correlation coefficient — we observed that GHI data from CRS performed the best overall, exhibiting the lowest rRMSE, rMBE and Cf with the ground measurements. The monthly trend analysis revealed a seasonal oscillation in CRS accuracy, with improved performance during clearer summer months (May–June) and reduced accuracy during winter months (December–January), which aligns well with the observed variation in the cloud cover. Among the components, DNI consistently showed the weakest agreement with ground-based measurements. This is primarily due to the inherent difficulty in capturing direct beam radiation from spaceborne platforms without precise alignment, as well as the greater sensitivity of DNI to errors in cloud detection and aerosol modeling. The findings underscore the utility of CRS data for solar energy applications in arid regions like Doha, especially for GHI. However, it is essential to note that calibration against ground-based measurements remains necessary even for GHI, to ensure optimal accuracy and reliability. Furthermore, caution should be exercised when relying on CRS-derived DNI, DHI values, particularly in cloudy or high-aerosol conditions.

Acknowledgement

Research reported in this work was supported by the Qatar Research Development and Innovation Council (Grant: ARG01-0523-230304). The content is solely the responsibility of the authors and does not necessarily represent the official views of Qatar Research Development and Innovation Council.

42nd European Photovoltaic Solar Energy Conference and Exhibition

Defining an Irradiance Quantity for Outdoor Assessment of PV System Performance

Anton Driesse

PV Performance Labs, Germany

anton.driesse@pvperformancelabs.com

James Blakesley

National Physical Laboratory, UK

james.blakesley@npl.co.uk

Reach out to us if you have suggestions or better ideas!

The Challenge

Performance indicators compare output energy to input energy, i.e. irradiance.

- In the lab, PV *module* performance is assessed using a light source facing the module and emitting a light of a known spectrum and intensity.

- In the field, PV *system* performance is observed under a wide variety irradiance conditions with spatial, spectral and intensity variations.

- Field performance indicators using pyranometer irradiance measurements are highly standardized, but produce high variability.

- Field Performance indicators using reference cell irradiance measurements are more consistent, but are only formally traceable under lab conditions.

How can we reduce the variability and improve the traceability?

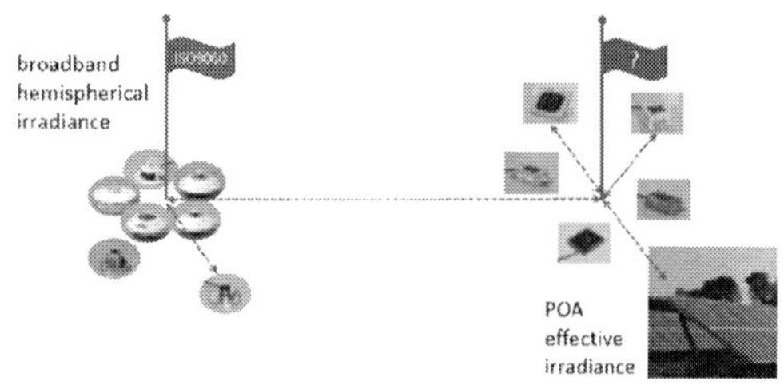

Solution

The way forward is to define an irradiance quantity that more closely represents the solar energy that is *available for conversion* to electricity, rather than the total solar energy.

The total solar energy received on a flat surface as measured by a pyranometer is the integral of the radiance over all directions and a wide range of wavelengths:

$$E_{PYR} = \frac{\int_0^{2\pi} \int_0^{\pi/2} \int_{300}^{3000} I(\lambda, \theta, \phi) \cdot \cos(\theta) \cdot \sin(\theta) \, d\lambda \, d\theta \, d\phi}{\int_{300}^{3000} E_{ref}(\lambda) \, d\lambda} \cdot E_{ref}$$

The solar energy available for conversion by a PV module is reduced by the directional response $\mathrm{IAM}(\theta)$, and the spectral response $S(\lambda)$:

$$E_{PV} = \frac{\int_0^{2\pi} \int_0^{\pi/2} \int_{300}^{1200} I(\lambda, \theta, \phi) \cdot S(\lambda) \cdot \mathrm{IAM}(\theta) \cdot \cos(\theta) \cdot \sin(\theta) \, d\lambda \, d\theta \, d\phi}{\int_{300}^{1200} E_{ref}(\lambda) \cdot S(\lambda) \, d\lambda} \cdot E_{ref}$$

Commercial reference cells already measure this quantity approximately, but a new standard is needed to define this quantity precisely.

Based on the proposed definition, accuracy classes (A,B,C) will be defined for reference cells based on how well they measure this quantity.

Directional Response

The directional response $\mathrm{IAM}(\theta)$ of PV modules varies due to different materials, coatings , textures. A single standard response is needed as a point of reference.

We propose a standard curve based on reflection at the air-glass interface, which can be calculated precisely using the Fresnel equations.

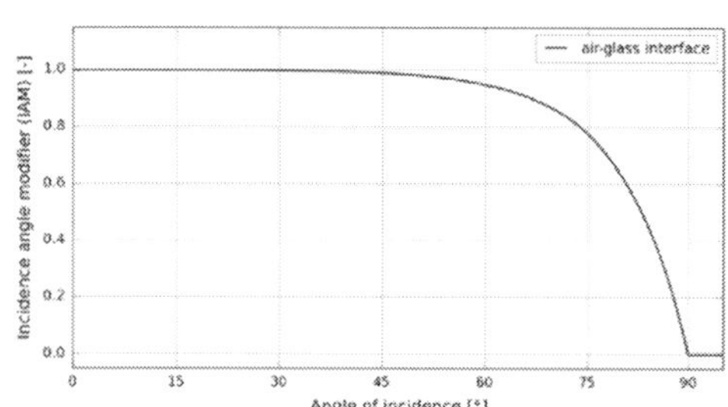

When compared to this standard response, PV modules with superior anti-reflective coatings and textures will achieve higher outdoor performance.

Spectral Response

The spectral response $S(\lambda)$ of PV modules varies due to different dimensions, materials, designs. A single standard response is needed as a point of reference.

We propose a standard curve to represents the response of a basic silicon PV cell. Shown here is a simple geometric definition which can be calculated precisely.

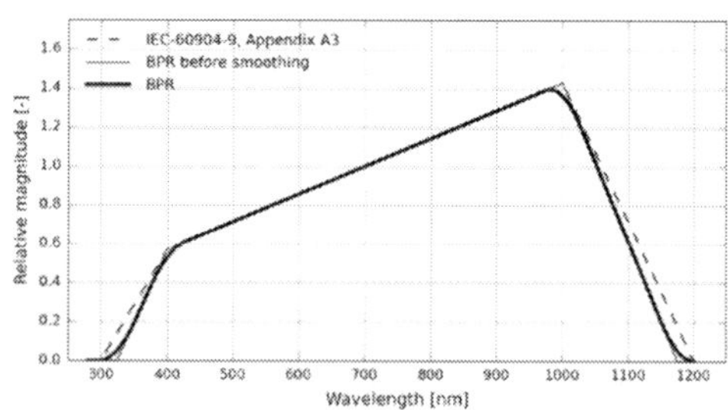

While broad spectral response can lead to higher absolute efficiencies, the link between spectral response and outdoor performance indicators is complex.

SOLiD-PV is a European Partnership on Metrology project that aims to quantify and reduce sources of uncertainty in key performance indicators for PV systems. https://www.solid-pv.ptb.de/home

PV Performance Labs provides a range of services in support of PV system R&D and operations including planning, measurements, simulation and analysis. PV Performance Labs participates in the SOLiD-PV project.

EUROPEAN PARTNERSHIP   Co-funded by the European Union

Funded by the European Union. Views and opinions expressed are however those of the author(s) only and do not necessarily reflect those of the European Union or EURAMET. Neither the European Union nor the granting authority can be held responsible for them.

020293-001

METROLOGY PARTNERSHIP   EURAMET

The project has received funding from the European Partnership on Metrology, co-financed from the European Union's Horizon Europe Research and Innovation Programme and by the Participating States.

TIME-RESOLVED ENERGY YIELD ESTIMATION OF RESIDENTIAL PHOTOVOLTAIC SYSTEMS: THE IMPACT OF TREE SHADING

Richard de jong[1,2,3], Patrizio Manganiello[1,2,3], Olivier Dupon[1,2,3], Sara Bouguerra[1,2,3], Arnaud Morlier[1,2,3]
[1]IMO-IMOMEC, Hasselt University, Wetenschapspark 1, 3590 Diepenbeek, Belgium, [2]imec, imo-imomec, Thor Park, Genk, Belgium, [3]EnergyVille, Genk, Belgium
richard.dejong@imec.be, arnaud.morlier@imec.be, Patrizio.Manganiello@imec.be, Olivier.dupon@imec.be, Sara.Bouguerra@imec.be

ABSTRACT: In this study, a methodology is developed to estimate the photovoltaic (PV) energy output of dwellings within a suburban setting. The primary goal of this methodology is to calculate the contribution of roof-mounted PV systems to individual household energy balances throughout the year, considering dwelling types, different azimuth orientations, and predefined roof-mounted PV system configurations. The methodology factors in PV module characteristics, sunlight absorption, ground albedo, ambient temperature, wind velocity, and other variables. Typical meteorological data from the PVGIS database is used to simulate energy yields. The study models four types of dwellings, creating specific 3D CAD models and simulating energy yields for each dwelling object. Detailed information about tree locations and dimensions is integrated into the simulation to accurately model tree shading effects. Results show that uniform tree heights of 15 m, 25 m, and 30 m would result in yearly median energy yield losses of approximately 15%, 25%, and 35%, respectively. Energy losses can be unevenly spread throughout the day and can also occur during peak consumption hours. This work lays the foundation for integrating real-time and forecast data into household digital twin models and presents a framework for simulating PV system yields in suburban environments.
Keywords: energy yield estimation, residential photovoltaic systems, tree shading

1 AIM AND APPROACH

The integration of photovoltaic (PV) systems in residential and community settings is becoming increasingly vital as solar power continues to expand its share in national electricity grids. In Belgium, solar energy saw a 23% increase in installed capacity in 2024, contributing to a record 29.8% of the electricity mix. This shift reflects a broader trend in which renewable energy sources are gradually replacing traditional gas-fired generation, which fell to an all-time low of 17.6% [1].

The primary aim of this work is to provide an accurate estimation of the PV solar energy output for dwellings in a suburban setting and its contribution to the energy balance of households. The case study considered in this work is the project of the existing social housing district Nieuw Texas in Genk, Belgium. The goal is to generate time-resolved simulations of the PV system output for each individual dwelling, accounting for variables such as system configuration, orientation, and environmental factors, with a special focus on the effect of shading from nearby trees.

The approach follows a multi-physics, bottom-up energy yield model developed by imec. This model incorporates PV module characteristics, geometries, and weather factors such as irradiance, ground albedo, ambient temperature, wind velocity, and humidity. Moreover, the simulation tool allows for performing simulations at the PV cell, module, and string levels. A flowchart of the energy yield simulation framework is shown in Figure 1. Weather data from the PVGIS database is used to simulate energy yields over a typical meteorological year (TMY).

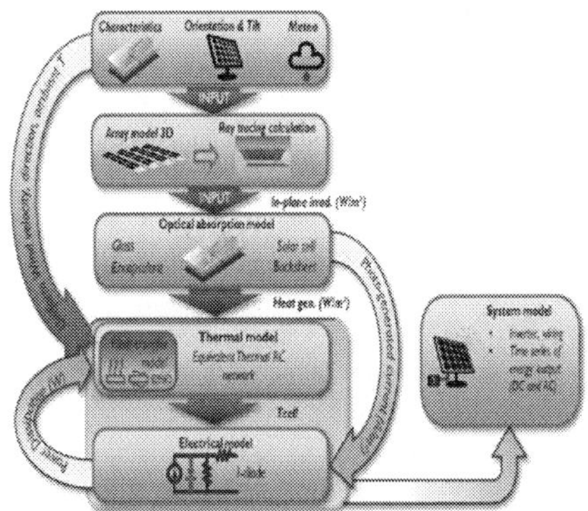

Figure 1: Energy Yield Simulation Framework

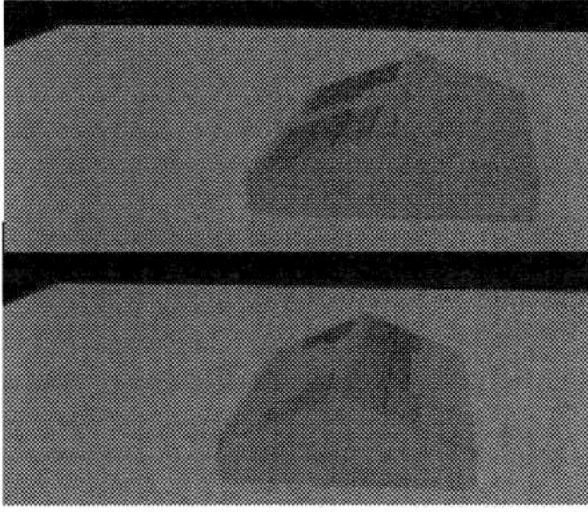

Figure 2: Two Examples of dwellings with two specific PV system layouts

The methodology integrates detailed 3D CAD models of the four types of dwellings present in the suburban Nieuw Texas district. This includes dwelling geometries, azimuth orientation, and specific roof PV system configurations. Twenty-eight roof-mounted PV system configurations were previously defined by an external party. Figure 2 shows two examples of similar dwellings with different orientations and, consequently, different PV systems projected onto their roofs.

The detailed 3D model also includes the precise positioning and dimensions of existing trees that may influence PV system performance (Figures 3 and 4). Tree locations and heights are incorporated using data from the Limburg Service Association (s-lim) [2]. By utilizing ray tracing, the simulation framework models the impact of shading on PV systems from trees and nearby buildings. The shadow effect is calculated over time, with hourly resolution, and spatially at the sub-cell level, using multiple sensing points per cell. These steps are crucial for accurate energy yield predictions.

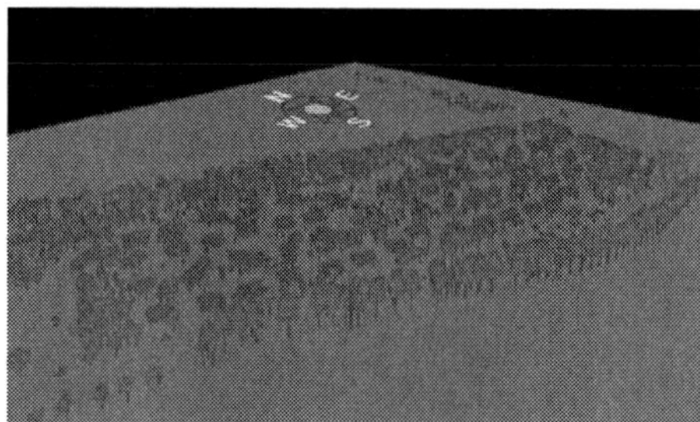

Figure 3: South-west view of the modelled Nieuw Texas district, Genk

Figure 4: Modelled dwelling with depiction of the irradiance inhomogeneity on the PV system during a morning hour

2 SCIENTIFIC INNOVATION AND RELEVANCE

The power output of residential PV systems under shading conditions has been evaluated in several studies. In [3], the impact of environmental factors such as ground albedo, module spacing, and tilt angle on annual energy generation was analyzed using PVSyst, enabling the optimization of system design to achieve a higher performance ratio. Another study [4] compared two different modeling software tools to evaluate shading losses in PV systems. The results showed an overestimation of 9% to 24% in energy output, primarily attributed to the simplification of 3D models and the lack of geometrical and optical details in the simulation. To address this gap, the method presented in this paper incorporates a detailed 3D model—based on polygons— for dwellings and nearby trees to predict shading loss more accurately. By integrating this 3D model with detailed optical and electrical-thermal models within the energy yield framework shown in Figure 1, a highly detailed, time-resolved energy yield model for photovoltaic (PV) systems in suburban environments is created. This allows for accurate simulation of energy output and quantification of the effects of both natural (trees) and artificial (e.g., buildings) surrounding objects on system performance.

Simulating energy yield in residential settings— especially when combined with real-time and forecast data—co-creates sustainable solutions within local communities and with residents. This empowers them to make informed decisions that improve energy efficiency, reduce carbon footprints, and enhance overall living conditions. This research is highly relevant to the objectives of the oPENlab project, particularly as part of the Genk Living Lab in which this study was done [5]. The accurate estimation of the energy provided by the PV system to the household is a crucial element towards the establishment of a digital twin of a dwelling, which integrates the solar energy yield from PV system with the contribution/consumption of individual HVAC, heat pumps and battery storages.

The project's methodology and findings could similarly be applied to other districts in Genk, as well as to suburbs of other cities. It promotes the integration of renewable energy into everyday life and contributes to broader sustainability goals.

3 RESULTS (OR PRELIMINARY RESULTS) AND CONCLUSIONS

The preliminary results of this study highlight the significant impact of tree height on the energy yield of photovoltaic (PV) systems in residential areas. Simulations were conducted on fifty-five dwellings, representing the most common dwelling type in the Nieuw Texas district. In the near future, each of these dwellings will be equipped with 14 PV modules. The simulations indicate that uniform tree heights of 15 m, 25 m, and 30 m would result in yearly median energy yield losses of approximately 15%, 25%, and 35%, respectively. This decline underscores the importance of accurately modeling tree-shading effects for reliable energy output predictions (Figure 5). Furthermore, the variation in calculated energy yield losses suggests that the impact of vegetation growth cannot be simplified into a one-size-fits-all approach for all PV systems within the same neighborhood.

Time-resolved analysis further shows that, on a typical November day, tree shading causes a 30% reduction in energy yield for a moderately shaded dwelling with 14 modules, with the greatest losses occurring during late morning hours (Figures 4 and 6). These findings highlight the necessity of regular tree maintenance and pruning to optimize PV system performance. The results of this analysis can inform property owners and local authorities about tree maintenance and pruning plans.

In conclusion, this study provides a robust framework for simulating PV energy output for individual dwellings in suburban environments by integrating both environmental and system-specific factors. Time-resolved simulations illustrate that energy loss is unevenly distributed throughout the day and emphasize the significant impact of shading, particularly during peak consumption hours. Additionally, the study underscores the importance of incorporating environmental constraints, such as trees, into the digital twins of seemingly identical systems to ensure accurate energy balance calculations for individual households. It also highlights the need for regular assessments of tree shading due to vegetation growth over a system's lifetime. This approach, combined with real-time and forecast data, co-creates sustainable solutions within local communities and with residents.

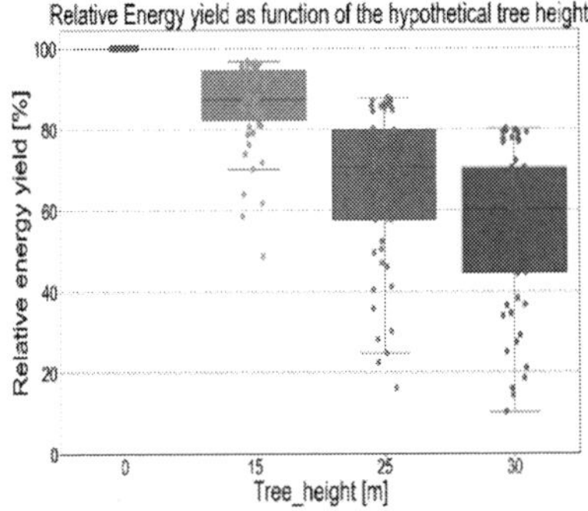

Figure 5: Relative Energy Yield of fifty-five dwellings, each with fourteen PV modules, calculated without trees (0 m) and with trees of three different uniform heights

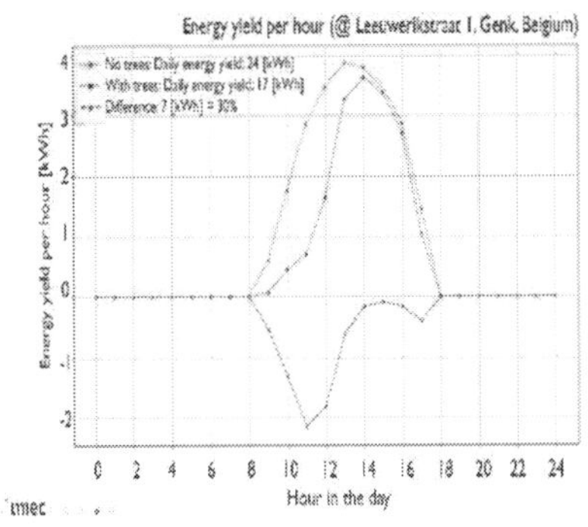

Figure 6: PV power output of a residential system, calculated without trees and with actual surrounding tree heights

References:

[1] Elia Group, "Electricity mix for Belgium in 2024: record international exchanges, significant increase in solar generation, and low use of gas-fired capacities." [Online]. Available: https://www.elia.be/en/press/2025/0120250102_electricity-mix.

[2] Limburg Service Association (s-lim) [Online]. Available: https://s-lim.be/

[3] J. Jamal, I. Mansur, A. Rasid, M. Mulyadi, M. Dihyah Marwan, and M. Marwan, "Evaluating the shading effect of photovoltaic panels to optimize the performance ratio of a solar power system," *Results in Engineering*, vol. 21, p. 101878, Mar. 2024, doi: 10.1016/j.rineng.2024.101878.

[4] E. D. Chepp, F. P. Gasparin, and A. Krenzinger, "Accuracy investigation in the modeling of partially shaded photovoltaic systems, "*Solar Energy*, vol. 223, pp. 182–192, Jul. 2021 doi: 10.1016/j.solener.2021.05.061.

[5] Positive Energy Neighbourhoods (oPEN) Living Labs: Tartu (Estonia), Pamplona (Spain), Genk (Belgium), funded by the European Union's Horizon 2020 Research and Innovation Programme: https://openlab-project.eu/

Time-Resolved Energy Yield Estimation of Residential Photovoltaic Systems: The Impact of Tree Shading

Richard de jong[1,2,3], Patrizio Manganiello[1,2,3], Olivier Dupon[1,2,3], Sara Bouguerra[1,2,3], Ismail Kaaya[1,2,3], Nikoleta Kyranaki[1,2,3], Arnaud Morlier[1,2,3]

[1]IMO-IMOMEC, Hasselt University, Wetenschapspark 1, 3590 Diepenbeek, Belgium, [2]imec, imo-imomec, Thor Park, Genk, Belgium, [3]EnergyVille, Genk, Belgium

Motivation

This study aims to provide an accurate **time-resolved energy yield estimation for dwellings** in a suburban setting and its **contribution to the energy balance of households**. This study is carried out as part of the oPENLab project [1]. It focuses on the New-Texas district in Genk, Belgium.

The geometric 3D model in the simulation considers:
- Specific dwelling types
- Different azimuth orientations
- Predefined roof-mounted PV system configurations
- Actual tree locations and dimensions [2,3,4]

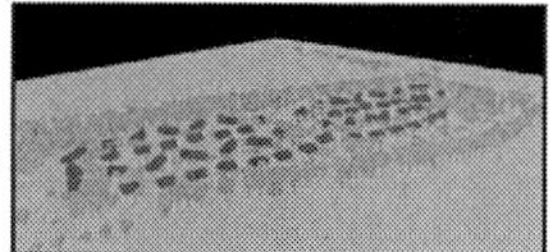

New-Texas district

Genk, Belgium

It is key to incorporate trees in the geometric 3D model to accurately predict the foreseeable tree-shading impact on the daily PV system efficiency: Today, and as trees mature over time.

Methodology

Simulations are done using **imec's PV-simulation framework** [5]:
- **Bottom-up, multi-physics energy yield model**
- **Incorporates:**
  - PV module characteristics
  - Weather data
    - Current: Typical Meteorological Year (TMY) for general predictions
    - Next phase: Live meteorological data for real-time modelling
  - **Detailed geometric 3D model**
    - **Dwellings**
    - **PV configurations on dwellings**
    - **Surrounding trees**

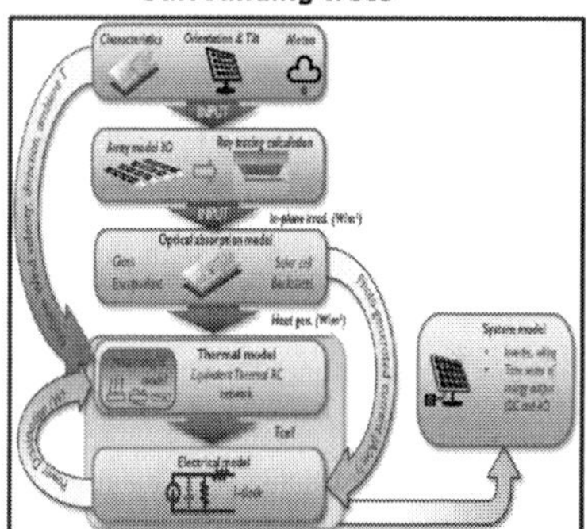

imec's multi-physics PV-simulation framework

Examples of dwellings with specific PV system layouts

Boxplot distribution of Energy Yield as function of the hypothetical tree height, relative to a treeless environment. Evaluated over a Typical Meteorological Year (TMY).

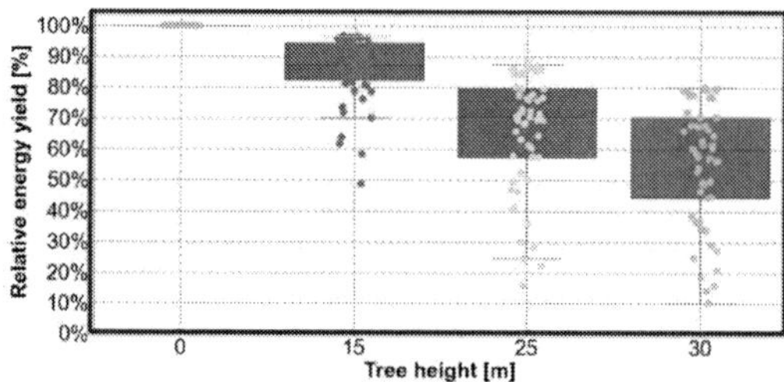

The shading effect is unevenly distributed throughout the day, with notable losses during peak consumption hours:

Hourly energy yield in a day: with/without surrounding trees.

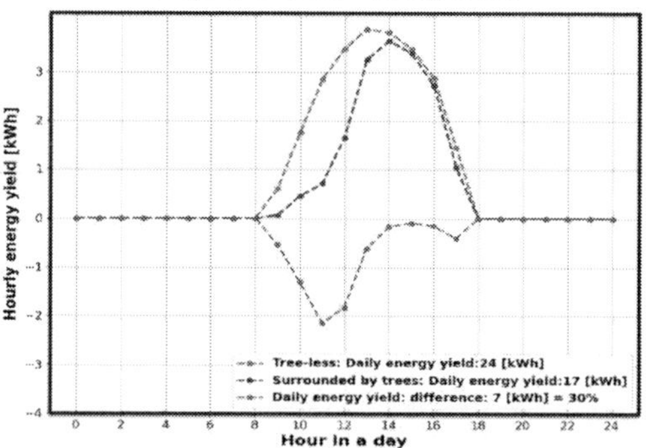

Modules partly shaded by trees in the morning

Results

Tree height significantly affects the energy yield of PV-modules (55 dwellings, 14 PV modules each):

Hypothetical tree height [m]	Median energy yield loss relative to a treeless environment [%]
15	15
25	25
30	35

Conclusion

This study emphasizes:
- **The importance of integrating environmental constraints** into digital twin models for accurate energy balance calculations.
- **The significant impact of surrounding trees on the energy yield.**
- **Unevenly distributed losses throughout the day demands time-resolved energy yield calculation.**
- **Regular tree maintenance and pruning is necessary** to optimize PV system performance.

Next

Next steps:
- Use LIDAR input to establish the 3D geometry of trees and dwellings.
- Use live meteorological data for real-time modelling.

Acknowledgments

The authors thank the Limburg Service Association (s-lim), Aster and EnergyVision for providing tree, dwelling, and PV-configuration data.

[1]Positive Energy Neighbourhoods (oPEN) Living Labs: Tartu (Estonia), Pamplona (Spain), Genk (Belgium), funded by the European Union's Horizon 2020 Research and Innovation Programme: https://openlab-project.eu/
[2] Limburg Service Association (s-lim) [Online]. Available: https://s-lim.be/
[3] EnergyVision: www.energyvision.be
[4] Aster: www.aster.vlaanderen
[5] T. Horvath et al., "Next Generation Tools for Accurate Energy Yield Estimation of Bifacial PV Systems – Best Practices, Improvements and Challenges,"
The oPEN Lab project has received funding from the European Union's Horizon 2020 Research and Innovation Framework Programme under Grant agreement No. 101037080. Views and opinions expressed are those of the author(s) only and do not necessarily reflect those of the European Union or the European Climate, Infrastructure and Environment Executive Agency (CINEA). Neither the European Union nor the granting authority can be held responsible for them.

020295-001

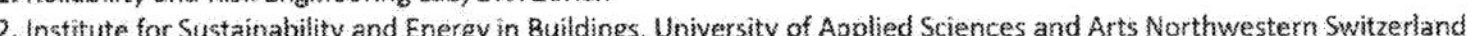

PV SYSTEM DESIGN WITH CURTAILMENT IN MIND: COSTS AND EMISSIONS AT THE PROSUMER LEVEL

Linda Brodnicke[1] Alissa Ganter[1], Giovanni Sansavini[1], Natasa Vulic[2]*

1. Reliability and Risk Engineering Lab, ETH Zürich
2. Institute for Sustainability and Energy in Buildings, University of Applied Sciences and Arts Northwestern Switzerland

Introduction / Background

The adoption of photovoltaic (PV) systems among end-consumers is expected to increase significantly. However, as the penetration of PV systems grows, grid congestion may lead to increased curtailment, negatively impacting the return on investment of PV systems that are designed under the assumption of favorable feed-in tariffs and unrestricted grid access. Given that PV systems represent long-term investments, decisions are often based on current conditions. These include existing feed-in tariffs, electricity prices, and the absence of export limitations. In this study, we investigate the following:

RQ1: How do **export limitations** influence the **optimal design of PV-battery systems** (system size, tilt, orientation, battery capacity) and their associated **life cycle costs and emissions**?

RQ2: What are the **impacts of incorrect foresight** about future export limitations (both overestimating and underestimating export freedom) on the **life cycle costs and emissions** of PV-battery systems?

Methodology

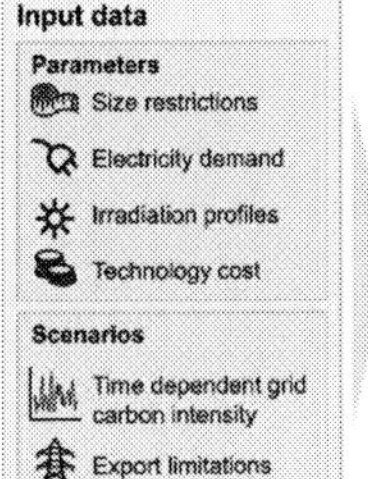
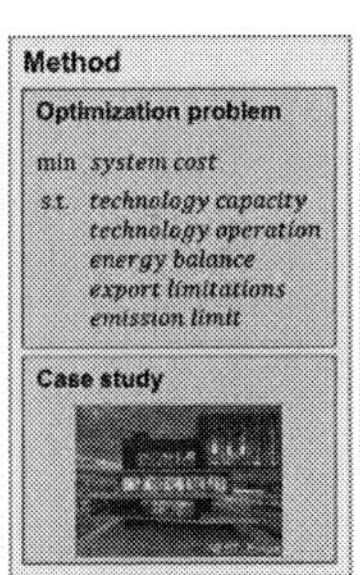
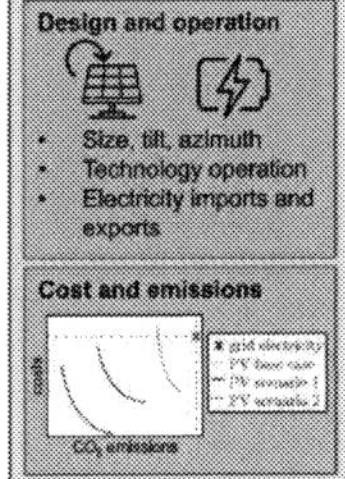

Brodnicke and Gartner, Energy and Buildings 2024

Optimization approach: Mixed-integer linear programming (MILP) formulated in Python (cvxpy, solved with Gurobi).

Objectives: Minimize

Annualized system cost → capital + operational − revenues

Annual GHG emissions → embodied + operational − export credits

Scenarios:
Base case (unlimited export, time-dependent grid carbon intensity)
Export limitations at 50%, 25%, and 0% of maximum feed-in in the base case

Scenario	Assumed during design	Export limit at operation
✓ Correct foresight (unl.)	Unlimited export	Unlimited export
✓ Correct foresight (cap)	Strict export cap	Strict export cap
⚠ Overestimate freedom	Unlimited export	Strict export cap
⚠ Underestimate freedom	Strict export cap	Unlimited export

Results and Discussion

RQ1: optimal design of PV-battery systems under export limitations

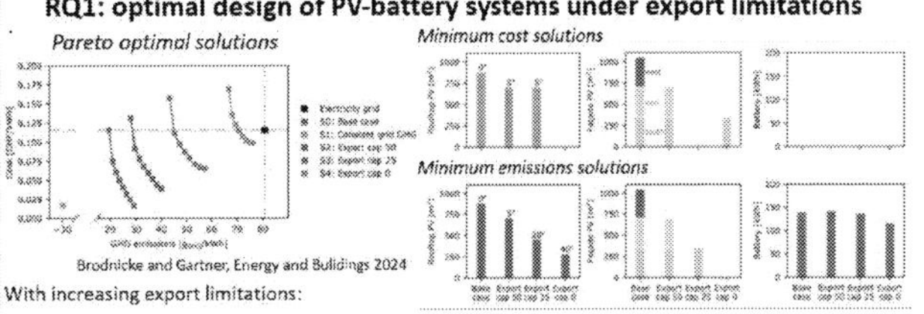

Brodnicke and Gartner, Energy and Buildings 2024

With increasing export limitations:

minimum cost solutions → more favorable than grid-only in terms of both costs and emissions
minimum emissions solutions → more favorable in terms of emissions, costlier than grid-only

minimum cost solutions → reduced PV size, no battery is installed in any of the export limitation scenarios
minimum emission solutions → reduced PV size with increased tilt, battery is installed in all scenarios

RQ2: impact of incorrect foresight about future export limitations

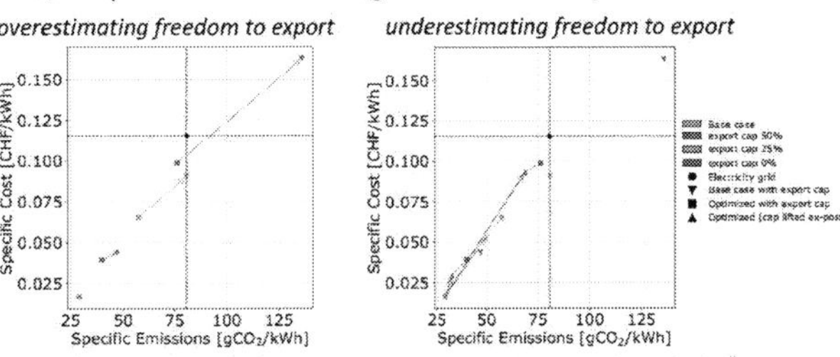

Compared to correct foresight (cap) at min. cost:
50% export cap → +11% cost, +18% emissions
25% export cap → +39% cost, +41% emissions
0% export cap → +65% cost, +79% emissions

Compared to correct foresight (unl) at min. cost:
50% export cap → +73% cost, +12% emissions
25% export cap → +210% cost, +71% emissions
0% export cap → +446% cost, +136% emissions

Conclusions

In response to the research questions posed above, the following key takeaways can be made based on the presented case study:

RQ1: optimal design of PV-battery systems under export limitations
- Export limits reduce both the emission reduction potential and its cost-effectiveness compared to the base case (no export limitations)
- Cost-optimal solutions with export limits outperform the grid-only by favoring smaller PV systems that self-consumption (rather than installing a battery)
- Emission-optimal solutions with export limits are more costly than grid-only solutions, with system design favoring increased tilt and a battery system

RQ2: impact of incorrect foresight about future export limitations
- **Overestimating freedom** → Export caps match the grid at best (25%), but can nearly double emissions for the strictest export case (0%)
- **Underestimating freedom** → Lifting caps restores revenue and credits, but leaves opportunities unrealized compared to the base case
- **50% cap assumption** → impact of incorrect foresight has a negligible impact in the two cases (both overestimating and underestimating export freedom)

Implications

- **High export limits** significantly influence both **economic viability** and **emission reduction** potential of PV installations → decision to install
- **Understanding export caps** is crucial for planning PV integration that is both **cost-effective and climate-aligned** → misjudging the benefits
- **For prosumers** → need robust investment strategies under uncertain export policies when planning their PV system installations
- **For policymakers** → regulations and incentives should explicitly account for curtailment effects to ensure promotion of renewable energy

Next steps

- Apply framework to other context (e.g. *dynamic tariffs, local energy communities* [2], *repowering decisions* [3]) to evaluate the impact on costs and emissions
- Expand to a *multi-stage optimization* [3] *approach* to evaluate how future conditions may impact operational or investment decisions for future stages

References

[1] L. Brodnicke, A. Ganter, S. Tröber, G. Sansavini, and N. Vulic, "Dynamic grid emission factors and export limits reduce emission abatement and cost benefits of building PV systems," Energy and Buildings, vol. 323, p. 114772, 2024. doi: 10.1016/j.enbuild.2024.114772

[2] Q. Li, N. Vulic, H. Cai, and P. Heer, "Flexibility implications of optimal PV design: Building vs. community scale," J. Phys.: Conf. Ser., vol. 2600, no. 8, p. 082002, 2023. doi: 10.1038/1742-6596/2600/8/082002.

[3] S. Ovaitt, H. Mirletz, B. Mirletz, and M. Prilliman, "Repowering PV systems demystified: Terms, motives, economics and impacts," in Proc. IEEE 53rd Photovoltaic Specialists Conf. (PVSC), Montreal, QC, Canada, 2025, doi: 10.1109/PVSC59419.2025.11132584

[4] F. Solèr, Y.-C. B. Chen, N. Vulic, and G. Mavromatidis, "Investigation of near-optimal solutions for building retrofit and portfolio optimization," presented at SBE25, 2025.

Prof. Dr. Natasa Vulic | Institut Nachhaltigkeit und Energie am Bau | natasa.vulic@fhnw.ch 020296-001

BIPV SIMULATION WITH CONVENTIONAL TOOLS AND MODELS; DO WE NEED MORE ACCURACY?

Ana Marcos-Castro [a,b], Nuria Martín-Chivelet [a], Jesús Polo [a], Carlos Sanz-Saiz [a]

[a] CIEMAT, Photovoltaic Solar Energy Unit, Av. Complutense, 40, 28040 Madrid, Spain
[b] Universidad Politécnica de Madrid, Av. de Juan de Herrera, 4, 28040 Madrid, Spain
ana.marcos@ciemat.es, nuria.martin@ciemat.es, jesus.polo@ciemat.es, carlos.sanz@ciemat.es

ABSTRACT: The present work compares two simulation tools, SAM and PVsyst, to assess their suitability in analysing the behaviour of BIPV systems, with special focus on their management of the effect of shading losses in energy output estimations, in addition to module temperature. The simulations are performed for Building 42 in CIEMAT headquarters, which was renovated in 2017 with monitored BIPV systems on the east, south and west façades. The shading tools in both software are capable of modelling the environment through simple geometric elements; moreover, PVsyst also allows the use of an external 3D file that can simplify the process. The results of this study manifest that the 3D scene method used to assess the effect of shading can have a strong impact on the reliability of energy output estimations. When using the same 3D scenes through their built-in tools, SAM shows better performance than PVsyst. In contrast, PVsyst energy output results improve significantly when using an imported 3D digital asset exchange file derived from Light Detection and Ranging data. This discrepancy in results remarks the need for special attention regarding the configuration and modelling of shading elements, which requires future work to better understand the simulation methods in each tool.
Keywords: BIPV modelling, PV simulation tools, BIPV shading.

1 INTRODUCTION

Although efforts are increasingly made towards decarbonisation and energy efficiency [1–3], integrating photovoltaic systems into building envelopes is still hindered by the limited availability of simulation tools that help justify the design and accurately estimate energy outcome of BIPV systems [4]. While this is mostly straightforward for PV plants, BIPV systems require software tools that can accommodate diverse boundary conditions, e.g., the surrounding environment and shading, the constructive solution and ventilation, and the tilt and azimuth angles of the modules.

Analysing and comparing simulation tools [5–7] provides valuable information to support future BIPV installations by helping decide which tools are suitable and to what extent for each case, based on aspects such as project specifications and design requirements, boundary conditions, and stakeholders' resources and skills.

The aim of this work is to assess the suitability of different software tools to estimate the behaviour of a BIPV system. Moreover, factors such as the ease-of-use, the simplicity or complexity of the base model and design process, the ability to include the environment and shading elements, or the customisability of the BIPV constructive system and module characteristics have been considered. All of these aspects are highly relevant in BIPV systems, especially in urban areas where buildings are subject to specific boundary conditions that need to be accounted for in the simulation stages of the project. Special focus is set on each tool's methodology for calculating module temperature, given that BIPV modules are generally poorly ventilated on their backside, causing an increase in their operating temperature and, therefore, a decrease in their PV energy performance. Therefore, module temperature determination can play a crucial role in energy estimation of BIPV systems.

2 PV MODELLING TOOLS APPLIED TO BIPV

SAM [8] and PVsyst [9] are two widely used photovoltaic simulation tools that provide means to estimate the behaviour of BIPV systems. Both offer 3D scene capabilities to account for shading with simple design features for buildings and vegetation. Furthermore, to better represent the operating conditions of a BIPV system, these programs include customisable features through the temperature model of the photovoltaic modules.

2.1 SAM

SAM is a free tool that offers two performance models to calculate the energy output of a BIPV system: a detailed model for an in-depth analysis and a basic model for a preliminary approach. Choosing one over the other depends on the availability of system specifications and input data, with the basic model requiring fewer parameters, mainly module efficiency, while resulting in less accurate calculations. Given that all necessary system specifications are known in Building 42, the study developed in this paper used the detailed model.

SAM provides a customisable mounting standoff option based on the distance between the module and the constructive element behind it, providing several distance ranges to choose from. The selected distance is taken into account for the calculations to better represent the effect of rear ventilation on the module's temperature. The model is based on the Nominal Operating Cell Temperature (NOCT), modified with temperature increments which are a function of the distance between the module and the constructive element behind it. The user can choose the mounting standoff distance that better suits the project design, ranging from lower than 0.5 inches, with NOCT increasing by 18 degrees, up to 3.5 inches, which leads to a NOCT increase of 2 degrees. This menu offers an additional 'building integrated' option, which instead of applying a default modification to the NOCT requires the user to manually include an NOCT value previously adjusted by the user based on the boundary conditions of the BIPV module.

2.2 PVsyst

PVsyst works similarly to SAM in terms of system

specifications and 3D design, though it has the additional feature of being able to import three external file types for 3D input scenes: 3DS (3D Studio), DAE (digital asset exchange) and PVC (PVcase). While useful for some cases, the calculation engine can only handle a limited amount of input data. As 3D scenes become more complex, the calculation time increases significantly and may not work properly.

To address the BIPV constructive system and boundary conditions, PVsyst allows the selection of three mounting options: free standing, fully insulated backside and semi-integration. These translate to the temperature model calculations by assigning specific values to the model's heat transfer coefficient uc (ranging from 15 to 29 W/m²K), which is then used to simulate module temperature. This coefficient is higher for well-ventilated modules and lower as backside ventilation decreases.

3 EXPERIMENTAL FACILITY AND MODEL PREPARATION

The selected tools are assessed in a BIPV monitored case study where experimental data are available: Building 42 at CIEMAT headquarters in Madrid, Spain (40.45° N, -3.74° E). The building was renovated in 2017, with the intervention including BIPV systems on the topmost areas of the east, south and west façades [10]. The constructive system for these BIPV modules is a ventilated façade with an air gap of approximately 70 mm in thickness, and a 15 mm top opening protected by a metal plate (Figure 1).

Figure 1: Southwest corner (up) and northeast corner (down) of Building 42.

This study focuses on a comparison of experimental to simulated values during the year 2019. Input data required in the simulation tools (module and inverter specifications, array and subarray setups) were set to match the existing system's products and design.

The main two parameters considered in the study are module temperature and PV energy output. In-situ measurements are compared to the estimated values calculated with the two simulation tools. This comparison

leads to identifying strengths and weaknesses of each tool and supporting the decision criteria when choosing the most suitable option for each project.

Energy calculations are performed using several meteorological variables, mainly irradiance, temperature and wind speed, which can be obtained from each tool's database or sourced from external sources and manually included in the tools. Instead of using the meteorological data available in both software individually, for the comparison study it was preferred to use the same meteorological data, minimising uncertainties caused by differing boundary conditions. The required data were obtained from Copernicus Atmosphere Monitoring Services (CAMS) for irradiation direct, diffuse and albedo components, and the Photovoltaic Geographical Information System (PVGIS) for ambient temperature and wind speed. CAMS was selected due to its good performance on previous studies that evaluate radiation data from several sources [11], and because irradiation data are not always available in BIPV façades.

Input data were processed to fit the specific weather file format required by each tool. In addition, simulation data were filtered to match the available experimental values, meaning that meteorological data values were set to zero for any timeframe when in-situ measurements were unavailable. This allows the comparison to only account for the actual available experimental data, and avoids deviations caused by data mismatch. In our case, this filtering criteria lead to approximately 4,200-4,300 daylight (i.e. measurements above zero) hourly values, depending on the façade.

4 RESULTS

Firstly, module temperature for the south façade was calculated for 2019 on an hourly basis using the tools' available configurations and then compared to experimental data. A statistical error analysis was developed with mean bias error (MBE) and root mean square error (RMSE) as the key indicators.

Table 1 presents SAM's results for module temperature estimation. For SAM's BIPV option, the module's NOCT was customised to 55.3 °C based on a regression analysis performed with experimental values [12]. All other configurations used the different default values provided by each software.

Table I: South façade statistical analysis of module temperature estimation for all configurations in SAM.

SAM	MBE (°C)	RMSE(°C)
BIPV	-3.3	6.2
<0.5 inch	-1.0	5.9
0.5-1.5 inch	-3.2	6.1
1.5-2.5 inch	-4.7	7.1
2.5-3.5 inch	-5.9	8.1

The RMSE is similar in all cases, with the lowest value at 5.9 °C for the <0.5-inch option. The negative values for the MBE indicate that the model consistently underestimates module temperature in all configurations between 1 °C and 5.9 °C. It should be noted that, while the <0.5-inch (12.7 mm) dimension does not accurately reflect the actual façade air gap of 70 mm, the small 15 mm opening at the top may reduce the effect of backside ventilation, which may cause this option to have lower error values. However, due to possible uncertainties in experimental data, it was preferred to use the option that matches the system's actual configuration, i.e., the 1.5-2.5 inch.

In PVsyst, the statistical analysis included the built-in 3D scene and the imported DAE file option, with results summarised in Table 2 below.

Table II: South façade statistical analysis of module temperature estimation for all configurations in PVsyst, including the built-in 3D scene (up) and an imported DAE file (down).

PVsyst (built-in)	MBE (°C)	RMSE (°C)
openback	-6.9	10.9
semi-BIPV	-3.0	8.7
BIPV	1.2	9.2

PVsyst (DAE)	MBE (°C)	RMSE (°C)
openback	-7.7	11.4
semi-BIPV	-4.3	9.0
BIPV	-0.5	8.8

The error module temperature estimation in PVsyst is similar for both 3D workflows. The RMSE is slightly higher than the values seen in SAM, ranging between 8.7 and 11.4 °C. The MBE shows underestimation in most cases, except for the BIPV configuration with the built-in 3D scene.

This statistical analysis can aid in selecting the constructive configuration that better represents the existing BIPV system's boundary conditions. For this study, the selected configurations were the 1.5-2.5 inch option in SAM and the BIPV in PVsyst. The statistical analysis was then extended to the remaining east and west façades (Table 3). For SAM's calculations, the NOCT value was adjusted for the east and west façades following the regression strategy used on the south façade.

Table III: Statistical analysis for module temperature estimation on the east and west façades for SAM (top) and PVsyst (bottom).

SAM	MBE (°C)	RMSE (°C)
East	2.5	5.1
West	5.2	7.2

PVsyst (built-in)	MBE (°C)	RMSE (°C)
East	2.4	7.1
West	-3.8	9.1

The average mean bias error is below 5.2 °C in SAM and -3.8 °C in PVsyst. On the contrary, SAM's quadratic deviation is slightly better by about 2 °C in both cases.

The next step was to evaluate energy output simulations, which were done monthly for the year 2019. To assess the effect of shading, energy simulations were firstly performed for the east façade with and without surrounding buildings and vegetation. This façade is highly affected by a nearby row of caduceus white poplar trees, which cause more shading during their leafy seasons, and some additional vegetation to a lesser extent. For this comparison, the shading scenes in both software were developed using their built-in shading tools. For comparable results, the same 3D building and tree elements were designed in both cases. Figure 2 shows the monthly results obtained in energy output estimations for 2019 when shading is considered as opposed to shading being ignored, and their comparison to experimental data.

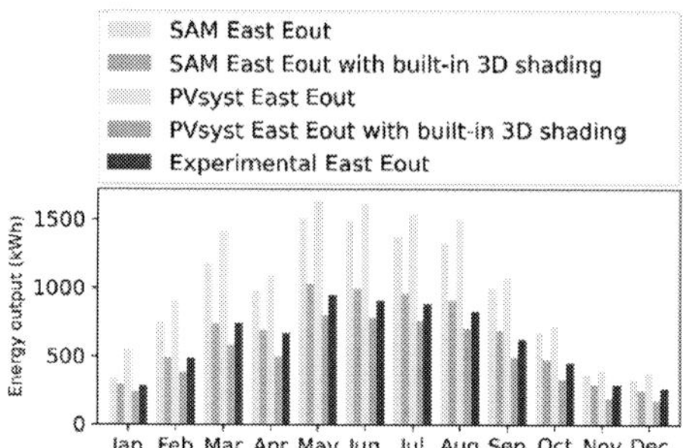

Figure 2: SAM and PVsyst energy output with and without shading comparison to experimental data for the east façade in 2019.

As expected, Figure 2 confirms that shading has a significant impact in BIPV energy simulations and should not be overlooked. Based on these results, energy output simulations for the south and west façades also included the surrounding shading elements. The south façade does not present significant nearby obstacles, while several trees affect the west façade and are accounted for in the calculations. Figure 3 includes charts comparing the experimental energy output to the values simulated with SAM and PVsyst respectively, both using the built-in 3D shading scene capabilities as explained earlier.

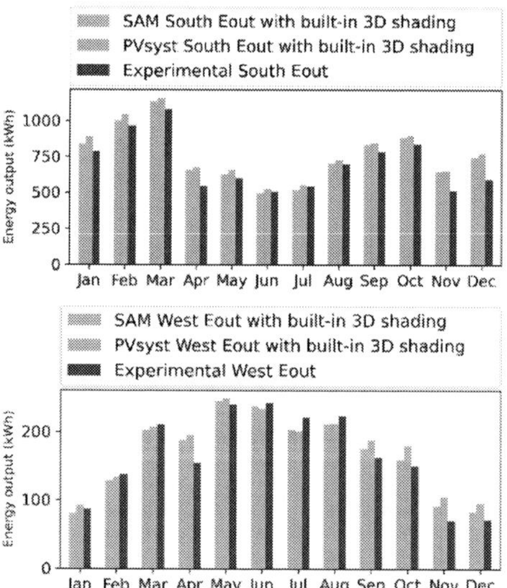

Figure 3: SAM and PVsyst energy output comparison to experimental data for the south (top) and west (bottom) façades in 2019.

Lastly, the study assessed the two available workflows for the 3D scene in PVsyst: the built-in option and an imported DAE file obtained from a Digital Surface Model (DSM) derived from Light Detection and Ranging

(LiDAR) data [13] (Figure 4).

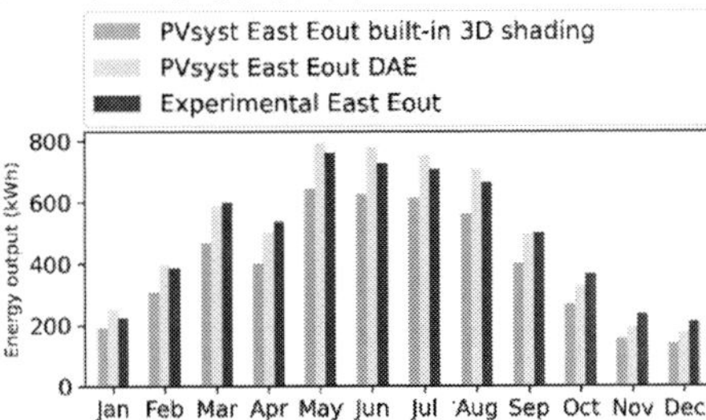

Figure 4: PVsyst energy output comparison to experimental data for the east façade based on the 3D the built-in scene creator and an imported DAE file.

This figure illustrates better performance in energy output estimations with the imported DAE file as opposed to the built-in scene creator.

To support the graphical analysis, the yearly normalised mean bias error (nMBE) and normalised root mean square error (nRMSE) for each façade in both tools are provided in Table 4 below. For PVsyst, the analysis was developed using both the built-in and the imported DAE 3D scene options.

Table IV: nMBE and nRMSE (%) analysis for SAM and PVsyst.

nMBE(%)	SAM (built-in)	PVsyst (built-in)	PVsyst (DAE)
South	7.9	12.1	-1.4
East	6.6	-20.9	1.1
West	1.9	6.9	-0.3

nRMSE(%)	SAM (built-in)	PVsyst (built-in)	PVsyst (DAE)
South	10.4	13.1	11.7
East	8.6	19.9	7.1
West	9.0	13.3	13.4

When comparing the built-in 3D scene with identical layout in both tools, energy output simulations show lower errors in SAM in all orientations, while the nMBE improves considerably when using PVsyst's imported DAE file. When evaluating the nRMSE, SAM and PVsyst's DAE option perform similarly, with the latter's built-in 3D scene having higher errors overall.

5 CONCLUSIONS

While several tools are available to perform PV simulations, few focus on BIPV specifically. For this purpose, some software solutions provide optional configurations that address BIPV specific boundary conditions, such as constructive configuration and surrounding elements. These tools may however be insufficient in certain detailed analyses and studies, such as shading from the urban context and nearby elements.

In this work, an exercise to model several small BIPV arrays working under different shading conditions is presented using two well-known tools (SAM and PVsyst). Energy output simulations confirmed that shading plays an essential role to ensure accuracy, leading to energy overestimation when shading is not considered, as presented in Figure 2.

Given the importance of shading in BIPV systems, proper design of the surrounding elements becomes one of the greatest challenges in BIPV simulations. This issue is addressed in the evaluated software by either providing a 3D scene design tool or an imported external 3D file. The present study reveals that the methods for configuring and imposing shading conditions in each tool need to be analysed carefully, since apparently equal shading conditions produce different results in each tool. In general, the results show more accuracy in SAM modelling than in PVsyst, although there is remarkable improvement in PVsyst estimations when detailed shading is provided from a DAE file containing an accurate 3D scene.

Because the discrepancy between the results of the equivalent 3D scenes in both software is significant, it is important to identify the possible causes, whether they are related to user experience during the design stages, or the tools' internal calculation methods for shadings and module temperature. To understand these differences, further work is required to understand and evaluate how each tool performs the calculations, especially their management of obstacles during the simulations.

Module temperature estimation is also key in BIPV installations, with both tools providing customisable options to account for different BIPV boundary conditions. This is another subject for further study since uncertainty in power estimations is partially conditioned by the accuracy in cell temperature determination.

The discrepancy between predicted and measured energy is not only the result of differences in irradiance and environmental data, but also the estimation of power losses due to factors such as module degradation, soiling, wiring losses, and others that affect the Performance Ratio (PR), which can be adjusted by the software user. Furthermore, the uncertainties in power estimation of BIPV arrays presented in this work are relative, since they include the uncertainty of the solar irradiance input (CAMS solar radiation service), the transposition model for the plane of array, and the modelling tool itself. However, beyond the quantitative comparison between both tools, the impact of how shading is input into the model is notable. Thus, further and more detailed analysis is needed before making recommendations on how to model BIPV power under shading conditions.

6 REFERENCES

[1] International Renewable Energy Agency (IRENA), Rise of Renewables in Cities: Energy Solutions for the Urban Future, Abu Dhabi, 2020.

[2] European Commission, "Fit for 55" delivering the EU's 2030 Climate Target on the way to climate neutrality, (2021).

[3] T. Reijenga, M. Ritzen, A. Scognamiglio, K. Kappel, Successful Building Integration of Photovoltaics A Collection of International Projects, (2020).

[4] N. Martin-Chivelet, M. Van Noord, F. Tilli, R.J. Yang, N. Weerasinghe, E. Daun, A. Baggini, BIPV Market Development: International Technological Innovation System Analysis, Buildings 15 (2025) 3011. https://doi.org/10.3390/buildings15173011.

[5] R. Jing Yang, Y. Zhao, S. Dev Sureshkumar Jayakumari, A. Schneider, S. Prithivi Rajan, J.

Leloux, P. Alamy, G. Prasetyo Raharjo, F. Rende, T. Samarasinghalage, A. Marcos Castro, N. Martin Chivelet, S. Woei Leow, P. Wijeratne, Y. Li, L. Zhang, C. Wu, X. Deng, D. Luo, Digitalising BIPV energy simulation: A cross tool investigation, Energy and Buildings 318 (2024) 114484. https://doi.org/10.1016/j.enbuild.2024.114484.

[6] J. Polo, N. Martín-Chivelet, M. Alonso-Abella, C. Sanz-Saiz, J. Cuenca, M. De La Cruz, Exploring the PV Power Forecasting at Building Façades Using Gradient Boosting Methods, Energies 16 (2023) 1495. https://doi.org/10.3390/en16031495.

[7] S. Sharma, G. Raina, S. Yadav, S. Sinha, A comparative evaluation of different PV soiling estimation models using experimental investigations, Energy for Sustainable Development 73 (2023) 280–291. https://doi.org/10.1016/j.esd.2023.02.008.

[8] System Advisor Model™ Version 2025.4.16 (SAM™ 2025.4.16). National Renewable Energy Laboratory. Golden, CO. Accessed May 23, 2025. https://https://sam.nrel.gov, (n.d.).

[9] PVsyst [Version 8.0.14]. Retrieved from PVsyst website, (n.d.).

[10] N. Martín-Chivelet, J. Gutiérrez, M. Alonso-Abella, F. Chenlo, J. Cuenca, Building Retrofit with Photovoltaics: Construction and Performance of a BIPV Ventilated Façade, Energies 11 (2018) 1719. https://doi.org/10.3390/en11071719.

[11] International Electrotechnical Commission, IEA-PVPS-T16-05-2023-Worldwide Benchmark of Modelled Solar Irradiance Data, (2023).

[12] A. Marcos-Castro, C. Sanz-Saiz, J. Polo, N. Martín-Chivelet, Performance Ratio Estimation for Building-Integrated Photovoltaics—Thermal and Angular Characterisation, Applied Sciences 15 (2025) 6579. https://doi.org/10.3390/app15126579.

[13] A. Marcos-Castro, N. Martín-Chivelet, J. Polo, Enhanced GIS Methodology for Building-Integrated Photovoltaic Façade Potential Based on Free and Open-Source Tools and Information, Remote Sensing 17 (2025) 954. https://doi.org/10.3390/rs17060954.

7 ACKNOWLEDGEMENTS

This publication is part of the R+D+I project "RINGS-BIPV Project (PID2021-124910OB-C31)", which is funded by the MICIU/AEI/10.13039/501100011033 and by ERDF/EU. The authors would also like to recognize the efforts, research and contributions of the expert groups of the IEA PVPS Program, in particular those corresponding to Task 15 (BIPV) and Task 16 (Solar Resource), where the authors have an active collaboration.

EU PVSEC
22 — 26
September
BEC
Bilbao Exhibition Centre
Bilbao
Spain
EU
PVSEC
2025
42nd European
Photovoltaic Solar Energy
Conference and Exhibition
030001-001

Conference Highlights

Robert Kenny

European Commission Joint Research Centre

EU PVSEC Technical Programme Chair

030001-003

EU PVSEC
FACTS & FIGURES | Presentations
EU PVSEC 2025
EU PVSEC Programme -
Distribution of
Presentations per Type
CONFERENCE PLENARIES & ORALS
349
CONFERENCE VISUALS
562
OPENING & CLOSING
6
1000+ PRESENTATIONS
4 PANEL DISCUSSIONS WITH 29 PANELISTS
PARALLEL EVENTS
110
INDUSTRY SUMMIT
44

030001-004

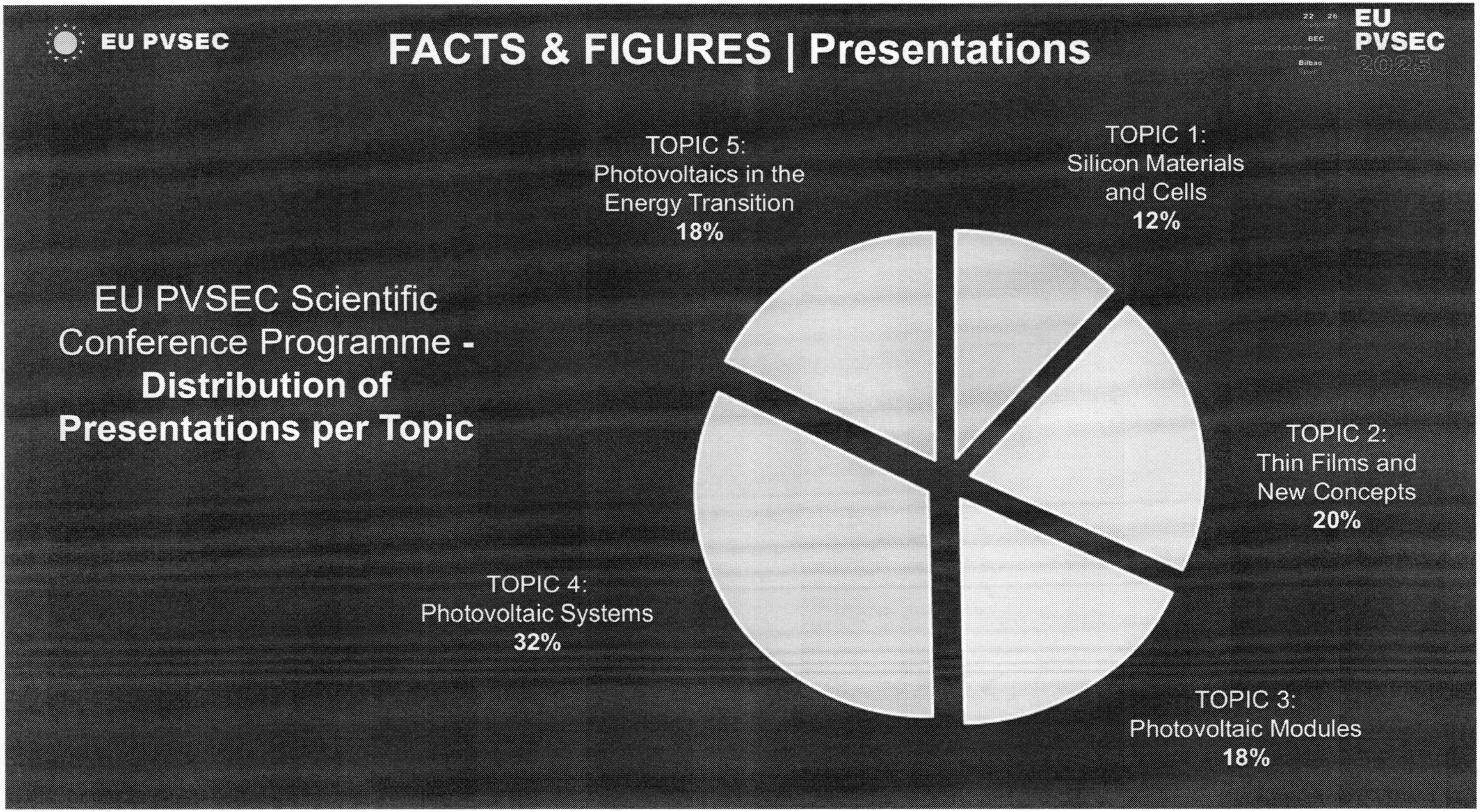

EU PVSEC
FACTS & FIGURES | Presentations
EU PVSEC 2025
EU PVSEC Scientific Conference Programme - Distribution of Presentations per Topic
TOPIC 1:
Silicon Materials and Cells
12%
TOPIC 2:
Thin Films and New Concepts
20%
TOPIC 3:
Photovoltaic Modules
18%
TOPIC 4:
Photovoltaic Systems
32%
TOPIC 5:
Photovoltaics in the Energy Transition
18%
030001-005

FACTS & FIGURES | Participants

Participants by Countries
Top 10

No	Country	Participants
1	Germany	310
2	Spain	270
3	France	108
4	Italy	90
5	The Netherlands	76
6	South Korea	67
7	Switzerland	62
8	Japan	55
9	Belgium	44
10	Norway	35

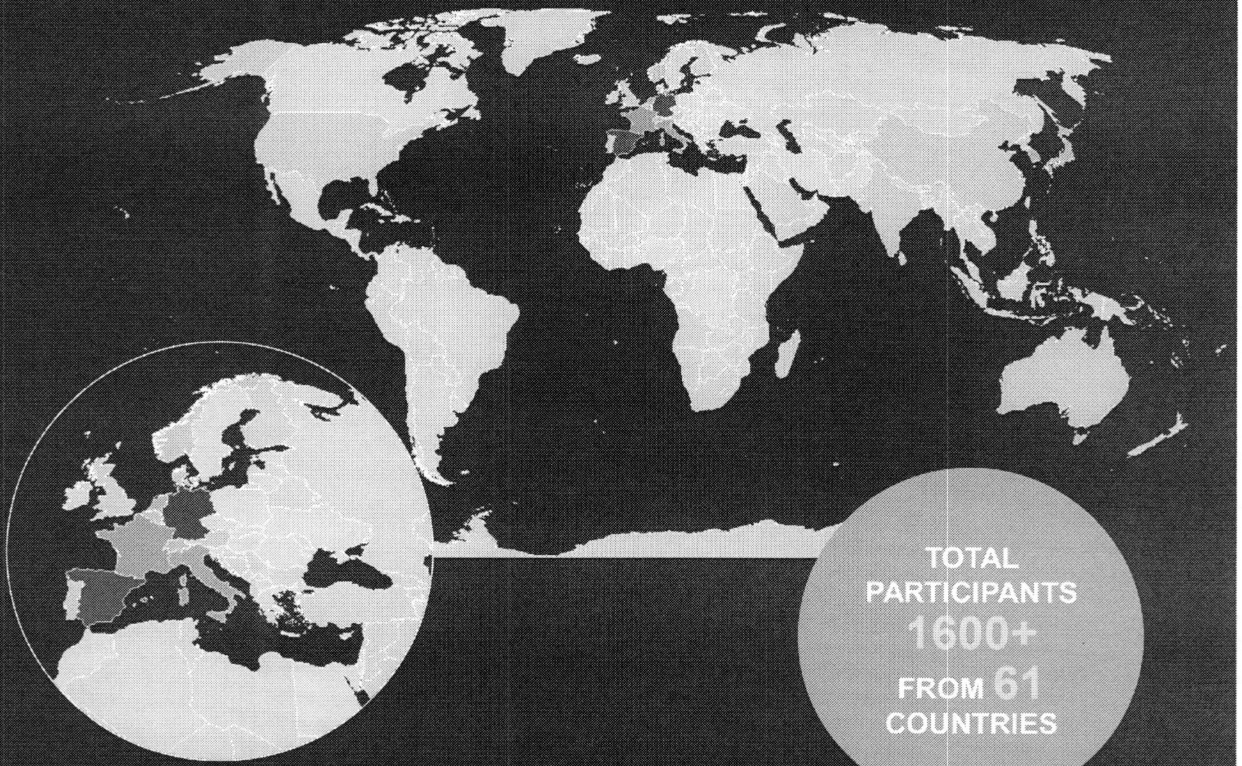

Plenary Session "PV Everywhere"
OPENING
Monday, 22 Sept. 2025
Becquerel Prize Ceremony
Welcome Messages
Jon DE GREGORIO
Carlos DEL CAÑIZO
Gaëtan MASSON
Key Note Speech "The Dual Face of Global Solar Growth"
Moderated Panel Discussion "Solar in Turbulent Times: Global Dynamics and the Way Forward"
Torsten BRAMMER

030001-007

EU PVSEC
PANEL DISCUSSIONS
22 26
BEC
Bilbao
EU PVSEC
2025

BO.13 Reliability and Bankability in PV
"The rapid developments of PV technology require increased attention to be paid to reliability testing."

CO.7 Challenges and Opportunities of PV up to 2030
"PV Technology is already reliable and cost effective, and even though improvements are welcome, key blockages are storage and grid strengthening. AI and robotics are essential to meet the scale of developments needed."

DO.13 Scalability and Manufacturability Prospects in Europe for New Technologies
"The prospects for reaching the 30GW target for PV module manufacturing in Europe were discussed and policy measures proposed."

CONFERENCE

KEY MESSAGES

Cross-cutting themes emerged throughout the programme, showcasing how solar technologies can be applied everywhere, from traditional to emerging fields.

- Sustainability and circularity remain central, with research focused on reducing material use, such as replacing silver with copper, and advancing end-of-life management of modules.

- Ensuring long-term stability and predictable energy yield is equally essential, with studies of degradation mechanisms such as UVID carried out.

- The role of AI across the PV value chain is rapidly expanding, from design to operations and maintenance, including drone applications.

CONFERENCE

Enhancements in IV measurement procedures

- Michael Rauer, Fraunhofer ISE: 1AO.4.5 *Universal Contacting Approaches for the Characterization of Solar Cells*
- Shuai Nie, UNSW: 1AO.4.6 *Contact-Free J-V: a Simple Technique for Universal State-of-the-Art Solar Cells*

Replacement of critical by sustainable materials:

- Reduced Ag consumpion e.g. by replacing by Cu (plating)
- In-free SHJ solar cells and Pero-Si tandems

EU PVSEC
EU PVSEC
22 26 September
BEC
Bilbao
2025

CONFERENCE

TOPIC 1:
SILICON
MATERIALS
AND CELLS

Great advance in understanding of UV induced degradation and Hydrogen related degradation

- Excellent PLENARY by Bram Hoex (presenting for Muhammad Umair Khan), UNSW: 1CP.3.5 *Understanding the Root Cause of UV-Induced Degradation in TOPCon and PERC Solar Cells*

Further high quality orals:

- Christina Hollemann, ISFH: 1AO.4.2 *Mitigating UV-Induced Degradation: Impact of PECVD and PEALD AlOx Layers Deposited in a Tube-Type Direct Plasma-Enhanced Chemical Vapor Deposition System*
- Hugo Lajoie, CEA: 1AO.4.3 *New Insights on UV-Induced Degradation of SHJ Solar Cells*
- Byungsul Min, ISFH: 1BO.3.6 *UV Stable Passivation Stack with Plasma-Enhanced Atomic Layer Deposition of Aluminum Oxide from an Industrial Tube-Type Direct Plasma-Enhanced Chemical Vapor Deposition System*
- Wolfram Kwapil, Fraunhofer ISE: 1AO.5.6 *Impact of Illumination on Solar Cell Properties: Insights into Atomic Hydrogen Release*

030001-011

TOPIC 1: SILICON MATERIALS AND CELLS

Advances in TOPCon and SHJ technology → Pushing the Limits of Performance

- Fantastic keynote lecture (PLENARY) on heterojunction solar cells by Dr. Guangtao Yang, Trina: 1CP.1.1 *Silicon Surface and Interface Study for >27% Efficient SHJ Solar Cell*
  - Deep insight into technological aspects eg. influence of rear side polishing on cell performance
  - Very high efficiencies for both-sides contacted HJT > 27%
  - Issues with CAPEX, sustainibility (Ag, In)
  - Pero-Si tandem cells on large area and modules

Late News Presentation on 27.8% efficient back contact silicon solar cells by Hua Wu, Longhi: 1DO.9.1 *Hybrid Interdigitated Back Contact Silicon Solar Cells with Superior Efficiency*

Late News Presentation as TOPCon for Bottom Solar Cells in Pero-Si Tandem devices by Jana Polzin-Isabelle Polzin, Fraunhofer ISE: 1DO.9.3 *Silicon Solar Cells – From High Efficiency Single-junction to Bottom Cells in Two-Terminal Perovskite-Silicon Tandem Devices*

EU PVSEC
EU PVSEC 2025
CONFERENCE

TOPIC 1:
SILICON
MATERIALS
AND CELLS

Further high quality orals:

- Hua Wu, Longhi: 1DO.9.1 Hybrid Interdigitated Back Contact Silicon Solar Cells with Superior Efficiency
- Daming Chen, Trina: 1AO.5.1 Large Area i-TOPCon Solar Cells with 25.9% Record Efficiency
- Maysa Sarsour, UNSW: 1AO.6.1 Evaluating Silicon Heterojunction Solar Cell Stability under Industrial Illuminated Hydrogenation Conditions

Bottom cell optimization for Pero-Si tandems

030001-013

CONFERENCE

A lot of focus on the long-term stability improvement and upscaling of tandem devices based on a variety of materials (hence not only pero-Si).

Many companies (e.g. Hanwha Q-cells, Oxford PV, Microquanta Seminconductor, Jinko Solar, Longi, etc. non-exhaustive list) presented impressive results on industrial size single-junction pero modules and pero-based tandem modules. A highlight here was the plenary talk from Hanwha Q-cells showing a record large area (M10) pilot-scale Pk/Si tandem cell of 28.6% efficiency.

EU PVSEC

EU
PVSEC
2025
22 - 26
DEC
Bilbao

CONFERENCE

In the field of pero-Si tandems, there is clearly more focus on improving the stability of the tandem devices than before with many contributions doing in-depth investigations into the different degradation mechanisms that can occur in pero-Si tandems.

In this respect, 2DO9.5 presented a consensus statement about reliability testing of perovskite-based tandems that is endorsed by specialists worldwide from both industry and research and presents a kind of minimum that should be done in terms of testing and reporting concerning the stability and lifetime of perovskite-based tandem devices.

More and more advanced characterization methods for perovskite and perovskite - silicon tandem solar cells are being used, hyperspectral imaging methods identify non-uniformities by layer for processing development.

CONFERENCE

TOPIC 2: THIN FILMS AND NEW CONCEPTS

Another clear trend is that pero-TOPCon cells are nearing the same record efficiencies as pero-Heterojunction cells. A highlight talk here was the certified 34.22% efficiency perovskite/ topcon tandem solar cell(1cm2) by Jinko Solar 2CO2.1

Another highlight was the 30.5% triple junction pero/pero/silicon cell by EPFL (2CO2.3)

In the field of perovskite single junction devices, 2DO.7.3 showed perovskite devices with remarkable reliability, withstanding 4 years of outdoor exposure. The degradation mechanism is attributed to the diurnal behaviour, also verified and replicated with indoor experiments.

2AO3.6 investigated experimental degradation and recovery of perovskite solar cells, improving the comprehension of instability's dynamics, to extend the lifetime of devices.

EU PVSEC
EU PVSEC 2025
CONFERENCE
TOPIC 2:
THIN FILMS
AND NEW
CONCEPTS
In the field of compound semiconductors, there were many presentations on alternative materials for perovskite in tandems. In this way, first monolithic (AgCu)(InGa)Se2 on Si tandem cells were demonstrated as well as 16.1% semitransparent Ag doped Cu(InGa)S2 sulfide top cells.
An exciting highlight in this field was 2BO8.2 in which UPC Barcelona achieved 18% efficiency under indoor lighting for kesterite solar cells with alkali doping

030001-017

EU PVSEC
EU PVSEC
2025

CONFERENCE

TOPIC 3:
PHOTOVOLTAIC
MODULES

"Reliable packaging to Maximize the energy yield from high efficiency cells"

big theme: Optimizing module materials and packaging for long lifetime and predictable energy yield from high efficiency cells. The industry and research community are moving quickly to assess and improve reliability.

- Understanding, accelerated testing, and mitigating UV-ID in n-type cells and modules
- How do you develop accelerated tests for constantly changing BOMs - new encapsulants, new metallization, thinner glass, and high efficiency cells

EU PVSEC
EU PVSEC 2025
22 26 September
BEC
Bilbao

CONFERENCE

TOPIC 3:
PHOTOVOLTAIC
MODULES

• Degradation and metastability in packaged perovskite tandems - understanding energy yield and realistic degradation rates

• Characterization out of the lab and into the field and factory - accurate outdoor performance, online quality control measurements for encapsulant cross linking

• Reducing silver content and metallization temperatures - reliability of low temperature and low silver metallization

• Developing glass qualification requirements to minimize breakage

030001-019

Advances in O&M of PV systems

(4CV.1) focuses on fault detection, cleaning optimization, soiling (and snow 4CO.8), UAV for autonomous monitoring and digital twin.

Data driven and AI based O&M (4CO.9) including a medicine-like workflow in Autonomous multi-AI agent system for health monitoring: a fully automated O&M pipeline with field robotics (4CO.9.4 D. Moser, EURAC)

PV Everywhere from space to agricultural applications like integration in vineyards (Mo, Opening plenary) and many other **integrated options** as we have seen throughout the week. On Thursday (4DO.4) agriPV, noise barriers and floating integrated systems. AgriPV technologies (4DO.2), BIPV

PV needs solar energy. **Solar resource and forecasting** (Mo, 4AO.7-9 & Tu 4BV.3). Shortly IEA PVPS T16 will publish minute irradiance data, some including GT over 220 stations worldwide with. Same format and quality controlled. (*Worldwide solar radiation measurement database with quality-control added value*, Anne Forstinger CSP Services, 4AO.7.1)

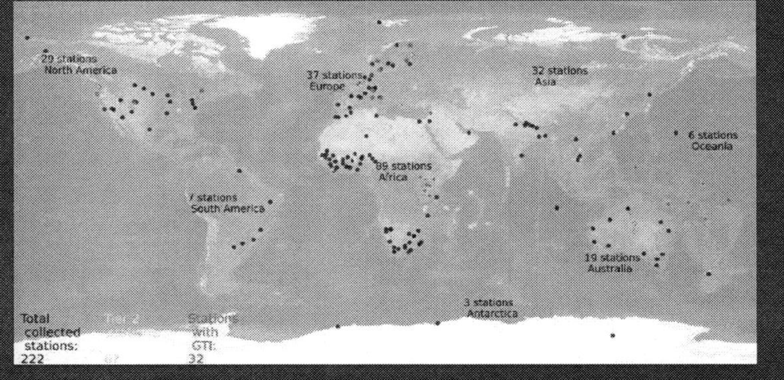

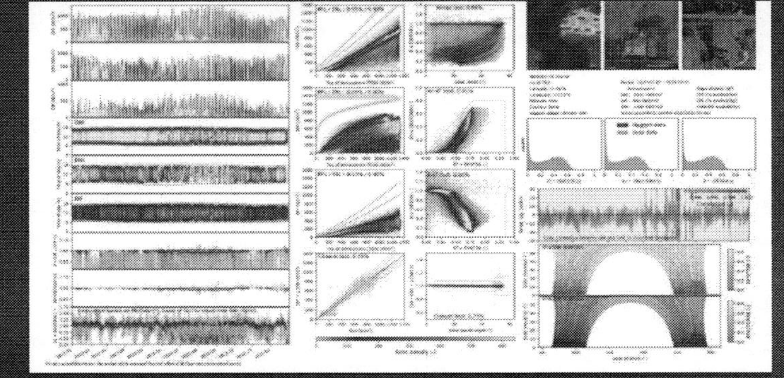

(4BV.3). Poster winner 4BV.3.12 *Advancing Very Short-Term Solar Irradiance Forecasting in Africa: A Low-Cost Sky Imaging and Machine Learning-Based Approach*, implications for PV deployment and grid integration (Martin Ansong, KIT). Runner-up 4BV.3.25 *Evaluating the Suitability of Köppen-Geiger Climate Classifications for Photovoltaic Systems: Micro-climate Analysis and Risk Assessment Maps*, with worldwide distribution of humidity related risk assessment for PV performance (Pavan Kumar Panda, Anhalt University of Applied Sciences).

030001-021

Integrated PV

BIPV (4BO.16) examples of coloured modules (which was main topic of the poster session along with fire concerns of BIPV, 4BV.4), lightweight solutions (4BO.5) and modelling partial shading effects 4BO.17.1, *Modelling partial shading at the cell level on PV modules*, Jean-Paul Calin, ENSTA) and 4BO.17.3, *Comparing the energy yield and degradation rates of smart PV modules compared to conventional PV system designs in shaded urban scenario's*, Youri Blom, TU DELF.

AgriPV 4DO.2 the room was fully packed showing the interest in the topic. 5 talks were on new ways of sharing light (2 spectral splitting before the PV conversion, 2 semitransparent PV modules both c-Si and CdTe, 1 on downshifting encapsulate) + 1 new AgrivPV like application with Algae instead of crops.

4DO.4 also included AgriPV and **Others types of integration like noise barriers and floating.** In addition to performance other aspects like (*Hydrological and ecological effects on floating PV,* Konstantin Ilgen, FHO ISe) have been highlighted this week

4DO4.2

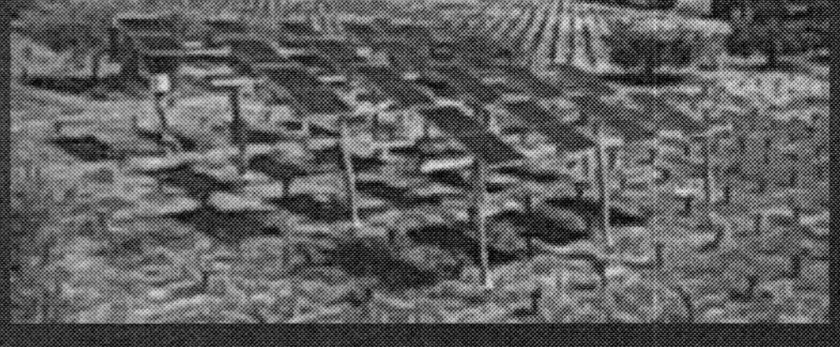

BOS and tracking systems (4DO.1) focused on backtracking strategies and terrains with complex topography.

4DO.1.4

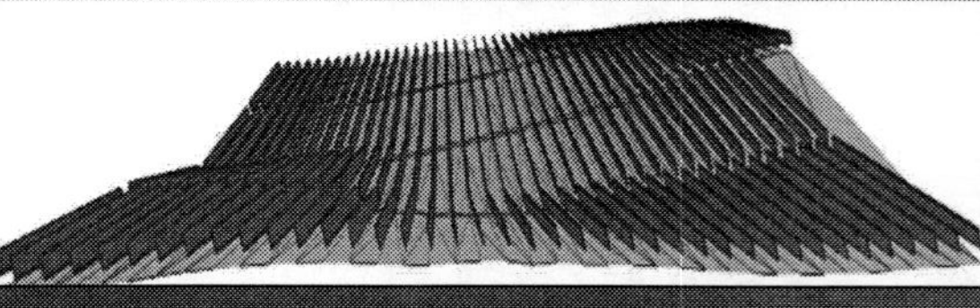

030001-022

CONFERENCE

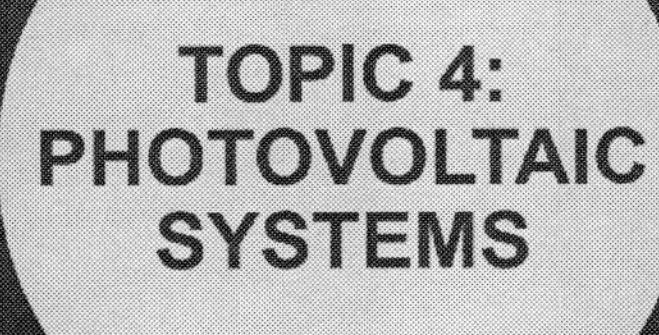

Reliability of PV systems

Several presentations focused long-term monitored degradation, failure modes and degradation modes identification techniques (non-destructive, aerial images, AI-based)

4BO.6.1 *Three decades, three climates: insights and lessons on PV reliability.* Good BOM offer very high reliability in power production, with 30-35 years old modules showing 0.24% degradation rate per year.

4BO.6.3 *Non-destructive detection of water ingress in solar modules using NIR spectroscopy* (Oleksandr Mashkow HI ERN) proved near-infrared absorption (NIRA) technique to detect water ingress in modules in the field, which correlated with the module degradation.

4BO.7.2 *Robust PV performance loss rate calculation for high latitudes* (Lauri Karttunen, Meteo Inst Helsinki) and 4BO.7. 3 *Detailed analysis of degradation rates of operating PV assets in tropical climate conditions* (Xioaqi Xu, Seris Singapore) Performance loss rates reported for high latitudes and tropics based on solid data sets. PLR in the tropics -1.4%/year

4DO.3.6 PV system design and assessment highlighted how inverter safety issues are extremely important and how more research about inverter safety and reliability is needed.

EU PVSEC
EU PVSEC 2025
22 26 September
BEC
Bilbao

CONFERENCE

TOPIC 5:
PHOTOVOLTAICS
IN THE ENERGY
TRANSITION

Main topics of interest :

- Flexibility

- Artificial intelligence

- EoL management

030001-024

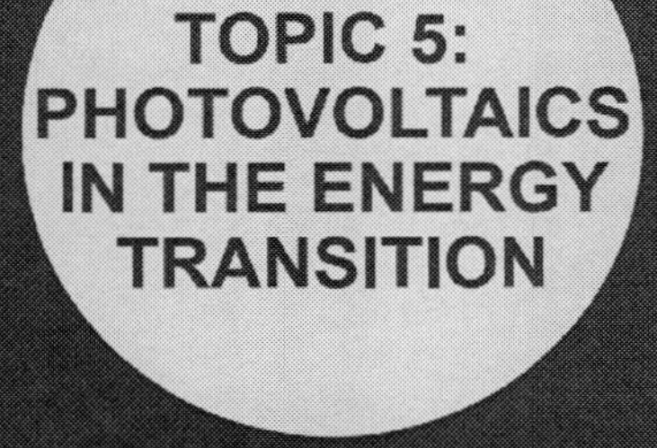

CONFERENCE

5.1 Grid Integration and Flexibility Enablers (2 sessions)

- Smoothing effect related to different orientations of PV systems in a given area allows 10 to 15% additional hosting capacity of the distribution grid compared to the conservative calculation that consists in summing the AC power. Such accurate calculation enabled by high resolution large area images and LIDAR and induces therefore very low costs.

5.2 Sustainability of PV (4 sessions)

- New inventories LCI and LCA for emerging technologies even though lack of data for perovskites, LCA showing a way for low environmental Impacts with technology improvement and localisation. / Technological improvements will contribute to the reduction of environmental Impact / Grid Efficiency has an Impact on the environmental Footprint.

- Manufacturing optimization / Reuse & recycling: results from the perspective of economic performance – would it convince manufacturer to consider it if economic benefit ?

- EoL Management /recycling -> emerging field attracting lots of activities / mainly EU projects (EVERPV / ICARUS / QASAR) – highlight on polymer, interesting question came up and to be debated for the next decade: is it worth it to consider polymer (EVA/ backsheet) recycling ?

- Major progress in methodology and indicators to assess sustainable design & circularity and improve transparency recyclability index, technical recyclability, digital passport)

CONFERENCE

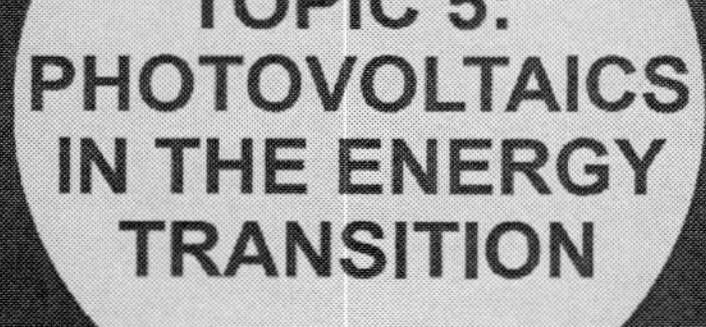

5.3 Scenarios for Renewables, Policy, Global Challenges (1 session)

- wide scope of contributions on the way to massive, medium- to long-term PV deployment -> should not be taken for granted despite positive projections since there can be limiting factors such as public acceptance / regulatory restrictions and effect of climate change

5.4 Costs, Economics, Finance and Markets (1 session)

- Annual installed capacity over 400 GWp / total cumulative installed capacity worldwide over 2.1 TWp / Clear mismatch between PV module installations rate worldwide and PV module production rate leading to bunch of inventories and drastically reduced prices.

5.6 Societal Challenges; Citizens' Participation, Awareness (1 session)

- data and analysis in gender aspects are emerging in PV! (poster session) + Highlight on innovation in education! On example that targets students & skilled workers -> mobile Lab for advanced experimental training PV-related to bring skills and characterization tools everywhere.

PARALLEL
EVENTS
Collaborat Network
Diversity
Prejudice
Justificat
Change
Needs — Profile Match
Avoid Blind Spots
Job Cost?
Integration
Lack of Attractivn
Resilience (People + Company)
Creativity
Different Communicat°
Internal Friction
More Efforts

030001-027

- Perovskite Innovation Roundtable: Driving EU Leadership in Perovskite Innovation
- Women in PV presents: Leading with Inclusion – Embracing the 6 Traits of Inclusive Leadership
- Unlocking the Potential of Integrated Photovoltaic Systems - European R&D Approach
- Why Do PV Plants Perform Lower than Expected? (Estimating losses by backtracking algorithms in undulating terrain & Analysis of the loss chain and identification of deviations from initial expectations)
- PV Made in the EU: How Do Companies Die and How Can They Thrive?

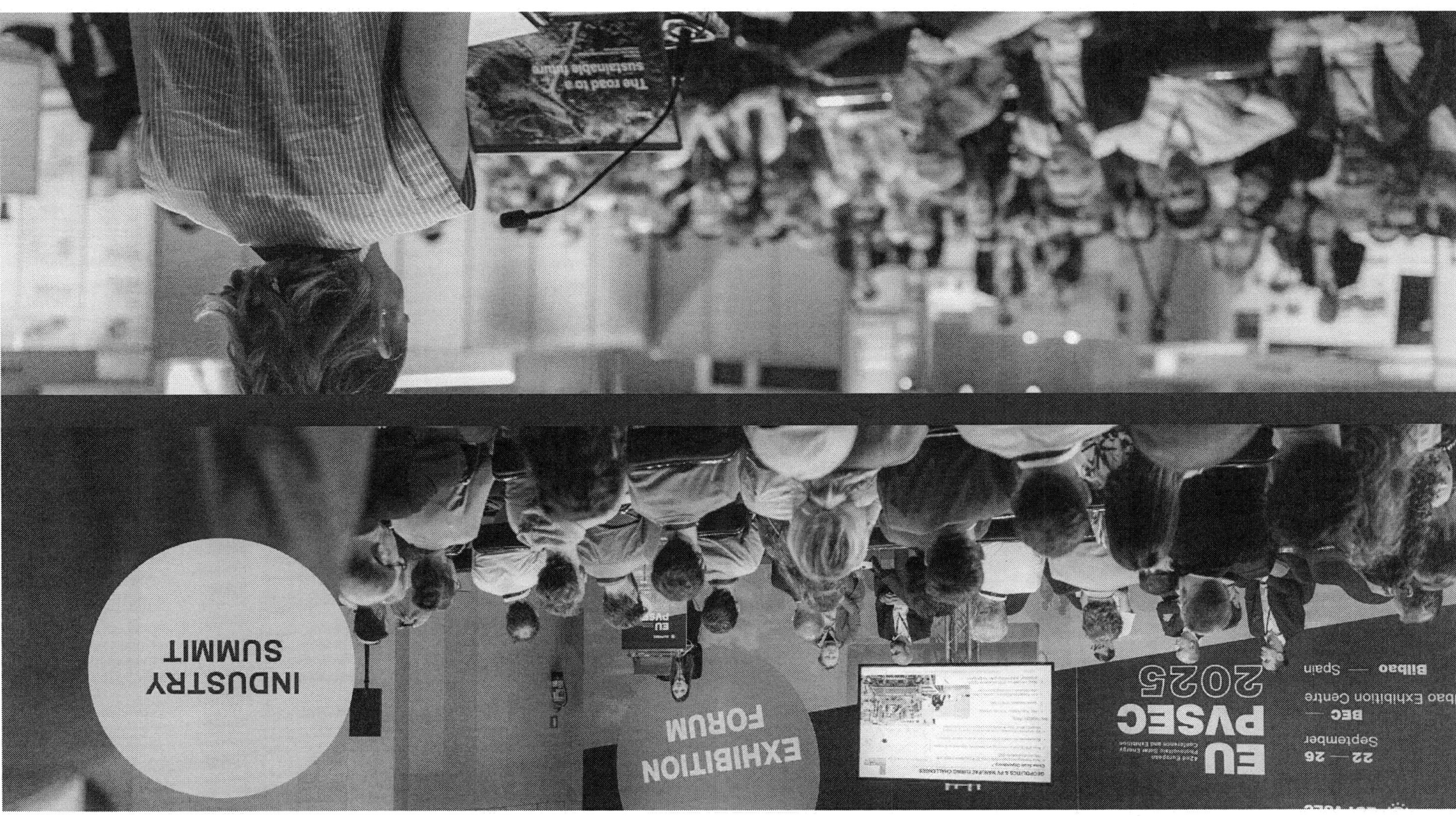

030001-029

EU PVSEC

EU PVSEC 2025
22 26 September
BEC
Bilbao

Industry Summit Opening (session I)

Session Title: Solar PV production in Europe - the way forward

Moderators: Begoña Molinete, Walburga Hemetsberger

Key Takeaway:

This session discussed the state of play of European manufacturing projects and whether there is enough European support. It was clear that political support is further lacking — only 3 Member States have developed schemes to support European manufacturing. While the Net Zero Industry Act is helpful to diversify supplies, it will not particularly support European manufacturing.

All panellists agreed that apart from further policy support (financing, derisking) collaboration is the way forward.

EU PVSEC

EU PVSEC 2025

INDUSTRY SUMMIT

Session II
Session Title: International corporations in the light of changing geopolitics
Moderators: Radovan Kopecek, Puzant Baliozian

Key takeaway:
EU machine builders are still supporting mostly Indian but also US and EU projects with their technology and expertise. The major arguments for choosing EU tech are quality, training, support and low OPEX.

Session III
Session Title: PV Systems: How do we get the produced electricity in Europe into the grid?
Moderators: Catarina Augusto, Peter Fath

Key Takeaway:
Hybrid PV + storage systems (co-located or distributed) are essential for integrating PV into electricity grids. Storage adds flexibility and stabilizes the grid, making it a cornerstone of resilient energy systems; while the technology is mature, scalable and bankable revenue models remain the key gap for widespread deployment.

LIST OF EXHIBITORS
(in alphabetical order)

Company name	Country
2nd Cycle FlexCo	Austria
9-Tech	Italy
Avalon ST / Pasan	Switzerland
BASQUENERGY Cluster	Spain
Becquerel Institute	Belgium
ECOPROGETTI	Italy
EKIENERGY	Spain
ESMC Pavilion	Belgium
Eternal Sun I WAVELABS	The Netherlands
EU PVSEC Startup Pavilion	
European Commission JRC	Italy
exateq	Germany
FLUXiM AG	Switzerland
G2V Optics	Canada
GALEA	Spain
halm elektronik	Germany
HighLine Technology	Germany
IEA PVPS	
Innovations in Optics, Inc.	United States of America
ISC Konstanz	Germany
LAB14	Germany
MBJ Solutions	Germany
Mondragon Assembly	Spain
Nagase Chemtex America	United States of America
NEO Messtechnik Holding	Austria
ODTÜ GÜNAM	Türkiye
Phoenixolar	China
PSE Instruments	Germany
PVsyst	Switzerland
RCT Future	Germany
RCT Solutions	Germany
RENA	Germany
ReNewPV-CA21148 / 5GSOLAR	Estonia
SALD B.V.	The Netherlands

SCIPRIOS	Germany
SEMILAB	Hungary
SINGULUS TECHNOLOGIES	Germany
Sinton Instruments	United States of America
SOLAR MATERIALS	Germany
SolarNL	The Netherlands
Soli Tek R&D	Lithuania
TAMURA ELSOLD	Germany
TECNALIA	Spain
The Netherlands Pavilion	The Netherlands
TNO	The Netherlands
University of the Basque Country	Spain
Vector Energy	Spain
VON ARDENNE	Germany
WCPEC-9	South Korea
WIP Renewable Energies	Germany
ZSW	Germany

We thank the EU PVSEC 2025 Sponsors

Platinum

Gold

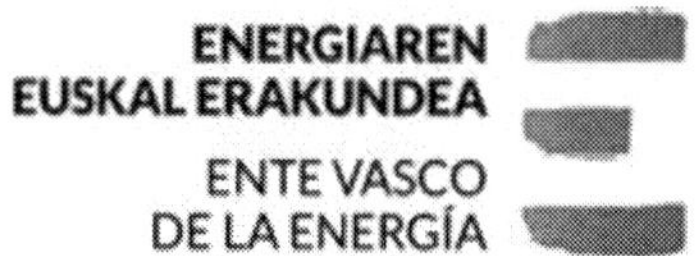

Silver

Bronze

AUTHORS OF EU PVSEC 2025 PROCEEDINGS PAPERS

Aghamohammadi, Amirhossain Amirkabir University of Technology, Tehran, Iran	020356
Aguirre, Aranzazu Hasselt Unversity, Genk, Belgium	020064
Ahmadi, Mehdi CNR-IMM, Catania, Italy	020066
Aiello, Andrea ACCA Software, Cosenza, Italy	020255
Aimé, Jérémie CEA / INES, Le Bourget-du-Lac, France	020217, 020311
Aissa, Brahim QEERI, Doha, Qatar	020042, 020075, 020108, 020109, 020146, 020147
Aizpurua, Jon Tecnalia, Donostia - San Sebastián, Spain	020139
Akbayrak, Serdar Necmettin Erbakan University, Konya, Türkiye	020020
Akram, M. Waqar Hohai University, Changzhou, China	020164
Al Katrib, Mirella IPVF, Palaiseau, France	020116
Alam, Habeel Lancaster University, Lancaster, United Kingdom	020394
Alberts, Vivian DEWA, Dubai, United Arab Emirates	020229
Albuquerque, Daniel P. Centre for New Energy Technologies, Sacavém, Portugal	020464
Alet, Pierre-Jean CSEM, Neuchâtel, Switzerland	020238, 020544
Alexandris, Nikos European Commission JRC, Ispra, Italy	020210
Alfieri, Felice Viegand Maagøe, Copenhagen, Denmark	020497
Ali, Adnan QEERI, Doha, Qatar	020147
Allen, Vince SunDrive Solar, Kurnell, Australia	020048
Alloji, Esma Necmettin Erbakan University, Konya, Türkiye	020020
Almeida Silva, José University of Évora, Évora, Portugal	020565
Almuneau, Guilhem LAAS-CNRS, Toulouse, France	020074
Alonso, Ricardo TECNALIA, Derio, Spain	020197, 020198, 020353, 020358
Alonso-Montesinos, Joaquín University of Almeria, Almeria, Spain	020100

Alonso-Montesinos, Joaquín   020336
University of Almería, La Cañada de San Urbano, Spain

Álvarez Hervás, José Domingo   020336
University of Almería, La Cañada de San Urbano, Spain

Alvarez, José   020040, 020058
CNRS, Gif-sur-Yvette, France

Álvarez, Marta   020300
CENER, Sarriguren, Spain

Álvarez-Pérez, Guillem   020062
IPVF, Palaiseau, France

Alvaro Høye, Ingar   020443
Solkraft Sør, Øyslebø, Norway

Alves e Silva, Kiane   020439, 020535, 020567, 020575
UPM, Madrid, Spain

Amaro e Silva, Rodrigo   020490
University of Lisbon, Lisbon, Portugal

Amatriain, Irati   020392
CENER, Sarriguren, Spain

Anamiati, Gaetana   020448, 020481
GreenPowerMonitor a DNV company, Barcelona, Spain

Anaya, Julian   020191, 020205
University of Valladolid, Valladolid, Spain

Ancillao, Andrea   020079
Polytechnic University of Turin, Turin, Italy

Anderlini, Alessandro   020155
Coveme, Gorizia, Italy

Andersen, Nanna L.   020250
DTU, Roskilde, Denmark

Andersen, Nanna Lysgaard   020306
DTU, Roskilde, Denmark

Andrade-Arvizu, Jacob   020094
IREC, Barcelona, Spain

Andreozzi, Federico   020494
University of Rome Tor Vergata, Rome, Italy

Anefnaf, Ikram   020093
University of Verona, Verona, Italy

Ansong, Martin   020272
KIT, Eggenstein-Leopoldshafen, Germany

Antognini, Luca   020196
PVsyst, Geneva, Switzerland

Antoine, C.   020508
IMDEA Nanoscience Institute, Madrid, Spain

Antón, Ignacio   020209, 020246, 020257, 020453, 020459
UPM, Madrid, Spain

Antonucci, Daniele   020551
Eurac Research, Bolzano, Italy

Apostoleris, Harry   020487
EPRI, Dubai, United Arab Emirates

Arakawa, Hayato   020436
NIED, Shinjo, Japan

Aranguren, Gerardo   020289, 020353
UPV/EHU, Bilbao, Spain

Arbaretaz, Sebastien   020317
CEA INES, Le Bourget-du-Lac, France

Ardissone, Bastien J. J.   020396
PV Lighthouse, Coledale, Australia

Arduino, Daniele   020079
Polytechnic University of Turin, Turin, Italy

Ariolli, Daniela Maria Godinho   020325
BayWa r.e, Rome, Italy

Ariza Camacho, Maria Jesus   020100
University of Almeria, Almería, Spain

Armstrong, Alona   020394
Lancaster University, Lancaster, United Kingdom

Arribat, Mathieu   020074
LAAS-CNRS, Toulouse, France

Arrizabalaga, Igor   020139
Tecnalia, Donostia - San Sebastián, Spain

Artegiani, Elisa   020057, 020089, 020093
University of Verona, Verona, Italy

Arumughan, Jayaprasad   020569
ISC Konstanz, Konstanz, Germany

Asaa, Shu-Ngwa   020393
imo-imomec, Genk, Belgium

Ascencio-Vásquez, Julián   020371
Univers, Courbevoie, France

Askins, Steve   020209, 020257
UPM, Madrid, Spain

Assaid, El Mahdi   020171
University of Chouaib Doukkali, El Jadida, Morocco

Aste, Niccolò   020249
Polytechnic University of Milan, Milan, Italy

Astigarraga, Alexander   020226
Eurac Research, Bolzano, Italy

Athienitis, Andreas   020248
Concordia University, Montreal, Canada

Aurrekoetxea, Olaia   020302
TECNALIA, Saint Sebastian, Spain

Awadallah, Carlos   020536
Wattkraft, Madrid, Spain

Azkona, Nekane   020055, 020097, 020153, 020287
UPV/EHU, Bilbao, Spain

Azzopardi, Brian   020318, 020334, 020520
FIR, Birkirkara, Malta

Azzopardi, Carmel   020334
FIR, Birkirkara, Malta

Babich, Francesco   020551
Eurac Research, Bolzano, Italy

Babics, Maxime   020217
CEA / INES, Le Bourget-du-Lac, France

Babin, Markus   020249, 020250, 020306, 020477
DTU, Roskilde, Denmark

Bachour, Dunia A.   020275, 020278
QEERI, Doha, Qatar

Bachour, Dunia   020291
QEERI, Doha, Qatar

Baderiya, Naman   020390
MARIN, Wageningen, The Netherlands

Badosa Franch, Jordi   020214
Polytechnic Institute of Paris, Palaiseau, France

Baeck, Pieter-Jan   020511
Flemish Institute for Technological Research (VITO), Genk,
Belgium

Bai, Jianbo   020164
Hohai University, Changzhou, China

Bailache, Simon   020303
CSTB, Marne-la-Vallée, France

Bakhtiari, Afshin   020121
AESOLAR, Koenigsbrunn, Germany

Balafoutis, Athanasios T.   020464
CERTH, Athens, Greece

Bald, Juan   020514
AZTI, PASAIA, Spain

Baldacchino, Alex J.   020065
UNSW, Sydney, Australia

Baležentienė, Skirmantė   020380
The Applied Research Institute for Prospective
Technologies, Vilnius, Lithuania

Baležentis, Algirdas   020380
The Applied Research Institute for Prospective
Technologies, Vilnius, Lithuania

Ballif, Christophe   020467
CSEM, Neuchâtel, Switzerland

Ballif, Christophe   020251
EPFL, Neuchâtel, Switzerland

Bandaru, Narendra   020039, 020043, 020104
Aarhus University, Aarhus, Denmark

Bang, Ole   020043
Technical University of Denmark, Copenhagen, Denmark

Barakel, Damien   020188
Toulon University, Marseille, France

Baraket, Mira   020039
ATLANT 3D, Taastrup, Denmark

Baranek, Philippe   020060
EDF R&D, Palaiseau, France

Barchi, Grazia   020485, 020489, 020544
Eurac Research, Bolzano, Italy

Bardizza, Giorgio   020181
TÜV Rheinland Italia, Milan, Italy

Bardizza, Giorgio   020208
TÜV Rheinland Solar, Cologne, Germany

Bardizza, Giorgio   020144
TÜV Rheinland, Cologne, Germany

Barguès, Anna   020505
Becquerel Institute France, Lyon, France

Barguès, Anna   020558
Becquerel Institute, Brussels, Belgium

Barnscheidt, Verena   020063, 020114
ISFH, Emmerthal, Germany

Barretta, Chiara   020325
PCCL, Leoben, Austria

Barrionuevo, Bruno   020464
CERTH, Athens, Greece

Barroso, João   020565
University of Évora, Évora, Portugal

Barrou, Alexis   020467
CSEM, Neuchâtel, Switzerland

Barrutia, Laura   020446, 020536
UPM, Madrid, Spain

Barth, Vincent   020134
CEA / INES, Le Bourget-du-Lac, France

Barth, Vincent   020019
CEA, Le Bourget-du-Lac, France

Barth, Vincent   020226
CEA/ INES, Le Bourget-du-Lac, France

Bartholomäus, Martin   020346
DTU, Roskilde, Denmark

Bartolo, Brian   020334
FIR, Birkirkara, Malta

Basta, Beata   020068
Roltec, Poznań, Poland

Basta, Marek   020068
Roltec, Poznań, Poland

Battisti, Kurt   020255
A-Null Development, Vienna, Austria

Bauhuis, Gerard   020067
Radboud University, Nijmegen, The Netherlands

Baumann, Kerstin   020470
bifa Umweltinstitut, Augsburg, Germany

Baumann, Sara   020063
ISFH, Emmerthal, Germany

Baumann, Ulrike   020006
ISFH, Emmerthal, Germany

Baur, Carsten   020246
European Space Agency, Noordwijk, The Netherlands

Beaucarne, Guy   020384
Dow Silicones Belgium, Seneffe, Belgium

Becker, Carl   020331
DLR, Almería, Spain

Behrensdorff Poulsen, Peter   020037
DTU, Lyngby, Denmark

Beinert, Andreas J.   020123
Fraunhofer ISE, Freiburg, Germany

Bejat, Timea   020225, 020500
CEA, Le Bourget-du-Lac, France

Belawadi, Aditya Girish   020231
Fraunhofer ISE, Freiburg, Germany

Belferkous, Brahim Anis   020325
PCCL, Leoben, Austria

Bellmann, Martin   020495, 020510
SINTEF, Trondheim, Norway

Bellvert, Eduard   020139
Tecnalia, Donostia - San Sebastián, Spain

Beltran-Condori, Sonia   020129, 020417
University of Antofagasta, Antofagasta, Chile

Belzunce, María Jesús   020514
AZTI, PASAIA, Spain

Bendix, Peter   020388
Next2Sun Technology, Dillingen, Germany

Bengoechea, Jaione   020181, 020300
CENER, Sarriguren, Spain

Bermudez Benito, Veronica   020146
QEERI, Doha, Qatar

Bermudez-Garcia, Anderson   020246
Thales Alenia Space, Cannes, France

Berrian, Djaber   020492
Belectric, Kolitzheim, Germany

Berson, Solenn   020134
CEA / INES, Le Bourget-du-Lac, France

Besson, Pierre   020373
INES, Le Bourget-du-Lac, France

Betak, Juraj   020241
Solargis, Bratislava, Slovakia

Bettucci, Ottavia   020077
University of Milano-Bicocca, Milan, Italy

Bhardwaj, Shashank   020515
TU Delft, Delft, The Netherlands

Bhatnagar, Shrey   020367
Nextracker, Fremont, United States of America

Biard, Yves   020303
SemperStyl, Eragny, France

Bieber, Lisa-Marie   020195
Fraunhofer ISE, Freiburg, Germany

Bilitu, Eddie   020393
Hasselt University, Hasselt, Belgium

Binani, Ashish   020225
TNO, Petten, The Netherlands

Binetti, Simona   020093
University of Milano Bicocca, Milan, Italy

Binetti, Simona   020087
University of Milano-Bicocca, Milan, Italy

Blakesley, James   020293
National Physical Laboratory, Teddington, United Kingdom

Blanc, Philippe   020291
MINES Paris, Nice, France

Blanco Aguiar, Adrián   020243
ieco.io, Vigo, Spain

Blieske, Ulf   020141
University of Applied Science Cologne, Cologne, Germany

Blieske, Ulf   020140
University of Applied Sciences Cologne, Cologne, Germany

Blstak Catlosova, Katarina   020274
Solargis, Bratislava, Slovakia

Blum, Niklas   020235, 020237, 020239
DLR, Almería, Spain

Boccardi, Roberto   020039
DTU, Copenhagen, Denmark

Boccardi, Roberto   020037
DTU, Lyngby, Denmark

Boccardi, Roberto   020028
DTU, Roskilde, Denmark

Boddaert, Simon   020302, 020303
CSTB, Marne-la-Vallée, France

Bokalič, Matevž   020047, 020319
University of Ljubljana, Ljubljana, Slovenia

Bolink, Henk J.   020226
University of Valencia, Paterna, Spain

Bonal, Victor   020085
UAM, Madrid, Spain

Bonnet, Martin   020141
University of Applied Science Cologne, Cologne, Germany

Bonnet-Eymard, Bénédicte   020251
CSEM, Neuchâtel, Switzerland

Borgers, Tom   020225
IMEC, Genk, Belgium

Borgna, Luciano   020369
BFH, Burgdorf, Switzerland

Borie, Benjamin   020039
ATLANT 3D, Taastrup, Denmark

Borowski, Peter   020307
Avancis, Munich, Germany

Borriello, Aniello   020378
ENEA, Portici, Italy

Borzi, Giovanni   020019
Enginsoft, Padua, Italy

Bosch, Elina   020252, 020543, 020564, 020573
Becquerel Institute, Brussels, Belgium

Bosma, Theo   020571
DNV, Arnhem, The Netherlands

Bothe, Karsten   020236
ISFH, Emmerthal, Germany

Bou-Nassif, Liliane   020338
CETHIL, Villeurbanne, France

Bouchier, Daniel   020058
CNRS, Palaiseau, France

Bouguerra, Sara   020156, 020294, 020389, 020393
imec, Genk, Belgium

Bourdin, Vincent   020406
CNRS, Paris, France

Bourgeois, Antoine   020102
SERIS, Singapore, Singapore

Bovesecchi, Gianluigi   020494
University of Rome Tor Vergata, Rome, Italy

Brabec, Christoph J.   020117
HI ERN, Erlangen, Germany

Bradford, David Roy   020077
Newcastle University, Newcastle upon Tyne, United
Kingdom

Brailovsky, Peter Henri   020475
Fraunhofer ISE, Freiburg, Germany

Braña, Alejandro F.   020508
Autonomous University of Madrid, Madrid, Spain

Brandstätter, Andreas   020227
Lenzing Plastics, Lenzing, Austria

Braun, Christian   020457
Luxembourg Institute of Science and Technology, Esch-sur-
Alzette, Luxembourg

Brecl, Kristijan   020269, 020319
University of Ljubljana, Ljubljana, Slovenia

Bredemeier, Dennis   020240
Leibniz University Hannover, Hannover, Germany

Breitenbücher, Marian   020225
Highline Technologies, Freiburg, Germany

Brendel, Rolf   020006, 020008, 020236, 020240, 020260,
ISFH, Emmerthal, Germany   020482

Brendstrup Møller, Clara Bolette   020028
DTU, Roskilde, Denmark

Bretzel, Tamara   020195
Fraunhofer ISE, Freiburg, Germany

Breyer, Christian   020479
LUT University, Lappeenranta, Finland

Brito, Miguel   020457
University of Lisbon, Lisbon, Portugal

Brivio, Elisabetta   020462
RSE, Milan, Italy

Brockmann, Lukas   020063
ISFH, Emmerthal, Germany

Brodnicke, Linda   020296
ETH, Zurich, Switzerland

Brueckner, Emanuel   020063
ISFH, Emmerthal, Germany

Bründlinger, Roland   020369
AIT, Vienna, Austria

Brun, Gonzalo   020414, 020517
ENDEF, Zaragoza, Spain

Bruno, Maddalena   020452
Fraunhofer ISE, Freiburg, Germany

Buceta, Alicia   020300
CENER, Sarriguren, Spain

Bucher, Christof   020179, 020322, 020359, 020369, 020386
BFH, Burgdorf, Switzerland

Buchholz, Florian   020035, 020225, 020569
ISC Konstanz, Konstanz, Germany

Buchmann, Johanna   020309
Berlin University of Applied Sciences, Berlin, Germany

Buck, Thomas   020033
ISC Konstanz, Konstanz, Germany

Buckland, Daniel   020119, 020218
Henkel, Düsseldorf, Germany

Buddana, Viswa Harinath   020482
DLR, Oldenburg, Germany

Bühlmann, Gian-Luca   020385
ZHAW, Winterthur, Switzerland

Buerhop, Claudia   020149, 020150, 020377
HI ERN, Erlangen, Germany

Buerhop-Lutz, Claudia   020185, 020230
HI ERN, Erlangen, Germany

Burgers, Antonius R.   020405
TNO, Petten, The Netherlands

Burri, Matthias   020179
BFH, Burgdorf, Switzerland

Busto, Chiara   020521
Eni, Novara, Italy

Butrichi, Fabio   020087
University of Milano-Bicocca, Milan, Italy

Butt, Nauman   020394
Lahore University of Management Sciences, Lahore,
Pakistan

C. Tavares, Fabiele   020090
Federal University of Rio de Janeiro, Duque de Caxias,
Brazil

Cabal, Raphael   020034
University Grenoble Alpes, Le Bourget-du-Lac, France

Caballero, Luis Jaime   020501, 020508
UPM, Madrid, Spain

Caballero, Raquel   020094
CSIC, Madrid, Spain

Caballero, Raquel   020085
IO-CSIC, Madrid, Spain

Cabecinha, Vasco   020565
Nova University Lisbon, Lisbon, Portugal

Cabello, Fatima   020085
IO-CSIC, Madrid, Spain

Caçapietra Pires da Silva, Lucas Teixeira   020025
PUCRS, Porto Alegre, Brazil

Caccavelli, Dominique   020551
CSTB, Bussy-Saint Georges, France

Caccivio, Mauro   020204, 020574
SUPSI, Mendrisio, Switzerland

Caffari, Francesca   020551
ENEA, Ispra, Italy

Calabrese, Nicolandrea   020551
ENEA, Ispra, Italy

Calin, Jean-Paul 020251
ENSTA Paris, Palaiseau, France

Çalışkan Arslan, Meriç 020006, 020135
Kalyon PV, Ankara, Türkiye

Caluori, Philip 020455
Virtual Vehicle, Graz, Austria

Camara, Assa 020274
Solargis, Bratislava, Slovakia

Cambarau, Werther 020139
Tecnalia, Donostia-San Sebastián, Spain

Campana, Pietro Elia 020381
Mälardalen University, Västerås, Sweden

Campos Guzman, Laura 020331
DLR, Almería, Spain

Cancro, Carmine 020378
ENEA, Naples, Italy

Canesse, Auriane 020196
PVsyst, Geneva, Switzerland

Cañizo, Carlos 020097
IES-UPM, Madrid, Spain

Cano, Francisco J. 020139
Tecnalia, Donostia - San Sebastián, Spain

Cano, Lucía 020127
ENDEF, Zaragoza, Spain

Cánovas, Enrique 020508
IMDEA Nanoscience Institute, Madrid, Spain

Cao, Han 020263
SERIS, Singapore, Singapore

Capitaine, Anna 020116
IPVF, Palaiseau, France

Cappelle, Jan 020329, 020351
KU Leuven, Ghent, Belgium

Capron, Guillaume 020217
CEA / INES, Le Bourget-du-Lac, France

Carballo López, José Antonio 020336
University of Almería, La Cañada de San Urbano, Spain

Cardenas, Luis Alejandro 020339, 020546
National University of Colombia, Bogotá, Colombia

Carmo, Paulo 020304, 020420
University of Évora, Évora, Portugal

Carrasco, Luis Miguel 020439, 020535, 020567
UPM, Madrid, Spain

Carrillo Mejía, Luis 020279
District University of Bogotá, Bogotá, Colombia

Carrillo, Rafael E. 020238
CSEM, Neuchâtel, Switzerland

Carroy, Perrine   020226
CEA/ INES, Le Bourget-du-Lac, France

Carstens, Justus   020003
ISC Konstanz, Konstanz, Germany

Cartenì, Fabrizio   020378
University of Naples Federico II, Naples, Italy

Casappa, Michele   020087
National Research Council, Parma, Italy

Casasola Paesa, Marta   020389
Hasselt University, Diepenbeek, Belgium

Castilla Nieto, María del Mar   020336
University of Almería, La Cañada de San Urbano, Spain

Castillo Patton, Daniel Jason   020326
Enertis Applus+, Madrid, Spain

Castro, Luis Guilherme   020530
Casa dos Ventos, Fortaleza, Brazil

Castro, Rui   020464
University of Lisbon, Lisbon, Portugal

Castro-Gallardo, Fernando   020417, 020422
University of Antofagasta, Antofagasta, Chile

Cavaco, Afonso   020304, 020565
University of Évora, Évora, Portugal

Cebecauer, Tomas   020274
Solargis, Bratislava, Slovakia

Çekerek, Gamze   020006
Kalyon PV, Ankara, Türkiye

Celik, Duygu   020551
WIP Renewable Energies, Munich, Germany

Çeliktaş, Melih Soner   020559
Ege University, İzmir, Türkiye

Centazzo, Massimo   020006
EnPV, Karlsruhe, Germany

Centeno Brito, Miguel   020421, 020490
University of Lisbon, Lisbon, Portugal

Cereceda, Eneko   020055, 020097, 020153, 020287
UPV/EHU, Bilbao, Spain

Ceretti, Mattia   020204
SUPSI, Mendrisio, Switzerland

Cesar, I.   020405
TNO, Petten, The Netherlands

Ceuppens, Ignas   020302
BUILD`UP, Aarschot, Belgium

Chatterji, Nithin   020071
SVNIT, Surat, India

Chen, Daniel   020048
SunDrive Solar, Kurnell, Australia

Chen, Syh-Homg   020161
ITRI, Hsinchu, Taiwan

Chen, Xiang   020111
Hohai University, Changzhou, China

Cheung, Kak Pong   020313
Kiel University of Applied Sciences, Kiel, Germany

Chhapia, Gaurang   020492
Belectric, Kolitzheim, Germany

Chiba, Takahiro   020436
Hokkaido University of Science, Sapporo, Japan

Chichignoud, Guy   020495
13Institut Polytechnique De Grenoble, Grenoble, France

Chicote, Beatriz   020289
Mondragon University, Arrasate-Mondragon, Spain

Chiesa, Matteo   020487
Khalifa University, Abu Dhabi, United Arab Emirates

Chini de Freitas, Felipe   020023
PUCRS, Porto Alegre, Brazil

Cho, Yunae   020045
KIER, Daejeon, South Korea

Choi, Kwan Bum   020102
SERIS, Singapore, Singapore

Chouder, Aissa   020301
University of M'sila, M'sila, Algeria

Chowdhury, Gofran   020276, 020544
3E, Brussels, Belgium

Christ, Anja   020063
ISFH, Emmerthal, Germany

Chrkavy, Daniel   020262
Solargis, Bratislava, Slovakia

Chueh, Wei-Lo   020021
TSEC, Hsinchu, Taiwan

Ciesla, Alison   020065
UNSW, Sydney, Australia

Cirimele, Vincenzo   020314
University of Bologna, Bologna, Italy

Clausing, Roland   020063, 020114
ISFH, Emmerthal, Germany

Clochard, Laurent   020031
Nines Photovoltaics, Dublin, Germany

Clochard, Laurent   020007
Nines Photovoltaics, Dublin, Ireland

Clyncke, Jan   020472, 020513
PV CYCLE, Brussels, Belgium

Coşkun, Özlem   020006, 020027, 020225
Kalyon PV, Ankara, Türkiye

Colberts, Fallon   020389
Zuyd University, Heerlen, The Netherlands

Colin, Hervé   020217, 020262
CEA / INES, Le Bourget-du-Lac, France

Collin, Stéphane   020074
C2N, Palaiseau, France

Colwell, Jack   020048
SunDrive Solar, Kurnell, Australia

Comak, Mertcan   020003
ISC Konstanz, Konstanz, Germany

Connolly, James Patrick   020058, 020060
CNRS, Gif-sur-Yvette, France

Cordeiro, Diogo   020464
EDP, Lisbon, Portugal

Cornago, Iñaki   020392
CENER, Sarriguren, Spain

Cornaro, Cristina   020494
University of Rome Tor Vergata, Rome, Italy

Correa, Guillermo   020412
Gonvarri MS R&D, Corvera - Asturias, Spain

Correia, Joana   020565
University of Évora, Évora, Portugal

Couderc, Romain   020217, 020311, 020546
CEA / INES, Le Bourget-du-Lac, France

Coutel, John   020244
SOLAÏS, Valbonne, France

Cowan, Don   020230
Kiwa PI Berlin, Hudson, United States of America

Cox, Joel D.   020250
SDU Climate Cluster, Odense, Denmark

Cox, Joel D   020306
SDU Climate Cluster, Odense, Denmark

Coz, Pier Luigi   020246
European Space Agency, Noordwijk, The Netherlands

Crespo, Carolina   020490
University of Lisbon, Lisbon, Portugal

Cristiane Pan, Aline   020548
UFRGS, Tramandaí, Brazil

Cristóbal, Ana Belén   020491, 020535, 020575
UPM, Madrid, Spain

Crozier McCleland, Jacqueline   020185, 020344
Nelson Mandela University, Port Elizabeth, South Africa

Cuadra, Juan Manuel   020318
CENER, Sarigurren, Spain

Cui, Jindan   020320, 020525
Tokyo University of Science, Tokyo, Japan

Culot, Dominique
Dow Silicones Belgium, Seneffe, Belgium
020384

Curon, Jonathan
Dow Silicones Belgium, Seneffe, Belgium
020384

Cusenza, Maria Anna
RSE, Milan, Italy
020466

D. Pinto, Luciana
Federal University of Rio de Janeiro, Rio de Janeiro, Brazil
020090

Daenen, Michael
imec, Genk, Belgium
020156, 020389, 020393

Dagla, Anastasia
3E, Brussels, Belgium
020276

Dahle, Arne
Norsun, Oslo, Norway
020225, 020495

Dahlioui, Dounia
University of Agder, Grimstad, Norway
020443

Dalibor, Thomas
Avancis, Munich, Germany
020307

Dalla Maria, Enrico
Eurac Research, Bolzano, Italy
020485

Dalla Torre, Francesco
Applied Materials, Treviso, Italy
020010

Dalmazzone, Didier
ENSTA Paris, Palaiseau, France
020251

Damon, Keanu
7SecondSolar, Cape Town, South Africa
020382

Danelli, Andrea
RSE, Milan, Italy
020462, 020466

Darsene Dimd, Berhane
SINTEF, Trondheim, Norway
020270

Das, Gourab
RCT Solutions, Konstanz, Germany
020005, 020222, 020463

Dasilva-Villanueva, Nerea
UPM, Madrid, Spain
020014, 020501, 020508

Daßler, David
Fraunhofer CSP, Halle, Germany
020313

Daßler, David
Fraunhofer IMWS, Halle, Germany
020355

Daume, Darwin
pvnode, Rosenheim, Germany
020361

Davidsen, Rasmus Schmidt
Aarhus University, Aarhus, Denmark
020028, 020039, 020043

De Almeida, Laura
LAAS-CNRS, Toulouse, France
020074

De Biasio, Martin   020504
Silicon Austria Labs, Villach, Austria

De Blasi, Mariam   020378
Enel Green Power, Pisa, Italy

de Graaf, Gertjan J.   020405
TNO, Petten, The Netherlands

de Groot, Koen M.   020405
TNO, Petten, The Netherlands

De Gruijter, Alvaro   020254
Eurac Research, Bolzano, Italy

de Jong, Minne M.   020169, 020425
TNO, Eindhoven, The Netherlands

De Jong, Richard   020156, 020294, 020389
imec, Genk, Belgium

de l`Epine, Mélodie   020252, 020505, 020543, 020564
Becquerel Institute France, Lyon, France

de l`Epine, Melodie   020225, 020334, 020520, 020558
Becquerel Institute, Brussels, Belgium

de l`Epine, Melodie   020570
IEA PVPS Task 1, Lyon, France

de la Casa Higueras, Juan   020269
University of Jaén, Jaén, Spain

de la Viuda, Eva   020205
University of Valladolid, Valladolid, Spain

de Meatza, Iratxe   020495
CIDETEC, San Sebastián, Spain

De Rose, Angela   020123
Fraunhofer ISE, Freiburg, Germany

De Rose, Jonas   020010
Fraunhofer ISE, Freiburg, Germany

Debastiani Benato, Betina   020019
AMIRES, Prague, Czech Republic

Deepti,   020563
SRM University, Sonipat, India

Del Campo, Valeria   020311
Federico Santa María Technical University, Valparaiso,
Chile

del Cañizo, Carlos   020014, 020501, 020507, 020508
UPM, Madrid, Spain

Del Pero, Claudio   020249
Polytechnic University of Milan, Milan, Italy

Del Pozo, Alberto   020197, 020198
TECNALIA, Derio, Spain

del Prado Santamaria, Rodrigo   020191, 020376
DTU, Roskilde, Denmark

del Ser, Javier   020358
UPV/EHU, Bilbao, Spain

Delgado-Sanchez, Jose Maria   020089
University of Seville, Seville, Spain

Delli Veneri, Paola   020378
ENEA, Naples, Italy

Denafas, Julius   020225, 020353
Solitek, Vilnius, Lithuania

Deniz, Engin   020559
Ege University, İzmir, Türkiye

Denke, Sebastian   020236
ISFH, Emmerthal, Germany

Dentz, Laurie   020058
CNRS, Palaiseau, France

Derin Gure, Pinar   020513, 020521, 020556
ODTU GUNAM, Ankara, Türkiye

Derj, Anyssa   020116
IPVF, Palaiseau, France

Dessì, Alessio   020077
CNR-ICCOM, Sesto Fiorentino, Italy

Devenson, Jan   020157
Center for Physical Sciences and Technology (FTMC),
Vilnius, Lithuania

Dhimish, Mahmoud   020346, 020376
DTU, Roskilde, Denmark

Di Matteo, Alfredo   020010
Enel Green Power, Catania, Italy

Diab, Mohanad   020203
Eurac Research, Bolzano, Italy

Diano, Marcello   020378
M2M Engineering, Naples, Italy

Diaz, Roberto   020300
Notio Association, Toledo, Spain

Díaz, Sara   020365, 020366
CENER, Sarriguren, Spain

Dietrich, Andreas   020355
DiSUN Deutsche Solarservice, Werder, Germany

Díez Alcántara, Eduardo   020501
UCM, Madrid, Spain

Díez, Eduardo   020508
UCM, Madrid, Spain

Dimd, Berhane Darsene   020495, 020510
SINTEF, Trondheim, Norway

Ding, Kaining   020233
FZJ, Jülich, Germany

Ding, Kung   020111
Hohai University, Changzhou, China

Dittmann, Sebastian   020318
Anhalt University of Applied Sciences, Köthen, Germany

Dittrich, Arne ISFH, Emmerthal, Germany	020240
Dizier, Antoine INES, Le Bourget-du-Lac, France	020373
Djeukeu, Ivanol Jaurece halm elektronik, Frankfurt am Main, Germany	020050
Dobreva, Petja University of Namibia, Windhoek, Namibia	020193
Dörenkämper, Maarten TNO, Eindhoven, The Netherlands	020169
Dörn, Markus A-Null Development, Vienna, Austria	020255
Doi, Minh Thong CEA INES, Le Bourget-du-Lac, France	020317
Domínguez, César UPM, Madrid, Spain	020209, 020246, 020257
Donadello, Alessandro Edyna, Bolzano, Italy	020485, 020489
Donėlienė, Jolanta Applied Research Institute for Prospective Technologies, Vilnius, Lithuania	020157
Donoso, José UNEF, Madrid, Spain	020570
Doppler, Christian Virtual Vehicle, Graz, Austria	020455
dos Reis, Givaldo University of São Paulo, São Paulo, Brazil	020348
dos Santos, Jeremias University of Évora, Évora, Portugal	020409
Doucet, Jean-Baptiste LAAS-CNRS, Toulouse, France	020074
Dovesi, Roberto Academy of Sciences of Turin, Torino, Italy	020060
Driesse, Anton PV Performance Labs, Freiburg, Germany	020211, 020293, 020452
Duarte, Dorivaldo University of Evora, Évora, Portugal	020418, 020565
Dubois, Sebastien University Grenoble Alpes, Le Bourget-du-Lac, France	020034
Dubravskij, Piotr Applied Research Institute for Prospective Technologies, Vilnius, Lithuania	020157
Dubravskij, Piotr Modern E-Technologies, Vilnius, Lithuania	020380
Duerinckx, Filip Hasselt Unversity, Genk, Belgium	020064, 020225

Düz, Cansel   020135
Kalyon PV, Ankara, Türkiye

Dullweber, Thorsten   020006, 020007, 020008, 020225
ISFH, Emmerthal, Germany

Dunlop, Ewan D.   020173, 020210, 020213
European Commission JRC, Ispra, Italy

Dupon, Olivier   020294
imec, Genk, Belgium

Dupuis, Julien   020188
EDF R&D, Moret Loing Orvanne, France

Dutykh, Denys   020338
Khalifa University, Abu Dhabi, United Arab Emirates

Duzellier, Sophie   020073
University of Toulouse, Toulouse, France

Dypvik Sødahl, Elin   020340
IFE, Kjeller, Norway

Ebert, Matthias   020426
Fraunhofer CSP, Halle, Germany

Ebert, Matthias   020355
Fraunhofer IMWS, Halle, Germany

Ebner, Rita   020318, 020334, 020521
AIT, Vienna, Austria

Echeverria, Oihane   020139
Tecnalia, Donostia - San Sebastián, Spain

Eder, Gabriele C.   020160, 020162, 020249, 020500, 020504
OFI, Vienna, Austria

Eelma, Tonis   020302
IBS, Tartu, Estonia

Efthymiou, Venizelos   020544
EPL Technology Frontiers, Dhali, Cyprus

Egan, Renate   020048
UNSW, Sydney, Australia

Egido, Miguel-Ángel   020407
UPM, Madrid, Spain

Eidtmann, Maximilian   020385
ZHAW, Winterthur, Switzerland

Eijgelaar, Marcel   020571
DNV, Arnhem, The Netherlands

Eikelboom, Erik   020225
Futurasun, Citadella, Italy

Einhaus, Roland   020312
ZSW, Stuttgart, Germany

Eisenacher, Matthias   020141
University of Applied Science Cologne, Cologne, Germany

Eiternick, Stefan   020004, 020052
Fraunhofer CSP, Halle (Saale), Germany

Ekins-Daukes, Nicholas J.   020065
UNSW, Sydney, Australia

El Ainaoui, Khadija   020171
Green Energy Park, Benguerir, Morocco

El mrabet, Yasmine   020171
Green Energy Park, Benguerir, Morocco

Elgaili, Mohamed   020166
QEERI, Doha, Qatar

Elhamaoui, Said   020171
Green Energy Park, Benguerir, Morocco

Ellis, Hanna   020213
European Commission JRC, Ispra, Italy

Engelen, Tine   020389
Hasselt University, Diepenbeek, Belgium

Erber, Alexander   020386
BFH, Burgdorf, Switzerland

Eryılmaz, Hande   020521
ODTÜ-GÜNAM, Ankara, Türkiye

Escudero, Ana   020414
IaSol, Zaragoza, Spain

Esmailifar, Seyyed Majid   020335, 020356, 020374, 020375
Amirkabir University of Technology, Tehran, Iran

Espinosa, Nieves   020497, 020506
University of Murcia, Murcia, Spain

Essam T. Mohammed, Sarah   020546
EU SOLARIS, Almeria, Spain

Esteras, Miguel   020358
TECNALIA, Derio, Spain

Eyhorn, Steffen   020369
Fraunhofer ISE, Freiburg, Germany

Fabel, Yann   020235, 020237, 020239
DLR, Almeria, Spain

Fabris, Francesca   020225
Futurasun, Citadella, Italy

Faes, Antonin   020251
CSEM, Neuchâtel, Switzerland

Falangas, Alexandros   020210
TRASIS International, Brussels, Belgium

Fang, Xue   020525
Tokyo University of Science, Tokyo, Japan

Fano, Vanesa   020055, 020097, 020153, 020287
UPV/EHU, Bilbao, Spain

Farhat, Mohammad   020428
Australian University, Kuwait City, Kuwait

Farina, Andrea   020066
CNR-IFN, Milan, Italy

Farrias-Basulto, Guillermo   020101
HZB, Berlin, Germany

Fath, Moritz   020463
RCT Solutions, Konstanz, Germany

Fath, Peter   020005, 020463
RCT Solutions, Konstanz, Germany

Fava, Henrique   020565
University of Évora, Évora, Portugal

Feichtner, Markus   020255
Sonnenkraft Energie, St. Veit/Glan, Austria

Feichtner, Markus   020160
Sonnenkraft Energy, St. Veit/Glan, Austria

Feldbacher, Sonja   020136, 020500
PCCL, Leoben, Austria

Feldhof, Anne Maren   020522
University of Applied Science Cologne, Cologne, Germany

Fernandes, Cláudia   020464
Centre for New Energy Technologies, Sacavém, Portugal

Fernández Solas, Álvaro   020331
DLR, Almería, Spain

Ferrando, Jorge   020226
University of Valencia, Paterna, Spain

Ferreira, Catarina G.   020250
SDU Climate Cluster, Odense, Denmark

Ferreira, Catarina   020306
SDU Climate Cluster, Odense, Denmark

Ferrero, Sergio   020079
Polytechnic University of Turin, Turin, Italy

Feuerherdt, Niels   020309
Berlin University of Applied Sciences, Berlin, Germany

Fialho, Luis   020203, 020254, 020261, 020304, 020403,
Eurac Research, Bolzano, Italy   020409, 020418, 020420, 020565

Figueroa, Andrés   020339
National University of Colombia, Bogotá, Colombia

Fischer, Stefan   020495
SGL Carbon, Meitingen, Germany

Fleischanderl, Martin   020136
voestalpine Stahl, Linz, Austria

Fleury, Perine   020513, 020521
Biosphere Solar, Delft, The Netherlands

Flouchi, Imane   020171
Green Energy Park, Benguerir, Morocco

Fodor, Nikoletta 020521
SolarPower Europe, Brussels, Belgium

Fontani, Daniela 020066
CNR-INO, Florence, Italy

Forster, Jacob 020135
Fraunhofer ISE, Freiburg, Germany

Forstinger, Anne 020331
CSP Services, Cologne, Germany

Franch, Jordi Badosa 020406
Ecole Polytechnique, Palaiseau, France

Franchi, Daniele 020077
CNR-ICCOM, Sesto Fiorentino, Italy

Franquet, Erwin 020259, 020428
Côte d'Azur University, Nice, France

Frasson, Nicola 020019
Applied Materials, San Biagio di Callalta, Italy

Freer, Solomon 020396
PV Lighthouse, Coledale, Australia

Freitag, Marina 020077
Newcastle University, Newcastle upon Tyne, United
Kingdom

Freund, Timo 020312
EnBW, Karlsruhe, Germany

Friansyah, Rizal 020376
DTU, Roskilde, Denmark

Friesen, Gabi 020160, 020249, 020574
SUPSI, Mendrisio, Switzerland

Friesen, Thomas 020249
Megasol Energie, Deitingen, Switzerland

Fritz Muñoz, Benjamín 020099
UPV, Valencia, Spain

Froebel, Jens 020121, 020142, 020192, 020223
Fraunhofer CSP, Halle, Germany

Frontini, Francesco 020249, 020253
SUPSI, Mendrisio, Switzerland

Fuentealba-Vidal, Edward 020129, 020311, 020342, 020417, 020422
University of Antofagasta, Antofagasta, Chile

Füreder-Kitzmüller, Friedrich 020136
voestalpine Stahl, Linz, Austria

Fuertes Marrón, David 020014, 020501, 020507, 020508
UPM, Madrid, Spain

Fuertes, David 020097
IES-UPM, Madrid, Spain

Furnari, Alessandro 020010
Enel Green Power, Catania, Italy

Fuß, Michael 020206
MBJ Solutions, Ahrensburg, Germany

Gabor, Andrew M.   020166
BrightSpot Automation, Boulder, United States of America

Gaete, Martin   020311
University of Antofagasta, Antofagasta, Chile

Gafert, Michael   020369
AIT, Vienna, Austria

Gageot, Tristan   020040
CEA / INES, Le Bourget-du-Lac, France

Gainza, Eusebio   020392
ALLOTARRA, Allo, Spain

Galarza, Alejandra   020461
IPVF, Palaiseau, France

Galbiati, Giuseppe   020119, 020218
Henkel, Düsseldorf, Germany

Galdikas, Algirdas   020157
Applied Research Institute for Prospective Technologies,
Vilnius, Lithuania

Galiana, Beatriz   020085
Charles III University of Madrid, Madrid, Spain

Galiazzo, Marco   020019
Applied Materials, San Biagio di Callalta, Italy

Gall, Stefan   020101
HZB, Berlin, Germany

Gallmetzer, Sandra   020261, 020509
Eurac Research, Bolzano, Italy

Galparsoro, Ibon   020514
AZTI, PASAIA, Spain

Gamarra, Ana Rosa   020502
CIEMAT, Madrid, Spain

Ganter, Alissa   020296
ETH, Zurich, Switzerland

Gaona García, Elvis Eduardo   020279
District University of Bogotá, Bogotá, Colombia

Garabetian, Thomas   020551
SolarPower Europe, Brussels, Belgium

García Campos, Enrique   020336
University of Almeria, La Cañada de San Urbano, Spain

García, Fernando   020326
UC3M, Madrid, Spain

García, Sonia   020139
Tecnalia, Donostia - San Sebastián, Spain

García-Cañas, Alejandro   020257
IMDEA Nanoscience, Madrid, Spain

García-Salinas, María José   020100
University of Almeria, Almería, Spain

Garcia-Sanchez, Almudena   020246, 020257
UPM, Madrid, Spain

Garg, Vivek   020069, 020071, 020081
SVNIT, Surat, India

Garraín, Daniel   020502
CIEMAT, Madrid, Spain

Gasse, Hugues   020073
University of Toulouse, Toulouse, France

Gassner, Anika   020160, 020162, 020500, 020504
OFI, Vienna, Austria

Gatti, Cesare   020541
PedersoliGattai, Milan, Italy

Gattu, Apoorva   020003
ISC Konstanz, Konstanz, Germany

Gautier, Damien   020505
Becquerel Institute, Brussels, Belgium

Gauvin, Xavier   020302
Bouygues Construction, Saint-Quentin-en-Yvelines, France

Ge, Hua   020249
Concordia University, Montreal, Canada

Gebhardt, Paul   020195
Fraunhofer ISE, Freiburg, Germany

Geerligs, L. J.   020030
TNO, Petten, The Netherlands

Gehrlein, Janek   020522
University of Applied Science Cologne, Cologne, Germany

Geier, Jutta   020234
PCCL, Leoben, Austria

Geml, Fabian   020031
University of Konstanz, Constance, Germany

Genovese, Maria   020378
Enel Green Power, Pisa, Italy

Georghiou, George E.   020534
University of Cyprus, Nicosia, Cyprus

Germani, Simone   020302
CEI, Milan, Italy

Getsiou, Maria   020181
Directorate General for Research and Innovation, Brussels,
Belgium

Geymayer, Lukas   020136
voestalpine Stahl, Linz, Austria

Ghahremani, Amirreza   020335, 020374
Amirkabir University of Technology, Tehran, Iran

Ghennioui, Abdellatif   020171
Green Energy Park, Benguerir, Morocco

Ghosh, Saptak   020519
CSTEP, Bengaluru, India

Greslou, Olivier   020551
CSTB, Bussy-Saint Georges, France

Grommes, Eva-Maria   020522, 020523
University of Applied Science Cologne, Cologne, Germany

Grosser, Stephan   020119, 020142, 020218
Fraunhofer CSP, Halle, Germany

Grünsteidl, Stefan   020307
Avancis, Munich, Germany

Gruginskie, Natasha   020067
Radboud University, Nijmegen, The Netherlands

Guedea, Isabel   020127, 020517
ENDEF, Zaragoza, Spain

Gülsoy, Eren Cihan   020521
METU, Ankara, Türkiye

Gümüs Çiftci, Burcu   020027
Kalyon PV, Ankara, Türkiye

Guerra, Gerardo   020448, 020481
GreenPowerMonitor a DNV company, Barcelona, Spain

Guidetti, Giulia   020541
Green Horse Advisory, Milan, Italy

Guillemoles, Jean François   020062
IPVF, Palaiseau, France

Guillevin, Nicolas   020225
TNO, Petten, The Netherlands

Gunbas, Gorkem   020113
ODTÜ-GÜNAM, Ankara, Türkiye

Gupta, Akshit   020551
Eurac Research, Bolzano, Italy

Gutierrez, Jose Ruben   020055, 020097, 020153, 020287
UPV/EHU, Bilbao, Spain

Gutjahr, Astrid   020030
TNO, Petten, The Netherlands

Haaland, Petry Kristine Nøttum   020476
NTNU, Trondheim, Norway

Haase, Felix   020063
ISFH, Emmerthal, Germany

Hadiwidjaja, Stella   020102
SERIS, Singapore, Singapore

Hadjipanayi, Maria   020064
University of Cyprus, Nicosia, Cyprus

Haedrich, Ingrid   020195, 020231
Fraunhofer ISE, Freiburg, Germany

Hämmer, Matthias   020470
bifa Umweltinstitut, Augsburg, Germany

Hafidi, Elias 020511
Inflights BV, Brussels, Belgium

Hagemann, Elizabeth M. 020416
Nelson Mandela University, Port Elizabeth, South Africa

Hallais, Géraldine 020058
CNRS, Palaiseau, France

Halle, Lasse 020359
BFH, Burgdorf, Switzerland

Hallensleben, Carina 020220
TAMURA-ELSOLD, Ilsenburg, Germany

Halm, Andreas 020218, 020220, 020221
ISC Konstanz, Konstanz, Germany

Halme, Janne 020249
Aalto University, Espoo, Finland

Hamada, Toshiyuki 020190
Osaka Electro-Communication University, Osaka, Japan

Hammer, Annette 020239
DLR, Oldenburg, Germany

Hamouda, Frederic 020058
CNRS, Palaiseau, France

Hanifi, Hamed 020121, 020125, 020137, 020223
AESOLAR, Koenigsbrunn, Germany

Hansen, Per-Anders 020017, 020503
Institute for Energy Technology, Kjeller, Norway

Harit, Amit Kumar 020064
Hasselt Unversity, Genk, Belgium

Harrison, Samuel 020225
CEA, Le Bourget-du-Lac, France

Hashem, Ahmad 020056, 020201
Anhalt University of Applied Sciences, Köthen, Germany

Hategan, Sergiu Mihai 020283
West University of Timisoara, Timisoara, Romania

Hauch, Jens 020117, 020149, 020150
HI ERN, Erlangen, Germany

Hauer, Martin 020255
Bartenbach, Vienna, Austria

Haverkamp, Helge 020008
centrotherm international, Blaubeuren, Germany

Hee Lee, Sang 020045
KIER, Daejeon, South Korea

Heidrich, Robert 020233
Fraunhofer CSP, Halle, Germany

Heikkinen, Kyösti 020423
VTT Technical Research Centre of Finland, Oulu, Finland

Heiser, Moritz 020230
Kiwa PI Berlin, Berlin, Germany

Helbig, Matthias   020220
ISC Konstanz, Konstanz, Germany

Helten, David   020331
CSP Services, Cologne, Germany

Hennig, Carsten   020313, 020355
saferay holding, Berlin, Germany

Hennig, Patrick   020313
Kiel University of Applied Sciences, Kiel, Germany

Heras, Jesús   020536
Wattkraft, Madrid, Spain

Hermle, Martin   020475
Fraunhofer ISE, Freiburg, Germany

Hernández Mora, Johann Alexander   020279, 020441
District University of Bogotá, Bogotá, Colombia

Hernández, Jaime J.   020257
IMDEA Nanoscience, Madrid, Spain

Hernández, Johann   020526
Francisco José de Caldas District University, Bogota,
Colombia

Herodotou, Panayiotis   020534
University of Cyprus, Nicosia, Cyprus

Herrera Leon, Fernando Augusto   020339, 020546
National University of Colombia, Bogotá, Colombia

Herrero, Leire   020139
Tecnalia, Donostia - San Sebastián, Spain

Herrero, Rebeca   020209, 020453, 020459
UPM, Madrid, Spain

Herrmann, Werner   020208
TÜV Rheinland Solar, Cologne, Germany

Herteleer, Bert   020329, 020351
KU Leuven, Ghent, Belgium

Herteleer, Bert   020574
SUPSI, Mendrisio, Switzerland

Hessler-Wyser, Aïcha   020251
EPFL, Neuchâtel, Switzerland

Heydari, Azim   020485
Eurac Research, Bolzano, Italy

Hinken, David   020236
ISFH, Emmerthal, Germany

Hladys, Bertrand   020010
CEA, Grenoble, France

Hoex, Bram   020065
UNSW, Sydney, Australia

Hofer, Leo   020322
BFH, Burgdorf, Switzerland

Hoffmann, Erik   020006
EnPV, Karlsruhe, Germany

Hulik Jansova, Marketa   020274
Solargis, Bratislava, Slovakia

Hung, Tzu Han   020552
ITRI, Taipei City, Taiwan

Hutterer-Tik, Thomas   020347
Watt Analytics, Vienna, Austria

Hwang, Hye-Mi   020324, 020357, 020561
KIER, Daejeon, South Korea

Iglesias, Unai   020139
Tecnalia, Donostia - San Sebastián, Spain

Ikeda, Kazuaki   020436
AIST, Koriyama, Japan

Infante, Paulo   020420
University of Évora, Évora, Portugal

Isabella, Olindo   020515
TU Delft, Delft, The Netherlands

Ishikawa, Ryousuke   020106, 020115
Tokyo City University, Setagaya, Japan

Iwaszko, Victorien   020495
ROSI Solar, Saint-Martin-d'Hères, France

Izquierdo-Roca, Victor   020094
IREC, Barcelona, Spain

J. N. Soares, Guillermo   020090
Federal University of Rio de Janeiro, Duque de Caxias,
Brazil

Jacob, Julieu   020302
METABUILD, Berlin, Germany

Jacobs, Ayesha   020382
Zutari, Cape Town, South Africa

Jaeckel, Bengt   020056, 020119, 020121, 020140, 020142,
Fraunhofer CSP, Halle, Germany   020175, 020192, 020201, 020223, 020229

Jäger Waldau, Arnulf   020570
European Commission, Rome, Italy

Jäger, Philip   020006
ISFH, Emmerthal, Germany

Jäggi, Adrian   020179
BFH, Burgdorf, Switzerland

Järventausta, Pertti   020445
Tampere University, Tampere, Finland

Jaffré, Alexandre   020058
CNRS, Gif-sur-Yvette, France

Jahn, Ulrike   020521, 020574
Fraunhofer CSP, Halle, Germany

Jahn, Ulrike Fraunhofer IMWS, Halle, Germany	020355
Jahreis, Sophia Fraunhofer CSP, Halle, Germany	020142, 020192
Jakomin, Roberto Federal University of Rio de Janeiro, Duque de Caxias, Brazil	020090
Jakubik, Martin Solargis, Bratislava, Slovakia	020274
Jakuza, Paola University of Padova, Padova, Italy	020089
Jalkh, Judy Virtual Vehicle, Graz, Austria	020455
Jandl, Ralf FFHS, Zurich, Switzerland	020204
Jankovec, Marko University of Ljubljana, Ljubljana, Slovenia	020197
Jaworczak, Kamil Technology Innovation Institute, Abu Dhabi, United Arab Emirates	020402
Jensen, Adam R. DTU, Kongens Lyngby, Denmark	020267
Jeong, Jungi K-water, Daejeon, South Korea	020323
Jeong, Kyung Taek KIER, Daejeon, South Korea	020045
Jeong, Minsoo KIER, Daejeon, South Korea	020045
Jeronimo, Pedro CEA, Grenoble, France	020010
Jiang, Zonghan Anhalt University of Applied Sciences, Köthen, Germany	020158, 020201
Jimenez, Maria Onyx Solar, Avila, Spain	020302
Jimeno, Juan Carlos UPV/EHU, Bilbao, Spain	020055, 020097, 020153, 020287, 020289, 020353
Jo, Hyunsik K-water, Daejeon, South Korea	020323
Job, Enzo Fraunhofer ISE, Freiburg, Germany	020231
Johnson, Mark Robert Institut Laue-Langevin (ILL), Grenoble, France	020546
Joo, Dongmyoung KETI, Wonmi-gu, South Korea	020449
Jooss, Wolfgang RCT Solutions, Konstanz, Germany	020005, 020222, 020463

Joseph, Daniel Christopher   020123
Fraunhofer ISE, Freiburg, Germany

Joshi, Deepak   020069, 020081
SVNIT, Surat, India

Joss, David   020359, 020369, 020386
BFH, Burgdorf, Switzerland

Jouini, Anis   020034
ECM Technologies, Grenoble, France

Jouttijärvi, Sami   020286, 020298, 020398
University of Turku, Turku, Finland

Joziak, Roman   020230
Kiwa PI Berlin, Berlin, Germany

Ju, Young-Chul   020324, 020357, 020561
KIER, Daejeon, South Korea

Jugo, Josu   020437
UPV/EHU, Leioa, Spain

Junge, Sebastian   020008, 020482
ISFH, Emmerthal, Germany

Kaaya, Ismail   020156, 020294, 020389, 020393
imec, Genk, Belgium

Kähler, Jan-Dirk   020482
Centrotherm International, Blaubeuren, Germany

Kahraman, Mert   020027
Kalyon PV, Ankara, Türkiye

Kainz, Konrad   020430
AIT, Vienna, Austria

Kaiser, Martin   020215
Fraunhofer ISE, Freiburg, Germany

Kaizuka, Izumi   020570
RTS Corporation, Tokyo, Japan

Kajari-Schröder, Sarah   020063
ISFH, Emmerthal, Germany

Kallioharju, Kari   020444, 020445
TUAS, Tampere, Finland

Kalliojärvi, Heidi   020194
Tampere University, Tampere, Finland

Kalshetty, Mahesh   020519
CSTEP, Bengaluru, India

Kaltenbach, Thomas   020195
Fraunhofer ISE, Freiburg, Germany

Kamphues, Joshua   020031
University of Konstanz, Constance, Germany

Kandiyoti-Eskenazi, Selin   020467
CSEM, Neuchâtel, Switzerland

Kang, Min Gu 020045
KIER, Daejeon, South Korea

Kapetanovic, Viktor 020367
Nextracker, Fremont, United States of America

Karhu, Juha 020286
Finnish Meteorological Institute, Helsinki, Finland

Kari, Thøger 020191, 020376
DTU, Roskilde, Denmark

Karimy, Hedayatullah 020052
Fraunhofer CSP, Halle (Saale), Germany

Karttunen, Lauri 020298, 020398
University of Turku, Turku, Finland

Kasper, Ruth 020167, 020232
University of Applied Sciences Cologne, Cologne, Germany

Katouli, Tannaz 020195
Fraunhofer ISE, Freiburg, Germany

Kaufmann, Kai 020355
DENKweit, Halle, Germany

Kawabata, Rudy 020092
PUC-Rio, Rio de Janeiro, Brazil

Kemp, Linda 020390
MARIN, Wageningen, The Netherlands

Kenchington, Ian 020225, 020474, 020558
Becquerel Institute, Brussels, Belgium

Kenny, Robert 020210
European Commission JRC, Ispra, Italy

Khan, Abeer Ali 020513
First Solar, Mainz, Germany

Khosravi, Arash 020381
Mälardalen University, Västerås, Sweden

Kikkert, Benjamin W. J. 020405
TNO, Petten, The Netherlands

Kilickaya, Seda 020020
ODTÜ-GÜNAM, Ankara, Türkiye

Kim, Jin-Hong 020449
KETI, Wonmi-gu, South Korea

Kim, Jun-Tae 020249
Kongju National University, Chungnam, South Korea

Kim, Kihwan 020112
KIER, Daejeon, South Korea

Kim, Seok Won 020449
KETI, Wonmi-gu, South Korea

Kim, Yong-Jin 020045
KIER, Daejeon, South Korea

Kinge, Sachin 020117
Toyota Motors Europe, Brussels, Belgium

Kolahi, Mohammad   020356, 020375
University of Isfahan, Isfahan, Iran

Konagai, Makoto   020106, 020115
Tokyo City University, Setagaya, Japan

Kono, Toru   020484
Hitachi, Kokubunji, Japan

Konu, Christopher Bruce   020132
HTW Berlin, Berlin, Germany

Kopecek, Radovan   020569
ISC Konstanz, Konstanz, Germany

Kopp, Nils   020220
TAMURA-ELSOLD, Ilsenburg, Germany

Korkmaz Arslan, Melisa   020020
ODTÜ-GÜNAM, Ankara, Türkiye

Korpås, Magnus   020476
NTNU, Trondheim, Norway

Kortetmäki, Aki   020444, 020445
TUAS, Tampere, Finland

Koskela, Juha   020444, 020445, 020554
Tampere University, Tampere, Finland

Kossen, Eric J.   020030
TNO, Petten, The Netherlands

Kowalski, Julia   020237
RWTH, Aachen, Germany

Kräling, Ulli   020215
Fraunhofer ISE, Freiburg, Germany

Kraft, Thomas M.   020423
VTT Technical Research Centre of Finland, Oulu, Finland

Krainer, Diana Maria   020430
AIT, Vienna, Austria

Krasilnikov, Inga   020379
Tel Aviv University, Tel Aviv, Israel

Krever Lopes, Bruno   020023
PUCRS, Porto Alegre, Brazil

Kribus, Abraham   020379
Tel Aviv University, Tel Aviv, Israel

Krishnan, Sasikumar   020361
Coburg University of Applied Sciences, Coburg, Germany

Kroon, Jan   020225
TNO, Petten, The Netherlands

Kuan, Ta-Ming   020021, 020053
TSEC, Hsinchu, Taiwan

Kubicek, Bernhard   020281, 020318, 020334, 020347, 020430
AIT, Vienna, Austria

Kucuk, E. Busra   020030
TNO, Petten, The Netherlands

Le Brun, Anton   020096
Australian Nuclear Science and Technology Organisation,
Lucas Heights, Australia

Lechón, Yolanda   020502
CIEMAT, Madrid, Spain

Ledesma, Javier R.   020337
UPM, Madrid, Spain

Ledesma, Javier   020446
UPM, Madrid, Spain

Lee, Chun-Wei   020021
TSEC, Hsinchu, Taiwan

Lee, Hyunju   020046
Meiji University, Kanagawa, Japan

Lee, Jieun   020323
K-water, Daejeon, South Korea

Lee, Jin-Seok   020324, 020357, 020561
KIER, Daejeon, South Korea

Legarrea, Aritz   020365
CENER, Sarriguren, Spain

Lelievre, Jean-Francois   020373
INES, Le Bourget-du-Lac, France

Lelong, Benoit   020373
Cythelia Energy, La Motte-Servolex, France

Leloux, Jonathan   020262
LuciSun, Villers-la-Ville, Belgium

Lenain, Philippe   020495
benkei, Lyon, France

Lennon, Alison   020048
UNSW, Sydney, Australia

Lenz, Markus   020226
School of Life Sciences FHNW, Muttenz, Switzerland

Lenzmann, Frank   020019
TNO Energy Transition, Petten, The Netherlands

Leone, Sander   020405
Novar, Rotterdam, The Netherlands

Leonforte, Fabrizio   020249
Polytechnic University of Milan, Milan, Italy

Leopold, Ulrich   020457
Luxembourg Institute of Science and Technology, Esch-sur-
Alzette, Luxembourg

Levrat, Jacques   020251, 020467
CSEM, Neuchâtel, Switzerland

Levtchenko, Alexandra   020116
IPVF, Palaiseau, France

Lewandowski, Simon   020073
University of Toulouse, Toulouse, France

Liu, Huiping GRÄNGES, Finspång, Sweden	020495
Liu, Mengdi TÜV Rheinland, Shanghai, China	020144, 020208
Liu, Yung-Tsung ITRI, Hsinchu, Taiwan	020053, 020083
Livera, Andreas University of Cyprus, Nicosia, Cyprus	020534
Lizin, Sebastien UHasselt, Hasselt, Belgium	020513, 020521
Llarena, María Elena ITER, Granadilla de Abona, Spain	020151
Loeckenhoff, Ruediger F. AZUR SPACE Solar Power, Heilbronn, Germany	020416
Löhning, Martha ISFH, Emmerthal, Germany	020063
Löhr, Johannes ISFH, Emmerthal, Germany	020063, 020114
Lokhat, Ismaël Cythelia Energy, La Motte-Servolex, France	020262
Lokhat, Ismael Trace Software, Saint-Romain-de-Colbosc, France	020373
Lombardo, Salvatore CNR-IMM, Catania, Italy	020066
Long, Yean-San ITRI, Hsinchu, Taiwan	020053, 020083
Longo, Giulia UPV, Valencia, Spain	020099
Lopes Gomes, Carlos Javier Sunveon, Madrid, Spain	020432, 020434
Lopes, Ana Patrícia University of Lisbon, Lisbon, Portugal	020464
López Cuéllar, Juan Manuel UCM, Madrid, Spain	020501
López Dalmau, Daniel Sunveon, Madrid, Spain	020432, 020434
López, Nuria DTU, Roskilde, Denmark	020451
Lorenz, Dieter MBJ Solutions, Ahrensburg, Germany	020206
Lorenzo Pigueiras, Eduardo UPM, Madrid, Spain	020363
Lorenzo, Celena UPM, Madrid, Spain	020337, 020536
Lorenzo, Eduardo UPM, Madrid, Spain	020439, 020446

Lossen, Jan
ISC Konstanz, Konstanz, Germany
020003, 020035

Louwen, Atse
Eurac Research, Bolzano, Italy
020203, 020226, 020261, 020509, 020546

Louwen, Atse
RISE, Boras, Sweden
020316

Lu, Huan-Wu
ITRI, Hsinchu, Taiwan
020161

Lu, Matthew
Kiwa PI Berlin, Shanghai, China
020230

Lucea, Aingeru
TECNALIA, Derio, Spain
020197, 020198

Lüdemann, Marius
Fraunhofer CSP, Halle, Germany
020233

Luís, Margarida
University of Lisbon, Lisbon, Portugal
020421

Lustoza de Souza, Patricia
UFRJ, Rio de Janeiro, Brazil
020092

Ly, Moussa
PUCRS, Porto Alegre, Brazil
020023, 020025

Lyubenova, Teodora
European Commission JRC, Ispra, Italy
020210

M. Bazilio, Willian
PUC-Rio, Rio de Janeiro, Brazil
020092

M. S. Kawabata, Rudy
Pontifical Catholic University of Rio de Janeiro, Rio de Janeiro, Brazil
020090

M. Torelly, Guilherme
Pontifical Catholic University of Rio de Janeiro, Rio de Janeiro, Brazil
020090

Ma Lu, Silvia
Mälardalen University, Västerås, Sweden
020381

Ma, Xiang
SINTEF, Oslo, Norway
020011

Macé, Philippe
Becquerel Institute, Brussels, Belgium
020225, 020252, 020474, 020505, 020543, 020558, 020573

Mack, Sebastian
Fraunhofer ISE, Freiburg, Germany
020031

Madsen, Morten
SDU Climate Cluster, Odense, Denmark
020250, 020306

Mahmood, Aysha
DTU, Roskilde, Denmark
020265, 020376

Maixner, Andreas
AESOLAR, Koenigsbrunn, Germany
020121, 020125, 020137, 020223

Maiz, Alexander   020437
UPV/EHU, Vitoria-Gasteiz, Spain

Majak, Martyna   020068
Roltec, Poznań, Poland

Makrides, George   020534
University of Cyprus, Nicosia, Cyprus

Malarkannan, Lavanya   020210
National Physical Laboratory, Teddington, United Kingdom

Malcorps, Philippe   020276
3E, Brussels, Belgium

Malik, Stephanie   020313
Fraunhofer CSP, Halle, Germany

Malik, Stephanie   020355
Fraunhofer IMWS, Halle, Germany

Maliutina, Kristina   020141
University of Applied Science Cologne, Cologne, Germany

Malo, Javier   020209
UPM, Madrid, Spain

Mancini, Simone   020425
TNO, Eindhoven, The Netherlands

Mandiola, Gotzon   020514
AZTI, PASAIA, Spain

Manganiello, Patrizio   020389
Hasselt University, Diepenbeek, Belgium

Manganiello, Patrizio   020294
imec, Genk, Belgium

Manito, Alex   020348
University of São Paulo, São Paulo, Brazil

Manochehrian, Rasoul   020539
Frankfurt University of Applied Sciences, Frankfurt am
Main, Germany

Manzolini, Giampaolo   020261
Polytechnic University of Milan, Milan, Italy

Maqsood, Ayman   020101
HZB, Berlin, Germany

Marangis, Demetris   020534
University of Cyprus, Nicosia, Cyprus

Marcos-Castro, Ana   020297
CIEMAT, Madrid, Spain

Marechal, Philippe   020217
CEA / INES, Le Bourget-du-Lac, France

Marí Soucase, Bernabé   020099
UPV, Valencia, Spain

Markert, Jochen   020231
Fraunhofer ISE, Freiburg, Germany

Marquardt, Cornelia   020063
ISFH, Emmerthal, Germany

Marteau, Baptiste   020034
ECM Technologies, Grenoble, France

Martín Rueda, Javier   020535
UPM, Madrid, Spain

Martín, Francisco José   020459
UPM, Madrid, Spain

Martín, Francisco   020209
UPM, Madrid, Spain

Martín-Chivelet, Nuria   020297
CIEMAT, Madrid, Spain

Martín-Rueda, Javier   020337, 020363
UPM, Madrid, Spain

Martínez González, Mario   020326
Enertis Applus+, Madrid, Spain

Martinez, Juan Ignacio   020252
Becquerel Institute Spain, San Sebastian, Spain

Martinez, Oscar   020191, 020205
University of Valladolid, Valladolid, Spain

Martínez-Barbeito, María   020243
ieco.io, Vigo, Spain

Maruyama, Rodrigo P.   020154, 020348
University of São Paulo, São Paulo, Brazil

Marzo, Aitor   020311, 020546
University of Granada, Granada, Spain

Mashkov, Oleksandr   020149, 020150, 020377
HI ERN, Erlangen, Germany

Massaro, Lorenzo   020541
PedersoliGattai, Milan, Italy

Masson, Gaëtan   020474, 020558, 020564, 020573
Becquerel Institute, Brussels, Belgium

Masson, Gaëtan   020570
IEA PVPS Task 1, Brussels, Belgium

Mateos, Yeray   020055, 020153
UPV/EHU, Bilbao, Spain

Maturi, Laura   020249, 020254, 020551
Eurac Research, Bolzano, Italy

Mayer-Ullmann, Philipp   020430
AIT, Vienna, Austria

Mazzoleni, Stefano   020378
University of Naples Federico II, Naples, Italy

McIntosh, Keith R.   020396
PV Lighthouse, Coledale, Australia

McNab, Shona   020065
UNSW, Sydney, Australia

Meereboer, Martijn   020225
Energyra, Westknollendam, The Netherlands

Meier, Rico   020132
HTW Berlin, Berlin, Germany

Meixner, Michael   020050
halm elektronik, Frankfurt am Main, Germany

Mekhaldi, Bouchra   020406
Ecole Polytechnique, Palaiseau, France

Melges de Andrade, Adnei   020154
University of São Paulo, São Paulo, Brazil

Melino, Francesco   020314
University of Bologna, Bologna, Italy

Mellone, Celeste   020541
Green Horse Advisory, Rome, Italy

Menard, Lionel   020291
MINES Paris, Nice, France

Mencaraglia, Denis   020058
CNRS, Gif-sur-Yvette, France

Menchaca, Iratxe   020514
AZTI, PASAIA, Spain

Mendes Ferreira Gomes, Amanda   020548
UFSC, Florianopolis, Brazil

Mendikoa, Iñigo   020514
Tecnalia, BRTA, Derio, Spain

Meneghini, Matteo   020089
University of Padova, Padova, Italy

Ménézo, Christophe   020317
LOCIE, Le Bourget-du-Lac, France

Menghini, Mariela   020508
IMDEA Nanoscience Institute, Madrid, Spain

Mercade Ruiz, Pau   020448, 020481
GreenPowerMonitor a DNV company, Barcelona, Spain

Merino, Amanda   020040
CEA / INES, Le Bourget-du-Lac, France

Merino, José Manuel   020085
UAM, Madrid, Spain

Mermoud, André   020196
PVsyst, Geneva, Switzerland

Merodio, Pablo   020337
UPM, Madrid, Spain

Mertens, Jan   020389
imec, Genk, Belgium

Mertens, Verena   020006, 020008
ISFH, Emmerthal, Germany

Meßmer, Marius   020031
Fraunhofer ISE, Freiburg, Germany

Messmer, Tobias   020218, 020221, 020225
ISC Konstanz, Konstanz, Germany

Miró-Llorente, Marta   020094
IREC, Barcelona, Spain

Misra, Prashant   020429
NISE, Gurugram, India

Miszczuk, Andrzej   020068
Roltec, Poznań, Poland

Mittag, Max   020137
Fraunhofer ISE, Freiburg, Germany

Mittal, Ankit   020318
AIT, Vienna, Austria

Mittelman, Gur   020379
Afeka Tel-Aviv Academic College of Engineering, Tel
Aviv, Israel

Mizushima, Io   020028
IPU P/S, Virum, Denmark

Mizushima, Io   020037
IPU, Virum, Denmark

Mngomezulu, Ndumiso   020344
PVinsight, Port Elizabeth, South Africa

Mo, Alvin   020065
UNSW, Sydney, Australia

Mockeviciute-Azzopardi, Austeja   020334
FIR, Birkirkara, Malta

Moe Nygård, Magnus   020340
IFE, Kjeller, Norway

Moehlecke, Adriano   020023, 020025
PUCRS, Porto Alegre, Brazil

Mohammadi, Mohammad Hossein   020037, 020104
Aarhus University, Aarhus, Denmark

Mollier, Stéphane   020262
CEA / INES, Le Bourget-du-Lac, France

Moltke, Asbjørn   020043
Technical University of Denmark, Copenhagen, Denmark

Mondaca-Cuevas, Gino   020422
University of Antofagasta, Antofagasta, Chile

Monokroussos, Christos   020181
TÜV Rheinland Shanghai, Shanghai, China

Monokroussos, Christos   020144, 020208
TÜV Rheinland, Shanghai, China

Monteiro Martins, Filipa   020317
Galp Energia, Lisbon, Portugal

Montes, Carlos   020151
ITER, Granadilla de Abona, Spain

Montoya, Josefa   020311
University of Antofagasta, Antofagasta, Chile

Morabito, Floriana   020066
CNR-IFN, Milan, Italy

Moradi Sizkouhi, Amirmohammad Concordia University, Montreal, Canada	020356, 020375
Moradi Zavie Kord, Soroush University of Helsinki, Helsinki, Finland	020400
Morales, Sergio UPM, Madrid, Spain	020491
Morantes Quintana, Giobertti Raul Eurac Research, Bolzano, Italy	020551
Mordvinkin, Anton Fraunhofer CSP, Halle, Germany	020233
Moreda, Guillermo P. UPM, Madrid, Spain	020407
Morin, Claire SolarPower Europe, Brussels, Belgium	020551
Morisset, Audrey CSEM, Neuchâtel, Switzerland	020068
Morlier, Arnaud Hasselt University, Genk, Belgium	020156
Morlier, Arnaud imec, Genk, Belgium	020294, 020389
Mortazavifar, Leila Anhalt University of Applied Sciences, Köthen, Germany	020056, 020158, 020201, 020284
Moruno, Ricardo UPM, Madrid, Spain	020209, 020453
Mosel, Frank PVA TePla, Wettenberg, Germany	020015
Moser, David Becquerel Institute Italy, Trento, Italy	020573
Moser, David Becquerel Institute, Bolzano, Italy	020316
Moser, David Bequerel Institute, Trento, Italy	020254
Moser, David Eurac Research, Bolzano, Italy	020203, 020226, 020261, 020325, 020485, 020489, 020546
Mouhoubi, Felicia CEA / INES, Le Bourget-du-Lac, France	020134
Müllejans, Harald European Commission JRC, Ispra, Italy	020208, 020213
Müller, Alexander Fraunhofer CSP, Halle, Germany	020119
Müller, Larissa University of Applied Sciences Cologne, Cologne, Germany	020523
Mugica, Maikel Tecnalia, Donostia - San Sebastián, Spain	020139
Mujovi, Fahradin CSEM, Neuchâtel, Switzerland	020251

Mukherjee, Srijani							020338
CEA / INES, Le Bourget-du-Lac, France

Mukhtar, Mariyam							020057
University of Verona, Verona, Italy

Mulder, Peter							020067
Radboud University, Nijmegen, The Netherlands

Muller, Matthew							020314
NREL, Denver, United States of America

Munkhammar, Joakim							020532
Uppsala University, Uppsala, Sweden

Muñoz Cerón, Emilio							020269
University of Jaén, Jaén, Spain

Muñoz, Delfina							020040, 020311, 020546
CEA / INES, Le Bourget-du-Lac, France

Muñoz, Delfina							020521
CEA, Le Bourget-du-Lac, France

Muñoz, Delfina							020226
CEA/ INES, Le Bourget-du-Lac, France

Muñoz, Ildefonso							020365, 020366, 020392
CENER, Sarriguren, Spain

Muñoz, Jesús Ángel							020508
UCM, Madrid, Spain

Muñoz-García, Miguel-Ángel							020407
UPM, Madrid, Spain

Murano, Giovanni							020551
ENEA, Ispra, Italy

Murillo, Asier							020497
CENER, Sarriguren, Spain

Musembi, Robinson J.							020272
University of Nairobi, Nairobi, Kenya

Nabipouor, Mohammad							020426
Anhalt University of Applied Sciences, Köthen, Germany

Nagel, Henning							020475
Fraunhofer ISE, Freiburg, Germany

Nakamura, Kyotaro							020046
Toyota Technological Institute, Nagoya, Japan

Nanno, Ikuo							020190
Nanno Energy Research Center, Yamaguchi, Japan

Nargelienė, Viktorija							020157
Center for Physical Sciences and Technology (FTMC),
Vilnius, Lithuania

Narsi Patel, Hitarth							020069
SVNIT, Surat, India

Narvarte, Luis							020337, 020446, 020491, 020535, 020536,
UPM, Madrid, Spain							020567, 020575

Nascimento, Lucas   020377
Solar Energy Research Laboratory Fotovoltaica/ UFSC,
Florianópolis, Brazil

Nasebandt, Lasse   020063
ISFH, Emmerthal, Germany

Nasser, Hisham   020226
ODTÜ-GÜNAM, Ankara, Türkiye

Naveiro, José Manuel   020414
ENDEF, Zaragoza, Spain

Nazififard, Mohammad   020259, 020428
Côte d'Azur University, Nice, France

Nejim, Ahmed   020058
SILVACO, St. Ives, United Kingdom

Nel, Paul   020382
7SecondSolar, Cape Town, South Africa

Nelson, Jenny   020394
Imperial College London, London, United Kingdom

Neuba, Adam   020114
Paderborn University, Paderborn, Germany

Neuber, Viola   020031
Fraunhofer ISE, Freiburg, Germany

Neuhaus, Holger   020123, 020140
Fraunhofer ISE, Freiburg, Germany

Neumaier, Lukas   020504
Silicon Austria Labs, Villach, Austria

Neussl, Vassilissa   020318, 020430
AIT, Vienna, Austria

Neykova, Neda   020107
Czech Technical University, Prague, Czech Republic

Nezhad, Mahyar   020230
Kiwa PI Berlin, Hudson, United States of America

Nguyen, Viet Xuan   020008
centrotherm international, Blaubeuren, Germany

Nicolet-dit-Félix, Kléber   020251
EPFL, Neuchâtel, Switzerland

Nicot-Senneville, Zoltan   020102
SERIS, Singapore, Singapore

Nielsen, Michael P.   020065
UNSW, Sydney, Australia

Nissen, Hauke   020313
Wattmanufactur, Galmsbüll, Germany

Nitsche, Tobias   020119, 020218
Henkel, Düsseldorf, Germany

Nobre, André M.   020263
PV Doctor, Singapore, Singapore

Noels, Serge   020472
PV CYCLE, Brussels, Belgium

Noh, Yong-Su 020449
KETI, Wonmi-gu, South Korea

Nold, Sebastian 020461
Fraunhofer ISE, Freiburg, France

Nold, Sebastian 020475
Fraunhofer ISE, Freiburg, Germany

Nordboe, Eirik 020495
Fiven Norge, Lillesand, Norway

Norde Santos, Fernanda 020331
DLR, Almería, Spain

Nouri, Bijan 020235, 020237, 020239
DLR, Almería, Spain

Nova, David 020339
National University of Colombia, Bogotá, Colombia

Núñez, Rubén 020209, 020453
UPM, Madrid, Spain

Núñez-Osorio, Alessia 020100
University of Almeria, Almeria, Spain

Nurmesjärvi, Antti 020423
VTT Technical Research Centre of Finland, Oulu, Finland

Nussbaumer, Hartmut 020385
ZHAW, Winterthur, Switzerland

Nyang'onda, Thomas N. 020272
University of Nairobi, Nairobi, Kenya

Obeidavi, Sahereh 020361
Coburg University of Applied Sciences, Coburg, Germany

Oberbeck, Lars 020461
TotalEnergies OneTech, Paris, France

Oberegger Filippi, Ulrich 020551
Eurac Research, Bolzano, Italy

Ocaña, Luis Manuel 020151
ITER, Granadilla de Abona, Spain

Ockert, Ajka 020312
EnBW, Karlsruhe, Germany

Odilio dos Santos, Daniel 020548
UFSC, Florianopolis, Brazil

Öhgren, Gustav 020532
Becquerel Sweden, Knivsta, Sweden

Öttl, Christian 020347
Watt Analytics, Vienna, Austria

Öz, Aksel Kaan 020135
Fraunhofer ISE, Freiburg, Germany

Özden, Talat 020226
ODTÜ-GÜNAM, Ankara, Türkiye

Özkalay, Ebrar 020160, 020204
SUPSI, Mendrisio, Switzerland

Ogura, Atsushi 020046
Meiji University, Kanagawa, Japan

Ohdaira, Keisuke 020131
JAIST, Ishikawa, Japan

Ohshita, Yoshio 020046
Toyota Technological Institute, Nagoya, Japan

Ojala, Aleksi 020554
Solarigo Systems, Pirkkala, Finland

Okawa, Hayato 020115
Tokyo City University, Setagaya, Japan

Okel, Lars A. G. 020030
TNO, Petten, The Netherlands

Oksanen, Jani 020067
Aalto University, Espoo, Finland

Oliosi, Michele 020196
PVsyst, Geneva, Switzerland

Olivares, Douglas 020311
University of Antofagasta, Antofagasta, Chile

Olivares, Gregorio 020365, 020366, 020392
CENER, Sarriguren, Spain

Oliveira Santos, João Victor 020188
EDF R&D, Moret Loing Orvanne, France

Oliveira, Helena 020420
University of Évora, Évora, Portugal

Oller Westerberg, Amelia 020570
Becquerel Sweden, Knivsta, Sweden

Ollo, Olatz 020139
Tecnalia, Donostia - San Sebastián, Spain

Oozeki, Takashi 020436, 020525
AIST, Koriyama, Japan

Opatovsky, Martin 020241, 020262
Solargis, Bratislava, Slovakia

Oreski, Gernot 020136, 020234, 020325, 020500, 020574
PCCL, Leoben, Austria

Ortega, Eneko 020055, 020153, 020287, 020353
UPV/EHU, Bilbao, Spain

Ortega, Eneko 020289, 020437
UPV/EHU, Leioa, Spain

Ortega, Pascal 020214
University of French Polynesia, Faa'a, French Polynesia

Ortiz-Pena, Aaron 020562
University of Castilla-La Mancha, Albacete, Spain

Ory, Daniel 020188
EDF R&D, Palaiseau, France

Ory, Daniel   020116
EDF, Palaiseau, France

Osman, Alaa   020006
ISFH, Emmerthal, Germany

Osuna, Jose Antonio   020358
MAGTEL, Córdoba, Spain

Osvald, Oliver   020274
Solargis, Bratislava, Slovakia

Otaegi, Aloña   020055, 020097, 020153, 020287
UPV/EHU, Bilbao, Spain

Otnes, Gaute   020169
Institute for Energy Technology, Kjeller, Norway

Otto, Nicolas   020101
HTW, Berlin, Germany

Otto, William   020390
MARIN, Wageningen, The Netherlands

Ou, Chao-Wei   020350
National Chin-Yi University of Technology, Taichung,
Taiwan

Ovaitt, Silvana   020314
NREL, Denver, United States of America

Ovaitt, Silvana   020574
NREL, Golden, United States of America

Oviedo Hernandez, Guillermo   020325
BayWa r.e, Rome, Italy

Ozer, Shay   020379
Agricultural Research Organization, Rishon LeZion, Israel

P. Pires, Maurício   020090
Federal University of Rio de Janeiro, Rio de Janeiro, Brazil

Pabiou, Herve   020338
CETHIL, Villeurbanne, France

Pabst, Elena   020312
ZSW, Stuttgart, Germany

Paiva, Lúcio   020530
Casa dos Ventos, Fortaleza, Brazil

Palais, Olivier   020188
Toulon University, Marseille, France

Palitzsch, Wolfram   020225, 020495
LuxChemTech, Freiberg, Germany

Palomino, Laura   020491, 020535
UPM, Madrid, Spain

Pamir Aly, Shahzada   020229
DEWA, Dubai, United Arab Emirates

Pamula, Bindu   020069
SVNIT, Surat, India

Panda, Pavan Kumar Anhalt University of Applied Sciences, Köthen, Germany	020284
Pandar, Matthias Fraunhofer CSP, Halle, Germany	020229
Pander, Matthias Fraunhofer CSP, Halle, Germany	020121, 020142, 020175, 020192, 020218, 020223, 020232
Panduri, Fabio BFH, Burgdorf, Switzerland	020322
Pantoja, Jaime Francisco José de Caldas District University, Bogota, Colombia	020526
Papantoni, Veatriki DLR, Oldenburg, Germany	020482
Paraficz, Danuta FFHS, Zurich, Switzerland	020204
Paraskeva, Vasiliki University of Cyprus, Nicosia, Cyprus	020064
Pardo, Eduardo Tecnova, Almeira, Spain	020414
Parfeniukas, Karolis ATLANT 3D, Taastrup, Denmark	020039
Parion, Jonathan Hasselt Unversity, Genk, Belgium	020064
Park, Hyeonwook KENTECH, Naju-Si, South Korea	020112
Parmar, Richa NISE, Gurugram, India	020429
Parra, Johan Ecole Polytechnique, Palaiseau, France	020406
Parra, Johan Polytechnic Institute of Paris, Palaiseau, France	020214
Parrilla, Carlos G. Fujairah Research Centre, Fujairah, United Arab Emirates	020402
Pascual Gallego, Valero UPM, Madrid, Spain	020407
Pasquier, Mathis DTU, Roskilde, Denmark	020451
Passaro, Marcello Sunzest Solar, Rotterdam, The Netherlands	020513
Patel, Dharm Fraunhofer IMWS, Halle, Germany	020355
Paul, Ananta SDU Climate Cluster, Odense, Denmark	020250, 020306
Paulescu, Marius West University of Timisoara, Timisoara, Romania	020283

Paviet-Salomon, Bertrand 020068, 020467
CSEM, Neuchâtel, Switzerland

Payno, David 020085, 020094
UAM, Madrid, Spain

Pearce, Pheobe 020065
UNSW, Sydney, Australia

Peche, René 020468, 020495
bifa Umweltinstitut, Augsburg, Germany

Pehlivanli, Ezgi 020521
METU, Ankara, Türkiye

Peibst, Robby 020006, 020063, 020114
ISFH, Emmerthal, Germany

Pelfort Ojer, Marta 020241
Solargis, Bratislava, Slovakia

Pelland, Sophie 020211
Natural Resources Canada, Varennes, Canada

Pelle, Martina 020249, 020254
Eurac Research, Bolzano, Italy

Peña-Bermudez, Julian 020110
University of the Caribbean, Santo Domingo, Dominican
Republic

Peng, Cheng-Yu 020350
National Chin-Yi University of Technology, Taichung,
Taiwan

Pera, David 020457
Luxembourg Institute of Science and Technology, Esch-sur-
Alzette, Luxembourg

Perani, Martina 020204
FFHS, Zurich, Switzerland

Peraticos, Elias 020064
University of Cyprus, Nicosia, Cyprus

Pereda, Ainhoa 020198, 020358
TECNALIA, Derio, Spain

Pereira Fialho, Luis Andre 020509
Eurac Research, Bolzano, Italy

Pereira, Sara 020403, 020418, 020565
University of Évora, Évora, Portugal

Pérez García, Manuel 020336
University of Almería, La Cañada de San Urbano, Spain

Pérez, Ernesto 020339
National University of Colombia, Bogotá, Colombia

Pérez, Jairo 020412
Gonvarri AgroTech, Corvera - Asturias, Spain

Pérez, Jorge 020412
Gonvarri AgroTech, Corvera - Asturias, Spain

Pérez, Luis 020412
Gonvarri MS R&D, Corvera - Asturias, Spain

Perez, Richard 020494
University at Albany, Albany, United States of America

Perez-Astudillo, Daniel 020275, 020278, 020291
QEERI, Doha, Qatar

Pérez-García, Manuel 020100
University of Almeria, Almería, Spain

Pérez-Rodríguez, Alejandro 020085, 020094
IREC, Barcelona, Spain

Pernas, Tomás 020412
Gonvarri AgroTech, Corvera - Asturias, Spain

Pernau, Thomas 020008
centrotherm international, Blaubeuren, Germany

Perrin, Marion 020544
Energy Pool, Le Bourget-du-Lac, France

Pervan, Nikolina 020136, 020234
PCCL, Leoben, Austria

Peter Amalathas, Amalraj 020107
University of Jaffna, Jaffna, Sri Lanka

Peter, Kristian 020569
ISC Konstanz, Konstanz, Germany

Peters, Ian Marius 020230, 020263
Forschungszentrum Jülich, Erlangen, Germany

Peters, Ian Marius 020149, 020150, 020377, 020574
HI ERN, Erlangen, Germany

Petersons, Karlis 020250, 020306
Stensborg, Roskilde, Denmark

Petkovski, Emil 020571
DNV, Arnhem, The Netherlands

Petzschmann, Jonas 020312
ZSW, Stuttgart, Germany

Pfau, Jan Hendrik 020240
Leibniz University Hannover, Hannover, Germany

Pfeiffer, Oliver 020141
University of Applied Science Cologne, Cologne, Germany

Pfeiffer, Oliver 020140
University of Applied Sciences Cologne, Cologne, Germany

Philipp, Daniel 020215, 020231
Fraunhofer ISE, Freiburg, Germany

Pierro, Marco 020489, 020494
Eurac Research, Bolzano, Italy

Pieters, Bart E. 020180
FZJ, Jülich, Germany

Pieterse, Marco 020495
Chemconserve, Bussum, The Netherlands

Pietralunga, Silvia Maria 020066
CNR-IFN, Milan, Italy

Pietsch, Veith   020331
Aquila Capital, Hamburg, Germany

Pilat, Eric   020311
CEA / INES, Le Bourget-du-Lac, France

Pilat, Eric   020317
CEA INES, Le Bourget-du-Lac, France

Pillai, Akhildev   020558
Becquerel Institute, Brussels, Belgium

Pinheiro, Philippe   020457
Luxembourg Institute of Science and Technology, Esch-sur-Alzette, Luxembourg

Pinho Almeida, Marcelo   020348
University of São Paulo, São Paulo, Brazil

Pinto, Cristina Leyre   020497
CENER, Sarriguren, Spain

Pinto, Luciana   020092
UFRJ, Rio de Janeiro, Brazil

Pitaval, Sébastien   020244
SOLAÏS, Valbonne, France

Pitz-Paal, Robert   020237, 020331
DLR, Cologne, Germany

Plakhotnyuk, Maksym   020039
ATLANT 3D, Taastrup, Denmark

Platero Gaona, Carlos A.   020332
UPM, Madrid, Spain

Plaza, Caroline   020543, 020564, 020573
Becquerel Institute France, Lyon, France

Polacchi, Cristina   020509, 020513
Eurac Research, Bolzano, Italy

Polo, Jaime   020300
CENER, Sarriguren, Spain

Polo, Jesús   020297
CIEMAT, Madrid, Spain

Polverini, Davide   020181
Directorate General for Internal Market, Industry, Entrepreneurship and SMEs, Brussels, Belgium

Polverini, Davide   020497
European Comission, Brussels, Belgium

Pongthanacharoenkul, Nattapark   020230
Kiwa PI Berlin, Berlin, Germany

Poortmans, Jef   020064
Hasselt Unversity, Genk, Belgium

Popescu, Lacramioara   020068
ISC Konstanz, Konstanz, Germany

Pospischil, Maximilian   020225
Highline Technologies, Freiburg, Germany

Poulsen, Peter B.   020039
DTU, Copenhagen, Denmark

Poulsen, Peter B.   020250, 020265, 020267, 020376, 020451
DTU, Roskilde, Denmark

Poulsen, Peter Behrensdorff   020028, 020306, 020346
DTU, Roskilde, Denmark

Pourshafi, Pouya   020121, 020125, 020137
AESOLAR, Koenigsbrunn, Germany

Pozza, Cristian   020551
Eurac Research, Bolzano, Italy

Prakash, Jai   020429
NISE, Gurugram, India

Prando, Davide   020485, 020489
Edyna, Bolzano, Italy

Prasad, Manjunath   020225
ISC Konstanz, Konstanz, Germany

Pravettoni, Mauro   020402
Technology Innovation Institute, Abu Dhabi, United Arab
Emirates

Preis, Pirmin   020003
ISC Konstanz, Konstanz, Germany

Preu, Ralf   020475
Fraunhofer ISE, Freiburg, Germany

Preuschoff, Jonas   020101
HTW, Berlin, Germany

Protti, Alexander Aguilar   020140
Fraunhofer ISE, Freiburg, Germany

Protti, Alexander   020137
Fraunhofer ISE, Freiburg, Germany

Provost, Marion   020116
IPVF, Palaiseau, France

Puel, Jean Baptiste   020062
IPVF, Palaiseau, France

Puertas López, Antonio Manuel   020100
University of Almeria, Almeria, Spain

Puttock, Claire   020367
Nextracker, Fremont, United States of America

Queste, Samuel   020068
Marie and Louis Pasteur University, Besançon, France

Quiroz, Mónica   020328
Qualifying Photovoltaics, Madrid, Spain

R. Ledesma, Javier   020363
UPM, Madrid, Spain

Rabanal Arabach, Jorge University of Antofagasta, Antofagasta, Chile	020183
Rabanal-Arabach, Jorge University of Antofagasta, Antofagasta, Chile	020129, 020342, 020417, 020422
Rabiei, Hossein ISFH, Emmerthal, Germany	020063
Rachdi, Lazhar ISC Konstanz, Konstanz, Germany	020035, 020068
Radzevicius, Aurimas Valoe Cells, Vilnius, Lithuania	020225
Rafiee, Hossein Frankfurt University of Applied Sciences, Frankfurt am Main, Germany	020539
Raginskis, Justinas Kaunas University of Technology, Kaunas, Lithuania	020380
Raievska, Oleksandra HI ERN, Erlangen, Germany	020117, 020149
Rajan, S. Prithivi LuciSun, Villers-la-Ville, Belgium	020262
Rajkiewicz, Katarzyna NAPE, Warsaw, Poland	020551
Rakotoniaina, Jean Patrice CEA / INES, Le Bourget-du-Lac, France	020311
Ramachandran Nair, Jishnu Fraunhofer CSP, Halle, Germany	020233
Ramesh, Santhosh imec, Genk, Belgium	020389
Ramírez Ledesma, Javier UPM, Madrid, Spain	020535
Ramirez, S. PV Lighthouse, Coledale, Australia	020396
Rampino, Stefano National Research Council, Parma, Italy	020087
Ramspeck, Klaus halm elektronik, Frankfurt am Main, Germany	020050
Ranisch, Tadeus HTW, Berlin, Germany	020101
Ranta, Samuli TUAS, Turku, Finland	020286, 020400
Ranta, Samuli Turku University of Applied Sciences, Turku, Finland	020298, 020398
Raposo, Mauro University of Évora, Évora, Portugal	020565
Ratnagiri, Abhinav Nextracker, Fremont, United States of America	020367
Raugewitz, Annika ISFH, Emmerthal, Germany	020063, 020114

Raval, Mehul   020005, 020222, 020463
RCT Solutions, Konstanz, Germany

Razanajao, Aina   020244
SOLAÏS, Valbonne, France

Razi, Umair   020085
IREC, Barcelona, Spain

Recart, Federico   020097
UPV/EHU, Bilbao, Spain

Redondo Cuevas, Marta   020332
UPM, Madrid, Spain

Redondo, Juan Manuel   020209
UPM, Madrid, Spain

Rehan, Muhammad   020112
KIER, Daejeon, South Korea

Rehman, Anees ur   020111, 020164
Hohai University, Changzhou, China

Reichart, Hannah   020167, 020232
University of Applied Sciences Cologne, Cologne, Germany

Reichel, Christian   020123, 020137, 020140
Fraunhofer ISE, Freiburg, Germany

Reichle, Julian   020005, 020222, 020463
RCT Solutions, Konstanz, Germany

Reinders, Angele   020253
TU Eindhoven, Eindhoven, The Netherlands

Reindl, Thomas   020263
SERIS, Singapore, Singapore

Reis, Luiz Filipe   020530
Casa dos Ventos, Fortaleza, Brazil

Rémondeau, Paul   020251
EPFL, Neuchâtel, Switzerland

Renard, Charles   020058
CNRS, Palaiseau, France

Rende, Fedele   020255
ACCA Software, Cosenza, Italy

Rennhofer, Marcus   020180, 020281, 020318, 020334, 020347,
AIT, Vienna, Austria   020430

Rentsch, Jochen   020475
Fraunhofer ISE, Freiburg, Germany

Rerat, Michel   020060
IPREM, Pau, France

Reshef, Liad   020379
Agricultural Research Organization, Rishon LeZion, Israel

Revol, Inès   020074
LAAS-CNRS, Toulouse, France

Reyal, Jean-Pierre   020303
SemperStyl, Eragny, France

Rodríguez-Gallegos, Carlos D.　020149, 020150
SERIS, Singapore, Singapore

Rodríguez-Romero, Sebastián　020342, 020417, 020422
University of Antofagasta, Antofagasta, Chile

Rodziewicz, Hanna　020498
Gdansk University of Technology, Gdansk, Poland

Römer, Udo　020006, 020063
ISFH, Emmerthal, Germany

Röver, Ingo　020225
LuxChemTech, Freiberg, Germany

Rojas, Christian A.　020422
Federico Santa María Technical University, Valparaíso, Chile

Rojas-Henríquez, Katalina　020129
University of Antofagasta, Antofagasta, Chile

Román, Eduardo　020139
Tecnalia, Donostia - San Sebastián, Spain

Romeo, Alessandro　020057, 020089, 020093
University of Verona, Verona, Italy

Romer, Pascal　020231
Fraunhofer ISE, Freiburg, Germany

Roodt, Roelof　020185
Nelson Mandela University, Port Elizabeth, South Africa

Roosloot, Nathan　020169
Institute for Energy Technology, Kjeller, Norway

Rosca, Victor　020030
TNO, Petten, The Netherlands

Rosen, Isaac　020225
Copprint, Jerusalem, Israel

Rosenfeld, Lavi　020379
Agricultural Research Organization, Rishon LeZion, Israel

Rosina, Konstantin　020241
Solargis, Bratislava, Slovakia

Rossa, Carlos　020432, 020434
Sunveon, Madrid, Spain

Rouffie, Brice　020068
SEGTON Advanced Technology, Versailles, France

Roulleau, Lea　020303
CSTB, Marne-la-Vallée, France

Rousset, Jean　020116
EDF, Palaiseau, France

Roy, Shantanu　020519
CSTEP, Bengaluru, India

Rudolph, Dominik　020003, 020068
ISC Konstanz, Konstanz, Germany

Rudzikas, Matas   020380
The Applied Research Institute for Prospective
Technologies, Vilnius, Lithuania

Rüther, Ricardo   020377
Solar Energy Research Laboratory Fotovoltaica/ UFSC,
Florianópolis, Brazil

Rüther, Ricardo   020548
UFSC, Florianopolis, Brazil

Ruf, Manuel   020455
Robert Bosch, Stuttgart, Germany

Ruiz Donoso, Elena   020331
DLR, Almería, Spain

S. Sousa, Graciana   020090
Federal University of Rio de Janeiro, Rio de Janeiro, Brazil

Safarian, Jafar   020011
NTNU, Trondheim, Norway

Sah, Dheeraj   020039
Aarhus University, Aarhus, Denmark

Sahin, Hasret   020479
LUT University, Lappeenranta, Finland

Saito, Kimihiko   020106
Tokyo City University, Setagaya, Japan

Salem, Mohammad   020428
Australian University, Kuwait City, Kuwait

Salerno, Giorgia   020077
University of Milano-Bicocca, Milan, Italy

Salis, Fabio   020541
Iberdrola, Rome, Italy

Salvador, Antonio   020358
MAGTEL, Córdoba, Spain

Sample, Tony   020213
European Commission JRC, Ispra, Italy

Samuolienė, Giedrė   020380
The Lithuanian Research Centre for Agriculture and
Forestry, Kaunas, Lithuania

San José, Luis Javier   020209, 020453
UPM, Madrid, Spain

Sánchez de León Peque, Miguel   020243
ieco.io, Vigo, Spain

Sanchez Garcia, Alfredo   020270
SINTEF, Trondheim, Norway

Sanchez, Hugo   020056, 020158, 020284
Anhalt University of Applied Sciences, Köthen, Germany

Sanchez, Jesus   020437
UPV/EHU, Vitoria-Gasteiz, Spain

Sanchez, Laura   020437
UPV/EHU, Leioa, Spain

Sánchez, Yudania   020085
IREC, Barcelona, Spain

Sanchez-Friera, Paula   020412, 020513, 020521
Solkeys, Gijón, Spain

Sanchez-Ruiz, Alain   020437
UPV/EHU, Vitoria-Gasteiz, Spain

Sansavini, Giovanni   020296
ETH, Zurich, Switzerland

Sansoni, Paola   020066
CNR-INO, Florence, Italy

Santamaría Fernández, Susanna   020249
TECNALIA, Derio, Spain

Santamaría-Sancho, Juan   020363
UPM, Madrid, Spain

Santos, Jose Domingo   020197, 020198, 020358
TECNALIA, Derio, Spain

Santos, Rodrigo   020530
Casa dos Ventos, Fortaleza, Brazil

Sanz Martinez, Asier   020546
Tecnalia, Bilbao, Spain

Sanz, Asier   020514
Tecnalia, BRTA, Derio, Spain

Sanz, Asier   020197
TECNALIA, Derio, Spain

Sanz-Cuadrado, Cristina   020575
UPM, Madrid, Spain

Sanz-Saiz, Carlos   020297
CIEMAT, Madrid, Spain

Sarafijanovic-Djukic, Natasa   020204
FFHS, Regensdorf, Switzerland

Saretti, Angelica   020301
Polytechnic University of Bari, Bari, Italy

Sarkadi, Monika   020569
ISC Konstanz, Konstanz, Germany

Sauer, Thomas   020140
EXXERGY, Gräfelfing, Germany

Saura, Juan Antonio   020506
University of Murcia, Murcia, Spain

Savisalo, Tuukka   020225
Valoe, Mikkeli, Finland

Saw, Min Hsian   020402
Technology Innovation Institute, Abu Dhabi, United Arab
Emirates

Saxena, Anmol Ratan   020429
NIT, Delhi, India

Sayed, Abdullah Abu	020180, 020230
Kiwa PI Berlin, Berlin, Germany

Scaltrito, Luciano	020079
Polytechnic University of Turin, Turin, Italy

Scerri, Kenneth	020334
University of Malta, Msida, Malta

Schading, Steve	020443
University of Agder, Grimstad, Norway

Schäfer, Aysim	020388
Next2Sun Technology, Dillingen, Germany

Schäfer, Sebastian	020539
Frankfurt University of Applied Sciences, Frankfurt am
Main, Germany

Schenk, Paul	020192
Fraunhofer CSP, Halle, Germany

Schermer, John	020067
Radboud University, Nijmegen, The Netherlands

Scherret, Jacqueline	020255
A-Null Development, Vienna, Austria

Schifferegger, Raffael	020162
OFI, Vienna, Austria

Schimanke, Sabrina	020006
ISFH, Emmerthal, Germany

Schirmer, Yoko	020101
HTW, Berlin, Germany

Schläger, Christian	020240
Leibniz University Hannover, Hannover, Germany

Schlatmann, Rutger	020101
HTW, Berlin, Germany

Schmidt Davidsen, Rasmus	020037, 020104
Aarhus University, Aarhus, Denmark

Schnaus, Dominik	020237
TUM, Garching, Germany

Schneider, Andreas	020129, 020183
University of Applied Sciences Gelsenkirchen,
Gelsenkirchen, Germany

Schneider, Astrid	020255
TU Wien, Vienna, Austria

Schneider, Friedrich	020482
LPKF SolarQuipment, Suhl, Germany

Schneider, Marc Gabriel	020522
University of Applied Science Cologne, Cologne, Germany

Schneiderlöchner, Eric	020033
VON ARDENNE, Dresden, Germany

Schnierer, Branislav	020262
Solargis, Bratislava, Slovakia

Schönau, Maximilian   020361
Coburg University of Applied Sciences, Coburg, Germany

Schönau, Maximilian   020544
smartblue, Munich, Germany

Schönheits, Markus   020468, 020470
bifa Umweltinstitut, Augsburg, Germany

Schranz, Christian   020255
TU Wien, Vienna, Austria

Schrempf, Michael   020199
PTB, Braunschweig, Germany

Schrijvers, Patrick   020390
MARIN, Wageningen, The Netherlands

Schröter, Nick   020142
Fraunhofer CSP, Halle, Germany

Schubert, Martin C.   020475
Fraunhofer ISE, Freiburg, Germany

Schubnel, Baptiste   020238
CSEM, Neuchâtel, Switzerland

Schüler, Marc Andre   020388
Next2Sun Technology, Dillingen, Germany

Schüler, Marc Andre   020411
Next2Sun, Dillingen, Germany

Schueler, Nadine   020015
Freiberger Instruments, Freiberg, Germany

Schulte-Huxel, Henning   020008, 020260
ISFH, Emmerthal, Germany

Schultz, Christof   020101
HTW, Berlin, Germany

Schulz, Philip   020060
IPVF, Palaiseau, France

Schulze, Achim   020361
Rosenheim Technical University of Applied Sciences,
Rosenheim, Germany

Schulze, Patricia S.C.   020475
Fraunhofer ISE, Freiburg, Germany

Schwenke, Almut   020495
SGL Battery Solutions, Meitingen, Germany

Sciuto, Marcello   020010
Enel Green Power, Catania, Italy

Scognamiglio, Alessandra   020541
ENEA, Naples, Italy

Scognamiglio, Alessandra   020378
ENEA, Portici, Italy

Sedaghat, Ahmad   020428
Australian University, Kuwait City, Kuwait

Seiffert, Christoph   020169
Institute for Energy Technology, Kjeller, Norway

Seiffert, Daniela 020008
centrotherm international, Blaubeuren, Germany

Seitz, Matthias 020468
bifa Umweltinstitut, Augsburg, Germany

Selj, Josefine H. 020169
Institute for Energy Technology, Kjeller, Norway

Senno, Maximiliano Alejandro 020226
University of Valencia, Paterna, Spain

Senturk, Bilge 020556
ODTU GUNAM, Ankara, Türkiye

Setien, Eneko 020198
TECNALIA, Derio, Spain

Šetkus, Arūnas 020157
Center for Physical Sciences and Technology (FTMC),
Vilnius, Lithuania

Shaaban, Ahmed 020402
Technology Innovation Institute, Abu Dhabi, United Arab
Emirates

Shah, Syed Fawad Ali 020112
KENTECH, Naju-Si, South Korea

Shanmugam, Raphael 020218, 020220
ISC Konstanz, Konstanz, Germany

Sharma, Rajesh Kumar 020071, 020081
SVNIT, Surat, India

Sharma, Sushma 020563
SRM University, Sonipat, India

Shen, Xinyi 020226
University of Oxford, Oxford, United Kingdom

Shen, Zhenjue 020001
YIST, Jiangyin, China

Shin, Donghyeop 020112
KIER, Daejeon, South Korea

Shin, Woo Gyun 020324, 020357
KIER, Daejeon, South Korea

Shin, Woo-gyun 020561
KIER, Daejeon, South Korea

Shirai, Yasuhiro 020115
NIMS, Tsukuba, Japan

Shirazi, Elham 020544
University of Twente, Enschede, The Netherlands

Shishavan, Amir Asgharzadeh 020367
Nextracker, Fremont, United States of America

Shishido, Hirotaka 020106
Tokyo City University, Setagaya, Japan

Shochet, Ofer 020225
Copprint, Jerusalem, Israel

Shyong, Yung-Jen   020163
ITRI, Hsinchu, Taiwan

Sicot, Lionel   020217
CEA / INES, Le Bourget-du-Lac, France

Sidler, Anika   020226
School of Life Sciences FHNW, Muttenz, Switzerland

Siebert, Michael   020206
ISFH, Emmerthal, Germany

Siefer, Gerald   020246
Fraunhofer ISE, Freiburg, Germany

Sierra, Daniel   020491
UPM, Madrid, Spain

Sigounis, Anna-Maria   020248, 020249
Concordia University, Montreal, Canada

Søiland, Anne-Karin   020495
ReSiTec, Kristiansand, Norway

Silva, José A.   020304, 020409, 020420
University of Évora, Évora, Portugal

Silva, José   020403
University of Évora, Évora, Portugal

Silvestre, Santiago   020301
UPC, Barcelona, Spain

Simeunovic, Jelena   020238
CSEM, Neuchâtel, Switzerland

Simón-Allué, Raquel   020127, 020414, 020517
ENDEF, Zaragoza, Spain

Singh, Ravi   020571
DNV, Arnhem, The Netherlands

Sinha, Amish Kumar   020463
RCT Solutions, Konstanz, Germany

Sinopoli, Alessandro   020042
QEERI, Doha, Qatar

Sivaramakrishnan Radhakrishnan, Hariharsudan   020064
Hasselt Unversity, Genk, Belgium

Sivaramakrishnan, Hariharsudan   020225
IMEC, Genk, Belgium

Snaith, Henry   020226
University of Oxford, Oxford, United Kingdom

Søndenå, Rune   020503
Institute for Energy Technology, Kjeller, Norway

Sobajima, Yasushi   020131
Gifu University, Gifu, Japan

Soler Toledo, Denet   020509
University of Antofagasta, Antofagasta, Chile

Solomon, Asfaw A.   020479
LUT University, Lappeenranta, Finland

Solórzano, Jorge	020328
Qualifying Photovoltaics, Madrid, Spain

Sondoqah, Mousa	020316
Becquerel Institute, Bolzano, Italy

Sondoqah, Mousa	020261
Eurac Research, Bolzano, Italy

Song, Hee-eun	020045
KIER, Daejeon, South Korea

Spagnolo, Sofia	020462, 020466
RSE, Milan, Italy

Spataru, Sergiu V.	020265, 020267, 020283, 020376, 020451
DTU, Roskilde, Denmark

Spataru, Sergiu Viorel	020346
DTU, Roskilde, Denmark

Spera, Fabian	020411
Next2Sun, Dillingen, Germany

Spihola, Jan	020355
DiSUN Deutsche Solarservice, Werder, Germany

Sraisth,	020005, 020222
RCT Solutions, Konstanz, Germany

Sraisth, Sraisth	020463
RCT Solutions, Konstanz, Germany

Staňková, Tereza	020107
Czech Technical University, Prague, Czech Republic

Steckenreiter, Verena	020063
ISFH, Emmerthal, Germany

Stegemann, Bert	020309
Berlin University of Applied Sciences, Berlin, Germany

Stegemann, Bert	020101
HTW, Berlin, Germany

Stellbogen, Dirk	020312
ZSW, Stuttgart, Germany

Stensborg, Jan F.	020250
Stensborg, Roskilde, Denmark

Stensborg, Jan	020306
Stensborg, Roskilde, Denmark

Stieldorf, Karin	020255
TU Wien, Vienna, Austria

Stierstorfer, Johannes	020225
WIP - Renewable Energies, Munich, Germany

Stierstorfer, Johannes	020551
WIP Renewable Energies, Munich, Germany

Stivanello, Juan José	020226
Eurac Research, Bolzano, Italy

Stoicescu, Liviu	020198
Solarzentrum Stuttgart, Stuttgart, Germany

Stowhas-Villa, Alejandro 020422
Federico Santa María Technical University, Valparaiso, Chile

Stoyanova Lyubenova, Teodora 020173
European Commission JRC, Ispra, Italy

Sträter, Hendrik 020211
PTB, Braunschweig, Germany

Strey, Jessica 020063, 020114
ISFH, Emmerthal, Germany

Strömberg, Rich 020472
University of Alaska, Fairbanks, United States of America

Stroyuk, Oleksander 020185
HI ERN, Erlangen, Germany

Stroyuk, Oleksandr 020117, 020149, 020150
HI ERN, Erlangen, Germany

Suárez Sánchez, Sergio 020326
Enertis Applus+, Madrid, Spain

Subasi, Dilara Maria 020475
Fraunhofer ISE, Freiburg, Germany

Sudbury, Ben A. 020396
PV Lighthouse, Coledale, Australia

Suemitsu, Issei 020484
Hitachi, Kokubunji, Japan

Suhonen, Riikka 020423
VTT Technical Research Centre of Finland, Oulu, Finland

Sulca, Kabir Paúl 020191, 020205
University of Valladolid, Valladolid, Spain

Svatos, Jan 020250
DTU, Roskilde, Denmark

Sylla, David 020063
ISFH, Emmerthal, Germany

Syre Wiig, Marie 020340
IFE, Kjeller, Norway

Szarek, Magda 020298, 020398
University of Turku, Turku, Finland

Taghipour Kani, Ghaem 020335, 020374
Amirkabir University of Technology, Tehran, Iran

Takahashi, Kanji 020106
Tokyo City University, Setagaya, Japan

Talvi, Micke 020528
Tampere University, Tampere, Finland

Tanahashi, Tadanori 020436
AIST, Koriyama, Japan

Tang, Kai 020011
SINTEF, Trondheim, Norway

Tang, Torben IPU P/S, Virum, Denmark	020028
Tang, Torben IPU, Virum, Denmark	020037
Tayebjee, Murad J. Y. UNSW, Sydney, Australia	020065
Taylor, Nigel European Commission JRC, Ispra, Italy	020210
Tellez Rodriguez, Eduardo Kiwa PI Berlin, Berlin, Germany	020230
Teppe, Andreas RCT Solutions, Konstanz, Germany	020005
Terheiden, Barbara University of Konstanz, Constance, Germany	020031
Terrados, Cristian University of Valladolid, Valladolid, Spain	020205
Thakur, Dhruv Singh SVNIT, Surat, India	020071, 020081
Theocharides, Spyros Univers, Courbevoie, France	020371
Thomas, Jean Ciel et Terre, Lille, France	020169
Thorning, Jacob K. DTU, Roskilde, Denmark	020267, 020283
Thorsteinsson, Sune DTU, Copenhagen, Denmark	020039
Thorsteinsson, Sune DTU, Lyngby, Denmark	020037
Thorsteinsson, Sune DTU, Roskilde, Denmark	020028, 020249, 020250, 020265, 020306, 020477
Timofte, Tudor ISC Konstanz, Konstanz, Germany	020218, 020221
Ting, San-Yu ITRI, Hsinchu, Taiwan	020161, 020163
Tissier, Corentin CSEM, Neuchâtel, Switzerland	020238
Tönies, Alexandra University of Applied Sciences Cologne, Cologne, Germany	020523
Tomšič, Špela University of Ljubljana, Ljubljana, Slovenia	020047
Tong, Yongfeng QEERI, Doha, Qatar	020108, 020109
Topič, Marko University of Ljubljana, Ljubljana, Slovenia	020047, 020269, 020319
Torabi, Narges University of Verona, Verona, Italy	020089

Torelly, Guilherme   020092
PUC-Rio, Rio de Janeiro, Brazil

Torre, Gorka   020437
UPV/EHU, Leioa, Spain

Torres Aguilar, Moira Itzel   020214
CentraleSupélec, Gif-sur-Yvette, France

Torres Aguilar, Moira Itzel   020406
CNRS, Gif-sur-Yvette, France

Torres Silva, Nicole   020546
ATAMOSTEC, Santiago, Chile

Torres, Oscar   020110
National University of Colombia, Bogotá, Colombia

Tosi, Irene   020037
IPU, Virum, Denmark

Tran Caliste, Thu Nhi   020546
European Synchrotron Radiation Facility (ESRF), Grenoble,
France

Treberspurg, Christoph   020255
Treberspurg und Partner Ziviltechniker, Vienna, Austria

Treberspurg, Martin   020255
Treberspurg und Partner Ziviltechniker, Vienna, Austria

Trefzer, Aaron   020135
Fraunhofer ISE, Freiburg, Germany

Trifiletti, Vanira   020087
University of Milano-Bicocca, Milan, Italy

Trigo-Gonzalez, Mauricio   020342, 020422
University of Antofagasta, Antofagasta, Chile

Tsai, Min-An   020053, 020083, 020161, 020163
ITRI, Hsinchu, Taiwan

Tsanakas, Ioannis (John) A.   020262
CEA / INES, Le Bourget-du-Lac, France

Tsanakas, Ioannis (John) A.   020544
CEA, Le Bourget-du-Lac, France

Tsanakas, Ioannis (John)   020546
CEA / INES, Le Bourget-du-Lac, France

Tsanakas, Ioannis (John)   020317
CEA INES, Le Bourget-du-Lac, France

Tsanakas, Ioannis (John)   020513, 020521
CEA, Le Bourget-du-Lac, France

Tsanakas, Ioannis   020217, 020338
CEA / INES, Le Bourget-du-Lac, France

Tsanakas, Ioannis   020500
CEA, Le Bourget-du-Lac, France

Tsanakas, John A.   020311
CEA / INES, Le Bourget-du-Lac, France

Tseberlidis, Giorgio   020093
University of Milano Bicocca, Milan, Italy

Tseberlidis, Giorgio 020087
University of Milano-Bicocca, Milan, Italy

Tsoi, Konstantin 020113
ODTÜ-GÜNAM, Ankara, Türkiye

Tsombou, Francois M. 020402
Fujairah Research Centre, Fujairah, United Arab Emirates

Tsuno, Yuki 020436
AIST, Koriyama, Japan

Tsunoda, Jun 020484
Hitachi, Kokubunji, Japan

Tsunoda, Jun 020186
Hitachi, Tokyo, Japan

Tulinski, Lona 020385
ZHAW, Winterthur, Switzerland

Tune, Daniel 020220, 020221, 020225
ISC Konstanz, Konstanz, Germany

Turcu, Mircea 020063
ISFH, Emmerthal, Germany

Turek, Marko 020004, 020052
Fraunhofer CSP, Halle (Saale), Germany

Ueda, Yuzuru 020320, 020525
Tokyo University of Science, Tokyo, Japan

Ujvari, Gusztav 020318, 020430
AIT, Vienna, Austria

Ulbikaitė, Vaidvilė 020157
Applied Research Institute for Prospective Technologies,
Vilnius, Lithuania

Ulbikas, Juras 020225
Protechnology, Vilnius, Lithuania

Ulyashin, Alexander G. 020011
SINTEF, Oslo, Norway

Unsur, Veysel 020020
ODTÜ-GÜNAM, Ankara, Türkiye

Urban, Harald 020255
TU Wien, Vienna, Austria

Useni, Yannick 020393
University of Lubumbashi, Lubumbashi, Congo (DRC)

Uzuner, Bahri Eren 020113
ODTÜ-GÜNAM, Ankara, Türkiye

Väisänen, Kaisa-Leena 020423
VTT Technical Research Centre of Finland, Oulu, Finland

Vaicikauskas, Viktoras 020157
Center for Physical Sciences and Technology (FTMC),
Vilnius, Lithuania

Valaski, Rogério 020090
National Institute of Metrology Quality and Technology, Rio de Janeiro, Brazil

Valencia, Felipe 020342, 020546
AtamosTec, Santiago, Chile

Vallerotto, Guido 020209, 020246, 020257
UPM, Madrid, Spain

van Aken, Bas B. 020405
TNO, Petten, The Netherlands

van der Heide, Arvid 020472
imec, Genk, Belgium

van der Zee, Friso F. 020405
Wageningen University and Research, Wageningen, The Netherlands

Van Dyck, Rik 020225
IMEC, Genk, Belgium

van Dyk, E. Ernest 020193, 020416
Nelson Mandela University, Port Elizabeth, South Africa

van Dyk, Ernest E. 020344
Nelson Mandela University, Port Elizabeth, South Africa

Van Overstraeten, Julien 020543
Becquerel Institute France, Lyon, France

Van Overstraeten, Julien 020252
Becquerel Institute, Brussels, Belgium

vanBaal, Rene 020492
Belectric, Kolitzheim, Germany

Vanhanen, Tuomas 020225
Valoe, Mikkeli, Finland

Vargas, Renzo 020348
University of São Paulo, São Paulo, Brazil

Varney, Valérie 020522
University of Applied Science Cologne, Cologne, Germany

Varney, Valérie 020523
University of Applied Sciences Cologne, Cologne, Germany

vas Dyk, Ernest 020185
Nelson Mandela University, Port Elizabeth, South Africa

Vasconcelos, Letícia 020530
Casa dos Ventos, Fortaleza, Brazil

Vavilkin, Tatjana 020302
Soltech, Genk, Belgium

Vázquez Adán, Alejandra 020501
UCM, Madrid, Spain

Vázquez, A. 020508
UCM, Madrid, Spain

Veas, Christian 020136, 020234
PCCL, Leoben, Austria

Vecino, Fernando Román 020346
DTU, Roskilde, Denmark

Veerman, Sebastian 020035
ISC Konstanz, Konstanz, Germany

Vega de Seoane, José Maria 020252
Becquerel Institute Spain, San Sebastian, Spain

Vega de Seoane, Jose 020546
Becquerel Institute, Brussels, Belgium

Vega-Herrera, Jorge 020342
University of Antofagasta, Antofagasta, Chile

Vehus, Tore Sandnes 020443
University of Agder, Grimstad, Norway

Veirman, Jordi 020203, 020226, 020254
Eurac Research, Bolzano, Italy

Velasco, Angel 020367
Nextracker, Fremont, United States of America

Veludo, Jorge 020317
Galp Energia, Lisbon, Portugal

Veneri, Alessandro 020093
University of Verona, Verona, Italy

Vergura, Silvano 020301
Polytechnic University of Bari, Bari, Italy

Verlinden, Pierre 020001
YIST, Jiangyin, China

Vermang, Bart 020064
Hasselt Unversity, Genk, Belgium

Vernay, Christophe 020244
SOLAÏS, Valbonne, France

Vero, Giuseppe 020301
Polytechnic University of Bari, Bari, Italy

Veronese, Elisa 020513
Eurac Research, Bolzano, Italy

Veurman, Welmoed 020063
ISFH, Emmerthal, Germany

Viani, Lucas 020326
Enertis Applus+, Madrid, Spain

Vicente-Laiglesia, Pablo 020181
European Climate, Infrastructure and Environment
Executive Agency, Brussels, Belgium

Vidal de Oliveira, Aline 020377
Solar Energy Research Laboratory Fotovoltaica/ UFSC,
Florianópolis, Brazil

Vidal, Beatriz Muñoz 020414
IaSol, Zaragoza, Spain

Vidal-Fuentes, Pedro 020094
IREC, Barcelona, Spain

Videla-Magnata, Natalia   020129
Universidad de Antofagasta, Antofagasta, Chile

Videla-Magnata, Natalia   020417
University of Antofagasta, Antofagasta, Chile

Vilches, Anna Morales   020388
Next2Sun Technology, Dillingen, Germany

Villalonga Palou, Joan Tomás   020432, 020434
Sunveon, Madrid, Spain

Villén, Raúl   020127, 020414, 020517
ENDEF, Zaragoza, Spain

Villodas, Aritz   020198
TECNALIA, Derio, Spain

Vincent, Laetitia   020058
CNRS, Palaiseau, France

Vincent, Robin   020196
PVsyst, Geneva, Switzerland

Viorel Spataru, Sergiu   020191
DTU, Roskilde, Denmark

Viriyaroj, Bergpob   020298
Aalto University, Espoo, Finland

Viti, Valeria   020541
Legance, Milan, Italy

Vitoshkin, Helena   020379
Agricultural Research Organization, Rishon LeZion, Israel

Vögeli, Pascal   020385
ZHAW, Winterthur, Switzerland

Vogt, Malte R.   020515
TU Delft, Delft, The Netherlands

Vogt, Thomas   020482
DLR, Oldenburg, Germany

Vollbrecht, Joachim   020063, 020114
ISFH, Emmerthal, Germany

Voltan, Alessandro   020010
Applied Materials, Treviso, Italy

von Friedeburg, Christoph   020557
CF Energy Research-Consulting-Operation, Berlin,
Germany

Voronko, Yuliya   020162, 020249
OFI, Vienna, Austria

Vorster, Frederik J.   020193, 020344, 020416
Nelson Mandela University, Port Elizabeth, South Africa

Vorster, Frederik   020185
Nelson Mandela University, Port Elizabeth, South Africa

Vuillon, Laurent   020338
CNRS, Chambery, France

Vulic, Natasa   020296
Univesity of Applied Arts and Sciences Northwestern
Switzerland, Muttenz, Switzerland

Vumbugwa, Monphias   020185, 020193, 020344
Nelson Mandela University, Port Elizabeth, South Africa

Waibel, Christoph   020511
Flemish Institute for Technological Research (VITO), Genk,
Belgium

Wakabayashi, Ryo   020484
Hitachi, Kokubunji, Japan

Wakazono, Kouzen   020131
Gifu University, Gifu, Japan

Wallner, Gernot M.   020227
University of Linz, Linz, Austria

Walpita, Harsha   020169
University of Oslo, Kjeller, Norway

Walsh, Yoselyn   020520
Costa Rica Institute of Technology, Cartago, Costa Rica

Wambach, Karsten   020468, 020470
bifa Umweltinstitut, Augsburg, Germany

Wang, Chia-Chen   020549
ITRI, Hsinchu, Taiwan

Wang, Shuo   020286, 020400
TUAS, Turku, Finland

Wang, Tzuya   020549
ITRI, Hsinchu, Taiwan

Wang, Xiaolin   020381
Mälardalen University, Västerås, Sweden

Wannenwetsch, Jann   020312
EnBW, Karlsruhe, Germany

Wargocki, Pawel   020551
DTU, Roskilde, Denmark

Waschl, Alfred   020255
buildingSMART, Vienna, Austria

Weber, Thomas   020180, 020230
Kiwa PI Berlin, Berlin, Germany

Weeber, Arthur W.   020515
TU Delft, Delft, The Netherlands

Wei, Wenpeng   020484
Hitachi, Kokubunji, Japan

Weihs, Philipp   020281
BOKU, Vienna, Austria

Weinrich, Frank   020177
PTB, Braunschweig, Germany

Weiß, Marius   020361
Coburg University of Applied Sciences, Coburg, Germany

Wellens, Christine
Fraunhofer ISE, Freiburg, Germany

020135

Whyatt, Duncan
Lancaster University, Lancaster, United Kingdom

020394

Wienands, Karl
ISC Konstanz, Konstanz, Germany

020218, 020220, 020221

Wiesenfarth, Maike
Fraunhofer ISE, Freiburg, Germany

020246

Wietler, Tobias
ISFH, Emmerthal, Germany

020063

Wilbert, Stefan
DLR, Almería, Spain

020235, 020237, 020239, 020331

Willers, Guido
Fraunhofer CSP, Halle, Germany

020201

Wilson, Helen R.
Fraunhofer ISE, Freiburg, Germany

020249

Winter, Renate
ISFH, Emmerthal, Germany

020063

Winter, Stefan
PTB, Braunschweig, Germany

020177, 020181

Wirtz, Wiebke
ISFH, Emmerthal, Germany

020260

Witkowska, Agnieszka
Gdansk University of Technology, Gdansk, Poland

020498

Wittmer, Bruno
PVsyst, Geneva, Switzerland

020196

Wolf, Andreas
Fraunhofer ISE, Freiburg, Germany

020031

Wong, Craig
Kiwa PI Berlin, Berlin, Germany

020230

Wu, Li-Guo
TSEC, Hsinchu, Taiwan

020021

Wu, Yu
TNO, Petten, The Netherlands

020030

Wyss, Philippe
CSEM, Neuchâtel, Switzerland

020068

Xiong, Weizhen
Tokyo University of Science, Tokyo, Japan

020320

Xu, Jiahui
YIST, Jiangyin, China

020001

Xu, Wenhao
TÜV Rheinland, Shanghai, China

020144, 020208

Xu, Xiaoqi
SERIS, Singapore, Singapore

020263

Xu, Yu   020263
SERIS, Singapore, Singapore

Xuereb, Steven   020180, 020230
Kiwa PI Berlin, Berlin, Germany

Yadav, Shivendra   020071, 020081
SVNIT, Surat, India

Yamaguchi, Yosuke   020484
Hitachi, Kokubunji, Japan

Yanagida, Masatoshi   020115
NIMS, Tsukuba, Japan

Yanar, T. Meriç   020027
Kalyon PV, Ankara, Türkiye

Yang, Donggeon   020323
K-water, Daejeon, South Korea

Yang, Hyoung-Kyu   020449
KETI, Wonmi-gu, South Korea

Yde, Leif   020250, 020306
Stensborg, Roskilde, Denmark

Ye, JiaYi   020102
SERIS, Singapore, Singapore

Yerci, Selcuk   020113
ODTÜ-GÜNAM, Ankara, Türkiye

Ylikunnari, Mari   020423
VTT Technical Research Centre of Finland, Oulu, Finland

Ylinen, Marko   020444
Satakunta University of Applied Sciences, Pori, Finland

Ylipaino, Juho   020444, 020445, 020554
TUAS, Tampere, Finland

Yılmaz, Büşra   020521
Kameleon Solar, Roosendaal, The Netherlands

Yordadov, Georgi   020389
imec, Diepenbeek, Belgium

Younes, Kareem   020487
Khalifa University, Abu Dhabi, United Arab Emirates

Yu, Cheng-Yeh   020021, 020053
TSEC, Hsinchu, Taiwan

Yu, Shusen   020406
Ecole Polytechnique, Palaiseau, France

Yuan, Xiao   020001
YIST, Jiangyin, China

Yun, Jae Ho   020112
KENTECH, Naju-si, South Korea

Zaimi, Mhammed   020171
University of Chouaib Doukkali, El Jadida, Morocco

Zanatta Britto, João Victor   020025
PUCRS, Porto Alegre, Brazil

Zanesco, Izete   020023, 020025
PUCRS, Porto Alegre, Brazil

Zaror, Yasmin   020225
WIP - Renewable Energies, Munich, Germany

Zarzalejo, Luis F.   020237, 020331
CIEMAT, Madrid, Spain

Zekri, Atef   020146
QEERI, Doha, Qatar

Zerafa, Steve   020334
PIXAM, Msida, Malta

Zhang, Geng   020001
Jolywood (ShanXi) Solar Technology, Taiyuan, China

Zhang, Jingwei   020111
Hohai University, Changzhou, China

Zhang, Kai   020233
FZJ, Jülich, Germany

Zhang, Wenjing   020001
YIST, Jiangyin, China

Zhang, Wuai   020101
HZB, Berlin, Germany

Zhang, Yating   020144, 020208
TÜV Rheinland, Shanghai, China

Zhou, Qilin   020102
SERIS, Singapore, Singapore

Zhu, Junjie   020017
Institute for Energy Technology, Kjeller, Norway

Ziaullah, Abdul Wahab   020278, 020291
QEERI, Doha, Qatar

Zilles, Roberto   020154, 020348
University of São Paulo, São Paulo, Brazil

Zimmermann, Iwan   020116
IPVF, Palaiseau, France

Zubillaga, Oihana   020139
Tecnalia, Donostia - San Sebastián, Spain

Zugasti, Eugenia   020334
CENER, Pamplona, Spain

Zugasti, Eugenia   020300
CENER, Sarriguren, Spain

Zwahlen, Theo   020369
BFH, Burgdorf, Switzerland

KEYWORDS OF EU PVSEC 2025 PROCEEDINGS PAPERS

Antireflection	020001
Antisoiling	020402
AOD	020278
Appearance	020250
Aquatic Ecosystem	020418
Architecture	020255
Arid Regions	020402
AROMP	020141
Artificial Intelligence	020544
Artificial Intelligence (AI)	020356, 020375
Artificial Neuronal Network	020342
Automation	020275
Autonomous Aerial Monitoring (AAM)	020356, 020375
Azimuth	020532
Back Contact	020006
Back Contact Solar Cell	020218
Backsheet	020151
Backsheet Degradation	020377
Backsheets	020150
Backtracking	020363
Backtracking 3D	020434
Backtracking Strategies	020434
Balancing Market Bid Planning	020525
Basin Test	020390
Battery	020429
Battery Energy Management	020490
Battery Energy Storage System	020490
Battery Energy Storage Systems	020492
Bifacial	020066, 020106, 020210, 020287, 020396, 020407
Bifacial Efficiency	020081
Bifacial Module	020379
Bifacial Modules	020181
Bifacial Photovoltaic	020443
Bifacial PV Modules	020154
Bifacial Technology	020342
Big Data	020328
Bio-based Polymers	020141

Characteristics Addition	020081
Characterization	020050, 020119, 020121, 020151, 020166, 020459
CIGS	020097
CIGS/Perovskite Solar Cell	020104
Circular Economy	020141, 020504, 020510, 020517
Circularity	020470, 020472, 020507, 020517
Citizen Participation	020491, 020575
Clay	020300
Clean Firm Power	020487
Clean Transportation	020428
Cleaning	020332
Cleaning Frequency	020348
Cleaning Optimization Asset Management	020339
Clear-sky	020278
Clear-Sky Detection	020340
Climate Change	020402
Climate-dependent Degradation	020150
Climate-responsive Design	020259
Climate-Specific PV O&M	020546
Cloud Detection	020267
Clustering	020243
Co-Extruded EPE	020135
Co-Visibility	020244
Collective Self-consumption	020490
Color Stability	020254
Colored Photovoltaics	020556
ColorFoil	020306
Comfort	020302
Compact Furnace	020025
Comparative Life Cycle Assessment (LCA)	020303
Competitiveness	020573
Compliance	020444
Composite Encapsulant	020139
Composites	020498
Computational Efficiency	020432
Computer Vision	020336, 020511
COMSOL	020104

Concentrator Photovoltaics	020257, 020416
Concentrator Photovoltaics (CPV)	020246
Condition Monitoring	020194, 020289, 020353
Conductive Adhesive	020220
Constitutive Model	020048
Constrained-Off	020530
Constructability	020302
Contact-failure	020055
Controller	020534
Convolutional Neural Networks (CNNs)	020374
Cooling Load Reduction	020259
Cooperation	020541
Copper Metallization	020035
Correction Factor	020446
Cost of Ownership	020482
Crack Detection	020201
Cracking	020151
Critical Minerals	020559
Cross-lateral Approach	020541
Crosslinking	020158
Crystalline Silicon	020175, 020265
Cu Contact	020020
Cu Plating	020028
Cu-plated Metallization	020037
Current-Voltage Curve	020185
Current–voltage Curve	020194
Curtailment	020332, 020530
Curved Photovoltaic Modules	020459
Czochralski Process	020015
Data Aggregation	020243
Data Center Energy Supply	020487
Data Evaluation	020183
Data Pipeline	020275
Data Quality	020275, 020371
Daylight Electroluminescence	020191
Daylight Luminescence	020205
DC-DC Converters	020422

Energy Management System	020534
Energy Management System (EMS)	020536
Energy Performance Directive	020477
Energy Performance of Buildings Directive (EPBD)	020551
Energy Poverty	020564
Energy Rating	020173, 020177, 020211
Energy Sharing	020564
Energy Storage	020428, 020487, 020534
Energy Testing	020171
Energy Transition	020479, 020537, 020541
Energy Yield	020175, 020181, 020210, 020286, 020318, 020443, 020453
Energy Yield Estimation	020294
Energy Yield Overestimation	020363
Energy Yield Simulations	020262
Environmental Impact	020418
Environmental Psychology	020523
Epitaxial Lateral Overgrowth	020058
Epoxy Bonding	020092
Epoxy–Fiberglass	020417
EROI	020479
ET	020522
Etching	020007, 020031
EU-LAC Collaboration	020546
Eurocode	020167
EV Charging	020428
Evaporation	020015
Experimental Testing	020127
Exports	020563
Facade-Integrated Photovoltaics (FIPV)	020192
Facade-mounted PV	020359
Failures	020328
Fault Analysis	020217
Fault Clustering	020351
Fault Detection	020337, 020346, 020353, 020375, 020511
Fault Signatures	020351
Field Measurements	020377

IEC 60904	020102
IEC 61853 Standard	020173
IEC 61853-1	020171, 020361
IEC Standards	020563
III-V	020058
III-V Semiconductors	020067
III-V/Silicon	020092
III−V/c-Si Tandem Cell	020046
In-line Post Processing	020010
In-situ Process Control	020132
Incidence Angle Modifier	020177
Individual Cells	020193
Indoor Photovoltaics	020069
Industrial	020304
Industry Foundation classes (IFC)	020255
Infrared Soldering	020123
Infrared Thermography	020376
InGaAs Camera	020191
Inhomogeneous Loads	020231
Injection Molding	020423
Innovation	020541
Innovative Agrivoltaics	020378
Inspection	020206
Installation Practices	020444
Insulations	020127
Intensity	020083
Interconnection	020119, 020123
Interfaces and Nanocomponents	020013
Inverter	020346, 020355
Inverter Efficiency	020355
Ion Implantation	020068
IoT Cloud Architecture	020334
IoT-based Energy Monitoring	020491
Irradiance	020276, 020307
Irradiance Dependence	020175
Irradiance Dependency	020056
Irradiance Fluctuations	020528
Irradiance Management	020400
Irradiance Measurement	020287

Irregular Terrain   020434
ISOS Protocols   020064
IV   020346
I–V and EL   020417
I–V Curve Emulation   020369
IV Data   020510
IV Testing   020050
IWO/SiO2 Stack   020046

Junction Box   020129

KPI   020302

Laboratory Measurements   020386
Laboratory Practices   020100
Lamination Monitoring   020132
Land Use   020398, 020543
Land Use Requirements   020476
Landscape   020549
Large Language Model   020544
Large-Size PV Modules   020161
Laser Processing   020023
Laser-grooved BC Technology   020037
LCA   020464, 020468, 020499, 020515
LCOE   020304
LCOE Reduction   020358
LCOH   020426
Lessons Learned   020567
Levelized Cost of Electricity   020482
Li-ion Batteries   020536
LID   020215
LiDAR   020262
Life Cycle Assessment   020511
Life Cycle Impact Assessment   020479
Life-Cycle Assessment   020559
Lifetime Financial Analysis   020367
Light Emitting Diodes   020067
Light Soaking   020010
Light Trapping (LT)   020104

Silicon	020007, 020058, 020097, 020468, 020495, 020501, 020507, 020508, 020515
Silicon Heterojunction	020040
Silicon Heterojunction Cell	020046
Silicon Kerf	020495
Silicon Photovoltaics	020144
Silicon Solar Cell	020001, 020013, 020023
Silicon Solar Cells	020006, 020068
Silicone	020384
Silver Recovery	020498
Simulation	020255, 020301
Simulation Acceleration	020243
Single-Axis Tracker Reliability	020314
Sizing Optimization	020530
Smart City	020420
Smart Energy System	020544
Smart Inverter IV Tracing	020361
SMARTS2	020278
Social Cognitive Career Theory (SCCT)	020569
Social Housing	020564
Social Innovation	020575
Social Risks	020505
Socio-Economics	020476
Software Tool	020183
Soil	020403, 020565
Soiling	020311, 020332, 020339, 020361
Soiling Loss Modeling	020317
Soiling Losses	020311, 020348
Soiling Mitigation	020311
Solar	020188, 020276
Solar Array Simulator Evaluation	020369
Solar Cell	020007, 020053, 020083
Solar Cells	020090, 020501, 020508
Solar Energy	020526
Solar Glass	020140
Solar Irradiance	020286
Solar Irradiance Forecasting	020267
Solar Irradiation	020412

Solar Mandate	020551
Solar Modules	020157
Solar Panel Reliability	020154
Solar Photovoltaic Technology	020569
Solar Photovoltaics	020479, 020564
Solar Power	020571
Solar Power Plant	020539
Solar PV	020476, 020549, 020552, 020559, 020573
Solar PV Systems in Buildings	020562
Solar Radiation	020275, 020283
Solar Railways	020421
Solar Resource Variability	020241
Solar Silicon	020011
Solar Water Pumping System	020429
Solder Paste	020220
Solid-State Reaction	020117
Solvent Additives	020096
Soxhlet Extraction	020135
Space	020053
Spatial Planning Integration	020552
Spatio-Temporal Analysis	020338
Spectral Composition	020416
Spectral Irradiance	020283
Spectral Mapping	020149
Spectroscopy	020227
Spectrum Splitting	020379
Stability	020096
Stakeholder Analysis	020556
Stall Detection	020314
Stance Detection	020522
Standardisation	020472
Standards	020211, 020444
STC Parameters	020183
Storage	020429, 020535
Storage Effect	020215
Storage System	020539
Stress Profile	020355
Structural Electronics	020423
Structuring	020031

Thermal Effects	020416
Thermal Image	020193
Thermal Stress	020153, 020260
Thermally Conductive Filler	020131
Thermomechanical Test	020497
Thermophotonics	020067
Thin Film	020071, 020180
Thin Films	020069, 020087
Thin-film	020094
Thin-Film Devices	020067
Thin-Film Solar Cells	020085
Tilt	020532
TOPCon	020010, 020021, 020028, 020031, 020037
TOPCON PV Modules	020229
Tracking Irradiation Gain	020363
Tracking Systems	020402
Transparency	020574
Transparent Conducting Oxide	020046
Tree Shading	020294

UAV-Based Monitoring	020335, 020374
Ultrasonic Characterization	020132
Ultraviolet Fluorescence	020158
Ultraviolet-Fluorescence Imaging	020185
Urban Planning	020420, 020526
Urban Shadowing	020457
Utility-Scale Photovoltaics	020348
Utility-Scale Solar PV	020382
UV Exposure	020229
UV Fluorescence	020166
UV Instability	020229
UV Laser Annealing	020079
UV Laser Scribing	020043
UV-Vis Spectroscopy	020081

Vacuum Refining	020011
Vacuum Thermal Evaporation	020558
Vacuum-Assisted Processing	020079
Validation	020390

Value Chain	020505
Vehicle Integrated Photovoltaics (VIPV)	020459
Vehicle-Integrated Photovoltaics	020453, 020457
Vehicle-Integrated Photovoltaics (VIPV)	020422
Vertical Bifacial PV	020262
Vertical PV	020388, 020400
Very Short-term Solar Forecasting	020272
Vibration Durability	020417
VIPV	020417, 020455
Virtual Power Plant	020554
Virtual Power Plants	020535
Visual inspection	020169, 020185
Water Quality	020418
Weather Station	020371
Weather Variables	020279
Wet Etching	020028
Yield	020180, 020307, 020396
YOLO Classifiers	020335, 020374
ZnSnO	020085

WIP – Renewable Energies
Sylvensteinstr. 2
81369 Munchen
Germany

ISBN 979-8-3313-2987-7